# WORLD GEOGRAPHY

## The Earth and Its People

# WORLD GEOGRAPHY
## The Earth and Its People

**Dr. Phillip Bacon**

**Harcourt Brace Jovanovich, Publishers**

Orlando    San Diego    Chicago    Dallas

## THE AUTHOR AND GENERAL EDITOR

**Dr. Phillip Bacon** is a professor Emeritus of Geography and Anthropology at the University of Houston. Dr. Bacon has served on the faculties of Columbia University and the University of Washington. Formerly Dean of the Graduate School of Peabody College for Teachers at Vanderbilt University, Dr. Bacon began his career in education as a teacher of elementary and secondary social studies. He is also a past president of the National Council for Geographic Education (NCGE).

Dr. Bacon is the author or editor of more than 36 books, including the *Life Pictorial Atlas of the World*. For 18 years Dr. Bacon served as a member of the Editorial Advisory Board of the *World Book Encyclopedia*. He also served as a member of the Council of the Association of American Geographers and for three years was chairperson of the AAG's Publications Committee.

Among his numerous honors and awards, Dr. Bacon received the NCGE's Distinguished Service Award, the highest honor the organization can bestow on a geographer. Dr. Bacon also holds the distinguished titles of Fellow of the Explorers Club and Fellow of the Royal Geographic Society of Great Britain. He is a three-time recipient of the Teaching Excellence Award at the University of Houston.

## CONTRIBUTING WRITERS

**Dr. Kempton Webb**
Professor of Geography
Columbia University

**Kathleen Braden**
Associate Professor of Geography
Seattle Pacific University

**Linda Wojtan**
Senior Consultant
Social Studies Development Center
Indiana University

## EDITORIAL CONSULTANT

**Patricia A. Rodriquez**

## CONTENT SPECIALISTS

**Dr. John Coffman**
Professor of Geography
University of Houston

**Dr. Lorrin Kennamer**
Professor of Geography
University of Texas

**Dr. George J. Demko**
Department of State
Office of the Geographer
Washington, D.C.

**Dr. George Hoffman**
Professor Emeritus
The University of Texas at Austin
Professorial Lecturer
George Washington University
Washington, D.C.

## CURRICULUM SPECIALISTS

**Alvin Borrero**
Consulting Teacher
Topeka, KS

**Lois Jordan**
Teacher
Nashville, TN

**Robert Rutherford**
Teacher
San Bernardino, CA

**Luis Cuevas**
Teacher
Gainesville, FL

**Dana Kurfman**
Social Studies Supervisor
Prince George's County, MD

**Barbara Wilson**
Teacher
Mount Vernon, IL

**Betty Dean**
Social Studies Chairperson
Houston, TX

**Richard Montgomery**
Teacher
San Antonio, TX

For permission to reprint copyrighted material, grateful acknowledgment is made to the following sources:

**ACKNOWLEDGMENTS:** *Georges Borchardt, Inc., on behalf of Ved Mehta:* From *The New India* By Ved Mehta. Copyright © 1971, 1974, 1975, 1976, 1977, 1978 by Ved Mehta. *Bradbury Press, an affiliate of Macmillan, Inc.:* From p. 9–10 in *Volcano: The Eruption and Healing of Mount St. Helens* by Patricia Lauber. Copyright © 1986 by Patricia Lauber. *Doubleday, a division of Bantam, Doubleday, Dell Publishing Group, Inc. and Walker Martineau:* From "The Romance of Travel" by Joseph Conrad. *E. P. Dutton, a division of NAL Penguin Inc.:* From *Brazil: The Infinite Country* by William Lytle Schurz. Copyright © 1961 by William Lytle Schurz. *Harcourt Brace Jovanovich, Inc.:* From pp. 130–131 in *South American Primer* by Katherine Carr Rodell. Copyright 1941 by Katherine Carr Rodell. From p. 271 in *Modern China and Japan: A Brief History* (Retitled: "Modern China and Japan") by Conrad Schirokauer. Copyright © 1982 by Harcourt Brace Jovanovich, Inc. *Harper & Row, Publishers, Inc.:* From *The Farmer Is Doomed* by Louis M. Hacker. Copyright 1933 by Louis M. Hacker. *This Is Our China* by Madame Chiang Kai-shek. Published by Harper & Brothers Publishers, 1940. *Henry Holt and Company, Inc.:* From pp. 10–11 in *Caravan: The Story of the Middle*

*(Acknowledgments continued on page 777)*

Printed in the United States of America
ISBM 0-15-373530-9

# CONTENTS

## UNIT 1

## UNIT 3

UNIT 4

# UNIT 5

# MIDDLE AMERICA 268

**UNIT 6**

**SOUTH
AMERICA                                                320**

**UNIT 8**

# UNIT 9

## UNIT 10

## SOUTH ASIA     568

# MAPS

# CHARTS, TABLES, AND GRAPHS

# DIAGRAMS

# CASE STUDIES

# DEVELOPING GEOGRAPHY SKILLS

# GEOGRAPHY IN THE WORKPLACE

# THE GEOGRAPHIC WEB

# CITY FOCUS

# PRIMARY SOURCES

# ATLAS

This Atlas includes 11 maps that provide you with information on the physical, political, and economic features of the world. Most two-page Atlas maps use the Robinson projection, and most maps are shaded to show relief, or elevation above sea level. The colors used on the physical maps in the Atlas reflect natural vegetation patterns. Dark green marks areas of heavy vegetation. Lighter green denotes areas of less vegetation. Tan marks areas of little vegetation. "Basic Land and Water Forms" provides a diagram of many of the geographical features found in the world. These include types of mountains, deserts, plains, rivers and other bodies of water that the student will learn about in the chapters of this textbook. The Atlas maps are designed for general reference and provide you with easy-to-use supplements to the maps of the specific regions that appear in the chapters.

Greenland

Baffin
Bay

*Bering
Sea*

R O C K Y

N O R T H

A M E R I C A

*Hudson
Bay*

APPALACHIAN MTS.

Mississippi R.

M T S.

*Sargasso
Sea*

Gulf of
Mexico

W E S T   I N D I E S

*Central
America*

*Caribbean Sea*

ATLANTIC

OCEAN

West    East

Prime

Meridian

Arctic    Circle

BRITISH
ISLES

*North
Sea*

*English
Channel*

ALPS

PYRENEES

Strait of
Gibraltar

ATLAS MTS.

Disputed

S A H A R A

SAHEL

*Cape
Verde*

HAWAIIAN
ISLANDS

PACIFIC

OCEAN

Tropic of Cancer

Equator

S O U T H

A M E R I C A

A
N
D
E
S

*Amazon* R.

ATLANTIC

OCEAN

Tropic of Capricorn

ATACAMA
DESERT

N

*Cape Horn*

**THE WORLD: Physical**

National boundary

MILLER CYLINDRICAL PROJECTION

| 0 | 1000 | 2000 Miles |
| 0 | 1000 | 2000 Kilometers |

Meridian

Prime

Antarctic Circle

ARCTIC OCEAN

Bering Strait

Sea of
Okhotsk

Bering
Sea

EUROPE

Danube CARPATHIAN
R. MTS

Black Sea

CAUCASUS
MTS

Caspian Sea

URAL MTS.

Baltic Sea

ASIA

GOBI
DESERT

He

Disputed

Huang

HIMALAYAS

Chang Jiang

East China
Sea

60°

30°

Mediterranean Sea

Arabian
Peninsula

Undefined

Persian G.

Red Sea

NUBIAN
DESERT

A

AFRICA

Ganges R.

Arabian
Sea

Bay of
Bengal

South
China
Sea

PACIFIC

OCEAN

Strait of Malacca

INDONESIA

Equator

0°

(Congo) R.

Zaire

INDIAN
OCEAN

KALAHARI
DESERT

Madagascar

AUSTRALIA

30°

Cape of
Good Hope

60°

30°

60°

90°

120°

150°

180°

60°

ANTARCTICA

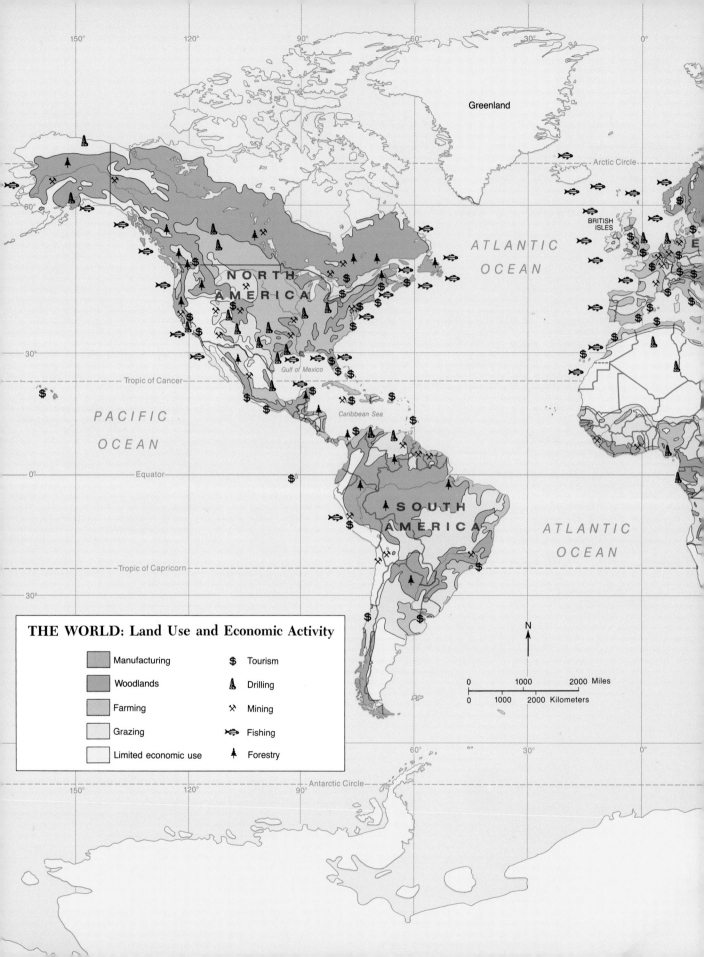

# THE WORLD: Land Use and Economic Activity

| | |
|---|---|
| Manufacturing | $ Tourism |
| Woodlands | Drilling |
| Farming | Mining |
| Grazing | Fishing |
| Limited economic use | Forestry |

Greenland

Arctic Circle

ATLANTIC
OCEAN

BRITISH
ISLES

NORTH
AMERICA

PACIFIC
OCEAN

Tropic of Cancer

Gulf of Mexico

Caribbean Sea

Equator

SOUTH
AMERICA

ATLANTIC
OCEAN

Tropic of Capricorn

30°

N

0        1000        2000 Miles

0    1000    2000 Kilometers

60°

30°

0°

Antarctic Circle

ARCTIC OCEAN

ASIA

EUROPE

Baltic Sea

Black Sea

Mediterranean Sea

AFRICA

INDIAN OCEAN

Madagascar

PACIFIC OCEAN

Tropic of Cancer

Equator

INDONESIA

AUSTRALIA

Tropic of Capricorn

NEW ZEALAND

ANTARCTICA

30° 60° 90° 120° 150° 180°

60°

30°

0°

30°

60°

Antarctic Circle

Duluth

**MINNESOTA**

Lake Superior

**M I C H I G A N**

Lake Huron

MAINE
★ Augusta

Minneapolis • ★ St. Paul

**WISCONSIN**

Mississippi River

Lake Michigan

Lansing ★

VERMONT
★ Montpelier
NEW HAMPSHIRE
★ Concord

Albany
★

Boston
●

Milwaukee ●
Madison ★

Detroit ●

Lake Erie

Lake Ontario

Rochester ●

**NEW YORK**

Hudson River

MASSACHUSETTS

Providence ●
RHODE ISLAND

**I O W A**

● Des Moines

Chicago ●
Gary ●

**OHIO**

Cleveland ●

Buffalo ●

Hartford ★
CONNECTICUT

New York ●

Omaha ●

River

**ILLINOIS**

Springfield ★

**INDIANA**

Indianapolis ★

Columbus ★

Pittsburgh ●

**PENNSYLVANIA**

Harrisburg ★

NEW JERSEY

Philadelphia ●
★ Trenton

Wilmington ●
★ Dover
DELAWARE

Kansas City ●

Cincinnati ●

Baltimore ●

Washington ⊛

40°

Topeka ★

St. Louis ●

River

Ohio River

Frankfort ★
Louisville ●

**WEST VIRGINIA**

Charleston ●

Annapolis ★
**MARYLAND**

70°

Jefferson City ★

**MISSOURI**

**KENTUCKY**

Richmond ★

**VIRGINIA**

Norfolk ●

Chesapeake Bay

**ATLANTIC OCEAN**

Tulsa ●

Mississippi River

★ Nashville

**TENNESSEE**

Tennessee River

**NORTH CAROLINA**

Raleigh ★

Charlotte ●

**ARKANSAS**

Memphis ●

A P P A L A C H I A N   M T S.

**SOUTH CAROLINA**

Columbia ★

Little Rock ★

★ Atlanta

Charleston ●

Birmingham ●

**GEORGIA**

Red River

**ALABAMA**

★ Jackson

Montgomery ●

Savannah ●

Jackson ★

**MISSISSIPPI**

Mobile ●

Jacksonville ●

★ Tallahassee

30°

**LOUISIANA**

Houston ●

Baton Rouge ★
New Orleans ●

**F L O R I D A**

Orlando ●

**Gulf   of   Mexico**

Tampa ●

Miami ●

N

## THE UNITED STATES

⊛ National capital
★ State capital
● Other city
━━ National boundary
── State boundary

ALBERS EQUAL AREA PROJECTION

0          250          500 Miles

0        250        500 Kilometers

90°

80°

**9**

SOVIET UNION

NORTH POLE

EUROPE

ARCTIC OCEAN

ICELAND

GREENLAND (DEN.)

Beaufort Sea

Baffin Bay

Aleutian Islands

Yukon R.

Anchorage

Gulf of Alaska

Mackenzie R.

Great Bear Lake

Great Slave Lake

Hudson Bay

ROCKY MOUNTAINS

Peace R.

Athabasca R.

Saskatchewan R.

CANADA

Nelson R.

Lake Winnipeg

Gulf of St. Lawrence

PACIFIC OCEAN

Vancouver

Calgary

Seattle

Portland

CASCADE RANGE

COASTAL RANGE

SIERRA NEVADA

Snake R.

Great Salt Lake

San Francisco

Missouri R.

Lake Superior

Minneapolis

Milwaukee

Lake Michigan

Chicago

UNITED

Omaha

Denver

Colorado River

Kansas City

STATES

St. Louis

Mississippi R.

Ohio R.

Detroit

Cleveland

Cincinnati

Pittsburgh

Lake Huron

Lake Erie

Toronto

Lake Ontario

Ottawa

Montreal

St. Lawrence R.

Québec

Halifax

Boston

New York

Philadelphia

Baltimore

Washington

APPALACHIAN MTS.

Hudson R.

ATLANTIC OCEAN

Los Angeles

San Diego

BAJA CALIFORNIA

Phoenix

Red River

Dallas

El Paso

San Antonio

Rio Grande

Houston

Memphis

New Orleans

Atlanta

Charleston

Savannah

Jacksonville

Tampa

Miami

BERMUDA (U.K.)

MEXICO

SIERRA MADRE

SIERRA MADRE

Monterrey

Gulf of Mexico

Nassau

BAHAMAS

Havana

CUBA

Santiago de Cuba

TURKS AND CAICOS IS. (U.K.)

PUERTO RICO (U.S.)

VIRGIN IS. (U.S.)

ST. MARTIN (NETH. & FR.)

ST. BARTHÉLEMY (FR.)

ST. CHRISTOPHER NEVIS

ANTIGUA

DOMINICA

Guadalajara

Mexico City

Cuernavaca

Veracruz

Oaxaca

YUCATÁN PENINSULA

CAYMAN ISLANDS (U.K.)

Kingston

JAMAICA

HAITI

Port-au-Prince

DOMINICAN REPUBLIC

Santo Domingo

MONTSERRAT (FR.)

GUADELOUPE (FR.)

MARTINIQUE (FR.)

ST. LUCIA

ST. VINCENT AND THE GRENADINES

BARBADOS

GRENADA

TRINIDAD AND TOBAGO

CURAÇAO (NETH.)

ARUBA (NETH.)

BONAIRE (NETH.)

BELIZE

Belmopan

GUATEMALA

Guatemala

San Salvador

EL SALVADOR

HONDURAS

Tegucigalpa

NICARAGUA

Managua

COSTA RICA

San José

Caribbean Sea

Panamá

PANAMA

SOUTH AMERICA

Tropic of Cancer

N

## NORTH AMERICA

⊛ National capital

• Other city

— National boundary

AZIMUTHAL EQUAL AREA PROJECTION

| 0 | 250 | 500 | 750 Miles |

| 0 | 250 | 500 | 750 Kilometers |

10

CARIBBEAN SEA

Barranquilla
Maracaibo
Caracas
VENEZUELA

Medellín
*Orinoco River*
Georgetown
Paramaribo
GUYANA
Cayenne
SURINAME FRENCH
GUIANA
(FR.)

Bogotá
COLOMBIA

*Magdalena River*

ATLANTIC
OCEAN

Quito
ECUADOR
Guayaquil

Iquitos

Manaus
*Amazon* River

Equator

Fortaleza

PERU

B R A Z I L

Recife

Lima

Lake
Titicaca
La Paz

BOLIVIA

Sucre

Salvador

Brasília
*São Francisco River*

Belo Horizonte

PARAGUAY

*Paraná River*

Rio de Janeiro
São Paulo

Tropic of Capricorn

Asunción

CHILE

*Paraguay River*

*Uruguay River*

Pôrto Alegre

Córdoba

Rosario

URUGUAY

ATLANTIC
OCEAN

PACIFIC

OCEAN

Valparaíso Santiago

Buenos Aires
Montevideo
*Río de la Plata*

ANDES

ARGENTINA
PAMPAS

N

**SOUTH AMERICA**

⊛ National capital

• Other city

— National boundary

AZIMUTHAL EQUAL AREA PROJECTION

0      250      500 Miles

0   250   500 Kilometers

Stanley
FALKLAND
ISLANDS
(U.K.)

TIERRA
DEL
FUEGO

Cape Horn

SOUTH
GEORGIA
(U.K.)

**11**

**EUROPE**

⊛ National capital

• Other city

⊥⊤⊤ Canal

— National boundary

AZIMUTHAL EQUAL AREA PROJECTION

Reykjavík
**ICELAND**

Arctic Circle

FAROE IS.
**(DEN.)**

SHETLAND IS.
**(U.K.)**

• Trondheim

**SWEDEN**

**NORWAY**

Gulf of Bothnia

• Bergen

⊛ Oslo

Uppsala •

• Stavanger

Stockholm ⊛

Göteborg •

Glasgow • • Edinburgh

Belfast •

**UNITED
KINGDOM**

**DENMARK**

Copenhagen ⊛

Baltic    Sea

North

Dublin ⊛

**IRELAND**

Liverpool •

• Manchester

Sea

Bornholm
**(DEN.)**

Kaliningrad
•

• Birmingham

**NETHERLANDS**

• Hamburg

Gdańsk •

Cardiff •

Bristol •

Thames R.

London •

The Hague ⊛ • Amsterdam

• Bremen

**EAST**

Vistula

Dover •

⊛ Berlin

**GERMANY**

Oder

**POLAND**

English    Channel

Calais •

Rotterdam •

**WEST**

Leipzig

**BELGIUM**

⊛ Brussels

**GERMANY**

• Bonn

Elbe

R.

⊛ Prague

Kraków •

ATLANTIC

Le Havre •

**LUXEMBOURG**

• Frankfurt

River

Seine

Paris ⊛

⊛ Luxembourg

**CZECHOSLOVAKIA**

R.

Loire     River

Strasbourg •

• Stuttgart

Danube

• Munich

Vienna ⊛

OCEAN

La Rochelle •

**FRANCE**

• Dijon

Rhine    R.

**LIECHTENSTEIN**

Zürich •

**AUSTRIA**

Budapest ⊛

Bern ⊛

**SWITZERLAND**

**HUNGARY**

Bay of
Biscay

• Bordeaux

Geneva •

Lyon •

**A L P S**

Rhône R.

• Zagreb

Garonne

R.

Milan •

Venice •

• Trieste

Turin •

Po River

**PYRENEES**

Genoa •

Belgrade •

**PORTUGAL**

• Porto

Ebro    River

**ANDORRA**

Marseille •

Nice •

**MONACO**

**SAN
MARINO**

**YUGOSLAVIA**

• Sarajevo

Tagus    R.

• Madrid

Florence •

**APENNINES**

Lisbon ⊛

**SPAIN**

Barcelona •

Corsica
**(FR.)**

Tiber

R.

⊛ Rome

Adriatic    Sea

Tiranë ⊛

**ITALY**

**ALBANIA**

• Seville

• Valencia

Sardinia
**(IT.)**

• Naples

Tyrrhenian

**BALEARIC ISLANDS
(SP.)**

Cádiz •

Sea

Ionian
Sea

Strait of
Gibraltar

M e d i t e r r a n e a n    S e a

Palermo •

**Sicily**

**A F R I C A**

◌ **MALTA**

GR

ARCTIC
OCEAN

URAL MOUNTAINS

White Sea

Arkhangelsk

North Dvina River

FINLAND

Lake Ladoga

Helsinki
Gulf of Finland
Leningrad

Tallinn

Gor'kiy

Riga

Moscow

Kuibyshev

Ural River

SOVIET     UNION

Vilnius

Minsk

Warsaw

Volgograd

Volga River

Kiev

Kharkov

CARPATHIAN MTS.

Dniester River

Don River

R.

Dnieper

Odessa

Sea of Azov

ROMANIA

CAUCASUS MTS.

Caspian Sea

Bucharest

Danube River

Sevastopol

Sea

BALKAN MTS.

Black

Sofia

BULGARIA

TURKEY

Istanbul

Aegean Sea

GREECE

N

A S I A

Athens

Crete

| 0 | 100 | 200 | 300 Miles |
|---|---|---|---|
| 0 | 100 | 200 | 300 Kilometers |

EUROPE

URAL MOUNTAINS

Ob
Irtysh
River
Yenisei
River

Sverdlovsk
Chelyabinsk
Omsk
Novosibirsk

Arctic Circle

Lake Balkhash

Black Sea
CAUCASUS
Caspian Sea
Aral Sea

Baku
Alma-Ata

Mediterranean Sea

Ankara
TURKEY
Tashkent
Samarkand

Nicosia
CYPRUS
SYRIA
Tigris
Euphrates
R.
Baghdad
Tehran
Kabul
AFGHANISTAN
Islamabad
Disputed
Lhasa

Beirut
Damascus
Jerusalem
Amman
ISRAEL
JORDAN
IRAQ
IRAN
R.
Lahore
PAKISTAN
HIMALAYAS
Brahmaputra R.

LEBANON
Kuwait
Neutral Zone
KUWAIT
Persian Gulf
Indus
New Delhi
NEPAL
Thimbu
BHUTAN
Katmandu
R.
Ganges

SAUDI
Manama
BAHRAIN
QATAR
Riyadh
Doha
UNITED ARAB
EMIRATES
Abu
Dhabi
OMAN
Muscat
Karachi
BANGLADESH
Dacca

Red Sea
Tropic of Cancer
Jiddah
Mecca
ARABIA
Undefined
OMAN
Bombay
INDIA
Calcutta

Sanaa
YEMEN
Undefined
PEOPLE'S DEMOCRATIC
REPUBLIC OF YEMEN
Arabian Sea
Madras
ANDAMAN
ISLANDS
(INDIA)
Bay of Bengal

AFRICA
Aden
of
Gulf
Socotra I.
(P.D.R. YEMEN)
LACCADIVE
ISLANDS
(INDIA)
SRI LANKA
NICOBAR
ISLANDS
(INDIA)

Colombo

Male
MALDIVES

N

Equator

INDIAN
OCEAN

0          500          1000 Miles

0     500     1000 Kilometers

**14**

ARCTIC OCEAN

Arctic Circle

80°

70°

Lena River

SOVIET UNION

Lena River

Lena River

Bering Sea

60°

Sea of Okhotsk

KAMCHATKA PENINSULA

50°

Lake Baikal

Amur River

•Ulaanbaatar

KURIL ISLANDS (U.S.S.R. & JAPAN)

MONGOLIA

•Harbin

GOBI (DESERT)

•Vladivostok

Sea of Japan

40°

Beijing ⊛

N. KOREA

Yalu R.

P'yongyang ⊛

Tianjin •

Truce Line

JAPAN

Seoul ⊛

Huang He

S. KOREA

Tokyo ⊛

CHINA

Kobe •

Yokohama

Yellow Sea

Osaka•

30°

Chang Jiang

Shanghai

East China Sea

RYUKYU IS. (JAPAN)

PACIFIC

•Chongqing

OCEAN

Xi River

Taipei•

Irrawaddy R.

Guangzhou•

TAIWAN

Tropic of Cancer

20°

BURMA

Hanoi•

MACAO (PORT.)

HONG KONG (U.K.)

LAOS

Vientiane•

Mekong R.

**ASIA**

Rangoon•

South China Sea

Philippine Sea

⊛   National capital

THAILAND

•   Other city

Bangkok•

VIETNAM

Manila•

PHILIPPINES

———   National boundary

CAMBODIA (KAMPUCHEA)

ROBINSON PROJECTION

Phnom Penh•

Ho Chi Minh City•

10°

BRUNEI

MALAYSIA

Bandar Seri Begawan ⊛

Kuala Lumpur ⊛

Singapore ⊛

SINGAPORE

Equator

0°

Java Sea

Jakarta ⊛

INDONESIA

10°

**15**

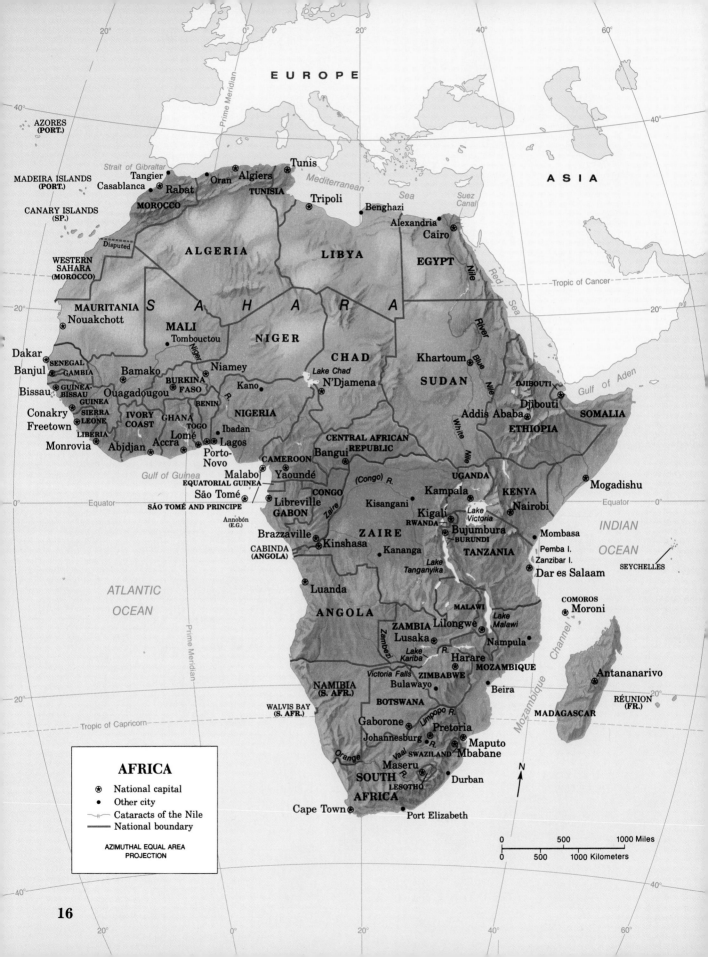

EUROPE

ASIA

AZORES
(PORT.)

MADEIRA ISLANDS
(PORT.)

CANARY ISLANDS
(SP.)

Strait of Gibraltar
Tangier
Casablanca
Rabat
MOROCCO

Oran
Algiers
TUNISIA

Tunis

Mediterranean
Sea

Tripoli

Benghazi

Suez
Canal

Alexandria
Cairo

WESTERN
SAHARA
(MOROCCO)

Disputed

ALGERIA

LIBYA

EGYPT

Nile

Tropic of Cancer

MAURITANIA
Nouakchott

S        A        H        A        R        A

Red

Sea

River

MALI

NIGER

Tombouctou

CHAD

Khartoum

Blue

Dakar
SENEGAL
Banjul GAMBIA
Bissau GUINEA-
BISSAU
GUINEA
Conakry
Freetown SIERRA
LEONE
Monrovia LIBERIA

Bamako

Niamey

Niger

Kano

R.

BURKINA
FASO
Ouagadougou

BENIN

IVORY
COAST GHANA
TOGO
Lomé
Accra

Abidjan

Lake Chad
N'Djamena

SUDAN

Nile

DJIBOUTI
Djibouti

Gulf of Aden

White

Addis Ababa
ETHIOPIA

SOMALIA

NIGERIA

Ibadan
Lagos
Porto-
Novo

CENTRAL AFRICAN
REPUBLIC
Bangui

Nile

Mogadishu

CAMEROON

Gulf of Guinea
Malabo
EQUATORIAL GUINEA
São Tomé
SÃO TOMÉ AND PRINCIPE
Annóbon
(E.G.)

Yaoundé

CONGO
Libreville
GABON

(Congo) R.

UGANDA

Kampala

KENYA

Kisangani

Zaire

ZAIRE

Kigali
RWANDA

Lake
Victoria

Nairobi

Mombasa
Pemba I.

Equator

Brazzaville
Kinshasa
CABINDA
(ANGOLA)

Kananga

Bujumbura
BURUNDI

TANZANIA

Zanzibar I.
Dar es Salaam

INDIAN

OCEAN

SEYCHELLES

ATLANTIC

OCEAN

Luanda

Lake
Tanganyika

MALAWI

COMOROS
Moroni

ANGOLA

ZAMBIA
Lusaka

Lilongwe

Lake
Malawi

Nampula

Prime Meridian

Zambezi

Lake
Kariba

R.

Harare

MOZAMBIQUE

Antananarivo

RÉUNION
(FR.)

Victoria Falls
ZIMBABWE
Bulawayo

NAMIBIA
(S. AFR.)
WALVIS BAY
(S. AFR.)

BOTSWANA

Beira

Mozambique Channel

MADAGASCAR

Tropic of Capricorn

Gaborone

Limpopo R.

Johannesburg
Orange
Vaal R.
SOUTH
AFRICA

Pretoria
Maputo
SWAZILAND Mbabane
Maseru
LESOTHO

Cape Town

Durban

Port Elizabeth

N

## AFRICA

⊛ National capital

• Other city

Cataracts of the Nile

National boundary

AZIMUTHAL EQUAL AREA
PROJECTION

0        500        1000 Miles

0      500    1000 Kilometers

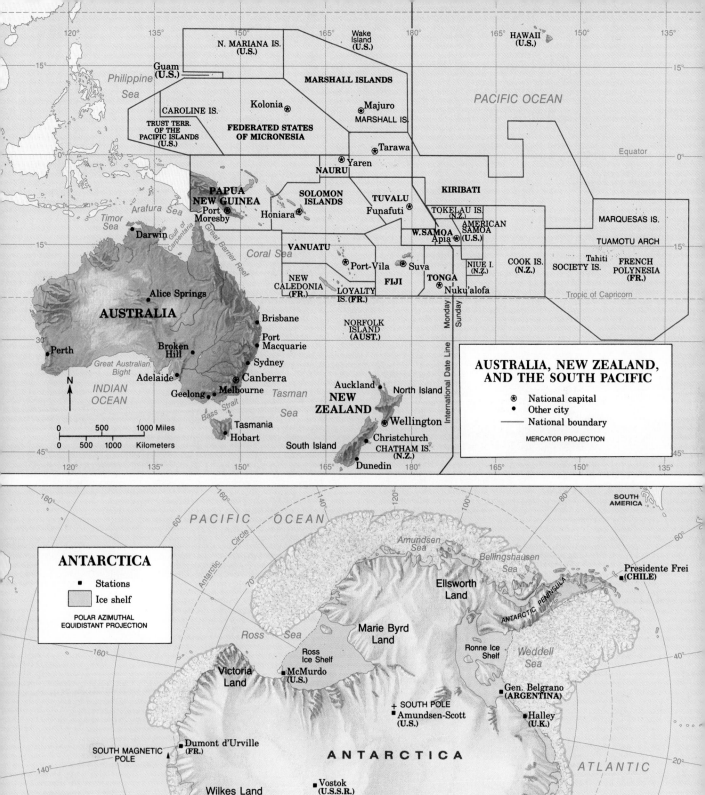

# AUSTRALIA, NEW ZEALAND, AND THE SOUTH PACIFIC

- ⊛ National capital
- • Other city
- — National boundary

MERCATOR PROJECTION

## Map labels (Australia, New Zealand, and South Pacific)

N. MARIANA IS. (U.S.)
Wake Island (U.S.)
HAWAII (U.S.)
Guam (U.S.)
Philippine Sea
MARSHALL ISLANDS
PACIFIC OCEAN
CAROLINE IS.
Kolonia
Majuro
MARSHALL IS.
TRUST TERR. OF THE PACIFIC ISLANDS (U.S.)
FEDERATED STATES OF MICRONESIA
Tarawa
Equator
Yaren
NAURU
KIRIBATI
PAPUA NEW GUINEA
Port Moresby
SOLOMON ISLANDS
Honiara
TUVALU
Funafuti
TOKELAU IS. (N.Z.)
MARQUESAS IS.
Timor Sea
Arafura Sea
Darwin
Gulf of Carpentaria
Great Barrier Reef
Coral Sea
VANUATU
Port-Vila
NEW CALEDONIA (FR.)
LOYALTY IS. (FR.)
FIJI
Suva
W.SAMOA
Apia
AMERICAN SAMOA (U.S.)
NIUE I. (N.Z.)
TONGA
Nuku'alofa
COOK IS. (N.Z.)
SOCIETY IS.
Tahiti
TUAMOTU ARCH.
FRENCH POLYNESIA (FR.)
Tropic of Capricorn
Alice Springs
AUSTRALIA
Brisbane
Port Macquarie
Sydney
Broken Hill
Perth
Great Australian Bight
Adelaide
Canberra
Geelong
Melbourne
Tasman Sea
NORFOLK ISLAND (AUST.)
Auckland
North Island
NEW ZEALAND
Wellington
Christchurch
CHATHAM IS. (N.Z.)
South Island
Dunedin
Bass Strait
Tasmania
Hobart
INDIAN OCEAN
N
Monday / Sunday
International Date Line

Scale:
0 500 1000 Miles
0 500 1000 Kilometers

# ANTARCTICA

- ■ Stations
- ▨ Ice shelf

POLAR AZIMUTHAL EQUIDISTANT PROJECTION

## Map labels (Antarctica)

PACIFIC OCEAN
SOUTH AMERICA
Antarctic Circle
Amundsen Sea
Bellingshausen Sea
Ellsworth Land
Presidente Frei (CHILE)
ANTARCTIC PENINSULA
Ross Sea
Marie Byrd Land
Ronne Ice Shelf
Weddell Sea
Ross Ice Shelf
McMurdo (U.S.)
Victoria Land
Gen. Belgrano (ARGENTINA)
SOUTH POLE
Amundsen-Scott (U.S.)
Halley (U.K.)
Dumont d'Urville (FR.)
SOUTH MAGNETIC POLE
ANTARCTICA
ATLANTIC OCEAN
Wilkes Land
Vostok (U.S.S.R.)
Queen Maud Land
Syoma (JAPAN)
Davis Sea
Mawson (AUSTRALIA)
Enderby Land
INDIAN OCEAN

Scale:
0 250 500 750 Miles
0 250 500 750 Kilometers

**17**

UNITED STATES*
Elevation

| Feet | Meters |
|---|---|
| 13,120 | 4,000 |
| 6,560 | 2,000 |
| 1,640 | 500 |
| 656 | 200 |
| 0 | 0 |
| Below sea level | Below sea level |

⊕ National capital
★ State capital
• Other city
━━ National boundary
── State boundary

ALBERS EQUAL AREA PROJECTION

19

Labels on illustration: Timberline, Glacier, Iceberg, Fjord, VALLEY, PLATEAU, Canyon, HIGHLAND, Lake, PLAIN, River, LOWLAND, Beach, Seacoast, Mouth of river, Lake, Natural Harbor, Channel, Isthmus, Cove, OCEAN, ARCHIPELAGO, SEA, PENINSULA, Cape

**archipelago**   Group or chain of islands

**basin**   Broad depression in the earth's surface

**bay**   Body of water that extends inland from a larger body of water and is smaller than a gulf

**beach**   Shore of an ocean, lake, river, or other body of water; covered by sand or rock

**breakwater**   Artificial offshore construction that protects the shore from wave damage and protects ships in a harbor

**canal**   Narrow body of water built for shipping, irrigation, or drainage

**canyon**   Narrow valley with steep sides that often has water flowing along its floor

**cape**   Land that extends into water, often marking the farthest extent of a land area, as Cape Hatteras

**channel**   Body of water between two land areas; or the deepest part of a river

**cliff**   Steep landform of rock or earth; sometimes called a **bluff**

**continent**   One of seven large landmasses on the earth's surface

**cove**   Small sheltered bay; sometimes called a **lagoon** or **inlet**

**dam**   Barrier built to hold water or to stop or slow its flow

**delta**   Land created from soils deposited at the mouth of a river

**desert**   Land affected by extremely dry conditions; usually support little or no vegetation

**divide**   Point from which rivers flow in opposite directions; usually known as a **continental divide**

**downstream**   Direction the water in a river or stream flows toward its mouth

**fjord**   Narrow body of water extending from the sea between steep cliffs

**foothills**   Hilly area at the base of a mountain range

**glacier**   Large mass of moving ice

**gulf**   Large body of water that extends inland from the ocean

**harbor**   Natural or artificial body of water deep enough to be navigable

**highland**   Area of mountains, hills, or plateaus

**hill**   Generally rounded land that rises at least 500 feet (152 meters) and has local relief of less than 2,000 feet (610 meters)

**iceberg**   Mass of floating ice that has broken off from a glacier

**inlet**   Small body of water that extends inland from a sea, lake, or river; *see* cove

**island**   Land area completely surrounded by water

**isthmus**   Narrow piece of land that connects two larger landmasses, as the Isthmus of Panama

**lake**   Body of water completely surrounded by land

**lowland**   Generally flat, low-lying land

**marsh**   Low land with moist soils and tall grasses

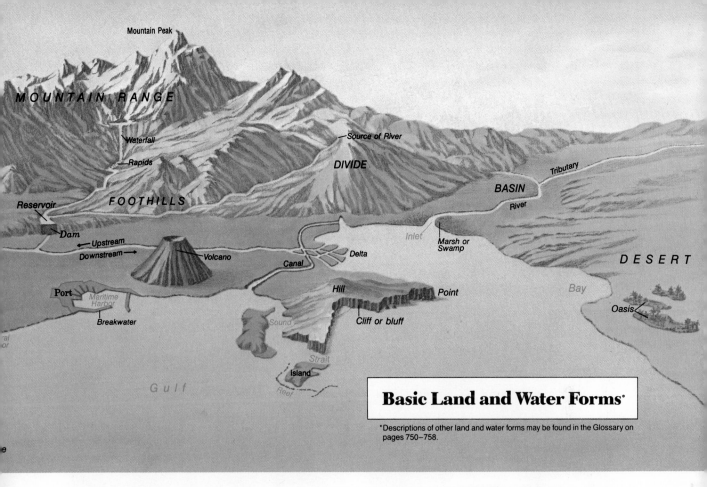

Mountain Peak

MOUNTAIN RANGE

Waterfall

Source of River

Rapids

DIVIDE

Tributary

BASIN

River

Reservoir

FOOTHILLS

Dam

Inlet

Marsh or Swamp

Upstream

Delta

Downstream

Volcano

Canal

DESERT

Port

Maritime Harbor

Hill

Point

Bay

Oasis

Breakwater

Cliff or bluff

Sound

Strait

Island

Gulf

Reef

## Basic Land and Water Forms*

*Descriptions of other land and water forms may be found in the Glossary on pages 750–758.

**mountain**  Landform distinguished by steep slopes, local relief of at least 2,000 feet (610 meters), and high elevation

**mountain peak**  Single mountain that rises from the surrounding land; or highest point of a mountain, sometimes called the **summit**

**mountain range**  Chain of mountains

**mouth**  Place where a river or stream enters a larger body of water

**oasis**  Fertile area where water is available surrounded by desert

**ocean**  Large body of saltwater that covers nearly three-fourths of the earth's surface; usually divided into four main components—Pacific, Atlantic, Indian, and Arctic—called oceans

**peninsula**  Narrow piece of land surrounded on three sides by water

**plain**  Landform characterized by nearly level or gently rolling land and with little slope and low local relief

**plateau**  Generally flat area that rises far above surrounding land on at least one side and has little slope, high elevation, and low local relief

**point**  Point of land that projects into a body of water

**port**  City where ships load and unload goods

**rapids**  Shallow, often rocky, part of a river where the current moves swiftly

**reef**  Landform composed of rock or sand at or near the water's surface

**reservoir**  Body of water used for water storage; often created by a dam

**river**  Large stream with a substantial flow of water

**sea**  Large body of water that is entirely or almost entirely surrounded by land, as the Baltic Sea

**seacoast**  Land area bordering a sea or ocean

**sound**  Broad inlet of the ocean usually parallel to the coast, as Long Island Sound; or a waterway separating islands from the mainland

**source**  Place where a river or stream begins

**strait**  Narrow body of water linking larger bodies of water, as the Strait of Gibraltar

**stream**  Body of water similar to but smaller than a river

**swamp**  Land that is always wet and sometimes covered with water; may be forested, often with mangrove trees

**timberline**  Line on a mountain above which trees do not grow; also called the **tree line**

**tributary**  Stream or river that flows into a larger river

**upstream**  Opposite direction of the flow of a river, toward the river's source and away from its mouth

**valley**  Low land between hills or mountains; a river often flows across the valley floor

**volcano**  Mountain or hill formed from layers of lava that solidify after an eruption and from which rocks, steam, gas, and ash may occasionally erupt

**waterfall**  Steep drop in a stream or river over which water flows

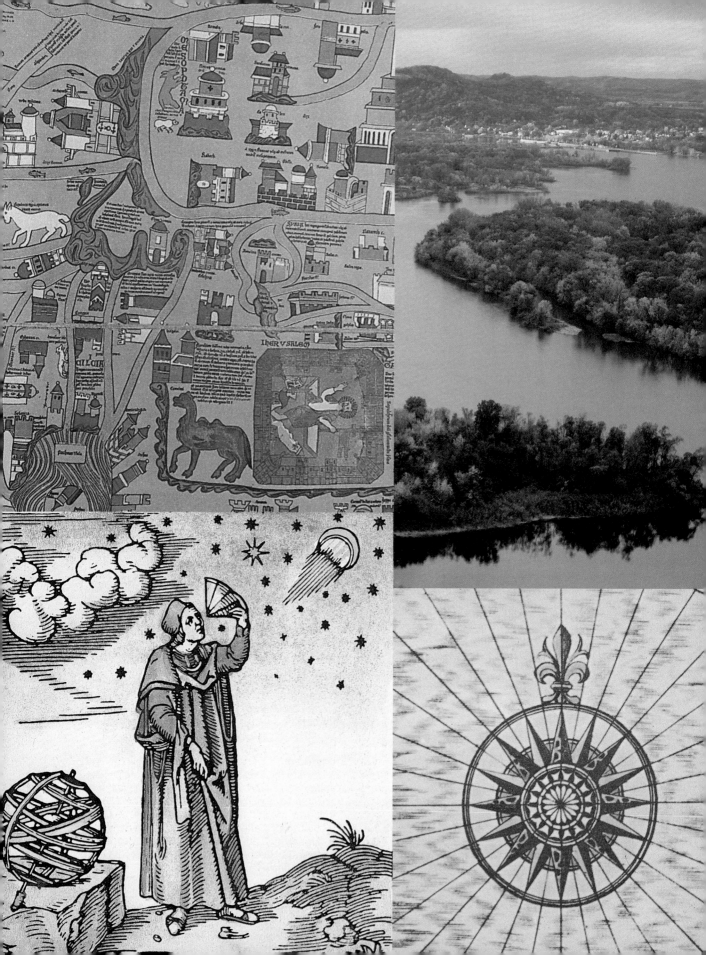

# UNIT 1

# THE NATURE AND PURPOSE OF GEOGRAPHY

**CHAPTER 1** The Nature of Geography
**CHAPTER 2** The Tools of Geography

23

# The Nature of Geography

# PUTTING THE CHAPTER IN FOCUS

Geography, which comes from the Greek words *geo,* meaning "earth," and *graphein,* meaning "description," is literally a study of the planet Earth. As trained scientists, geographers describe and analyze the physical characteristics of our planet and the ways in which people interact with these physical characteristics and with each other. From this study of the earth and its people, geographers have identified five basic themes—location, place, relationships within places, movement, and regions. These themes remain the basis of geographic study.

## Ideas to Understand

In studying about the nature of geography, use these ideas to give direction to your reading.

1 Geographers attempt to describe the earth accurately.
2 Modern geography focuses on five basic themes.

## Terms to Define

The following terms are some of the key terms in the chapter. Defining them will help you understand the nature of geography.

| | |
|---|---|
| geography | equator |
| environment | hemisphere |
| geographer | parallel |
| physical geography | meridian |
| cultural geography | prime meridian |
| culture | relative location |
| human habitat | place |
| cultural diffusion | relationships |
| absolute location | within places |
| axis | movement |
| rotate | region |

## Places to Locate

Locating the following places will add to your knowledge of geography.

| | |
|---|---|
| North Pole | Northern Hemisphere |
| South Pole | Southern Hemisphere |

## 1 Geographers attempt to describe the earth accurately.

Throughout history people who ventured even short distances from where they lived became keenly aware of differences that distinguish one place from another and one group of people from another. Many of these travelers formed mental images of the places that they had visited and told others what they had seen. They sometimes scratched crude maps on rocks or on pieces of cloth or leather to improve the accuracy of their descriptions.

**Geography,** the study of the relationship between people and their physical surroundings, or **environments** (in·vy·rehn·mehnt), grew directly out of these attempts by early explorers to describe what they had seen on their travels. Today those who study geography describe and analyze the earth to explain what is where, why it is there, and what significance it has.

### The Study of the Earth

Earth is only one of nine planets in our solar system that revolves around the sun—a minor star in the universe. A **planet** is an object or body that is made of various solids and gases and that circles a star. A star and the planets and other related bodies such as asteroids that revolve around it are known as a **solar system.**

◀ *A view of earth from space*

Earth is the third planet in distance from the sun, which is 93 million miles (150 million kilometers) away. Even though the sun, with a diameter of 864,000 miles (1,393,548 kilometers), ranks as one of the smaller stars in the universe, it is huge when compared to Earth, which has a diameter of more than 7,926 miles (12,783 kilometers). The sun's heat and light provide most of the energy that makes life on Earth possible. It is this life and the physical features of the earth* that **geographers,** scientists who study the relationship between people and their environments, attempt to describe and analyze. Most geographers focus on one of the two major branches of geography, physical geography and cultural geography, or on one of its more specialized fields.

## Physical Geography

The earth offers many different natural, or physical, features. Low-lying, sweltering jungles mark some places on the earth. Ice-covered, windswept mountain peaks dominate other places. Each location derives its physical character from combinations of the shapes of the land, climate, soils, plants, animals, and other naturally occurring phenomena. These combinations of physical features and their variations from place to place are the special concern of **physical geography,** the study of the physical features and changes of the earth's surface.

## Cultural Geography

In marked contrast to physical geography, **cultural geography** focuses on the impact of human ideas and actions on the earth. The sum of what a human group acquires through living together, such as language, knowledge, skills, art, literature,

laws, customs, and life styles, is known as that group's **culture.** Cultural features are evident in a group's tools, foods, government, religions, and other characteristics.

Each group of people leaves a distinct imprint on its **human habitat** (HAB·eh·tat), or the place where that group lives. This imprint, or effect, is known as the **cultural landscape.** Examples of cultural landscapes include the fields people clear and farm, the crops and livestock they raise, and the style and distribution of the villages and cities they build.

The skyscrapers of New York City's cultural landscape, for example, show how humans there have changed the environment. People have constructed multistory buildings to make better use of a very limited amount of space. Even remote villages in The Himalaya or in the Amazon Basin show how a **society,** or group of people who share traditions, institutions, activities, and interests, changes its habitat. For example, farmers in the Amazon Basin burn away parts of the forest to provide space to grow crops and cut down trees to use to build houses.

Along with the cultural landscape, cultural geographers also study the process of **cultural diffusion** (dif·YOO·zhehn), or the spread of parts of a culture from one area to another. The spread of Christianity from Palestine to other parts of the Middle East and to Europe between the years A.D. 100 and 600 is one example of cultural diffusion. The spread of the alphabet is another example. The alphabet originated in the Middle East about 2000 B.C. and gradually spread to most parts of the world. Today many different cultures use various forms of the alphabet to write their languages.

The process of cultural diffusion continues today. The spread of rock music from the United States to Great Britain and other parts of the world illustrates modern cultural diffusion.

---

* The word *earth* is capitalized only in discussions of planets in the solar system.

*Text continues on page 28.*

Ancient geography came to an end with the work of Ptolemy (TAHL·uh·mee), the best-known and most widely acclaimed astronomer and geographer of the ancient world. Little is known about Ptolemy's life other than that he worked in the Roman Empire's great library in Alexandria, Egypt, between A.D. 127 and 150. It was in Alexandria, the cultural center of the ancient world, that he wrote his most important work on astronomy. Ptolemy entitled the work *Mathematical Composition.* It was so admired, however, that it became known as the *Almagest,* a combination of Greek and Arabic terms meaning "the greatest."

### A Guide to Geography

After completing his work on astronomy, Ptolemy began preparing *A Guide to Geography,* an eight-volume work on all aspects of geography. Ptolemy began the work with a detailed discussion of different methods of mapmaking and a lengthy list of all of the known places in the world, together with their latitudes and longitudes. The book also contained 26 colored maps and a carefully planned new map of the world. Ptolemy adopted the grid of latitude and longitude lines developed by the Greek geographer Hipparchus (hip·AHR·kuhs) nearly 300 years earlier. This grid was based on the division of a circle into 360 parts. Using this system, every place on the earth could be given a precise location.

### The Problem of Accuracy

Despite its appearance of accuracy, however, Ptolemy's geography was a compilation of errors. In his time, for example, latitude could only be approximated and there was no exact way of determining longitude at all. Therefore each listing of latitude and longitude was, at best, only a rough estimate.

*Ptolemy with astronomy tools*

Furthermore Ptolemy greatly exaggerated the size of the land area from Spain to China, vastly underestimated the size of the Atlantic Ocean, and estimated the circumference of the earth to be about half its actual size. Based on Ptolemy's inaccurate calculations, Christopher Columbus believed that Asia was close to Europe on the west. It was actually Ptolemy's error that encouraged Columbus to set forth on his westward voyage across the Atlantic Ocean.

### A Lasting Impact

In spite of mistakes made more from the lack of accurate instruments than from ignorance, Ptolemy was extremely well respected. *A Guide to Geography* was such a monumental work that its significance to the development of the field of geography cannot be overestimated. His work remained the major geographic study for nearly 1,000 years.

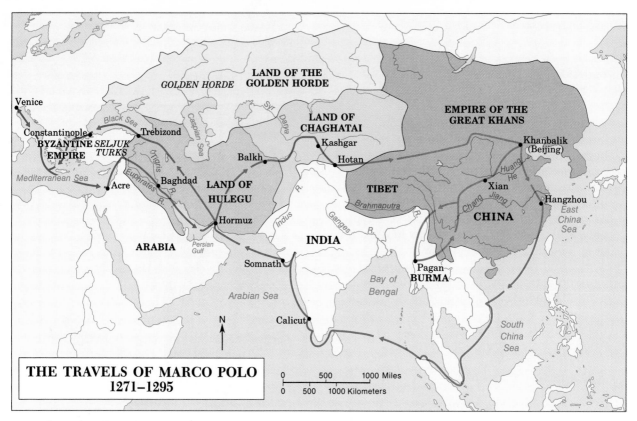

THE TRAVELS OF MARCO POLO
1271–1295

**Learning from Maps.** *Marco Polo traveled across lands that he had never seen and managed to return to Venice. How do you think his expedition found its way home?*

## Other Fields of Geography

Geographers study many aspects of the physical and cultural landscapes. These different approaches have led to the development of specialized fields of geography.

**Biophysical geography** is the study of the natural environment and the interrelationships of all the living things in that environment. It examines the shapes of the land and bodies of water, or **topography** (tuh·PAHG·ruh·fee), of a given location, along with its climate, soil, plants, and animals.

The fields of political, social, and economic geography make up parts of cultural geography and they often overlap. **Political geography** focuses on the political organization of areas. It deals with the administration of areas, territorial acquisitions, political boundaries, and patterns of government. Political geography is closely tied

to **social geography,** the study of the interrelationships of groups and communities. This field includes the study of human movements within and between communities. **Economic geography** focuses on resources and resource use, agriculture and land use, and global trade interactions. It also examines such diverse geographic ideas as factory locations, transportation networking, and market distribution. Economic geography forms one of the broadest subdivisions of cultural geography and relies heavily on information from other fields.

**Historical geography** examines the ways in which the relationship between people and their environments has changed over time. This field attempts to bring time and space together. Because understanding the present requires knowledge of the past, geographers place a great deal of emphasis on the study of historical geography.

**28**

# GEOGRAPHY IN THE WORKPLACE
## Cartographers

In a way we are all cartographers, or mapmakers. Each of us has sketched simple maps to show friends how to get to our house or to a good camping or fishing ground.

Each of us also has used the products of professional cartographers. Vacationers use maps to determine the best routes to their destinations. People in the armed forces use maps to plan troop movements and lines of defense. People in business often use maps to plan sales campaigns, to determine the best route for the distribution of their products, and to identify the least costly way of getting raw materials from their source to the factory.

In one sense, then, cartography is an occupation that almost everyone practices and uses. Yet it also is a highly specialized science that offers exciting and rewarding careers to those who successfully complete the required training.

Cartography offers a wide variety of employment opportunities. The United States government employs more than 20,000 cartographers to prepare the wide variety of maps it requires in its daily operations. Every civilian and military branch of government has its own highly specialized map needs and its own staff of cartographers to meet those needs.

One of the most important mapping agencies of our government is the United States Geological Survey (USGS). The USGS prepares huge numbers of topographic, or terrain, maps. Such maps are readily available in many stores that carry camping and sporting equipment. These USGS topographic maps have been drawn for the entire nation and are under continuous revision. Most are large-scale maps that provide the user with a vast amount of cultural information, as well as an accurate portrayal of the terrain.

The National Ocean Survey is responsible for charting the coastlines of our nation. It prepares navigational charts vital to all sailors, from the captains of supertankers to weekend recreational sailors. The Oceanographic Office of the Navy develops both coastal and worldwide ocean maps. The Air Force, which operates a large cartographic establishment in St. Louis, employs over 500 cartographers who prepare aeronautical charts. The Army Map Service, which is probably the largest of all the government mapping agencies, draws and prints topographic maps for military use. Among the dozens of other government agencies that employ cartographers are the Census Bureau, the Forest Service, the Bureau of Indian Affairs, the Soil Conservation Service, the Department of Agriculture, and the Department of State.

Private firms also need cartographers to prepare maps. These firms produce highway maps; maps that appear in newspapers, magazines, and on television news programs; maps designed for schools; and the maps that appear in encyclopedias and other references that contain information about places around the world.

**Urban geography** focuses on the locations of cities, the services cities provide, and the movements of goods and people to and from cities. The rapid growth of cities in the modern world has made this field an increasingly important area of study.

**Cartography** is the art and science of mapmaking. Recent developments in mathematics, computers, and electronics have expanded cartography to include the study and analysis of aerial photographs and remotely sensed images (see page 49).

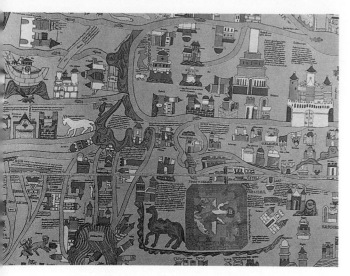

**Learning from Pictures.** *Ancient maps, such as this one of Jerusalem in 1240, detail places of interest. How do modern maps identify absolute location?*

You may wish to refer to the GEOGRAPHY IN THE WORKPLACE features for more information about these fields of geography.

---

**SECTION 1 REVIEW**

1. **Define** geography, environment, planet, solar system, geographer, physical geography, cultural geography, culture, human habitat, cultural landscape, society, cultural diffusion, biophysical geography, topography, political geography, social geography, economic geography, historical geography, urban geography, cartography
2. **Tracing Ideas** How did the study of geography develop?
3. **Summarizing Ideas** What are the two major branches of geography?
4. **Applying Ideas** List three examples of the cultural landscape in your area.
5. **Categorizing Ideas** Which fields of geography are more closely related to (a) physical geography and (b) cultural geography? (c) Why is cartography related to both fields?

---

## 2 Modern geography focuses on five basic themes.

Modern geography deals with five major themes, or topics. They are location, which is classified as absolute or relative; place; relationships within places; movement; and regions. Each of these five themes offers insights about connections between the physical earth and its human inhabitants.

### Absolute Location

One of the basic tasks in geography is to describe exactly what is where on the earth. To do this, geographers must identify the **absolute location,** or the precise spot on the earth, of each place. The spherical shape of the earth makes describing locations difficult. A sphere has no corners, edges, or other useful reference points.

Like all spheres, the earth has an **axis** (AK·sehs), or an imaginary line extending through its center. Unlike other spheres, however, the earth's axis is tilted. In addition, the earth **rotates,** or spins on its axis, making one complete rotation every 24 hours. As the earth rotates, one-half of the planet faces toward the sun and is in daylight. The other half faces away from the sun and is in darkness. The ends of the axis are the North Pole in the northern part of the earth and the South Pole in the southern part. The two poles serve as important reference points in a system geographers created to pinpoint absolute locations. As you will see, a grid formed by a series of imaginary lines drawn around the earth serves as the basis of this system.

**Lines of latitude.** The **equator** is an imaginary line drawn around the globe halfway between the North and South poles. The equator divides the earth into two halves, or **hemispheres** (HEM·eh·sfeer)—the Northern Hemisphere and the Southern

Hemisphere. Several shorter imaginary lines circle the earth parallel to the equator and on both sides of it. They are called **parallels,** or **lines of latitude.**

Parallels are used to locate places north and south of the equator through a special numbering system based on a unit of measurement known as degrees. In the Northern Hemisphere the parallels are numbered from zero degrees (0°) at the equator to ninety degrees (90°) north (N) at the North Pole. In the Southern Hemisphere they run from 0° at the equator to 90° south (S) at the South Pole.

In addition to the equator, geographers identify two other lines of latitude as especially important. The first is the Tropic of Cancer, located at 23.5° N. The second is the Tropic of Capricorn, located at 23.5° S. These parallels form the boundaries of the tropical regions of the earth. You will read more about them in Chapter 4.

**Lines of longitude.**  To complete the system for determining absolute locations,

geographers drew a second set of imaginary lines on the earth from pole to pole. These lines are called **meridians** (meh·RIHD·ee·uhns), or **lines of longitude** (LAHN·jeh·tood). Unlike lines of latitude, meridians are not parallel, or equal distances apart. Instead, the distances between meridians vary, with the farthest point between lines at the equator and the closest point at the poles.

In 1884 an international conference of astronomers agreed that the meridian passing through the Royal Observatory in Greenwich, England, near London, would serve as 0° longitude. This meridian is called the **prime meridian.** The meridian directly opposite the prime meridian, on the other side of the globe, is the 180° meridian. Just as the equator divides the earth into Northern and Southern hemispheres, the prime meridian and the 180° meridian divide the earth into Eastern and Western hemispheres. The Eastern Hemisphere covers the half of the earth that extends east of the prime meridian to the 180° meridian. The Western Hemisphere covers the half of

*Learning from Diagrams.*  *This diagram outlines the imaginary lines of latitude and longitude. At what coordinates do the equator and the prime meridian intersect?*

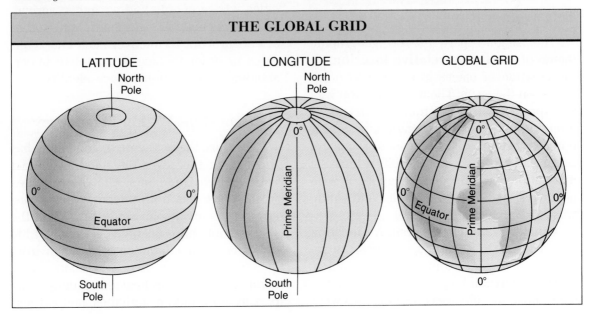

THE GLOBAL GRID

LATITUDE

LONGITUDE

GLOBAL GRID

31

the earth west of the prime meridian to the 180° meridian.

The meridians in the Eastern Hemisphere are numbered from 0° at the prime meridian to 180°. The meridians in the Western Hemisphere also are numbered from 0° to 180°. Through this numbering system, the meridians are used to locate places east and west of the prime meridian. For example, Rangoon, Burma, is at 96° east (E) longitude while Bakersfield, California, is at 119° west (W) longitude.

**The global grid.** Parallels and meridians cross each other to form an imaginary grid over the earth. Because each degree can be broken into 60 minutes (′) and each minute can be broken into 60 seconds (″), this grid can be used to fix the precise location of any point on the earth's surface. To identify an absolute location, list latitude coordinates first, followed by longitude coordinates. The Statue of Liberty in New York harbor, for example, is at 40°41′22″ N, 70°40′24″ W. The powder magazine in the center of the Alamo in San Antonio, Texas, is at 29°25′30″ N, 98°29′8″ W.

## Relative Location

The second part of the geographic theme of location is **relative location,** or the position of places in relation to other places on the earth. The most common way to express relative location is in terms of direction. The relative location of Singapore, for example, is southeast of Rangoon, Burma, because that is the city's location in relation to Rangoon. Singapore is also northwest of Jakarta, Indonesia, and southwest of Manila, Philippines.

Other ways to express relative location are in terms of distances, nearness to resources, and accessibility to trade routes. Such information helps geographers understand how specific areas develop and what

roles they play in world affairs. Singapore, for example, lies on one of the busiest trade routes in the world.

## Place

Every location on earth has unique characteristics and traits that distinguish it from all other locations. Geographers describe each location in terms of both physical and human characteristics. The physical characteristics of a location include the shapes of the land, bodies of water, climate, animal life, and vegetation. The human characteristics include the features of the cultural landscape. Together these physical and cultural aspects of a location make up its **place** identity.

The characteristics of a place as they appear today are a part of a location's place identity. Keep in mind, however, that place identity also includes the characteristics of a place as they appeared years ago. In many areas physical features obscure a cultural landscape that shows how humans of earlier times changed their environment. The dense forests of the Yucatán Peninsula in Mexico, for example, hide ruins of great cities whose people had advanced agricultural systems. Geographers and other scientists work to uncover such characteristics in order to have a complete understanding of a location's place identity.

## Relationships Within Places

The third major theme of geography has to do with the ways that people interact with their environments. Almost every area of the earth has both advantages and disadvantages for human settlement. Over the years people have adapted their way of life in order to accommodate their environment. People who live in climates with harsh winters wear heavier clothing, take part in more indoor activities, and eat less

fresh fruits and vegetables during the winter months than during the summer months, for example. At the same time, people have modified their physical surroundings. They have dug irrigation canals, mined coal, built tunnels, and cleared forests. Geographers classify all of these interactions between people and their natural environments as **relationships within places.**

The theme of relationships within places includes not only the interactions of people and their environments but also both the positive and negative consequences of those interactions. Consider this example. To produce energy industries burn coal, oil, and gas. The positive consequence is energy. The negative consequence is that sulfur and other pollutants are released into the air. In the air the chemicals in the pollutants combine with the water vapor and fall to the ground as the polluted precipitation commonly known as **acid rain.** Most of the acid rain falls on northeastern North America and Western Europe.

## Movement

The fourth theme of geography involves the interaction of humans with each other. Geographers call these interactions among people **movements.**

Each day people throughout the world interact with each other through travel, telecommunications, and the exchange of goods and services.

Geographers study movements, including your everyday interactions with people around the world, because they help to explain the relationships and connections between people. How and why do people move from one place to another? How do new ideas spread throughout the world? The study of movements also helps geographers understand the world as we know it today and predict changes that may occur in the future.

***Learning from Pictures.*** *Workers in Bangladesh dig a ditch to irrigate their parched fields. What positive and negative consequences do you think the ditch might have?*

## Regions

The fifth major theme of geography is regions. In order to study parts of the earth more closely, geographers divide the earth's surface into smaller units called **regions.** Regions vary in size from those that cover several countries to those that include only a part of a city. However, the particular feature or features that characterize an area set it apart from other regions. Hundreds of different features define the regions of the world. This means that one area may be a part of many different regions, and that the boundaries of one region often overlap the boundaries of another. Physical features, such as mountains or plains, or cultural features, such as religion or economic activity, define most regions of the world.

**Physical regions.** Features that define the physical regions of the earth include climate, soils, vegetation, and the shapes of the land. A mild climate and rich soils, for

*Text continues on page 35.*

Textbooks are carefully planned not only to present the facts of geography, mathematics, or biology, but also to give you practice in reading for understanding. Information about each major topic is usually contained in a chapter.

### How to Read a Chapter

Follow these guidelines to read a chapter in this textbook.

1. **Study the chapter's opening pages.** Read the chapter title and study the picture. Together they give you an idea of the chapter's theme.
2. **Use the chapter's study helps.** Take time to read "Putting the Chapter in Focus," which gives you a brief introduction to the main ideas contained in the chapter.
3. **Look at the way the page is divided.** Note that the size and style of type give clues to chapter organization. Sections of the chapter have headings like this:

> **1 Geographers attempt to describe the earth accurately.**

Subsections look like this:

> **The Study of the Earth**

The topics dealt with in the subsections have headings that look like this:

> **Lines of longitude.**

In fact, if you copied the headings from the text, indenting for each change in type size, you would have an outline of the chapter.

4. **Look at the illustrations and their captions.** Note that graphics add information as well as interest to the written material. "Reading" the assignment means "reading" the graphics.
5. **Make sure you know the meanings of key words.** Recognize that new terms appear in **boldface** type. They are defined **in context,** which means in terms of the subject you are studying.
6. **Read the Chapter Summary.** Make sure you have not missed any key information. You will note that the summary repeats the points outlined in "Putting the Chapter in Focus."

An assignment to "read" certain pages or to "study" a chapter should include all of these steps.

### Applying the Skill

Make an outline of Chapter 2 by copying the headings. Your outline for the first section should resemble the following one.

I. Globes and maps are useful models of the earth.
  A. Globes
    1. Advantages
    2. Disadvantages
  B. Maps
    1. Advantages
    2. Disadvantages
  C. Components of Maps
    1. Title
    2. Legend
    3. Direction indicator
    4. Scale
  D. Map Projections
    1. Correct shape
    2. Correct size
    3. Correct distance
    4. Correct direction

*To practice this skill, see Practicing Geography Skills on page 37.*

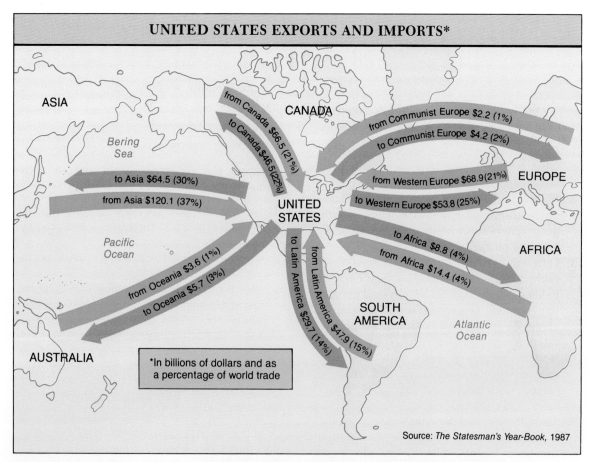

**UNITED STATES EXPORTS AND IMPORTS***

ASIA

CANADA

EUROPE

AFRICA

SOUTH
AMERICA

AUSTRALIA

Bering
Sea

Pacific
Ocean

Atlantic
Ocean

from Canada $66.5 (21%)

to Canada $46.5 (22%)

from Communist Europe $2.2 (1%)

to Communist Europe $4.2 (2%)

to Asia $64.5 (30%)

from Asia $120.1 (37%)

from Western Europe $68.9 (21%)

to Western Europe $53.8 (25%)

UNITED
STATES

to Africa $8.8 (4%)

from Africa $14.4 (4%)

from Oceania $3.6 (1%)

to Oceania $5.7 (3%)

to Latin America $47.9 (15%)

from Latin America $29.7 (14%)

*In billions of dollars and as
a percentage of world trade

Source: *The Statesman's Year-Book*, 1987

***Learning from Maps.*** *World trade provides people with products not available in their own countries. Where does the United States send the highest percentage of exports?*

example, distinguish the Fertile Triangle of the Soviet Union from parts of the country with features less favorable for farming. Similarly, high mountain ranges and rugged cliffs distinguish the Rocky Mountain region in the United States and Canada from less mountainous regions of North America.

**Cultural regions.** Human or cultural features also define regions of the earth. Geographers identify Anglo America and Latin America as cultural regions defined by language. Language, however, is only one of many features that distinguish cultural regions. Others include economic systems, political systems, and religion.

**SECTION 2 REVIEW**

1. **Define** absolute location, axis, rotate, equator, hemisphere, parallel, line of latitude, meridian, line of longitude, prime meridian, relative location, place, relationships within places, acid rain, movement, region
2. **Locate** North Pole, South Pole, Northern Hemisphere, Southern Hemisphere
3. **Summarizing Ideas** What are the five themes of modern geography?
4. **Interpreting Ideas** Why is the global grid significant?
5. **Analyzing Ideas** Why do geographers study movement?

# CHAPTER 1 REVIEW

## Chapter Summary

The following list contains the key concepts you have learned about the nature of geography.

1. Geographers study the earth to determine what is where, why it is there, and what significance it has.
2. Physical geographers study the natural and physical settings of the earth, while cultural geographers study human actions and their impacts on the earth.
3. Different approaches to the study of geography have led to the development of other fields of study, such as biophysical geography, political geography, social geography, economic geography, historical geography, urban geography, and cartography.
4. Modern geography deals with five basic themes: location—absolute and relative; place; relationships within places; movement; and regions.
5. Absolute location describes exactly where a place is on the earth; relative location describes where a place is in relation to other places.
6. Imaginary lines, called parallels and meridians, are drawn around the globe to form a grid. The grid is used to identify a point's absolute location on the earth's surface.
7. Place identity describes a location's unique characteristics.
8. Geographers study relationships within places to identify how humans interact with their natural surroundings.
9. Geographers study movement, or how humans interact with each other, to explain the relationships and connections between people.
10. Geographers divide the earth into regions distinguished by one or more physical or cultural features.
11. Ptolemy's *A Guide to Geography*, though it contained many inaccuracies, compiled much of the geographic information of the ancient world and called attention to the study of geography.

On a separate sheet of paper, complete the following review exercises.

## Reviewing Geographic Terms

Supply the geographic term that correctly completes each sentence.

1. ____ is the study of the relationship between people and their physical surroundings, or environments.
2. The place where a group lives is its ____ ____.
3. The sum of what a human group acquires through living together, including language, knowledge, skills, art, literature, law, customs, and life styles, is called ____.
4. The spread of certain parts of cultures from one part of the world to another is known as ____ ____.
5. ____ is the study of the natural environment and the interrelationships of all living things in that environment.
6. The art and science of mapmaking is ____.
7. ____ ____ is the term for the position of places in relation to other places on the earth.
8. Together, the physical and cultural characteristics of each location represent its ____ identity.
9. ____ is the interaction of humans with each other.
10. Geographers divide the earth's surface into units with common characteristics called ____.

## Developing Critical Thinking Skills

1. **Summarizing Ideas**   From what does each location derive its physical character?
2. **Contrasting Ideas**   How does the study of cultural geography differ from the study of physical geography?
3. **Seeing Relationships**   (a) What do lines of latitude measure?   (b) What do lines of longitude measure?

4. **Distinguishing Ideas** What is the difference between the geographic themes of relationships within places and movement?
5. **Analyzing Ideas** How did Ptolemy's contribution to geography affect the course of American history?
6. **Writing About Geography** In a well-written paragraph, discuss one of the following ideas. **(a)** What are the similarities between early travelers and explorers of the earth and those who explore the frontiers of the solar system? **(b)** Why is the quest for geographical knowledge important in terms of the past, the present, and the future?

## Using Primary Sources

In the following excerpt from *Decline of Geographical Discovery*, James Richardson describes the reasons for the lack of geographical knowledge. As you study the reading, compare what the author writes with today's view of geography.

National vanity, and ignorance, . . . are equally mighty obstacles to the progress and attainment of geographical knowledge; and it is only by unremittingly cultivating and nourishing a spirit of discovery that the world can be known as it is, in all its entirety and exactitude of relations. . . .

People must either advance or recede, progress or decline in their science, power, virtue, and greatness, . . . as proved in the history of all the empires which have been planted and taken root in our solid earth. It is the same also with particular sciences and discoveries of art, . . . which constitute the riches, the might, and renown of a great nation. If, therefore, I can make out a case of decline in our geographical enterprises, it will then become a serious question how and by what means this [backward] motion can be stopped, and how far the spirit of geo-

graphical discovery can be . . . restored to its . . . vigor of other and past days.

1. According to the author, what obstacles hinder geographical progress?
2. Why, according to Richardson, do we need to stop the "decline in our geographical enterprises"?

## Practicing Geography Skills

*Before completing this activity, review Developing Geography Skills on page 34.*

**Using This Textbook** Scan Chapter 2 and complete the following activities.

1. List all the words in **boldface** type.
2. Compare your list to the list in **Terms to Define.** How many new terms did you find as you scanned the chapter?

## Exploring Geography

1. Interview a geography professor from a local college. During the interview ask the professor which of the seven subdivisions of geography is his or her favorite area of study. Then ask the professor how he or she goes about gathering information for geographical studies and for what purposes he or she employs this information. Share your findings with the rest of the class.
2. Reread the section titled "Place" on page 32. Then construct a two-column table about the place characteristics of your community. Label the first column "Physical Characteristics" and the second column "Human Characteristics." In the first column, place such items as the shapes of the land, bodies of water, climate, animal life, and vegetation found in your community. The second column should include features of your community's cultural landscape, such as types of farms and styles of architecture. Share your completed table with the rest of the class.

# PUTTING THE CHAPTER IN FOCUS

Geographers use a variety of tools to carry out their work. The tools that most people identify with geography are those that are still most important to geographers today—globes and maps. Modern geographers, however, also use tools such as aerial photographs, satellite images, and computer programs to help them analyze the interactions between people and their environments. The best tool to use often depends on the geographic theme that is the focus of the research.

## Ideas to Understand

In studying about the tools of geography, use these ideas to give direction to your reading.

1 Globes and maps are useful models of the earth.
2 Aerial photographs and satellite images offer new information about the earth's surface.

## Terms to Define

The following terms are some of the key terms in the chapter. Defining them will help you understand the tools of geography.

| | |
|---|---|
| globe | cardinal directions |
| great circle | map scale |
| plane | map projection |
| map | remote sensing |
| atlas | aerial photograph |
| distortion | stereoscope |
| legend | stereoplotter |
| key | multispectral |
| relief | scanner |
| contour line | Landsat |
| compass rose | |

## Places to Locate

Locating the following places will add to your knowledge of geography.

| | |
|---|---|
| Chicago | South America |
| Greenland | |

---

# 1 Globes and maps are useful models of the earth.

A thread linking each theme of modern geography is, of course, the earth. Each of the geographic themes—location, place, relationships within places, movement, and regions—relates to the physical features of the earth itself or to the living things found on the earth. For this reason it would be impossible for geographers to carry out their work without accurate representations, or models, of the earth. Two of the most useful models of the earth are globes and maps.

Globes and maps serve as the basic tools of geographers. Yet they also are fa-miliar tools of everyday life. At one time or another you probably have referred to a globe found in your classroom or in a library. Or perhaps you have been lost and have used a map to find your way.

As important as they are to the study of geography, however, globes and maps do not provide perfect representations of the earth. Each has specific advantages as well as disadvantages.

## Globes

**Globes** are three-dimensional models of the earth. Most globes, such as the globe shown on page 40, are mounted on a central rod, or axis. Spin the globe slowly and it looks much like the earth does as it rotates on its axis in space.

◀ *Map of the Americas, 1520*

*Learning from Pictures.* *Many globes show very detailed information such as the different shapes of the land. Why are most globes mounted on a central rod or axis?*

**Advantages.** The most important advantages of globes relate to their shape. A globe is the only model of the earth in the shape of a sphere, just like the earth. A globe, then, provides the most accurate representation of the shape of the earth.

Because a globe follows the spherical shape of the earth, the landmasses and bodies of water it illustrates have the same shapes as they do on the earth's surface. In addition, a globe accurately represents the earth's grid of parallels and meridians, as well as direction and distance from one place to another.

The spherical shape of the earth also makes it possible for globes to show great circles more clearly than other models of the earth's surface. A **great circle** is the edge of any imaginary flat surface that divides the earth into two equal parts. Geographers refer to such a flat surface as a **plane.** The equator, which divides the earth

into the Northern and Southern hemispheres, is one of countless great circles that can be drawn on the earth.

Great circles are especially important when measuring distances between places. A great circle or any part of a great circle is the shortest distance between two points on the earth. If you trace a great circle on a globe, then, you are tracing the shortest route of travel between points on that circle. To save time, navigators often try to plan great circle routes, or air and sea routes that follow great circles.

**Disadvantages.** Among the disadvantages of globes is that they often are not practical to use. Globes are expensive and most are too big and bulky to carry around. In addition, people can view only one-half of a globe at a time. This makes it impossible, for example, to look at Canada and India at the same time because they lie on opposite sides of the globe, just as they lie on opposite sides of the earth.

Another disadvantage of globes concerns the problem of detail. Because globes represent the entire earth, the individual areas that they illustrate are relatively small. As a result, globes cannot show the detailed features of an area, such as roads, streams, forests, and parks.

*Learning from Maps.* *This graphic compares a great circle route between Orlando and Taipei with a route that follows the compass direction. How much longer is the straight route?*

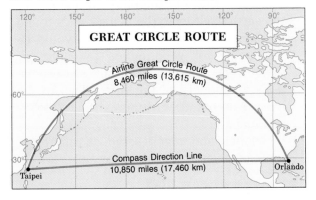

GREAT CIRCLE ROUTE

Airline Great Circle Route
8,460 miles (13,615 km)

Compass Direction Line
10,850 miles (17,460 km)

Taipei

Orlando

## Maps

**Maps** are flat representations of the earth. Maps vary in size from small maps that appear in pocket references to huge wall maps. As you will see, maps also vary in purpose.

**Advantages.** One of the most obvious advantages of maps over globes is that they are handier to use. Maps can be rolled and folded and are easy to carry around. Maps and related material can also be collected in an **atlas** to provide an easy-to-use refernce (see the Atlas section of the textbook on pages 2–17).

Another advantage of maps is that they offer flexibility in terms of the subject matter to be illustrated. Maps can show all of the earth's surface at one time, or just a part of it. Maps that focus on a small part of the earth have the additional advantage of being able to illustrate the area in far more detail than a globe. Only the largest and bulkiest globe, for example, could show the many small towns located within 10 miles (16 kilometers) of the city of Chicago, Illinois. A map of the Chicago area, however, can easily show these towns.

Maps also can present information about a wide range of topics related to both the physical and cultural features of the earth. Using different colors and symbols, maps can illustrate many kinds of topics, including rainfall, mineral resources, and religions. Presenting such a variety of information about an area often helps geographers to see regions and relationships otherwise difficult to visualize.

**Disadvantages.** It is impossible to accurately show a three-dimensional object like the earth on a flat, two-dimensional map. For this reason all maps have one or more inaccuracies, called **distortions.** As you will see, the problem of distortion remains the major disadvantage of maps.

HERMAN®

8/24

©1987 Universal Press Syndicate

"I can't find Australia. Are you sure it's on here?"

***Learning from Cartoons.*** *This cartoon illustrates the need for geographic literacy. How can you find out where Australia is located without using a globe?*

## Components of Maps

Despite their variety, all maps have similar components, or parts. These include a title; a legend, or key; a direction indicator; and a scale.

**Title.** The title of a map identifies what the map is about and what parts of the earth it shows. The title of some maps includes a date. Dates are useful on maps showing features that change over time. A map with the title "Distribution of Population in the United States: 1920," for example, should not be used when looking for figures on the present population of the United States.

**Legend.** A **legend,** or **key,** explains the meaning of colors and symbols used on a map. A map with areas shown in green, red, and blue might be misunderstood unless the user knows what the green, red, and

***Learning from Pictures.*** *This compass rose is from a map of colonial Virginia drawn in 1606. How do you know which direction on the compass rose is north?*

blue represent. The legend also explains the meaning of symbols used on a map, such as stars for capital cities.

Another part of the legend found on some maps is a key to the **relief,** or the elevations of the land illustrated. Elevation is a place's distance above or below sea level. Some maps use different colors to show relief. Each color represents a different elevation. By studying the colors, you can distinguish flat plains from rugged mountain ranges. Relief also can be shown by using **contour lines,** or lines on a map that connect points of equal elevation on the earth's surface (see the SPECIAL FEATURE on page 234).

**Direction indicator.** Every map should have an indicator that identifies direction. One such indicator is a north arrow—a single arrow labeled "N" that points north. The maps in this book use north arrows (see page 44). Another direction indicator is a **compass rose.** The arms of a compass rose

point to all four **cardinal directions,** north, south, east, and west.

A different way to find directions on a map is to study the parallels and meridians. East and west directions follow parallels, or lines of latitude. North and south directions follow meridians, or lines of longitude.

**Scale.** A **map scale** provides statistical information used to measure distances on a map. The most common kinds of map scales include statement scales, bar scales, and representative fraction scales.

Statement scales use a statement or phrase to relate a distance on the map to the distance it represents on the earth. "One inch to 100 miles" and "One inch represents 100 miles" are statement scales. Statement scales also may be expressed in kilometers.

A bar scale is a short line divided into equal parts. Each part of the line is labeled in intervals by miles or kilometers. The length of the line on the scale represents that number of miles or kilometers on the earth's surface. The maps in this textbook use bar scales (see the map on page 44).

Representative fraction, or RF, scales relate distance on a map to distance on the earth, using the same unit of measurement. On some maps representative fraction scales are written as a ratio, such as 1:1,000,000. On other maps they are written as a fraction, such as 1/1,000,000. Both of these examples indicate that one inch on the map equals 1 million inches on the earth's surface.

## Map Projections

While they have similar components, maps do not always show areas of the world in exactly the same way. The size and shape of North America, for example, may look somewhat different on two different maps. The differences occur because the two maps use different **map projections,** or methods by which the features of the

*Text continues on page 45.*

# CASE STUDY
## EXPLORING IDEAS: Perspective—Scale and Distance

A rumbling freight train with more than 100 loaded cars and 4 huge diesel engines appears enormous when viewed from a railroad crossing along a road. The same train seen from an airplane seems like a toy. The difference is scale. In both cases, however, even though the scales are quite different, we are able to recognize the train for exactly what it is.

### In the Heart of the Ituri Forest

In the northwest corner of Zaire (zah·YR), just a short distance north of the equator, lies the Ituri (i·TUHR·ee) Forest, a vast area of dense, dark, damp, and seemingly impenetrable rain forest. In the heart of the forest huge trees are always dripping from intense rainstorms. Above all, there is an eerie silence in this dense forest that often overpowers people from the outside, giving them a feeling of isolation and desperate loneliness. To the Mbuti (muh·BOO·ty), the people who have called the Ituri Forest home for thousands of years, however, the forest provides a good and protective world.

The forest gives the Mbuti a very special view of the world. Living below a dense canopy of branches and leaves, and hemmed in on all sides by lush, green forests, these people of the rain forest rarely see anything far away. As a result, their idea of scale and distance is quite different from that of people who live in open areas.

### A Mbuti Sees the Outside

Imagine what it would be like to have spent your whole life in the confines of a vast rain forest and then, suddenly, to be placed in an open environment where you could see for miles. This is exactly what happened to Kenge, a Mbuti.

A scientist who had spent many years living with the Mbuti—and who had earned their friendship and trust—was planning a

*Scale and distance in the Sahara in Algeria*

visit to a national park on the open grasslands of Uganda. Kenge asked to come along. On seeing the grassland, Kenge stopped and stood absolutely still. His mouth opened, but he said nothing. Before him stretched a seemingly endless plain.

When Kenge noticed a herd of buffalo grazing lazily far in the distance, he turned to his friend and asked, "What insects are those?" When told that they were buffalo, Kenge told his friend to stop telling him stupid lies. As they drove closer to the herd of buffalo, however, Kenge saw that the "insects" were getting larger and larger.

### Scale and Distance

Kenge could not believe that what he saw were real buffalo. He could not accept something that we take for granted. We correct for changes in the sizes of images as objects move closer or farther away. Kenge, familiar only with the forest, was bewildered by distance and scale. He could not accept the message his eyes were sending because he had never seen objects in the distance. Just as seeing a broad expanse of plain helped Kenge gain perspective, seeing places on maps helps us understand scale and distance.

# DEVELOPING GEOGRAPHY SKILLS
## INTERPRETING VISUALS: Reviewing Map Basics

Geography helps us to "see" or visualize the earth. The tools used to see the earth include diagrams, charts, graphs, globes, and illustrations. But the oldest and most important visual record is a map.

A map is a reference work like a dictionary or an almanac, but it must be read in its own language. A map illustrates the information it contains in words and symbols including typeface, colors, shadings, lines, signs, and labels.

### How to Read a Map

Follow these guidelines to interpret a map.

1. **Note the map's title.** Each map has a special purpose that will be stated in its title.
2. **Study the map's legend, or key.** The legend contains information that ex-

plains any special symbols used on the map. Using the legend, you can identify what each symbol represents.

3. **Note differences in labels.** Some of the helpful symbols used on maps are not explained in the key. In this textbook, for instance, labels printed in *italic type like this* mark natural features such as mountains and oceans. The labels for oceans also appear in blue type. Political features, such as boundary lines, are labeled in roman, or regular, type.

4. **Check the map's directions.** Most maps have a direction arrow or compass rose. *NORTH IS NOT ALWAYS TOWARD THE TOP OF THE MAP,* but if there is no direction indicator and the longitude lines run toward the top of the map, you may assume that it is.

5. **Study the distance scales.** A small map may picture the whole world while a large one may illustrate only a few miles. A common scale indicator is a bar scale, which appears as a short line with tick marks. It indicates the distance in a straight line between two points. In this textbook, bar scales give the distance in both miles and kilometers.

### Applying the Skill

Study the map on the left. Note the title. The subject is land use and economic activity in Mexico. Study the key. It shows the colors that indicate different types of land use. (For example, manufacturing areas are orange.) It also shows the symbols used to illustrate economic activities. (Tourist attractions are marked with $.) Note the north arrow and the distance scale. With the scale, you can tell that Mexico City is about 190 miles (300 kilometers) from the Gulf of Mexico.

*To practice this skill, see Practicing Geography Skills on page 53.*

MEXICO
Economic Activity

| | | | |
|---|---|---|---|
| Manufacturing | | $ | Tourism |
| Woodlands | | ⚒ | Drilling |
| Farming | | ⚒ | Mining |
| Grazing | | 🐟 | Fishing |
| Mixed farming and grazing | | 🌲 | Forestry |
| Limited economic use | | | |

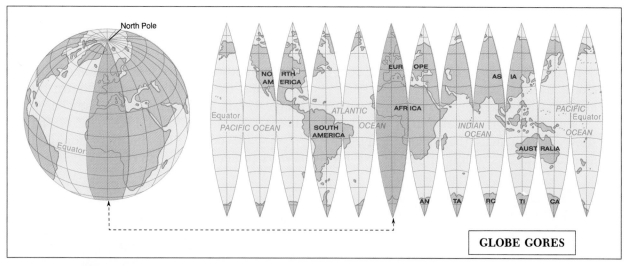

North Pole

Equator

Equator

PACIFIC OCEAN

NORTH AMERICA

ATLANTIC OCEAN

SOUTH AMERICA

EUROPE

AFRICA

INDIAN OCEAN

ASIA

AUSTRALIA

ANTARCTICA

PACIFIC OCEAN

Equator

**GLOBE GORES**

*Learning from Maps.* *With the help of mathematical equations, cartographers peel back the surface of the earth. What purpose does this serve?*

earth's curved surface are transferred onto a flat map.

The diagram on page 46 shows how some map projections look. The projections used for the physical/political maps in the chapters in this book and for all of the Atlas maps are labeled near each map's legend. The maps in the Atlas (see pages 2–17) use several different projections, while many of the maps in the chapters use the Robinson projection (see page 47).

No matter which projection is used, every map has some distortions that are inherent in the process of illustrating the earth's spherical surface on a flat map. Certain distortions, however, are worse on some projections than on others. Mapmakers choose which projection to use depending on what undistorted features, or map properties, are most important to the area being illustrated. The four most useful map properties are correct shape, correct size, correct distance, and correct direction.

No world map can have all four map properties. Maps of smaller areas, however, may have less distortion than maps of larger areas. The Robinson projection attempts to reduce distortions in shape, size, distance, and direction.

**Correct shape.** Maps using projections that maintain true shape are called **conformal maps** because the shapes of land areas conform to, or look like, the shapes shown on a globe. One quick way to check for conformity on a map is to look at the way parallels and meridians cross. If they cross at right angles, as on a globe, the map is a conformal map.

A conformal map such as the Mercator (muhr·KAYT·uhr) projection on page 46 greatly distorts distances and sizes because the parallels all are the same length. On a globe the parallels near the poles are shorter than the parallels near the equator. The parallels on a Mercator projection also are farther apart toward the poles, instead of being regularly spaced as they are on a globe. Such inaccuracies make landmasses near the poles look larger than they really are. Greenland, for example, is actually one-ninth the size of South America. But on a Mercator projection, Greenland and South America appear to be about the same size.

**Correct size.** Maps using projections that show correct relative area are called **equal-area maps.** Such maps are especially

useful for comparing factors affected by an area's size, such as farm output or population size. The Albers projection is a commonly used equal-area projection (see the maps in Chapter 11).

Even though equal-area projections show area correctly, they distort shapes. In general, this distortion is greater at the edges of equal-area projections than at the center. The Mollweide (mawl·VYD·uh) projection shown in the left column of this page and the Peters projection shown on page 47 are two examples of equal-area maps. (See the SPECIAL FEATURE on the next page comparing the Robinson and Peters projections.)

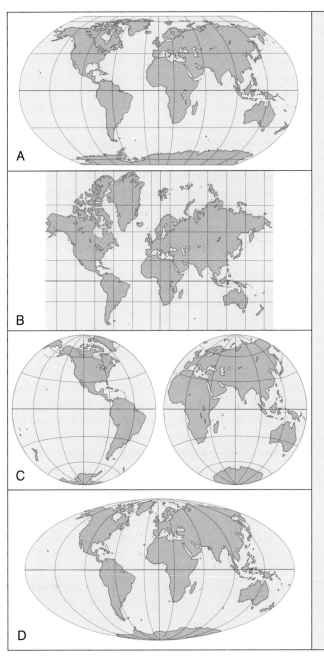

A

B

C

D

The projections are, from top to bottom, A–Robinson, B–Mercator, C–Azimuthal, and D–Molleweide.

## SPECIAL FEATURE: Identifying Projections

Every map contains distortion. Most maps show one of the map properties accurately, but distort the others. The Robinson projection, the top map shown to the left, is unique because it is a *compromise projection.* It maintains no single property but minimizes overall distortion.

Below the Robinson projection is a Mercator projection. This projection, named for the cartographer who developed it in 1569, is a conformal projection. Landmasses retain their true shapes, but the projection distorts the relative size of land areas. Notice that the latitude and longitude lines on the projection cross at right angles.

The third projection shown is an azimuthal projection. Azimuthal projections, which are circular, show true direction. The bottom projection is a Molleweide projection. It is an equal-area projection that shows relative size accurately but distorts shapes.

1. How can you quickly identify **(a)** a Mercator projection and **(b)** an azimuthal projection?
2. Describe the differences in the latitude and longitude lines on **(a)** a conformal projection and **(b)** an equal-area projection.

**Correct distance.** Maps using projections that show the correct distances between the places illustrated are called **equidistant** (ee·kweh·DIHS·tehnt) **maps.** Maps of small areas can be drawn with little distortion of distance. Maps of the whole world, however, can never show all distances correctly because it is impossible to show the lengths of all parallels and meridians as accurately as on a globe. (See the map on page 40, for example.)

**Correct direction.** Maps using projections that show true compass direction are called **azimuthal** (az·uh·MUHTH·uhl) **maps.** Azimuthal maps, like the polar map on page 17, are circular. Although directions on an azimuthal map are correct, they cannot be shown on a compass rose because north and south follow the radiating meridians on the map rather than straight lines. Remember to refer to the compass rose to determine directions on other maps.

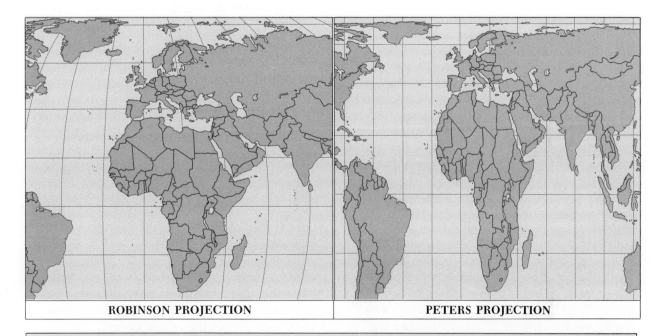

| ROBINSON PROJECTION | PETERS PROJECTION |

## SPECIAL FEATURE: Comparing Projections

Compared to the world illustrated by the Robinson projection shown on the left above, the world illustrated by the Peters projection shown next to it looks quite different. This is because the Robinson projection is a compromise projection that minimizes distortion but maintains no single property. The Peters projection is an equal-area map that shows the relative sizes of landmasses correctly but distorts their shapes.

South America and Africa, for example, appear to be more narrow and much longer on the Peters projection than they do on

the Robinson projection. Although their shapes are distorted, however, South America and Africa are actually as large in terms of relative land area as they appear to be on the Peters projection.

1. **(a)** What type of projection is the Peters? **(b)** What does the Peters projection distort?
2. **(a)** Describe the differences in the size and shape of Greenland as illustrated by the Mercator projection on page 46 and the Peters projection. **(b)** How do you account for these differences?

*Learning from Pictures.* *During World War I the airplane, still in the early stages of development, was used to take aerial photographs. What are the advantages of aerial photographs?*

# 2 Aerial photographs and satellite images offer new information about the earth's surface.

Even though globes and maps remain the most familiar tools of geographers, they are not the most recent. Rapid developments in technology have made several new tools available. These tools already have provided a wide range of valuable information about the earth's surface. **Remote sensing,** the gathering and recording of information through aerial photographs and satellite images, ranks among the most important of the new methods.

## Aerial Photographs

Geographers use **aerial photographs**—pictures taken from above the earth—to study relationships involving people and places that are not easily seen from ground level. Aerial photographs of traffic patterns, for example, can be used to help plan new highways. Military planners can see troop movements and rocket launch sites. Foresters can spot diseased or insect-infested trees in rugged terrain that would be hard to reach on foot. Aerial photographs even show features of the ocean floor.

Because aerial photographs provide such accurate and detailed information, cartographers have come to rely on them as a source of information when making maps. Most aerial photographs used to make maps are taken by cameras in high-altitude airplanes and are developed in strips of overlapping pictures. An instrument called a **stereoscope** converts a pair of overlapping aerial photographs into a three-dimensional view of the area shown.

Elevations appear somewhat distorted on aerial photographs because the camera taking the pictures is closer to the tops of the mountains than to the valleys. As a re-

***Learning from Pictures.*** *A Landsat satellite produced the image of the Mekong Delta shown above. What instrument on the satellite is responsible for recording observations?*

sult, mountains appear larger than the more distant valleys. This distortion is corrected by using a viewing instrument called a **stereoplotter,** which gives a more accurate three-dimensional view of the earth shown in the pictures.

## Satellite Images

Many of the satellites circling the earth have special sensors called **multispectral** (muhl·tee·SPEC·trahl) **scanners,** or MSS. These scanners record observations electronically and send them to ground stations. Computers then translate the data into electronic images, making false-color pictures such as the one on this page. Even though the pictures are taken from far in space, they are so detailed that they can show houses or even sailboats on a lake.

An extraordinary group of earth viewers known as **Landsats** take many of the satellite images. These satellites circle the earth 14 times every 24 hours, silently scanning, collecting, and sending back a greater view of the world than any earthbound eye could ever see.

## Other Tools

In addition to globes, maps, and remotely sensed images, geographers use tables, charts, graphs, and diagrams to help them in their work. Geographers also use computers to solve geographic problems as well as to make maps and graphics.

### SECTION 2 REVIEW

1. **Define**   remote sensing, aerial photograph, stereoscope, stereoplotter, multispectral scanner, Landsat
2. **Interpreting Ideas**   Why are aerial photographs and satellite images especially useful to geographers?
3. **Organizing Ideas**   Why do elevations appear somewhat distorted on aerial photographs?
4. **Analyzing Ideas**   How do computers help geographers?

**49**

# THE GEOGRAPHIC WEB
## The Puzzle of Geographic Names

One of the most puzzling problems in cartography is the selection of the correct spelling of place names. This problem involves language, changes in government, and changes in national policy.

### Language

In general, cartographers print names in their own language, even though the inhabitants of the region call the place by a different name. For example, on an American-made map of Europe you will probably see a label for the Danube River. The same river would be labeled *Donau* on a German map, *Duna* on a Hungarian map, and *Dunarea* on a Romanian map. On the same American-made map you would see labels for Finland and Hungary, even though the people of these nations call their countries *Suami* and *Magyarorszag.*

Another language problem involves repetition. For example, *rio* means "river," *sierra* means "mountain," and *sahara* means "great desert." Therefore labels such as Rio Grande River, Sierra Nevada Mountains, and Sahara Desert are repetitious. They actually mean "River Grande River," "Mountain Nevada Mountains," and "Desert Desert."

### Pinyin

Maps of China create special problems for American cartographers. Until recently maps used the Wade-Giles system of transcribing the Chinese alphabet into English. In 1979, however, the Chinese government adopted a new system of transcription called Pinyin that more accurately reflects the sounds of the Chinese words for places. For a time many Western nations resisted the new spellings because they seemed so strange and so completely different from the Wade-Giles system. Today, however, many Western publications, including this textbook, use Pinyin.

### Changing Names

Cartographers also must deal with name changes. In recent years many nations have

*A map with English names*

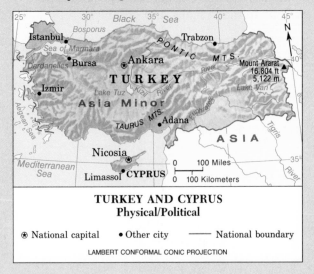

**TURKEY AND CYPRUS**
**Physical/Political**

⊛ National capital　• Other city　—— National boundary

LAMBERT CONFORMAL CONIC PROJECTION

*A map with French names*

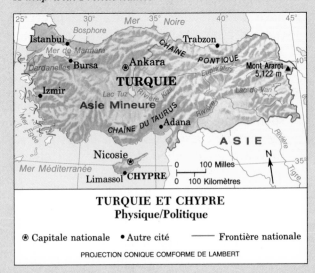

**TURQUIE ET CHYPRE**
**Physique/Politique**

⊛ Capitale nationale　• Autre cité　—— Frontière nationale

PROJECTION CONIQUE COMFORME DE LAMBERT

*Indians of the southeastern United States named this river "Great River," or Mississippi.*

taken on new names. After World War II, for example, Germany was divided into the Federal Republic of Germany (West Germany) and the German Democratic Republic (East Germany). As European colonies throughout the world gained their independence, many changed their names. In Africa the former Belgian Congo became Zaire, the former British colony of Southern Rhodesia became Zimbabwe, and the former French colony of Dahomey became Benin. In the Pacific the New Hebrides (HEB·ruh·deez) became the Republic of Vanuatu (vahn·oo·WAHT·oo) and the islands of Yap, Kusaie, Truk, and Ponape (PUHN·ah·pay) became the Federated States of Micronesia.

Even internal political changes in a nation can bring about important place-name changes. In the Soviet Union, for example, the nation's second largest city, Leningrad, has had three names since 1914. Before 1914 the city was called St. Petersburg. It was named for its founder, Tsar Peter I.

After Russia went to war with Germany in 1914 the name was changed to Petrograd, which means "Peter's City" in Russian. This name change took place in order to drop the German ending (burg) in the original name. Finally, in 1924, the Communist government changed the city's name again to its present one—Leningrad—to honor the founder of the Soviet Communist party, Vladimir Ilyich Lenin.

## Choosing the Correct Names

Governments around the world have established agencies to help cartographers choose the correct place names and spellings on maps. In the United States this agency is the United States Board on Geographic Names (BGN). In Britain it is the British Permanent Committee on Geographical Names (PCGN). Argentina, Brazil, Canada, and most European countries have similar agencies.

# CHAPTER 2 REVIEW

## Chapter Summary

The following list contains the key concepts you have learned about the tools of geography.

1. Geographers use a wide variety of tools in their attempts to understand the earth and its people.
2. Globes accurately portray the earth's three-dimensional shape. They are also useful in determining correct latitude and longitude and in locating great circles.
3. Maps, because they are flat, cannot portray all shapes, sizes, distances, and directions as accurately as globes. Despite these limitations, maps serve as the principal tool of geographers because of the almost limitless number of topics related to both the physical and cultural features of the earth that they can illustrate.
4. Components common to most maps are a title; a legend, or key; a direction indicator; and a scale.
5. Cultural backgrounds determine how people perceive distance and scale.
6. Four of the most useful map properties are correct shape, correct area, correct distance, and correct directions.
7. Remotely sensed images, including aerial photographs and satellite images, have greatly improved the making of maps. Their "bird's eye view" permits mapmakers to depict terrain changes far more accurately than could be done from surveys made at ground level.
8. Geographers use a wide variety of other graphics to present the information they have gathered.

On a separate sheet of paper, complete the following review exercises.

## Reviewing Geographic Terms

Match each of the following terms with the correct definition.

a. great circle
b. legend
c. map projection
d. conformal map
e. equal-area map
f. remote sensing
g. aerial photograph
h. stereoscope
i. multispectral scanner
j. Landsat
k. distortion

_____ 1. Map using a projection that maintains true shape
_____ 2. Gathering and recording information from a distance through aerial photographs and satellite images
_____ 3. Picture taken from above the earth
_____ 4. Instrument that makes a pair of overlapping aerial photographs into a three-dimensional view
_____ 5. Edge of any imaginary plane that divides the earth into two equal halves
_____ 6. Instrument that records observations from space electronically and sends them to ground stations where computers translate the data into electronic images
_____ 7. Satellite that views the earth
_____ 8. One of many different ways to show the spherical earth's surface on a flat map
_____ 9. Map that shows sizes correctly
_____ 10. Explains the meaning of symbols and colors used on a map
_____ 11. Types of inaccuracies contained on maps—a major disadvantage

## Developing Critical Thinking Skills

1. **Comparing Ideas**  What are the advantages and disadvantages of globes?
2. **Interpreting Ideas**  What advantages do maps have over globes?
3. **Classifying Ideas**  Classify each of the following three map projections as conformal, equal-area, equidistant, or azimuthal:  **(a)** Mercator,  **(b)** Peters,  **(c)** polar.
4. **Analyzing Ideas**  How might people's cultural backgrounds affect their ability to understand distance and scale?

5. **Writing About Geography** In a clearly written paragraph, discuss one of the following ideas. **(a)** What are the advantages and disadvantages of each of the following types of maps: conformal maps, equal-area maps, equidistant maps, and azimuthal maps? **(b)** How do geographers use new advances in technology to acquire data?

## Using Primary Sources

In the following excerpt from *The Romance of Travel*, Joseph Conrad describes his view of geography and cartography. As you study the reading, consider the contrast between how maps were constructed during the Middle Ages and how they are constructed today.

Descriptive geography, like any other kind of science, has been built on the experience of certain phenomena and on experiments prompted by that unappeasable curiosity of [people] which their intelligence has elevated into a quite respectable passion for acquiring knowledge. Like other sciences it has fought its way to truth through a long series of errors. . . .

Geography had its phase . . . which had nothing to do with the pursuit of truth, but has given us a curious glimpse of the medieval mind playing in its ponderous childish way with the problems of our earth's shape, its size, its character, its products, its inhabitants. Cartography was almost as pictorial then as some modern newspapers. It crowded its maps with pictures of strange pageants, strange trees, strange beasts, drawn with amazing precision in the midst of theoretically conceived continents. It [outlined] imaginary kingdoms of Monomotapa and of Prester John, the regions infested by lions or haunted by unicorns. . . .

1. How did geography find its way to the truth?
2. How was cartography in the Middle Ages different from cartography today?

## Practicing Geography Skills

*Before completing this activity, review Developing Geography Skills on page 44.*

**Reviewing Map Basics** Study the map on pages 6–7 and answer the following questions.

1. **(a)** What is the map's title? **(b)** What information is shown on the map?
2. How does the map illustrate **(a)** land use and **(b)** economic activities?
3. What symbol is used for **(a)** drilling, **(b)** fishing, and **(c)** mining?
4. How many manufacturing areas in the United States are shown on the map?

## Exploring Geography

1. Study the Landsat image on page 49. Such colorful satellite images provide a mass of information on physical geography and highlight the major physical features of the areas shown. The technology to make such images is constantly changing and improving. Use recent magazine and newspaper reports to find information on these developments. You might also write to the National Aeronautics and Space Administration for further information. After you have finished your research, prepare an oral presentation of your findings.
2. The map on page 38 is only one of thousands of examples of maps that early cartographers drew. Because the geographical knowledge that these early cartographers possessed was limited, many of the maps are filled with inaccuracies. Use resources in your school or public library to find other examples of early maps and prepare a brief report detailing their inaccuracies.

# UNIT 1 REVIEW

## Unit Summary

The following list contains the key concepts you have learned about the nature and purpose of geography.

1. Geographers study the earth to determine what is where, why it is there, and what significance it has.
2. The two major divisions of geography are physical geography and cultural geography. Physical geographers study the natural and physical settings of the earth. Cultural geographers study human actions and their impact on the earth.
3. The five basic themes of modern geography are location, place, relationships within places, movement, and regions.
4. Globes and maps are the basic tools of geography. Both have advantages and disadvantages. Globes accurately portray the earth's three-dimensional shape but are bulky and cannot show details of small areas. Maps are convenient to use and can show specific details that even the largest globes cannot show, but they cannot portray all shapes, sizes, distances, and directions as accurately as globes.
5. Geographers use remotely sensed images, including aerial photographs, as well as a wide variety of other graphics to present the information they have gathered.

On a separate sheet of paper, complete the following review exercises.

## Checking Your Understanding

1. What are the two major branches of geographic study?
2. In what way does a human group leave a distinct imprint on its human habitat? Cite specific examples from the textbook.
3. What are the major components of maps?
4. How do the three main types of map scale differ?

## Applying Critical Thinking Skills

1. **Analyzing Ideas** (a) What are the major subdivisions of geography? (b) What are some of the ways that they reflect the role of technology in the study of geography?
2. **Interpreting Ideas** (a) What are the five major themes of modern geography? (b) Why are they significant in today's world? (c) Which is the most important to study? Why?
3. **Analyzing Ideas** How can an understanding of relative location help you understand the world's political problems?
4. **Synthesizing Ideas** Review the CASE STUDY in Chapter 2. (a) Describe the major place characteristics of the Mbuti's habitat. (b) How does place identity explain the perspective of the Mbuti? (c) Why is an understanding of less advanced societies often helpful to geographers who study complex societies?
5. **Seeing Relationships** (a) Why is the polar map on page 17 considered to be an azimuthal map? (b) What is the advantage of using an azimuthal projection for this subject area?

## Reviewing Unit Features

1. **Geography in the Workplace** How do vacationers, people in the armed forces, and people in business use the products of professional cartographers?
2. **The Geographic Web** In cartography, what problems does the selection of the correct spellings of place names involve?

## Using Map Skills

1. Study the map entitled, "Great Circle Route" on page 40. Explain why the route between Orlando and Taipei appears as a curved line.
2. Examine the map entitled, "The Travels of Marco Polo" on page 28. (a) What type of distance scale is used on the map? (b) Approximately how far did Polo travel?

## Investigating Geography

1. Use a map showing latitude and longitude to identify the absolute location of the city where you live. (You should identify the location within 5° latitude and longitude.)

2. Use references in the school library to identify and list the physical and human characteristics that represent the place identity of one of the following: Buenos Aires, Argentina; Lima, Peru; Rio de Janeiro, Brazil; Godthaab, Greenland; Kinshasa, Zaire; or San Francisco, California. Then answer this question: How do the physical characteristics of each area affect the human characteristics of each location? Report your findings to the class.

3. **Preparing a Written Report** Reread the section on map projections in Chapter 2. Then go to your school or public library to find information on at least four different map projections that are not mentioned in the text. Prepare a written report detailing the advantages and disadvantages of each projection. Illustrate your report by tracing an example of each projection.

## Further Readings

### Chapter 1

Dixon, Dougal. *Geography*. New York: Franklin Watts, Inc. Discusses earth's land, oceans, atmosphere, seasons, weather, human settlement, and people's effect on the landscape. A glossary is included.

Hapgood, Fred. *Space Shots: An Album of the Universe*. New York: Times Books. Discusses the planets and moons of the solar system.

Holt-Jensen, Arild. *Geography: Its History and Concepts. A Student's Guide*. Totowa, New Jersey: Barnes & Noble Books. Describes the history of geographic ideas from early times to the present day.

National Geographic Society, Special Publications Division. *Nature's World of Wonders*.

Washington, D.C.: The National Geographic Society. Describes journeys to seven continents through the skillful use of photographs and commentary.

Ordway, Frederick I. *Pictorial Guide to Planet Earth*. New York: Thomas Y. Crowell. Uses a large number of stunning photographs taken from Skylab and other satellites to provide a history of satellite-image gathering. Also explains how modern geographers and cartographers collect, use, and analyze such images.

### Chapter 2

Carey, Helen H. *How to Use Maps and Globes*. New York: Franklin Watts, Inc. Highlights the types of data that can be found on a map or globe and discusses the ways to use maps as visual aids in papers and presentations.

Frazee, Steve. *Where Are You?* New York: Meredith Press. Presents the history of maps and mapmaking, why maps are needed, and the ways early explorers used them.

Hammond Incorporated. *The World Atlas*. New York: Random House. Includes detailed maps of all the major continents, views of the earth as a water planet, an index of statistics, a gazetteer of the world, and a list of common abbreviations.

Rand McNally. *Rand McNally Student's World Atlas*. Chicago: Rand McNally and Company. Contains chapters on how to use and understand maps, information on the planets, and satellite imagery as well as detailed maps of world cities, landscapes, terrain, and other geographic information.

Schere, Monroe. *The Story of Maps*. Englewood Cliffs, New Jersey: Prentice-Hall. Describes the history of maps and the mapmaking process, including a short section on some of the aspects of modern mapmaking.

Wilford, John Noble. *The Mapmakers*. New York: Alfred A. Knopf. Discusses the history of cartography, detailing the techniques mapmakers have used to map the earth, the oceans, and the planets.

## UNIT 2

# THE EARTH'S PHYSICAL SETTING

# Earth's Changing Surface

# PUTTING THE CHAPTER IN FOCUS

The features of the earth's surface range from expansive plains to towering mountain peaks, from tablelike plateaus to deep ocean floors. For centuries scientists have devised theories to help explain the diversity of the earth's surface features and the forces that change those features.

## Ideas to Understand

In studying about the earth's changing surface, use these ideas to give direction to your reading.

**1** The earth's surface displays an amazing variety of landforms.
**2** The earth's interior offers clues to a restless planet.
**3** Movements of the earth's plates have changed its surface features.
**4** Weathering and erosion create distinctive landforms.

## Terms to Define

The following terms are some of the key terms in the chapter. Defining them will help you understand the earth's changing surface.

landfo                    seismic wave
slope
eleva
loca
pla
pl
h
mountai

## Places to Locate

Locating the following places will add to your knowledge of geography.

Grand Canyon        The Himalaya
San Andreas Fault    Andes

---

## 1 The earth's surface displays an amazing variety of landforms.

The surface of the earth is wrinkled, warped, folded, twisted, and broken. Powerful forces continue to change the earth, giving rise to many different **landforms,** or shapes on the earth's surface. Plain, plateau, hill, mountain, canyon, valley, island, ridge, and fjord are a few of the names given to these landforms. As you read about these landforms in this chapter, you may wish to refer to the graphic entitled, "Basic Land and Water Forms" on pages 18–19.

Landforms help to characterize the physical setting of each place on the earth. The **physical setting,** also known as the **natural landscape,** is the combination of a place's physical features. Other aspects of the physical setting include climate, vegetation, and soils.

### Landforms and People

Landforms have an important impact on human activity. People study the "lay of the land" when building a house, for example, and planners consider the physical setting when designing roads and highways. Farmers follow the contours of the land when laying out and plowing fields.

Most landforms have both advantages and disadvantages for human use and settlement. Consider this example. Many river valleys in Asia are more densely settled than neighboring areas. Soils in these valleys are rich—an advantage—but the risk of flooding is high—a disadvantage. To the people who live in these valleys, the advantage outweighs the disadvantage.

*◀ Mount St. Helens*

## Types of Landforms

Geographers group landforms into different categories, depending on each landform's characteristics. Two characteristics that prove especially useful in categorizing landforms are slope and local relief. **Slope** refers to the slant of the land. The slant may be very steep, or it may be so gentle that the land appears almost flat. Local relief relates to a landform's elevation. **Elevation** is a place's distance above or below sea level. The difference in elevation between the highest and lowest points in an area is known as **local relief.**

Geographers identify four of the most common types of landforms as plains, pla-

*Learning from Graphs.* Continents make up the vast majority of the earth's land surface. What is the smallest continent?

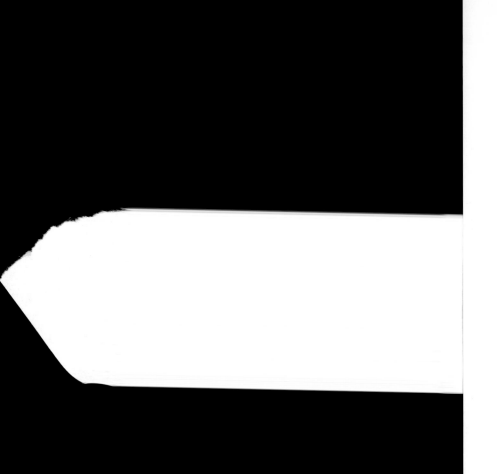

**LAND SURFACE OF THE EARTH**

AUSTRALIA
5%
2.9 million sq. mi
4.6 million sq. km

ASIA
30%
16.9 million sq. mi
27 million sq. km

AFRICA
21%
11.6 million sq. mi
18.6 million sq. km

NORTH AMERICA
15%
8.4 million sq. mi
13.4 million sq. km

EUROPE
7%
3.8 million sq. mi
6.1 million sq. km

SOUTH AMERICA
12%
6.8 million sq. mi
10.9 million sq. km

ANTARCTICA
10%
5.5 million sq. mi
8.8 million sq. km

teaus, hills, and mountains. Although they are classified differently, all four landforms exist under the sea as well as on the continents. A **continent** is one of the seven large landmasses found on the earth's surface. The seven continents are North America, South America, Europe, Asia, Africa, Australia, and Antarctica.

**Plains.** Geographers classify a landform characterized by nearly level or gently rolling land as a **plain.** If you were to look out over a large plain, you would see no dramatic changes in the landscape. The land would look generally flat all the way to the horizon, with few rocks or other features to break up the view.

Plains have little slope and, by definition, a local relief of less than 500 feet (150 meters). Most plains exist at low elevations—less than 1,000 feet (305 meters) above sea level. The Gulf Coastal Plain of the United States, for example, stretches from the Gulf of Mexico to southern Illinois, but no part of it is higher than 500 feet (150 meters) above sea level. A few plains, such as the western Great Plains of the United States, however, are located at much higher elevations.

**Plateaus.** A generally flat area that rises far above the surrounding land on at least one side characterizes a **plateau.** Plateaus also are known as tablelands. This term provides a helpful image of the characteristics of a plateau. Like a tabletop, a plateau is flat and high off the ground.

High elevation serves as one of the most distinguishing features of many plateaus. The Colorado Plateau of the western United States, for example, lies 7,000 to 8,000 feet (2,135 to 2,440 meters) above sea level. The Plateau of Tibet in China lies more than 15,000 feet (4,572 meters) above sea level. Some plateaus, however, exist at relatively low elevations.

# GEOGRAPHY IN THE WORKPLACE
## Physical Geographers

Air pollution, contaminated water, fuel shortages, and droughts that cause mass starvation concern all of us. Stories about such problems appear with great frequency in newspapers and magazines and on radio and television newscasts. Such stories make people more aware of their physical surroundings. They also illustrate a need for more knowledge of the earth and people's relationship with it. Only by understanding the cause-and-effect relationships between people and the natural environment can we solve problems growing from those relationships. For this reason, physical geographers play a vital role in studying our natural world.

Physical geographers study the natural landscape and how people change the land and water forms, climates, soils, and vegetation on the earth. Physical geographers study, for example, the soil erosion that results from the reckless plowing of steep slopes. They consider the effects of strip mining on landforms and vegetation, and the way burning fossil fuels send large amounts of carbon dioxide into the atmosphere, changing rainfall patterns.

Because physical geography is such a large and complex field, most physical geographers concentrate on a specialized subject area. Those who specialize in the study of weather, for example, are called meteorologists; those who study climate are known as climatologists. Physical geographers who specialize in the study of landforms are called geologists. Those who focus their work on the world's oceans are called oceanographers. Physical geographers interested in the earth's vegetation often work as foresters or range management specialists.

These and many other specialties of physical geography provide outstanding career opportunities for those interested in the natural world. Students who enjoy the out-of-doors and who are interested in learning more about the physical environment that surrounds them may wish to investigate the range of exciting careers in the field of physical geography.

---

The slope and local relief of a plateau are both high because the plateau rises above the surrounding area. But broad and flat land usually covers the top of a plateau. This gives the top of the plateau little slope and low local relief. Deep canyons that cut into some plateaus often break this pattern, however. The canyons have high slope and local relief. For example, the Grand Canyon, which the Colorado River carved into the Colorado Plateau, has a local relief of more than 5,000 feet (1,525 meters).

**Hills.** A **hill** features generally rounded land that rises at least 500 feet (152 meters) above the land in the surrounding area. The slope of hills varies from very gentle to very steep. By definition, however, the local relief of a hill must be less than 2,000 feet (610 meters).

**Mountains.** A dramatic type of landform that rises sharply from the surrounding land to heights thousands of feet above sea level is called a **mountain.** Steep slope and local relief of at least 2,000 feet (610 meters) characterize mountains. The **summit,** or highest point, of a mountain is typically smaller and more sharp than the summit of a hill.

High elevations also distinguish mountains from other landforms. Mount Everest in The Himalaya in Asia ranks as the highest mountain in the world. Mount Everest soars to an elevation of 29,028 feet (8,848 meters). Geographers are currently using sophisticated equipment to measure another mountain that may come close to rivaling Mount Everest for the distinction of being the highest mountain in the world. This mountain, called K2, also lies in The Himalaya.

## 2 The earth's interior offers clues to a restless planet.

The earth is constantly changing. As scientists observe these changes, they obtain a more complete picture of what the earth is like, what changes its surface has undergone, and what changes may take place in the future.

### The Little-Known Interior

Scientists have studied the surface of the earth for centuries. Yet each year brings new information about the earth's surface that is added to the data already known. Direct observation of the earth's deep interior, however, remains impossible. Currently scientists can gather information about the center of the earth only through indirect evidence.

**Investigating the earth's interior.** Vibrations of the earth, or **seismic waves,** tell much about the earth's interior. Earthquakes or explosions set off seismic waves, which travel outward from the disturbance. These waves travel faster through solid material than through molten material. **Molten material** consists of rocks and stones that have been melted by heat.

Instruments called seismographs track seismic waves as they pass through the earth. By studying the wave patterns, scientists can learn a great deal about the earth's interior. From such studies they have concluded that different layers of solid and molten materials make up the interior of the earth. The three major layers are the core, the mantle, and the crust.

**Earth's core, mantle, and crust.** The deepest layer of the earth's surface, located at the center of the earth, is known as the **core.** The core is divided into two parts—the inner core and the outer core. Scientists believe that the inner core, with a radius of about 700 miles (1,120 kilometers), is solid. The outer core, thought to be liquid, surrounds the inner core and is about 1,500 miles (2,400 kilometers) thick.

The next layer of the earth's interior, surrounding the liquid outer core, is the **mantle.** The mantle measures about 1,800 miles (2,900 kilometers) thick and makes up about 80 percent of the earth's total volume. Scientists believe that the mantle is solid except for a very soft layer of partially molten material in the upper mantle. This soft layer lies about 63 miles (100 kilometers) below the earth's surface.

*Text continues on page 64.*

# DEVELOPING GEOGRAPHY SKILLS
## INTERPRETING VISUALS: Interpreting Physical Maps

Physical maps are special-purpose maps that focus on topography and the natural landscape. They show the locations and extent of physical features. For example, a physical map of the United States (see page 195) tells you that the Great Lakes are located in the north central part of the country. It shows that the Central Plains and Great Plains stretch more than 1,200 miles (1,900 kilometers) from Ohio to Colorado. A physical map also illustrates the relative locations of various features. The same physical map of the United States shows the location of California's Central Valley in relation to the Sierra Nevada and Coast Ranges.

Because elevation, access to water routes, and other physical features influence the choices humans make, it is important for you to be able to read a physical map.

### How to Interpret a Physical Map

Follow these steps to interpret a physical map.

1. **Use basic map skills.** Review the basic map-reading steps presented in Reviewing Map Basics on page 44. Study the colors used to illustrate elevations and specific natural features.
2. **Study shapes.** Look closely at the shapes shown on the map. A peninsula will appear as an arm of land reaching into the water. An isthmus will be a narrow strip of land between water bodies. The unique shapes of other natural features, such as deltas, capes, bays, and islands, also will appear.
3. **Note relative locations.** Study the map as a whole. Note where one feature appears in relation to other features. Make comparisons and draw conclusions about the effect of topography on settlement patterns and economic activity.

### Applying the Skill

Study the map below, which illustrates the physical features of Central America. Note that a mountainous spine occupies the center of the region, forming a land bridge linking North America and South America. Even today these mountains hinder transportation and communication in Central America. Cartographic art, or special colored shading, indicates the rugged nature of this mountain chain. Also note that, as you learned in the skill lesson in Chapter 2 (see page 44), black italic type designates natural features such as the Mosquito Coast. Blue italic type marks water features such as the Gulf of Panamá, the Gulf of Honduras, the Caribbean Sea, and the San Juan River. All of the physical maps in this textbook follow the style of this map.

*To practice this skill, see Practicing Geography Skills on page 77.*

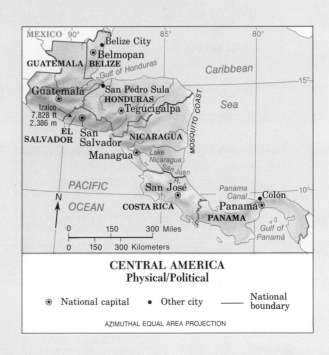

**CENTRAL AMERICA**
**Physical/Political**

⊛ National capital    • Other city    —— National boundary

AZIMUTHAL EQUAL AREA PROJECTION

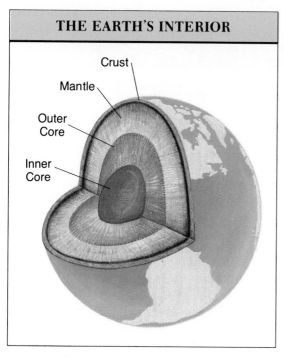

## THE EARTH'S INTERIOR

Crust
Mantle
Outer Core
Inner Core

*Learning from Diagrams. Above is a cross section of the earth's interior showing its different layers. On what layer are the continents located?*

The **crust** forms the solid outermost layer, or skin, of the earth. It is much thinner in proportion to the earth's size than the shell of an egg. Because it lies on or near the surface, more is known about the crust than about any of the other layers of the earth's interior. The crust under the continents is some 25 miles (40 kilometers) thick, while the crust under the ocean is only about 3 miles (5 kilometers) thick. Scientists who specialize in the study of the earth's crust, including its different rock formations, are known as **geologists.**

## Constant Change

The earth today is very different from the earth of millions of years ago. The texture of the land, the locations of the landmasses, and the climate have undergone tremendous changes—changes that scientists even now can only begin to understand.

**A shrinking earth.** For many years scientists thought that the continents were permanently fixed on the earth, never changing in size, shape, or location. The lands and seas developed, the scientists said, as the earth cooled from its original molten state. The mountains, too, were believed to be ancient and permanent features of the earth. They formed, it was thought, as the earth cooled, much as wrinkles form on the skin of a drying apple.

Scientists also believed that this cooling process caused the earth to shrink as it hardened. In time scientists abandoned the "shrinking earth" idea largely because there was no evidence that the earth had actually gotten smaller.

**Drifting continents.** Over the years a new description of the earth's surface—one that suggested that the continents were actually moving and changing—developed. One of the first proponents of this idea was Francis Bacon, a seventeenth-century scientist. After studying the latest maps of the earth and trying to piece together the shapes of the continents, Bacon concluded that the continents once were joined, forming one huge landmass. Over time, he believed, the continents separated and moved and were still moving.

In the years following Bacon's studies, other scientists announced similar conclusions. None, however, were able to offer enough evidence to prove that the idea was true. Then in 1858 the work of a scientist named Antonio Snider-Pelligrini attracted renewed attention to Bacon's idea that the continents had once been joined. Snider-Pelligrini drew a map showing Africa, Europe, and the Americas nestled together as one landmass. He stated that the similarity of plant fossils found in Europe and North America could only be explained by the idea of a single continent. In 1912 a German geographer named Alfred Wegener took up

*Text continues on page 67.*

It is a dark winter night in 1620 in England. A fire glows in the fireplace, warming the cold study, as a man sits alone at his desk. Several candles on the desk cast shadows on the wall. The man is poring over some new maps drawn from the charts of sailors who have sailed the coasts of Africa and South America.

Tracing the coasts with his finger, the man suddenly stops, seeing something unusual. He pulls the candles closer for better light. Then, taking some scissors from his desk, he cuts out the shapes of the two continents and tries to fit them together like pieces of a jigsaw puzzle.

The pieces nearly fit! The bulge of the east coast of South America fits almost exactly below the bulge of Africa's west coast. In the man's mind, questions fight for attention. What does this mean? Were these two great landmasses, now separated by the Atlantic Ocean, once connected?

## Searching for Likenesses

The man in the study was Francis Bacon, a famous scientist. Bacon wrote that scientists ought "to observe resemblances, for they unite nature." Resemblances suggest ways in which things are related. The idea that the two large continents might once have been joined appealed to him. As a scientist, he always searched for ways of using observation and experimentation to explain things found in nature.

## Establishing a Theory

Bacon's interest in the resemblances of the shapes of all the continents led him to study them. He looked especially for relationships between what he called the "Old World" and the "New World." He developed a **hypothesis,** or scientific assumption, that all the landmasses fit together. He wrote that "the New and Old World are both of

*Portrait of Francis Bacon*

them broad and expanded toward the north and narrow and pointed toward the south."

The large map at the top of page 66 supports the very same hypothesis that Francis Bacon formulated and wrote about in 1620. The smaller maps below it illustrate the **theory**—an idea for explaining something that is not proven—that developed from Bacon's hypothesis.

In the nearly four hundred years since he first wrote about the possible connections between continents, many scientists have offered similar theories. Each theory suggested that at one time, millions of years ago, all of the continents were joined as a single supercontinent. At some time in the distant past, the supercontinent broke up and the continents began drifting apart.

For hundreds of years most scientists did not accept such theories. No one then knew of a mechanism strong enough to pull the continents apart. As you will see, however, recent findings that help to explain how the continents move tend to support the theory of continental drift.

# PANGAEA AND THE DRIFTING CONTINENTS

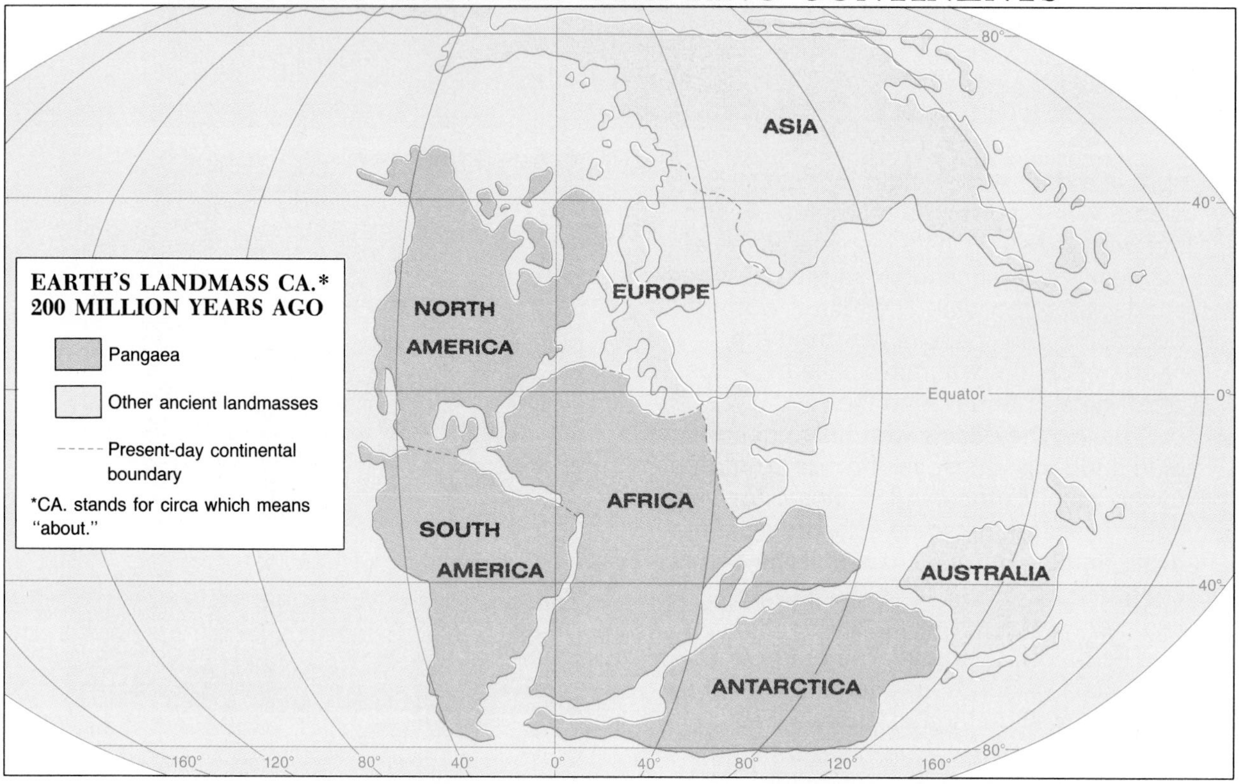

EARTH'S LANDMASS CA.* 200 MILLION YEARS AGO
Pangaea
Other ancient landmasses
Present-day continental boundary
*CA. stands for circa which means "about."
NORTH AMERICA
SOUTH AMERICA
EUROPE
ASIA
AFRICA
AUSTRALIA
ANTARCTICA
Equator
80°
40°
0°
160°
120°
80°
40°
0°
40°
80°
120°
160°


190 MILLION YEARS AGO

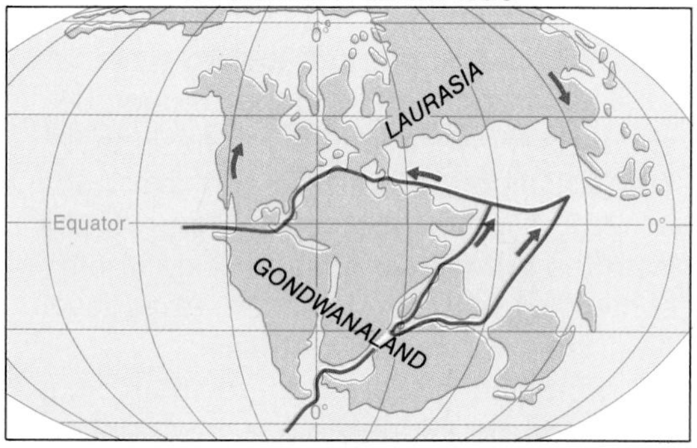

LAURASIA
GONDWANALAND
Equator
0°


65 MILLION YEARS AGO

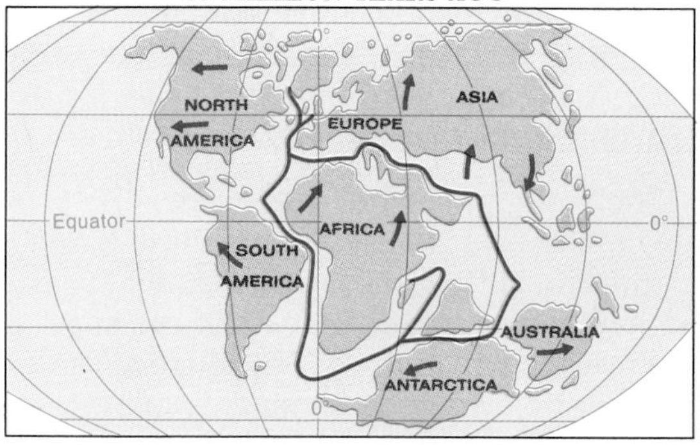

NORTH AMERICA
EUROPE
ASIA
AFRICA
SOUTH AMERICA
AUSTRALIA
ANTARCTICA
Equator
0°


PRESENT

NORTH AMERICA
EUROPE
ASIA
AFRICA
SOUTH AMERICA
AUSTRALIA
ANTARCTICA
Equator
0°


**THE DRIFTING CONTINENTS FROM 190 MILLION YEARS AGO TO THE PRESENT**

- Landmasses
- Tectonic plate boundary
- Direction of tectonic plate movement

***Learning from Maps.*** *The maps above illustrate continental drift. What do the solid red lines on the maps represent?*

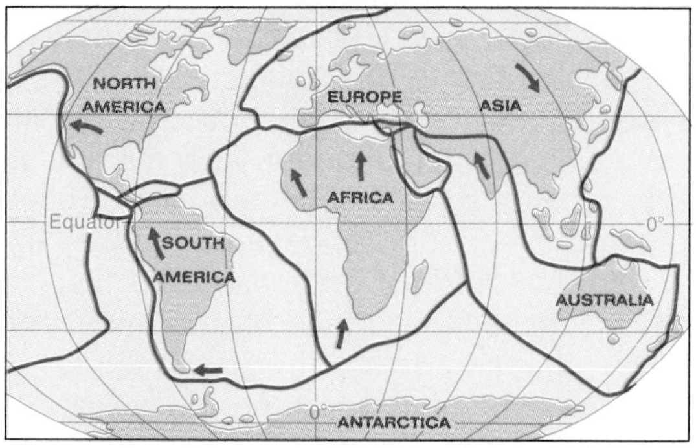

the work of Bacon and Snider-Pelligrini, offering a new idea he called the "theory of **continental drift.**"

Wegener believed that there was once a single supercontinent that he called Pangaea, from the Greek words *pan*, meaning "all," and *ge*, meaning "the earth." According to Wegener, Pangaea split apart millions of years ago to form two huge continents—Laurasia in the Northern Hemisphere and Gondwanaland in the Southern Hemisphere. Ultimately, said Wegener, Laurasia broke up to form North America, Europe, most of Asia, and Greenland. In the Southern Hemisphere, Gondwanaland split apart into Africa, South America, Antarctica, Australia, and India. Wegener believed that the landmasses drifted for millions of years before arriving at their present locations. He also claimed that the process of continental drift was still going on—that the continents were still on the move.

In order to support the theory of continental drift, Wegener and his followers pointed to similarities in the fossils of the southern continents. Fossils of the same ferns and freshwater reptiles had been found in all of the southern continents. To those who supported Wegener's ideas, the presence of such fossils strongly suggested that South America, Africa, India, and Australia had once been part of the same continent. They claimed that such land-based life could never have crossed the wide seas that now separate these lands. Critics of the theory, however, said that the animals may have crossed the waters on ancient land bridges. However, no evidence of such land bridges in the Southern Hemisphere has been found.

Wegener's theory caused a storm of controversy. Despite fossil and geological evidence, most scientists could not accept the idea. They argued that it was scientifically impossible for the continents to move across the solid seafloor. At the time,

Wegener and his supporters could not conclusively prove their arguments. New studies of the seafloor, however, have given more scientific evidence to support the theory of continental drift.

---

**SECTION 2 REVIEW**

1. **Define** seismic wave, molten material, core, mantle, crust, geologist, hypothesis, theory, continental drift
2. **Interpreting Information** How can scientists obtain information about the deep interior of the earth?
3. **Summarizing Ideas** What are the three major layers of the earth?
4. **Contrasting Ideas** How does the shrinking earth theory differ from the theory of continental drift?
5. **Synthesizing Ideas** How did the work of Antonio Snider-Pelligrini and Alfred Wegener support Francis Bacon's theory?
6. **Analyzing Ideas** Why did Wegener's theory cause controversy?

---

## 3 Movements of the earth's plates have changed its surface features.

More than 50 years after Wegener first presented the idea of continental drift, a new theory about changes on the earth's surface developed. This theory—the theory of plate tectonics—revolutionized scientific thinking about the earth and showed that continental drift may, in fact, occur.

### Evidence from Under the Sea

In the 1950s scientists began studying the ocean floor in more detail than ever before. Special **sonar** (SOH·nar) equipment that uses sound waves to detect underwater objects helped scientists gather informa-

tion. Their observations showed that the seafloors were slowly spreading apart along well-defined oceanic ridges. They called their discovery seafloor spreading.

Seafloor spreading begins when molten materials rise from the soft layer of the earth's upper mantle. The molten materials break through the oceanic crust, build up high ridges or rises, and solidify. As they solidify, the molten materials become part of the crust. As new oceanic crust is formed at the ridges, older parts of the crust are pushed outward, away from the ridges.

Studies of **paleomagnetism** (pay·lee·oh· MAG·neh·tihz·ehm), or the ancient patterns of magnetism recorded in rocks, confirm the process of seafloor spreading. By examining the magnetic field of rocks, scien-

***Learning from Pictures.*** *This Pterodactyl fossil is from Bavaria, a region in West Germany. How do scientists use fossils to support the theory of seafloor spreading?*

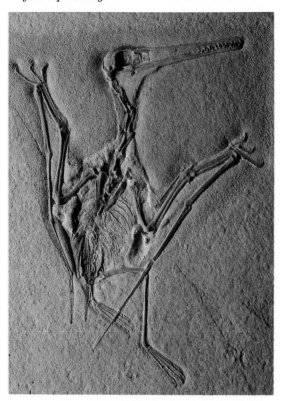

tists can tell whether or not the rocks have moved from the place where they originated. Evidence indicates that the rocks on the ocean floor have indeed moved, supporting the idea of seafloor spreading.

**Core samples,** or samples taken from the earth's interior, also support the idea of seafloor spreading. Core samples help scientists date the **sediments,** or the solids deposited by water, that constantly accumulate on the seafloor. The samples are obtained from holes drilled into these sediments. Tiny fossils in the core samples show, almost without exception, that the age of sediments on the seafloor increases outward from the oceanic ridges. The youngest part of the seafloor lies closest to the ridges, and the oldest part of the floor lies farthest from them. This age difference, scientists believe, can only be explained by seafloor spreading.

## Plate Tectonics

The discovery of seafloor spreading provided the evidence for the theory of plate tectonics. The theory of **plate tectonics** (tek·TON·iks) states that the earth's outer shell—including both the crust and parts of the upper mantle—is not one solid piece as was previously thought. Instead, great **faults,** or cracks in the crust of the earth, divide it into huge sections called plates. These plates, on which the continents and ocean lie, have a total thickness of about 63 miles (100 kilometers) and are continuously moving.

The plates move along on top of the molten material in the upper mantle as if the mantle serves as a giant conveyor belt. The plates move very slowly, perhaps no more than 1 to 2.4 inches (1 to 6 centimeters) a year. Nonetheless, even such small movements can carry continents across great distances over the course of millions of years. The map on page 69 illustrates the major plates and their direction of

*Text continues on page 70.*

**68**

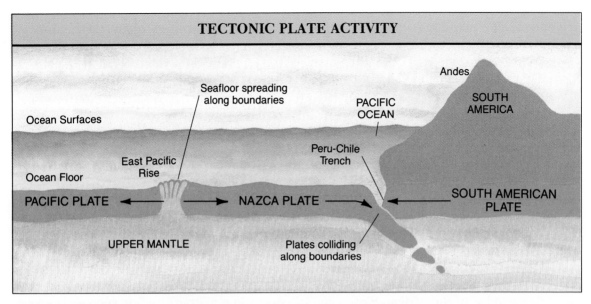

## TECTONIC PLATE ACTIVITY

Andes

Seafloor spreading
along boundaries

PACIFIC
OCEAN

SOUTH
AMERICA

Ocean Surfaces

East Pacific
Rise

Peru-Chile
Trench

Ocean Floor

PACIFIC PLATE ← → NAZCA PLATE → ← SOUTH AMERICAN
PLATE

UPPER MANTLE

Plates colliding
along boundaries

***Learning from Diagrams.*** *Tectonic plate movement is constantly changing the earth's surface. What is happening to the Peru-Chile Trench?*

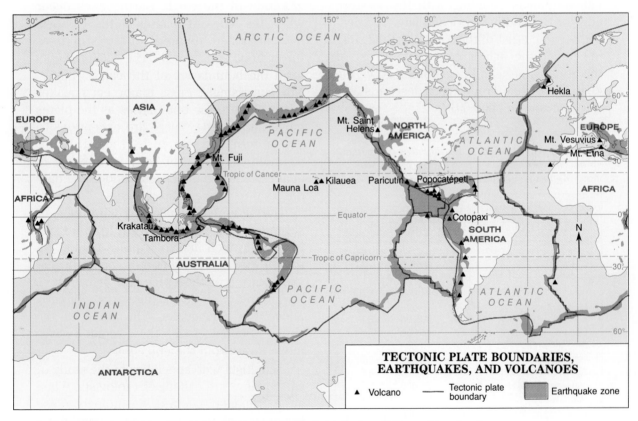

### TECTONIC PLATE BOUNDARIES, EARTHQUAKES, AND VOLCANOES

▲ Volcano    — Tectonic plate boundary    ▓ Earthquake zone

***Learning from Maps.*** *The map above outlines the boundaries of the earth's tectonic plates. Why are earthquake zones located along these boundaries?*

movement. The two largest plates are the Pacific Plate, which covers about one-fifth of the earth's surface, and the Eurasian Plate. Other large plates include the North American, South American, Australian, African, and Antarctic plates.

As the plates move, some move away from each other, while others move closer together. The North American and Eurasian plates, for example, have been moving apart along the mid-Atlantic Ridge (see the map on pages 134–35) for millions of years. The North American Plate is moving to the west, while the Eurasian Plate is moving to the east. Farther south the South American Plate is moving westward, away from the mid-Atlantic edge of the African Plate.

Plates moving closer together sometimes collide head-on. For example, the eastward-moving Nazca Plate under the Pacific Ocean is colliding with the western edge of the South American Plate. The denser oceanic crust of the Nazca Plate is sinking under the lighter continental crust of the South American Plate, pulling down the deep Peru-Chile Trench as it descends (see the diagram on page 69).

*Learning from Charts.* *Earthquakes can cause an enormous amount of destruction. Where was the most intense recorded earthquake of this century?*

### WORST EARTHQUAKES OF THE TWENTIETH CENTURY

| Date | Place | Death Toll* | Richter Scale |
|------|-------|-------------|---------------|
| July 28, 1976 | China | 242,000 | 8.0 |
| May 22, 1927 | China | 200,000 | 8.3 |
| December 16, 1920 | China | 180,000 | 8.6 |
| December 28, 1908 | Italy | 75,000 | 7.5 |
| December 26, 1932 | China | 70,000 | 7.6 |
| May 31, 1970 | Peru | 66,800 | 7.8 |
| September 1, 1923 | China | 43,000 | 8.3 |
| January 29, 1939 | Chile | 39,000 | 8.3 |
| May 31, 1935 | India | 30,000 | 7.5 |
| January 13, 1935 | Italy | 30,000 | 7.0 |

*Estimated      Source: *Time,* September 30, 1985

Other plates brush against each other as they move side by side. The movements of the Pacific Plate, which carries part of California, and the North American Plate, which carries the rest of North America, provide one example. As the Pacific Plate moves slowly toward the northwest, it grinds against the edge of the North American Plate. This movement takes place along the San Andreas Fault, which separates the two plates in California.

The movement of the earth's plates often triggers great upheavals on the earth's surface. These upheavals, which can be violent, can result in tremendous changes in an area's landforms. Some of these changes occur in a matter of a few seconds. Others, however, occur over millions of years.

**Earthquakes.** An **earthquake** is a sudden vibration of the earth. Earthquakes occur when the sides of a fault shift. Scientists have identified hundreds of faults in areas throughout the world. The major faults form the boundaries of the earth's plates. Not surprisingly, most major earthquakes occur along these boundaries as the plates move and collide. There are exceptions to this pattern, however. In 1811 and 1812, for example, a series of very strong earthquakes centered in Missouri shook the middle section of the United States.

During an earthquake the vibrations, or seismic waves, travel outward from the disturbance, much like the ripples made by a rock thrown into a pond. The strongest shock is felt at the **epicenter** (EHP·ih·sent·uhr), or point on the earth's surface directly above the earthquake. The force of the shock diminishes as the seismic waves move away from the epicenter.

Scientists who specialize in the study of earthquakes are called seismologists. When an earthquake occurs, seismologists use seismographs to record the time and force of the seismic waves. By comparing seis-

***Learning from Pictures.*** *Earthquakes and volcanoes are among the most spectacular displays of nature. How is the intensity of earthquakes measured?*

mograph readings from different locations, seismologists can pinpoint the exact location of an earthquake's epicenter.

In 1935 a California seismologist named Charles F. Richter created a scale for measuring the intensity of earthquakes. The **Richter** (RIK·tuhr) **scale** uses numbers ranging from 0 to 9 to describe an earthquake's intensity. An earthquake with a force of 8 or more on the Richter scale causes enormous damage. In some cases buildings collapse, dams burst, gas lines break and ignite, and roads buckle.

Seismologists estimate that the earthquake that shook San Francisco, California, in 1906 measured 8.3 on the Richter scale. That earthquake and the fires that resulted destroyed most of San Francisco. A 1976 earthquake in northeast China registered 8.2 and leveled the city of Tangshan. Smaller earthquakes, while not as devastating, still can cause major damage.

**Volcanic eruptions.** Like earthquakes, volcanic eruptions usually occur near the boundaries of the earth's plates, either on land or under the sea (see the map on page 69). During a volcanic eruption, molten rock, or magma, finds its way up through the earth's crust and spills out as **lava** (LAHV·uh) at the surface. The lava solidifies and builds up, layer upon layer, to form mountains with cones of different shapes. These mountains are called **volcanoes.**

Shield volcanoes create broad and gently sloping cones. In the Pacific Ocean, the cones of shield volcanoes rise more than 20,000 feet (6,100 meters) from the ocean floor to form the Hawaiian Islands. The eruptions of shield volcanoes, while spectacular, remain relatively nonviolent. Lava flows out of the crater and down the slopes of the cones in fiery tongues until it cools and solidifies.

Mount Fuji in Japan and Mount Hood in Oregon are composite volcanoes, generally the most recognizable type of volcano. Cones of composite volcanoes have steep slopes built of a mixture of lava and rock fragments. Eruptions are violent, hurling lava, superheated rocks, volcanic ash, and steam and other gases into the air with great force. An unusually violent eruption devastated Krakatau, an Indonesian island,

71

in 1883. After the eruption only the black-ened stump of the volcano remained. So great was the explosion that it was heard in Singapore, 868 miles (1,400 kilometers) away, and volcanic ash fell on China, 1,875 miles (3,000 kilometers) away.

The highest concentration of earth-quakes and volcanic eruptions circles the rim of the Pacific Ocean. Alaska and Cali-fornia experience earthquakes each year as the Pacific Plate grinds against the North American Plate (see the map on page 69). Other countries bordering the Pacific also record many earthquakes. Frequent vol-canic eruptions, both on land and under the sea, also threaten these areas. Because of the high degree of earthquake and volcanic activity, the Pacific rim is often called the "Ring of Fire."

**Mountain building.** You have read about the spectacular changes that earthquakes and volcanic eruptions can create on the earth's surface in a matter of seconds. While such changes are immediately notice-able, the movement of the plates also causes other, equally dramatic changes that are not as apparent. These are changes brought about by the process of mountain building—a process that can take millions of years. Depending on how the mountains are formed, geographers classify them as one of four types of mountains: fault block, folded, dome, or volcanic.

**Fault-block mountains** develop in places where the earth's crust breaks into enormous blocklike pieces, some of which have been pushed slowly upward. The Him-alaya, for example, were formed—and are still forming—as a result of the slow colli-sion of the continental crust of India on the Australian Plate with the continental crust of the Eurasian Plate. The Andes are form-ing somewhat differently, as the lighter con-tinental crust of South America buckles up over the denser oceanic crust of the Nazca Plate.

**Folded mountains** look like a huge cor-rugated roof. Because of the shifting of the tectonic plates, the earth's surface is always under stress. In some places this stress re-sults in the squeezing together of rocks into a series of rounded waves that appear to rise and fall in great folds. The Jura moun-tain range that covers parts of Switzerland and France is a classic example of folded mountains.

**Dome mountains** form as molten rock from within the earth pushes up layers of soft rock. The soft rock slowly wears away, exposing the rounded shape of the now-

*Learning from Diagrams.* *Volcanoes force lava and dust from deep in the earth to spill out over the earth's surface. What kind of volcano is illus-trated in this diagram?*

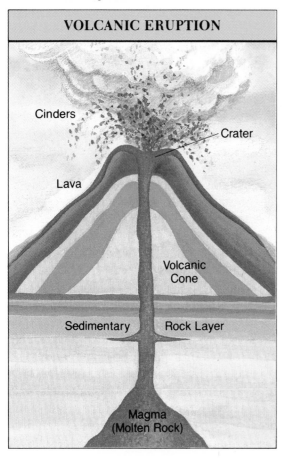

**VOLCANIC ERUPTION**

Cinders

Crater

Lava

Volcanic Cone

Sedimentary    Rock Layer

Magma (Molten Rock)

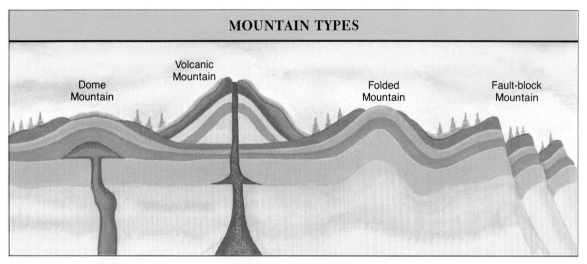

**MOUNTAIN TYPES**

Dome Mountain

Volcanic Mountain

Folded Mountain

Fault-block Mountain

*Learning from Diagrams.* *This diagram shows the four ways that mountains are formed. Which of the mountain types are formed by molten rock?*

hardened rock from below. The Black Hills of South Dakota and Wyoming provide examples of dome mountains.

As you read earlier in the chapter, geographers identify two types of **volcanic mountains,** or mountains formed from volcanic eruptions. These types are shield mountains and composite mountains.

---

**SECTION 3 REVIEW**

1. **Define** sonar, paleomagnetism, core sample, sediment, plate tectonics, fault, earthquake, epicenter, Richter scale, lava, volcano, fault-block mountain, folded mountain, dome mountain, volcanic mountain
2. **Locate** San Andreas Fault, The Himalaya, Andes
3. **Summarizing Ideas** (a) What is seafloor spreading? (b) According to the theory of plate tectonics, on what do the plates move?
4. **Interpreting Ideas** Why is the Pacific rim called the "Ring of Fire"?
5. **Evaluating Information** How do mountains form?

---

## 4 Weathering and erosion create distinctive landforms.

As plate movements reshape the earth's continents and ocean floor, certain external processes are at work, changing surface and subsurface features. These processes work much more slowly than earthquakes and volcanoes. In fact, like the process of mountain building, they often go unnoticed for generations. Over time, however, they can produce results as dramatic as the Grand Canyon and the Badlands of North and South Dakota. Two such external processes are weathering and erosion.

### Weathering

The slow process that breaks rocks down into smaller and smaller pieces is called **weathering.** Two kinds of weathering—physical and chemical—take place over time. Both types of weathering often occur simultaneously.

The major agent of physical weathering is frost wedging. The alternate freezing and

**Learning from Pictures.** *This Bristlecone Pine is an agent of weathering. If the pine continues to grow on the side of this cliff, what will eventually happen to the rocks?*

limestone dissolves in water. The minerals in the limestone that contain iron eventually oxidize and corrode, just as manufactured iron products rust if left outside. Even granite, one of the hardest rocks, slowly decomposes in the chemical weathering process. The chemicals present in acid rain speed the process of chemical weathering even more. As you learned in Chapter 1, pollutants released into the air combine with water vapor to form acid rain. In addition to speeding the chemical weathering process, acid rain pollutes lakes and rivers, kills fish, and damages crops, forests, and even buildings.

## Erosion

Each day parts of the earth's surface slowly wear away in a gradual process known as **erosion.** The major agents of erosion include running water, waves, moving ice, and wind.

Running water, found almost everywhere, probably does more to change the earth's surface than any other agent of erosion. Water running down a slope during a heavy rainfall carries away weathered rock and soil, cutting deep ruts and gullies in the slopes. Running water in streams and rivers carves valleys in much the same way—wearing away land in some places and depositing the eroded materials elsewhere.

Waves cause erosion and other changes along the shores of the ocean and large lakes. Along rocky coasts waves pound away at the bases of cliffs until the cliffs collapse. In other spots waves wash up eroded materials to form pebble and sand beaches.

Large masses of moving ice, known as **glaciers** (GLAY·shur), erode the land in the colder regions of the world. Glaciers in the form of large ice sheets travel across areas like monstrous bulldozers, scraping the land bare and pushing the eroded material

thawing of water found in the cracks of rocks causes frost wedging. When the water freezes it expands as much as 10 percent, forcing the cracks to widen. This cycle of freezing and thawing eventually breaks down even the largest and hardest rocks. Sometimes seeds take root in the cracks of rocks caused by the wedging and plants or trees grow. This speeds the process of physical weathering. As the plant or tree grows, the roots exert more pressure on the rocks, causing them to break apart (see the photograph above).

Chemical weathering alters the chemical makeup of rocks. Chemicals present in the air and water are a part of this process, although water is the most important agent of chemical weathering. Water mixes with the chemicals in the rocks, leading to their decomposition. Over time, for example,

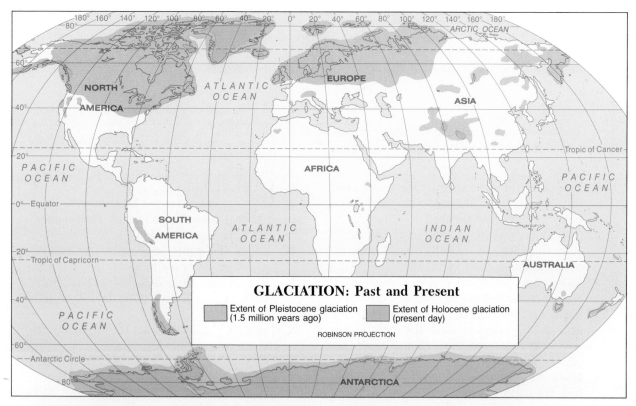

GLACIATION: Past and Present

| | Extent of Pleistocene glaciation (1.5 million years ago) | | Extent of Holocene glaciation (present day) |

ROBINSON PROJECTION

***Learning from Maps.*** *Present-day glaciers cover about 10 percent of the earth. Which is the most glaciated continent?*

in front of them. At the edge of an ice sheet, where melting occurs, deposits of eroded materials accumulate. Often huge boulders are left strewn here and there across the land when the ice sheet recedes. Smaller valley glaciers also are agents of erosion in mountain regions. As the glaciers move through mountain passes, they create distinctive U-shaped mountain valleys by eroding soil and rocks from the valley floor and walls.

Wind is a powerful agent of erosion, especially in regions that receive little rainfall. Continual strong winds stripped soil from parts of the Great Plains in the 1930s and carried the soil as far east as Boston, Massachusetts. Winds carry sand, volcanic ash, and even gravel. High winds carrying such windblown materials sandblast even the hardest rocks into many different and often fantastic shapes.

## SECTION 4 REVIEW

1. **Define** weathering, erosion, glacier
2. **Comparing Ideas** How does physical weathering differ from chemical weathering?
3. **Summarizing Ideas** What are the most important agents of **(a)** physical weathering, **(b)** chemical weathering, and **(c)** erosion?
4. **Analyzing Ideas** How can erosion change the appearance of a landscape over time?
5. **Interpreting Ideas** Why does acid rain speed the chemical weathering process?
6. **Evaluating Ideas** Which changes—those caused by weathering or those caused by erosion—have had the greatest impact on human activity? Explain your answer.

## Chapter Summary

The following list contains the key concepts you have learned about the earth's changing surface.

1. The variety of landforms that cover the face of the earth have advantages and disadvantages for human settlement.
2. Geographers use slope, local relief, and other characteristics to classify landforms as plains, plateaus, hills, or mountains.
3. Fossils and geological evidence are helping scientists understand the changes the earth has undergone over the years. Scientists are also seeking answers about the earth's interior—the exact structure of the core, the mantle, and the crust.
4. Many theories have been presented about how the earth has changed over time. Francis Bacon was among the first to suggest that the continents were once joined as one huge landmass.
5. The evidence to support the theory of plate tectonics was provided by the discovery of seafloor spreading. The theory of plate tectonics states that the earth's outer shell is not one solid piece but is broken into plates that are constantly moving.
6. Earthquakes and volcanoes, which cause violent changes on the earth's surface, occur most often near major faults on the edges of the earth's plates.
7. Weathering and erosion can produce dramatic changes in the surface of the earth over time.

On a separate sheet of paper, complete the following review exercises.

## Reviewing Geographic Terms

Supply the geographic term that correctly completes each sentence.

1. The shapes on the earth's surface are called ____.

2. ____ is a place's distance above or below sea level.
3. The ____ forms the solid outermost layer of the earth.
4. An idea for explaining something that is not proven is called a ____.
5. A ____ is characterized by a generally flat area that rises far above the surrounding land on at least one side.
6. ____ is the study of ancient patterns of magnetism recorded in rocks.
7. ____ ____ are formed as molten rock from within the earth pushes up layers of soft rock.
8. The ____ ____ uses numbers to measure the intensity of an earthquake.
9. The slow process of breaking down rocks into smaller and smaller pieces is called ____.
10. ____ are solids deposited by water.

## Developing Critical Thinking Skills

1. **Interpreting Ideas** Why do people live in areas that have some disadvantages for human use and development? Provide an example from the textbook to support your answer.
2. **Drawing Conclusions** Why have scientists concluded that the interior of the earth consists of different layers of solid and molten materials?
3. **Evaluating Ideas** What evidence did scientists use to confirm the theory of seafloor spreading?
4. **Analyzing Information** (a) What does the theory of plate tectonics state? (b) How does this theory relate to scientific knowledge about earthquakes and volcanic eruptions along the Pacific Coast of the United States?
5. **Writing About Geography** In a clearly written paragraph, complete one of the following activities. (a) Contrast the shrinking earth theory with the theory of plate tectonics. (b) Discuss the physical changes of

the earth and the value of the scientific study of these changes to the inhabitants of the planet.

## Using Primary Sources

In the following excerpt from *The Innocents Abroad, or the New Pilgrim's Progress*, Mark Twain describes his visit to Pompeii, which was destroyed when Mount Vesuvius erupted in A.D. 79—nearly 1,800 years before Twain's visit. As you study the reading, consider what an erupting volcano might do to a modern city.

They pronounce it Pom-*pay*-e. I always had an idea that you went down into Pompeii with torches, by the way of damp, dark stairways, just as you do in silver mines, and traversed gloomy tunnels with lava overhead and something on either hand like [run-down] prisons gouged out of the solid earth, that faintly resembled houses. But you do nothing of the kind. Fully one-half of the buried city, perhaps, is completely [dug up] and thrown open freely to the light of day; and there stand the long rows of solidly-built brick houses (roofless) just as they stood eighteen hundred years ago, hot with the flaming sun; and there lie their floors, clean swept, and not a bright fragment tarnished or wanting of the labored mosaics that pictured them with the beasts, and birds, and flowers which we copy in perishable carpets to-day; . . . and there are the narrow streets and narrower sidewalks, paved with flags of good hard lava, the one deeply rutted with the chariot-wheels, and the other with the passing feet of the Pompeiians of bygone centuries; and there are the bakeshops, the temples, the halls of justice, the baths, the theatres—all clean-scraped and neat, and suggesting nothing of the nature of a silver mine away down in the bowels of the earth.

1. What surprised Twain about Pompeii?
2. What did Twain notice about the ruins at Pompeii?

## Practicing Geography Skills

*Before completing this activity, review Developing Geography Skills on page 63.*

**Interpreting a Physical Map**   Study the map on page 511 and answer the following questions.

1. What is the name of the cape at the southern end of Africa?
2. What natural feature forms the border between Tanzania and Zaire?
3. **(a)** What small African nation overlooks the narrow strait between the Red Sea and the Gulf of Aden?   **(b)** Why does this location have strategic importance?
4. **(a)** What major landform lies directly to the north of the Sahel?   **(b)** How might this relative location affect the landscape and people of the Sahel?

## Exploring Geography

1. To better understand the theory of continental drift, outline the section "Establishing a Theory" in the CASE STUDY on text page 65.
2. If you have ever witnessed an earthquake or visited the site of an active volcano, prepare a short speech on your experiences. Your speech on earthquakes should include information on where the earthquake occurred, what its Richter scale measurement was, how much damage it caused, and how you felt while it was taking place. Speeches on volcanoes should include such points as the location of the volcano, the last time it erupted, the amount of damage this eruption caused, and how you felt about being so close to a potentially dangerous area. If you have not personally witnessed these natural phenomena, you might interview someone who has.

# CHAPTER 4
# Weather, Climate, and Vegetation

# PUTTING THE CHAPTER IN FOCUS

The atmosphere—the air—shapes the weather, climate, and vegetation found on the earth. Without air there would be no day-to-day weather changes. It would be scorchingly hot during the day and bitterly cold at night. And, there would be no oxygen and no carbon dioxide to support human and plant life.

## Ideas to Understand

In studying about weather, climate, and vegetation, use these ideas to give direction to your reading.

1 The atmosphere makes life on the earth possible.
2 Four conditions in the earth's atmosphere cause weather.
3 Changing atmospheric conditions can create violent weather.
4 Three climatic controls influence the distribution of climates.
5 Global vegetation regions are related to global climate regions.

## Terms to Define

The following terms are some of the key terms in the chapter. Defining them will help you understand weather, climate, and vegetation.

| | |
|---|---|
| atmosphere | precipitation |
| weather | front |
| temperature | atmospheric pressure |
| insolation | climate |
| water cycle | plant community |
| relative humidity | biome |

## Places to Locate

Locating the following places will add to your knowledge of geography.

| | |
|---|---|
| Glasgow, Scotland | Amazon Basin |
| Labrador, Canada | Tibet |

---

## 1 The atmosphere makes life on the earth possible.

Earth is unique among the planets in the solar system. One of the most unique features of Earth is the presence of a stable atmosphere. The various gases that surround a planet make up its **atmosphere** (AT·muh·sfehr). Earth's atmosphere shapes our weather, climate, and vegetation patterns and makes life as we know it possible.

### Components of the Atmosphere

A great "ocean" of gases surrounding the earth for thousands of miles forms the earth's atmosphere, usually known simply as the air. More than 98 percent of the gases that make up the atmosphere, however, are found within 16 miles (26 kilometers) of the earth's surface. Farther above the earth, the gases—and the air—gradually thin out.

Air in its natural state is a colorless, odorless, tasteless mixture of gases. Nitrogen makes up 78 percent of dry air, oxygen makes up 21 percent, and other gases such as carbon dioxide, helium, and ozone make up the remaining 1 percent.

Along with gases, air nearly always contains small amounts of water vapor, dust, soot, pollen, seeds, and other particles. Winds, forest fires, and volcanic eruptions sweep many of these particles into the air naturally. Other particles spew from chimneys, smokestacks, automobiles, and other polluters. Together, these particles create polluted air, such as the haze and smog that hangs over many cities today.

◀ *Earth from space*

## Concerns About the Atmosphere

The gases in the atmosphere combine in a delicate balance that supports life. In recent years, however, many scientists have become increasingly concerned that this delicate balance may be in jeopardy.

The level of carbon dioxide ($CO_2$) in the air, for example, has been increasing for the last 100 years. Many scientists trace the rise to the emergence of heavy industries, which burn coal, oil, and other fossil fuels to produce energy. Because $CO_2$ helps warm the air by absorbing energy from the sun, scientists are afraid that higher $CO_2$ levels will warm the lower atmosphere. Such a warming process could melt the earth's ice sheets, causing flooding and changes in the world's weather patterns.

Scientists also have become alarmed about the level of another gas in the air— ozone ($O_3$). Most ozone is found in the **stratosphere,** or upper atmosphere, between 10 and 25 miles (16 and 40 kilometers) above the earth's surface. This thin ozone layer protects the earth from the dangerous ultraviolet rays of the sun.

Scientists suspect that emissions from supersonic airplanes and certain manufactured products such as aerosol spray cans damage the ozone layer. In fact, they have found a large hole in the ozone layer over Antarctica. Concern over damage to the ozone layer prompted 46 nations, including the United States, to sign a 1987 agreement to conserve ozone.

---

**SECTION 1 REVIEW**

1. **Define** atmosphere, stratosphere
2. **Summarizing Ideas** What are the components of the atmosphere?
3. **Interpreting Ideas** Why are some scientists concerned about the atmosphere's levels of **(a)** carbon dioxide and **(b)** ozone?

---

## 2 Four conditions in the earth's atmosphere cause weather.

The people of Chicago have a saying: "If you don't like the weather, wait an hour." They are referring to how quickly weather conditions in the area can change. One minute, billowing black thunderheads shower the city with rain. The next, sunshine filters through the clouds.

Chicagoans are not alone in observing how quickly weather changes. By its very nature, weather changes constantly. The term **weather** describes the condition of the atmosphere for a short period of time in a specific area. Because the atmosphere changes constantly, the weather, too, changes constantly. Four variable conditions in the atmosphere affect an area's weather: temperature, moisture, atmospheric pressure, and wind.

### Temperature

When most people talk about the weather, one of the first things they describe is the temperature. **Temperature** is a measurement of heat and cold—the lack of heat. The temperature of the air controls the temperature of a place on the earth's surface.

Temperature is measured in degrees, using a thermometer with either a Fahrenheit (F) or a Celsius (C) scale. Thermometers using the Fahrenheit scale are most common in the United States.

**How the atmosphere is warmed.** The earth receives its warmth from sunlight, or solar radiation. The process by which sunlight warms the earth is called **insolation.**

Only about 48 percent of all sunlight actually reaches the earth's surface. Gases in the atmosphere either absorb or reflect the rest back into space. Land and water

absorb the sunlight that does reach the earth's surface and change it into heat energy. This heat energy radiates back into the atmosphere, where it warms the air. Air closest to the land and water warms first, followed by the air in the higher layers of the atmosphere. At night the earth and the air slowly cool.

**The greenhouse effect.** Heat energy does not pass through the air as easily as sunlight does. The lower atmosphere temporarily traps the heat, much like a greenhouse traps warmth. In a greenhouse the sunlight passes through the glass roof and walls and warms the air. The heat, however, does not immediately pass back through the glass to the outside air. Instead the heat is temporarily trapped in the warm air, keeping the greenhouse warm, just as heat energy is temporarily trapped in the lower atmosphere, keeping the earth warm. This process, called the **greenhouse effect,** constantly warms the earth.

## Moisture

Moisture is the second variable element of weather. The air in the lower atmosphere always contains some amount of moisture. However, air higher than 4 miles (6.4 kilometers) above the earth's surface rarely contains moisture.

**The water cycle.** Moisture in the air occurs as a part of the **water cycle,** or

*Learning from Diagrams.* *Water evaporates from the earth into the atmosphere and returns to the earth as precipitation. What are the four kinds of precipitation shown?*

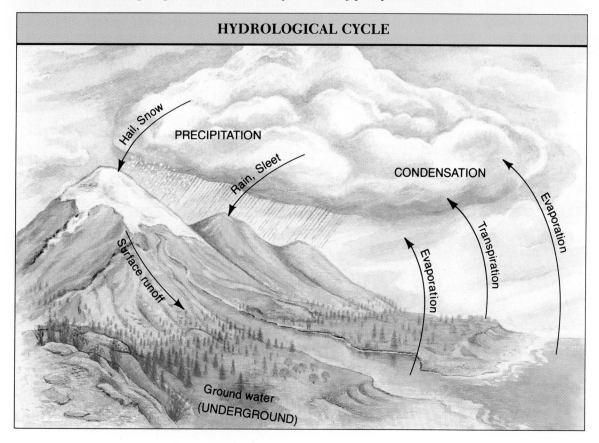

### HYDROLOGICAL CYCLE

Hail, Snow

PRECIPITATION

Rain, Sleet

CONDENSATION

Surface runoff

Evaporation

Transpiration

Evaporation

Ground water
(UNDERGROUND)

hydrological cycle (see the diagram on page 81). Moisture enters the air through **evaporation** (ee·vap·uh·RAY·shuhn), the process by which water changes from a liquid form to a gaseous water vapor. Evaporation takes place continuously over the ocean, rivers, lakes, and other wet surfaces.

You cannot see water vapor in the air until **condensation** changes the gaseous water vapor back into liquid water. This liquid water falls to the earth as rain or snow. The rain and snow then drain into the ocean, rivers, lakes, and streams to begin the water cycle again.

**Absolute and relative humidity.** The amount of moisture in the air is called **humidity** (hyoo·MIHD·eht·ee). Humidity can be measured in two ways. **Absolute humidity** measures how much the water vapor in the air weighs. **Relative humidity,** always expressed as a percentage, compares the weight of the water vapor present in the air with the maximum amount of water vapor the air could hold. Suppose, for example, that a cubic foot of air con-

tains 8 grams of water vapor but could hold 16 grams. The absolute humidity of that sample of air would be 8 grams and the relative humidity would be 50 percent.

As a rule warm air can hold more moisture than cold air. When air contains all the moisture it can, it becomes saturated and has a relative humidity of 100 percent. If the saturated air cools, the extra moisture condenses to a liquid state, forming clouds and fog.

**Precipitation.** When the drops of water condensing in cooling air become large enough, they form **precipitation** (pri·sip·uh·TAY·shuhn)—rain, snow, sleet, or hail. Rain forms when condensation takes place at temperatures above 32°F (0°C). Snow, sleet, and hail form when condensation takes place below 32°F (0°C).

Precipitation can be placed into several different categories, depending on how the precipitation formed. The three major types of precipitation are orographic, convectional, and frontal. Each type is illustrated on the diagrams that follow.

*Text continues on page 84.*

*Learning from Diagrams.* *Cool, moist air forms precipitation after a high landform causes it to rise. How is this air different after it passes over the landform?*

*Learning from Diagrams.* *As warm air rises it cools and forms precipitation. How is convectional precipitation directly related to the fact that cool air can hold less moisture than warm air?*

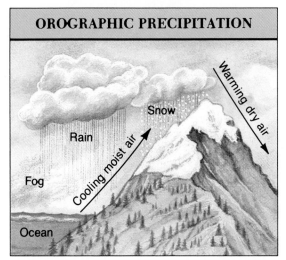

**OROGRAPHIC PRECIPITATION**

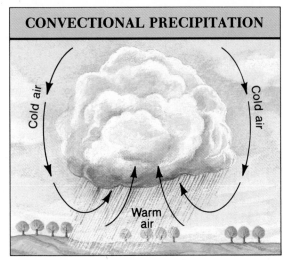

**CONVECTIONAL PRECIPITATION**

# DEVELOPING GEOGRAPHY SKILLS
## INTERPRETING VISUALS: Understanding Diagrams

Geographers use diagrams to present a variety of different types of information. Some show the steps in a process, such as the diagram of the water cycle on page 81. Some illustrate interactions, such as the diagram of tectonic plate activity on page 69. Others provide tidy and eye-catching ways of presenting graphic information, such as the diagram of the earth's interior on page 64. In order to effectively interpret a diagram, you must understand the labels and translate the symbols into ideas.

### How to Understand Diagrams

Follow these guidelines to effectively understand diagrams.

1. **Note the title.** Study the title. Each diagram has a special purpose, which is explained by the title. The title also may contain dates, locations, or other important information.
2. **Study the key.** Locate and read the key if one exists. Like a map key, the key to a diagram tells you what the symbols used in the diagram mean.
3. **Read the labels.** Note all labels and captions. Diagrams often give much of their information in labels and short captions.
4. **Study the parts of the diagram.** Identify the information given by each part of the diagram. Note relationships between its parts.
5. **Check for footnotes.** Refer to all footnotes. An asterisk or number will refer you to an explanation of some important information in the diagram, such as a special circumstance surrounding data collection.
6. **Form ideas out of the information diagramed.** Translate the symbolic illustration into sentences. Be sure to check your understanding of all the information the diagram contains.

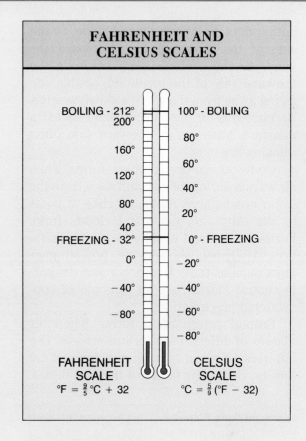

**FAHRENHEIT AND CELSIUS SCALES**

BOILING - 212°
200°
160°
120°
80°
40°
FREEZING - 32°
0°
−40°
−80°

100° - BOILING
80°
60°
40°
20°
0° - FREEZING
−20°
−40°
−60°
−80°

FAHRENHEIT SCALE
°F = $\frac{9}{5}$°C + 32

CELSIUS SCALE
°C = $\frac{5}{9}$(°F − 32)

### Applying the Skill

Study the diagram above. Note that its title is "Fahrenheit and Celsius Scales." The diagram illustrates both scales side by side. Labels at the bottom identify the scales—Fahrenheit on the left and Celsius on the right—and provide the formulas for converting temperatures from one scale to the other. Temperatures (in increments of 20 degrees) are labeled along the vertical sides of the thermometers. These labels provide a visual comparison of the two scales. Labels also mark the freezing points (32°F/0°C) and the boiling points (212°F/100°C).

*To practice this skill, see Practicing Geography Skills on page 105.*

Orographic precipitation forms when a high landform, such as a mountain, forces moist air to rise up into the atmosphere. As the air rises, it cools and sheds excess moisture, resulting in rain or snow. This precipitation falls on the **windward** slope, or the side of the mountain facing toward the wind. As the cooler air moves down the **leeward** side of the mountain, or the side facing away from the wind, it slowly warms. Because this air has already shed its extra moisture, however, the leeward side often remains dry.

Convectional precipitation forms when air warms during the day and rises from the lower atmosphere. As the air rises, it cools to the saturation point and clouds form. Further rising and cooling cause precipitation. Afternoon showers on hot summer days, such as those that occur almost daily in central Florida, are an example of convectional precipitation.

Frontal precipitation forms when air masses of different temperatures meet. The different air masses do not mix. Instead the **fronts,** or leading edges of the air masses,

## FRONTAL PRECIPITATION

Warm air

Cool air

*Learning from Diagrams. When the front edges of warm and cool air masses meet they often create precipitation. Why does the collision of such fronts result in precipitation? Why are fronts created when warm and cool air masses meet?*

clash with each other. Eventually one front forces the other front up over it. Clouds and precipitation form as the warm air mass rises and cools.

### Atmospheric Pressure

The third variable element of weather is **atmospheric pressure,** or the weight of the air. A barometer measures atmospheric pressure. The standard pressure exerted by the atmosphere at sea level is 14.7 pounds per square inch (1,030 grams per square centimeter), equal to a barometric pressure of 29.92 inches (760 millibars).

**Effects of altitude and temperature.** The distance above the earth's surface—**altitude**—has a major effect on atmospheric pressure. At high altitudes pressure is lower because the earth's gravity holds fewer gas molecules. At 18,000 feet (5,486 meters), for example, the air exerts only half as much pressure as it does at sea level.

Temperature also affects air pressure. Warm air weighs less and exerts less pres-

*Learning from Pictures. Two fronts collide over the Great Plains, causing a storm. Why does the warm front rise up over the cold front in these situations?*

sure than cool air. As the light, warm air rises, a low-pressure center forms below it. Cool air is denser than warm air and tends to sink, forming a high-pressure area.

**Global pressure belts.** In general, low-pressure areas tend to have unstable weather with clouds, rain, and storms. High-pressure areas tend to have more clear, calm weather. Scientists have identified seven different low- and high-pressure areas, known as pressure belts, that affect the world's weather. These pressure belts, which are illustrated on the diagram below, include the equatorial low, two subtropical highs, two subpolar lows, and two polar highs.

Rising warm air and descending cool air create the seven pressure belts. Near the equator, for example, solar heating causes warm air to rise and form a low-pressure area—the equatorial low. This pressure belt causes the drying responsible for equatorial deserts. At the poles the air is cold and heavy. As it sinks, this air forms high-pressure areas. The mixture of warm and cold air, forced to the surface by the rotation of the earth and blown by wind, forms the pressure belts between the equator and the poles.

## Wind

Wind is the fourth variable element of weather. **Wind** blows when air moves from high-pressure areas to low-pressure areas. It can be thought of as a river of air flowing from a "hill" of high atmospheric pressure to a "valley" of lower atmospheric pressure. The greater the differences in pressure, the stronger the wind blows.

**Prevailing winds.** The winds that flow continually between global pressure belts are called **prevailing winds.** The three prevailing winds are the trade winds, the westerly winds, and the polar easterlies. The diagram below names and shows the directions of these global winds.

Trade winds blow out from the subtropical highs toward the equatorial low. They do not flow on a direct course, however, due to the force of the earth's rotation. The earth's rotation produces a force known as the **Coriolis** (kor·ee·OH·les) **force** that deflects winds to the right of their intended course in the Northern Hemisphere and to the left in the Southern Hemisphere. For this reason, the trade winds of the Northern Hemisphere blow from the northeast, rather than from the north, and are called

*Text continues on page 88.*

***Learning from Diagrams.*** *Except for almost-windless areas called doldrums, prevailing winds flow continuously between global pressure belts. What are the three types of prevailing winds?*

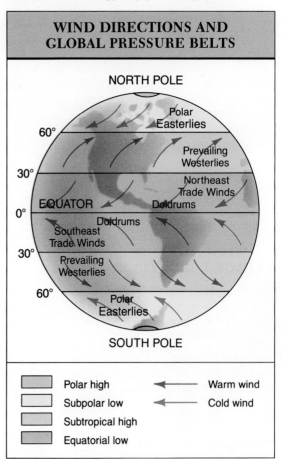

**WIND DIRECTIONS AND GLOBAL PRESSURE BELTS**

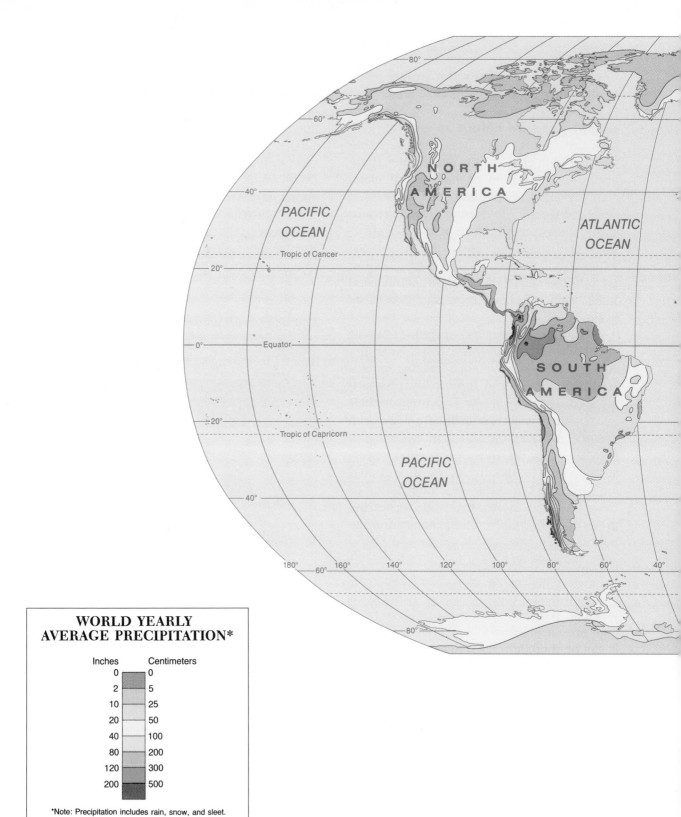

**WORLD YEARLY
AVERAGE PRECIPITATION***

| Inches | Centimeters |
|--------|-------------|
| 0 | 0 |
| 2 | 5 |
| 10 | 25 |
| 20 | 50 |
| 40 | 100 |
| 80 | 200 |
| 120 | 300 |
| 200 | 500 |

*Note: Precipitation includes rain, snow, and sleet.

ARCTIC OCEAN

Arctic Circle

EUROPE

ASIA

AFRICA

ATLANTIC
OCEAN

PACIFIC
OCEAN

Equator

INDIAN OCEAN

AUSTRALIA

N

0        1000        2000 Miles
0    1000    2000 Kilometers

20°    0°    20°    40°    60°    80°    100°    120°    140°    160°    180°

Antarctic Circle

ANTARCTICA

the northeast trades. The northeast trades are the winds that carried the first sailing ships from Europe to the Caribbean Sea. The trade winds of the Southern Hemisphere blow from the southeast and are called the southeast trades.

The westerly winds blow from the subtropical highs to the subpolar lows. They are found in the middle latitudes (from 30° to 60°) and are the prevailing winds of the United States, Canada, and Europe. In the Northern Hemisphere the westerlies blow from the southwest. In the Southern Hemisphere they blow from the northwest.

The polar easterlies blow from the polar highs. In the Northern Hemisphere they blow from the northeast as the northeast polar winds. In the Southern Hemisphere they blow from the southeast as the southeast polar winds. In winter the polar easterlies blow cold polar air into the middle latitudes. In summer they blow welcome cool air.

**The jet stream.** During World War II American pilots discovered another type of wind—the jet stream. The **jet stream** includes three bands of swiftly moving high-altitude winds—the polar jet, the subtropical jet, and the equatorial jet. All three bands have winds in excess of 60 miles (96 kilometers) per hour. The winds of the

***Learning from Maps.*** *Daily newspapers publish weather maps to inform people of forecasted weather conditions. On this map, what kind of front is located over Denver?*

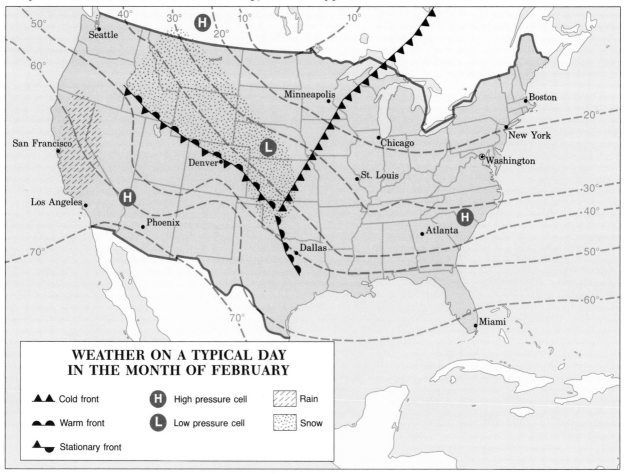

equatorial jet stream blow from east to west, while the winds of the subtropical and polar jet streams blow from west to east.

The jet stream influences weather in the United States, particularly during the winter when it blows cold Arctic air masses throughout much of the country. The winds also affect airplanes. Airplanes flying into the winds fly slower, while airplanes flying in the same direction as the winds fly faster.

*Learning from Pictures.* *Lightning strikes the earth about 100 times each second. Why is lightning dangerous?*

---

**SECTION 2 REVIEW**

1. **Define** weather, temperature, insolation, greenhouse effect, water cycle, evaporation, condensation, humidity, absolute humidity, relative humidity, precipitation, windward, leeward, front, atmospheric pressure, altitude, wind, prevailing winds, Coriolis force, jet stream
2. **Summarizing Ideas** What four atmospheric conditions cause weather?
3. **Distinguishing Ideas** How do orographic, convectional, and frontal precipitation differ?
4. **Interpreting Ideas** **(a)** What are the seven global pressure belts? **(b)** How are they formed?
5. **Analyzing Ideas** **(a)** Why are the northeast trades especially important to American history? **(b)** How does the jet stream affect the climate of the United States?

---

## 3 Changing atmospheric conditions can create violent weather.

Thunderstorms, tornadoes, hurricanes, and typhoons can create a spectacular display of weather—a display that also can be dangerous. Such unstable weather conditions result from certain combinations of temperature, moisture, atmospheric pressure, and wind.

### Thunderstorms

Thunderstorms occur whenever hot and humid air rises rapidly. Electrical charges build up in the rising air as moisture condenses, clouds form, and rain begins to fall. When the negative charges in the clouds make contact with the positive charges on the earth's surface, a streak of lightning flashes across the sky. Thunder, the shock waves caused by the lightning bolt, rumbles after the flash.

Lightning is one of nature's most dangerous elements. Each lightning bolt carries a powerful electric charge. When these charges touch people or buildings, they can cause death and property damage.

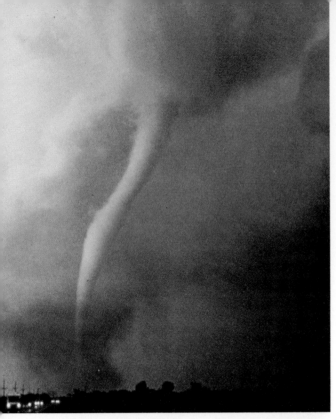

***Learning from Pictures.*** *This tornado in Oklahoma is one of about 700 reported each year in the United States. How fast is the speed of the winds in a typical tornado?*

## Tornadoes

Tornadoes, with winds of between 300 and 500 miles per hour (480 and 800 kilometers per hour), rank among the most violent of nature's storms. The twisting, funnel-shaped cloud of a **tornado** often descends from the clouds of a severe thunderstorm. As the tornado gets closer to the earth's surface, its winds swirl everything in its path into the funnel. It is not uncommon for the powerful winds to lift small buildings and move them hundreds of yards.

Although very destructive, tornadoes are usually small. The path of destruction of an average tornado measures only a few hundred yards wide and 16 miles (26 kilometers) long. Even though tornadoes occur throughout the world, they most often strike the central and eastern United States.

## Hurricanes and Typhoons

Large low-pressure areas with strong winds can create violent storms over tropical ocean areas, usually in the late summer and early fall. The storms that form over the Atlantic Ocean and the Gulf of Mexico are called **hurricanes.** Similar storms that form over the Pacific Ocean are called **typhoons** (ty·FOONS).

Winds must blow 74 miles (119 kilometers) per hour or more before a storm is classified as a hurricane or a typhoon. Once formed the storms are circular, with "eyes" of very low pressure at their centers. The air in the eye usually remains calm, but winds swirl around it at high speeds. Hurricanes and typhoons typically measure 100 to 600 miles (160 to 960 kilometers) across. The eye of most storms has a diameter of 10 to 25 miles (16 to 40 kilometers).

Hurricanes and typhoons move in unpredictable patterns, eventually pounding coastlines with high winds, high waves, and heavy rains. Because they gather their strength from the warm ocean waters, however, they usually die out quickly once they reach land—not, however, before causing tremendous damage to coastal areas.

Unlike other storms, hurricanes and typhoons have names. Each year the National Hurricane Center in Coral Gables, Florida, chooses an alphabetical listing of names to identify the season's storms. The names selected for the first three hurricanes of 1989 were Allison, Barry, and Chantal.

---

### SECTION 3 REVIEW

1. **Define**   tornado, hurricane, typhoon
2. **Summarizing Ideas**   How is lightning formed?
3. **Analyzing Ideas**   What violent weather patterns characterize **(a)** thunderstorms, **(b)** tornadoes, and **(c)** hurricanes and typhoons?

*Text continues on page 92.*

On August 3, 1980, a hurricane was born. Its place of birth was 12° N, 40° W, in the Atlantic Ocean midway between the west coast of Africa and the Caribbean island of Trinidad (see the map on page 304). The storm, with initial wind speeds of more than 74 miles (119 kilometers) per hour, was named Allen—the name chosen for the first hurricane of the season.

### The Saffir-Simpson Hurricane Scale

The Saffir-Simpson Hurricane Scale rates hurricanes from 1 to 5, according to their strength and potential damage to life and property. A rating of 5 classifies a hurricane as catastrophic and warns that it might cause widespread loss of life and billions of dollars worth of property damage. Over the last 100 years only three hurricanes have been rated as a 5 on the scale. Allen received such a rating.

As Allen gained strength, a United States Navy hurricane-hunting airplane flew into the storm and measured wind speeds of 215 miles (345 kilometers) per hour. A round-the-clock weather watch began as the "storm of the century" moved across the ocean.

### An Erratic Path

Allen zigzagged across the Caribbean Sea, eventually threatening Haiti and Jamaica and the western end of Cuba. But the storm avoided the islands, continued to gather strength from the moisture-laden air, and changed course. Allen skirted the resort areas of Cancún and Cozumel on the coast of Mexico's Yucatán Peninsula and moved into the Gulf of Mexico.

On August 9 radar and satellite images showed an alarming picture of the huge storm that now stretched across the Gulf of Mexico from the Yucatán Peninsula to the coast of Louisiana. Emergency weather re-

*Satellite image of hurricane Allen*

ports predicted that the center of the swirling storm would hit land at Galveston on the Texas coast. Suddenly the storm swung away from its predicted track and headed toward Corpus Christi, Texas, 200 miles (320 kilometers) to the southwest.

### Allen Comes Ashore

Finally, on the morning of Sunday, August 10, the erratic hurricane came ashore. It arrived not at Corpus Christi as feared but in a sparsely populated area between Corpus Christi and Brownsville. It brought flooding to southern Texas and heavy rains as far north as Kansas. Like most hurricanes, however, Allen quickly lost its fury once it was over land. By Tuesday Allen had completely disappeared from the weather maps. Losses were far less extensive than originally predicted.

Today Allen is best remembered for its erratic course. It serves as an example of the unpredictability of hurricanes. This erratic nature makes preparation difficult and nerve-racking. But in Allen's case, the erratic path meant a catastrophe that never happened.

## 4 Three climatic controls influence the distribution of climates.

Weather is the condition of the atmosphere for a short period of time at a specific location. The average of daily weather conditions over a long period of time is known as **climate.** Certain location and place factors influence the distribution of climates over the earth's surface. These factors, known as **climatic controls,** are latitude, altitude, and proximity to land and water.

### Latitude

Latitude is the most important climatic control. An area with an absolute location in the high latitudes (60° to 90°) has a much cooler climate than an area with an absolute location in the low latitudes (0° to 30°). The climate is cooler, in part, because of the differences in the angle at which the sun's rays hit the earth.

*Learning from Pictures. Chicago's average high temperature for the month of January is 32°F (0°C). Why are the low latitudes warmer?*

**Angle of the sun's rays.** The angle at which the sun's rays strike the earth helps to determine the amount of the sun's energy a place receives. For example, the sun's rays hit the earth almost vertically at the equator for most of the year. Vertical rays concentrate energy from the sun in a small area, giving a place more heat. As a result, the equator receives more of the sun's energy, and therefore more of the sun's heat, than any other latitude.

The amount of the sun's energy that the earth receives decreases toward the poles as the sun's rays strike at more of a slant. The slanting rays spread the sun's energy over a wider surface area. Areas in the middle and high latitudes receive these slanting rays and are cooler than places near the equator.

**Seasonal differences.** The angle at which the sun's rays strike the earth changes with the seasons. As you can see in the diagram on page 93, such changes occur because the earth tilts 23.5° on its axis. While this tilt never changes, the angle at which the sun's rays hit the earth does change as the earth makes its yearly journey around the sun.

An **equinox** occurs when the sun's rays strike the equator directly. It is the only time when days and nights are of equal length everywhere on the earth. At the spring equinox in March, the sun's rays hit the equator directly. The Northern Hemisphere, tilted away from the sun during the winter, now moves toward the sun, bringing spring to the Northern Hemisphere and fall to the Southern Hemisphere.

A **solstice** occurs when the sun's rays hit either the Tropic of Cancer (23.5° N) or the Tropic of Capricorn (23.5° S) directly. During a solstice the earth's poles reach their maximum tilt toward or away from the sun. At the summer solstice, when the vertical rays of the sun hit the earth directly

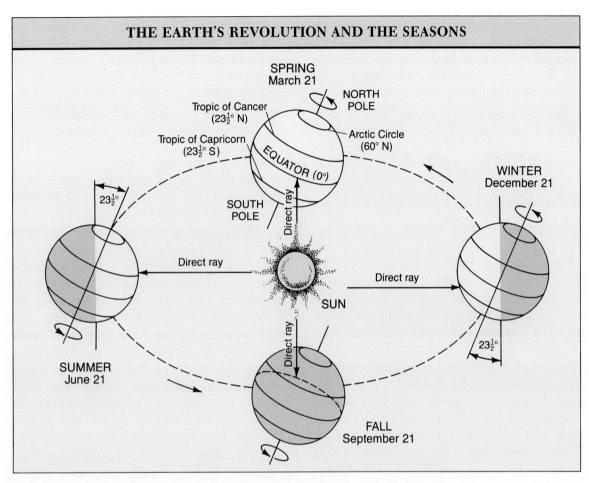

**Learning from Diagrams.** *The angle of the sun's rays changes with the seasons. What season begins in the Southern Hemisphere on March 21?*

at the Tropic of Cancer, the Northern Hemisphere reaches its maximum tilt toward the sun. This brings summer and more hours of daylight to the Northern Hemisphere. Only slanting rays hit the Tropic of Capricorn at the summer solstice, bringing winter to the Southern Hemisphere.

As the earth continues to move following the summer solstice, the tilt of the Northern Hemisphere eventually moves away from the sun. In September the fall equinox brings fall to the Northern Hemisphere and spring to the Southern Hemisphere. A few months later, at the winter solstice, the sun's rays strike directly on the Tropic of Capricorn. This brings winter to

the Northern Hemisphere and summer to the Southern Hemisphere.

## Altitude

Altitude controls climate in two ways. The first has to do with temperature. Lower layers of the atmosphere are nearly always warmer than higher layers of the atmosphere. Air temperatures decrease at an average of 3.6°F (2°C) for every 1,000-foot (305-meter) increase in altitude. If, for example, the temperature is 50°F (10°C) at the base of a mountain, a mountain climber can expect a temperature of 14°F (−10°C) at 10,000 feet (3,000 meters).

**93**

Altitude also can affect climate through the orographic effect. As you will recall, rainfall varies from one side of a mountain to the other. Abundant rain falls on the windward side, while the leeward side remains dry. This helps to explain the presence of lush grasslands and forests on windward slopes and deserts and semiarid conditions on leeward slopes of mountains.

## Proximity to Land and Water

Land and water heat and cool at different rates. As a result, lands near the ocean or another large body of water have a different climate from lands that are far away from large bodies of water. A place's relative location, then—particularly its proximity to land and water—affects its climate.

**Marine and continental influences.** Because land is a solid and water is a liquid, land heats more rapidly and to a higher temperature than water. The heat, however, does not penetrate far below the surface. When cooling begins, the land loses its heat

*Learning from Pictures.* The vast plains of Nebraska have a continental climate. What climatic influence do winds have on these plains in winter?

rapidly. Water, because of its swiftly moving currents, warms to greater depths than land. As soon as layers of water in the ocean begin to warm, currents circulate the warm water, spreading the heat. When cooling begins water cools more slowly than land.

As a result, land surfaces heat up rapidly throughout the summer months, while the ocean waters stay mild. When winter comes the land surfaces cool rapidly, while the ocean waters retain their summer warmth.

These varying heating and cooling rates result in two major climatic controls—marine and continental influences. The climate of lands swept by winds from the ocean has a **marine influence.** The winds keep the climate mild and moist in winter and cool and moist in summer. The climate of lands separated from the ocean by mountains or by hundreds of miles of land has a **continental influence.** Winds that blow across vast expanses of land keep the climate cold and dry in winter and hot in summer.

The different effects of marine and continental influences can be seen by comparing the climates of San Francisco and St. Louis. At about 38° N, the cities are nearly the same distance north of the equator. But San Francisco has a marine location near the Pacific Ocean, while St. Louis has a continental location far inland. The average January temperature remains a mild 50°F (10°C) in San Francisco, but a cool 33°F (0.6°C) in St. Louis. In July cool ocean breezes keep San Francisco's average temperature 59°F (15°C). St. Louis, deep in the continental interior, heats up rapidly and has an average July temperature of 80°F (26.6°C).

Proximity to land and water, however, is not the only factor that determines marine and continental influences. At first glance, for example, it would seem that Washington, D.C., also located at 38° N but near the

*Text continues on page 98.*

# MAJOR CLIMATE TYPES AND SUBTYPES

| Type and Subtype | Characteristics |
| --- | --- |
| TROPICAL | Hot all year; average temperature for the coolest month about 64°F (18°C)<br>Occur between 0° and 30° north and south of the equator<br>Receive the largest amount of rainfall for all climatic types |
| Wet | Close to the equator<br>Average monthly temperature above 80°F (27°C) with little month-to-month variation<br>Usually more than 60 inches of rainfall per year |
| Wet and Dry | Rainy season in summer; dry season as temperature cools<br>Cover about one-third of the earth's land area |
| DRY | Covers about one-third of the earth's land area |
| Semiarid | Occur in continental interiors<br>Border deserts on one side and tropical wet-and-dry regions on the other side<br>Usually receive 10 and 20 inches (25 and 50 centimeters) of rain per year |
| Desert | Occur in continental interiors because they are cut off from rain-bearing winds<br>Occur in low-lying coastal depths because of a cold ocean current nearby<br>Occur in tropical deserts because of descending air in subtropical high pressure belts |
| MOIST, MILD WINTER | Usually occur in the midlatitudes; no month averages less than 32°F (0°C) |
| Mediterranean | Mild and dry in winter; hot and dry in summer<br>Occur in western areas of the continents |
| West Coast Marine | Occur in western areas of the continents where winds blow marine influences on shore<br>Cool summers<br>Rain all year but more in winter |
| Humid Subtropical | Occur near the tropics in eastern sections of continents<br>Winter temperatures above 32°F (0°C); hot summers<br>More rain in summer than winter |
| CONTINENTAL | Severe winters; summers vary<br>Occur in eastern sections of continents in the midlatitudes<br>Occur only in Northern Hemisphere |
| Humid Continental with Hot Summer | Severe winters; hot rainy summers<br>Average summer temperatures between 70° and 78°F (21°C and 25°C) with possible daytime highs of 100°F (37°C) |
| Humid Continental with Cool Summer | Severe winters; hot and fairly dry summers<br>Average summer temperature between 60° and 67°F (16° to 20°C)<br>Usually more than one winter month averages below 32°F (0°C) |
| POLAR | Occur close to the earth's poles; very cold; no month warmer than 50°F (10°C) |
| Boreal | Brief, chilly summers but warm enough to support coniferous forests |
| Subarctic | Long, cold winters due to closeness to the poles and low insolation from slanting sun rays<br>At least one month above 50°F (10°C); too cool for most crops |
| Tundra | Brief, chilly summers with at least one month warmer than 32°F (0°C) |
| Ice Cap | Covered with permanent frost, snow, and ice; no vegetation<br>Average monthly temperatures below 32°F (0°C) all year |
| MOUNTAIN (highland) | Determined by elevation, relative location, and exposure |

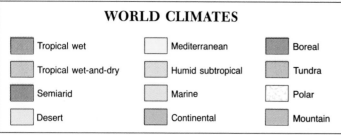

## WORLD CLIMATES

- Tropical wet
- Tropical wet-and-dry
- Semiarid
- Desert
- Mediterranean
- Humid subtropical
- Marine
- Continental
- Boreal
- Tundra
- Polar
- Mountain

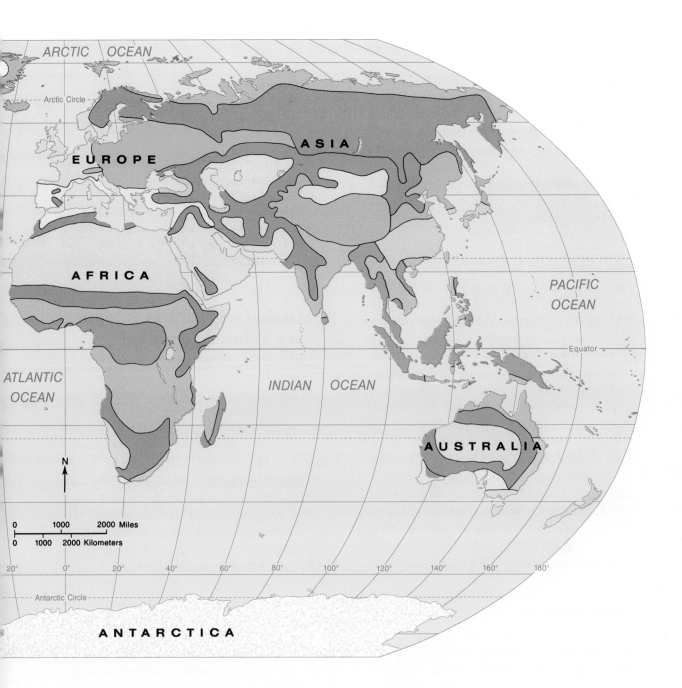

ARCTIC OCEAN

Arctic Circle

EUROPE

ASIA

AFRICA

PACIFIC
OCEAN

Equator

ATLANTIC
OCEAN

INDIAN OCEAN

AUSTRALIA

N

0        1000        2000 Miles
0    1000    2000 Kilometers

20°    0°    20°    40°    60°    80°    100°    120°    140°    160°    180°

Antarctic Circle

ANTARCTICA

Atlantic Ocean, should have a climate similar to that of San Francisco. Yet the average July temperature of Washington, D.C.—78°F (26°C)—is closer to that of St. Louis than of San Francisco. What accounts for Washington's heat? Remember that the prevailing winds in the Northern Hemisphere blow from west to east. These winds are warm and dry after crossing the entire country, giving even areas close to the Atlantic Ocean a climate with strong continental influences.

**The effects of ocean currents.** Warm and cold ocean currents also modify marine influences. The Gulf Stream, for example, is a warm ocean current (see the map on page 130). It originates in the Caribbean Sea and flows northeastward across the Atlantic Ocean to Europe as the warm North Atlantic Current (Drift). It warms Glasgow, Scotland, located at 56° N latitude. So in spite of its location far to the north of the equator, Glasgow has an average January temperature of 39°F (4°C). Nain, at 56° N latitude on the other side of the Atlantic Ocean in Labrador, Canada, remains much colder. The Labrador Current, a cold current from the Arctic Ocean, washes the shores of Labrador. The average January temperature of Nain is a very cold −7°F (−21°C).

### World Climates

Geographers use the elements of weather and the climatic controls to divide the world into various global climates. There are 6 main types and 13 subtypes of global climates. The main types of climate are tropical; dry; moist, mild winter; continental; high-latitude; and mountain. The chart on page 95 describes the characteristics of each main type, as well as the characteristics of the 13 major subtyes. The map on pages 96–97 also illustrates the locations of the 12 global climates.

**SECTION 4 REVIEW**

1. **Define** climate, climatic control, equinox, solstice, marine influence, continental influence
2. **Locate** Glasgow, Scotland; Labrador, Canada
3. **Summarizing Ideas** What factors are known as climatic controls?
4. **Synthesizing Ideas** **(a)** Why does the angle of the sun's rays affect climate? **(b)** How does the angle of the sun's rays change with the seasons?

## 5 Global vegetation regions are related to global climate regions.

Many different kinds of vegetation dot the earth's surface. In some areas towering trees grow close together, and in others dense underbrush makes it almost impossible to walk. In still other areas, sand, punctuated by drought-resistant shrubs and bushes, stretches as far as the eye can see.

The map on pages 100–01 shows the distribution of vegetation over the earth's land surfaces. Because plants respond directly to differing sunlight, warmth, and moisture, you will notice that the vegetation regions are closely tied to the climate regions shown on the map on pages 96–97.

The growth patterns of various plants also affect vegetation regions. One kind of plant, for example, seldom grows in isolation. Instead many kinds of plants grow together in the same location. These groups are known as **plant communities.** Geographers call a plant and animal community that lives in a particular climate region a **biome** (BY·ohm), or **ecosystem.**

Plant communities thrive in biomes in which they are most suited. The process by which a plant community becomes estab-

lished can be a long one, taking many years. Over time the plants that are not suited to a particular climate begin to die out. Slowly the plants that can adapt to the area begin to grow, pushing out the weaker plants. The process by which one type of vegetation replaces another is called **plant succession.**

The plant community that eventually takes over an area in the last phase of plant succession is called a **climax community.** Natural events such as storms and fires, or human activities such as clearing and logging, may destroy a climax community. This forces the process of plant succession to begin again.

## Forestlands

Forests cover one-fourth of the earth's land surface. Trees need a regular supply of moisture and at least one month per year with average temperatures above 50°F (10°C). Once these requirements are met, trees can adapt to many conditions.

**Evergreen broadleaf forests.** In hot and rainy areas the trees stay green all year long and have broad, flat leaves. The rain forests, such as those found in equatorial Africa and the Amazon Basin, are evergreen broadleaf forests (see the map on pages 100–01). In these forests many different kinds of trees grow together, and their treetops form a thick canopy that shades the forest floor below. Only certain kinds of plants can live on the shady forest floor of the rain forest. Many of the trees that thrive in rain forests, such as mahogany, teak, and ebony, have valuable wood.

**Needleleaf forests.** Only very hardy trees can live in subarctic and continental cool summer climates (see the map on pages 100–01). Because their narrow, spike-like leaves expose very little surface area

to the cold, needleleaf trees adapt to the cold conditions better than most other trees. Needleleaf trees include pines, firs, and spruces. Evergreen forests of these and other needleleaf trees cover much of northern Canada and the Soviet Union.

Sometimes a needleleaf forest consists of only one kind of tree. These trees often grow close together, making logging easier than in rain forests, where one kind of tree may be scattered and hidden among many others. Softwood from needleleaf trees is often used to make wood pulp, paper, plastics, and other synthetics.

*Learning from Pictures.* *This tropical rain forest shows how broad and flat leaves shade the forest floor. What type of trees from the rain forest are valuable?*

*Text continues on page 102.*

## WORLD VEGETATION PATTERNS

Evergreen broadleaf forest

Needleleaf forest

Mixed broadleaf and needleleaf forest

Scrub forest and Mediterranean

Savanna

Steppe and prairie grassland

Arid and desert

Tundra

Mountain

Ice cap

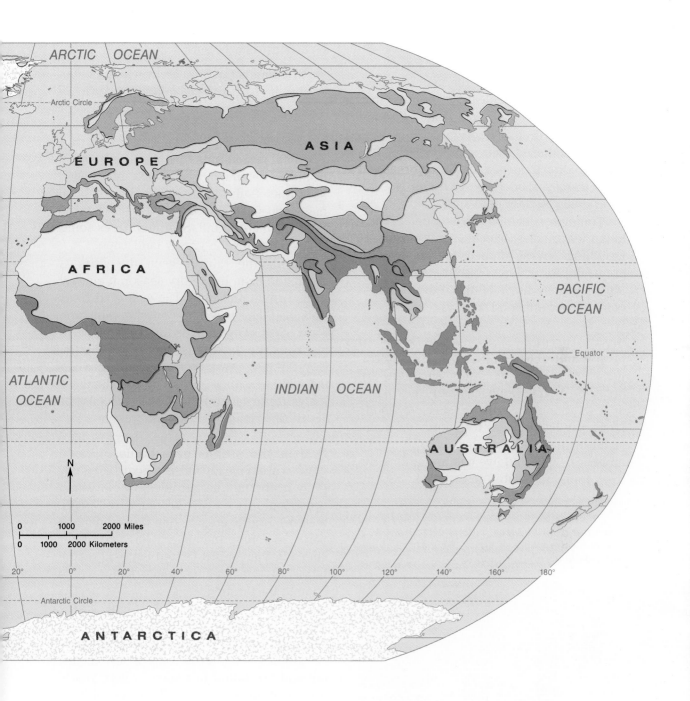

ARCTIC OCEAN

Arctic Circle

EUROPE

ASIA

AFRICA

PACIFIC OCEAN

ATLANTIC OCEAN

INDIAN OCEAN

Equator

AUSTRALIA

N

0 1000 2000 Miles
0 1000 2000 Kilometers

20° 0° 20° 40° 60° 80° 100° 120° 140° 160° 180°

Antarctic Circle

ANTARCTICA

**Mixed forests.**  Moist, mild winter climates support mixed forests of needleleaf and broadleaf trees (see the map on pages 100–01). The needleleaf trees are usually evergreens. The broadleaf trees are **deciduous** (di·SIDZH·uh·wuhs). They stop growing and shed their leaves when it gets cold or dry. In a mixed forest broadleaf trees usually shed their leaves in the fall and remain leafless until spring.

Common deciduous trees include oaks, hickories, maples, beeches, and chestnuts. Deciduous trees, often called hardwoods, are useful for making furniture and lumber. Many different kinds of nuts and fruits also come from hardwood trees.

**Scrub forests.**  Only certain kinds of bushes and trees can live in the Mediterranean climate region, where summers are hot and dry. These bushes and trees make up a scrub forest. Scrub forests have woody bushes and short trees with corky bark and small leathery or waxy leaves to conserve moisture. Olive and live oak are among the trees found in scrub forests.

*Learning from Pictures.  Many wild animals live on the grasslands of Africa. What are the tropical grasslands of Africa called?*

## Grasslands

Grasslands thrive in areas where precipitation is too low, usually less than 20 inches (50 centimeters), or too irregular for trees.

**Tropical grasslands.**  Grasslands found in tropical wet-and-dry climates are called **savannas** (suh·VAN·uhs); (see the map on pages 100–01). The coarse grass often grows 8 feet (2 meters) tall. Scattered trees sometimes interrupt the grassy landscape.

During the rainy season the grass is green and lush. In the dry season it quickly turns brown and dies. The scattered trees also shed their leaves to conserve moisture. Fires often sweep across the dry land, burning away the dead grass and preparing the way for new grass to start growing when the rainy season returns. The grasslands of Kenya in Africa and the *llanos* (LAHN·os) of South America are savannas.

**Prairie and steppe grasslands.**  Prairie grasses are typically tall and luxuriant. They grow in the middle latitudes, where yearly precipitation exceeds 20 inches (50 centimeters). Prairie grasses once covered many parts of Ohio, Indiana, Iowa, and other states in the central United States. Precipitation in this area is heavy and reliable enough for farming.

Steppe grasses, named for a large grassy plain in the southern Soviet Union known as the **steppe** (STEP), are shorter than prairie grasses. They grow only a few inches tall and are found in regions where yearly precipitation is less than 20 inches (50 centimeters). Steppe grasses once covered the Great Plains of the United States.

## Vegetation in Dry and Cold Regions

Few plants can live in very dry or very cold conditions. Plants able to live in deserts survive by adapting to the extremely

dry conditions. In cold areas some vegetation survives by growing rapidly during the short period when the ground thaws.

**Arid and desert lands.** Plants able to live in deserts need little water (see the map on pages 86–87). Some, such as cacti, store water or have shiny, waxy leaves that prevent the loss of moisture. Thick, leathery leaves also help plants live through the hot days and cold nights of the deserts. Other desert plants lie dormant for years. When rain falls, they spring to life, grow quickly, drop their seeds, and die. The seeds may lie on the desert soil for months or even years before another shower makes them sprout, and the growth cycle renews.

**Tundras.** Often called cold deserts, areas called **tundras** are found where summers last three months or less and are too cold for trees and most other plants to live. When the ground thaws, however, tundra vegetation springs to life. Millions of flowering plants color the landscape. They often grow in scattered clusters, separated by barren ground. Typical tundra plants include grasses, mosses, lichens, herbs, and a few dwarfed shrubs. Northern North America is an example of a tundra.

## Mountain Vegetation

Tibet, Switzerland, and other lands covered by the world's highest mountains have mountain vegetation. This vegetation can be divided into zones that change with altitude. On the lower slopes of mountains the vegetation resembles that of the surrounding land. As altitude increases, however, vegetation changes.

For example, the lower, windward slopes of a mountain in the rainy tropics may be covered by a rain forest. Higher up, as temperatures cool, the vegetation becomes a mixed forest. Still higher only hardy needleleaf trees grow. Alpine mead-

*Learning from Pictures.* *This tundra near Valdez, Alaska, is in full bloom. What kinds of plants are typical tundra vegetation?*

ows with short grasses and hardy flowering plants grow above the tree line. The **tree line** marks the place on a mountain where the growth of trees stops. Areas above the tree line remain too cold for trees to grow. The **snow line** marks the place where snow and ice lie permanently on the ground.

### SECTION 5 REVIEW

1. **Define** plant community, biome, ecosystem, plant succession, climax community, deciduous, savanna, steppe, tundra, tree line, snow line
2. **Locate** Amazon Basin, Tibet
3. **Interpreting Ideas** How is vegetation related to climate regions?
4. **Summarizing Information** **(a)** What two conditions are required for forestlands to grow? **(b)** What distinguishes the four types of forests?
5. **Classifying Ideas** What are the different types of grasslands?
6. **Analyzing Ideas** How do plants adapt to overcome the climatic limitations of **(a)** arid and desert lands and **(b)** tundras?

# CHAPTER 4 REVIEW

## Chapter Summary

The following list contains the key concepts you have learned about weather, climate, and vegetation.

1. The atmosphere is made up of gases. The two that are of the most concern to modern scientists are carbon dioxide ($CO_2$) and ozone ($O_3$).
2. The four conditions that cause weather are temperature, moisture, atmospheric pressure, and wind.
3. Thunderstorms, tornadoes, hurricanes, and typhoons are among the most spectacular displays of weather and can be very dangerous and destructive.
4. Latitude, altitude, and proximity to land and water are controls that determine climate patterns.
5. The world has 6 major climate types and 13 subtypes.
6. Vegetation responds directly to climatic conditions and plant-growth patterns.
7. Global vegetation regions include forestlands, grasslands, vegetation in dry and cold regions, and mountain vegetation.

On a separate sheet of paper, complete the following review exercises.

## Reviewing Geographic Terms

Match each of the following terms with the correct definition.

a. deciduous
b. savanna
c. climate
d. continental influence
e. weather
f. atmospheric pressure
g. precipitation
h. condensation
i. wind
j. humidity
k. temperature
l. biome
m. evaporation

____ 1. Condition of the atmosphere for a short period of time
____ 2. Process in which gaseous water vapor changes to a liquid
____ 3. Moisture in the air
____ 4. Condensation in the form of rain, snow, sleet, or hail
____ 5. Force exerted by the air
____ 6. Movement that occurs when air flows from high-pressure to low-pressure areas
____ 7. Average of daily weather conditions over a long period of time
____ 8. Climatic effect on lands separated from the ocean by mountains or by hundreds of miles of land
____ 9. Broadleaf trees that stop growing and shed their leaves when it gets cold or dry
____ 10. Grassland found in tropical wet-and-dry climates
____ 11. Plant and animal community that lives in a particular climate region
____ 12. Measure of heat or cold
____ 13. Change of water from its liquid form to gaseous water vapor

## Developing Critical Thinking Skills

1. **Contrasting Ideas**   In what ways do orographic, convectional, and frontal precipitation differ?
2. **Interpreting a Chart**   Study the chart of the hydrological cycle on page 81. How do ocean waters help fill lakes?
3. **Interpreting Ideas**   What is the Saffir-Simpson Hurricane Scale?
4. **Classifying Ideas**   Study the chart entitled "Major Climate Types and Subtypes" on page 95. **(a)** Where do tropical climates occur? **(b)** Which climatic control is primarily responsible for this type of climate?
5. **Analyzing Ideas**   Which climatic control has the most influence on the vegetation zones of mountain vegetation?
6. **Writing About Geography**   In a clearly written paragraph, complete one of the following activities.   **(a)** Study the chart entitled "Major Climate Types and Subtypes" on page 95. Then describe what types of vege-

tation you might find in each climate subtype. **(b)** Study the map entitled "World Climates" on pages 96–97 and identify the climate type shown for your area. Then describe the climate that affects your area. Finally, answer the question: How closely does your description match the one given in the chart on page 95?

## Using Primary Sources

In the following excerpt from *Volcano: The Eruption and Healing of Mount St. Helens*, Patricia Lauber describes how the eruption of Mount St. Helens destroyed vegetation. As you study the reading, consider other consequences of a volcanic eruption.

The May 18 eruption began with an earthquake that triggered an avalanche. . . . The pilot and passengers of a small plane saw the north side of the mountain rippling and churning. . . .

The avalanche tore open the mountain. A scalding blast shot sideways out of the opening. It was a blast of steam, from water heated by rising magma [molten rock].

Before the eruption Mount St. Helens was like a giant pressure cooker. The rock inside it held superheated water. The water stayed liquid because it was under great pressure, sealed in the mountain. When the mountain was torn open, the pressure was suddenly relieved. The superheated water flashed to steam. Expanding violently, it shattered rock inside the mountain and exploded out the opening, traveling at speeds of up to 200 miles [320 kilometers] an hour.

The blast flattened whole forests of 180-foot-high [55-meter-high] firs. It snapped off or uprooted the trees, scattering the trunks as if they were straws. At first, this damage was puzzling. A wind of 200 miles [320 kilometers] an hour is not strong enough to level forests of giant trees. The explanation, geologists later discovered, was that the wind carried rocks ranging in size from grains of sand to blocks as big as cars. As the blast roared out of the volcano, it swept up and carried along the rock it had shattered.

The result was what one geologist described as "a stone wind." It was a wind of steam and rocks, traveling at high speed. The rocks gave the blast its great force. Before it [the wind], trees snapped and fell. Their stumps looked as if they had been sandblasted. The wind of stone rushed on. It stripped bark and branches from trees and uprooted them, leveling 150 square miles [390 square kilometers] of countryside. At the edge of this area other trees were left standing, but the heat of the blast scorched and killed them.

1. How did geologists account for the blast's extremely destructive power?
2. What is a stone wind and what are the effects of such a wind?

## Practicing Geography Skills

*Before completing this activity, review Developing Geography Skills on page 83.*

**Understanding Diagrams**  Study the diagram on page 84 and answer the following questions.

1. What is the subject of the diagram?
2. What labels does the diagram have?
3. According to the diagram, what happens in the process shown?

## Exploring Geography

Interview a meteorologist from a nearby office of the National Weather Service or a weather reporter from a local television station. Ask how local weather forecasts are developed. Share your interview results with the class.

# The Earth's Resources

# PUTTING THE CHAPTER IN FOCUS

Resources help people satisfy their needs and wants. Natural resources occur as part of the environment and are an important part of an area's place characteristics. Renewable resources can be used over and over again, but scarce and nonrenewable resources must be conserved or recycled for use by future generations.

## Ideas to Understand

In studying about the earth's resources, use these ideas to give direction to your reading.

1 People use natural resources in many different ways.
2 Energy resources support industrialization.
3 Human innovations help the earth produce more agricultural resources.

## Terms to Define

The following terms are some of the key terms in the chapter. Defining them will help you understand the earth's resources.

natural resource
mineral
renewable resource
nonrenewable
  resource
humus
water table
recycling

fossil fuel
petroleum
geothermal energy
commercial farming
cash crop
subsistence farming
aquaculture
malnutrition

## Places to Locate

Locating the following places will add to your knowledge of geography.

Saudi Arabia
Indonesia

Sahel
Pakistan

## 1 People use natural resources in many different ways.

Earth is a planet rich in the materials necessary to support life. Further, humans are enormously clever. They convert the things that nature provides into useful machines, tools, shelters, and foods.

Even the most desolate and isolated areas of the world contain at least some **resources,** or materials that people use to meet basic needs and wants. Needs are those goods and services that people must have in order to survive. Needs include food, water, clothing, and housing. Those goods and services that people use beyond what is needed to survive, such as television sets and jewelry, fulfill what are called wants.

◀ *Solar energy plant*

## Natural Resources

All places on the earth have advantages and disadvantages for human settlement. A **natural resource**—a naturally occurring material that can be used to produce goods and services—is a great advantage to a group of people able to use it. Land, soil, and water are examples of natural resources. Other examples include fish, wildlife, vegetation, and minerals. **Minerals** are inorganic substances found in the earth's crust, such as coal, copper, and iron ore.

As groups use natural resources, they change the natural landscape. Changes in the landscape brought about by mining and farming illustrate this idea, which is an example of relationships within places (see Chapter 2). Yet the use of natural resources also brings about changes in the cultural landscape. Centuries ago the Romans built

stone aqueducts to carry water to many parts of the Roman Empire. For some people, this made water readily available for the first time. Today freight cars carry coal and other minerals along thousands of miles of railroad track. Vehicles use highways, canals, and airways to speed the movement of valuable resources throughout the world.

## Using Natural Resources

Not all people in the world use natural resources in the same way. Factors that affect a group's use of natural resources include cultural differences, technological change, economic factors, and geopolitics.

**Cultural differences.** A group's culture directly affects how its people value and use natural resources. People in different cultures may view resources in different ways. Years ago, for example, Native Americans viewed the Great Plains of the United States as hunting grounds, while settlers

*Learning from Pictures.* *Large leaves serve as natural umbrellas. How might technological change and economic factors alter the use of the giant leaves in Bali?*

moving west across the frontier saw the Great Plains as a place for farms and towns.

Even people in the same culture may view and use resources differently. A farm family with an ax or a chain saw may see a forest as a source of winter warmth and cooking fuel. Loggers may see the forest as a place to find jobs. Campers may see the forest as a recreational area in which to spend vacations.

**Technological change.** New technology also affects how people value and use natural resources. Before tractors and trucks, farmers considered mules to be a highly valued resource. Mules pulled plows and carried crops to market. Today tractors and trucks do the work once done by mules. For this reason, people value mules less than they did in the past.

Technological change also creates uses for previously unvalued natural materials. In the 1700s people did not use uranium ores and did not value them as natural resources. Uranium ores gained value only after modern advances made them useful as a resource for nuclear energy.

**Economic factors.** Economic factors also play an important part in the way people use natural resources. Scarcity and rising prices have always led people to seek cheaper substitutes for costly resources. In colonial days, for example, people burned whale oil for lighting. As demand for whale oil rose, more and more whales were hunted. Eventually overhunting made whales harder to find and prices rose. People then looked for cheaper substitutes. In time they found a way to make kerosene from petroleum. Because kerosene cost less than whale oil, it quickly replaced whale oil as a lighting fuel.

**Geopolitics.** Another factor that affects the use of natural resources is **geopolitics**—

the relationship between geography and political policy. The international trade of scarce minerals provides an example of the importance of geopolitics in today's world.

Most mineral deposits are unevenly distributed across the earth (see the map on pages 110–11). This uneven distribution has resulted in increased world trade as countries lacking certain mineral resources buy what they need from other countries. Depending on the circumstances, a price increase or interruption in supply could result in great changes in the country importing the mineral.

Geopolitics is becoming an increasingly important force in the world today. Because it affects the availability of resources—not only resources such as manganese but also resources such as food and oil—it also affects their use.

## Renewable and Nonrenewable Resources

Natural resources can be categorized as either renewable or nonrenewable. **Renewable resources** are replaced naturally and can be used over and over again. **Nonrenewable resources,** however, are almost impossible to replace and their supplies lessen with each use.

**Renewable resources.** For many years people thought that water was one of the most abundant natural resources. Scientists classify water as a renewable resource because it is constantly recirculated by the water cycle (see Chapter 4). As the feature on pages 112–13 explains, however, water is a fragile resource. Water reentering the water cycle often carries traces of fertilizers, pesticides, industrial chemicals, and sewage. These contaminants pollute the water and can destroy its value as a resource.

Scientists classify many other natural resources as renewable—but with certain

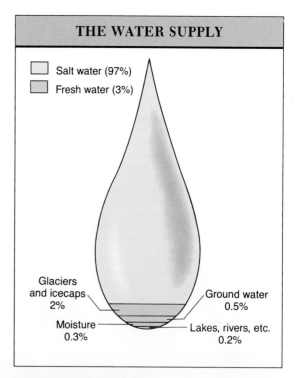

**THE WATER SUPPLY**

Salt water (97%)
Fresh water (3%)

Glaciers and icecaps 2%
Ground water 0.5%
Moisture 0.3%
Lakes, rivers, etc. 0.2%

*Learning from Diagrams.* As you can see from the diagram, most of the water on the earth is in the oceans. What percentage of the world's water supply is fresh water?

stipulations. Forests are renewable resources if people plant new trees to replace those cut down. Fish and wildlife are renewable resources if people leave enough fish and wildlife to reproduce and if people preserve natural habitats.

Perhaps the natural resource that people most take for granted is soil. As surprising as it may seem, however, even soil must be protected if it is to remain a valuable resource.

Soil has three general levels. Decayed plants and animals, or **humus** (HYOO·muhs), make up the top level. Soil rich in humus is usually fertile and is black or dark brown. Below the humus lies a layer of mineral particles that washes down from the humus. Finally, there is a layer of **parent material,** or solid rock. The weathering of this rock forms most of the soil.

*Text continues on page 114.*

**109**

## WORLD RESOURCES
### Mineral and Fuel Deposits

| | | | | | | | |
|---|---|---|---|---|---|---|---|
| bx | Bauxite | gl | Gold | nk | Nickel | tg | Tungsten |
| cb | Cobalt | ir | Iron | ph | Phosphate | tn | Tin |
| ch | Chromium | ld | Lead | pl | Platinum | ur | Uranium |
| cl | Coal | mb | Molybdenum | pt | Petroleum | zc | Zinc |
| cp | Copper | mg | Manganese | sf | Sulfur | | |
| dm | Diamonds | ng | Natural gas | sl | Silver | | |

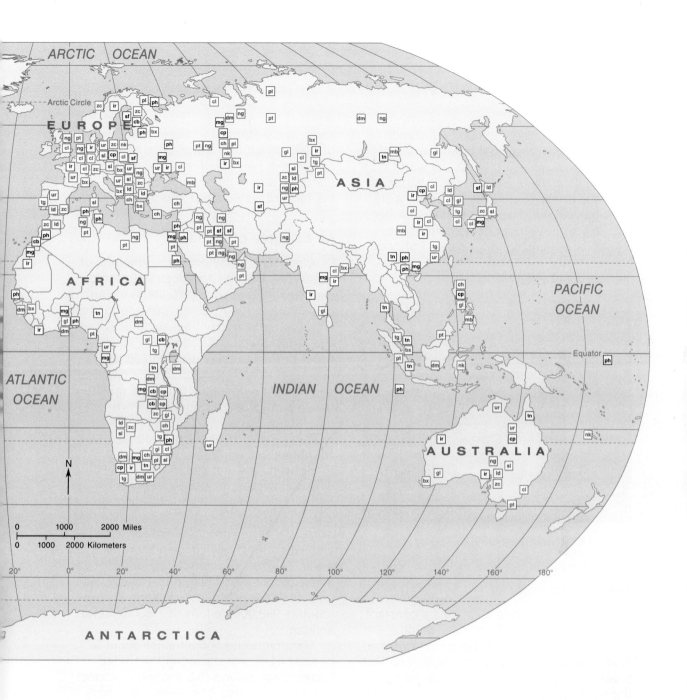

ARCTIC OCEAN

Arctic Circle

EUROPE

ASIA

PACIFIC OCEAN

AFRICA

ATLANTIC OCEAN

INDIAN OCEAN

Equator

AUSTRALIA

N

| 0 | 1000 | 2000 Miles |
| 0 | 1000 | 2000 Kilometers |

ANTARCTICA

20°    0°    20°    40°    60°    80°    100°    120°    140°    160°    180°

Water is the most common substance on earth. It covers almost three-fourths of the earth's surface and forms the world's ocean, lakes, rivers, and ice caps. Water is essential to life. Every living thing consists principally of water and must take in water regularly to live. About 65 percent of the human body is made up of water. Potatoes consist of about 80 percent water, and tomatoes about 90 percent.

*A public water fountain in Italy*

### World Water Balance

The earth's surface maintains a constant amount of moisture. There is as much water now as there ever was or ever will be. This is because water is a renewable resource that is continually replenished by the water cycle (see Chapter 4).

The chart on page 109 shows the location of the world's water supply. Most of the world's water is seawater, which is too salty to drink or to use for irrigation or manufacturing. A process known as **desalinization** can be used to remove the salt from seawater. This process, however, is extremely costly and is not likely to be useful in providing a source of fresh water

soon. The water not found in the ocean, in glaciers, in ground water, or in other water bodies (0.3 percent of the total moisture) is unevenly distributed around the world in the form of water vapor and precipitation.

### An Example of Demand

Americans today use huge amounts of water. The average American household uses about 70 gallons (265 liters) of water a day. This is not surprising, considering how much water everyday household activities use. It takes about 3 gallons (11 liters) of water to flush a toilet, between 30 and 40 gallons (110 to 150 liters) to fill a bathtub, and at least 5 gallons (19 liters) a minute to take a shower. An automatic dishwasher uses about 10 gallons (38 liters) and a washing machine uses about 30 gallons (110 liters) per wash.

Household water use in the United States, however, makes up a very small part of the total demand. About 41 percent of all water used in the United States is used for irrigation. Crops produce higher yields per acre when they receive ideal amounts of water. To grow properly to maturity, for example, an acre of wheat requires 652,000 gallons (2,464,560 liters) of water. Cotton requires 983,000 gallons (3,715,740 liters) an acre.

Manufacturing accounts for about 52 percent of all water used in the United States. Each pound (0.5 kilogram) of steel produced requires 27 gallons (102 liters) of water. Each pound (0.5 kilogram) of paper manufactured takes 25 gallons (95 liters). Each quart (0.9 liter) of gasoline takes 10 gallons (38 liters) of water.

Unfortunately, industries use most of this water for cooling and cleaning, making the water warm and dirty. If returned to the water cycle in this state, it could pollute clean water sources.

*A portable broadcast sprinkler for irrigation*

## A Fragile Resource

Water occurs naturally as an odorless, colorless, and tasteless liquid. These desirable characteristics are quickly lost when water is abused. Pollution of surface waters is the most common abuse. Oil spills and the dumping of chemicals, raw or partially treated sewage, and industrial wastes pollute the ocean, rivers, and lakes. Circulating waters then carry this pollution to every part of the world.

Ground water in the United States also is threatened. It is being depleted at an alarming rate as people take more water from wells and springs than precipitation replaces. In some areas the **water table,** or upper surface of ground water, has dropped so low that wells have dried up. In addition, ground water is becoming contaminated in many areas. Farm and industrial chemicals, untreated sewage, and hazardous wastes seep through the ground into the ground water. These poisons are often found in wells many miles from the dump sites. Because many of the poisons do not break down and wash away, they will affect water quality for years to come.

## An International Concern

Problems with the global water supply are an international concern. Because water circulates, its problems are widespread. Ocean currents or water vapor found in windblown clouds carry pollution far from its source.

Both scientists and politicians realize the sensitive nature of the water supply. Both groups have held conferences seeking ways to avoid harming this most important resource. In the United States, local communities have passed strict laws against polluting water supplies, while state and federal laws protect interstate and international waterways. On the international level, United Nations agencies and conferences are writing agreements designed to conserve and preserve the water supply for future generations.

**Learning from Pictures.** *Conservationists hope that seedlings planted today will grow into forests in the future. What stipulation do scientists make when they say that forests are renewable resources?*

Clearing the land of its natural vegetation encourages soil erosion. Farming the same crops in the soil depletes it of valuable minerals. Irrigating the soil can result in salinization, or a salt build-up that eventually destroys the soil's productivity. For these and other reasons, scientists consider soil to be a renewable resource only if people take measures to prevent erosion, grow plants that restore nutrients, or use natural or chemical fertilizers.

**Nonrenewable resources.** Such important resources as coal, oil, natural gas, iron ore, copper, bauxite (the principal source of aluminum), gold, and silver are nonrenewable resources. As people use these resources, they cannot be replaced.

**Recycling.** Resource depletion can be slowed through recycling. **Recycling** is the process by which products that have been used and discarded can be reused. **Conservationists,** people who work to protect natural resources and natural environments, support recycling because it slows the use of the earth's resources.

Paper, which is made from trees, is one of the most commonly recycled materials. Youth groups and charitable organizations often collect newspapers and other paper products to sell to recycling factories. The factories grind up the old paper and make it into new paper. Many greeting cards, for example, are printed on recycled paper. Recycling paper saves millions of trees each year.

---

**SECTION 1 REVIEW**

1. **Define** resource, natural resource, mineral, geopolitics, renewable resource, nonrenewable resource, humus, parent material, desalinization, water table, recycling, conservationist
2. **Summarizing Ideas** How can the use of natural resources change **(a)** the natural landscape and **(b)** the cultural landscape?
3. **Interpreting Ideas** What different factors affect the value and use of natural resources?
4. **Analyzing Ideas** In order to be classified as a renewable resource, what steps must be taken to protect the soil?
5. **Organizing Ideas** Why do many people favor recycling?

---

## 2 Energy resources support industrialization.

Muscle power was once the chief source of energy. The muscles of men, women, children, and animals provided the energy needed to plow fields, raise crops, move

goods, and manufacture finished products. Today the industrialized countries of the world largely use fuels instead of muscles for energy. To produce the fuels needed, these countries constantly search for energy resources—a search that underscores the geographic themes of location, place, relationships within places, movement, and regions.

## Fossil Fuels

Coal, oil, and natural gas generate electricity and power vehicles and machinery throughout the United States and the world. These materials are **fossil fuels,** energy sources formed from the remains of plants and animals that died millions of years ago. Fossil fuels provide the major sources of energy in the United States today (see the graph on page 116).

**Coal.** Coal ranks as the most abundant fossil fuel, with deposits of about 660 billion tons. At the present rate of use, that is enough coal to meet the world's needs for 200 years. The United States, the Soviet Union, the People's Republic of China, West Germany, and Australia have more than 80 percent of all known coal deposits.

**Oil.** Oil, or **petroleum,** is a liquid fossil fuel. Petrochemicals and gasoline constitute the major products made from oil. **Petrochemicals** are oil-based materials used to manufacture plastics, synthetic fibers, fertilizers, insecticides, and pesticides. Gasoline, which is refined from crude oil, powers many different sizes and types of internal-combustion engines.

Oil replaced coal in the 1950s as the world's most important energy source. Scientists now believe, however, that more than half of all the world's oil will be used up by the year 2050. This has resulted in attempts by the oil-consuming nations to

*Learning from Pictures.* *The technology necessary to remove the oil from tar sands is currently being developed. When did oil replace coal as the world's most important energy source?*

rely less on oil, turning instead to other energy sources. This also has resulted in new political and economic importance for countries with large oil reserves.

To guarantee oil supplies, oil-consuming countries have formed trade partnerships with oil-producing countries. Oil-producing countries also have formed their own partnership. In 1960 five major oil-producing countries—Saudi Arabia, Kuwait, Iraq, Iran, and Venezuela—formed the Organization of Petroleum Exporting Countries, or OPEC. Indonesia, Nigeria, Gabon, Libya, Qatar, Ecuador, and the United Arab Emirates soon joined OPEC. OPEC members try to control world oil prices.

**Natural gas.** Natural gas is used to generate electricity and for heating, cooling, and cooking. It is often found in the same places as crude oil. Scientists believe that at the current rates of use, known supplies of natural gas will last about 150 years. The largest reserves of natural gas underlie the Soviet Union, which uses a pipeline to send the fuel to Eastern and Western Europe.

**115**

## Other Energy Sources

Due to dwindling supplies, many countries want to become less dependent on fossil fuels. These countries are searching for ways to use nuclear energy, hydroelectricity, and solar energy to meet energy needs. Geothermal, wind, and tidal energy also are other alternative energy sources.

**Nuclear energy.** The chief benefit of nuclear energy is that the electricity it generates is inexpensive. Because it requires only small amounts of uranium, costs per unit of electricity are low.

Nuclear energy has certain negative costs, however. Construction costs for a nuclear plant, for example, run into the millions. And a safe way to move and dispose of hazardous wastes from nuclear power plants has not yet been found. What concerns most people about nuclear energy, however, is that nuclear materials are extremely dangerous. A 1979 accident at Pennsylvania's Three Mile Island and a more devastating accident at Chernobyl in the Soviet Union in 1986 illustrate the potential danger of nuclear energy. In addition, by-products of nuclear energy—which could fall into the wrong hands—can be used to make atomic bombs.

**Hydroelectricity.** Hydroelectric plants use the energy of moving water or steam to drive engines that generate electricity. Such plants are costly to build but efficient to run because water is an abundant and renewable resource.

**Solar energy.** The sun provides an inexpensive and virtually inexhaustible power source. Several devices have been built to harness solar energy, but most remain experimental. Devices that use mirrors to collect the sun's energy, for example, are not yet practical for home or industrial heating. Some types of solar collectors placed on rooftops, however, can help supplement the traditional energy sources used in a home or other building.

**Experimental energy sources.** Experiments with geothermal, wind, and tidal energy seek to harness the power these sources provide. **Geothermal energy** uses water and gases heated under the earth's surface to power engines that generate electricity. Because it is found in only a few places on the earth's surface, however, it is not widely used. The same problem limits the use of tidal energy, which can be harnessed in only a few areas (see page 131). Wind energy, used to power engines connected to windmills, is widely available but is less reliable than other sources because of inconsistencies in wind intensity.

*Text continues on page 118.*

***Learning from Graphs.*** *This graph indicates the percentages of the total energy supply produced by various energy sources. What sources might be classified as "Other"?*

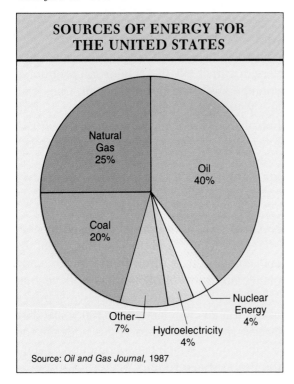

### SOURCES OF ENERGY FOR THE UNITED STATES

Natural Gas 25%

Oil 40%

Coal 20%

Other 7%

Hydroelectricity 4%

Nuclear Energy 4%

Source: *Oil and Gas Journal*, 1987

To learn from reading, you must make the ideas in a book or article memorable to you. The information needs to take orderly form in your mind if you are to remember and use it. As you read, whether during leisure time or for an assignment, your mind must sort out the important points and identify the details offered to support, prove, or add interest to these points.

### How to Recognize Main Ideas

To recognize main ideas, follow these guidelines.

1. **Use the features of the text.** Introductions, summaries, and headings outline the main ideas. Other helps also are supplied to guide your reading.
2. **Find the topic sentence.** A writer organizes information for you by separating topics into paragraphs. Each paragraph, unless it is meant to illustrate an idea further, has a separate point to make. Often that point is summarized in a *topic sentence,* which usually appears as the opening or closing sentence of the paragraph. Sometimes the main idea or topic is only implied and the reader must identify the topic sentence from the information given.
3. **Identify supporting details.** Note illustrations and examples that support the main point.

### Applying the Skill

Read the following excerpt about conservation on Cape Hatteras, a barrier island. Then identify the main idea and the supporting details.

The Park Service is now firmly opposed to promoting boom development of Hatteras. North of the National Seashore, a thickly developed stretch already

*Cape Hatteras lighthouse*

runs up Nags Head, Kill Devil Hills and Kitty Hawk to the mainland bridge, with jumbles of expensive homes and clusters of prefab sun shanties near where the Wright brothers first took to the air.

The topic sentence, *The Park Service is now firmly opposed to promoting boom development of Hatteras,* is the paragraph's opening sentence. The author describes "the thickly developed stretch" from Nags Head to the mainland bridge and the "jumbles of expensive homes and prefab sun shanties." These are details that identify why the Park Service opposes development on Hatteras.

*To practice this skill, see Practicing Geography Skills on page 125.*

*Learning from Pictures.* Cotton fields stretch for miles in Texas. Why is cotton a cash crop?

## 3 Human innovations help the earth produce more agricultural resources.

Food is a need. It gives humans the energy necessary to live. The world's farmers feed most of the people on the earth. Feeding more than 5 billion people, however, is no easy task. Since farming first began 10,000 to 20,000 years ago, farmers have learned how to best use the earth's natural resources to yield steadily increasing amounts of food.

Absolute and relative location, physical and cultural characteristics, and economic considerations often determine what can and will be grown in a given area. The chart on page 119 lists the major agricultural products of the world, where they are raised, and how each is used.

### Types of Farming Activities

The world's farmers practice two very different kinds of farming. Many farmers in the United States and other industrialized countries practice **commercial farming.** Commercial farmers grow crops and animals to sell. These are called **cash crops.** Most of the farmers in nonindustrialized countries practice **subsistence** (sub·SIS·tuhns) **farming,** raising only enough food to feed themselves and their families.

**Commercial farming.** Commercial farmers use scientific farming methods developed only in the last 250 years. Modern machinery, advanced farming techniques, and chemical fertilizers and herbicides help them raise large crops. Commercial farming can be categorized as either mixed or specialized farming.

Between 5 and 10 percent of the commercial farmers practice mixed farming, raising several different crops and animals for income. Farmers in the central United

*Text continues on page 120.*

118

# MAJOR AGRICULTURAL PRODUCTS

| Product | Growing Conditions | Major Producing Nations | Major Uses |
|---|---|---|---|
| WHEAT | Winter wheat: mild winters with ample precipitation Spring wheat: growing season long enough to mature | United States, Soviet Union, China, India, Canada, France | Breakfast foods, macaroni products, livestock feed |
| RICE | Long, wet summers | China, India, Indonesia, Japan | Food |
| CORN | Adequate rainfall, long growing season | United States, China, Brazil, Romania | Flour, starch, cooking oil, livestock feed |
| BARLEY | Hot, dry summers or cool summers; tolerates cold, dry climates | Soviet Union, United States, France, United Kingdom | Food, livestock feed, malt |
| OATS | Cool, moist summers | Soviet Union, United States, China | Oatmeal, flour, livestock feed |
| RYE | Cool summers; tolerates poor soil | Soviet Union, Poland | Flour, bread |
| SORGHUM | Tolerates dry, cool conditions | United States, India, China, Argentina, Mexico | Livestock feed |
| MILLET | Tolerates dry, cool conditions | India, Soviet Union | Food products, livestock feed |
| POTATOES | Moist climates, loose, well-drained soils | Soviet Union, Poland, United States, China | Food |
| CASSAVA | Hot, rainy climates | Central and South America, Southern United States | Flour, tapioca |
| SOYBEANS | Adequate rainfall, all types of soil | United States, Canada, China, Japan | Bean sprouts, tofu, soy sauce, livestock feed |
| COTTON | Sunny, irrigated, dry land | China, Soviet Union, United States, India | Clothing |
| WOOL | Sheep herded on open pastureland | Australia, New Zealand | Clothing, blankets, carpets |
| RUBBER | Hot, humid climates | Malaysia, Indonesia, Thailand | Tires, shoes, aircraft and machine parts |
| SUGARCANE | Hot, humid climates | India, Brazil, Cuba | Sweetener |
| SUGAR BEETS | 5-month growing season | Soviet Union, France. West Germany, United States | Sweetener |
| TEA | Temperate climates | India, China, Sri Lanka, Indonesia, Japan | Beverage |
| COFFEE | Tropical climates; 3,000–6,000 feet above sea level | Brazil, Colombia, Indonesia, Ivory Coast, Central America | Beverage |
| CACAO | Shade, heavy rainfall, hot temperatures | Ivory Coast, Brazil, Ghana, Nigeria | Chocolate, cocoa butter, cocoa powder |

**Learning from Cartoons.** *Farming can be an unpredictable venture. What farming problems are illustrated by this cartoon?*

States, for example, raise both corn and livestock to sell on the market. On a typical mixed farm in Pennsylvania or New York, farmers grow corn, alfalfa, and soybeans. The difficulties of mixed farming include choosing crops or animals that can be raised together and buying the different kinds of machinery needed to raise several crops.

Despite the difficulties, mixed farming has several important benefits. Growing different crops allows farmers to alternate crops in the fields. This practice of crop rotation replaces nutrients that the previous crops took from the soil. Economically, growing different crops makes farmers less vulnerable to falling prices for farm products. Falling prices can mean economic disaster to farmers who grow only one crop. Farmers growing several crops, however, can count on other products as sources of income if the price of one crop drops.

Most commercial farmers practice specialized farming, raising a single cash crop or kind of animal for income. Specialized commercial farmers on **plantations,** or very large farms, raise most of the world's cotton, wheat, cattle, sheep, dairy products, poultry, rubber, rice, sugarcane, pineapples, bananas, tobacco, coffee, and tea.

On most specialized farms, one crop or kind of livestock brings in more than half the farm's income. The benefit of specialized farming is that farmers need machinery for only one crop. The danger, however, is that market prices may suddenly go down. Because they rely on the income from one crop or kind of livestock, specialized farmers can go bankrupt when prices fall.

**Subsistence farming.** Millions of farmers in Africa, Asia, Latin America, and other nonindustrialized regions practice subsistence farming. In many of these countries over 75 percent of the workers are farmers.

Farmers practice different kinds of subsistence farming, based on their needs and locations. Farmers in the densely populated river valleys of India, the People's Republic of China, and Southeast Asia use intensive subsistence farming, planting as much food as possible on any lands that will support crops. Farmers grow rice in areas with warm, rainy summers. In cooler, drier regions they grow wheat and millet.

Farmers who move from place to place in search of richer soils practice **slash-and-burn agriculture.** When they find a new place to plant, farmers cut down trees and brush, burn them to add fertilizing ash to the soil, and plant crops. After a few years, when successive crops have drained the soil of its fertility, the farmers move to another location. Farmers practice slash-and-

burn agriculture only in sparsely populated regions, particularly in tropical wet climates where rains constantly wash the nutrients from the soil.

Nomadic herders also move from place to place. Nomadic farming dominates many dry regions of Africa and Asia. Camels, goats, sheep, and cattle make up the major herd animals. They provide meat, milk, clothing, tools, hides for tents, and most other necessities.

Nomadic herders lead difficult lives. When drought or overgrazing damages grazing lands, herds die off and people begin to starve. A major famine is now occurring in some African countries of the Sahel region, near the Sahara. Somalia, Chad, Niger, Ethiopia, Mali, Mauritania, Senegal, and Burkina Faso have been receiving emergency food supplies from the United Nations Disaster Relief Organization since 1984. The United Nations Food and Agricultural Organization also works to teach nomadic herders in the region how to plant drought-tolerant pastures and how to prevent overgrazing.

## Increasing the Food Supply

Problems faced by people like those in the Sahel, who wonder if there will be enough food to keep them alive from day to day, have raised important issues. Some people believe that the world's population eventually will outgrow the food supply. They predict severe food shortages and famines. Others, however, are more hopeful, pointing to scientific research currently under way to find new ways of growing more food.

**Farming more land.** One way to grow more food is to **cultivate,** or farm, more land. This can be done by converting sparsely settled areas into farmland. In South America and Africa farmers clear

***Learning from Pictures.*** *Subsistence farming villages, like this one in Niger, are usually small. Where is subsistence farming practiced?*

rain forests for farmland. Soon advances in irrigation will make it possible to bring deserts under cultivation, especially when scientists find a cost-effective way to remove salt from seawater. Subarctic and other short-summer regions also may be farmed in the years ahead, once scientists develop new types of quick-growing crops.

**Increasing yields.** Increasing the present agricultural **yield,** or amount grown per acre or hectare, also will increase food supplies. Wider use of fertilizers and irrigation boosts crop yields. Scientific farming also makes greater yields possible.

In the 1960s and 1970s, for example, scientists planted new, more productive varieties of rice, corn, and wheat. They also taught farmers in countries such as Mexico, India, and Pakistan to use modern fertilizers and watering techniques. By the 1980s many of the countries using the new seeds and techniques were raising more than enough grain to feed their people.

*Text continues on page 123.*

**121**

# CASE STUDY
## EXPLORING IDEAS: World Food Supplies

In June 1987 experts from around the world met in Beijing in the People's Republic of China, to discuss the problems of hunger and **malnutrition,** the lack of proper diet. The experts concluded that there are more than 500 million hungry and malnourished people and that the number grows at a rate of nearly 8 million people a year.

Hunger exists in almost every country, and children are the chief victims. Estimates indicate that every day 140,000 children die of hunger-related causes.

### Surplus Food, Starving People

Hunger is on the rise in many of the poorer countries because slow economic

*Food for the children*

development has made it impossible for many people to grow or buy enough food. The fact remains, however, that many countries have huge food surpluses that could help feed the hungry elsewhere.

World stocks of grain, sugar, and butter remain at record levels, and food surpluses are expected to grow larger by the year 2000. Even countries such as India and Indonesia, which used to have terrible famines, now sell food to other countries. Unhappily, they sell food elsewhere because many of their own hungry people cannot afford to buy it.

### The Problems

How can there be food surpluses and millions of starving people at the same time? This important question has no easy answer. Part of the answer lies in economic conditions, and part lies in political ones.

Since the early 1980s economic growth in industrial countries has slowed. Economic geographers believe that this slowdown lowers the incomes of the world's poorest countries. With sharply lower incomes, people are no longer able to buy food, even though plenty remains available.

Political conditions also can hinder attempts to feed the poor. In spite of efforts by the United Nations, many countries refuse to send help to countries with different political ideologies. Local political problems also slow the flow of food to starving people. Millions of tons of food shipped to hungry people around the world each year fail to reach the people in need.

Yet hope for the future remains. Experts believe that there is enough food to feed everyone on the earth. However, as one agricultural expert put it, "We know how to increase food output now. What we can't do so well is insure that the poor get access to this increased output."

**Cutting crop and food losses.** Each year farmers lose tons of crops to disease. Tragically, many of the crops that survive spoil before they reach the market. New methods to reduce crop and food losses would greatly increase food supplies.

Farmers who plant disease-resistant crops and use pesticides and fungicides lower crop damage and, in turn, increase yields. In addition, vaccines and antibiotics help protect animals from sicknesses. New food-processing methods help keep foods from spoiling and lengthen the shelf life of fruits, vegetables, beans, and meats. Often simply making improvements in storage facilities can cut losses of stored grains and other crops.

**Crops for the future.** Another way to raise farm production is to expand the use of crops grown today and to cultivate new crops. Soybeans may become an important source of protein in the future. Soybeans can be eaten raw or cooked, made into cheeselike *tofu*, or ground into protein-rich flour and meal.

One promising new crop is *amaranth*, a grass that grows wild in Mexico. Amaranth can be used as a grain or as a green vegetable. It grows well in many locations.

Farmers also are experimenting with other new crops. Channel millet is a grain found in the Australian desert that needs only one watering to produce a crop. Quinoa is a protein-rich grain used by the Incas before the Spanish Conquest, but now rarely cultivated. A bean native to the Andes, tarwi is high in protein and tolerates frost, drought, and poor soils. The high-protein winged bean, which grows wild in southeast Asia, grows easily and improves soil fertility. The marama bean, native to semidesert areas of southern Africa, is rich in protein and other nutrients. The prickly pear, a nutritious cactus, grows in desert regions.

**Aquaculture.** When most people think of agriculture, they think of farmers harvesting fields of grain or raising herds of cattle. Aquaculture, however, also is a kind of agriculture. **Aquaculture** consists of raising fish in ponds and coastal areas. Farmers raise catfish, trout, and salmon in artificial ponds and lakes. Oysters and other shellfish develop in special beds built in shallow coastal waters. Aquaculture already has succeeded in increasing the supply of fish. Farmers in the People's Republic of China, for example, harvest large numbers of fish from artificial ponds each year.

**Genetic engineering.** Many scientists also believe that world food supplies can be increased through genetic engineering. Using genetic engineering scientists transfer certain genes from one plant or animal to another. Scientists foresee a time in the near future when plants can be specially "designed" to be high in protein and other nutrients and to resist frost or repel damaging insects.

---

### SECTION 3 REVIEW

1. **Define** commercial farming, cash crop, subsistence farming, plantation, slash-and-burn agriculture, cultivate, yield, malnutrition, aquaculture
2. **Locate** Sahel, Pakistan
3. **Summarizing Ideas** How do farming activities differ between industrialized and nonindustrialized countries?
4. **Evaluating Ideas** What are **(a)** the benefits and **(b)** the disadvantages of mixed farming?
5. **Analyzing Ideas** **(a)** In what ways can farmers increase the food supply? **(b)** What are some of the scientific innovations that have helped increase food supplies?

# CHAPTER 5 REVIEW

## Chapter Summary

The following list contains the key concepts you have learned about the earth's resources.

1. The use and value placed on the earth's abundant resources are affected by cultural differences, changing technologies, economic factors, and geopolitics. Technological advances have changed the patterns of resource use throughout the world.
2. Natural resources are naturally occurring materials that are used to produce goods and services.
3. Some natural resources are renewable—they are replaced naturally and supplies can be used over and over again. Other natural resources are nonrenewable—their supplies diminish with use and are not replaced.
4. Mineral resources are unevenly distributed on the earth. This uneven distribution leads to global interdependence.
5. Energy resources are essential to industrial societies. Coal, oil, and natural gas are non-renewable fossil fuels. Hydroelectricity and solar energy are based on abundant or renewable resources, but each of these alternative energy sources, along with nuclear energy, currently has disadvantages.
6. Farmers use natural resources, such as soil and water, to produce a variety of foods and other agricultural resources.
7. Commercial farmers raise crops or livestock for income. Most commercial farms are specialized, growing a single cash crop. A smaller but growing number are mixed farms.
8. Several types of subsistence agriculture are practiced in the nonindustrialized countries of the world.
9. Several scientific and farming techniques to increase the world's food supply are currently being explored.

On a separate sheet of paper, complete the following review exercises.

## Reviewing Geographic Terms

Supply the geographic term that correctly completes each sentence.

1. Materials people use to meet basic needs are called ____.
2. A ____ ____ can be replaced naturally and can be used over and over again.
3. A ____ is an inorganic substance in the earth's crust, such as gold and iron ore.
4. ____ is the soil layer that consists of decayed plants and animals.
5. ____ makes it possible to reuse products that have been used and discarded.
6. A person who works to protect natural resources is a ____.
7. ____ are oil-based materials.
8. An energy source that has been formed from the remains of plants and animals that died millions of years ago is known as a ____ ____.
9. ____ is the amount of a crop grown per acre or hectare.
10. The term for fish farming is ____.

## Developing Critical Thinking Skills

1. **Summarizing Ideas**  Why are natural resources important?
2. **Organizing Ideas**  How did technological advances and economic factors change the way people met their lighting needs?
3. **Seeing Relationships**  (a) How do the oil-consuming nations attempt to guarantee oil supplies?  (b) What five oil-producing nations formed OPEC?
4. **Synthesizing Ideas**  Refer to the chart entitled "Major Agricultural Products" on page 119 and examine the different climatic conditions in which each crop grows. Then refer to the textbook to answer the following questions.  (a) What factors determine what can and will be grown in a given place?  (b) Why do you think the Soviet Union is not a leading rice producer?

5. **Writing About Geography** In a clearly written paragraph, complete one of the following activities. (a) Describe the experiments with new energy sources and discuss why these sources are needed. (b) Explain the problems confronting the efforts to feed the world's people and discuss the attempts to meet these problems.

## Using Primary Sources

In the following excerpt from *The Farmer Is Doomed*, Louis M. Hacker describes the loss of international markets for the American farmer during the Great Depression of the 1930s. As you study the reading, compare the current problems of the American farmer with those that Hacker describes.

There is no place for it [American commercial agriculture] either in the international or, for that matter, in the home market. In the fullness of time the United States has arrived at the stage of finance capitalism where our economy today is dependent upon the exploitation of foreign markets both for finished goods and capital. To produce manufactured goods cheaply we must feed our factory populations cheaply. It hardly matters whether the bacon comes from our own corn belt or from Poland, the Irish Free State or the Netherlands; whether the wheat comes from Kansas or from Russia, Manchuria, Argentina or Canada; whether the butter comes from Wisconsin or from New Zealand, Denmark or Belgium: so long as the cost of living is cheap and wages low so that our automobiles, electrical appliances, typewriters, and tin cans can be shipped from Europe, our metals, oils, chemicals, agricultural machinery and railroad equipment to South American and Far Eastern countries, and our surplus capital to every nook and corner of the earth where there are still raw materials to be mined from the earth's surface and subsurface. . . .

1. Why is there no place for American commercial agriculture at home and abroad?
2. What does the United States export?

## Practicing Geography Skills

*Before completing this activity, review Developing Geography Skills on page 117.*

**Recognizing Main Ideas** Reread the last full paragraph in column one on page 109. It discusses water as a renewable resource. Then answer the following questions.

1. (a) What is the main idea of this paragraph? (b) What is the topic sentence?
2. What are two points given in the paragraph that support the topic sentence?

## Exploring Geography

1. Reread the section "Technological change." on text page 108. Then select a natural resource other than the ones mentioned in the section and research how it was used in the past, how it is used today, and what technological developments led to this change in use. Prepare an oral or written presentation focusing on how technological improvements have changed the way the natural resource that you have chosen is used.
2. Secure an outline map of the world from your teacher. Then use the map of world economic activity on pages 6–7 and the information in Chapter 5 to locate the world's leading oil-producing areas. Color in these areas on your outline map. In a different color trace the routes that the oil must travel in order to reach markets in the United States. On the back of the map write a brief essay on how political problems in the Middle East might affect oil supplies in the United States.

CHAPTER
**6** **The World Ocean**

# PUTTING THE CHAPTER IN FOCUS

Oceans, seas, and other bodies of salt water cover 70 percent of the earth's surface. This vast "world ocean," which is still being explored, forms an important component of the physical setting. It interacts with the atmosphere, affects world climates, influences world trade routes, provides a source of energy, and contains a wealth of mineral and fish resources. In recent years "ownership" of the ocean has become an increasingly important question as nations squabble over the rights to use it and to harvest its resources.

## Ideas to Understand

In studying about the world ocean, use these ideas to give direction to your reading.

1  The waters of the world ocean are interconnected.
2  The waters of the world ocean move constantly.
3  Spectacular landforms lie beneath the ocean.
4  Nations look to ocean waters for a wealth of resources.

## Terms to Define

The following terms are some of the key terms in the chapter. Defining them will help you understand the world ocean.

| | |
|---|---|
| strait | salinity |
| oceanographer | food chain |
| continental shelf | territorial limit |
| nodule | biodegradable |

## Places to Locate

Locating the following places will add to your knowledge of geography.

| | |
|---|---|
| Indian Ocean | Strait of Malacca |
| Arctic Ocean | Mediterranean Sea |

## 1 The waters of the world ocean are interconnected.

A series of narrow waterways and other sea passages connect the earth's oceans, forming a single world ocean. Around the edges of this vast world ocean lie seas, gulfs, and bays that extend its waters.

The world ocean is usually subdivided into four main oceans—the Pacific, Atlantic, Indian, and Arctic (see the table on page 128). These oceans can be thought of as components of the world ocean.

### The Pacific Ocean

The Pacific Ocean is by far the largest component of the world ocean (see the map on pages 134–35). It covers nearly one-third of the earth's surface, or more than the entire area covered by all of the earth's land surfaces combined. The Pacific Ocean extends 9,600 miles (15,500 kilometers) north and south from the Bering Strait to Antarctica, and stretches 13,225 miles (21,160 kilometers) east and west from Malaysia to Colombia.

The Panama Canal and the Strait of Malacca form the two chief trade links of the Pacific Ocean. The Panama Canal in Central America (see page 299) connects the Atlantic and Pacific oceans across the narrow Isthmus of Panama. The Strait of Malacca in Southeast Asia connects the Pacific and Indian oceans.

Most of the Pacific Ocean's major seas extend from its western edge. The Bering Sea, between Alaska and the Soviet Union,

*Surf pounding Cape Kiwanda, Oregon*

| OCEANS OF THE WORLD | | | |
|---|---|---|---|
| Ocean | Area | Average Depth | Greatest Known Depth |
| PACIFIC | 63,800,000 sq. mi<br>165,200,000 sq. km | 14,050 ft<br>4,280 m | 35,810 ft<br>10,915 m |
| ATLANTIC | 31,530,000 sq. mi<br>81,660,000 sq. km | 14,000 ft<br>4,270 m | 28,373 ft<br>8,648 m |
| INDIAN | 28,350,000 sq. mi<br>73,440,000 sq. km | 13,000 ft<br>3,900 m | 23,376 ft<br>7,125 m |
| ARCTIC | 5,430,000 sq. mi<br>14,120,000 sq. km | 4,360 ft<br>1,330 m | 17,880 ft<br>5,450 m |
| Source: *The World Book*, 1986 | | | |

**Learning from Tables.** *The ocean with the largest area does not carry the greatest volume of trade. Which ocean carries the most trade?*

and the Sea of Okhotsk (oh·KAHTSK), between mainland Asia and the Kamchatka (kam·CHAT·kuh) Peninsula, are important politically because of their relative locations. Each separates nations that have different ideas and beliefs. The Sea of Japan, the East China Sea, and the Yellow Sea are important economically because they are used heavily for fishing and shipping.

## The Atlantic Ocean

The vast stretch of the world ocean separating Europe and Africa from the Americas is called the Atlantic Ocean (see the map on pages 134–35). The Atlantic Ocean is about half the size of the Pacific, but it carries more world trade than the Pacific or any other ocean.

The Mediterranean Sea forms the Atlantic's largest extension and is located on its eastern edge. Ships carrying goods throughout the world travel this busy waterway continuously. The Suez Canal links the Mediterranean Sea with the Indian Ocean. Two **straits,** or narrow bodies of water linking large bodies of water, connect the Mediterranean Sea and the Black Sea. These two straits are the Dardanelles and the Bosporus.

The English Channel, which separates the United Kingdom from France, also extends from the eastern edge of the Atlantic Ocean. This busy trade route carries goods to and from Western Europe.

## The Indian Ocean

The Indian Ocean ranks as the third largest of the four components of the world ocean. It is strategically important because of its relative location—the Red Sea and the Persian Gulf both stretch along its northwestern edges. The Red Sea is the southern outlet for the Suez Canal, the major trade link between Europe and Asia. The Persian Gulf serves as an outlet for trade with nearby oil-producing nations.

## The Arctic Ocean

The Arctic Ocean makes up the smallest component of the world ocean. Because parts of it are covered by ice year-round, it carries little shipping. Airplanes frequently fly over the Arctic Ocean, however, as they follow great circle routes between North America, Europe, and Asia. A great circle route between New York and Tokyo, for example, crosses the Arctic Ocean.

### SECTION 1 REVIEW

1. **Define**  strait
2. **Locate**  Indian Ocean, Arctic Ocean, Strait of Malacca, Mediterranean Sea
3. **Summarizing Ideas**  **(a)** What are the four main components of the world ocean?  **(b)** Where is each component located?
4. **Interpreting Ideas**  What are some examples of major trade links between each ocean component?

## 2 The waters of the world ocean move constantly.

The amount of water on the earth remains constant. As you learned in earlier chapters, the water cycle continually recirculates water from the ocean to the atmosphere to the earth's surface. At the same time, other forces also move water through all of the components and extensions of the world ocean. The most important of these forces are currents and tides.

### Ocean Currents

Gigantic river-like streams called **ocean currents** circulate the waters deep within the world ocean (see the map on page 130). These currents redistribute the sun's heat energy through the ocean in much the same way that the prevailing winds redistribute heat energy through the atmosphere.

Geographers identify two types of ocean currents. *Warm* ocean currents flow from the equator toward the North and South poles. They carry warm water into cold regions and help make climates milder, especially in winter. *Cold* ocean currents flow from the poles toward the equator or rise up from the deepest layers of the ocean's water. They carry cool or cold water into warm regions. As you learned in Chapter 4, ocean currents strongly influence the climates of nearby coastal regions.

Ocean currents do not flow in a direct course due to the earth's rotation. The Coriolis force deflects moving water in much the same way as it deflects the prevailing winds. In the Northern Hemisphere, ocean currents deflect to the right of their intended course. In the Southern Hemisphere, they deflect to the left. This deflection produces a clockwise circulation of water in northern oceans and a counterclockwise circulation in southern oceans (see the map on page 130).

*Learning from Pictures.* *The world ocean absorbs much of the sun's energy that reaches earth. What are some of the effects that the sun's energy has on the ocean?*

**Atlantic Ocean currents.** The Gulf Stream and the North Atlantic Current are warm currents in the North Atlantic Ocean. The Gulf Stream originates in the tropical waters of the Caribbean Sea. From there it moves into the Gulf of Mexico and along the east coast of North America as far north as Newfoundland. The warm waters then cross the Atlantic as the North Atlantic Current, bringing mild winters to northwestern Europe.

The cold Labrador Current flows south along the shores of Canada as far as Newfoundland. It carries icebergs with it, and it keeps the coastal regions of northeastern Canada very cold in the winter and cool in the summer. The cold Canary Current flows south on the eastern side of the Atlantic to complete the circulation.

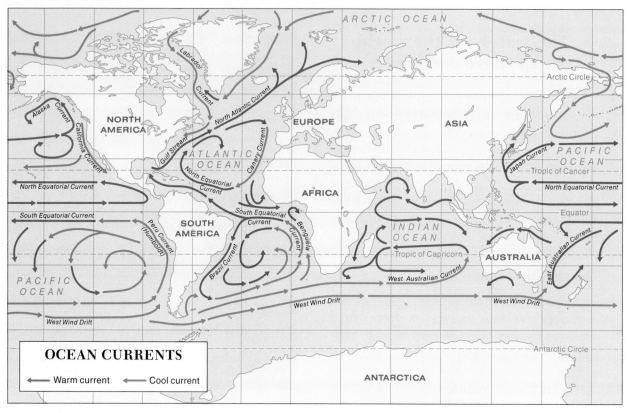

**Learning from Maps.** *The patterns of ocean currents resemble the patterns of the prevailing winds. Which current circles the earth?*

**Pacific Ocean currents.** Currents in the Pacific Ocean follow the same general pattern as those in the Atlantic. In the northern Pacific the warm Japan, or Kuroshio, Current and the North Pacific Current carry warm water past southern Japan to Alaska and northwestern Canada, giving those regions unusually mild winters (see the map on this page). Northeast Asia, a region swept by the cold Kamchatka, or Oyashio, Current, has much colder winters. The cold California Current completes the circulation of waters in the North Pacific.

In the South Pacific the warm East Australian Current washes along the east coast of Australia. The cold Peruvian, or Humboldt, Current flows north along the west coast of South America.

**Finding hidden flow patterns.** A new technique has enabled **oceanographers,** scientists who study the ocean, to learn much more than they ever knew before about the circulation patterns of ocean currents. This new technique, called **ocean acoustic tomography** (uh·KOO·stik toh·MAHG·reh·fee), provides three-dimensional images of the movement of ocean water.

Preliminary studies indicate that ocean currents are as complex as movements in the atmosphere. Studies also show that the image of a smoothly circulating system of ocean currents is a misconception. In fact, only the surface currents have been mapped, while major deep currents remain hidden. For example, oceanographers have just identified a vast flow of salt water running beneath the Gulf Stream and in the opposite direction. This previously unknown flow is a key factor in the workings of the Gulf Stream, which affects the world's climates.

Oceanographers now realize that ocean currents do change and are, to some extent, unpredictable. In addition, currents play a far greater role in determining climate than previously thought. Scientists hope that new information about ocean currents will help them predict major changes in climate conditions in the future.

## Tides

Oceans also move in regular rises and falls called **tides.** Tides are formed chiefly by the gravitational pull of the moon. When the moon is directly overhead, it causes the water beneath it to bulge toward the moon. At the same time, the water on the side of the earth opposite the moon also bulges. In this case, however, the bulge forms as the moon's gravity pulls the earth away from the water (see the diagram on this page). High, or incoming, tides occur where waters bulge. Low, or ebb, tides occur in the areas of ocean between the bulges. Two high tides and two low tides, spaced about six hours apart, occur each day as the earth rotates on its axis.

Tides in the open ocean remain surprisingly low. Most rise and fall less than 3 feet (1 meter). Higher tidal ranges, the difference between high and low tides, occur in shallow seas at the edges of continents and in coastal inlets. Parts of the North Sea, for example, have a tidal range of 15 feet (5 meters)—enough to delay the docking or departure of oceangoing ships in North Sea ports.

The world's highest tidal range occurs in Canada's Bay of Fundy, an arm of the Atlantic Ocean. The Bay of Fundy narrows as it moves inland, causing tides to build up a gigantic wall of water called a **tidal bore.** This creates tidal ranges of up to 70 feet (21 meters). Broad mud flats, exposed when the water recedes at low tide, flood each day at high tide.

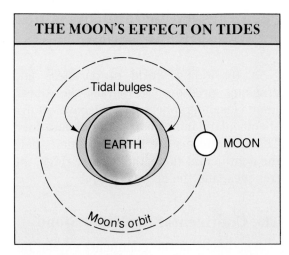

**THE MOON'S EFFECT ON TIDES**

*Learning from Diagrams.* *This diagram illustrates the effect of the moon's gravity on the water in the world ocean. How many tides occur each day?*

Incoming tides produce an enormous amount of energy—energy that may prove useful for generating electricity. One experimental tidal energy plant is located on the Rance River near Saint-Malo in France. Incoming tides measuring up to 44 feet (13.2 meters) high roar up the river twice a day. The rushing waters turn turbines and produce electricity cleanly and efficiently from a renewable resource base.

**SECTION 2 REVIEW**

1. **Define** ocean current, oceanographer, ocean acoustic tomography, tide, tidal bore
2. **Locate** North Sea, Bay of Fundy, Saint-Malo
3. **Summarizing Ideas** What forces continually move water in the world ocean?
4. **Interpreting Ideas** **(a)** What are the two types of ocean currents? **(b)** In what direction do these currents generally flow?
5. **Analyzing Ideas** What causes ocean tides to form?

## 3 Spectacular landforms lie beneath the ocean.

A forbidding world of darkness and crushing pressure surrounds the ocean floor. Oceanographers have discovered five spectacular landforms on the ocean floor. These landforms are the continental shelf, the continental slope, the oceanic ridge, the trenches, and the abyssal plains.

### The Continental Shelf and Slope

The edges of the continents extend beneath the ocean to form a platform called the **continental shelf** (see the map on pages 134–35). This shelf extends outward from the continents and slopes gradually downward to a depth of 100 fathoms (600 feet; 180 meters). Oil and natural gas deposits frequently underlie the continental shelf and fish are abundant (see the maps on pages 110–11 and 138).

The outer edge of the continental shelf ends abruptly in a steep drop called the **continental slope,** or escarpment. The slope drops about 10,000 feet (3,000 meters) over a distance of several miles. Large submarine canyons, which are similar to canyons cut by rivers on land, slash across it. Many of these submarine canyons lie off-shore from the mouths of large rivers. For example, deep canyons exist far from the mouths of the Hudson and Mississippi rivers (see the map on pages 134–35).

Oceanographers are uncertain about the origin of submarine canyons. The canyons lie too far below sea level to have been carved by rivers. Even during the Ice Age, when sea level fell as much as 425 feet (130 meters), the continental slope remained below sea level. Today most scientists believe the canyons form when sediment-laden water slips down the steep continental slope during an earthquake or other disturbance.

### The Oceanic Ridge

A range of submarine mountains called the **oceanic ridge** ranks as the earth's most prominent landform. It is 950 miles (1,500 kilometers) wide and 52,500 miles (84,000 kilometers) long, and rises 10,000 feet (3,000 meters) from the ocean floor.

The mountains of the ridge wrap around the earth like the seam of a baseball. They extend in an unbroken line across the Pacific, Indian, and Atlantic oceans. Iceland is one of the few places where the oceanic ridge rises above sea level.

A great **rift,** or wide crack, lies at the crest of the ridge. The rift is about 30 miles

***Learning from Diagrams.*** *The ocean floor has landforms as varied as those above the sea. What are the deepest parts of the ocean floor called?*

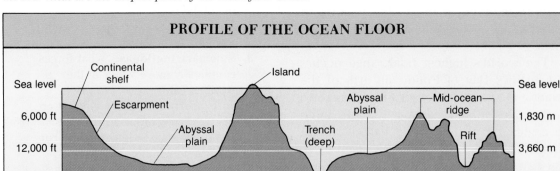

PROFILE OF THE OCEAN FLOOR

Sea level · Continental shelf · Island · Sea level · 6,000 ft · Escarpment · Abyssal plain · Mid-ocean ridge · 1,830 m · Abyssal plain · Trench (deep) · Rift · 12,000 ft · 3,660 m · 18,000 ft · 5,540 m

(48 kilometers) wide and contains active volcanoes. Molten materials rise from the earth's upper mantle and break through the oceanic crust at the rift. As the lava rises and solidifies, it builds up the high mountains of the oceanic ridge. As you read in Chapter 3, this process also causes seafloor spreading and related movements of the continents.

## Trenches and Abyssal Plains

Long and narrow V-shaped valleys called **trenches** or **deeps** form the deepest parts of the ocean. Many trenches lie near the edges of the continental shelf (see the map on pages 134–35). The deepest known trench is the Mariana Trench in the western Pacific Ocean, where a depth of more than 36,000 feet (11,022 meters) has been recorded. Many other trenches circle the edges of the Pacific Ocean.

According to the theory of plate tectonics, ocean trenches develop where the edge of an ocean plate descends under the edge of a continental plate (see the diagram on page 69). As the ocean plate sinks, its edge forms a deep trench, while the edge of the continental plate crumples into mountains. The Peru-Chile Trench off the west coast of South America, for example, occurs where the edge of the Nazca Plate under the Pacific Ocean sinks under the South American Plate (see the map on pages 134–35). The Andes are forming from the crumpled edge of the South American Plate. Other deep trenches off the shores of Japan and the Philippines are similarly associated with mountains at the edge of the Pacific Plate. Because of the unsettled nature of the plates, many of the mountains remain active volcanoes.

While dramatic, trenches represent only a small portion of the total area of the vast ocean basin. The **abyssal** (uh·BIS·uhl) **plains** cover extensive parts of the seafloor between the oceanic ridge and the continental slope. Like plains on land, the abyssal plains are generally smooth and flat.

---

### SECTION 3 REVIEW

1. **Define** continental shelf, continental slope, oceanic ridge, rift, trench, deep, abyssal plain
2. **Locate** Iceland, Mariana Trench
3. **Summarizing Ideas** What are the five major underwater landforms?
4. **Analyzing Ideas** What, according to scientists, might be the origin of submarine canyons?
5. **Evaluating Ideas** According to the theory of plate tectonics, how do ocean trenches develop?

---

## 4 Nations look to ocean waters for a wealth of resources.

Ocean waters hold vast mineral and food resources. Scientists believe that the ocean's mineral resources could supplement the decreasing reserves of nonrenewable resources on land. Nations struggling to feed growing populations hope that the ocean's food resources ultimately will help feed people in need. Those who use the ocean's resources, however, must proceed with caution. All agree that the ocean's wealth must be conserved so that it can be used by future generations.

### Mineral Resources

The ocean floor contains a variety of mineral resources. Some valuable minerals simply lie on the ocean floor. Other resources, mainly oil and natural gas, have formed in the rocks of the seafloor. Still other resources, including salt and other minerals, are found in seawater.

*Text continues on page 136.*

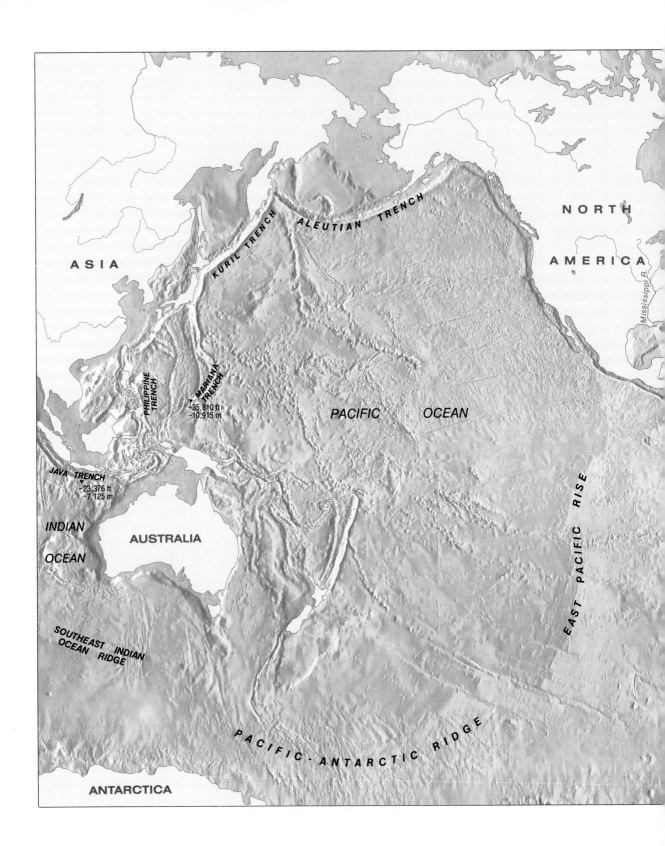

NORTH

AMERICA

ASIA

*Mississippi R.*

KURIL TRENCH

ALEUTIAN TRENCH

PHILIPPINE
TRENCH

MARIANA
TRENCH

−35,810 ft
−10,915 m

*PACIFIC*     *OCEAN*

JAVA TRENCH
−23,376 ft
−7,125 m

*INDIAN*

*OCEAN*

AUSTRALIA

EAST PACIFIC RISE

SOUTHEAST INDIAN
OCEAN RIDGE

PACIFIC−ANTARCTIC RIDGE

ANTARCTICA

134

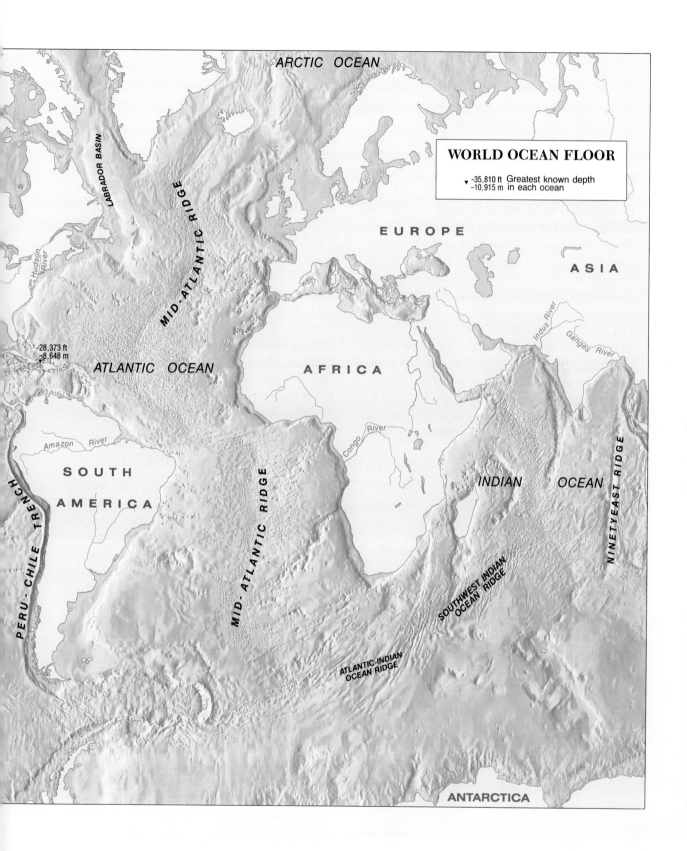

WORLD OCEAN FLOOR

▼ -35,810 ft   Greatest known depth
  -10,915 m   in each ocean

ARCTIC OCEAN

EUROPE

ASIA

LABRADOR BASIN

MID-ATLANTIC RIDGE

Hudson River

-28,373 ft
-8,648 m

ATLANTIC OCEAN

AFRICA

Indus River

Ganges River

Amazon River

SOUTH
AMERICA

Congo River

MID-ATLANTIC RIDGE

INDIAN        OCEAN

NINETYEAST RIDGE

PERU-CHILE TRENCH

SOUTHWEST INDIAN OCEAN RIDGE

ATLANTIC-INDIAN
OCEAN RIDGE

ANTARCTICA

**Nodules.** Unusual potato-sized lumps of magnesium, phosphorus, cobalt, iron, and nickel lie on many areas of the seafloor. These mineral lumps are called **nodules** (NAHJ·ools). Scientists believe that nodules form during chemical reactions in seawater that result in small, highly concentrated lumps of almost pure minerals. Although costly, some countries have begun mining nodules. To supplement limited sources of manganese, for example, the United States has begun to mine manganese nodules. Interest in such mining operations has risen sharply in recent years as land-based supplies of valuable minerals have dwindled.

**Oil and natural gas.** Offshore oil fields account for about 20 percent of the world's oil production today. In all, about 320 drilling rigs work at more than 60 drilling sites. All known offshore oil fields are located in waters above the continental shelf. Two of the more important fields underlie the Gulf of Mexico and the North Sea.

The continental shelf also contains vast supplies of natural gas. Today, there are over 100 offshore natural gas platforms,

*Learning from Pictures. Nodules settle in the soft sand of the Pacific Ocean floor. What are some problems associated with mining nodules such as these?*

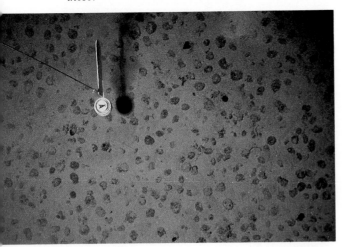

many of which are located off South Asia. One platform pumps natural gas from an offshore gas field to the refinery near Bombay, India, through 70 miles of pipeline.

**Ocean water.** Ocean water contains traces of all the minerals found on land. These minerals, which exist in the water in the form of salts, account for seawater's **salinity** (say·LIN·uht·ee), or salt content. If all the water in the world ocean were to dry up, the salts would form a layer on the ocean floor 500 feet (152 meters) thick.

The most abundant salt in seawater is sodium chloride, or table salt. Sodium chloride makes up 78 percent of the mineral content of seawater. It is "mined" by evaporating seawater in pools and gathering the residue. More sophisticated techniques recover magnesium, bromine, and other difficult-to-extract minerals and chemicals from seawater.

## An Abundance of Marine Life

The world ocean makes up the largest biological environment of our planet. **Marine biologists,** scientists who study the ocean's plants and animals, can only estimate the number of living things that inhabit the ocean. Each form of life, however, is a part of a complex process in which small plants and animals provide nourishment for larger animals living in the sea.

**Mysteries of the deep.** Sea monsters, so feared by sailors hundreds of years ago, seem unlikely discoveries in the ocean depths today. Enormous sea creatures, however, undoubtedly exist. A research ship from Denmark, for example, once caught the larva of an eel so large that the fully developed eel would have been 89 feet (27 meters) long. Another research ship hooked something at a depth of 1,000 feet (305 meters). What it was, the researchers

never learned. The "creature," however, was so big and powerful that it bent a 3-foot (1-meter) steel hook and escaped.

Marine biologists continually discover new species of life as changing technology allows them to probe deeper and deeper into the world ocean. For example, oceanographers exploring volcanic mountain ranges on the floor of the Atlantic Ocean in 1986 discovered a vast wonderland of strange deep-sea creatures, including a previously unknown type of shrimp and a mysterious six-sided creature.

**The ocean food chain.**  A complex feeding system, or **food chain,** provides nourishment for the multitude of sea creatures (see the diagram in the next column). Microscopic plants and animals called plankton make up the bottom of the food chain. Marine biologists call the microscopic plants phytoplankton. They call the microscopic animals zooplankton.

Plankton supply the complete diet for many small fish such as herring, menhaden, and mackerel. Carnivorous, or flesh-eating, sea creatures such as tuna and sharks, prey, in turn, on plankton eaters. However, not all plankton eaters are small. Some whales and other large sea animals also live entirely on a diet of plankton.

Like all plants, phytoplankton need sunlight to survive. For this reason, they and the creatures that eat them are most abundant where sunlight penetrates the ocean waters. They usually live within the top 300 feet (92 meters) of the sea. Deeper waters are too dark for plant life. Carnivores specially adapted to an environment with little light inhabit these darker waters.

Temperature also affects marine life. Different types of plankton and fish are associated with warm and cold waters. Mixed waters, where cold and warm ocean currents meet, have the greatest variety of sea life. The Grand Banks of Newfoundland,

## FOOD CHAIN FOR A HUMPBACK WHALE

1
Humpback
Whale

5,000
Herring

35,000,000
Krill

4,000,000,000,000
Phytoplankton
and
Zooplankton

***Learning from Diagrams.***  *In the ocean food chain large creatures feed on smaller ones. How do some large sea animals, such as whales, complicate ocean food chains?*

where the cold Labrador Current mixes with the warm Gulf Stream and North Atlantic Current, for example, holds one of the world's great fishing grounds (see the maps on pages 130 and 138).

## Fishing Resources

Fishing ranks among the world's most important economic activities. It employs more than 6 million people. Each year fishing fleets extract millions of tons of food and raw materials for industry from the oceans. These catches consists mainly of fish, shellfish, and seaweed.

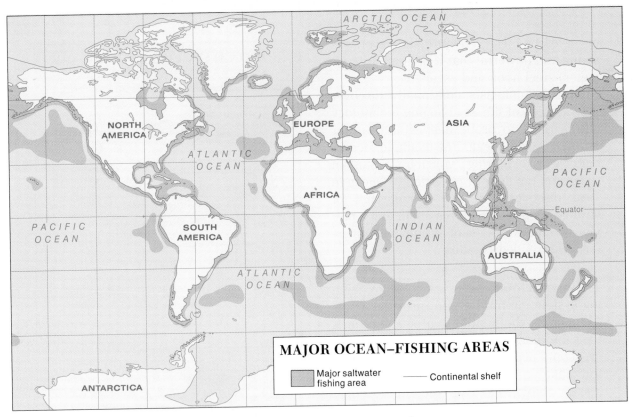

MAJOR OCEAN–FISHING AREAS

| | Major saltwater fishing area | | Continental shelf |

**Learning from Maps.** *Most major fishing areas are above continental shelves. Why are continental shelves rich fishing areas?*

**Fish for food.** The present annual marine catch totals about 150 billion pounds (67,500 million kilograms). Fish comprise more than 90 percent of the catch. Herring and codfish lead the list of edible fish taken by commercial fishers worldwide. The remaining 10 percent of the catch consists mainly of shellfish such as shrimp, lobsters, crabs, oysters, clams, and squid.

**Fish for industry.** Much of the world's fish catch is fed to livestock or used in industry. Fishers catch large quantities of anchoveta, a species similar to anchovy, off the west coast of South America. Processors grind part of the catch into fish meal for livestock feed. They use the remainder to make soap, linoleum, paint products, and fertilizer. Menhaden, a small fish caught in huge quantities off the coast of the United States and Canada, has similar uses.

## Potential Problems

For centuries coastal nations have abused the ocean while benefiting from it. They have used it to carry trade and also to dump wastes. They have harvested its fish with little thought of protecting that renewable resource for use by future generations. Today many people are working to protect this vital resource.

**Politics and the sea.** For centuries nations have argued about who controls nearby waters. Since the 1600s coastal nations claimed control over sea territories 3 miles (4.8 kilometers) from their coasts.

As nations began realizing the value of fishing grounds and underwater mineral deposits, some governments began extending their nation's sea claims, or **territorial limits.** By tradition, most countries today

*Text continues on page 140.*

# CASE STUDY
## EXPLORING PLACES: Tromelin Island

Tromelin Island is located off the east coast of Africa in the Indian Ocean, 300 miles (480 kilometers) east of Madagascar and 300 miles (480 kilometers) north of Mauritius (see the map on page 557). It has a few coconut palms and a weather station, but no drinking water and no inhabitants. Once important for the harvesting of bird droppings, from which fertilizer is made, Tromelin has little economic value today. Nevertheless, the pear-shaped piece of sand that measures less than 1 mile (1.6 kilometers) by a few hundred feet is the center of an international dispute.

### Ownership Claims

France, Mauritius, Madagascar, and the Seychelles all claim Tromelin as part of their national territory. France presently governs Tromelin as part of the Réunion Islands, a French possession since 1638. Neighboring Mauritius claims Tromelin as well as the rest of the Réunion Islands. Mauritius was itself part of the Réunion group before gaining independence in 1968. Madagascar, the nearest nation geographically to Tromelin, insists that Tromelin and the four other uninhabited islands of the Réunion group were part of Madagascar long before the French arrived. The Seychelles also makes a claim based on geography, stating that Tromelin belongs to it as part of the Seychelles-Mauritius Plateau under the sea.

### What's at Stake?

At first glance a territorial dispute over such an insignificant island seems ridiculous. In today's world, however, it appears that the nation that owns Tromelin can claim ownership of a 200-mile (320-kilometer) exclusive economic zone around the island. This claim will give the successful claimant the ownership of fishing rights

*Tromelin Island*

and mineral resources in some 125,000 square miles (323,750 square kilometers) of seafloor around Tromelin.

### No Settlement in Sight

No settlement of the dispute is in sight, although the United Nations seeks to prevent scrambles for islands such as Tromelin. As early as 1967 the United Nations General Assembly voiced concern over potential conflicts arising from territorial sea claims. A series of UN actions led to the Third Law of the Sea Conference in 1973. At this conference general agreements were reached on a number of ocean-related issues. These agreements eventually led to the adoption of the Law of the Sea Treaty in 1982. That treaty grants ownership of territorial sea only to islands capable of sustaining life or economic activity. Of course, only nations signing the treaty feel obliged to abide by its laws. France refuses to sign the controversial treaty, so it is not bound by any of the decisions made by the United Nations based on the treaty.

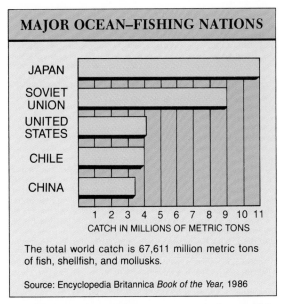

## MAJOR OCEAN–FISHING NATIONS

JAPAN
SOVIET UNION
UNITED STATES
CHILE
CHINA

1 2 3 4 5 6 7 8 9 10 11
CATCH IN MILLIONS OF METRIC TONS

The total world catch is 67,611 million metric tons of fish, shellfish, and mollusks.

Source: Encyclopedia Britannica *Book of the Year,* 1986

***Learning from Graphs.*** *Japan leads the world in fish caught. What physical aspect of Japan makes it different from the other nations on the chart?*

recognize a 200-mile (320-kilometer) territorial limit.

Several international laws have been created to regulate the use of the world ocean and avoid disputes among countries. Several nations, for example, have signed the Law of the Sea Treaty, sponsored by the United Nations. The United States and many nations of Western Europe, however, disagree with certain provisions of the treaty and have refused to sign it.

Despite longstanding practice and international laws, however, many countries contest territorial claims over the world ocean. The United States and the Soviet Union, for example, dispute territorial limits in the Bering Sea.

**Overfishing.** Advances in technology make modern fishing highly efficient. Radar and electronic equipment, for example, locate large schools of fish. Motor-driven nets and other devices haul in everything in the sea within their reach. But it is possible to **overfish,** or to take more fish from the sea than can be naturally replaced. Overfishing leaves few mature fish in the ocean to rebuild the marine populations. Numbers of some marine animals, including the blue whale, have been greatly reduced by overfishing. Others may already be extinct.

**Pollution.** The ocean has long served as a dumping ground for waste products. Today the effects of this long-term dumping are becoming increasingly obvious. The water in many areas is now too polluted for fish to survive. Oil spills from drilling rigs and ship collisions pollute the ocean. The dumping of industrial and other wastes far out at sea adds to the problem.

Pollution of the ocean concerns all nations. Some pollutants are **biodegradable** (by·oh·dee·GRAYD·uh·buhl), or easily broken down by natural means, and are harmless to the sea. Other pollutants, however, are nonbiodegradable. They enter the ocean's food chain, where they remain for years. In addition, ocean currents carry pollutants far from where they originally entered the water. For example, the pesticide DDT has never been used in Antarctica. Yet scientists have discovered its presence in the livers of penguins and seals living in Antarctic waters.

### SECTION 4 REVIEW

1. **Define** nodule, salinity, marine biologist, food chain, territorial limit, overfish, biodegradable
2. **Interpreting Ideas** What minerals are found on the ocean floor?
3. **Studying Charts** What are the steps in the ocean food chain?
4. **Analyzing Ideas** Why are fishing resources important?
5. **Synthesizing Ideas** (a) How is ocean pollution carried far from the original source? (b) What is an example of this process?

# DEVELOPING GEOGRAPHY SKILLS
## INTERPRETING VISUALS: Gathering Data from Photographs

Imagine you are an oceanographer. As your deep-sea probe dives toward the ocean floor, you see a variety of creatures and landscapes. The probe's video cameras film the underwater scene and its mechanical arms collect samples. The observations you make are as important as the physical samples collected by the probe's arms because observing your surroundings is the easiest way to gather data.

Students of geography do not always have the opportunity to be firsthand observers of new and different surroundings. You can, however, become a skilled observer by carefully studying the pictures in this textbook.

*Exploring the ocean depths*

### How to Gather Data from Photographs

Follow these guidelines to gather data from photographs.

1. **Determine your purpose.** Study all the information. Identify the relationships between the photograph, the caption, and the textbook's contents.
2. **Examine the photograph.** Look closely for unique features, especially those that illustrate information in the caption or in the textbook's content.
3. **Formulate questions about what is being observed.** What information does the photograph contain? How does it illustrate key concepts?
4. **Reexamine the details.** Look carefully at all aspects of the photograph. Make sure you have answers to all your questions. Ask yourself if there is anything else you need to know before finishing your observation of the photograph.

### Applying the Skill

Imagine once again that you are an oceanographer. You are searching the ocean floor for nodule deposits large enough to mine commercially. Study the picture on page 136. Your purpose in studying the picture is to see if a sizeable deposit of nodules is present on this part of the ocean floor. As you study the picture, you should ask the following questions: *Are there nodules in the picture? Do there seem to be a large number of nodules on this part of the ocean floor? Does it appear that the nodules will be difficult to mine?*

By studying the picture and answering the questions, you collect data about nodules on this part of the ocean floor. You should note that there are nodules in the picture. As you can see, many nodules dot this part of the ocean floor. And the nodules appear to be sitting on the ocean floor rather than embedded in it. Therefore, the nodules are probably not difficult to mine. Based on the information you gathered from the picture, you would probably decide that there are enough nodules on this part of the ocean floor to mine efficiently.

*To practice this skill, see Practicing Geography Skills on page 143.*

## Chapter Summary

The following list contains the key concepts you have learned about the world ocean.

1. Oceans, seas, and other bodies of salt water cover 71 percent of the earth's surface.
2. These bodies of salt water are interconnected, forming a single world ocean that is usually divided into four main parts—the Pacific, Atlantic, Indian, and Arctic oceans.
3. The world ocean helps determine climate and shapes landforms.
4. The waters of the ocean are in constant motion. The most important movements are caused by the circulation of ocean currents and by tides.
5. Spectacular landforms and abundant mineral resources lie beneath the sea.
6. Ocean waters hold a wealth of food resources. They are part of a complex food chain built on plankton.
7. Many problems, such as territorial disputes, overfishing, and pollution, cloud the future use of the world ocean. Such problems arise from the absence of universally accepted rules governing ownership of the ocean and its resources.
8. The world's nations recognize the ocean's importance and are continually seeking solutions to territorial disputes and other potential problems.

On a separate sheet of paper, complete the following review exercises.

## Reviewing Geographic Terms

Match each of the following terms with the correct definition.

a. ocean acoustic tomography
b. nodule
c. rift
d. food chain
e. continental shelf
f. abyssal plain
g. oceanographer
h. trench
i. biodegradable
j. strait

_____ 1. Narrow body of water linking large bodies of water
_____ 2. Technique that provides a three-dimensional image of water movement
_____ 3. Scientist who studies the ocean
_____ 4. Edge of a continent extending beneath the ocean
_____ 5. Wide crack in the oceanic ridge
_____ 6. Deepest part of the ocean
_____ 7. Very wide, smooth, and flat section of seafloor
_____ 8. Potato-sized lump of minerals
_____ 9. Complex feeding system that nourishes sea creatures
_____ 10. Easily broken down by natural means

## Developing Critical Thinking Skills

1. **Summarizing Ideas** List some specific extensions of the Atlantic Ocean, Pacific Ocean, and Indian Ocean.
2. **Connecting Ideas** (a) How do ocean currents affect climate? (b) What ocean current was recently identified, and how does it affect the world's climates?
3. **Interpreting Ideas** Why do high tides and low tides occur?
4. **Analyzing Ideas** How is overfishing related to the expansion of territorial limits?
5. **Writing About Geography** In a clearly written paragraph, complete one of the following activities. (a) Analyze the impact of the ocean's currents, tides, and resources on the earth and on human activity. (b) Analyze the Tromelin Island situation. Then state your opinion regarding which country you think should have the territorial rights to the island.

## Using Primary Sources

In the following excerpt from *The Sea Around Us*, Rachel Carson describes the relationship between the wind and the water of the sea. As you study the reading, consider the beauty and the mystery of the sea.

The waves move toward the coast, and the wind that created them controls their destiny. As the storm continues and the waves move shoreward, they receive energy from the wind and increase in height. Up to a point they will continue to take to themselves the fierce energy of the wind, growing in height as the strength of the gale is absorbed, but when a wave becomes about a seventh as high from trough to crest as the distance to the next crest it will begin to topple in foaming whitecaps. Winds of hurricane force often blow the tops off waves by their sheer violence; in such a storm the highest waves may develop after the wind has begun to subside.

But to return to our typical wave, born of wind and water far out in the Atlantic, grown to its full height on the energy of the winds, with its fellow waves forming a confused, irregular pattern known as a "sea." As the waves gradually pass out of the storm area their height diminishes, the distance between successive crests increases, and the "sea" becomes a "swell," moving at an average speed of about 15 miles an hour. Near the coast a pattern of long, regular swells is substituted for the turbulence of open ocean. But as the swell enters shallow water a startling transformation takes place. For the first time in its existence, the wave feels the drag of shoaling bottom. Its speed slackens, crests of following waves crowd in toward it, abruptly its height increases and the wave form steepens. Then with a spilling, tumbling rush of water falling down into its trough, it dissolves in a seething confusion of foam.

An observer sitting on a beach can make at least an intelligent guess whether the surf spilling out onto the sand before him has been produced by a gale close offshore or by a distant storm. Young waves, only recently shaped by the wind, have a steep, peaked shape even well out at sea. From far out on the horizon you can see them forming whitecaps as they come in; bits of foam are spilling down their fronts and boiling and bubbling over the advancing face, and the final breaking of the wave is a prolonged and deliberate process. But if a wave, on coming into the surf zone, rears high as though gathering all its strength for the final act of its life, if the crest forms all along its advancing front and then begins to curl forward, if the whole mass of water plunges suddenly with a booming roar into its trough—then you may take it that these waves are visitors from some very distant part of the ocean, that they have traveled long and far before the final dissolution at your feet.

1. What controls a wave's destiny?
2. How do wind waves created near shore differ from those created far offshore?

## Practicing Geography Skills

*Before completing this activity, review Developing Geography Skills on page 141.*

**Gathering Data from Illustrations** Study the pictures on pages 102 and 115. Then complete these activities.

1. Using complete sentences, describe what you see in each photograph.
2. What details does the caption direct you to note about each picture?
3. Rewrite each caption to direct attention to other interesting details in each picture.

## Exploring Geography

Look through newspapers and magazines for photographs, paintings, diagrams, and other illustrations of the ocean floor. Gather all these visual materials together and make a collage for display on the bulletin board.

# UNIT 2 REVIEW

## Unit Summary

The following list contains the key concepts you have learned about the earth's physical setting.

1. Slope and local relief help to determine whether a landform is classified as a plain, plateau, hill, or mountain.
2. A variety of internal and external forces constantly changes the surface of the earth. Among these forces are earthquakes, volcanoes, physical and chemical weathering, and erosion.
3. The four variable conditions in the atmosphere that affect an area's weather are temperature, moisture, atmospheric pressure, and wind. The climatic controls of latitude, altitude, and proximity to land and sea influence the distribution of climates over the earth's surface.
4. The elements of weather and the climatic controls determine which of the 6 major climate types and 13 subtypes a location has. Climate also affects a location's vegetation, including forests, grasslands, deserts, tundras, and mountain vegetation.
5. Both renewable and nonrenewable natural resources help people satisfy their needs and wants.
6. Industrial societies depend on nonrenewable energy sources but are experimenting with other sources such as hydroelectricity, nuclear energy, and solar energy.
7. Agriculture may be either commercial or subsistence. Commercial farms may be specialized, growing a single cash crop, or mixed, growing several cash crops. Many different types of subsistence agriculture are practiced in the nonindustrialized countries of the world.
8. The waters of the ocean are interconnected and are in constant motion.
9. Spectacular landforms, including the continental shelf and slope, the oceanic ridge, oceanic trenches, and the abyssal plains, lie beneath the ocean.
10. Territorial disputes, overfishing, and pollution cloud the future use of the world ocean. Such problems arise from the absence of universally accepted rules governing ownership of the ocean and its wealth of resources.

On a separate sheet of paper, complete the following review exercises.

## Checking Your Understanding

1. (a) What causes earthquakes? (b) Explain what happens during an earthquake.
2. What are the effects of (a) altitude and (b) temperature on atmospheric pressure?
3. Study the map on pages 96–97 and refer to the chart entitled "Major Climate Types and Subtypes" on page 95. Then answer the following questions. (a) What climate type and subtype do you find near the tropics in eastern sections of continents? (b) Why are there no continental climates in the Southern Hemisphere? (c) What climate might you find in the highest submarine mountains if they were not submerged in water?
4. (a) How, according to scientists, do nodules form? (b) Why are nodules important to many nations today?

## Applying Critical Thinking Skills

1. **Interpreting Ideas** How might aquaculture help to resolve conflicts over territorial limits?
2. **Analyzing Ideas** (a) What technique can scientists use to specially design plants to produce proteins and fight off disease? (b) How might this help reduce world hunger?
3. **Seeing Relationships** How does the Coriolis effect change the course of (a) prevailing winds and (b) ocean currents?
4. **Synthesizing Ideas** Why would vegetation patterns be affected if ocean currents were completely altered?

## Reviewing Unit Features

1. **Geography in the Workplace**  Why do physical geographers play a vital role in studying our natural world?
2. **The Geographic Web**  Why are problems with water an international concern?

## Using Map Skills

1. Study the map entitled "World Climates" on pages 96-97. In what climate zone do you live?
2. Study the map entitled "Ocean Currents" on page 130.  **(a)** In which direction do the ocean currents in the Southern Hemisphere tend to move—clockwise or counterclockwise?  **(b)** What are the major ocean currents of the Atlantic Ocean and  **(c)** the Pacific Ocean?  **(d)** Is the Gulf Stream a warm or a cold current?

## Investigating Geography

1. Use references in the library to further research the Law of the Sea Treaty. Prepare two written reports, one that supports the treaty and another that opposes it. Pass them out to the class and ask them to vote for one of them. Then tell the class whether you are for the treaty or not.
2. Find out which climatic controls influence the climate where you live. Write a weather forecast for a given day and explain which elements of weather served as a basis for your prediction.

## Further Readings

### Chapter 3
Fodor, R. V. *Earth in Motion: The Concepts of Plate Tectonics*. New York: Morrow. Describes the theory of continental drift and discusses the historical background of plate tectonics.

Gilfond, Henry. *The New Ice Age*. New York: Franklin Watts. Shows how an ice age occurs, how volcanic eruptions influence climate, and why glaciers move, and discusses the possibility of a new ice age.

### Chapter 4
Lehr, Paul E., R. Will Burnett, and Herbert S. Zim. *Weather*. New York: Golden Press, Western Publishing Co. Reviews the causes of weather and various aspects such as storms and tornadoes. Also describes weather maps and weather forecasting.

Purvis, George, and Ann Purvis. *Weather and Climate*. New York: Franklin Watts, Inc., Bookwright Press. Discusses weather, climate, and atmosphere.

### Chapter 5
Douglas, John H., and the Editors of Grolier. *The Future World of Energy*. New York: Epcot Center Book, Grolier. Discusses where energy can be found, why it is important to the world, and the various types of energy—oil, sun, wind, and water.

Pringle, Laurence. *Water: The Next Great Resource Battle*. New York: Macmillan Co., Inc. Deals with water and why it is important for human survival, which parts of the earth have less water and why, and the potential effects of chemicals and other pollutants on the water supply.

Smith, Norman F. *Energy Isn't Easy*. New York: Coward-McCann. Discusses traditional forms of energy and renewable resources.

### Chapter 6
Lambert, David. *The Oceans*. New York: Franklin Watts, Bookwright Press. Covers various aspects of the oceans including waves, tides, currents, the seashore, and the ocean floor.

Sedge, Michael H. *Commercialization of the Oceans*. New York: Impact Books, Franklin Watts. Defines commercialization of the ocean and describes how it began.

Weiss, Malcolm E. *One Sea, One Law. The Fight for a Law of the Sea*. Orlando: Harcourt, Brace, Jovanovich. Discusses how the ocean might be protected by international law.

# UNIT 3

# THE EARTH'S CULTURAL SETTING

# Cultural Patterns

# PUTTING THE CHAPTER IN FOCUS

Every human group leaves a distinct imprint on the earth. A variety of cultural patterns reflects this imprint. The earth's cultural variety finds expression in different population trends, social characteristics, political systems, and economic systems.

## Ideas to Understand

In studying about the earth's cultural patterns, use these ideas to give direction to your reading.

1 Geographers study population trends.
2 Language and religion form important parts of the cultural setting.
3 The world today is divided into more than 160 nations.
4 World nations feature differing levels of development and differing economies.

## Terms to Define

The following terms are some of the key terms in the chapter. Defining them will help you understand cultural patterns.

| | |
|---|---|
| cultural setting | compact nation |
| demographer | fragmented nation |
| life expectancy | one-crop economy |
| population density | developed nation |
| migration | developing nation |
| language family | capitalism |

## Places to Locate

Locating the following places will add to your knowledge of geography.

| | |
|---|---|
| Pakistan | China |
| Indonesia | Japan |
| India | Israel |

## 1 Geographers study population trends.

Landforms, climate, weather, vegetation, resources, and the world ocean make up parts of the earth's physical setting. As you know, however, the study of geography involves much more than a study of the earth's physical features. Just as important is a study of the earth's various cultural features, or the **cultural setting.** As you read in Chapter 1, **culture** is the sum of what a human group acquires through living together, including language, knowledge, skills, art, literature, law, customs, and life styles.

When studying about a group's culture, it helps to divide cultural characteristics into two categories—material culture and nonmaterial culture.

**Material culture** includes all the physical objects that people make. Examples of material culture include buildings, clothing, tools, paintings, and other artifacts. The ideas of a society—expressed in its language, values, political and economic systems, and so on—make up its **nonmaterial culture.**

Both material and nonmaterial culture tell us a great deal about a society's way of life. As you will see later in this chapter, they also help us to understand **acculturation** (uh·kul·chuh·RAY·shuhn), the process by which a person from one culture adopts traits of another culture. Cultural diffusion is a part of this process. You will remember that **cultural diffusion** is the spread of certain parts of cultures from one area of the world to another.

The cultural setting focuses on people—particularly the imprint that people make on the earth. To begin a study of the cultural setting, then, it is important to begin with a study of people. Changes in the

◀ *Rath Yatra festival in India*

**149**

number of people, their distribution, and the movement of people from place to place especially interest geographers.

## Stages of Population Growth

Earth's **population,** or the number of people living on the planet, constantly increases. In fact, in the time it takes you to read this sentence at least two more people will be born. Such population growth places pressure on the resources of an already crowded world.

The population growth rate has not always been as high as it is today. Keep in mind, too, that the growth rate differs in different parts of the world. **Demographers** (dih·MOG·reh·fer), scientists who study population trends, have found that population growth rates vary with the levels of a country's economic development. Based on this information, they have identified four general stages of population growth known as the **demographic transition.** Population changes in Europe as it industrialized in the late 1800s and early 1900s served as a model for the stages.

In the first stage of population growth the number of people increases slowly. The **birth rate,** or the number of children born per 1,000 people, is high. But the **death rate,** the number of people who die per 1,000 people, also is high. Few children live to be adults. Sickness, malnutrition, and starvation kill large numbers of people every year. **Life expectancy**—the average number of years a person is expected to live—is only about 30. This means that the **rate of natural increase,** or the difference between the birth rate and the death rate, remains low.

In the second stage of population growth technological advances in farming, nutrition, medicine, and sanitation result in increased food supplies and improvements in health care. So people live longer and many more children than before live to become adults. The death rate drops rapidly and the population begins to grow rapidly.

In the third stage most children live to be adults. In order to raise their standard of living, however, many adults begin limiting the size of their families, thus lowering the birth rate. The population still grows, but at a slower rate than before.

Finally, in the fourth stage both the birth rate and the death rate are very low. At this stage, the population growth rate slows dramatically and may even approach **zero population growth,** or the point at which the birth rate and the death rate are about equal. In stage four the rate of natural increase is almost as slow as it was in stage one.

The four stages of population growth may not always apply to every country of the world. Understanding the demographic transition, however, helps put the world's population growth since 1800 into perspective. It explains why the world's population grew slowly for thousands of years before 1800. It also explains why the population grew rapidly after 1800, from only 1 billion in 1850 to more than 5 billion today.

## An Uneven Distribution

The world's population is not evenly distributed over the earth. In some places hundreds of thousands of people live within the limits of a single city. In other places only a few people live scattered over miles and miles of farmland or wilderness. The **spatial** (SPAY·shul) **distribution of population** describes the way the population is distributed over the earth.

**Measuring distribution.** One of the most important ways to measure population distribution is to calculate the **population density,** or the number of people per square mile (or square kilometer) of a given land

*Text continues on page 154.*

# CASE STUDY
## GEOGRAPHY AND PEOPLE: Thomas Malthus

Thomas Malthus, a member of the English clergy as well as a historian and economist, was one of the most famous and important early population experts. In 1798 Malthus wrote *An Essay on the Principle of Population as It Affects the Future Improvement of Society.*

Malthus wrote that population grows more rapidly than food output. He stated that population tends to grow in a geometric progression—1, 2, 4, 8, 16, 32, and so on—so that the number of people doubles every 25 years as each generation grows to maturity. Food output, on the other hand, increases in an arithmetic progression—1, 2, 3, 4, 5, 6, and so on.

Malthus concluded that the population would eventually outgrow the food supply. When this happens, he predicted, millions of people will starve to death, bringing population back into line with the food supply. Famine, Malthus believed, served to check population growth.

*Thomas Malthus*

### Was Malthus Right or Wrong?

Malthus's book caused a whirlwind of protest and debate. Between 1798 and 1826 he changed his writings several times. Never in any of the revisions, however, did he change his belief that population would outgrow the food supply. He simply added more evidence to support his position.

So far Malthus's predictions have not come true, even though famines have plagued many parts of the world. Malthus did point out that migration and better farming methods might delay the problems caused by a growing population. But he could not foresee how colonization and migration in the 1800s and early 1900s would change world food production. These movements brought millions of acres of new farmland into production. Nor could Malthus predict the many changes that

have occurred in world transportation and marketing systems. These changes make it possible to quickly send food to famine-stricken parts of the world. Finally, Malthus could not foresee the huge harvests that high-yielding seeds, advanced machinery, and effective fertilizers make possible.

### The Debate Continues

Many of today's population experts believe that Thomas Malthus was correct, although his predictions proved premature. Called neo-Malthusians, these people respect Malthus as the first person to warn the world that this small planet cannot feed an ever-growing number of people.

Other population experts take a more optimistic view. They do not believe that famines are inevitable. These people refer to the neo-Malthusians as "prophets of doom." Both groups agree, however, that the earth's resources must be used wisely.

## WORLD POPULATION DENSITY

| Persons per square mile | | Persons per square kilometer | |
|---|---|---|---|
| 0–25 | | 0–10 | |
| 26–60 | | 11–25 | |
| 61–125 | | 26–50 | |
| 126–250 | | 51–100 | |
| over 250 | | over 100 | |

• Cities with more than 5 million inhabitants

Ice cap

ARCTIC OCEAN

Arctic Circle

EUROPE

London•

Moscow•

ASIA

Beijing•
Tianjin•
Seoul•
Tokyo•
Shanghai•

Cairo•

Karachi•

Bombay•

AFRICA

PACIFIC OCEAN

Equator

ATLANTIC OCEAN

INDIAN OCEAN

Jakarta•

AUSTRALIA

N

1000    2000 Miles

1000    2000 Kilometers

0°    20°    40°    60°    80°    100°    120°    140°    160°    180°

Antarctic Circle

ANTARCTICA

area. Population density can be measured in two ways—by calculating arithmetic density and physiological density.

The **arithmetic** (ar·ith·MET·ik) **density** refers to the average number of people per square mile or square kilometer in a given country. You can figure this number by dividing a country's area by its population. For example, the Philippines has an arithmetic density of 531 people per square mile (204 per square kilometer).

Calculating arithmetic densities provides a useful way to compare the population densities of various countries. Yet these statistics do not reflect the fact that population is distributed unevenly. Many of

*Learning from Pictures.* Populi *is published by the United Nations to inform people throughout the world about population problems. Why is world population distribution uneven?*

the more rugged parts of the Philippines, for example, have almost no people. This means that more people crowd onto the habitable land. To get a more accurate picture of how crowded a country is, geographers often calculate the **physiological** (fihz·ee·uh·LAHJ·ih·kuhl) **density,** or the number of people per square mile of cultivated land. The Philippines has a physiological density of 1,397 people per square mile (537 per square kilometer).

**Factors that affect population density.** A world population map, such as the one on pages 152–53, shows at a glance the uneven distribution of the world's people. Nearly 90 percent of the world's land area remains "empty" or sparsely populated. The remaining 10 percent is densely populated. What explains this uneven distribution? Two of the most important factors include the place characteristics of an area and the level of technology of the people.

It is easy to understand why the place characteristics of an area directly affect its population density. More people live in areas with fertile soil and a mild climate, for example, than in areas with rugged terrain and a harsh climate. Of course, advances in technology make it possible for people to live in even extreme conditions. Yet many sparsely populated areas may never have high populations. They are too cold, too dry, too mountainous, too infertile, or otherwise too unattractive to support large numbers of people.

The level of technology of the people also affects population density. In some areas, for example, the people are tied to the land, still using traditional methods of farming. Muscle power provides the energy for farm work, rather than machine power. In such areas more people settled farmland that lies close to a water supply, such as the land along the banks of a river, than outlying areas.

In areas with high levels of technology, machines replaced human power in the fields. This freed many people from work on the farm and eventually led to the development of cities, where large numbers of people live today.

Look again at the world population map on pages 152–53. Try to identify the three areas of the world that have the highest population densities. The People's Republic of China and other countries in East Asia rank first. India and other countries in South and Southeast Asia rank second. Western and Eastern Europe rank third.

In the two most densely populated areas of Asia millions of people crowd into a few coastal plains, deltas, and river valleys where soils are rich and the climate is favorable for growing rice and wheat. Especially large concentrations of people live along three great rivers—the Ganges (GAN·jeez) in India and the Huang He (HWAHNG HUH) and Chang Jiang (CHAHNG JYAHNG) in the People's Republic of China.

Now study the population density of Europe. Before Europe industrialized in the 1800s and early 1900s, climate and soil fertility determined population density. Today, however, more than 90 percent of the European people live in or around cities. Especially large clusters of population occupy industrial and commercial centers.

## Migration

Along with population growth and distribution, geographers also study **migration** (my·GRAY·shuhn), or the movement of people from place to place. Migration does not add to world population. But it does change the population of specific areas. Migration from one country to another can be classified as emigration or immigration. **Emigration** is the movement of people out of a country. **Immigration** is the movement of people into a country.

People migrate for many reasons. Oppression, war, or natural catastrophes force some people from their homes. Other people move to an area because they are attracted by better conditions or new opportunities—political or religious freedom, better jobs, a more favorable climate, and so on. In the 1800s, for example, more than 50 million people left their homelands in Europe to seek better opportunities in North and South America.

Migration also occurs within countries as people move from one region or city to another. Such internal migration can have a direct effect on the distribution of a country's population. Internal migration is very common in the United States, where 20 percent of the people move each year. In recent years the trend has been for Americans to move to the states of the South and West.

### SECTION 1 REVIEW

1. **Define** cultural setting, culture, material culture, nonmaterial culture, acculturation, cultural diffusion, population, demographer, demographic transition, birth rate, death rate, life expectancy, rate of natural increase, zero population growth, spatial distribution of population, population density, arithmetic density, physiological density, migration, emigration, immigration
2. **Interpreting Ideas** Describe the four stages of population growth.
3. **Using Map Skills** Study the world population map on pages 152–53. What area of the United States has the highest population density?
4. **Contrasting Ideas** How are patterns of population density affected by **(a)** place characteristics and **(b)** the level of technology?
5. **Analyzing Ideas** Why do people move from one location to another?

*Text continues on page 157.*

# THE GEOGRAPHIC WEB
## All That Trash

Americans dispose of about 800 million pounds of garbage every day. That is enough to fill 40,000 large garbage trucks. Most of the garbage is simply dumped onto the ground at large **landfills,** sites for the disposal of garbage. There garbage trucks dump their loads of trash and snorting bulldozers push it into mountains of garbage. Yet the space for trash is fast running out.

### Where to Put It All

By the early 1990s half of our nation's landfills will be used up. Unless alternatives on land are found, a fleet of garbage scows (bargelike ships) might be forced to put out to sea in search of new dump sites as one did in 1987. The most frightening thought of all is that, in desperation, the ocean itself could become a huge dumping ground.

How long can we continue to dispose of our trash this way? Some cities, such as Philadelphia, Pennsylvania, have long been searching for an answer. Much of Philadelphia's garbage is now trucked to Ohio. The rest is burned. Plans were made to ship the ash to Panama, which would use it as roadbed and landfill. But Panamanian officials changed their minds, stating, "If it is not good for the United States, neither can it be any good for Panama." Many other cities routinely transport their garbage by truck, rail, or barge over distances as much as 150 miles (242 kilometers) to landfills in more open areas.

### Finding Alternatives

In Europe, where there are even fewer landfill sites than in the United States, the trash is often burned. But there is growing concern over air pollution caused by burning garbage. This concern has encouraged recycling. Swiss firms have developed machinery that can convert smelly garbage into reusable products such as glass, ceramics, plastics, paper fiber, metals, and fertilizer. Several American cities have purchased Swiss recycling plants and expect them to be operational in 1988.

Recycling efforts help. But the world's population is growing very rapidly. And, despite recycling options, people today throw away far more material than earlier generations did. The problems of the garbage explosion will not go away easily. As garbage continues to pile up, scientists around the world continue to look for solutions.

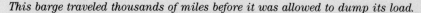

*This barge traveled thousands of miles before it was allowed to dump its load.*

## 2 Language and religion form important parts of the cultural setting.

Population patterns indicate the number of people, where they settle, and why they move from place to place. Other aspects of a group's culture, such as language and religious patterns, however, reveal much more about the people's everyday lives.

### Language

Language, both spoken and written, makes it possible for people to communicate with each other. Cultural geographers have identified over 3,000 different languages used in the world today.

**Local and global languages.** Cultural geographers divide the world's languages into local and global languages. **Local languages** are spoken by relatively small numbers of people. Only about 200,000 people in northern India, for example, speak Khasi (KAH·see). **Global languages** are spoken by millions of people. Global languages include English, which is the official language of many countries around the world, and Chinese, which more than 600 million people speak. Many global languages illustrate cultural diffusion. Most of these languages began in one area and then spread to other parts of the world.

**Language families.** Scholars believe that the thousands of languages spoken today developed from a few common languages. As early people migrated throughout the world and lost contact with other groups, different languages evolved. Geographers classify languages that have the same origins as **language families.** The two largest language families in the world today are the Sino-Tibetan family, spoken mainly in Asia,

| MAJOR LANGUAGES OF THE WORLD | |
|---|---|
| Language | Speakers |
| MANDARIN CHINESE | 788,000,000 |
| ENGLISH | 420,000,000 |
| HINDI | 300,000,000 |
| SPANISH | 296,000,000 |
| GREAT RUSSIAN | 285,000,000 |
| ARABIC | 177,000,000 |
| BENGALI | 171,000,000 |
| PORTUGUESE | 164,000,000 |
| MALAY/INDONESIAN | 128,000,000 |
| JAPANESE | 122,000,000 |

Source: *The World Almanac*, 1987
*The 1987 Information Please Almanac*

**Learning from Charts.** *Global languages vary—some are spoken by many people in a populous country while others are spoken in many different countries. Why are global languages a good example of cultural diffusion?*

and the Indo-European family, of which English is a part.

Even though most speakers of different languages within the same language family cannot understand each other's languages, certain words are similar. The English word *sister*, for example, resembles the word for sister in several other Indo-European languages. The French *soeur*, the German *schwester*, the Italian *sorella*, and the Russian *sestra* reflect common origins.

Language is never static. It always changes and develops. Changes in languages can take place over a relatively short period of time. The most notable recent additions include terms related to technological advances, such as the words *computer chip* and *software*.

157

***Learning from Pictures.*** *Children prepare to attend this small Christian church in Jamaica. Why are the methods of worship within a religion often similar regardless of location?*

## Religion

Religion makes up another part of a group's nonmaterial culture. Every culture in the world has religion in one form or another. In most cultures **religion** is a set of beliefs in a supreme being or beings.

In general, religions give people a model for human behavior. Most include the idea that good behavior will be rewarded and that bad behavior will be punished. Often a trained group of religious leaders leads the people in religious observances. Priests, ministers, and rabbis, for example, conduct weekly services and preside at confirmations, baptisms, weddings, and funerals.

Religion affects many aspects of daily life. In the United States, for example, many

workers have Sundays off because that is the traditional day of Christian church services. In Israel, a Jewish country, most workers have Saturdays off because Saturday is the Sabbath, or day of rest.

Three major world religions—Christianity, Judaism, and Islam—began in the Middle East. From there they spread to other parts of the world through the process of cultural diffusion. Two of the world's religions, Hinduism and Buddhism, began in ancient India. Even though these religions have followers scattered all over the world, most Hindus and Buddhists live in Asia. Confucianism remains largely confined to China and Japan.

## Cultural Regions

Geographers divide the world into several **cultural regions,** or areas in which the people share similar cultural characteristics. They identify the cultural regions of the world in many different ways. The following list reflects one way accepted by geographers—Anglo America, Latin America, Europe, North Africa and the Middle East, Africa South of the Sahara, South Asia, East Asia, Southeast Asia, and Oceania. You will study more about each cultural region in Chapters 10 to 36.

---

**SECTION 2 REVIEW**

1. **Define** landfill, local language, global language, language family, religion, cultural region
2. **Locate** Pakistan, Indonesia, India, China, Japan, Israel
3. **Evaluating Ideas** Why do global languages provide excellent examples of cultural diffusion?
4. **Analyzing Ideas** In general, what do the different religions of the world have in common?

# 3 The world today is divided into more than 160 nations.

Geographers refer to distribution patterns on the earth as **spatial relationships.** Along with the spatial distribution of population, another spatial relationship that forms an important part of the earth's cultural setting is the pattern of international boundaries that divides the world. Today political boundaries divide the world into more than 160 different nations.

## Political Boundaries

The map on pages 4–5 shows the current political boundaries of the world. Many international boundaries follow physical landforms on the earth. The high Andes Mountains, for example, divide Peru from Brazil and Chile from Argentina. The Rhine River forms part of the border between France and Germany. Other boundaries, however, do not follow physical features. The long border between Canada and the western United States, drawn along the 49° N latitude line, cuts across many different landforms for thousands of miles.

Many political boundaries separate groups of people with different heritages. The border between Spain and France, for example, separates the Spanish people, with their distinctive culture and language, from the French people, who have their own traditions. In other cases, however, the boundaries are arbitrary lines that encompass several different, and often opposing, groups. Many boundaries in Africa, for example, were drawn by Europeans, who ruled much of that part of the world until the mid-1900s. Such countries often have serious difficulties because so many different groups are within their borders.

In some cases, political boundaries serve as brutal reminders of different political systems at odds with one another. The wall separating the German cities of East and West Berlin is one such reminder. Often disputes over such boundaries lead to war. In recent years boundary disputes have resulted in wars between Israel and Egypt, the People's Republic of China and India, India and Pakistan, and Iraq and Iran.

Finally, some groups of people who share the same heritage and think of themselves as a separate nation have no political boundaries that separate them from other countries. Such groups include the Armenians, who live near the Black Sea in Asia, and the Ukrainians, who are ruled by the Soviet Union. Even though many Armenians and Ukrainians want their own governments, they remain part of other countries.

## Size

A political map illustrates the variety of sizes of the countries of the world today. Some countries span continents and cover several different time zones. Others are so tiny that a person can walk across them in a single day. Geographers call such small countries **microstates** (MY·kroh·stayt).

Years ago size was a measure of a country's pride. Wars were fought to acquire more land and to add to a country's prestige. However, big does not always mean better. Large countries are more likely to have a large workforce and an adequate supply of natural resources. Yet they face potential problems concerning food supplies, defense, transportation, communication, and political unity.

## Shape

Countries vary not only in size but also in shape. Political geographers often classify nations according to their shape, or spatial form. Two of the most common classifications they use are compact nations and fragmented nations.

**Compact nations.** As the term suggests, **compact nations** have generally round or rectangular shapes and land areas not separated by large bodies of water or by the territory of other countries. In a compact nation all points on the country's borders lie about the same distance from the geographic center of the country. This makes communication and transportation easier. Examples of compact nations include Poland, Uruguay, and Kenya.

**Fragmented nations.** Geographers classify nations that have land areas that are geographically separated from other parts of the country as **fragmented nations.** New Zealand, which occupies several islands in the South Pacific, is one example of a fragmented nation. Other examples include Italy, Indonesia, and Japan. Alaska and Hawaii, which are geographically separated from the rest of the United States, make it a fragmented nation.

Fragmented shapes make communication and transportation more difficult than in compact nations. In fact, some fragmented nations have had such serious breakdowns in communication that they eventually divided into two or more countries. East and West Pakistan, for example, originally were part of the same country. Communication and government administration were difficult because the two parts of the country were thousands of miles apart, separated by India. Finally, in 1971 the people of East Pakistan revolted and formed their own nation—Bangladesh.

## Types of Government

Each of the 160 nations of the world has its own form of government. Although each is unique, the governments of the world may be placed in general categories according to organization and power.

**Organization.** Organization rates as one of the most important characteristics of a government. A key question to consider when studying government organization is, Does the country have several levels of government, or only one?

Many countries, such as France, Spain, and Austria, have unitary governments. In a **unitary** (YOO·nuh·tehr·ee) **system,** a central government located in the national capital has the complete authority to govern.

Other countries, such as the United States, Mexico, and India, have federal governments. In a **federal system** the national government and regional, state, or local governments share the authority to govern. In the United States, for example, the national government makes laws that affect all the people. State and local governments,

*Learning from Pictures.* The Acropolis in Greece was the birthplace of Western democracy. Why is direct democracy impossible today?

however, also pass and enforce laws that affect state and local residents.

**Power.** Governments can also be categorized in terms of the exercise of power. How many people govern? Do those who do not hold office play a role in government? To answer such questions, political geographers identify two basic forms of government—dictatorship and democracy.

In a **dictatorship** (dik·TAYT·uhr·ship) one person or a select group of people exercises power. The rulers answer only to themselves, hold power by force, and attempt to eliminate all opponents. If elections are allowed, there usually is no choice of candidates because only one person is listed for each office. Authoritarian dictatorships usually exercise political control, but allow the people some freedoms in their everyday lives. Authoritarian dictatorships control several Central American governments. Totalitarian dictatorships not only exercise political control, but also attempt to control the people's economic, social, cultural, and religious lives. Examples of totalitarian dictatorships include Nazi Germany (1933–1945) and the Soviet Union.

The word *democracy* is a combination of two Greek words: *demos,* meaning "the people," and *kratos,* meaning "rule." Together they mean "rule by the people," which defines **democracy** and indicates that the people hold the power to govern.

In the earliest forms of democracy the citizens themselves ruled the government. Countries today, however, have millions of people, making direct democracy impossible. Instead the people elect representatives to exercise political power for them. This system is called representative democracy.

Almost every country claims to be a democracy. But as Abraham Lincoln stated, the major quality of democracy remains government "of the people, by the people, and for the people."

**SECTION 3 REVIEW**

1. **Define** spatial relationship, microstate, compact nation, fragmented nation, unitary system, federal system, dictatorship, democracy
2. **Summarizing Ideas** **(a)** What different purposes do political boundaries serve? **(b)** What problems can political boundaries cause?
3. **Interpreting Ideas** Why is the United States an example of a fragmented nation?
4. **Classifying Ideas** What are the two types of governmental organization?
5. **Analyzing Ideas** What is the basic difference between a dictatorship and a democracy?

## 4 World nations feature differing levels of development and differing economies.

The economic features of a country—the way it produces, distributes, and exchanges goods and services—form an important part of its cultural setting. Economic geographers study economic patterns to understand how countries meet the needs and wants of their people.

### Levels of Economic Development

The countries of the world today reflect a wide range of economic development. Some countries are highly industrialized, producing a variety of goods and services. The United States, for example, has an economy that supports agriculture, manufacturing, and a variety of service industries. Other countries have **one-crop economies** that specialize in the production of one or a very few products. Most often

**161**

agricultural products or raw materials make up these goods. Such specialization leads to instability because the whole economy depends on the world price of a single good. The Ivory Coast, for example, depends on coffee production. If the price of coffee remains high, its economy grows. If the price drops, however, the economy suffers.

The level of development of a country's economy largely depends on its **factors of production**—natural resources or raw materials, human resources or labor, and capital resources or capital. Natural resources that are especially important to a nation's economy are its fossil fuels, minerals, trees, and water. **Human resources** include a country's workers. **Capital resources** in-

clude the money, tools, equipment, and inventory used in the production process.

A country lacking any one of the factors of production finds it difficult to reach a high level of economic development. Without energy resources, for example, a country lacks the power needed to run factories. A country without a skilled workforce or technical equipment may be unable to support heavy industries.

Economic geographers divide the countries of the world into two broad categories—developed and developing nations. Each country's level of economic development forms the basis of its classification.

**Developed nations.** Highly industrialized nations with high standards of living fall into the **developed nations** category. Today only about 30 of the world's countries, or barely 25 percent of the world's people, fit this category. These nations, which include the United States, Canada, and most countries of Western and Eastern Europe, use advanced technology to make their systems of farming, manufacturing, and distribution highly productive. They also have highly skilled workers and good educational systems.

International trade accounts for much of the wealth of developed nations. They import goods they lack and goods they cannot produce as cheaply as other countries. They export surplus goods and goods they can produce more efficiently than other countries.

Developed nations offer most of their citizens adequate food, clothing, and housing. Their governments also offer such services as fire and police protection; transportation and communication systems; and schools, libraries, and museums. In general, the people have a high standard of living.

Economic geographers often use per capita gross national product to determine a country's standard of living. You can fig-

*Text continues on page 166.*

# DEVELOPING GEOGRAPHY SKILLS
## STUDYING ECONOMIC GEOGRAPHY: Reading Economic Maps

• Where are the major mineral deposits in the United States located?
• Where are the nation's major manufacturing centers?

You can find the information to answer these questions on economic maps. An economic map is a special-purpose map that shows information about land use, resource distribution, types of agriculture, products, trade, and other economic topics. In this textbook these economic maps are subtitled, "Economic Activity."

### How to Interpret an Economic Map

To effectively interpret an economic map, follow these guidelines.

1. **Read the map.** Review the guidelines for reading a map listed in the skill lesson on page 44.
2. **Pay special attention to the symbols.** Study the key to understand the economic information given by the map's symbols.
3. **Note important relationships.** Study all the data on the map. Observe how distributions of economic activities and other data on the map relate.
4. **Use the map's information in critical thinking.** Ask yourself, "Why does that take place there?" Draw conclusions about economic activities.

### Applying the Skill

Study the map at the right. Note that the title, "SOUTH AMERICA: Economic Activity," tells you that it contains economic information about South America.

The key shows that colors are used to identify the locations of such land uses as farming, grazing, and manufacturing. By closely studying the map you can determine how land throughout South America is used. The key also shows what symbols

mark the locations of economic activities such as fishing and drilling. Type giving the names of specific products shows where they are located or produced.

*To practice this skill, see Practicing Geography Skills on page 169.*

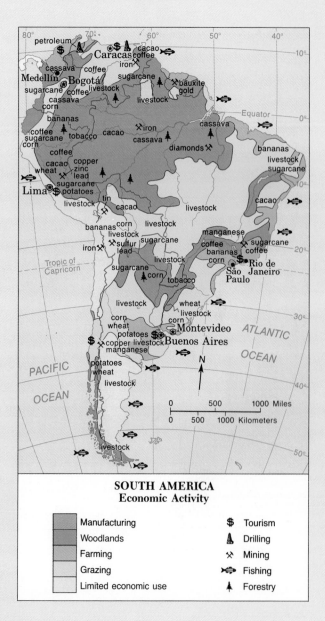

**SOUTH AMERICA**
**Economic Activity**

Manufacturing
Woodlands
Farming
Grazing
Limited economic use

$ Tourism
⚒ Drilling
⚒ Mining
🐟 Fishing
🌲 Forestry

# DEVELOPED AND DEVELOPING

## PHYSICAL AREA

The size of each nation reflects its actual size compared with the total land surface of the earth.

Developed nation
Developing nation

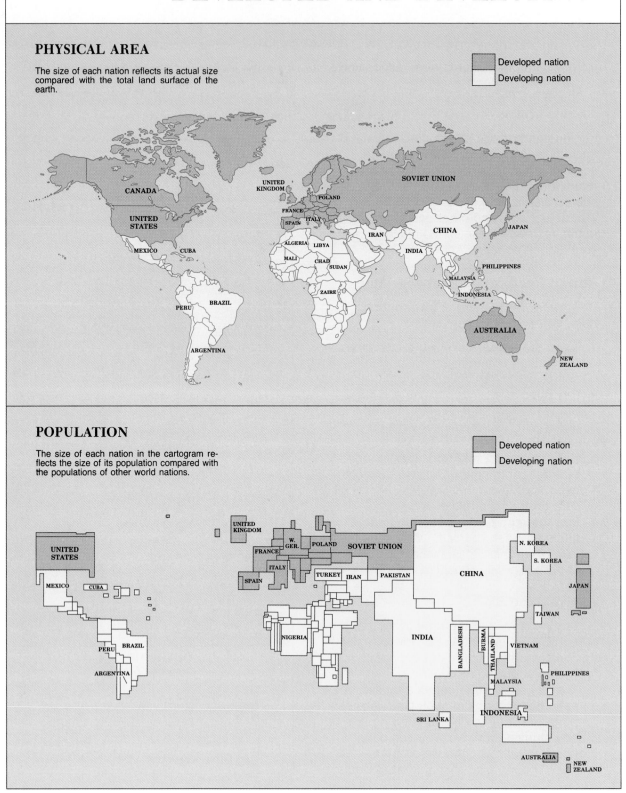

## POPULATION

The size of each nation in the cartogram reflects the size of its population compared with the populations of other world nations.

Developed nation
Developing nation

# NATIONS OF THE WORLD

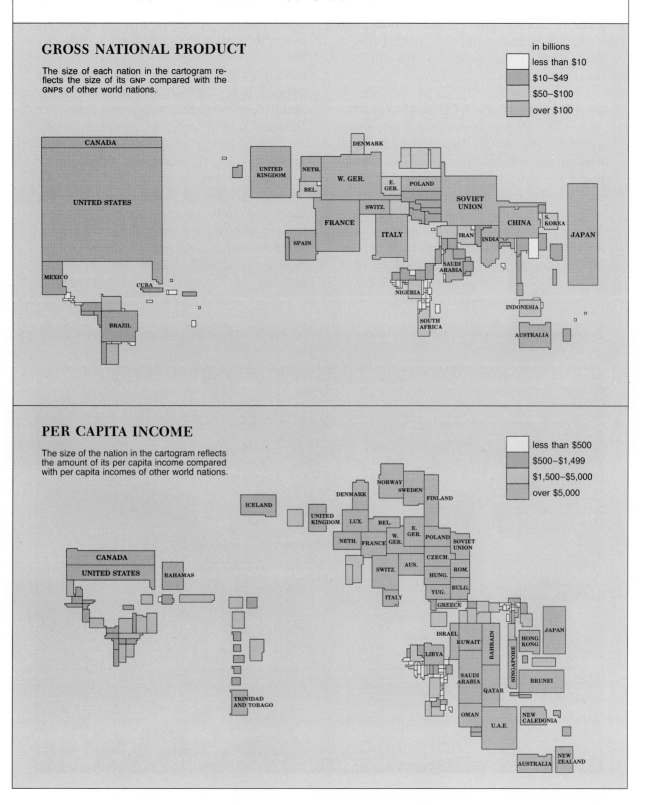

## GROSS NATIONAL PRODUCT

The size of each nation in the cartogram reflects the size of its GNP compared with the GNPS of other world nations.

in billions

- less than $10
- $10–$49
- $50–$100
- over $100

## PER CAPITA INCOME

The size of the nation in the cartogram reflects the amount of its per capita income compared with per capita incomes of other world nations.

- less than $500
- $500–$1,499
- $1,500–$5,000
- over $5,000

ure **per capita gross national product,** or per capita GNP, by dividing the total dollar value of all goods and services produced in a country by the number of people living in the country. The per capita GNPs of developed nations tend to be high.

**Developing nations.** Economists classify more than 130 countries of the world today as developing nations. **Developing nations** feature agricultural economies and traditional life styles. These countries have little or no industry. Some lack the energy resources to power factories. Others lack money to develop the resources they have. As a result, developing nations must depend on the countries of the developed world to satisfy all or part of their needs and wants.

The per capita GNPs of developing nations tend to be low. Although some developing nations have several large cities, overcrowding, inadequate housing and sanitation, and unemployment present serious problems. Most of the people in developing nations live in rural parts of the country and depend on subsistence agriculture. The **literacy** (LIHT·uh·ruh·see) **rate,** or the percentage of people who can read and write, is low. Usually, there are few workers with specialized training.

Most developing nations have high birth rates and declining death rates. As a result, their populations grow rapidly. Often, developing nations cannot feed, educate, or care for their people. In Ethiopia and Bangladesh, for example, the growing popula-

*Learning from Pictures.* *This market scene characterizes the traditional life style of an agricultural economy. How many countries are classified as developing nations?*

tion strains resources and contributes to the outbreak of famines.

## Types of Economic Systems

The countries of the world have a wide variety of economic systems. Although unique, each system can be placed in one of two general categories: traditional economies and mixed economies.

**Traditional economies.** In a **traditional economy** customs, habits, laws, and religious beliefs that were developed by the society long ago form the basis of economic activities. The same goods and services are produced in the same ways as they have been for centuries. Farming supports most traditional economies, which still exist in parts of Latin America, Africa, Asia, and the Middle East. For example, the Dinka of central Africa still herd their cattle and grow their crops on the plains of southern Sudan as they have for generations.

**Mixed economies.** Economists list most of the world's economies as mixed economies. **Mixed economies** combine a variety of methods to produce, distribute, and exchange goods and services.

Economists classify mixed economies according to the degree of control that the government exercises. Under **capitalism** individuals and private corporations own most of the businesses. The government provides some regulation, but its intervention is limited. A Scottish economist named Adam Smith first outlined the principles of capitalism in *An Inquiry into the Nature and Causes of the Wealth of Nations*, published in 1776.

Because individuals remain free to own and operate businesses, exchange goods and services, and seek jobs of their own choosing, capitalist systems are often called **free enterprise systems.** Today examples of capitalist economies include the economies of the United States and Japan.

Under **socialism** (SOH·shuh·liz·uhm) the government owns or controls the means of production to varying degrees. Under **authoritarian** (ah·thar·uh·TER·ee·uhn) **socialism,** or **communism** (KAM·yuh·niz·uhm), the government owns almost all of the businesses and controls the entire economy. This economic plan was first described by a German philosopher named Karl Marx in *The Communist Manifesto*, published in 1848. The Soviet Union and Cuba have Communist economies today.

In between capitalism and authoritarian socialism is **democratic socialism.** In this system the government owns many businesses but individuals maintain basic human rights and control over economic planning through the election of government officials. Democratic socialism guides the economies of Britain, Sweden, West Germany, and many other countries of Western Europe.

---

**SECTION 4 REVIEW**

1. **Define** one-crop economy, factor of production, human resource, capital resource, developed nation, per capita gross national product, developing nation, literacy rate, traditional economy, mixed economy, capitalism, free enterprise system, socialism, authoritarian socialism, communism, democratic socialism

2. **Classifying Ideas** (a) What two categories describe the levels of economic development of the nations of the world? (b) What are the characteristics of each?

3. **Analyzing Ideas** What hampers economic growth in developing nations?

4. **Organizing Ideas** How do economists classify mixed economies?

# CHAPTER 7 REVIEW

## Chapter Summary

The following list contains the key concepts you have learned about cultural patterns.

1. Cultural geographers divide cultural characteristics into material culture—all of the objects that people make—and nonmaterial culture—ideas such as language and religion.
2. As a country industrializes, it goes through four stages of demographic transition.
3. Nearly all of the 5 billion inhabitants of the earth live on about 10 percent of the earth's land surface.
4. Even though migration does not add to world population, it does change the population of specific regions or countries.
5. Thomas Malthus predicted that population growth would eventually outpace the food supply, resulting in starvation.
6. Many different languages and religions are a part of the cultural landscape. Geographers divide the earth into cultural regions according to various aspects of the cultural landscape.
7. The more than 160 nations of the world have different sizes, shapes, and types of governmental organization.
8. Governments may be organized as unitary or federal. Depending on who exercises power, governments may be classified as dictatorships or democracies.
9. The world is divided into developed, or industrial, nations and developing, or nonindustrial, nations.
10. Most of the economic systems of the world, including capitalist and socialist systems, are classified as mixed economies.

On a separate sheet of paper, complete the following review exercises.

## Reviewing Geographic Terms

Match each of the following terms with the correct definition.

a. democracy
b. capital
c. physiological density
d. unitary government
e. fragmented nation
f. immigration
g. nonmaterial culture
h. demographer
i. per capita GNP
j. culture

____ 1. Number of people per square mile (square kilometer) of cultivated land
____ 2. Scientist who studies population trends
____ 3. Movement of people into a country
____ 4. Country in which part of the territory is geographically isolated from other areas of the country
____ 5. System in which a central government has complete authority to govern
____ 6. Measure of wealth obtained by dividing the total dollar value of all goods and services produced in a country by the number of people living in the country
____ 7. Money, tools, machinery, equipment, and inventory used in the production process
____ 8. Sum of what a human group acquires through living together, including knowledge, skills, customs, and life styles
____ 9. Ideas of a society
____ 10. Government in which the people control the power

## Developing Critical Thinking Skills

1. **Analyzing Ideas**  What do the patterns of population density in a country reveal about its people?
2. **Interpreting Ideas**  Why is a country's physiological density often more helpful in describing population patterns than its arithmetic density?
3. **Evaluating Ideas**  (a) Why was Malthus called the "Population Prophet"?  (b) What new ideas did he suggest?  (c) Why do geographers still debate his opinions?

4. **Analyzing Charts**   Refer to the chart on page 157. What language is the world's most widely spoken?
5. **Using Map Skills**   Study the maps (cartograms) on pages 164–65.  **(a)** What relationship do you see between per capita income and the classification of countries as developed or developing nations?  **(b)** Cite two specific examples from the maps to support your opinions.
6. **Contrasting Ideas**   What are the basic differences between  **(a)** traditional and mixed,  **(b)** capitalist and socialist, and  **(c)** Communist and democratic socialist economic systems?
7. **Writing About Geography**   In two clearly written paragraphs, discuss one of the following ideas.  **(a)** What are the components of population growth?  **(b)** What has been the influence of cultural diffusion on language and religion?

## Using Primary Sources

In the following excerpt from *The Law of Population*, Annie Besant quotes English economist Thomas Malthus on the relationship between the food supply and population growth. As you study the reading, consider the population problems in the world today.

"The ultimate check to population appears to be a want of food. . . . But this ultimate check is never the immediate check, except in cases of actual famine. The immediate check may be stated to consist in all those customs and all those diseases, which seem to be generated by a [lack] of . . . [food]; and all those causes, independent of this [lack], whether of a moral or physical nature, which tend [early] to weaken and destroy the human frame." These causes which retard the growth of population by killing human beings, either slowly or rapidly, are all classed together by Malthus under the head of "positive" checks; they are the "natural" checks to population, common alike to vegetables, to animals, to [people].

1. What is the ultimate check to population?
2. What is the immediate check to population growth?

## Practicing Geography Skills

*Before completing this activity, review Developing Geography Skills on page 163.*

**Interpreting Maps**   Study the map entitled "The World: Land Use and Economic Activity" in the Atlas on pages 6–7. Then answer the following questions.

1. What is the main land use in  **(a)** Australia,  **(b)** Eastern Europe,  **(c)** Indonesia, and  **(d)** western South America?
2. Where in  **(a)** South America,  **(b)** Western Europe, and  **(c)** SubSaharan Africa have oil deposits been tapped?  **(d)** How can you tell?
3. In a sentence or two, make a general statement about land use in the northern parts of Canada and the Soviet Union.
4. **(a)** Is fishing a more important economic activity in the low (0–30), middle (31–60), or high (61–90) latitudes?  **(b)** Why might this be true?

## Exploring Geography

Research the various technological developments and medical breakthroughs that, in one way or another, contributed to population growth in the past. Then construct a time line showing these developments and breakthroughs. Use your time line as the basis for a brief oral presentation explaining to the rest of the class how the developments and breakthroughs you noted contributed to population growth.

# Patterns of Urbanization

# PUTTING THE CHAPTER IN FOCUS

Cities originated more than 8,000 years ago when the development of agriculture freed groups of people from the need to search for food on a daily basis. In the 1700s and 1800s cities began growing more rapidly. Over the years they have continued to grow. Today cities serve as a focal point of the earth's cultural setting.

## Ideas to Understand

In studying about patterns of urbanization, use these ideas to give direction to your reading.

1 The development of agriculture made cities possible.
2 Cities today serve many functions.
3 More people than ever before now live in urban areas.
4 Modern cities are organized into four distinct zones.

## Terms to Define

The following terms are some of the key terms in the chapter. Defining them will help you understand patterns of urbanization.

| | |
|---|---|
| city | central place |
| nomad | service area |
| specialization of labor | suburb |
| | primate city |
| site | urbanization |
| situation | metropolitan area |

## Places to Locate

Locating the following places will add to your knowledge of geography.

| | |
|---|---|
| Athens | Rotterdam |
| Beijing | Montreal |
| Donetsk | Canberra |
| Nashville | Brasilia |

## 1 The development of agriculture made cities possible.

**Cities,** centers of population, came into being after early people made one of the greatest of all discoveries—that it was possible to obtain food by planting crops. This discovery freed many members of the population from the drudgery of hunting and gathering and allowed them to spend their time building, crafting, teaching, and performing many other tasks.

### The First Human Settlements

Before the development of farming many early people were **nomads** (NOH·mads), always on the move hunting game and gathering food that grew wild. These hunters and gatherers were at the mercy of nature. If their numbers became too large, or if the animals that they hunted and the wild foods that they gathered were in short supply, some starved. Once the food supply in one place was used up, the group had to move on or go hungry.

About 10,000 years ago, in the Middle East, India, Southeast Asia, and China, people discovered that they could raise their own food by planting and cultivating the foods that they had previously gathered. As their knowledge of **agriculture** (AG·rih·kuhl·chuhr)—the art and science of farming—increased, people found that they could grow enough food to meet their needs. No longer were they forced to search for food. This meant that they could build permanent settlements. Over hundreds of years these settlements developed into cities.

◀ *Vancouver, British Columbia, harbor at twilight*

171

Scholars believe that the first cities developed about 8,000 years ago in the Tigris–Euphrates (yoo·FRAY·tees) River Valley, where farmers learned to grow surpluses of food. These surpluses meant that it was no longer necessary for all the people to devote all of their energy to growing food. Instead some people could work at other tasks, such as making tools or weaving cloth. Dividing tasks among workers is called **specialization of labor.**

The first cities were actually tiny villages. Over time some of these villages grew larger and larger, eventually becoming great cities. Yet even the greatest cities of the past, such as Athens, Greece, and Beijing (BAYZ·ing), China, would not be considered large today. They included no more than 100,000 people. Today many cities have populations in the millions.

## Cities and Industrialization

During the 1700s and 1800s machine power began to replace human power as the major source of labor. This process, known as **industrialization** (in·duhs·tree·uh·luh·ZAY·shuhn), encouraged the growth of business. New industries sprang up everywhere.

Industrialization encouraged the growth of cities. Factory-made farm tools helped farmers raise more food with fewer workers. In time unemployed farm workers left the fields in search of work. Many found new jobs in factories, which were being built near energy sources. Cities developed near the factories to meet the needs of the growing numbers of factory workers.

Some of the earliest American industrial cities, such as Paterson, New Jersey, and Lowell, Massachusetts, grew up in the shadows of factories powered by water energy. When coal replaced water power as an energy source, other industrial cities sprang up near coal fields. Some of the largest were Birmingham in Britain, Essen in West Germany, Pittsburgh in the United States, and Donetsk (duh·NETSK) in the Soviet Union.

Newer technologies, especially long-distance transmissions of electricity and movements of oil and natural gas by pipelines and tankers, had an enormous impact on the development of cities. These changes freed cities from their close ties to energy sources. New industrial cities quickly arose and older industrial cities either adapted to the changing conditions or declined in importance.

## Site and Situation

The first cities grew in areas with fertile land and a climate favorable for farming—place characteristics. Later, cities sprang up close to factories powered by nearby energy sources—an example of the importance of relative location. These two geographic themes, place and location, illustrate two very important concepts concerning cities—site and situation.

Urban geographers use the term **site** to describe the physical features of the place that a city occupies. A city, for example, may be located along the banks of a river, in the middle of a vast plain, or at the foothills of a mountain. Its land may be covered by hard clay or rich soil. Climate also makes up part of a city's site.

Years ago one of the most important features of a city's site was its defensibility. A city located in a valley protected by high mountains was much more desirable than one on the open plains where it was defenseless against attack. Today, however, geographers view a city's site somewhat differently. The high mountains that once protected a city from invaders may restrict air circulation, adding to pollution problems. When studying a city's site, urban geographers consider both the advantages and disadvantages of a location's physical features.

While the term site describes a city's place characteristics, the term **situation** describes its relative location. Is the city located near agricultural activity? Does traffic flow through the city, bringing business to storeowners, or does a major highway carry traffic around and away from the city? Such questions that concern a city's situation are important to every city and may even determine whether or not a city will thrive.

*Text continues on page 175.*

***Learning from Maps.*** *Rome has been a major world city for over 2,000 years. What date was St. Peter's Basilica constructed?*

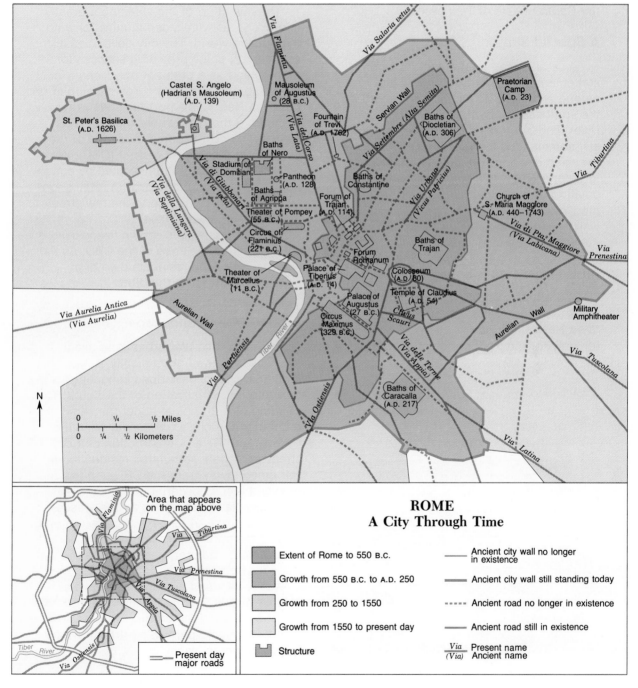

**ROME**
**A City Through Time**

Extent of Rome to 550 B.C.

Growth from 550 B.C. to A.D. 250

Growth from 250 to 1550

Growth from 1550 to present day

Structure

Ancient city wall no longer in existence

Ancient city wall still standing today

Ancient road no longer in existence

Ancient road still in existence

*Via* Present name
(Via) Ancient name

Present day major roads

Area that appears on the map above

**173**

In 1775 settlers from North Carolina founded Nashville on land they had acquired from the Cherokee Indians. The settlers wanted to build a trading post to serve the Central Basin of Tennessee.

## A Special Site

Several environmental factors favored settlement at the Nashville site. Chief among them was its location on a bluff on the southeastern bank of the Cumberland River. The bluff was high above flood levels, commanded a sweeping view of the river and surrounding areas, and was easy to defend. The site also benefited from its position on a navigable river feeding into the Ohio and Mississippi rivers, a large saltwater spring, and a freshwater spring within the walls of the fort.

## An Unpromising Situation Improves

At the time of settlement more than 200 miles (320 kilometers) of wilderness separated Nashville from the nearest town. Fortunately for the frontier community, wealthy

*A southeastern railroad hub*

cotton planters soon settled nearby. The town quickly grew into a service center for surrounding farms and a trading center for cotton farmers.

The invention of the steamboat greatly improved Nashville's communication with the outside world. The city developed both as a central place providing services for farmers and as a break-of-bulk center for incoming and outgoing cargoes shipped on the river. Nashville's port facilities were built along the river where the bluff was lowest. The port became the focus of the city's central business district (CBD). Warehouses and office buildings used by cotton merchants were built nearby. A retail shopping district grew up along the few streets in the CBD that were level.

Most of Nashville's early citizens lived within walking distance of the CBD. As the city grew, wealthy residents paid high prices for houses on the bluff.

## A New Urban Landscape

After the Civil War urban land use in Nashville changed dramatically. A new industrial district developed, reflecting the increasing industrialization of the South. The building of railroads at about the same time redirected the city's trade away from the Cumberland River. Construction of a city streetcar system stimulated residential development away from the CBD and the crowded lands bordering the river.

Today Nashville serves as Tennessee's capital and one of its largest cities, second only to Memphis. More people now work in government and manufacturing than in services for farmers.

Nashville also has become known as "Music City, U.S.A." More than 180 recording companies, 23 recording studios, and about 450 music-publishing firms have their headquarters in Nashville.

## SECTION 1 REVIEW

1. **Define** city, nomad, agriculture, specialization of labor, industrialization, site, situation
2. **Locate** Tigris–Euphrates River Valley, Athens, Beijing, Donetsk
3. **Summarizing Ideas** What discovery led to the beginning of cities?
4. **Analyzing Ideas** How did industrialization encourage the growth of cities?
5. **Seeing Relationships** Describe the site and situation of your city or a city nearby.

## 2 Cities today serve many functions.

From the earliest times cities of all sizes have served many of the same functions. Even the smallest city serves as the **central place,** or the location of specialized activities and services, for the area around it. This surrounding area is called the **service area.** Service areas vary greatly in size.

Though every city acts as the central place for an area, many have taken on distinctive characteristics. Some cities serve as transportation hubs, for example, while others act as centers of trade or as cultural centers. Today we recognize many cities by the special functions that they provide. Among the most important functions of cities are as transportation, manufacturing, commercial, and administrative centers. Keep in mind, however, that most cities serve several functions at the same time.

### Transportation Centers

Many of the world's largest cities act as **break-of-bulk centers** where workers transfer goods from one form of transportation to another. Seaports are one kind of break-of-bulk center. In seaports, workers transfer goods from oceangoing ships to land-based or river-based transportation. Rotterdam, Netherlands; Yokohama, near Tokyo, Japan; and New York City rank among the world's largest seaports.

Lake and river ports also serve as break-of-bulk centers. Workers in Chicago, a major port on the Great Lakes, transfer goods from ships on Lake Michigan and distribute them to a wide area over a large network of roads and rail lines. Other break-of-bulk cities such as Cincinnati, Ohio; Kinshasa, Zaire; and Montreal, Canada have developed along rivers where waterfalls or shallows interrupt navigation.

A second kind of transportation center develops at **transportation hubs,** where road, rail, river, or air routes cross. Two cities in Missouri—St. Louis, located on the Mississippi River, and Kansas City, located on the Missouri River—developed where travelers arriving on early road and rail routes boarded river vessels. Salt Lake City,

*Learning from Pictures.* Hong Kong harbor is one of the world's busiest ports. The harbor illustrates what important function of cities?

175

A visitor to a large city often feels that the entire area is under reconstruction. New buildings constantly replace old ones. Sewer lines, water lines, and gas and electric lines are continually dug up, repaired, and replaced. Streets are closed to be repaved or are turned into pedestrian malls between rows of stores. And throughout the city, traffic patterns are continually changed to ease the flow of traffic.

All of these changes, and many more, are the work of urban planners. Urban planners are problem solvers who tackle the challenges of today's modern cities. They carry out their work using many different approaches.

Urban planners may be researchers seeking specific data to complete a traffic plan. Or they may be historians checking old maps of city sites or street plans because, in spite of dramatic changes in the urban landscape, a city's past influences its present. Urban planners may be educators, trying to show both politicians and the public how their ideas will work. And perhaps above all, they may be politicians who influence their city through its government.

Students thinking about a career in urban planning must be sensitive to the environment and to history. They must enjoy analyzing complex problems and developing imaginative solutions to these problems. And they must truly enjoy working with people, because much of their contact with people is in a highly charged political situation. If these qualities appeal to you, you might want to consider a career in urban planning.

Atlanta, and Dallas began as transportation hubs. Other such hubs include Frankfurt, West Germany; and Shanghai, in the People's Republic of China.

## Manufacturing Centers

Many of the world's largest cities serve as manufacturing centers—cities with industries that produce goods. The growth of manufacturing centers depends on access to resources, labor, and markets.

Support industries often develop in the larger manufacturing centers. In mining areas, for example, miners work in the mines while other workers run the plants that reduce the thousands of tons of ore to smaller amounts of a valuable metal such as gold, silver, or copper. Johannesburg, South Africa, serves as a mining and processing center for gold and other minerals. Large oil-refining operations center in Houston, Texas.

While many of the world's largest cities serve as manufacturing centers, some manufacturing cities remain quite small. In addition, the size of any manufacturing city can change dramatically over a short period of time. When prices for their products are high, manufacturing cities grow rapidly. But they lose population just as rapidly when prices decline.

Some cities even disappear. Cities centered on raw material production become ghost towns when supplies of a nonrenewable resource on which they depend are used up or are no longer needed. In the 1950s, for example, 2,000 people lived and worked in Cobalt, Oregon, a town that sprang up near a large cobalt mine. By the 1980s the mine had closed and all of the people had moved away.

## Commercial Centers

Commercial centers focus on the buying, selling, and trading of products. Even the smallest city has a few businesses that sell goods or services to residents. Cities that grow to depend on selling goods and services as their primary function are known as commercial centers.

Most commercial centers sell a variety of different products to residents. Even small commercial centers have businesses such as grocery stores, pharmacies, clothing stores, restaurants, and so on. They also have doctors, lawyers, and bankers, who offer essential services to residents. A commercial center also might carry other products if there is a special need in a certain area. Commercial cities near large farming areas, for example, have stores that sell farmers the seed and fertilizer they need. Such cities also have grain elevators, warehouses, and stockyards to store and sell farm products.

As commercial centers grow larger, they offer a greater variety of products. Only the very largest cities, however, have theaters, ballet and opera companies, stock exchanges, specialized import and export firms, international airports, and other specialized businesses. Because people do not need such services on a daily basis, the cities' specialized businesses and services need to draw customers from a very large service area in order to be profitable.

## Administrative Centers

Cities that provide special administrative, or management, services are known as administrative centers. Capital cities and cities with military bases, large universities, colleges, or other institutions fit this category.

Seats of government serve as the largest administrative centers. National capitals have service areas covering whole coun-

**Learning from Pictures.** *The Texas Capitol at Austin is the largest state capitol building. What is the chief function of capital cities?*

tries. Depending on the country and the form of government, other cities such as provincial or state capitals and county seats also serve as administrative centers.

Because centers of government always attract settlers, Australia and Brazil decided to build their national capitals in isolated inland areas that they wanted to develop. The population of Canberra, the Australian capital, grew from 85,800 in 1967 to 264,300 in 1984. Brasilia's population soared from 120,000 in 1960 to 1,576,000 in 1985.

---

### SECTION 2 REVIEW

1. **Define** central place, service area, break-of-bulk center, transportation hub
2. **Locate** Nashville, Rotterdam, Montreal, Canberra, Brasilia
3. **Organizing Ideas** What are the four most important functions of cities?
4. **Interpreting Ideas** How do the goods and services offered by commercial centers change as the center grows larger?

*Text continues on page 179.*

# DEVELOPING GEOGRAPHY SKILLS
## WRITING ABOUT GEOGRAPHY: Summarizing Information

This textbook introduces the subject of geography. In learning about geography, however, it is not important to remember every word you read. As you read, your mind identifies the main ideas (see the skill lesson on page 117). It then notes the supporting details. In short, your mind summarizes the information presented. You should follow the same steps in writing a summary.

A summary highlights the main points about a certain topic. Minor points are usually excluded because the purpose of a summary is to bring out main points.

### How to Summarize Information

Follow these guidelines in writing summaries.

1. **Identify main ideas.** As you read material to be summarized, note the main ideas (see the skill lesson on page 117). Also note all important supporting evidence.
2. **Use your own words.** Restate the main ideas in your own words. Using your own words helps you understand the main ideas. (If you have trouble stating the ideas in your own words, reread the material until you feel you understand and can restate it.)
3. **Recognize relationships.** Think in broad terms. Write a list of the main ideas. Look for main ideas that are related and state that relationship as a broad topic. Link all the main ideas to broader topics. Identify a general idea that links all the main ideas and use this idea as your first sentence.

### Applying the Skill

The following excerpt is from page 171 of this textbook. Key sentences have been underlined. Read the excerpt as a whole. Then reread only the underlined sentences.

Before the development of farming many early people were nomads, always on the move hunting game and gathering food that grew wild. These hunters and gatherers were at the mercy of nature. If their numbers became too large, or if the animals that they hunted and the wild foods that they gathered were in short supply, some starved. Once the food supply in one place was used up, the group had to move on or go hungry.

About 10,000 years ago, in the Middle East, India, Southeast Asia, and China, people discovered that they could raise their own food by planting and cultivating the foods that they had previously gathered. As their knowledge of agriculture—the art and science of farming—increased, people found that they could grow enough food to meet their needs. No longer were they forced to search for food. This meant that they could build permanent settlements. Over hundreds of years these settlements developed into cities.

The following paragraph is a summary of the excerpt. In it the underlined sentences have been restated.

Before the development of farming early people constantly had to search for food. They moved whenever food sources got too low. About 10,000 years ago people discovered that they could control their food supplies by planting and cultivating plants. Because they no longer had to move in search of food, they could build permanent settlements.

*To practice this skill, see Practicing Geography Skills on page 187.*

## 3 More people than ever before now live in urban areas.

Cities are unevenly distributed over the earth's land surfaces. Some areas have so many cities that it is difficult to tell where one city stops and another starts. Other areas have no cities at all—only miles and miles of uninhabited land.

Geographers classify towns and cities as **urban areas,** from the Latin word *urbs,* meaning "city." Places outside cities are classified as **rural areas,** a term borrowed from the Latin word for "countryside." Today modern forms of transportation often blur the distinctions between urban and rural areas. Automobiles, buses, subways, and trains allow people to live in **suburbs,** or communities just outside the cities, and travel to work in the city each day. Sometimes city boundaries expand so that a suburb falls within a city's limits. More often suburbs choose to keep their political independence while benefiting from their strong ties to nearby cities.

Just as the distribution of cities varies widely, so do their spatial patterns. Many regions, for example, have several large cities of a similar size. Other regions have one city that is so much larger than any other that it dominates the region. Geographers call such a city a **primate city.** Mexico City, with a projected population of 30 million by the year 2000, is a primate city. So too is Moscow, which is more than twice as large as any other city in the Soviet Union.

### Urbanization Today

**Urbanization,** or the large-scale movement of people from rural to urban areas, characterizes modern industrial societies. But levels of urbanization vary greatly from country to country. In the United States 74 percent of the people now live in urban areas, up from 51 percent in 1920 and 40 percent in 1900. At the same time the number of American farmers has steadily declined from 40 percent of the population in 1890 to less than 4 percent today. The chart below compares urbanization in 10 countries of the world today, including the United States.

Cities grow rapidly today. London, the capital of Britain and the world's largest city for many years, did not reach 1 million inhabitants until 1800. Today 16 cities in the world have more people than London and some 200 cities have more than 1 million people.

The graph on page 182 lists the world's 20 largest cities according to the size of

*Text continues on page 182.*

**Learning from Graphs.** *Modern farming methods allow more people to live in cities. What percentage of Japan's population is urbanized?*

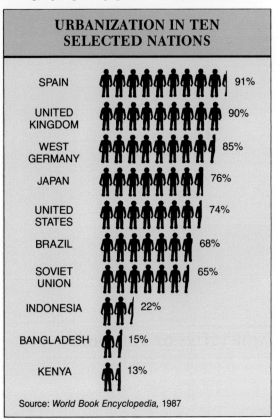

**URBANIZATION IN TEN SELECTED NATIONS**

| | |
|---|---|
| SPAIN | 91% |
| UNITED KINGDOM | 90% |
| WEST GERMANY | 85% |
| JAPAN | 76% |
| UNITED STATES | 74% |
| BRAZIL | 68% |
| SOVIET UNION | 65% |
| INDONESIA | 22% |
| BANGLADESH | 15% |
| KENYA | 13% |

Source: *World Book Encyclopedia,* 1987

**MAJOR CITIES OF THE WORLD**

ARCTIC OCEAN

Arctic Circle

EUROPE

• Stockholm
Glasgow •
• Copenhagen • Leningrad
North • Moscow • Gor'kiy
Birmingham • Sea • Minsk
London • • Berlin • Warsaw • Kharkov
Paris • • Budapest • Kiev
Milan • • Bucharest
Barcelona • • Rome • Istanbul • Black Sea
Lisbon • • Madrid • Athens • Ankara • Baku
Algiers • Tunis • Mediterranean Sea • Beirut • Damascus • Tehran
Casablanca • • Tripoli • Alexandria • Baghdad • Kabul
• Cairo • Amman
• Riyadh

ASIA

• Novosibirsk

• Tashkent

Shenyang • • Harbin
Beijing • • P'yongyang
Tianjin • • Seoul • Kyoto • Tokyo
Xi'an • • Pusan • Osaka
Chengdu • • Nanjing
• Chongqing • Wuhan • Shanghai
• Delhi • Guangzhou • Taipei
• Karachi • Dacca • Hong Kong
Ahmadabad • • Calcutta • Hanoi
• Bombay • South China Sea
Arabian Sea • Hyderabad • Rangoon • Manila
• Madras • Bangkok • Philippine Sea
• Ho Chi Minh City

AFRICA
Red Sea

Abidjan • • Lagos
Addis Ababa •

• Nairobi

• Singapore

• Kinshasa
Luanda •

ATLANTIC OCEAN

INDIAN OCEAN

Jakarta • 
• Surabaya

Equator

PACIFIC OCEAN

• Harare

AUSTRALIA

• Johannesburg

N

Cape Town •

• Sydney
Melbourne •

0    1000    2000 Miles
0   1000   2000 Kilometers

20°   0°   20°   40°   60°   80°   100°   120°   140°   160°   180°

ANTARCTICA

**181**

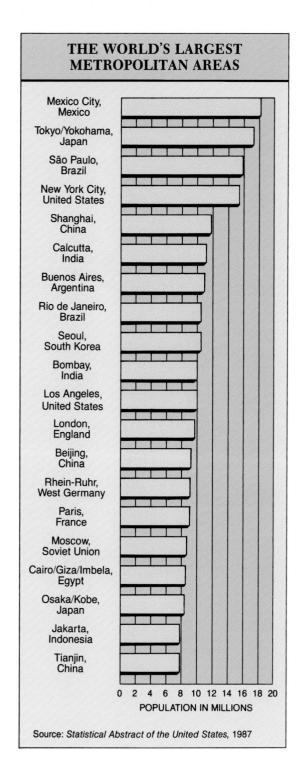

## THE WORLD'S LARGEST METROPOLITAN AREAS

Mexico City, Mexico

Tokyo/Yokohama, Japan

São Paulo, Brazil

New York City, United States

Shanghai, China

Calcutta, India

Buenos Aires, Argentina

Rio de Janeiro, Brazil

Seoul, South Korea

Bombay, India

Los Angeles, United States

London, England

Beijing, China

Rhein-Ruhr, West Germany

Paris, France

Moscow, Soviet Union

Cairo/Giza/Imbela, Egypt

Osaka/Kobe, Japan

Jakarta, Indonesia

Tianjin, China

0  2  4  6  8  10  12  14  16  18  20
POPULATION IN MILLIONS

Source: *Statistical Abstract of the United States*, 1987

***Learning from Graphs.*** *Metropolitan areas include the populations of world cities beyond city boundaries. What is the population of Mexico City?*

their metropolitan areas. A **metropolitan area** includes both the city proper, or the area within a city's boundaries, and the dependent smaller cities and suburbs. Because it includes the people who live near a city and use its services, a metropolitan area often provides a more meaningful measure of a city's size than the city proper.

## Differing Definitions

The countries of the world define the terms urban area, rural area, and metropolitan area in different ways. In the United States, the United States Bureau of the Census provides the official definitions of these terms.

In 1980 the bureau classified a place with 2,500 or more inhabitants, together with the smaller places directly connected to it, as an urban area. It defined a metropolitan area as a place with a central core of at least 50,000 people. The metropolitan area includes all places that show strong economic ties to the central core. Sometimes, as in the Los Angeles–Long Beach or the Washington, D.C.–Baltimore metropolitan areas, places within the area have strong ties to more than one central core.

## Urban Land Use

City dwellers make use of urban lands in a variety of ways. They use much of the urban land area for commercial purposes—to provide goods and services. Often these goods and services are available in the city's downtown, also known as its commercial center or **central business district** (CBD). Department stores, office buildings, banks, hotels, and restaurants all characterize a CBD. Outlying business areas, especially suburban shopping centers, also may provide such goods and services.

Along with commercial businesses, industries occupy urban lands. Industries use

land both inside and around the edges of a city. Regardless of where it is located, however, almost every city has an area of industries.

Housing also occupies city land. The land taken up by apartment buildings, condominiums, and single-family homes is called residential land. Residential land use occurs in all parts of an urban area. Some people live in or close to the city center, some live near businesses and industries, and some live in the suburbs.

**SECTION 3 REVIEW**

1. **Define**  urban area, rural area, suburb, primate city, urbanization, metropolitan area, central business district
2. **Locate**  London
3. **Summarizing Ideas  (a)** In the United States, which governmental agency defines the terms urban area, rural area, and metropolitan area? **(b)** What definitions of urban area and metropolitan area were used in the 1980 census?
4. **Interpreting Ideas**  What are the major categories of urban land use?
5. **Analyzing Graphs**  What is the largest metropolitan area in Europe?

## 4 Modern cities are organized into four distinct zones.

You can easily list some of the problems that many of today's cities face: air and water pollution, traffic jams, noise, slums, crime, and many more. With all their problems, however, cities also offer residents many opportunities—theater and musical performances, museums, libraries, sports teams, and zoos.

To understand the geographic nature of the problems and opportunities of cities, it helps to examine the various parts of a city. Urban geographers divide modern cities, particularly those in the United States and Western Europe, into four major zones: the inner zone, the middle zone, the suburban zone, and the outer zone. In every city the precise shape and size of each zone differs somewhat. Even so, the general pattern remains similar to the pattern in the map below.

### The Inner Zone

The inner zone lies in the center of the city and is usually the place where the city was first settled. Often the inner zone serves as the home of the city's busy central

*Learning from Maps.*  *Modern cities have specific districts where land use differs. What is the downtown district called?*

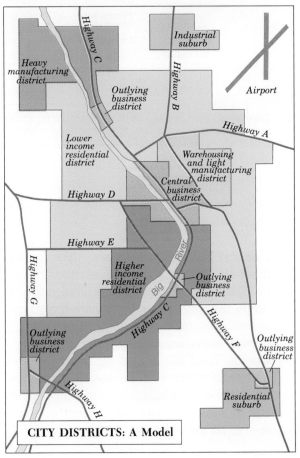

CITY DISTRICTS: A Model

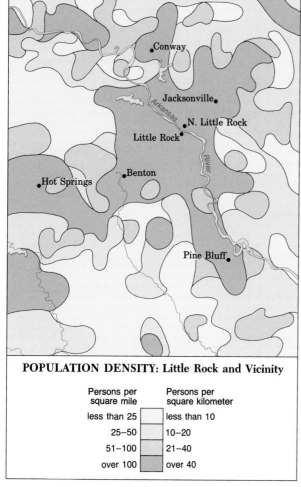

**POPULATION DENSITY: Little Rock and Vicinity**

| Persons per square mile | Persons per square kilometer |
|---|---|
| less than 25 | less than 10 |
| 25–50 | 10–20 |
| 51–100 | 21–40 |
| over 100 | over 40 |

*Learning from Maps. Many United States cities were founded along rivers. How does the population density around Little Rock reflect the process of urbanization?*

business district and contains some of the city's oldest buildings.

**Central business districts.** The central business district forms the economic core, or downtown, of most American cities. It offers the most desirable location for businesses. Central business districts typically occupy compact areas—often only a few blocks. The CBD makes up for its lack of horizontal space with its intense use of vertical space. Most buildings rise many stories and include far more square feet of space above the ground than at ground level.

**At the edges of the CBD.** An area of old and run-down buildings surrounds many central business districts. Usually low-rent apartments, warehouses, light manufacturing industries, and small offices occupy this area.

The areas on the edges of a central city were not always run-down. In the days before automobiles, areas within walking distance of the CBD were filled with the expensive homes of wealthy businesspeople. Modern transportation, however, made it possible for people to live outside the inner zone and commute to work in the CBD. Today most of a city's wealthier citizens prefer to live either in exclusive apartments in the CBD or in the suburbs.

In many cities CBDs have expanded and the decaying buildings along its edges have been torn down and replaced by new highrises funded by urban renewal projects. In many cases rents have risen and forced low-income residents to move to other parts of the city.

## The Middle Zone

In most large cities the middle zone makes up about one-third of all urban space. The middle zone of many American cities was settled by young families in the 1920s. Now elderly members of the original families make up many of the residents of the zone. Children raised there grew up and moved away long ago. As a result, many schools in the middle zone have closed and services catering to older residents are often strained.

**Middle-zone housing.** The quality of housing in the middle zone is usually mixed. Some homes remain well kept while others badly need repair. The middle zone also looks crowded because building lots are small. In addition, freeways and highways often crisscross the area. Widened residen-

tial streets that are within 10 to 20 feet (3 to 6 meters) of the front doors of many middle-zone homes serve as many of these highways. As a result, problems such as noise and air pollution plague this zone.

**Commercial development.** Stores in middle zones are typically small. Most residents shop in the CBD and depend on neighborhood stores only for groceries and other necessities. Many department stores have branches in certain areas of the middle zone. But these branches rarely carry the variety of goods available in the CBD.

## The Suburban Zone

Suburbs, when compared with the inner and middle zones, are quite new. Suburbs first appeared after World War II, when improved highways, better public transportation, and increased automobile ownership made it practical to live outside the city and commute to work.

Suburbanization largely takes place outside the political boundaries of a city. Suburbanites choose to be independent of the city for many reasons. Like a city, suburbs govern themselves. This means that suburban residents can influence how schools are run and can pass laws governing land uses within their community.

Because many suburbs lie far from the CBD, they have their own shopping districts, which often include multipurpose shopping malls. In addition, many suburbs have light manufacturing and service industries. Shopping malls and adequate services make it unnecessary for suburban residents to depend on the CBD in their daily lives.

## The Outer Zone

The outer zone of a city's metropolitan area marks the transition from urban to rural life. The transition is not abrupt. Roads lined with houses gradually change to open

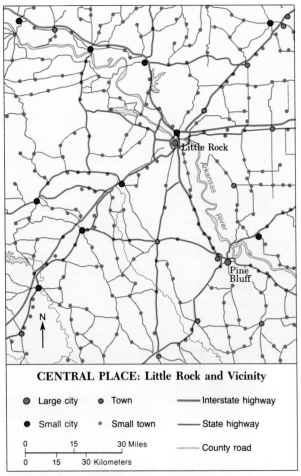

**CENTRAL PLACE: Little Rock and Vicinity**

| | | |
|---|---|---|
| ⬤ Large city | ● Town | —— Interstate highway |
| ● Small city | · Small town | —— State highway |
| | | —— County road |

0    15    30 Miles
0    15    30 Kilometers

***Learning from Maps.*** *The automobile and the building of highways changed the course of urban development. How has this affected the CBDs?*

farmland. In many places people have become alarmed as city growth has overtaken productive farmland.

**SECTION 4 REVIEW**

1. **Summarizing Ideas** **(a)** Into what four major zones do geographers often divide cities? **(b)** How do these zones differ?
2. **Evaluating Ideas** What changes made living in the suburbs popular?
3. **Analyzing Ideas** Why do suburbanites often choose to be independent of the city?

# CHAPTER 8 REVIEW

## Chapter Summary

The following list contains the key concepts you have learned about patterns of urbanization.

1. Agriculture made the development of cities possible, because people no longer had to travel constantly in search of food.
2. Industrialization encouraged the growth of cities in several important ways. As farms became more mechanized, fewer farm workers were needed. Unemployed farm workers moved to cities to find work in the rapidly growing factories. Cities grew up near the factories because workers needed to live close to their jobs.
3. Site describes the place characteristics of a city. Situation describes the city's relative location.
4. The four most important functions of cities are as transportation, manufacturing, commercial, and administrative centers. Most cities serve more than one of these functions at the same time.
5. Modern cities, spurred by industrial and commercial development, often extend over traditional city boundaries to form large metropolitan areas. Although definitions of metropolitan areas differ, today's metropolitan areas have a central core of at least 50,000 people in a city and its suburbs. All places that show strong economic ties to the central core are classified as a part of the metropolitan area.
6. Land uses in modern cities include a mixture of residential, commercial, and industrial purposes.
7. City lands are organized into four zones: the inner, middle, suburban, and outer zones. The inner zone includes the central business district and generally is located on the city's original site. Transition between urban and rural areas is not abrupt.
8. Nashville grew from a frontier settlement to become a large city. Today Nashville is the capital of Tennessee as well as "Music City, U.S.A."

On a separate sheet of paper, complete the following review exercises.

## Reviewing Geographic Terms

Supply the geographic term that correctly completes each sentence.

1. Another name for a center of population is a ___.
2. ___ is the art and science of farming.
3. Dividing tasks among farmers, merchants, metalworkers, teachers, and others is called ___ ___ ___.
4. ___ is the large-scale movement of people from rural to urban areas.
5. A ___ ___ includes both the city proper and the dependent smaller cities and suburbs nearby.
6. Goods and services are available in a city's commercial center, or ___ ___ ___.
7. Urban geographers use the term ___ to describe the physical features of the place a city occupies.
8. The term used to describe a city's relative location is ___.
9. A city that is so much larger than any other city that it dominates an area is called a ___ ___.
10. Road, rail, river, or air routes cross at a ___ ___.

## Developing Critical Thinking Skills

1. **Summarizing Ideas** (a) Where do scholars believe that the first cities developed? (b) Why did cities develop there?
2. **Seeing Relationships** How did industrialization influence the transition from largely rural to largely urban life styles?
3. **Interpreting Ideas** How did site and situation affect the growth of (a) Chicago and (b) Nashville?
4. **Comparing Ideas** How do transportation, industrial, commercial, and administrative centers differ?

5. **Classifying Ideas**   What are nonurban areas called?
6. **Evaluating Ideas**   How might decisions made in the CBDs of large cities affect the lives of people throughout the world?
7. **Writing About Geography**   In two clearly written paragraphs, discuss one of the following ideas. **(a)** Why do some cities grow into sprawling metropolitan areas, while others remain small? **(b)** How do the life styles for residents of each of the four zones of a city differ?

## Using Primary Sources

In the following excerpt from *The Living City*, Frank Lloyd Wright describes his views of the modern city. As you study the reading, consider the modern city and contrast it with Wright's views.

> Centralization — without plan — has overbuilt. Urban happiness of the properly citified citizen consists in crowding in confusion—lured by the hypnotic warmth, . . . of the crowd? The screech and mechanical uproar of the big city turns the citified head, fills citified ears — as the song of birds, wind in the trees, animal cries, or as the voices and songs of . . . loved ones once filled [the person's] heart. . . .
>
> Thus the properly citified citizen becomes a broker of profit-system ideas, a vendor of gadgetry. . . . A speculator in frailties continually dealing in the ideas and inventions of others—or become an avid spectator. This puller of levers, pusher of the buttons of vicarious power, has power . . . only by way of mechanical craft. . . .
>
> Perpetual to-and-fro excites this citified citizen, robs [the person] of deeper sympathy. . . .
>
> So exists the properly citified urbanite! Still a slave to the herd-instinct, fatally committed to vicarious power—a *slave* in any final analysis just as the medieval laborer, not so long before . . . was slave to caprice of king or state.

1. How does the author view the big city?
2. According to the author, what happens to a person in such a city?

## Practicing Geography Skills

*Before completing this activity, review Developing Geography Skills on page 178.*

**Summarizing Information**   Read the first two paragraphs of Section 4 on page 183. Then complete the following activities.

1. List the main ideas in each paragraph.
2. Write a summary of the information by restating the main ideas in your own words.

## Exploring Geography

1. Reread the information on site and situation on pages 172–73. Then use the information to write a description of the site and situation of the city where you live or the city nearest to where you live. Your report should include two paragraphs—one on the city's site, the other on its situation.
2. Study the map of Rome on page 173. Then select one of the other cities mentioned in the section and draw a map of that city. Your map should contain information that indicates the major function that the city serves. You should use resources in the school and public libraries to locate the information necessary to complete this activity.
3. Research the history of the city where you live or the city closest to where you live. Focus your research on why the city is located where it is, what conditions caused the city to grow, and how the city has dealt with urban problems over the last 25 years. Present your findings in an illustrated written report.

# UNIT 3 REVIEW

## Unit Summary

The following list contains the key concepts you have learned about the earth's cultural setting.

1. Cultural characteristics include both material culture—all of the objects that people make—and nonmaterial culture—ideas such as language and religion.
2. The 5 billion inhabitants of the earth are unevenly distributed over the earth's surface.
3. A variety of languages, religions, and other social characteristics are a part of the earth's cultural setting.
4. The nations of the world have different sizes, shapes, types of governments, levels of economic development, and economic systems.
5. Advancements in farming more than 8,000 years ago led to the development of cities.
6. With industrialization, the size and growth rates of cities have increased.
7. Both site and situation are important to the growth of cities.
8. The four most important functions of cities are as transportation, manufacturing, commercial, and administrative centers.
9. Modern cities, which are divided into inner zones, middle zones, suburbs, and outer zones, include a mixture of commercial, industrial, and residential land.

On a separate sheet of paper, complete the following review exercises.

## Checking Your Understanding

1. **(a)** What is the relationship between advances in modern technology and changes in the English language? **(b)** Cite specific examples from the textbook.
2. **(a)** What are the classifications of government according to **(a)** organization and **(b)** power? **(c)** What two classifications describe a country's level of economic development? **(d)** How are economic systems classified?
3. How do geographic features and industrialization influence the origin of the two types of transportation centers?
4. What do geographical studies indicate about the changes in central business districts from the early 1900s to the present?
5. Why did Nashville, Tennessee, become both a break-of-bulk center and a transportation hub?

## Applying Critical Thinking Skills

1. **Synthesizing Ideas** Review the four functions of cities. **(a)** Which of these functions would differ considerably between cities in countries with a unitary government and countries with a federal government? **(b)** How might the functions of cities differ in developed nations and developing nations?
2. **Synthesizing Ideas** Why do transportation centers often become cultural centers? Support your answer with specific facts from the textbook.

## Reviewing Unit Features

1. **Geography in the Workplace** What is the role of urban planners?
2. **The Geographic Web** What are the two main reasons that the problem of trash will not go away?

## Using Map Skills

1. Examine the map of world cities on pages 180–81. **(a)** Which continent includes the most major cities? **(b)** Are most of the nations on this continent developing or developed? **(c)** Why might this be true?
2. Using a map from the library, **(a)** identify and list the geographic features that originally encouraged settlement of the area where you live. **(b)** In a well-written paragraph, evaluate the importance of those same geographic features to the area today.

## Investigating Geography

1. As a report topic, select a nation that has had severe famine in the last 10 years. Research the population increases for that nation over the same time period. In a written statement, compare your findings to Thomas Malthus's theories. Does your research seem to confirm or disprove his theory that famine serves to check population growth? Support your answer with facts.
2. Select an example of advanced technology. Make a list of new terms added to the English language because of this invention. Share your findings with the class.
3. Obtain two copies of the prologue to *The Canterbury Tales* by Geoffrey Chaucer from your school or public library. One copy should show the prologue in Middle English. The other should show the prologue in modern English. Study the two selections carefully. Then prepare a written or oral report detailing what changes in the English the two versions of the prologue illustrate. Conclude your report with a discussion of how the English language continues to change.

## Further Readings

### Chapter 7

Jones, Claire, Steve J. Gadler, and Paul H. Engstrom. *Pollution: The Population Explosion.* Minneapolis, Minnesota: Real World Book, Lerner Publications Company. Deals with rapidly growing populations and the problems of crowded cities, pollution, and fewer resources.

MacDonald, Dick, comp. and ed. *The Population Story: From Now to 2000.* London, Canada: Western Journalism Library. Reviews the possible problems of population growth, as well as some possible solutions, as the twentieth century comes to a close.

McHugh, Kevin E. "Black Migration Reversed in the United States." *Geographical Review* 77, no. 2 (April 1987): 171–182. Describes the reverse flow of black Americans from the North back to the South.

Pringle, Laurence. *What Shall We Do with the Land? Choices for America.* New York: Thomas Y. Crowell. Covers the continuing problem of how to use the land—to retain it as farmland or pasture, or to develop it.

Stwertka, Eve, and Albert Stwertka. *Population: Growth, Change, and Impact.* New York: Franklin Watts. Provides an overview of many aspects of our world's rapidly increasing population.

Wells, Robert V. *Uncle Sam's Family. Issues in and Perspectives on American Demographic History.* Albany, New York: State University at Albany Press. Focuses on demographic trends in the United States.

### Chapter 8

Fullerton, H. "The 1995 Labor Force: A First Look." *Monthly Labor Review* 103, no. 12: 11–21. Describes what the work force in the year 1995 might look like.

Gapp, Paul. *The American City. An Urban Odessey to 11 U.S. Cities.* New York: The Chicago Tribune Company. Illustrates through text and photographs 11 major American cities.

Habenstreit, Barbara. *Cities in the March of Civilization.* New York: Franklin Watts. Explores the various types of cities found throughout the world, shows how humans first developed cities, and traces the growth of cities up to modern times.

Hanmer, Trudy. *The Growth of Cities.* New York: Franklin Watts. Describes the growth of cities in the United States from colonial times to the present and discusses the future of American cities.

Van der Ryn, Sim, and Peter Calthorpe. *Sustainable Communities: A New Design Synthesis for Cities, Suburbs, and Towns.* San Francisco: Sierra Club Books. Deals with the current problems of cities such as overcrowding, pollution, crime, and decaying inner city areas, and how to deal with them.

# UNIT 4

# THE UNITED STATES AND CANADA

191

# CHAPTER 9

# The Physical Setting of the United States

# PUTTING THE CHAPTER IN FOCUS

The United States ranks as the world's fourth-largest nation in land area. Its long coastline fronts three oceans: the Pacific on the west, the Atlantic on the east, and the Arctic on the northern shores of Alaska. Land areas extend over 52° of latitude—from 19° N in Hawaii to 71° N in Alaska—and 106° of longitude—from 67° W in Maine to 173° W in Alaska. Climates vary from very wet to very dry and from tropical to polar. With a few exceptions, natural resources are abundant.

## Ideas to Understand

In studying about the physical setting of the United States, use these ideas to give direction to your reading.

1 The United States can be divided into eight physical regions.
2 Climates and vegetation patterns vary widely in the United States.
3 The United States has a wealth of natural resources.

## Terms to Define

The following terms are some of the key terms in the chapter. Defining them will help you understand the physical setting of the United States.

physical region     glaciated
estuary     shield
subregion     continental divide
fall line     microclimate

## Places to Locate

Locating the following places will add to your knowledge of geography.

Atlantic and Gulf     Blue Ridge
    Coastal Plains     Central Lowland
Appalachian     Great Plains
    Highlands     Rocky Mountains

## 1 The United States can be divided into eight physical regions.

If you took an airplane flight from New York City to Los Angeles, you would fly over some of the world's most varied and spectacular landforms. Imagine that you are on such an airplane flight. As your plane banks over the narrow coastal plain and begins flying west, you look out the window to see the heavily forested Appalachian Mountains. Later in your flight you cross the seemingly endless expanses of the Great Plains, whose farms feed people throughout the world.

Eventually you fly over the snowcapped peaks of the Rocky Mountains, then you cross miles and miles of rugged, arid land. Soon you look out and see deep canyons—you might even see the Grand Canyon, formed by the raging waters of the Colorado River. Nearing the end of your flight west, you see tall mountains, wide plateaus, and a barren desert area. When your airplane begins its descent into Los Angeles, you see the rugged coastline as you circle over the Pacific Ocean.

Even though your flight took you across much of the country, you still would not have seen all of the physical regions of the United States. Shapes on the earth's surface define an area as a **physical region**. Physical geographers divide the United States into eight physical regions (see the map on page 195). Moving from east to west, these physical regions are the Atlantic and Gulf

*Glacier National Park, Montana*

193

Coastal Plains, the Appalachian Highlands, an extension of the Canadian Shield, the Interior Plains, the Rocky Mountains, the Intermountain region, the Pacific Coastal region, and the Hawaiian Islands.

The physical regions of the United States are based on its physical features. As you know, however, the study of geography includes much more than the study of the earth's physical setting. It also includes a study of the people on the earth, or the cultural setting. For this reason geographers also divide the United States into **cultural regions,** or areas in which the people share similar cultural characteristics. Most cultural geographers divide the United States into seven cultural regions. These regions are the Northeast, the Southeast, the Great Lakes, the Plains, the Mountain region, the Southwest, and the Pacific region.

You will learn about the cultural regions of the United States in Chapter 11. In this chapter you will learn about the country's physical regions. The presentation of physical regions will start with those on the east coast and move west—in the same direction as your imaginary airplane flight.

## Atlantic and Gulf Coastal Plains

A continuous coastal plain borders the eastern coast of the United States along the Atlantic Ocean and the southern coast along the Gulf of Mexico.

The vast plain extends from New York to Texas. The plain is narrow in the north and many bays and **estuaries** (ES·chuh·wer·ees), or water passages where the tide meets a river current, interrupt it. The plain widens in the south to include all of Florida and the Mississippi River Valley as far north as Cairo, Illinois. Elevations on the coastal plain range from sea level along the coast to generally less than 600 feet (200 meters) above sea level inland.

The Atlantic and Gulf Coastal Plains were the site of the first European settlements in the 1500s and 1600s. The relative locations of the plains on the coast closest to Europe made them logical sites for these early settlements.

## Appalachian Highlands

The Appalachian Highlands rise beyond the coastal plain from Maine to Alabama. They consist of eroded, or worn-down, remnants of an old and once much higher mountain chain that existed millions of years before the Rockies and other western mountains were formed. Today the highlands generally rise less than 6,000 feet (2,000 meters) above sea level.

The Appalachian Highlands can be divided into five **subregions,** or smaller units. These subregions are the Piedmont, the Blue Ridge, the Ridge and Valley, the Appalachian Plateaus, and the New England Appalachians.

**The Piedmont.**  Foothills with elevations between 500 and 1,000 feet (150 and 300 meters) above sea level form the Piedmont. The Piedmont joins the Atlantic Coastal Plain at the **fall line.** Along this line, rivers drop from the foothills to the coastal plain in small waterfalls. Several cities developed at these falls, either as break-of-bulk points or as manufacturing centers with factories powered by the falling water. Philadelphia, Baltimore, Richmond, and Raleigh all lie along the fall line.

**The Blue Ridge.**  The Blue Ridge subregion forms the highest part of the Appalachian Highlands. It rises to 6,684 feet (2,037 meters) in North Carolina at Mount Mitchell, the highest point in the United States east of the Mississippi River. This subregion, which includes the Blue Ridge and Great Smoky mountains, was difficult for

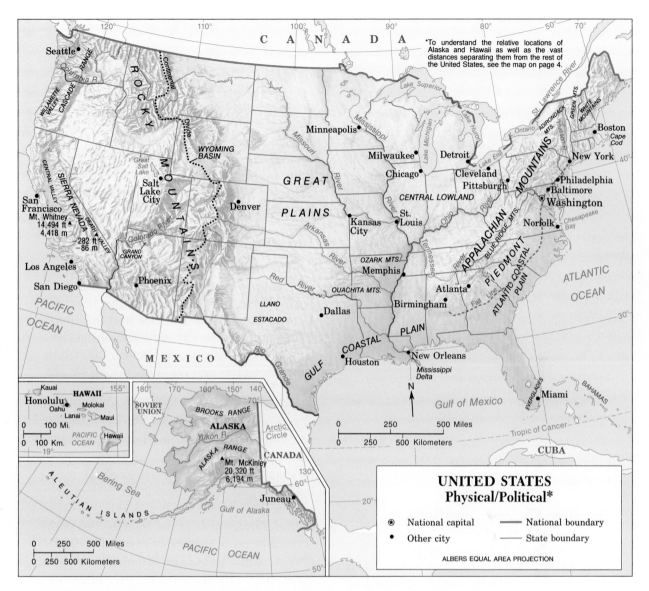

*Learning from Maps.* Two major mountain ranges stretch generally north to south in the continental United States. What are the names of these mountain ranges?

early pioneers to cross in their search for new lands in the west.

**The Ridge and Valley.**   West of the Blue Ridge subregion lies the Ridge and Valley subregion. Over the years the folds of the mountains in this subregion slowly eroded, forming long, parallel rows of steep-sided ridges and narrow lowlands. They extend from northeast to southwest. Many rivers drain the region and the fertile soil of the

valleys attracted settlers to this rugged territory.

**The Appalachian Plateaus.**   The Appalachian Plateaus begin as a steep cliff west of the Ridge and Valley subregion. To the west of this cliff lie the rolling and sometimes hilly lands of the Cumberland Plateau in Kentucky and Tennessee and the Allegheny Plateau in Pennsylvania, Ohio, and West Virginia. Rock layers underlying the plateaus

**195**

**Learning from Pictures.** *American pioneers moving west often went through Tennessee's Cumberland Gap, shown above. In which subregion is the Cumberland Plateau located?*

hold rich coal reserves in Kentucky, West Virginia, and Pennsylvania.

**The New England Appalachians.** The New England Appalachian subregion covers all of New England except for Cape Cod. During the Ice Age this area was **glaciated** (GLAY·she·ayt·ed), or covered by ice. Advancing ice sheets scraped much of the topsoil away and smoothed the land. When the ice sheets melted they left piles of boulders, rocks, and stones. These rocks and stones make the subregion generally unsuitable for large-scale agriculture.

## Extensions of the Canadian Shield

Two parts of the United States—the Adirondack Mountains in New York State and the Superior Upland around the shores of Lake Superior—occupy the continental **shield,** an area of exposed ancient rock. The rest of the shield lies in Canada and is called the Canadian, or Laurentian,* Shield. (See the CASE STUDY on page 251).

Geologists believe the shield, which has been worn down over millions of years by ice and water, is the oldest part of North America. As in many other shield areas around the world, soils remain generally thin and infertile. The Adirondacks and the Superior Upland, however, have important mineral deposits.

## Interior Plains

The Interior Plains cover a vast area in the center of the continent. Longitude 100° West divides the Interior Plains into the Central Lowland in the east and the Great Plains in the west. The elevation of the Central Lowland averages between 500 and 2,000 feet (150 and 600 meters) above sea level. The Great Plains rise gradually westward to elevations of more than 5,000 feet (1,500 meters) above sea level. Glaciers scoured both areas in the Ice Age, but left generally smoother and more fertile deposits than those in rocky New England, making the region more suitable for agriculture.

The Mississippi River and its major tributaries drain much of the Interior Plains. A **tributary** is a stream or river that flows into a larger river. The tributaries of the Mississippi River include the Missouri, Ohio, and Tennessee rivers. Some northern rivers of the plains drain into the Great Lakes. Small rivers and lakes connect the Great Lakes to form a continuous waterway that drains eastward into the St. Lawrence River and the Atlantic Ocean. This river and lake system offers convenient transportation between various parts of the plains.

Parts of the plains are amazingly flat, but small hills and mountains break the flatness in some areas. The Black Hills interrupt the plains in the north. Other mountains,

---

* The shield is named Laurentian after the St. Lawrence River.

*Text continues on page 198.*

# DEVELOPING GEOGRAPHY SKILLS
## THINKING GEOGRAPHICALLY: Classifying Information

One key to learning the large amount of information in a subject such as geography is to classify the information. To classify means to organize items or information into categories, or groups, according to common characteristics.

Organizing information into a chart or table is one common method of classifying information. Classifying information into charts, tables, and other graphics highlights common themes and makes relationships among seemingly unrelated data more easily recognizable. Geographers often classify geographic data.

### How to Classify Information

To classify information, follow these steps.

1. **Identify a purpose.** Before information can be charted, a purpose for classifying must be set. Make sure your purpose is clear and logical.
2. **Select categories.** Study the information with your purpose for classifying it in mind. Identify categories that reflect your purpose. Choose an item from the list of items to be classified and place it in the category in which it fits. Continue this classifying process until you have placed all the items or information into a category.
3. **Develop a chart.** Charts are devices that help to make relationships among facts clear. Turn your purpose for classifying into a chart title. Use the categories you identified as column or row headings. Finally, place your categorized items in the proper columns and rows of your chart.

### Applying the Skill

Study the chart in the next column. The title tells you that the subject of the chart is

| SUBREGIONS OF THE APPALACHIAN HIGHLANDS | | |
|---|---|---|
| **Subregion** | **Relative Location** | **Physical Characteristics** |
| PIEDMONT | Joins Atlantic Coastal Plain at fall line | Foothills with elevations between 500 and 1,000 feet (150 and 300 meters) |
| BLUE RIDGE | Rises to the west of the Piedmont subregion | Highest mountains east of the Mississippi River |
| RIDGE AND VALLEY | Extends from northeast to southwest beyond the Blue Ridge | Long, parallel rows of steep-sided ridges and narrowed lowlands |
| APPALACHIAN PLATEAUS | West of the Ridge and Valley subregion | Steep cliff with rolling and sometimes hilly lands to the west |
| NEW ENGLAND APPALACHIAN | Covers all of New England | Rocky land dotted with boulders, rocks and stones |

the subregions of the Appalachian Highlands. The categories of information are the relative locations and physical characteristics of each of the subregions. Listed in each column is specific information about the subregion. The chart shows how the information on the subregions is related. It shows where each subregion lies relative to other subregions. It also illustrates the similarities and differences in landforms among the subregions.

*To practice this skill, see Practicing Geography Skills on page 207.*

**197**

which are known collectively as the Interior Highlands, rise above the plains in parts of Missouri, Arkansas, and Oklahoma. They include the Ozark Mountains.

## The Rocky Mountains

The Rocky Mountains extend northward across the United States from New Mexico into Canada and onto the Brooks Range in Alaska. The Rockies soar over 14,000 feet (4,500 meters) in places and contain North America's continental divide. A **continental divide** is a water parting between river systems that flow in opposite directions. In North America, rivers flow either eastward or westward from the continental divide.

## The Intermountain Region

Plateaus characterize the Intermountain region, which lies between the Rocky Mountains and mountains farther west. The Colorado Plateau in the southern part of the region reaches the highest elevation—5,000 feet (1,500 meters) above sea level. Streams on this plateau drain into the Colorado River. Lower plateaus lie along the Columbia and Snake rivers in parts of Washington, Oregon, Idaho, and Alaska.

## Pacific Coastal Region

The Pacific Coastal region consists of two very high and roughly parallel mountain ranges. The Coast Ranges rise near the Pacific coast. They are geologically young mountains and are still forming. A second mountain system stretches farther inland. It extends from California to Alaska and includes the Sierra Nevada, Klamath Mountains, Cascade Range, and Alaska Range.

Earthquakes and occasional volcanic eruptions caused by the movements of the tectonic plates occur throughout both mountain systems. In fact, the San Andreas Fault extends across the Coast Ranges in California east of Los Angeles to San Francisco. As you learned in Chapter 3, this fault lies above a plate boundary between land on the North American Plate and land and sea on other plates to the west (see the map on page 69).

Some lowlands suitable for farming exist in this mountainous region. The most extensive lowlands lie in the Central Valley of California between the Coast Ranges and the Sierra Nevada. Farther to the north the Puget Sound Lowland and the Willamette Valley lie between the Coast Ranges and the Cascades.

*Text continues on page 200.*

***Learning from Diagrams.*** *Plains and lowlands occupy the interior of the United States. What landform comprises North America's continental divide?*

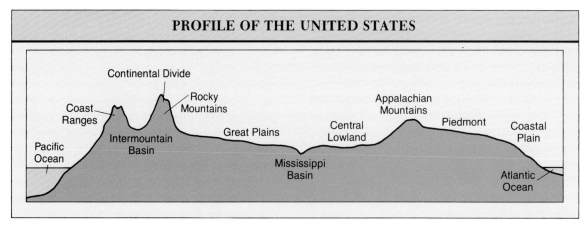

PROFILE OF THE UNITED STATES

In the spring and summer of 1980 a volcano named Mount St. Helens suddenly and violently awoke after 120 years of inactivity. The volcano is located in the Cascade Range about 75 miles (120 kilometers) south of Seattle, Washington. On March 27 a huge new crater opened at the top of Mount St. Helens, and steam and smoke poured out for the first time in memory. The emissions continued sporadically for the next 51 days.

### A Devastating Blast

May 18 brought an enormous and devastating blast that riveted the attention of all Americans on the erupting volcano. An earthquake registering about 5 on the Richter scale shook the north slope of the mountain. Gases pent up within the mountain suddenly escaped with a force great enough to send a column of steam and volcanic ash 70,000 feet (21,300 meters) into the air. No lava erupted, but the blast blew away the entire north slope of the once cone-shaped volcano.

Trees in the way of the blast were blown down like matchsticks. Torrents of boiling mud and water, traveling at over 200 miles (320 kilometers) an hour, flowed down the mountain into the Toutle River and eventually into the Columbia River. Seventy people died or were declared missing because of the blast. More than 11 million fish died in the heated water of the rivers. Thousands of birds and animals also died.

Prevailing winds picked up volcanic ash from the eruption and carried it eastward across the Cascades. The ash-choked skies reduced visibility to zero in Yakima, Washington, and other nearby cities. Road and rail traffic came to a standstill. Airplane travel within a radius of several hundred miles was canceled. A 2-inch (5-centimeter) layer of ash blanketed the land as far away

*Fireweed and herbs signal life's renewal.*

as Idaho. Smaller particles stayed aloft in the air surrounding the entire earth during the next 17 days.

### Nature Bounces Back

Mount St. Helens looked like a completely different place when, after four more big blasts, it finally became quiet. It had a different shape, a lower elevation, and upper slopes that were totally devastated. Yet life began to return to the mountain immediately. Within a week spiders busily spun webs. By the end of the summer ferns, other ground covers, and even trees sprouted from the ashes.

### Will It Happen Again?

Peace and quiet once again prevail in the scenic Cascade Range. But the mountains, located on the North American plate, lie directly above the descending edge of the Juan de Fuca Plate. Geologists fear that another eruption will occur somewhere in the Cascades in the near future.

## The Hawaiian Islands

Landforms in the Hawaiian Islands are totally unlike those in other parts of the United States. Tops of undersea volcanoes located on the floor of the Pacific Ocean actually form the islands. The highest peak, Mauna Loa, rises to 13,679 feet (4,170 meters) above sea level on the island of Hawaii. Because the base of this still-active volcano lies 18,000 feet (5,400 meters) below sea level on the ocean floor, Mauna Loa actually measures higher from base to top than Mount Everest, the highest mountain on earth. Today Mauna Loa has become one of the most popular and spectacular tourist spots on the Hawaiian Islands.

Thousands of miles separate Hawaii and Alaska from the other 48 states of the United States. To understand the relative locations of these two states as well as the vast distances separating them from the rest of the United States, see the map on page 195.

---

### SECTION 1 REVIEW

1. **Define** physical region, cultural region, estuary, subregion, fall line, glaciated, shield, tributary, continental divide
2. **Locate** Atlantic and Gulf Coastal Plains, Appalachian Highlands, Piedmont, Blue Ridge, Central Lowland, Great Plains, Rocky Mountains, Colorado Plateau
3. **Organizing Ideas** Why do geographers divide the United States into physical and cultural regions?
4. **Summarizing Ideas** What are the eight physical regions of the United States?
5. **Studying Maps** Refer to the map on page 195. **(a)** Which physical region includes the area where you live? **(b)** What are the primary landform characteristics of your region?

---

## 2 Climates and vegetation patterns vary widely in the United States.

The United States has 11 of the 13 global climate types described in Chapter 4. The climate map on page 201 shows the distribution of these climate types.

### Tropical and Subtropical Climates

A tropical climate is found only in two places in the United States—Hawaii and the southern tip of Florida. In Hawaii the northeast trade winds bring more than 400 inches (1,000 centimeters) of rain a year to some mountainous areas in the northeast. Areas on the leeward side of the mountains just a few miles away get less than 20 inches (50 centimeters) of rain a year. Southwest winds from the Gulf of Mexico influence southern Florida's tropical wet-and-dry climate and carry occasional hurricanes to shore. Rainfall, mostly from summer storms, averages between 60 and 80 inches (150 and 200 centimeters) a year.

The southeastern area of the United States has a humid subtropical climate. Summers are hot and humid. Winters are mild, although severe freezes occur every winter throughout the area.

### Humid Continental Climates

Most of the central and eastern parts of the United States have a humid continental, hot summer climate. Daytime highs during the summer occasionally reach 100°F (38°C), while winters are cold and snowy.

Extreme northeastern sections of the United States such as Maine have a humid continental, cool summer climate with bitterly cold winters. This climate region extends in a broad band along the eastern half of the boundary between the United States and Canada.

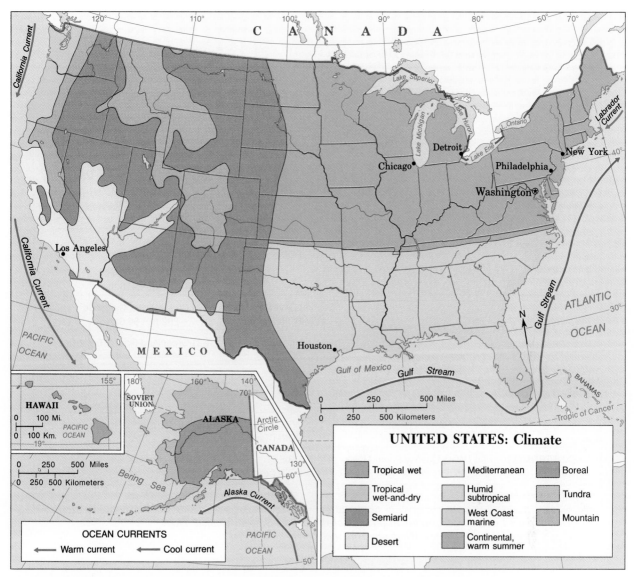

**Learning from Maps.** *Americans can experience most of the world's climate types within the country's borders. What climate type does Hawaii have?*

## Semiarid and Desert Climates

The western Great Plains and Inter-mountain region of the United States have a semiarid climate. Yearly precipitation generally totals less than 25 inches (60 centimeters). Extremes of weather threaten the areas year-round. Frequent droughts, sometimes severe enough to ruin crops and pastures, plague these areas. Summers often bring dangerous thunderstorms and tor-

nadoes. Winters remain mild in the south but are much colder, with snow and occasional blizzards, in the north.

The southwestern interior of the United States has a desert climate that extends across several physical regions from western Texas into New Mexico, Arizona, Utah, Nevada, and California (see the map on this page). It is a land of little rainfall, low relative humidity, clear skies, and bright sunshine. Daytime temperatures in the sum-

201

## GEOGRAPHIC HIGHLIGHTS OF THE UNITED STATES

| | | |
|---|---|---|
| **WESTERNMOST POINT** | ⑥ | Cape Wrangell, Attu Island, Alaska<br>53°08' N, 173°18' E |
| | ⑦ | Cape Alava, Washington*<br>48°10' N, 124°43' W |
| **GEOGRAPHIC CENTER** | ⑧ | Butte County, South Dakota<br>44°58' N, 103°46' W |
| | ⑨ | Smith County, Kansas*<br>36°50' N, 98°35' W |
| **HIGHEST POINT** | ⑩ | Mt. McKinley, Alaska<br>20,320 ft/6,096 m |
| | ⑪ | Mt. Whitney, California*<br>14,494 ft/4,418 m |
| **LOWEST POINT** | ⑫ | Death Valley, California<br>−282 ft/−84.6 m |
| **HOTTEST POINT** | ⑬ | Greenland Ranch, California<br>134° |
| **COLDEST POINT** | ⑭ | Prospect Creek Camp, Alaska<br>−80° |
| **WETTEST POINT** (annual) | ⑮ | Mt. Waialeale, Hawaii<br>460 in/1,168 cm |
| **DRIEST POINT** (annual) | ⑯ | Phoenix, Arizona<br>7.11 in/18 cm |

| | | |
|---|---|---|
| **NORTHERNMOST POINT** | ① | Point Barrow, Alaska<br>71°20' N, 156°0' W |
| | ② | Angle, Minnesota*<br>49°26' N, 94°14' W |
| **SOUTHERNMOST POINT** | ③ | Ka Lae (South Point), Hawaii<br>18°52' N, 155°30' W |
| | ④ | Key West, Florida*<br>24°31' N, 81°47' W |
| **EASTERNMOST POINT** | ⑤ | West Quoddy Point, Maine<br>45°5' N, 67°12' W |

*excluding Alaska and Hawaii

***Learning from Charts.*** *Geographic highlights of the United States changed when Alaska and Hawaii became states. What remains the easternmost point?*

mers can soar to 120°F (49°C). Winters only occasionally bring snow or freezing temperatures.

## Mediterranean and West Coast Marine Climates

Most of California has a Mediterranean climate. Such a climate features mild and rainy winters and hot and almost completely dry summers.

A west coast marine climate extends along the Pacific coastal regions from San Francisco to the northern end of the Alaska panhandle (see the map on page 201). Pre-vailing westerly winds and a warm ocean current offshore keep winter temperatures unusually mild for the latitude. Although its relative location is closer to the Arctic Circle, Juneau, Alaska, for example, is often warmer in winter than Chicago and New York City.

The northwest coastal regions are the wettest parts of the United States outside of Hawaii. Some areas receive more than 100 inches (250 centimeters) of rain a year. High mountains running north and south along the coast bring orographic moisture from weather systems that the prevailing

westerly winds sweep in from the Pacific Ocean (see Chapter 4).

## Subarctic and Polar Climates

Central Alaska has a subarctic climate in which winter is the dominant season. Cold, harsh winters last more than half of the year. Snow covers the land from early fall until May. Summers are short, although daylight lasts for 24 hours in areas north of the Arctic Circle. Despite days and sometimes weeks of warm summer weather, summers stay too cool to grow most crops. Because summer days in the central part of the state are mild and have daylight for at least 20 hours, crops that do grow ripen quickly. Most fruits and vegetables that tolerate cool nights can grow in the short Alaskan summers.

A tundra, or polar, climate exists along the extreme northern edge of Alaska facing the Arctic Ocean. Only a few mosses and grasses survive in this cold climate.

## Mountain Climates

High mountain areas have a highland, or mountain, climate (see the map on page 201). In such regions temperature and precipitation vary so much from place to place that climate generalizations mean little. In fact, each mountain slope develops its own **microclimate,** or temperature and rainfall characteristics that are locally determined. For example, Mount Whitney, the tallest mountain in the continental United States, has several microclimates.

## Vegetation

Vegetation patterns follow much the same outlines as the country's physical regions. For example, mixed broadleaf deciduous and needleleaf evergreen forests cover much of the east, while prairie grasses cover the Great Plains.

***Learning from Pictures.*** *When the ground thaws, tundra vegetation blooms for a short period of time. Do trees grow in the tundra?*

**SECTION 2 REVIEW**

1. **Define** microclimate
2. **Studying Maps** Refer to the climate map on page 201. **(a)** What are the general locations of the 11 United States climate regions? **(b)** Which climate type or subtype exists in the area where you live?
3. **Contrasting Ideas** **(a)** How do humid continental climates differ from semiarid and desert climates? **(b)** How do Mediterranean and west coast marine climates differ from subarctic and polar climates?
4. **Organizing Ideas** Why do climate generalizations mean little in mountain areas?
5. **Studying Maps** Study the vegetation map on pages 100–01. Then develop a chart that lists the major vegetation type for each of the physical regions of the United States.

# 3 The United States has a wealth of natural resources.

The United States has abundant supplies of natural resources, including much of what it needs for agriculture and industry.

## Renewable Resources

Forests, water, soils, and fish comprise the principal renewable resources in the United States. If properly managed, supplies of these resources will be available to Americans for generations to come.

**Forests.**   Forests once covered all but the very cold and arid areas of the United States. Although they have been cut down and replaced by farmlands in many areas, forests still cover nearly one-third of the nation. The largest forests are in areas too mountainous or too cold for farming.

Three mountainous and rainy states in the Pacific Northwest—Washington, Oregon, and Alaska—contain the nation's most extensive forests. These states produce nearly one-half of all the lumber cut in the United States and much is exported.

**Water.**   The United States has an abundant water supply—a supply used for a variety of purposes. The country contains ample supplies of surface water and ground water for drinking and irrigation, for example. In addition, the United States has a good system of navigable waterways. One of the largest systems, the Mississippi River system, is navigable throughout the central part of the nation. The Mississippi itself is navigable as far as Minneapolis and St. Paul, Minnesota; the Missouri as far as Sioux City, Iowa; and the Ohio as far as Pittsburgh, Pennsylvania. The Great Lakes-St. Lawrence River system forms a second navigable waterway. Oceangoing vessels travel inland on this system to Lake Superior.

**Soils.**   Naturally fertile soils cover the Interior Plains, the Mississippi River Valley, and the Columbia Plateau. Other, less-fertile soils produce well when farmers use modern seeds, fertilizers, and other scientific farming methods. As a result, the United States now produces far more food than it uses.

**Fish.**   Fish and other seafoods make up an important resource in coastal areas. The Gulf of Mexico serves as the principal fishing area. It provides large quantities of shrimp, oysters, redfish, and red snapper. Fishers catch cod, flounder, herring, and menhaden in the deeper waters of the Atlantic Ocean. Shallow coastal waters yield lobsters, clams, oysters, crabs, and scallops. Fishing fleets in the Pacific Ocean catch salmon, halibut, and tuna.

## Nonrenewable Resources

Nonrenewable resources found in the United States include most metals as well as energy fuels such as coal, oil, and natural gas. Supplies of these resources continue to dwindle and need to be conserved for future use.

**Minerals.**   Metals needed for American industries are found in varying amounts in many parts of the country. The Superior Upland of Minnesota and Michigan once contained rich deposits of iron ore. However, the rich deposits were exhausted by the 1950s. Steel makers now use lower-grade ore from that region or import iron ore from Canada and Venezuela.

Mines in Arizona and Utah produce large amounts of copper. The United States also imports copper from Canada, Chile, and Peru.

# GEOGRAPHY IN THE WORKPLACE
## Conservationists

It has always been easier to find ways to use natural resources than to find ways to protect them. Human use easily damages some of these resources, while not harming others.

Conservationists focus their attention on resources that are likely to be damaged or that can be significantly improved. Areas of most critical concern include farmland, forestland, bodies of water, mineral deposits, wildlife—both animals and plants—and areas of scenic beauty.

The conservation field offers a variety of job opportunities. National and state parks, wildlife refuges, and wilderness areas employ large numbers of conservationists. Under the sponsorship of the Department of Agriculture, soil conservationists work in districts all over the United States to protect rich farmlands, and foresters work to improve our forestlands. In addition, in all the states conservationists enforce fish and game laws and manage wildlife resources. And finally, the Environmental Protection Agency (EPA) and many state agencies with similar goals try to protect the environment from pollution. Their conservationists work to clean up the air, land, and water.

As fine as all of the combined efforts of the many agencies and their workers are, however, the problems of protecting and conserving our resources is far from solved. The nation needs more conservationists—some as employees of federal and state agencies, but even more as volunteers. To truly succeed, conservation requires the daily involvement of everyone. We must do all we can to protect and conserve our environment. In this way we are all conservationists.

---

The United States has deposits of uranium, used to fuel nuclear power plants, and molybdenum (muh·LIB·duh·nuhm), used in steel making. It also has deposits of lead, gold, and silver.

**Coal.** Coal, used to generate electricity and to manufacture steel, is abundant in the United States and ranks as a major export. The principal coal fields lie in the Appalachian Highlands. Eastern Kentucky, West Virginia, and western Pennsylvania produce 75 percent of the nation's coal supply.

**Oil and natural gas.** Supplies of oil and natural gas, while abundant, fail to meet the nation's current energy needs. The map on page 219 shows the principal oil and natural gas fields. Texas, Alaska, Louisiana, and California rank as the leading oil-producing states. Texas, Louisiana, Oklahoma, and New Mexico lead the list of natural gas producers.

---

### SECTION 3 REVIEW

1. **Summarizing Ideas** What needs are met by the many resources in the United States?
2. **Interpreting Ideas** Why is it important to properly manage resources?
3. **Classifying Ideas** **(a)** What are the principal renewable resources in the United States? **(b)** Why are water and soil important resources for the United States?
4. **Analyzing Ideas** How are nonrenewable resources used in the United States?

## Chapter Summary

The following list contains the key concepts you have learned about the physical setting of the United States.

1. The eight physical regions of the United States are the Atlantic and Gulf Coastal Plains, the Appalachian Highlands, extensions of the Canadian Shield, the Interior Plains, the Rocky Mountains, the Intermountain region, the Pacific Coastal region, and the Hawaiian Islands.
2. In 1980 Mount St. Helens in Washington State erupted with frightening fury.
3. The United States has 11 of the 13 global climate types. They include tropical wet in parts of Hawaii, tropical wet-and-dry in southern Florida, humid subtropical in the southeast, humid continental with hot summers in most of the central and eastern United States, humid continental with cool summers in extreme northeastern sections of the nation, semiarid in the western Great Plains and Intermountain region, desert in the southwestern interior, Mediterranean in much of California, west coast marine north of San Francisco, subarctic in central Alaska, and polar in northern Alaska.
4. The United States has a wealth of renewable resources, such as forests, water, soils, and fish; and nonrenewable resources, such as coal, oil and natural gas, iron ore, copper, uranium, molybdenum, gold, and silver.

On a separate sheet of paper, complete the following review exercises.

## Reviewing Geographic Terms

In the following sentences the underlined terms are incorrect. Rewrite each sentence using the correct term.

1. Cultural geographers often divide the United States into seven underlined areas, or areas identified by cultural characteristics.
2. The United States has eight fall lines, areas identified by shapes on the earth's surface.
3. The Piedmont joins the Atlantic Coastal Plain at the terraced land where rivers drop in small waterfalls from the foothills to the coastal plain.
4. During the Ice Age much of New England was eroded, or covered by ice.
5. Two parts of the United States are on a continental plateau, an area of exposed ancient rock.
6. The Mississippi River and its major channels—the Missouri, Ohio, and Tennessee rivers—drain most of the Interior Plains.
7. In the United States the mountain divide separates rivers draining west to the Pacific Ocean from rivers draining east to the Atlantic Ocean and Gulf of Mexico.
8. High mountain areas have locally determined temperature and rainfall characteristics called glaciers.

## Developing Critical Thinking Skills

1. **Summarizing Ideas** (a) What are the subregions of the Appalachian Highlands? (b) What are the physical characteristics of each subregion?
2. **Interpreting Ideas** (a) What is the primary natural resource under the rock layer of the plateaus in Kentucky, West Virginia, and Pennsylvania? (b) Which parts of the United States lie on the continental shield and what important resources do they yield?
3. **Analyzing Ideas** How did the presence of glaciers during the Ice Age affect the surface features of the New England subregion?
4. **Contrasting Ideas** (a) How do the Appalachian Highlands differ from the Rocky Mountains? (b) How do landforms on the Hawaiian Islands differ from those in other parts of the United States?
5. **Understanding Ideas** Why is Juneau, Alaska, often warmer in winter than some cities that have relative locations farther south of the Arctic Circle?

6. **Synthesizing Ideas** **(a)** What three states contain the chief forest resources of the United States? **(b)** In what physical region are these three states located? **(C)** Why do large forests still exist in those states?
7. **Writing About Geography** In two clearly written paragraphs, complete one of the following activities. **(a)** Assume that you were on the scene when Mount St. Helens erupted. Record your observations in a well-organized essay that documents the geographical and human effects of this event. **(b)** What effect did the unique geographic features found in the Piedmont subregion have on human activity?

## Using Primary Sources

In an excerpt from *God's Country and Mine*, Jacques Barzun discusses the physical geography of the United States. As you study the reading, consider what effects geography has had on shaping the American character.

The solemn [scientists] who call any spot in the United States part of the Temperate Zone are kidding. A change of thirty degrees between sunup and sundown, repeated without warning of season fifty times a year; highs of 90°[F; 32°C] to 120°[F; 49°C] in summer, with natural steam provided free; lows of zero and less in winter, with snowfalls and blizzards and ice-storms — none of these can be called temperate except in the sense of tempering. If they don't kill, they give a steel-like elasticity to the [body].

But although the country is fertile, almost tropical in vegetation and rich in minerals, its food is bland. Everything that grows here is large but not [delicious]. The juices are not concentrated —as if to discourage self-indulgence through the belly. And just as there are but few delicate . . . landscapes, so there is a lack of concentrated drama in the mountains. We have nothing like the Alps. Our bareness is diffuse, it is diluted— once again—in space. Our overwhelming masses of mountain timber are unbroken by any grassy islands. . . . Our pure rock and eternal snows are remote, instead of rising from the midst of our daily life.

1. Why, according to the author, is the United States not really a temperate zone?
2. How does the author describe food grown in the United States?

## Practicing Geography Skills

*Before completing this activity, review Developing Geography Skills on page 197.*

**Classifying Information** Reread Section 1 of the chapter. Then develop a chart classifying information about the eight physical regions of the United States. Include the relative locations of the regions and the physical characteristics of the regions.

## Exploring Geography

1. Use the map of climates in the United States on text page 201 to identify the climate region in which you live. Then turn back to Chapter 4 to find a description of this climate. Prepare a written report comparing the climate of your area to the climate described in Chapter 4. Your report should note the similarities and differences and suggest reasons that might account for the differences.
2. Interview a representative of a company involved in the development of energy resources—an oil company or a coal company, for example. Before the interview, prepare questions on such topics as the problems involved in extracting the resource from the earth, the future supply of the resource, and the future of all energy resources. Share the results of your interview with the class.

# The Cultural Setting of the United States

# PUTTING THE CHAPTER IN FOCUS

In only a little more than 200 years, the United States has risen from a British colony to become one of the most powerful nations in the world. A diverse population, a high standard of living, and democratic political institutions make the United States unique in the world.

## Ideas to Understand

In studying about the cultural setting of the United States, use these ideas to give direction to your reading.

1 The population of the United States is diverse.
2 Population patterns in the United States have changed dramatically.
3 The culture of the United States, like its people, is diverse.

## Terms to Define

The following terms are some of the key terms in the chapter. Defining them will help you understand the cultural setting of the United States.

reservation          Sun Belt
acculturation        cultural pluralism
age distribution     bilingual
megalopolis          free enterprise system

## Places to Locate

Locating the following places will add to your knowledge of geography.

Bering Strait        Chicago
Baltimore            Cleveland
Puerto Rico          Detroit
Cuba                 St. Louis

## 1 The population of the United States is diverse.

The United States has a population vastly different from that of most other nations. With the exception of Native Americans, all the people in the United States are immigrants or descendants of immigrants who settled in North America after 1500. Today the approximately 250 million people of the United States include many groups with many different backgrounds, customs, and life styles.

### Native Americans

Native Americans make up less than 1 percent of the population and are one of the nation's smallest ethnic groups. Today approximately 2.5 million Native Americans live in the United States. Native Americans are descendants of people who crossed onto the North American continent from northeast Asia about 25,000 years ago, when sea levels were much lower than today. At that time a land bridge connected the two continents. Today the Bering Strait separates the continents (see the map on pages 2–3).

American Indians form the largest Native American group. They retain many different life styles and are widely distributed across the nation. Two other Native American groups are Aleuts and Eskimos, most of whom live in Alaska.

The most Indians—more than 200,000—live in California. Oklahoma, Arizona, New Mexico, North Carolina, and Alaska also have large Indian populations.

Today most Indians speak English. More than half of them live in urban areas and have adopted modern American ways. Many Indians, however, choose to live on **reservations,** lands that the United States

◀ *Ninth Avenue Cultural Festival, New York City*

**209**

government set aside for them. Indian reservations cover some 55 million acres (22 million hectares) of land in the United States.

## White Americans

The 195 million white Americans living in the United States make up about 78 percent of the population. Nearly all are descended from European immigrants. Their ancestors spoke many different languages and had a variety of cultural traditions.

More than 33 million Europeans representing almost every nation in Europe settled in the United States between 1815 and 1920. Many immigrants settled in eastern cities such as Boston, New York City, Philadelphia, and Baltimore. The locations of

*Learning from Graphs.* *Asian Americans are the fastest-growing group in the country. How many Asian Americans live in the United States?*

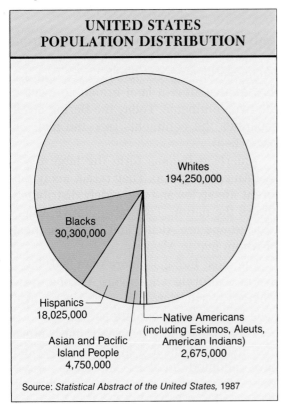

**UNITED STATES POPULATION DISTRIBUTION**

Whites
194,250,000

Blacks
30,300,000

Hispanics
18,025,000

Asian and Pacific
Island People
4,750,000

Native Americans
(including Eskimos, Aleuts,
American Indians)
2,675,000

Source: *Statistical Abstract of the United States*, 1987

these cities made them convenient places to settle for immigrants arriving in ships from Europe.

Often unfamiliar with the English language and American customs, many newly arrived immigrants lived in neighborhoods that other people from their country had already settled. Eventually, through the process of acculturation, they learned English and became used to different customs in the United States. As you read in Chapter 7, a person from one culture takes on the traits of another culture through the process of **acculturation.** Although many immigrants moved away from ethnic neighborhoods, most retained some elements of their native cultures. These elements bring much diversity to American life today.

## Black Americans

Thirty million black Americans make up about 12 percent of the nation's population. Most trace their descent to slaves brought to the United States against their will between 1619 and 1865.

The United States abolished slavery in 1865. Yet for many years blacks suffered discrimination that kept them apart from other Americans. Many states, for example, had laws requiring blacks to use separate facilities, including schools, parks, swimming pools, and restrooms. After years of struggle such laws were declared unconstitutional. A movement to recognize the civil rights of black citizens, led during the 1960s by the Reverend Dr. Martin Luther King, Jr., has resulted in great gains for black Americans. Work toward social and economic equality continues.

## Hispanic Americans

The term *Hispanic* refers to the people, language, or culture of Spain, Portugal, or Latin America. Hispanics may be people of any race. About 18 million Hispanics, or 7

percent of the total population, live in the United States, and this number is increasing steadily. In fact, Hispanics form one of the fastest-growing minority groups. The Population Reference Bureau estimates that by the year 2080 there will be nearly 60 million Hispanics living in the United States.

Mexican Americans comprise more than half of all Hispanics living in the United States. Many are descendants of Mexican citizens who were living in the southwestern United States at the time the United States annexed the region by treaty in the 1800s. Today Mexican Americans form one of the largest groups immigrating to the United States. States with high concentrations of Mexican Americans include California, Arizona, New Mexico, and Texas.

Puerto Ricans make up the second-largest Hispanic group in the United States. They originally came from the island of Puerto Rico, an American territory since 1898. Puerto Rico now has special status as a self-governing commonwealth within the United States (see Chapter 15). People travel freely back and forth between the island and the 50 states. Puerto Ricans are United States citizens. About 2 million Puerto Ricans live permanently in the United States, with the largest concentration in New York City.

Cuban Americans constitute the third-largest group of Hispanics in the United States. Approximately 800,000 Cuban Americans now live permanently in the United States. They originally came from Cuba, a Spanish-speaking island nation just south of Florida. A large concentration of Cuban Americans now lives in the Miami area in southern Florida.

## Asian Americans

About 4 million Asian Americans live in the United States today. They make up about 2 percent of the American popula-

*Learning from Pictures.* Americans celebrate their cultural heritages through festivals. What group of people are represented at this festival?

tion. Although Asian Americans form a tiny minority group, their numbers are increasing rapidly. From 1924 to 1965 Asians were largely excluded from the United States under the immigration quota system then in effect. Today they account for nearly half of all new immigrants.

People of Chinese, Filipino, and Japanese descent comprise the largest Asian groups. Many Indians, Koreans, and Vietnamese also now live in the United States. Some Chinese and Japanese Americans trace their descent to immigrants who entered the United States in the 1800s. Most Asian Americans, however, are recent immigrants.

## Pacific Islanders

Pacific Islanders make up the smallest of the nation's principal minority groups. Many Pacific Islanders are Hawaiians, descendants of people who lived in Hawaii long before Europeans colonized the islands in the 1800s.

**211**

## 2 Population patterns in the United States have changed dramatically.

In the late 1700s the United States consisted of the 13 original states located on the Atlantic seaboard, or eastern edge of the continent. All 13 states as well as parts of the continent to the west were sparsely populated and predominantly rural.

### Components of Population Change

At the time of the first federal census in 1790, the population of the United States was 3.9 million. It had increased to 76 million in 1900 and is expected to reach 260 million by the year 2000.

Despite such overall increases, the American population is growing more slowly than in the past. Limited immigration and a falling rate of natural increase account for the slower growth.

**Limited immigration.** In the 1800s and early 1900s there were few limitations on immigration. Millions of people from around the world entered the United States each year. The era of unlimited immigration ended in 1921, however. From 1921 until new laws were enacted in 1965, immigrants were admitted under a strict quota system based on national origin. Today, under new immigration laws, would-be immigrants from around the world compete equally for entry into the United States.

**Falling rate of natural increase.** A second reason for the decline in population growth in the United States is a low rate of natural increase. The birth rate in the United States has fallen from 55 live births per 1,000 people in 1820 to around 16 live births per 1,000 people today.

The death rate also has fallen. In 1900 the rate was 17 deaths per 1,000 people. It is 9 deaths per 1,000 people today. The decline results from major improvements in health care and nutrition.

Despite lower death rates, the lower birth rates have resulted in a low rate of natural increase, which is calculated by finding the difference between the birth rate and the death rate. The rate in the United States today is 0.9 percent. This rate remains far lower than the 1.7 percent found in the world as a whole.

### A Changing Population Structure

Changes in immigration and in the rate of natural increase have created other changes in the structure, or makeup, of the American population. Important changes have occurred in the male-female balance, life expectancy, and age distribution.

In 1900 males accounted for 51 percent of the population; females accounted for 49 percent. Today females make up 51.5 percent of the population while males make up only 48.5 percent.

In 1900 life expectancy was just 47 years. Improvements in health care and nutrition have raised that to 75 years today.

Declines in the birth rate and improvement in life expectancy have caused changes in the nation's **age distribution,**

*Text continues on page 214.*

# DEVELOPING GEOGRAPHY SKILLS
## INTERPRETING VISUALS: Reading Graphs

This textbook contains many graphs. Graphs are ways of presenting information visually. A *pie,* or *circle, graph* shows percentages. For example, the pie graph on page 214 shows the relative size of America's age groups.

A *line graph* shows changes in two variables. It most often shows changes over time. The line graph in the next column shows the changes in the U.S. rural population.

A *bar graph* shows comparisons, making highs and lows stand out clearly. The bar graph on page 182 shows the number of people in the world's largest cities.

A *pictograph* is a special graph using a picture of the subject to present the information. The pictograph on page 179 illustrates urbanization in certain selected countries.

### How to Read a Graph

Follow these guidelines to read a graph.

1. **Read the title.** The title will tell you the subject and purpose of the graph and may contain other information, such as the appropriate time period.
2. **Study the labels on the vertical and horizontal axes.** Line and bar graphs show two sets of data, one displayed along the vertical axis and the other displayed along the horizontal axis. Labels on these axes identify the data and units of measurement, when appropriate.
3. **Analyze the data.** Note all changes, trends, and relationships. Note increases and decreases in quantities.
4. **Put the data to use.** Form generalizations and hypotheses and draw conclusions based on the data.

### Applying the Skill

Study the bar graph. Its title tells you that subject of the graph is the number

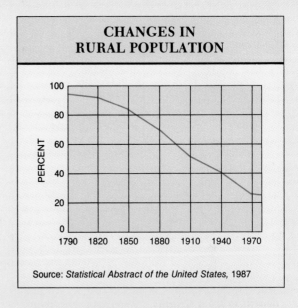

Source: *Statistical Abstract of the United States,* 1987

of people in the United States fed by one farm worker. The vertical axis tells you the years in which the statistics apply. The horizontal axis shows the number of people fed, divided into 10-person segments. You can see from the graph that one farm worker fed about 5 people in 1900, about 12 people in 1940, and about 75 people in 1987.

*To practice this skill, see Practicing Geography Skills on page 221.*

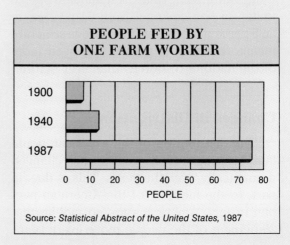

Source: *Statistical Abstract of the United States,* 1987

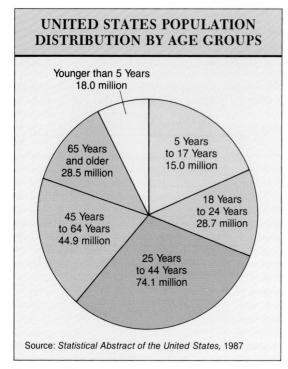

### UNITED STATES POPULATION DISTRIBUTION BY AGE GROUPS

Younger than 5 Years
18.0 million

65 Years and older
28.5 million

5 Years to 17 Years
15.0 million

18 Years to 24 Years
28.7 million

45 Years to 64 Years
44.9 million

25 Years to 44 Years
74.1 million

Source: *Statistical Abstract of the United States, 1987*

***Learning from Graphs.*** *Americans are living much longer today than in 1900. What is one conclusion you can draw about life in the United States from data on this graph?*

or the relative sizes of different age groups (see the graph above). For example, the number of people who are 65 years of age and older, the fastest-growing group, has increased from 4 percent in 1900 to 12 percent today. At the same time the number of people under 18 has declined from 44 percent to 26.5 percent. Such a shift in the age structure means that elderly people will need more of the nation's resources than ever before.

## Changes in Distribution

The distribution of the American population throughout the country has changed dramatically over the years. This is due, in part, to the mobility of the American people. In fact, Americans are so mobile that 20 percent of the people move every year.

**Urbanization.** Rural and urban distributions have changed dramatically since 1790. In 1790 the United States was a nation of farmers. Ninety-five percent of the people lived in rural areas. Today only 25 percent of the people live in rural areas and only 5 percent actually live on farms. Seventy-five percent of Americans today live in cities or their suburbs.

What caused the population to shift from rural to urban? Over the years, American agriculture improved greatly in both its methods and equipment. As a result, fewer people were needed to work on the farms to supply food for the population (see the graph on page 213). At the same time, industries were growing rapidly and creating new jobs in urban areas. These economic changes brought a steady flow of workers from rural areas to urban centers.

The urban population of the United States today is unevenly distributed throughout the country (see the map on page 215). The highest population densities in the United States are in the eastern half of the nation, particularly in the megalopolis that stretches from Boston to Washington, D.C. A **megalopolis** (meg·uh·LAHP·oh·luhs) is a supercity consisting of several cities that have grown together. The South has a moderate population density, with high concentrations near large cities such as Atlanta, Georgia. Western sections remain generally sparsely populated, except for scattered clusters of dense population along the Pacific coast. Alaska is the least-populated state, with large unsettled areas.

**Black movement from the South.** Another change in population distribution has been the movement of black Americans. Blacks lived mainly in the southern states before the abolition of slavery in 1865. Attracted by higher-paying jobs in northern factories, many black Americans moved to the North in the 1900s. Nine out of every

**214**

ten blacks lived in the South in 1900. Today only five out of ten blacks live in the South. Also, the black population, once almost entirely rural, has become highly urban. In four cities—Atlanta, Baltimore, Newark, and Washington, D.C.—blacks make up more than 50 percent of the population. In many other cities—Chicago, Birmingham, Cleveland, Detroit, Memphis, New Orleans, Richmond, and St. Louis—blacks comprise more than 40 percent of the population.

**Draw of the Sun Belt.**   Another change in distribution has occurred more recently. During the last 20 years people have moved from the colder northern states—called the Frost Belt or Snow Belt—to the warmer southern and southwestern states—called the **Sun Belt.**

Retired people make up a large group of those moving to the Sun Belt. New jobs that are opening up in expanding industries attract others.

*Text continues on page 217.*

***Learning from Maps.***   *The population densities below indicate the uneven population distribution of the United States. What cities have populations over 2 million?*

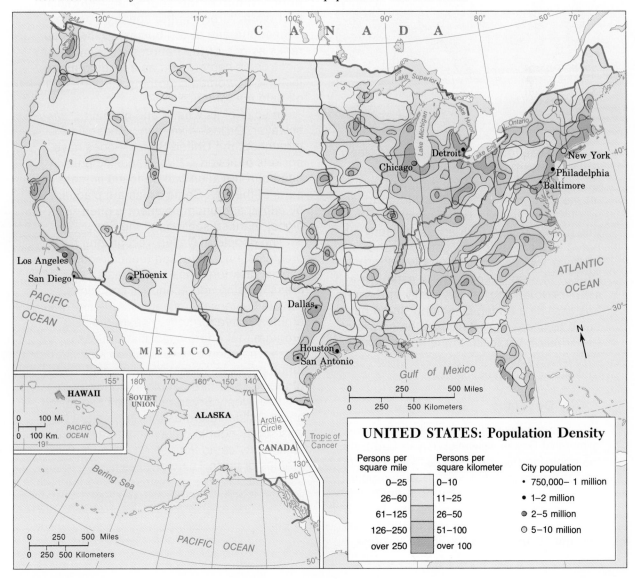

UNITED STATES: Population Density

| Persons per square mile | Persons per square kilometer | City population |
|---|---|---|
| 0–25 | 0–10 | • 750,000– 1 million |
| 26–60 | 11–25 | • 1–2 million |
| 61–125 | 26–50 | ◉ 2–5 million |
| 126–250 | 51–100 | ○ 5–10 million |
| over 250 | over 100 | |

**215**

# CITY FOCUS
## Dallas, Texas

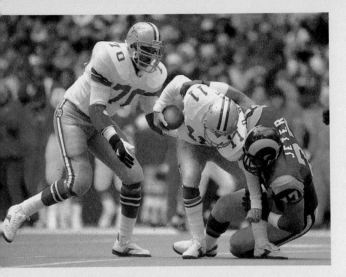

*The Dallas Cowboys*

When the founder of Dallas, John Neely Bryan, arrived in 1841 with his horse and dog, a rifle, some lead for shot, and a skillet, he thought that he had found an ideal site for a settlement. Bryan concluded that this grassy, rolling prairie was perfectly situated at the head of navigation on the Trinity River that flowed southeastward to the Gulf of Mexico. He planned to establish a steamboat landing on the Trinity and set up business as a trader. One thing Bryan had failed to check, however, was the nature of the Trinity River itself. In the entire next century only two boats made it all the way to Dallas on this shallow river.

### A City Develops

Lack of river traffic did not hamper the growth of Dallas, however. Bryan had built his cabin on the route of westward-bound wagon trains and was soon busily supplying their needs. He also found a ready market for trade both with Indians and buffalo hunters. Throughout the rest of the 1800s and the 1900s, Dallas continued to grow.

### Dallas Today

Many Dallas residents call "Big D," as their city is affectionately known, the most optimistic big city in the United States. Indeed, Dallas thrives on the energy of its people. In spite of its age, it looks new and clean. It is a city of skyscrapers, parks, and beautiful residential areas, and the home of the Dallas Cowboys. It serves as the transportation hub of the Southwest. The Dallas-Fort Worth Airport is the country's second-largest and one of the busiest. Dallas also ranks as one of the nation's most important electronics centers and as a leading manufacturer of women's clothing, aircraft, and oil-field equipment.

In spite of its wealth and glamour, however, Dallas—like many other cities throughout the United States—does have pockets of poverty. Public housing units in need of renovation can be found in these parts of the city. Some areas are plagued by crime, and unemployment is often much higher in these sections of the city.

The people of Dallas, recognizing these problems, have attacked them directly. A special task force has been created to address housing and economic conditions. Private businesses, along with the city government, have formed a "share the risks" program that offers special incentives to those who open businesses and manufacturing plants in certain impoverished areas of the city and hire people living there.

John Neely Bryan may have been wrong about Dallas' future as a river port, but he was surely right in believing that a dynamic community could flourish on the rolling prairies of north Texas. Dallas stands today as a tribute to free enterprise and to the imagination and drive of its people.

# 3 The culture of the United States, like its people, is diverse.

Some people have called the United States a great melting pot because so many people from so many backgrounds have worked hard to learn a common language and to realize common dreams. Others call the United States a perfect example of **cultural pluralism**—a way of life in which people share a common culture while retaining parts of their traditional cultures. All agree that America's society provides its citizens with many advantages.

## Social Patterns

Cultural geographers divide cultural characteristics into two categories—material culture and nonmaterial culture. Both of these aspects of culture illustrate the cultural pluralism of the United States.

Differences in food, art, and architecture reflect diversity within the material culture. Language and religion reflect a similar diversity in the nonmaterial culture. A growing number of Americans are **bilingual** (by·LIN·gwuhl), or fluent in two languages. Many continue to speak their native language in addition to English. Americans also practice a wide variety of religions. Christianity is the dominant religion, followed by Judaism. Many Americans, however, practice other religions. Despite this diversity, the American people, linked by modern communication and transportation systems, reflect many common cultural traits.

## Political Patterns

The political boundaries of the United States divide the country in the north from Canada and in the south from Mexico. The Atlantic Ocean forms the eastern boundary of the nation while the Pacific Ocean forms its western boundary. Throughout the nation's history these ocean boundaries have influenced trade and prevented invasion.

The United States is a fragmented nation. Part of Canada separates Alaska from the other states on the continent, while the Pacific Ocean separates Hawaii from the mainland.

The United States has a federal system of government. Under this system the national government and the states share power. Because the United States is a democracy, however, the power to govern ultimately rests in the hands of the people. The nation's plan of government—the Constitution of the United States—outlines the responsibilities of the leaders of government and the rights of the people.

## Economic Patterns

Today the economic system of the United States provides Americans with one

*Text continues on page 219.*

**217**

*The Great Plains—America's Breadbasket*

Francisco Vasquez de Coronado and Major Stephen H. Long were two of the first Europeans to explore the Great Plains. Although they saw the same grassy plains, they came to vastly different conclusions about the area's potential settlement value.

### Two Expeditions

In the 1540s Coronado led a military expedition for Spain across what is now the southwestern United States. The expedition was searching for the fabled "Seven Cities of Cibola" that had been described as "seven very large towns which had streets of silver." When the Spanish explorers reached the legendary cities, however, they saw only an adobe-walled pueblo inhabited by Zuñi Indians.

The next spring the Coronado party journeyed north in search of another legendary city called "Quivira." As they headed across the Great Plains, they marveled at the huge herds of buffalo they saw grazing on seemingly endless grassy plains. They were less impressed by Quivira—a collection of grass huts inhabited by Wichita Indians.

Nearly 300 years later, on June 6, 1820, a United States Army officer named Stephen H. Long began another expedition across the Great Plains. Long and his men traveled across what are now the states of Iowa, Nebraska, Colorado, Kansas, Oklahoma, and Arkansas.

### Same Place, Different Viewpoints

Although Coronado was disappointed at the lack of gold and silver, he was impressed by the richness of the land he saw. "The country itself," he said, "is the best that I have ever seen for producing all of the crops of Spain."

Long, by contrast, was struck by the treelessness and seeming worthlessness of the Great Plains. On the map that accompanied his report, he labeled the Great Plains the "Great American Desert."

### Two Very Different Cultural Origins

How could two intelligent explorers have such different opinions about the Great Plains? The answer lies in their different cultural backgrounds and experiences.

Coronado grew up on a dry and treeless plateau in central Spain and spent many years in the dry lands of Mexico. He compared the grass-covered Great Plains with the arid lands he knew and saw them as lush and suitable for farming.

In contrast, Long spent his early life in the humid and densely forested lands of the eastern United States. He saw the treelessness of the Great Plains as a sign that the land was far too dry for farming. In Long's experience, only deserts were treeless.

Just as each explorer evaluated the Great Plains from a particular cultural perspective, so each society views its place and resources. What is useful to one society may seem useless to others.

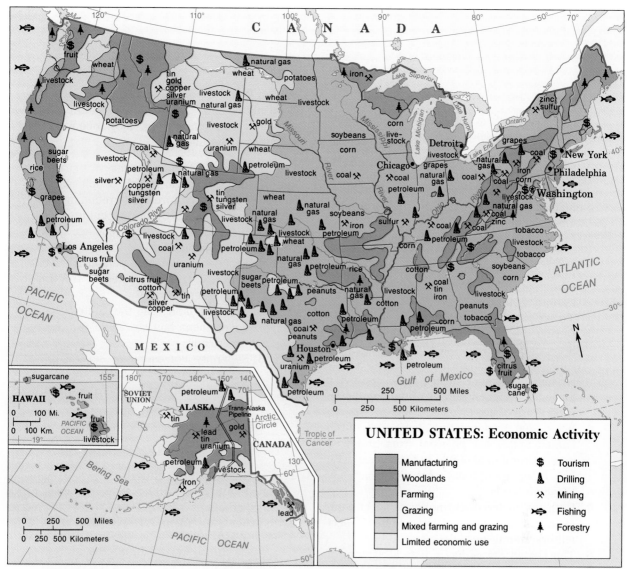

**Learning from Maps.** *Climate and natural resources help determine economic activities. What are Hawaii's main economic activities?*

of the highest standards of living in the world. Under the American **free enterprise system,** business is conducted freely with limited government intervention.

With a per capita gross national product (GNP) of $16,400 a year, the United States ranks as one of the wealthiest of the developed nations. While poverty exists in the United States, the free enterprise system provides the opportunity for all Americans to benefit from the economic system.

**SECTION 3 REVIEW**

1. **Define** cultural pluralism, bilingual, free enterprise system
2. **Summarizing Ideas** Why is the United States an example of cultural pluralism?
3. **Evaluating Ideas** What advantages does the free enterprise system provide for Americans?

## Chapter Summary

The following list contains the key concepts you have learned about the cultural setting of the United States.

1. The United States includes six major population groups: Native Americans, whites, blacks, Hispanics, Asian Americans, and Pacific Islanders.
2. In the 1800s and early 1900s immigration and a high birth rate helped the United States population grow rapidly. In recent years restrictions on immigration as well as a lower rate of natural increase have resulted in slower population growth.
3. During the 1900s the male-female balance, life expectancy, and age distribution of the American population have changed. Today women outnumber men, people are living longer, and a larger portion of the population is 65 years of age or older.
4. Since 1790 the population distribution of the United States has changed from about 95 percent rural to about 25 percent rural, with only 5 percent of today's Americans actually living on farms.
5. Both the material and nonmaterial cultural characteristics of the United States reflect cultural pluralism.
6. The United States has a federal system of government and is a democracy in which the people rule.
7. The United States is a developed nation with a free enterprise system that provides Americans with one of the highest standards of living in the world.
8. Dallas has grown into a major world city.

On a separate sheet of paper, complete the following review exercises.

## Reviewing Geographic Terms

Match each of the following terms with the correct definition.

a. Sun Belt
b. acculturation
c. age distribution
d. cultural pluralism
e. bilingual
f. reservation
g. megalopolis

_____ 1. Fluent in two languages
_____ 2. Way of life in which people share a common culture while retaining many parts of their traditional culture
_____ 3. Relative sizes of different age groups in a population
_____ 4. Process by which a person from one culture learns and takes on the traits of another culture
_____ 5. Tract of land that the United States government has set aside for Native Americans
_____ 6. Supercity consisting of several cities that have grown together
_____ 7. Area made up of southern and southwestern states

## Developing Critical Thinking Skills

1. **Comparing Ideas** How do the lives of many Native Americans differ from the lives of other groups?
2. **Synthesizing Ideas** (a) Why is there a need today to use more of the nation's resources for elderly people than there was in 1900? (b) What has caused the change?
3. **Interpreting Ideas** In what ways is the United States a good example of cultural pluralism?
4. **Analyzing Ideas** How do the conclusions Coronado and Long reached in their evaluations of the Great Plains mirror the relationships between human groups and their environments?
5. **Writing About Geography** In two clearly written paragraphs, discuss one of the following ideas. (a) Why did Coronado and Long come to vastly different conclusions about the usefulness of the Great Plains? (b) Why do you think many Native Americans have chosen to remain on reservations?

## Using Primary Sources

In the following excerpt from *God's Country and Mine*, Jacques Barzun discusses the importance of baseball to American culture. As you study the reading, consider how both baseball and society have changed. Then decide whether the sport of baseball has a similar impact on modern American culture.

Baseball *is* Greek in being national, heroic, and broken up in the rivalries of city-states. How sad that Europe knows nothing like it! Its Olympics generate anger, not unity, and its interstate politics follow no rules that a people can grasp. At least Americans understand baseball, the true realm of clear ideas.

That baseball fitly expresses the powers of the nation's mind and body is a merit separate from the glory of being the most active, agile, varied, articulate, and brainy of all group games. It is of and for our century. . . . The idea of baseball is a team, an outfit, a section, . . . in short, a twentieth-century setup of opposite numbers. . . .

The rules keep pace with this imaginative creation so rich in allusions to real life. How excellent, for instance, that a foul tip muffed by the catcher gives the batter another chance. It is the recognition of Chance that knows no argument. But on the other hand, how wise and just that the third strike must not be dropped. This points to the fact that near the end of any struggle life asks for more than is needful in order to clinch success. A victory has to be won, not snatched. We find also our American innocence in calling "World Series" the annual games between the winners in each big league. The world doesn't know or care and couldn't compete if it wanted to, but since it's us children having fun, why, the world is our stage. I said baseball was Greek. Is there not a poetic symbol in the new meaning— our meaning—of "Ruth hits Homer"?

1. **(a)** Why does the author say that baseball is Greek? **(b)** Do you agree with this comparison? Explain your answer.
2. **(a)** In the author's opinion, why is baseball better than the Olympics? **(b)** In what ways does baseball reflect modern American society?

## Practicing Geography Skills

*Before completing this activity, review Developing Geography Skills on page 213.*

**Reading Graphs** Study the graph on page 214. Then complete the following items.

1. **(a)** What type of graph is illustrated? **(b)** What is its title?
2. **(a)** What age group in the United States makes up the largest segment of its population? **(b)** the smallest segment?
3. Convert the data on the graph to a bar graph. Label the vertical axis "People (in millions)" and divide the axis into 5 segments—20, 40, 60, 80, and 100. Label the horizontal axis with the age groups.

## Exploring Geography

1. Study the pie graph, "United States Population Distribution" on page 210. Remember that the purpose of a pie graph is to show not only the relationship of each section to the other sections, but also the relationship of the sections to the whole. Keeping the purpose of pie graphs in mind, write three statements that make generalizations about the racial and ethnic makeup of the United States population.
2. Imagine that you are an immigrant to the United States. Write a three-minute speech detailing where you are leaving and why you want to immigrate.

# Cultural Regions of the United States

# PUTTING THE CHAPTER IN FOCUS

As you learned in Chapter 9, physical geographers divide the United States into physical regions according to the country's varied landforms. Cultural geographers also divide the country into regions, according to the areas in which the people share cultural characteristics. In this chapter you will learn about the major characteristics of the seven cultural regions of the United States. These cultural regions include the Northeast, the Southeast, the Great Lakes, the Plains, the Southwest, the Mountain region, and the Pacific region.

## Ideas to Understand

In studying about the cultural regions of the United States, use these ideas to give direction to your reading.

1 The two eastern regions are the most densely populated.
2 Interior regions reflect a diversity of agricultural and industrial activities.
3 Western areas are now experiencing rapid population growth.
4 The last territorial expansion brought a major population shift.

## Terms to Define

The following terms are some of the key terms in the chapter. Defining them will help you understand the cultural regions of the United States.

truck farming          locational advantage
reforestation          twin cities

## Places to Locate

Locating the following places will add to your knowledge of geography.

Boston                 San Francisco
New York City          Seattle
Philadelphia           Portland
Kansas City            Anchorage
Dallas                 Honolulu

## 1 The two eastern regions are the most densely populated.

The Northeast and Southeast regions form the historic core of the United States. Many events associated with the country's beginnings unfolded there. Today, nearly 400 years after European settlement began, these regions remain more densely populated than the other United States regions.

### The Northeast Region

The Northeast region forms part of the Atlantic seaboard, or eastern edge, of North America. It includes the New England states—Maine, New Hampshire, Vermont, Massachusetts, Rhode Island, and Connecticut—and the Middle Atlantic states—New York, Pennsylvania, New Jersey, Delaware, Maryland, and West Virginia (see the maps on pages 224 and 225).

**Agriculture.** Farmers in the Northeast produce vegetables, fruits, poultry, and dairy products for sale to people living in the region (see the chart on page 227). In New England, climate and rocky soil limit what farmers can raise. Dairy and poultry farming rank as the area's most important agricultural activities. In New England's valleys farmers grow several specialized crops such as cranberries, blueberries, pears, apples, peaches, potatoes, and tobacco.

*Frontier Days Rodeo in Cheyenne, Wyoming*

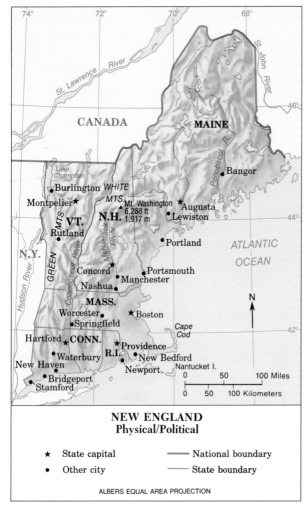

St. Lawrence River

St. John River

CANADA

MAINE

46°

Lake Champlain

Burlington • WHITE

Montpelier ★ MTS.

Bangor •

Penobscot R.

★ Mt. Washington
6,288 ft
1,917 m

Augusta
Lewiston •

44°

VT. N.H.

Rutland •

GREEN MTS.

Merrimack River

Connecticut River

Portland •

ATLANTIC
OCEAN

N.Y.

Hudson River

Concord ★

Portsmouth •

Nashua • Manchester •

MASS.

N

Worcester •
• Springfield

★ Boston

Cape
Cod

42°

Hartford ★ CONN.

• Waterbury R.I.

Providence ★

New Haven

Newport • New Bedford •

Nantucket I.

• Bridgeport
Stamford •

0    50    100 Miles

0    50    100 Kilometers

**NEW ENGLAND**
Physical/Political

★    State capital      ——   National boundary

•    Other city      ——   State boundary

ALBERS EQUAL AREA PROJECTION

*Learning from Maps. Coastal ports and cities on rivers helped to determine New England's economic development. Which New England ports are also capital cities?*

Farmers in New Jersey, Delaware, Maryland, and much of New York concentrate on **truck farming,** growing fresh fruits and vegetables for immediate sale in the cities. Mixed commercial farms in Pennsylvania and New York supply beef, pork, and grains (see Chapter 5). Specialized commercial farms in many parts of the region provide poultry, especially chickens and turkeys, and dairy products.

**Forestry, fishing, and mining.** Forestry remains important in sparsely populated sections of the Appalachian Highlands (see Chapter 9). Maine and New Hampshire have the Northeast's largest lumbering operations, which mainly supply the region's pulp and paper industries. New England also supplies half of the country's maple syrup. Although most of New England's original forests were cleared, reforestation projects have helped to cover 75 percent of New England with trees. **Reforestation** is the planting of new trees on lands that were once covered by forests.

Fishing ranks as a major industry in the Northeast. The shallow waters above the continental shelf off the New England coast hold haddock, cod, flounder, mackerel, and shellfish such as lobster. Farther south Chesapeake Bay waters contain plentiful supplies of fish and shellfish such as clams, oysters, and crabs.

The Northeast region contains many different mineral resources. Mines in New England yield granite and high-grade marble. In addition, Vermont leads the nation in the production of asbestos. Mines in western Pennsylvania and West Virginia produce coal, one of the region's key natural resources. The Appalachian Highlands of New York, Pennsylvania, and West Virginia also hold small supplies of petroleum and natural gas.

**Industry.** The Northeast ranks as the largest manufacturing and trading region in the United States. Today high-tech industries as well as many different kinds of manufacturing and service industries make key contributions to the region's economy. Many industrial and commercial centers that include factories, banks, investment houses, and insurance companies are located in and around large coastal ports such as Boston, New York City, Philadelphia, and Baltimore. Raw materials for local industries enter the ports, which also offer access to large overseas markets in Europe.

**Cities.** The Northeast is highly urbanized. Cities, towns, and suburbs form a nearly continuous urban corridor, or **megalopolis,** that extends for 450 miles (725 kilometers) along the Atlantic coast from Boston, Massachusetts, to Washington, D.C. Today the megalopolis contains nearly 39 million people and about 60 percent of the country's industrial, financial, and commercial production.

Major cities of the megalopolis include Boston, New York City, Philadelphia, Baltimore, and Washington, D.C. Other smaller cities and suburbs now almost completely cover the once undeveloped land between these major cities. Even in the few remaining open areas, such as southern New Jersey, rail lines, multilane highways, and multiwired power lines provide reminders of growing urbanization.

**Regional perspective.** The teeming cities of the Northeast reflect the cultural pluralism of the United States. Recent immigrants often live in neighborhoods with other immigrants from the same country, giving each area a distinctive cultural identity.

After World War II many of the Northeast's shoe, clothing, and heavy manufacturing industries closed because of rising fuel costs and foreign competition. Many other businesses moved to the Sun Belt. Today state and local governments work to keep factories open and to attract new businesses. In addition, many of the region's cities work to revitalize decaying neighborhoods, further attracting new businesses and residents (see the CASE STUDY on page 226).

## The Southeast Region

The Southeast spans a large part of the continent and lies completely within the Sun Belt. The region includes Virginia, Kentucky, Tennessee, North Carolina, South Carolina, Georgia, Florida, Alabama, Mississippi, Louisiana, and Arkansas. For many years a farming region, the Southeast has been undergoing rapid urbanization and industrialization.

**Agriculture.** The area's fertile soil and mild climate, which provides ample rainfall and a long growing season, favor agriculture. In the past cotton was considered "king" and the Southeast was called the Cotton Belt. Today cotton is somewhat less important but remains the region's

*Text continues on page 227.*

*Learning from Maps.* *Cities between Washington, D.C., and New York City form part of the eastern seaboard's megalopolis. What cultural imprints mark growing urbanization?*

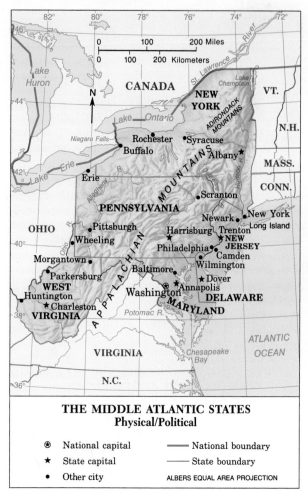

**THE MIDDLE ATLANTIC STATES**
**Physical/Political**

| ⊛ | National capital | —— | National boundary |
| ★ | State capital | —— | State boundary |
| • | Other city | | ALBERS EQUAL AREA PROJECTION |

*Assembling industrial robots in Connecticut*

New England has been a center of manufacturing since the early Industrial Revolution. Many factors helped New England become an industrial center. Poor farming conditions forced people to seek other livelihoods. The steady stream of skilled and unskilled immigrants who poured into the Northeast provided a cheap and plentiful supply of labor. The many waterfalls scattered throughout the countryside supplied the power to turn the wheels of industry.

### Advantages Became Handicaps

New England led the country's industrial production into the early 1900s. But by 1920 the region's early advantages had become liabilities. New England's factories produced goods made of cloth, wood, or leather. By 1900, however, industry had become metal-based. And synthetic materials were replacing the materials on which New England's industries depended.

In addition, New England's early energy advantage belonged to a past era. Waterfalls could not meet the rising power needs of modern industry. Coal, natural gas, and oil became more important and the need to import these energy resources drove up the costs of manufacturing in New England.

Labor, long one of New England's great assets, also became a liability. In New England labor unions were strong, wages were high, and strict laws protected workers. These conditions, however attractive to workers, raised costs and made the region unattractive to plant owners.

Adding to the other problems, many New England factories were old and their machinery obsolete. Rather than rebuild in a high-cost region, many owners simply closed their New England mills. They built new factories in areas where land, labor, raw materials, and power were all readily available at lower costs.

### A Dramatic Comeback

Until the 1940s New England continued to decline. Today, however, New England has once again become a booming industrial region and is more prosperous than at any other time in its history. In spite of the loss of thousands of jobs in the traditional industries, total industrial employment has risen dramatically. Major new industries began to appear during World War II.

The most important new industry is high-tech electronics. High-tech industries employ engineers, scientists, technicians, and computer specialists at a rate that is at least 1.5 times higher than the national average. The presence of a highly skilled labor force has attracted a large number of high-tech firms. Clear evidence of this phenomenon is the dense concentration of new electronics firms in the outer suburbs of Boston. From there electronics industries are spreading outward into the very towns where textile mills once dominated the industrial landscape of New England.

| LARGEST CITIES IN THE UNITED STATES | | LARGEST METROPOLITAN AREAS IN THE UNITED STATES | |
|---|---|---|---|
| City | Population | Metropolitan Area | Population |
| NEW YORK | 7,165,000 | NEW YORK | 17,931,000 |
| LOS ANGELES | 3,097,000 | LOS ANGELES | 12,738,000 |
| CHICAGO | 2,992,000 | CHICAGO | 8,065,000 |
| HOUSTON | 1,706,000 | SAN FRANCISCO/OAKLAND | 5,809,000 |
| PHILADELPHIA | 1,647,000 | PHILADELPHIA | 5,776,000 |
| DETROIT | 1,089,000 | DETROIT | 4,581,000 |
| DALLAS | 974,000 | BOSTON | 4,051,000 |
| SAN DIEGO | 960,000 | HOUSTON | 3,623,000 |
| PHOENIX | 853,000 | DALLAS | 3,512,000 |
| SAN ANTONIO | 843,000 | WASHINGTON | 3,490,000 |

Source: *State and Metropolitan Area Data Book*, 1986

***Learning from Charts.*** *Metropolitan area population figures include suburbs. What cities drop in rank on the chart if metropolitan area figures are included?*

most valuable crop. Although Texas and California produce more cotton than any other states, Mississippi, Arkansas, and Louisiana rank as the leading cotton-producing states in the Southeast.

Tobacco, grown in the Southeast since colonial times, ranks as the region's second most valuable crop. North Carolina, Virginia, and Kentucky lead the nation in the production of tobacco. Rice, another traditional crop, now grows mainly in Louisiana and Arkansas.

Farmers in the Southeast also grow many other crops. Citrus fruits—oranges, grapefruits, and lemons—grow in Florida, and sugarcane grows in parts of Florida and Louisiana. Peaches, apples, pecans, and vegetables grow in the eastern part of the region. Farmers raise peanuts for peanut oil, food products, and livestock feed in Georgia, Alabama, Virginia, and North Carolina. In addition, cattle, hogs, chickens,

and grain crops have become increasingly important agricultural products.

**Forestry, fishing, and mining.** The Southeast's mild climate also favors forestry. Pine and other softwoods—useful both for lumber and in the manufacture of pulpwood for paper—grow quickly in the Southeast. They mature in 15 to 20 years, instead of the 25 to 50 years it takes in cooler regions. In addition, the Southeast supplies nearly half of the country's hardwood. Abundant in the Appalachian Highlands, hardwoods support a large furniture-making industry in North Carolina.

Fishing along the Gulf Coast provides a major source of income in the Southeast. Fishers harvest shrimp, oysters, and scallops along with many species of fish.

Abundant energy and mineral resources support industrialization in the Southeast today. Mines in Kentucky and Tennessee

produce coal. Louisiana, Mississippi, and Arkansas have large deposits of oil and natural gas. The Tennessee Valley Authority makes hydroelectricity and coal-fired electricity available at low cost throughout the region. Deposits of iron ore in Alabama, zinc in Tennessee, bauxite in Arkansas, and phosphate in Florida, North Carolina, and Tennessee add to the region's mineral riches.

**Industry.** Today manufactured items produced in the Southeast have six times the value of agricultural products. Textile prod-

*Learning from Maps.* *River ports and seaports no longer remain the only leading cities of the Southeast. What are today's leading urban centers?*

THE SOUTHEASTERN STATES
Physical/Political

★ State capital    —— State boundary
● Other city    ■ Point of interest

ALBERS EQUAL AREA PROJECTION

ucts remain a leading moneymaker, though output has declined because of foreign competition. The Southeast's low taxes and abundance of inexpensive land attract hundreds of other industries, such as chemical production and food processing. As a result, states such as Arkansas and North Carolina have industrialized rapidly.

Growing industrialization requires a growing labor force. In recent years the Southeast's population has grown faster than that of any other region except the West. Such growth provides workers for the many new manufacturing jobs. Industrialization also has helped the Southeast's per capita income rise faster than that of any other region.

**Cities.**   In the 1700s and 1800s the major cities of the Southeast were river ports and seaports such as New Orleans and Memphis. Today rapidly-developing urban areas characterize all parts of the region. The largest include Atlanta, Nashville, Miami, Jacksonville, Birmingham, Louisville, Baton Rouge, and Charlotte.

**Regional perspective.**   Traditionally an agricultural region, the cultural landscape of the Southeast is changing rapidly. More and more people are moving to the region, attracted by the climate and the job opportunities in the Sun Belt. Increasing population growth rates, industrialization, and urbanization strain resources yet bring important economic benefits.

In stark contrast to this progress are the pockets of poverty that dot the region. Incomes in many parts of rural Mississippi, Arkansas, and elsewhere in Appalachia remain among the lowest in the United States. Regional agencies work to improve conditions in these areas.

As in other regions, the Southeast reflects the cultural pluralism of our country. Black influences are strong throughout the region.

*Learning from Pictures.*   *This couple is fishing in a Louisiana bayou. How have the original French settlements influenced Louisiana's cultural landscape?*

Cuban Americans have a large community in southern Florida. In Louisiana, originally settled by the French, French influences in architecture and state laws are evident.

## SECTION 1 REVIEW

1. **Define**   truck farming, reforestation, megalopolis
2. **Locate**   Boston, New York City, Philadelphia, Atlanta, Birmingham
3. **Summarizing Ideas**   What states are included in  (a) The Northeast region and  (b) the Southeast region?
4. **Contrasting Ideas**   What are the major problems of  (a) the Northeast region and  (b) the Southeast region?  (c) How is each region handling its unique problems?
5. **Synthesizing Ideas**   In what ways do agriculture, forestry, fishing, mining, and industry support the populations of  (a) the Northeast and  (b) the Southeast?

## 2 Interior regions reflect a diversity of agricultural and industrial activities.

Geographers often divide the vast lands in the interior of the United States—the land between the Appalachian and Rocky mountains—into the Great Lakes region and the Plains region. These regions cover 50 percent of the country's land area and are home to 25 percent of its people. Today the Great Lakes region has both industry and agriculture. The Plains region remains mainly agricultural. Together they form one of the world's most productive regions.

### The Great Lakes Region

The Great Lakes region covers five states—Ohio, Indiana, Illinois, Michigan, and Wisconsin. It lies between the Appalachian Mountains, the Mississippi River, the Ohio River, and the Great Lakes (see the map on page 231). The Mississippi and Ohio rivers and the Great Lakes all are navigable. This transportation network has played a major role in the settlement and industrialization of the region.

**Agriculture.** Few places in the world have soil as fertile as Ohio, Indiana, and Illinois. Farms, many of them large farms run by corporations known as agribusinesses, cover the central and northern parts of these states. This area makes up part of the Corn Belt that stretches from Ohio to South Dakota, Nebraska, and Kansas. Corn, used mainly as a feed grain for cattle and hogs, serves as the chief crop. Other crops, such as soybeans, oats, wheat, and hay, help to replenish the nutrients that corn removes from the soil. Farmers often rotate these crops to maintain soil fertility.

In Wisconsin, where summers stay too cool to grow corn, farmers specialize in dairy and truck farming. They sell the vegetables and some of the milk fresh in nearby cities. Processors convert the rest of the milk into butter, cheese, and other dairy products.

**Mining.** Neither forestry nor fishing ranks as a major economic activity in the Great Lakes region. The area's many mineral resources, however, make mining important. Mines in Illinois, Indiana, and Ohio produce coal. Indiana produces the most limestone in the nation.

**Industry.** The Great Lakes region produces most of the country's steel. The Steel Belt extends from Pittsburgh to Chicago and includes Buffalo, New York; Youngstown, Cleveland, and Toledo, Ohio; and Gary, Indiana. These steel cities grew because of their **locational advantages,** or the benefits of their locations. The cities were either near the raw materials needed for steel making—coal, iron ore, and limestone—or on waterways on which the raw materials could be easily and cheaply transported. These same waterways still carry many raw materials and finished goods in and out of the region today.

In recent years the region's steel industry has suffered a rapid decline. Mills rate as old and inefficient by modern standards and do not make steel at as low a cost as newer plants in other countries. As a result, foreign competition has caused many steel mills to close.

Many other industries have developed around the area's steel centers. Farm and transportation equipment rank as major products of the Great Lakes region. The Detroit area, for example, is known as the automobile capital of the world. Other industries produce machinery, tools, wire, household appliances, rubber, plastics, and metals.

## THE GREAT LAKES STATES
### Physical/Political

★ State capital     —— National boundary
● Other city        —— State boundary
■ Point of interest

ALBERS EQUAL AREA PROJECTION

**Learning from Maps.** *The Great Lakes comprise the world's largest body of fresh water. Which state is divided in two by the lakes?*

**Cities.** The Great Lakes region, like the Northeast region, has many large cities. Most of the cities have grown up along the region's waterways, which still serve as the major transportation link. A highly urbanized belt stretches from Pittsburgh to Milwaukee. Most of the cities along the lakes developed around a major industry. Chicago ranks as the largest city in the Great Lakes region. Other large cities include Detroit, Indianapolis, Cleveland, Columbus, Cincinnati, and Toledo.

*Text continues on page 233.*

# THE GEOGRAPHIC WEB
## Preserving Nature

Today's world would surely seem strange to the pioneers who established new beginnings in the vast wilderness of the United States and Canada. The forests and grasslands have been replaced by towering concrete, glass, and steel cities and flashing neon lights. The empty silences have been replaced with blaring horns and the sounds of rushing traffic. Is this what our ancestors struggled for?

Despite lifetimes spent in cities and in air-conditioned buildings, almost all of us feel a need to make contact with nature—to breathe the air, to listen to the wind as it sings its way through tall trees, to walk on a wave-swept beach. In the United States and other countries, conservationists work hard to preserve an environment where such air, forests, and beaches remain.

### Early Attitudes

To Americans in the 1800s untouched land seemed endless. But then state gov-

*The Nashua River after a major cleanup*

ernments, railroad companies, war veterans, and more than 1 million families claimed 761 million acres (305 million hectares) of grasslands, forests, and mountain slopes under laws passed by Congress. Eastern forests were cut and lumberjacks began removing the forests of the West. Hunters killed all the passenger pigeons, once America's most plentiful bird, and slaughtered buffalo by the millions. By the 1850s many people were shocked at the destruction of both wildlife and landscape.

### Conservation

Conservationists alerted the American people. As early as the 1830s frontier artist George Catlin suggested that the government create preserves where future generations could view "the wild freshness of nature." A few years later Henry David Thoreau, the author of *Walden,* added his voice to Catlin's, stating "In Wilderness is the Preservation of the World." Perhaps the most vocal early conservationist was John Muir—naturalist, writer, and devoted lover of the wilderness. Muir campaigned to save the Yosemite River; the western mountains; the glaciers, fjords, and forests of Alaska; and the sequoias (si·ᴋᴡᴀᴡ·uh), the giant trees in California. With the establishment of Yellowstone and Yosemite National parks, conservation efforts began to pay off.

From that start the move to preserve nature has grown. The list of American forest reserves, national wildlife refuges, and areas of historic or natural interest grows each year. It now includes the Grand Canyon, the Petrified Forest, and Muir Woods, site of the giant sequoias that John Muir so dearly loved. These natural areas remind Americans of the way the country was when pioneers first headed west. Canadians, too, are actively protecting the beauty and wilderness of their country.

**THE PLAINS STATES**
**Physical/Political**

★ State capital
• Other city
━━ National boundary
── State boundary
■ Point of interest

ALBERS EQUAL AREA PROJECTION

***Learning from Maps.*** *Abundant agricultural yields from the Plains states have resulted in low prices and falling incomes for farmers. What major river flows southeast through the region?*

**Regional perspective.** Large cities and rural areas combine to form the cultural landscape of the Great Lakes states. Many of the region's lands were first settled by immigrants from Scandinavia and Germany, giving the region a unique cultural flavor.

Yet the Great Lakes region faces some of the same problems that the Northeast faces. Many of its factories have closed and many of its people have moved out of the region. State and city governments work to improve the area's economy. In addition,

*Text continues on page 235.*

# SPECIAL FEATURE: Contour Maps

Some maps show the **contour,** or changes in elevation, of an area. The map below, called a quadrangle map, is produced by the United States government and shows the landscape of a small area along the Wisconsin–Minnesota border.

The "rings" on the map show changes in elevation. Smaller rings indicate the top of a hill. Numerous narrow rings mark spots where the elevation changes rapidly, such as a cliff or ridge. Such a ridge, marked by contour lines, can be seen running up the middle of the inset map.

Study the map and answer the following questions.

1. What do you think the 900 along the ridge measures?
2. How can you tell that St. Croix Dalles is an area of hills, plateaus, and valleys?

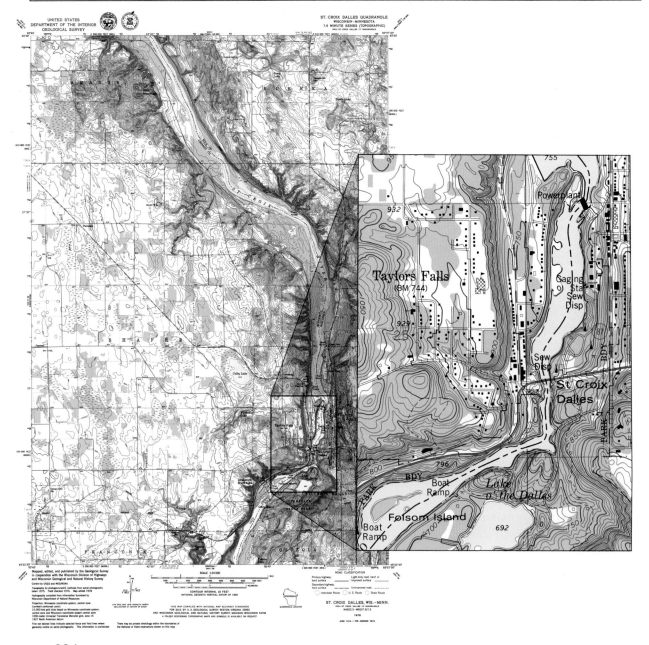

industries such as automaking have incorporated new technology and other improvements to compete more successfully with foreign firms.

## The Plains Region

The Plains region includes seven states—Minnesota, Iowa, Missouri, Kansas, Nebraska, North Dakota, and South Dakota—located west of the Mississippi River (see the map on page 233). Farming and related food-processing industries give a distinctive personality to the region.

**Agriculture.** In the Plains region rich soil, adequate rainfall, and level plains are well suited to mechanized farming. Large agribusinesses run many of the farms.

Corn and wheat rate as the region's most important crops. Farmers grow corn from Minnesota and Iowa to eastern Kansas. In areas to the west, which receive less rainfall, wheat serves as the most important crop. Western Kansas and Nebraska lie at the heart of the Winter Wheat Belt. The cooler Dakotas form part of the Spring Wheat Belt.

Beef cattle and hogs eat much of the corn grown in the region. Cattle arrive from other parts of the United States to be fattened for market in feedlots, enclosures where animals remain generally inactive as they eat. More cattle stand in feedlots in Iowa and Nebraska than in any other states. Farmers in the region raise two-thirds of the country's hogs.

**Mining.** Iron ore remains the major mineral resource of the Plains region. The Mesabi (muh·SAHB·ee) Range in northern Minnesota holds major iron ore deposits. Though the richest iron ore in these deposits has been mined, mines still produce a low quality ore called taconite (TAK·uh·nyt) that is made into pellets. Workers load the

***Learning from Pictures.*** *Cars from Detroit today must compete in the international automobile market. What countries provide the major competition in the United States automobile market?*

pellets onto freighters bound for steel centers along the Great Lakes.

**Industry.** Manufacturing in the Plains region relates closely to farming. Some factories process farm products. Meat packing and flour milling lead the food-processing industries. Other industries manufacture machinery, fertilizers, and other farm goods.

**Cities.** Although vast expanses of several states in the region, such as Minnesota and Nebraska, are sparsely settled and two states—North Dakota and South Dakota—have no large cities, the region does have some urban areas of note.

Two cities in Missouri, St. Louis and Kansas City, are the largest in the region. Other large cities, in order of size, include Minneapolis, Omaha, Wichita, St. Paul, and Des Moines. All developed around food-processing and transportation links.

**Twin cities** are an unusual feature of the urban geography of the Plains region. These are pairs of cities located on facing

235

banks of a river. Probably the best known twin cities are Minneapolis and St. Paul, Minnesota. They lie on opposite banks of the Mississippi River. On the Missouri River, which forms several state boundaries in the Plains region, some of the twin cities lie in different states. Kansas City, Missouri, for example, is the twin city of Kansas City, Kansas. Together these twin cities form a metropolitan area of nearly 1.5 million people.

**Regional perspective.** The Plains region, along with parts of the Great Lakes region, forms an area often called the "Breadbasket of the United States" because its fertile lands supply food to much of the nation and, in fact, the world. Yet the area's farmers must deal with serious challenges. Farm income has steadily declined. Farmers produce such large surpluses that they cannot find enough buyers. In many cases the federal government buys these crops or pays farmers to not farm part of their land. Despite this, the number of farmers facing bankruptcy continues to rise.

*Learning from Pictures.* *This cattle and hog farm is near Iowa City, Iowa. What two states have the most cattle feedlots in the country?*

## 3 Western areas are now experiencing rapid population growth.

Recent increases in population have greatly affected two of the cultural regions in the West—the Southwest and the Mountain region. In both areas the rapid influx of businesses and people has provided many economic opportunities. At the same time the effects of uncontrolled population growth have made leaders painfully aware of the need for future planning.

### The Southwest Region

Four states—Arizona, New Mexico, Oklahoma, and Texas—make up the Southwest region (see the map on page 237). The warm and sunny climate, multicultural population, and rapid growth of these states give the region its special personality.

**Agriculture.** Beef cattle provide the leading source of farm income in all four

states of the Southwest. Dairy products rank second in Texas, New Mexico, and Arizona. Wheat ranks second in Oklahoma. Rice, sugarcane, and citrus fruits grow well in the humid subtropical climate of the Gulf coast of Texas. Cotton, grown on irrigated land, serves as a major crop in many areas of Texas and Arizona.

Irrigation has made large-scale farming possible in the semiarid parts of the Southwest. The Rio Grande and the Colorado, Salt, and Gila rivers provide water for irrigation. Throughout the Southwest many deep wells have also been drilled to tap ground water resources.

**Fishing and mining.** Fishing remains an important industry along the Texas Gulf coast. Fishers catch shrimp, fish, and other seafoods.

The region has large deposits of mineral and energy resources. Abundant oil and natural gas supplies underlie Texas and Oklahoma. Not surprisingly, many of the jobs in Houston, Tulsa, Dallas, and Oklahoma City relate to the oil industry. Deposits of oil and natural gas also have been tapped in New Mexico. In addition, about 60 percent of the country's copper comes from strip mines in Arizona.

**Industry.** Factories dot the Southwest region. Oil refining and processing lead the major industries, particularly in Texas and Oklahoma. Food processing, especially meat packing, also rates as an important

*Learning from Maps.* Water shortages are a problem in Arizona and several other states. What human-made features on the map depict management of the water supply?

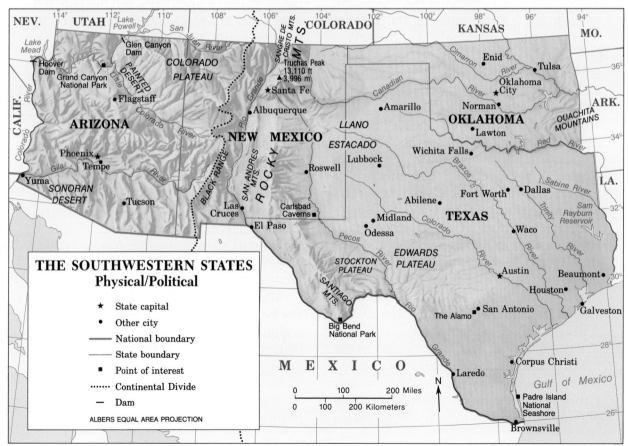

THE SOUTHWESTERN STATES
Physical/Political

★ State capital
• Other city
— National boundary
— State boundary
■ Point of interest
······ Continental Divide
— Dam

ALBERS EQUAL AREA PROJECTION

**Learning from Pictures.** *These oil workers drill for oil in Texas. What other major industries in Texas and Oklahoma are related to oil?*

industry in the region. In recent years the electronics industry has developed rapidly in the Southwest, sparking the expansion of such fast-growing cities as Dallas, Fort Worth, Austin, San Antonio, and Phoenix.

**Cities.** Houston grew with the oil boom and remains the largest city in the Southwest. Other major cities include Dallas, Fort Worth, San Antonio, El Paso, Phoenix, Albuquerque, and Oklahoma City.

**Regional perspective.** The mixture of Hispanic, Native American, and American, or "Anglo," cultures helps make the Southwest different from all other regions. Spanish influences, in particular, abound. Since the 1960s, however, industrial growth fueled by the oil boom and the movement of people to the Sun Belt has changed the face of the Southwest region. Even though a worldwide oil glut hurt the economies of Texas, Oklahoma, and New Mexico in the 1980s, rapid industrial and population growth go on, helping to make the economic future of the Southwest look bright. Along with growth, however, come the problems

of heavy demands on transportation systems, services, and the environment.

## The Mountain Region

Fewer people live in the Mountain region than in any other region in the United States because the rugged landscape makes settlement difficult in many places. Population density measures less than two people per square mile (0.5 people per square kilometer) over more than half of the region. Six states—Montana, Wyoming, Colorado, Idaho, Utah, and Nevada—make up the region (see the map on page 239).

**Agriculture.** Most agricultural land lies in the eastern section of the region. Wheat and beef cattle lead the farm products. In some places irrigation helps farmers grow alfalfa, sugar beets, vegetables, and other crops. Farmers use alfalfa and the pulp left after sugar is squeezed from sugar beets as feed for cattle. In drier areas sheep ranching serves as the major agricultural activity. Potatoes are a specialty in Idaho. An especially rich irrigated farming region lies along the foothills of the Wasatch Range near Great Salt Lake. This region was developed by Mormons, who arrived in 1847.

**Forestry and mining.** Steep, forested mountains cover much of the Mountain region. Lumbering is important in Montana, Idaho, and Colorado. In other forested areas, however, steep and inaccessible land makes lumbering impossible.

Mining brought the first settlers to the Rocky Mountains and other parts of the region. Mines still produce gold, silver, and copper. Colorado leads the world in the production of molybdenum, a metal used in making alloys. The region also has deposits of tungsten, zinc, lead, and oil shale—a rock from which oil can be extracted.

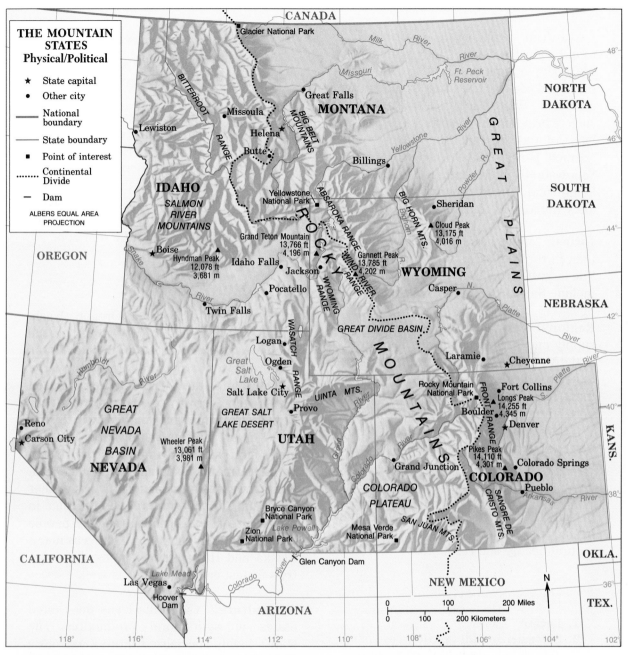

THE MOUNTAIN
STATES
Physical/Political

★ State capital
• Other city
— National boundary
— State boundary
■ Point of interest
···· Continental Divide
— Dam

ALBERS EQUAL AREA
PROJECTION

CANADA

Glacier National Park

Milk River

NORTH DAKOTA

Missouri River

Ft. Peck Reservoir

Great Falls

Missoula

MONTANA

Helena ★

Lewiston

BITTERROOT RANGE

BIG BELT MOUNTAINS

Butte

Billings

Yellowstone R.

SOUTH DAKOTA

IDAHO

Yellowstone National Park

SALMON RIVER MOUNTAINS

Sheridan

BIG HORN MTS.

Powder R.

▲ Cloud Peak 13,175 ft 4,016 m

Grand Teton Mountain 13,766 ft 4,196 m

ABSAROKA RANGE

Boise

Hyndman Peak 12,078 ft 3,681 m

Idaho Falls

Jackson

WIND RIVER RANGE

Gannett Peak 13,785 ft 4,202 m

WYOMING

Casper

Bighorn R.

OREGON

Shake River

Pocatello

WYOMING RANGE

NEBRASKA

Twin Falls

GREAT DIVIDE BASIN

Platte River

Humboldt River

Logan

WASATCH RANGE

Laramie

Cheyenne ★

GREAT NEVADA BASIN

Ogden

Great Salt Lake

Rocky Mountain National Park

Fort Collins

FRONT RANGE

Longs Peak 14,255 ft 4,345 m

Salt Lake City ★

UINTA MTS.

Boulder

Reno

Carson City ★

Wheeler Peak 13,061 ft 3,981 m ▲

Provo

Green River

Denver ★

NEVADA

GREAT SALT LAKE DESERT

UTAH

MOUNTAINS

Pikes Peak 14,110 ft 4,301 m ▲

Colorado Springs

Grand Junction

COLORADO

Pueblo

KANS.

Bryce Canyon National Park

COLORADO PLATEAU

Lake Powell

Mesa Verde National Park

SAN JUAN MTS.

SANGRE DE CRISTO MTS.

Arkansas River

CALIFORNIA

Zion National Park

Colorado River

Glen Canyon Dam

OKLA.

Lake Mead

NEW MEXICO

N

Las Vegas

Hoover Dam

Colorado River

ARIZONA

TEX.

0    100    200 Miles
0    100    200 Kilometers

*Learning from Maps.* The sparsely populated Mountain region has rugged natural beauty. Which city is nearest the continental divide?

Recent discoveries of oil and natural gas reserves have encouraged settlement in Montana and Wyoming. These two states also have begun to strip mine coal, much of which is used to generate electricity at power plants in the Plains region.

**Industry.** In the Mountain region wood and paper processing and oil and mineral processing rank as the major industries. Many of these industries developed around Denver. High-tech businesses stretch from Colorado Springs to Boulder.

**239**

Tourism remains an important year-round industry. Cool, sunny summers attract people from around the country and the world seeking to escape from high temperatures. Winter snows attract skiers to such world-famous resorts as Aspen and Vail, Colorado, and Jackson Hole, Wyoming. National parks such as Glacier in Montana; Yellowstone in Wyoming, Montana, and Idaho; and Rocky Mountain in Colorado draw millions of tourists each year.

**Cities.**   Many more people live in cities than in rural areas in the Mountain region. The largest city is Denver. Other large cities include Salt Lake City and Las Vegas.

**Regional perspective.**   A limited water supply and rugged landforms limit growth in the Mountain region. Many places remain either too dry or inaccessible for development. Most of the water and level land support farming and ranching.

Many of the region's population centers, however, have grown so fast that air pollution, traffic congestion, and inadequate housing present constant problems. Plans to accommodate growth in the region, especially in large cities such as Denver, must be made in order to protect the region's natural beauty and resources.

---

**SECTION 3 REVIEW**

1. **Locate**   Dallas
2. **Summarizing Ideas**   How have mining and industry helped the Southwest region grow?
3. **Interpreting Ideas**   What makes the Southwest region different from the other regions you have studied so far?
4. **Organizing Ideas**   What states are located in the Mountain region?
5. **Synthesizing Ideas**   What problems of booming growth must the regions' planners tackle?

---

## 4 The last territorial expansion brought a major population shift.

In recent years the Pacific region has experienced rapid population growth. Today 14 percent of the American people live in this area. Population increases present a challenge to the people of the region. Many growth-related problems have been solved. But as the population continues to grow, more problems may be on the horizon.

### The Pacific Region

Five states—California, Oregon, Washington, Alaska, and Hawaii—make up the Pacific region (see the map on page 241). Settlers began to arrive in the area in large numbers after the United States organized the Oregon Territory—today's states of Oregon, Washington, and Idaho—in 1848. The discovery of gold in California in 1849 led many more settlers to move to the region. Settlers have been arriving ever since. California now has more people than any other state and 16 times more people than in 1900. Oregon has 6 times as many people as in 1900; Washington has 8 times as many. Alaska and Hawaii rank among the country's fastest-growing states as well.

**Agriculture.**   California leads the United States in agricultural production. The state's highly specialized farms raise more than half of the apricots, artichokes, avocados, broccoli, brussels sprouts, cauliflower, dates, figs, garlic, grapes, lemons, lettuce, peaches, plums, and walnuts consumed in the United States.

The Central Valley and the Imperial Valley near the mouth of the Colorado River form California's two major farming regions. Farmers in both areas use irrigation extensively. A great aqueduct carries water

*Text continues on page 243.*

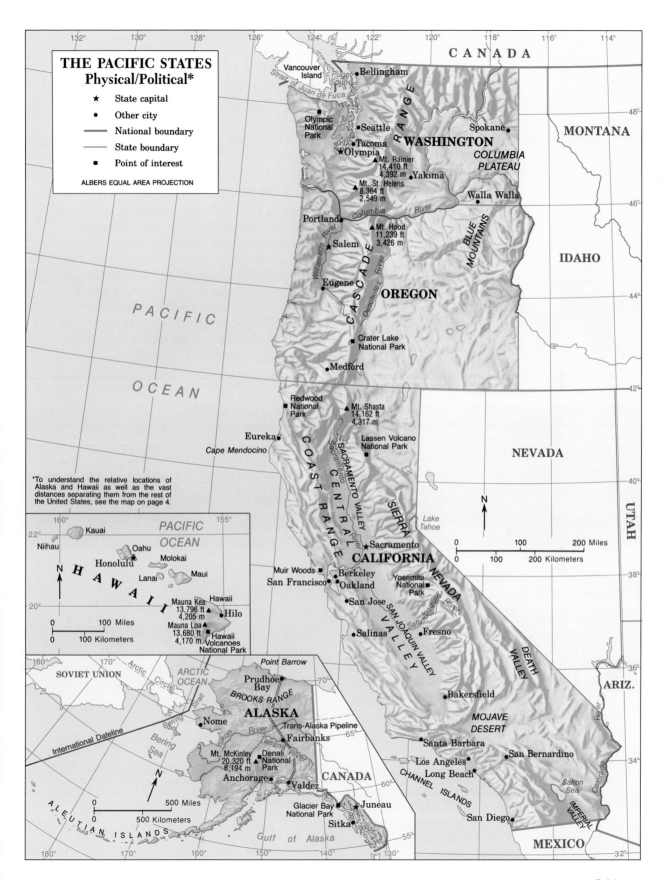

THE PACIFIC STATES
Physical/Political*

★ State capital
● Other city
— National boundary
— State boundary
■ Point of interest

ALBERS EQUAL AREA PROJECTION

*To understand the relative locations of Alaska and Hawaii as well as the vast distances separating them from the rest of the United States, see the map on page 4.

CANADA

Vancouver Island
● Bellingham
CASCADE RANGE
Olympic National Park
● Seattle
● Spokane
● Tacoma
★ Olympia
WASHINGTON
COLUMBIA PLATEAU
▲ Mt. Rainier 14,410 ft 4,392 m
● Yakima
▲ Mt. St. Helens 8,364 ft 2,549 m
● Walla Walla
Columbia River
● Portland
▲ Mt. Hood 11,239 ft 3,426 m
BLUE MOUNTAINS
Willamette River
★ Salem
Deschutes River
● Eugene
OREGON
■ Crater Lake National Park
● Medford

MONTANA

IDAHO

PACIFIC

OCEAN

■ Redwood National Park
▲ Mt. Shasta 14,162 ft 4,317 m
● Eureka
Cape Mendocino
■ Lassen Volcano National Park
SACRAMENTO VALLEY
COAST RANGE
CENTRAL VALLEY
Sacramento River
SIERRA NEVADA
Lake Tahoe

NEVADA

UTAH

N

0    100    200 Miles
0    100    200 Kilometers

★ Sacramento
CALIFORNIA
■ Muir Woods
● Berkeley
● San Francisco ● Oakland
● San Jose
● Yosemite National Park
San Joaquin River
● Salinas
SAN JOAQUIN VALLEY
● Fresno
● Bakersfield
DEATH VALLEY
MOJAVE DESERT
● Santa Barbara
● San Bernardino
● Los Angeles
● Long Beach
CHANNEL ISLANDS
Salton Sea
Colorado River
● San Diego
IMPERIAL VALLEY

ARIZ.

MEXICO

PACIFIC OCEAN
160°    155°
22°
● Kauai
● Niihau
● Oahu
Honolulu ★
● Molokai
● Lanai
● Maui
HAWAII
N
Mauna Kea 13,796 ft 4,205 m ▲
Hawaii
● Hilo
Mauna Loa 13,680 ft 4,170 m ▲
■ Hawaii Volcanoes National Park
20°
0    100 Miles
0    100 Kilometers

160°    170°
SOVIET UNION
Arctic Circle
ARCTIC OCEAN
Point Barrow
● Prudhoe Bay
BROOKS RANGE
70°
International Dateline
ALASKA
Bering Strait
● Nome
Yukon River
Trans-Alaska Pipeline
Tanana River
● Fairbanks
65°
Bering Sea
▲ Mt. McKinley 20,320 ft 6,194 m
■ Denali National Park
● Anchorage
● Valdez
CANADA
60°
ALEUTIAN ISLANDS
N
0    500 Miles
0    500 Kilometers
■ Glacier Bay National Park
★ Juneau
● Sitka
Gulf of Alaska
55°
180°    170°    160°    150°    140°    130°

**241**

Maps are reference tools. When they are grouped together in a book, they form a reference tool called an atlas. (The map section at the beginning of this textbook provides one example of an atlas.) One of the most common and useful types of atlases is a road atlas. With a road atlas you can plan routes and calculate distances for a trip.

Most road atlases have two basic parts. The first part is a series of maps showing information about various areas such as states or countries. This information usually includes cities, points of interest, major highways, and important geographical features such as lakes, rivers, and mountains. The second part is a mileage chart that lists the distances between major cities and other points of interest. The mileage chart is a grid with city names listed along the top and down the side. Mileage between cities is listed in the columns and rows. To best use a road atlas to plan a trip, you should be able to use both the map and the mileage chart.

### How to Use an Atlas to Plan a Trip

To use a road atlas to plan a trip, follow these guidelines.

1. **Plan ahead.** List your destination and the places you wish to visit on your trip. Decide if your pace is to be leisurely or more hurried.
2. **Study the map or maps.** Note the roads and highways that lead to your points of interest and destination. Plan a route along these roads and highways that suits your needs. Thin lines indicate state and county roads; thicker lines mark interstate highways.
3. **Check the mileage chart.** Locate your city or the city nearest the one you are starting from. Then locate the city that is your destination. The mileage between

those cities* is shown where the column and row meet.

### Applying the Skill

Study the map and mileage chart below. Note that the most direct route from Billings, Montana, to Boise (BOY·see), Idaho, follows Interstate 90 to Butte (BYOOT), then Interstate 15 to Pocatello, and Interstate 86 to Interstate 84 to Boise. The map also shows several other routes between the two cities. The mileage chart tells you that your trip along the most direct route will cover 606 miles (975 kilometers).

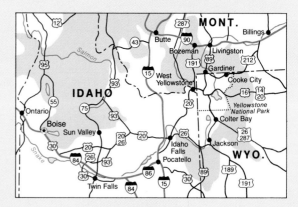

| | Albany, NY | Albuquerque, NM | Atlanta, GA | Baltimore, MD | Billings, MT | Birmingham, AL | Boise, ID | Boston, MA | Buffalo, NY | Charleston, SC |
|---|---|---|---|---|---|---|---|---|---|---|
| Acadia N.P. ME | 440 | 2459 | 1330 | 666 | 2468 | 1508 | 2958 | 274 | 733 | 1219 |
| Albany NY | | 2041 | 1010 | 339 | 2098 | 1071 | 2518 | 169 | 301 | 880 |
| Albuqueque NM | 2041 | | 1404 | 1890 | 991 | 1254 | 940 | 2220 | 1773 | 1703 |
| Atlanta GA | 1010 | 1404 | | 654 | 1799 | 148 | 2223 | 1108 | 907 | 291 |
| Baltimore MD | 339 | 1890 | 654 | | 1916 | 771 | 2406 | 427 | 365 | 568 |
| Big Bend N.P. TX | 2239 | 586 | 1341 | 1907 | 1421 | 1192 | 1702 | 2297 | 1923 | 1623 |
| Billings MT | 2098 | 991 | 1799 | 1916 | | 1775 | 606 | 2197 | 1721 | 2175 |
| Birmingham AL | 1071 | 1254 | 148 | 771 | 1775 | | 2065 | 1226 | 902 | 441 |
| Boise ID | 2518 | 940 | 2223 | 2406 | 606 | 2065 | | 2685 | 2214 | 2493 |
| Boston MA | 169 | 2220 | 1108 | 427 | 2197 | 1226 | 2685 | | 465 | 936 |

*To practice this skill, see Practicing Geography Skills on page 247.*

---

* Note that not every city is listed on the mileage chart. In calculating distances you may have to use the nearest city listed.

## REGIONS OF THE UNITED STATES

| Region | Population | Area (sq. mi/sq. km) | Principal Industries | Principal Agricultural Products |
|---|---|---|---|---|
| NORTHEAST 12 States | 56,642,000 | 206,168/ 533,975 | Electronics, chemicals, plastics, food processing, printing and publishing, machinery, clothing, metals, computers, transportation equipment, tourism, textiles, paper | Poultry, vegetables, dairy products, soybeans, potatoes, apples, corn, cranberries, livestock, hay, maple syrup |
| SOUTHEAST 11 states | 53,753,000 | 525,449/ 1,361,042 | Food processing, pulp and paper products, furniture, chemicals, tourism, tobacco products, textiles, electronics, transportation equipment | Cotton, tobacco, peanuts, corn, citrus fruits, sugarcane, soybeans, vegetables |
| GREAT LAKES 5 states | 41,602,000 | 248,283/ 643,053 | Automobiles, transportation equipment, machinery, electronics, metals, machine tools, chemicals, food processing | Corn, wheat, dairy products |
| PLAINS 7 states | 17,516,000 | 517,247/ 1,339,970 | Food processing, farm machinery, chemicals, aircraft, tires, electronics, clothing, stone and glass | Livestock, corn, wheat, barley, oats, sorghum |
| SOUTHWEST 4 states | 23,764,000 | 572,832/ 1,483,365 | Electronics, oil, printing, tourism, food processing, machinery, oil field equipment | Livestock, cotton, sugar beets, sorghum, wheat, grains |
| MOUNTAIN 6 states | 8,077,000 | 628,312/ 1,627,328 | Food processing, minerals, tourism, wood products, electronics, aerospace, computers, machinery, stone and glass | Livestock, wheat, corn, potatoes, peas, barley, alfalfa, apples, beans |
| PACIFIC 5 states | 34,137,000 | 916,728/ 2,347,326 | Tourism, food processing, aerospace, metals, machinery, clothing, wood products, pulp and paper, fish products | Vegetables, grapes, oranges, sugarcane, wheat, barley, potatoes, apples |

Source: *Statistical Abstract of the United States,* 1987

**Learning from Charts.** *The different regions of the United States produce great varieties of goods. Which region has the largest population?*

from the rainy northern parts of the Central Valley into the drier southern parts. Though favored by a year-long growing season and fertile soil, the arid Imperial Valley can produce crops only with water that the Colorado River supplies.

Hawaii's fertile volcanic soil and abundant rainfall also support farming. Plantations on the wetter, eastern sides of the mountains produce sugarcane, the leading crop. Pineapples rank as the second major crop. They, too, grow on plantations, but usually on the drier sides of the islands. Advanced machinery, scientific methods, and a large labor force now make pineapple cultivation a major industry. Farmers also grow papayas, coffee, macadamia nuts, and flowers. Large cattle ranches supply over 50 percent of the beef for the island's people.

The cooler states of Oregon, Washington, and Alaska are less suited to farming than California and Hawaii. Strawberries, pears, filbert nuts, vegetables, and flower bulbs lead the crops grown in Oregon.

Washington produces more apples, dried peas, and hops than any other state. The semiarid Columbia Plateau in the interior of both states contains many wheat farms and cattle ranches. Water from the Columbia River irrigates farms on the semiarid plateau. Cold weather and a short growing season limit farming in Alaska to gardens and small farms.

**Forestry, fishing, and mining.** Beautiful redwood and sequoia forests cover broad expanses of the Pacific states. These trees are among the largest and oldest living things on earth. Some trees live several thousand years and grow more than 320 feet (100 meters) tall.

The region's states rank among the leaders in lumbering. Redwood rates as the most important timber tree cut in California. Douglas fir and western cedar make up the principal trees cut in Oregon and Washington. Alaska exports much of the lumber and pulp it produces to Japan. Construction companies use most of the lumber cut in the rest of the region. Throughout the region large lumber companies have planted tree farms and started reforestation projects to replenish the area's forests.

Fishing contributes to the economies of all five states in the Pacific region. Fishing villages and commercial fishing ports dot their coasts. Alaska leads the country in fishing. Fishers catch salmon, herring, halibut, shrimp, and crabs in the cool waters of the Gulf of Alaska and the Bering Sea. The United States tuna industry centers in California, while fishing fleets in Washington and Oregon catch salmon, halibut, and herring. Fishing also is important in Hawaii.

California and Alaska were long famous for gold and silver deposits. Though mines continue to produce these minerals—as well as copper, mercury, and tungsten—rich oil and natural gas deposits prove more important today. In Alaska these deposits are located under the North Slope near Prudhoe Bay. The Trans-Alaska Pipeline carries oil 800 miles (1,300 kilometers) to Valdez on the southern coast. In California, oil deposits lie near Los Angeles and Bakersfield. Efforts are also underway to extend oil production offshore. Environmentalists, however, protest the drilling because they fear oil spills will damage wildlife and beaches along the coast.

**Industry.** Tourism ranks as the leading industry in the Pacific region. Each year millions of tourists come to see the great scenic beauty of these states. Hawaii and California lead the region's well-developed and successful tourist industries.

The Pacific region has a variety of other successful industries. The manufacture of transportation equipment rates as the leading industry in California and Washington. Seattle, Burbank, Long Beach, and San Diego are aircraft manufacturing centers. Shipbuilding remains important, but has de-

*Learning from Pictures.* *The beautiful city of San Diego is known for its harbor and beaches. What is the largest city in the Pacific region?*

244

clined in the face of foreign competition. The largest concentration of computer and electronics industries in the United States is in Silicon Valley between San Francisco and San Jose. Large factories process fruits, vegetables, and fish in California. Food processing and wood pulp and paper manufacturing lead industries in Oregon.

**Cities.** Los Angeles ranks as the largest city in the Pacific region and the second largest in the United States (see the map on page 215). San Francisco, Oakland, Berkeley, and San Jose form the second-largest urban area on the Pacific coast. Other large cities include San Diego, Seattle, and Portland. Anchorage is the largest city in Alaska, while Honolulu is the largest city in Hawaii.

**Regional perspective.** The Pacific region has a cultural landscape as diverse as its physical landscape. The urban areas of southern California reflect Spanish influences in language, cooking, and architecture. The area's many Asian Americans also contribute to the region's cultural pluralism.

The Pacific states must deal with the same rapid growth as the Southeast and Southwest. The major growth-related issues are water shortages, environmental protection, the high cost of living, and the strain on government services.

## Alaska and Hawaii

Some geographers group Alaska and Hawaii together in a single cultural region. They do so because both states share significant characteristics, including geographic isolation, a varied ethnic mix, a high cost of living, and strategic locations.

Long distances separate both Alaska and Hawaii from the other 48 states. Honolulu is over 2,000 miles (3,200 kilometers)

southwest of San Francisco. Part of Canada and the Pacific Ocean separate Alaska from other mainland states.

Alaska and Hawaii also have unique mixtures of people. In Alaska about one-third of the people are Native Americans belonging to three different groups. Eskimos live mainly in the colder northern regions of the state. American Indians live widely scattered over the state. Aleuts live mainly on the Aleutian Islands.

Native Hawaiians trace their descent from Polynesians who traveled in canoes thousands of miles across the Pacific Ocean from Tahiti to settle the islands. Today Hawaiians make up a small minority in the state. Asian Americans, including people of Japanese and Filipino descent, now form the major ethnic group.

Because so many necessities must be shipped from the other states, Alaska and Hawaii have a much higher cost of living than other parts of the United States. Salaries and wages are also high, however, to compensate for the high living costs.

Alaska and Hawaii both have locations that are important to military defense. Alaska, as the state nearest the Soviet Union, has special strategic value for the defense of North America. In Hawaii Oahu is the center of the United States Pacific defense. Pearl Harbor, in Honolulu, serves as an important naval base.

---

**SECTION 4 REVIEW**

1. **Locate**   San Francisco, Seattle, Portland, Anchorage, Honolulu
2. **Summarizing Ideas**   What states make up the Pacific region?
3. **Contrasting Ideas**   What are the differences in agriculture within the states of the Pacific region?
4. **Comparing Ideas**   How are  **(a)** forestry, fishing, mining, and  **(b)** industry similar in the Pacific region?

# CHAPTER 11 REVIEW

## Chapter Summary

The following list contains the key concepts you have learned about the cultural regions of the United States.

1. The United States can be divided into seven cultural regions: the Northeast, the Southeast, the Great Lakes, the Plains, the Southwest, the Mountain region, and the Pacific region. Each region has a unique personality, or combination of features, that makes it different from other places in the United States.
2. The Northeast and Southeast form the nation's historic core. Today the Northeast is dominated by manufacturing and trade concentrated in a great urban area called a megalopolis. The Southeast is industrializing and changing rapidly.
3. Manufacturing in the United States began in New England. Several developments in the 1800s turned New England's advantages into handicaps. Today, however, the area is home to a flourishing high-tech industry.
4. Interior regions support a diversity of agricultural and industrial activities. Soil and climate support a productive agriculture largely based on corn. Dairying is important in cooler regions, wheat in drier regions. The Great Lakes region is more industrial than agricultural. The Plains region is predominantly agricultural.
5. The population of the western United States is growing rapidly. Growth in the Southwest is dependent largely on oil, natural gas, irrigation, and the electronics industry. Growth in the Mountain region is based mainly on coal, oil, natural gas, and tourism. In the Pacific region productive agriculture and a wealth of natural resources have led to rapid industrialization.
6. Alaska and Hawaii have some surprising things in common. Among the aspects these states share are geographic isolation, a varied ethnic mix, a high cost of living, and strategic locations.

On a separate sheet of paper, complete the following review exercises.

## Reviewing Geographic Terms

Supply the geographic term that correctly completes each sentence.

1. A pair of cities located on facing banks of a river are called ____ ____.
2. Cities on waterways or near raw materials have ____ ____.
3. Growing fresh fruits or vegetables for sale in the city is called ____ ____.
4. Cities, towns, and suburbs forming a nearly continuous urban corridor are called a ____.
5. ____ is the process of planting new trees on lands once forested.

## Developing Critical Thinking Skills

1. **Summarizing Ideas** (a) What are the seven cultural regions of the United States discussed in this chapter? (b) Which of the physical regions described in Chapter 9 are located in each cultural region?
2. **Interpreting Ideas** Why are the Northeast and Southeast regions more densely populated than the rest of the country?
3. **Seeing Relationships** (a) How did technological innovations change New England's early advantages into handicaps? (b) How did World War II change the economic future of New England?
4. **Analyzing Ideas** Why is the Great Lakes region still vital to the United States economy even though many of its factories have closed and people are moving out of the region?
5. **Contrasting Ideas** (a) How are the cultural landscapes of the Northeast region and the Mountain region different? (b) Why is the cultural landscape of the Mountain region likely to remain very different from that of other cultural regions of the United States?

**6. Writing About Geography** In two well-written paragraphs, discuss one of the following ideas. **(a)** Why is the Plains region undergoing changes in farming? **(b)** If you were an urban planner, how would you resolve growth-related issues in your community or the city nearest your home?

## Using Primary Sources

In the following excerpt from *Their Blood Is Strong*, John Steinbeck describes the migrants in California in the late 1930s. As you study the reading, consider modern migrants and compare them with those described by Steinbeck in 1938.

At the season of the year when California's great crops are coming into harvest, the heavy grapes, the prunes, the apples and lettuce and the rapidly maturing cotton, our highways swarm with the migrant workers, that shifting group of nomadic, poverty-stricken harvesters driven by hunger and the threat of hunger from crop to crop, from harvest to harvest, up and down the state and into Oregon. . . . There are at least 150,000 homeless migrants wandering up and down the state, and that is an army large enough to make it important to every person in the state. . . .

The unique nature of California agriculture requires that these migrants exist, and requires that they move about. . . .

Thus, in California we find a curious attitude toward a group that makes our agriculture successful. The migrants are needed, and they are hated. Arriving in a district they find the dislike always [given] out by the resident to the foreigner, the outlander. . . . They are never received into a community nor into the life of a community. Wanderers in fact, they are never allowed to feel at home in the communities that demand their services.

1. **(a)** According to Steinbeck, why do the migrants move from job to job? **(b)** How is there a contradiction in how migrants are received?
2. At the time the excerpt was written, how many migrants did the author estimate worked in California?

## Practicing Geography Skills

*Before completing this activity, review Developing Geography Skills on page 242.*

**Using Road Atlases** Study the road map and mileage chart on page 242. Then complete the following questions.

1. How many miles apart are **(a)** Boise, Idaho, and Boston? **(b)** Birmingham and Baltimore?
2. What highways would you take on a trip from Butte, Montana, to Idaho Falls, Idaho?
3. What national park would you travel through on a trip from Livingston, Montana, to Jackson, Wyoming?

## Exploring Geography

1. Choose one of the cities of the United States mentioned in this chapter. Then look through newspapers and magazines to find photographs, paintings, diagrams, or maps of this city. Use these illustrations to construct a poster highlighting the cultural and physical settings of the city. You might also include a brief chart at the bottom of your poster showing the city's population, land area, absolute location, and major industries.
2. Choose one of the regions discussed in this chapter. Then use the map "United States: Economic Activity" on page 219 and the content of the chapter to construct a simple table showing economic activities in the region you have chosen. The table should consist of two columns, one headed "State" and the other headed "Economic Activities."

# PUTTING THE CHAPTER IN FOCUS

Canada stretches more than 3,000 miles (4,800 kilometers) east and west and more than 2,000 miles (3,200 kilometers) north and south in North America. It is divided into ten provinces and two territories. Canada is located to the north of the United States along the longest unguarded border in the world. Historically, economically, and culturally, the two countries have remained closely linked throughout their histories.

## Ideas to Understand

In studying about the physical and cultural settings of Canada, use these ideas to give direction to your reading.

1 Many of Canada's physical regions extend from United States regions.
2 A unique blend of two cultures forms Canada's cultural setting.
3 Great differences exist among Canada's cultural regions.

## Terms to Define

The following terms are some of the key terms in the chapter. Defining them will help you understand Canada.

peninsula            secede
*cordillera*         native peoples
tree line            Indian reserve

## Places to Locate

Locating the following places will add to your knowledge of geography.

Quebec               Yukon Territory
New Brunswick        Labrador
Nova Scotia          Northwest
Prince Edward          Territories
  Island             British Columbia
Newfoundland         Alberta
St. Lawrence River   Saskatchewan
Ontario              Manitoba
Mackenzie River

## 1 Many of Canada's physical regions extend from United States regions.

Canada stretches across the northern half of North America from the Atlantic Ocean to Alaska. It ranks as the world's second-largest country in area, after the Soviet Union. Much of Canada lies in the cold, icy north, along Arctic waters. Towering peaks, broad prairies, blue lakes, and rocky soils cover much of the land. The climate is cold—often too cold for farming—and natural resources are plentiful.

### Physical Regions

Canada features seven physical regions—the Appalachian Highlands, the Canadian Shield, the Great Lakes–St. Lawrence Lowlands, the Interior Plains, the Cordilleran region, the Hudson Bay Lowland, and the Arctic Islands. The first five regions are continuations of physical regions in the United States.

**Appalachian Highlands.** The Appalachian Highlands, also called the Laurentian Highlands, extend northward from New England into southeastern Quebec, New Brunswick, Nova Scotia, Prince Edward Island, and Newfoundland (NOO·fuhn·luhnd) (see the map on page 253). Except on tiny Prince Edward Island, forested hills and rounded mountain peaks highlight the landscape. As in New England, glaciers once scraped the entire area, leaving the soil thin, rocky, and poorly suited for farming.

◀ *Changing of the guard at Canada's Parliament*

**249**

**Canadian Shield.** Much of Canada between the St. Lawrence River, Lake Superior, and Great Slave Lake (see the map on page 253) lies on the Canadian Shield. This shield extends south into the United States (see page 196). The shield has very poor soil but contains a wealth of minerals (see page 251). The region remains rugged and heavily forested and supports a large lumbering industry. Glacial lakes dot the region, which also is crisscrossed by rapidly flowing rivers. Waterfalls and rapids on many of the rivers have become sites for hydroelectric plants.

**The Great Lakes-St. Lawrence Lowlands.** The Great Lakes–St. Lawrence Lowlands cover less than 2 percent of the land. The Great Lakes Lowland, or Ontario Peninsula, in southern Ontario extends from the Central Lowland of the United States (see page 195). As you learned from the graphic on pages 18–19 entitled "Basic Land and Water Forms," a **peninsula** is a narrow piece of land surrounded on three sides by water.

The St. Lawrence Lowland borders the St. Lawrence River. A narrow valley of rich soil sandwiched between the Appalachian Highlands and the Canadian Shield, the lowland supports many productive farms.

**Interior Plains.** The Great Plains of the United States merge into the Interior Plains of Canada. The Interior Plains extend north to the Arctic Ocean along the Mackenzie River. Like the Great Plains, Canada's Interior Plains hold rich oil and natural gas reserves. In the south they support productive farms and ranches.

**Cordilleran region.** Western Canada lies in what Canadians call the Cordilleran region. The name comes from the Spanish word *cordillera* (kaurd·uhl·YER·uh), meaning "mountain system." Three landforms from the United States extend across the border into the Cordilleran region. The Rocky Mountains rise along the Alberta–British Columbia border at its eastern edge. The Intermountain Plateaus form a rugged strip of valleys, plateaus, and basins in interior British Columbia. The Coast Mountains, extensions of the Coast Ranges of the United States, rise along Canada's western coast. Mount Logan, the highest point in the cordillera and in all of Canada, rises to 19,850 feet (6,050 meters) in southwestern Yukon Territory.

**Hudson Bay Lowland.** A flat coastal plain along the shores of Hudson Bay forms the Hudson Bay Lowland. The lowland remains too cold and marshy for large-scale settlement and has only a few trading posts. The port of Churchill, which was constructed in 1931 to ship wheat to Europe, stays open for trade only during the short summer season, when Hudson Bay is clear of ice.

**Arctic Islands.** Canada's Arctic Islands are north of the Arctic Circle (66.5° N). Baffin and Ellesmere are the two largest islands. Oil and natural gas have been found in the Arctic Islands, but high production and transportation costs in this remote region discourage development.

## Rivers and Lakes

Canada boasts plentiful water resources. The waterway made up of the Great Lakes and the St. Lawrence River forms a vital water route. It remains open for trade from April to mid-December, but closes because of ice in winter. Canals and locks make the entire waterway navigable by ocean vessels. Ships and barges transport even bulky cargoes such as wheat, iron ore, and coal on the waterway to various lake ports and to the Atlantic.

Canada's other long river, the Mackenzie, proves less useful for trade. It flows

*Text continues on page 252.*

# EXPLORING NATURE: The Canadian Shield

The earth's shields hold particular interest for geologists. They usually call the shield in North America the Canadian Shield. Its other names include Laurentian Shield, Laurentian Upland, and Laurentian Plateau.

## Ancient Rocks

Geologists call the rocks of the shield *Precambrian,* meaning they were formed before fossils were abundant. (Abundant fossils first appear in rock from the Cambrian period.) Precambrian rocks range from 500 million to 5 billion years old.

Ancient rocks are more likely to contain concentrated deposits of metals and other ores than younger rocks because mineral ores form as earth movements, such as mountain building, alter the rocks. The older the rocks, the more they have changed.

## Effects of the Ice Age

The surface of the Canadian Shield was changed dramatically during the Ice Age. Great ice sheets crept southward across the region, smoothing and scraping the land with the power of thousands of bulldozers. The results are visible everywhere. One important result is the almost complete lack of soil. Only a few spots have soil suitable for farming.

A second result of the Ice Age is a landscape filled with lakes and swamps. Debris left by melting glaciers blocked original channels and forced rivers out of their banks. Water filled low areas, creating thousands of lakes and wildly winding rivers.

## Geographic Effect

The shield also holds interest for cultural geographers, who study it as a human

*Mining on the Canadian Shield*

habitat. For example, geographers note that the lack of soil suitable for farming has limited settlement of the shield. They also note the importance of the area's great mineral wealth. Mines near Sudbury, Ontario, supply 90 percent of the nickel mined in the non-Communist world. They also produce copper, silver, gold, and other minerals. Mines in Labrador supply iron ore.

## Land of the Future?

Canadians have steadily, if slowly, migrated north onto the Canadian Shield. Mining opportunities draw many settlers. Quebec Province, a leader in developing these lands, looks to the region's vast hydroelectric potential to attract more settlers. It is developing one of the world's largest hydroelectric plants on the La Grande River near James Bay. The availability of energy, it is hoped, will attract other businesses and settlers to the region.

***Learning from Pictures.*** *Maligne Lake in Alberta is an example of Canada's beautiful physical setting. Where is Canada's mildest climate type?*

from Great Slave Lake to the Arctic Ocean (see the map on page 253). In summer huge barges carry cargoes along the Mackenzie into isolated northern mining communities. In winter, when the river freezes, trailer trucks use its frozen surface as a highway.

## Climates

Canada's climates are colder versions of climates found in the northern United States (see the map on page 201). The mildest climate, a west coast marine climate, occurs in southwestern British Columbia.

Colder, more extreme continental climates occur inland. On the Interior Plains the long winters feature bitterly cold temperatures and occasional deep snows and blizzards. Somewhat less extreme conditions prevail in the Ontario Peninsula, where surrounding lakes moderate temperatures. Farther east, very long, cold, and snowy winters affect Quebec and the Atlantic Provinces, while summers remain short and cool.

Harsh subarctic and polar climates limit settlement in northern areas. Subarctic conditions, made even colder by the icy blasts of the jet stream, prevail in Labrador, northern Quebec and Ontario, the northern Prairie Provinces, and the Yukon Territory. A tundra climate dominates much of the Northwest Territories. Permanent ice caps cover much of the Arctic Islands.

Precipitation patterns also resemble those found in the northern United States. The heaviest precipitation falls on the west coast. Dry conditions prevail on the intermountain plateaus and interior plains. Eastern Canada receives moderate amounts of precipitation.

## Vegetation and Soils

A vast **boreal,** or northern, forest of pines, hemlocks, and other coniferous trees, extends across much of subarctic Canada. The northern limit of the forest, called the tree line, runs from the delta of the Mackenzie River to the middle of the Hudson Bay region, and eastward to Labrador and the Atlantic Ocean. North of the **tree line** conditions remain too cold for trees; only tundra vegetation can survive.

A mixed forest of maples and birches grows in southeast Canada. A needleleaf forest of Douglas firs and cedars thrives along the rainy Pacific coast.

Prairies originally covered the dry southern sections of the Interior Plains. Most were plowed under in the late 1800s and early 1900s. Humus makes soils on the prairies rich (see page 109) and naturally fertile.

## Resources

Natural resources play a major role in Canada's economy. Though it has limited agricultural resources, other natural resources—including forests, fish, and minerals—are abundant.

**Agriculture.** Climate and poor soils limit Canada's agriculture to the southern edge of the country. The best farmlands lie on the Interior Plains. There, farmers grow cool-weather crops such as wheat, oats, and barley. Farmers in southeast Canada produce dairy products, potatoes, and apples.

*Learning from Maps.* *The movement of great ice sheets shaped many of Canada's landforms. In what province does the tree line extend farthest south?*

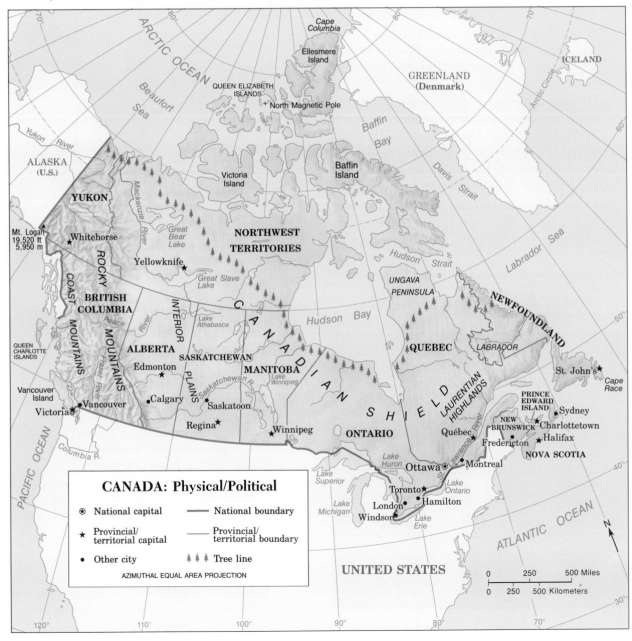

**CANADA: Physical/Political**

⊛ National capital
★ Provincial/territorial capital
• Other city

━━━ National boundary
──── Provincial/territorial boundary
♣♣♣ Tree line

AZIMUTHAL EQUAL AREA PROJECTION

0   250   500 Miles
0   250   500 Kilometers

**Forestry.** Forests provide a major resource to the Canadian economy. Forests cover about 50 percent of the land and serve as the basis for large lumbering and pulpwood industries. However, logging operations now tap only about 35 percent of the commercially useful forests.

**Fishing.** Canadian waters hold many kinds of fish and seafood. The Grand Banks off Canada's Atlantic coast rank among the world's richest. Atlantic fishers catch large amounts of cod, lobsters, herring, scallops, and other seafoods. In the Pacific Ocean, fishers catch salmon, halibut, and herring.

**Mining.** Mining makes major contributions to the Canadian economy. Canada leads the world in the value of mineral exports. Mining is a key force that draws settlers northward. Large deposits of oil and natural gas exist beneath the Interior Plains. Mines throughout Canada produce nickel, coal, gold, copper, zinc, and iron ore.

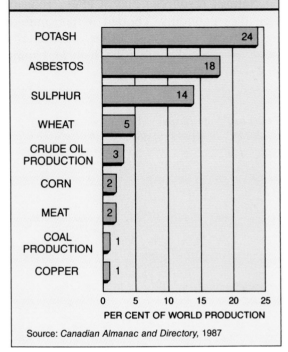

### MINERAL AND AGRICULTURAL RICHES OF CANADA

| Resource | Per cent of world production |
|---|---|
| POTASH | 24 |
| ASBESTOS | 18 |
| SULPHUR | 14 |
| WHEAT | 5 |
| CRUDE OIL PRODUCTION | 3 |
| CORN | 2 |
| MEAT | 2 |
| COAL PRODUCTION | 1 |
| COPPER | 1 |

PER CENT OF WORLD PRODUCTION

Source: *Canadian Almanac and Directory,* 1987

***Learning from Graphs.*** *Canada's natural resources are among the world's richest. What resource on the graph accounts for the largest percentage of the world total?*

***Learning from Pictures.*** *Lumber products are the major source of manufacturing income in British Columbia. What percentage of Canada's forests is being logged?*

---

### SECTION 1 REVIEW

1. **Define** peninsula, cordillera, boreal, tree line
2. **Locate** Quebec, New Brunswick, Nova Scotia, Prince Edward Island, Newfoundland, St. Lawrence River, Ontario, Mackenzie River, Yukon Territory, Labrador, Northwest Territories
3. **Summarizing Ideas** What are the seven physical regions of Canada?
4. **Comparing Ideas** How are Canada's **(a)** climates and **(b)** precipitation patterns different from or similar to those in the United States?
5. **Evaluating Ideas** Are forests, fish, and minerals economically important to Canada? Explain.

## 2 A unique blend of two cultures forms Canada's cultural setting.

Canada's culture reflects a mixture of French and English beliefs, ideas, and traditions. Languages and life styles have existed side by side. At times this mixture has caused conflicts, but it continues to give a special flavor to Canadian life.

### A Brief History

As in the United States, early people inhabited Canada thousands of years before Europeans colonized the region. Anthropologists believe Canada's first inhabitants were nomads who crossed the land bridge from Asia thousands of years ago. Many of these first inhabitants remained in the northern parts of Canada.

French and English explorers came to Canada in the 1500s and early 1600s. Both European countries founded colonies in the vast land. In 1763 the British defeated France and gained control of the French territory. Together with the British colonies of Ontario and New Brunswick, these new possessions formed an important British colony for 100 years.

In 1867 Ontario, Quebec, Nova Scotia, and New Brunswick united and gained independence as a country named Canada. Other provinces later joined Canada, the most recent admission being the two-part province of Newfoundland (officially called Newfoundland and Labrador) in 1949.

### Population Patterns

About 26 million people—one-tenth as many as in the United States—live in Canada. Canada has a mostly urban and nonagricultural population. About 76 percent of the people live in urban areas. Of the 24 percent who live in rural areas, only 6 percent live on farms. Toronto, Montreal, and Vancouver rank as the three largest cities.

French Canadians, English-speaking Canadians, and native peoples form the three largest population groups. Each group has contributed greatly to a diverse Canadian culture.

**French Canadians.** French Canadians number about 7.5 million and make up 29

*Learning from Graphs.* As the graph shows, except for land area, the United States and Canada differ greatly. How do you account for these differences?

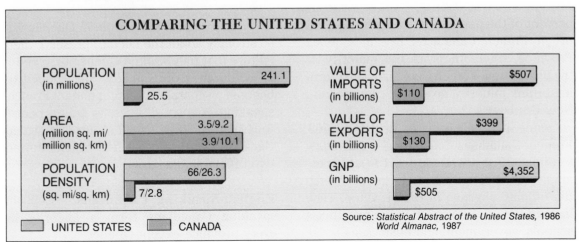

**COMPARING THE UNITED STATES AND CANADA**

| | UNITED STATES | CANADA |
|---|---|---|
| POPULATION (in millions) | 241.1 | 25.5 |
| AREA (million sq. mi/ million sq. km) | 3.5/9.2 | 3.9/10.1 |
| POPULATION DENSITY (sq. mi/sq. km) | 66/26.3 | 7/2.8 |
| VALUE OF IMPORTS (in billions) | $507 | $110 |
| VALUE OF EXPORTS (in billions) | $399 | $130 |
| GNP (in billions) | $4,352 | $505 |

Source: *Statistical Abstract of the United States*, 1986
*World Almanac*, 1987

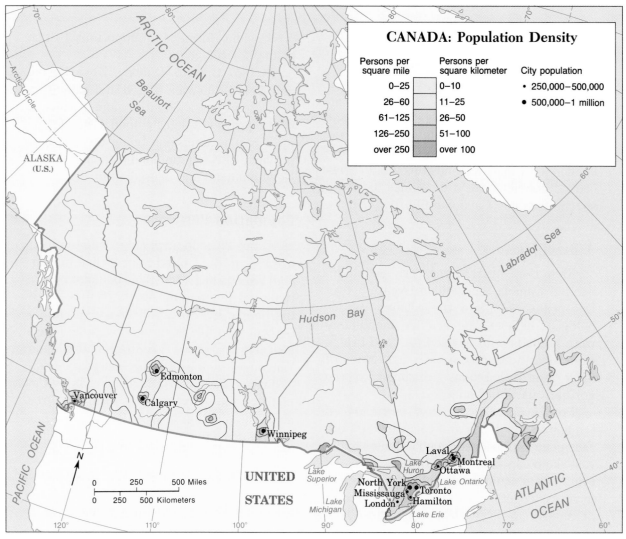

### CANADA: Population Density

| Persons per square mile | Persons per square kilometer |
|---|---|
| 0–25 | 0–10 |
| 26–60 | 11–25 |
| 61–125 | 26–50 |
| 126–250 | 51–100 |
| over 250 | over 100 |

City population
- 250,000–500,000
- 500,000–1 million

**Learning from Maps.** *Most of the population of Canada lives in the southeastern provinces. Between what latitudes do almost all Canadians live?*

percent of the population. About 80 percent of all French Canadians live in Quebec Province, where they are the majority of the population. French Canadians also form important minority groups in Ontario and New Brunswick.

Since their defeat by the British in 1763, French Canadians have fought for equal treatment. For a while in the 1970s, for example, Quebec's leaders declared French the official language of the province. They banned the use of English in the province's schools, government, and businesses.

At that time some people in Quebec felt so strongly about the need to preserve their culture that they wanted Quebec to **secede,** or withdraw, from Canada. They hoped to become a separate and independent French-speaking country. The crisis ended peacefully in 1982 when Quebec's leaders signed Canada's Constitutional Act, which allowed two official languages.

**English-Speaking Canadians.** English-speaking Canadians form a majority in every province except Quebec.

*Text continues on page 258.*

# DEVELOPING GEOGRAPHY SKILLS
## THINKING GEOGRAPHICALLY: Analyzing Primary Sources

> Quebec, with its citadel and fortifications crowning the precipitous heights which overhang the St. Lawrence, and where the deep and broad river is enlivened with a variety of shipping, struck us as the most picturesque city we had seen since we landed in America.

Thanks to journals such as Charles Lyell's *Travels in North America,* we know a great deal about what the continent looked like long ago. Lyell traveled throughout North America in 1841 and 1842.

Lyell's descriptions are eyewitness accounts of places and events. Such eyewitness, or firsthand, accounts are called **primary sources.** *Primary* means "original." Any original account—diaries, birth certificates, letters, ships' logs, bank records, newspapers, movies, photographs, records and tapes, videotapes, paintings, poetry, and songs—can be primary sources.

To analyze a source means to break apart its information into pieces, such as facts and opinions and causes and effects. Analyzing helps you see the relationships among the pieces.

### How to Analyze a Primary Source

To analyze a primary source effectively, follow these steps.

1. **Read the source carefully.** Identify the main ideas and supporting details. Before analyzing the information, you must understand what you are reading.
2. **Separate fact from opinion.** Remember that facts are provable. They can be confirmed by more than one source. Opinions are beliefs that may or may not be provable. Often words and phrases such as *it is believed* or *it would appear* precede opinions.
3. **Search for bias.** Some sources present a one-sided view. Be alert to words, phrases, and facts that support only a single viewpoint when it seems likely that more than one viewpoint exists.
4. **Check for relationships.** Look for clue words that indicate cause-and-effect and time relationships.
5. **Investigate.** Find out about the author. Who wrote the source? Why was it written? How accurate is it?
6. **Use your findings.** After analyzing the data, use what you have found. Draw conclusions, make inferences, or form a generalization or hypothesis.

### Applying the Skill

Read the excerpt below. It is written by David S. Boyer, a senior writer for *National Geographic.* Boyer quotes Sheila Joseph, an Indian, who writes about Canada's Indians. The subject is Canada's Fraser River. Most of Joseph's comments seem to be opinions, and her claim that the hydro engineers would ruin the river seems to indicate her bias. The existence of salmon keeps the engineers from damming the river. Their disappearance would allow the river to be "developed."

> Sometimes I try to imagine how it was before the white man came. Just a quiet gathering of Indian fishermen. . . . The hydro engineers have always had their eyes on this river. They can't dam it, because of the salmon. If we don't save our salmon now, they'll say, Well, there's no longer any good reason to save the river, is there? They'll ruin it, like they did the Columbia!

*To practice this skill, see Practicing Geography Skills on page 265.*

About 45 percent, or 11.7 million, of those Canadians who speak English are of British descent. Immigrants from other countries, however, also learn to speak English once they become acculturated. Recent immigrants entered Canada in two great waves. The first wave of people settled in Canada from 1900 to 1914. Most were British, but large numbers of Germans, Ukrainians, and other European settlers added to Canada's cultural diversity. Canada's second wave of immigration began in 1945 and continues today. Many Germans and Italians arrived first. Later, large numbers of Asians, East Indians, and Caribbean Islanders moved to Canada. Blacks form a small minority in Canada and have come mostly from the Caribbean islands.

**Native peoples.**   Today the first inhabitants of Canada, or **native peoples,** make up less than 2 percent of the country's people. Indians rank as the most numerous native peoples. The Six Nations of the Grand River, the Blood, and the Kahnawake (kahn·uh·wah·KEE) make up the largest bands, or tribes as they are called in Canada.

Indians live in all the provinces, with the largest numbers in British Columbia and Ontario. Most live on one of approximately 2,200 reservations, which are called **Indian reserves.**

Inuit, as Eskimos prefer to be called, form a minority numbering only about 20,000 people. Nearly 70 percent of them live in towns or villages along the Arctic shores of the Northwest Territories. Many continue to fish and hunt for a living.

Canada's people are unevenly distributed across the country. Nearly all Canadians live within 200 miles (320 kilometers) of the United States border. Along this border the features of Canada's physical setting—its landforms, climate, soils, vegetation, and lakes and rivers—are most attractive for settlement.

## Social Patterns

The Canadian government recognizes both French and English, expressions of two different cultures, as official languages. Canadians can use either language when dealing with the government and courts. They also can have their children educated in either language.

Canada's religious diversity follows the same patterns as its language. Heavy concentrations of Roman Catholics live in the historically French areas of eastern Canada. Throughout the rest of the country most people are Protestants. Cities such as Montreal and Toronto have large, active Jewish communities.

## Political Patterns

Canada's ten provinces and two territories form a compact nation. Its provinces make up part of a federal system similar to that of the United States. The **prime minister** heads the national government. In addition, each province has its own government to deal with provincial concerns. The national government governs Canada's two territories directly.

## Economic Patterns

Economists classify Canada as a developed nation. Its economy has grown rapidly in the last 30 years. Today Canada's GNP ranks among the world's highest.

Canada has a free enterprise system similar to that of the United States. In both countries individuals and corporations own most businesses. However, there is more government involvement in the economy of Canada than in the United States. For example, the Canadian government owns many telephone, transportation, and other communications networks.

Abundant natural resources provide the basis for Canada's economy. Mining, the

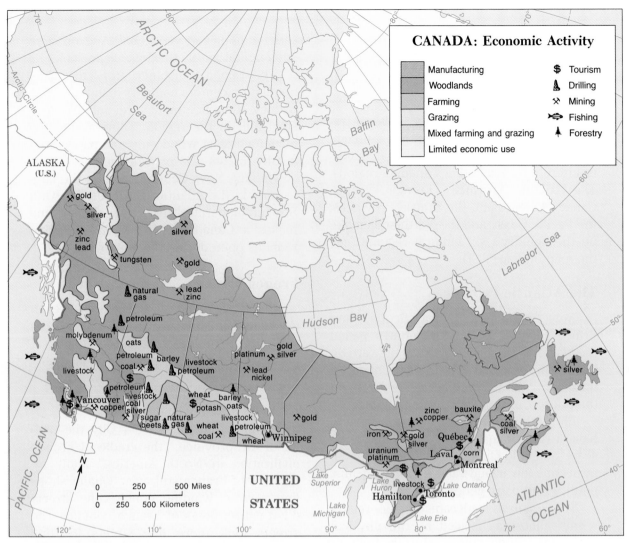

**CANADA: Economic Activity**

Manufacturing
Woodlands
Farming
Grazing
Mixed farming and grazing
Limited economic use

$ Tourism
Drilling
Mining
Fishing
Forestry

***Learning from Maps.*** *The St. Lawrence Lowlands, southern Quebec, and Ontario are known as the heartland of Canada. What is the economic activity of the Arctic regions?*

processing of mineral resources, and food processing lead Canada's industries. Canada ranks as the world's leading exporter of zinc and ranks second in the export of molybdenum, uranium, and asbestos. Canada also ranks as a leading exporter of paper and wood products.

Like other developed nations, Canada carries on extensive trade. It exports mostly raw materials and imports mostly manufactured goods such as vehicles, appliances, and electronic equipment. The United States serves as Canada's chief trading partner.

**SECTION 2 REVIEW**

1. **Define** secede, primary source, native peoples, Indian reserve, prime minister
2. **Locate** British Columbia
3. **Summarizing Ideas** How have French Canadians acted to preserve their language and culture?
4. **Comparing Ideas** (a) Why is Canada considered a developed nation? (b) How are the economies of Canada and the United States similar? (c) How are they different?

**259**

# 3 Great differences exist among Canada's cultural regions.

Geographers identify six cultural regions in Canada. Each region has a unique personality, or set of qualities, that makes it different from all other Canadian regions. The Atlantic Provinces, French Canada, Canada's Heartland, the Prairie Provinces, the Pacific Coast, and the Northlands make up the country's six cultural regions (see the map on page 253).

## The Atlantic Provinces

New Brunswick, Nova Scotia, and Prince Edward Island (sometimes called the Maritime Provinces because they are on the ocean) combine with Newfoundland to form the Atlantic Provinces. They remain the poorest of Canada's settled regions.

The Atlantic Provinces are hilly and have a rugged coastline. Their rough landscape and cold climate limit farming. Small farms in a few inland valleys produce fruits, poultry, and dairy goods.

The cultural landscape of the region seems almost as rugged as the physical landscape. Stone homes, sturdily built to keep out the harsh winter cold, dot the countryside.

Most people in the Atlantic Provinces trace their descent to English, Irish, and Scottish settlers. However, a sizable group of French Canadians also live in the region.

Fishing provides the main economic activity of the Atlantic Provinces. The Grand Banks off the east coast of Newfoundland rank as one of the world's best fishing areas. Fishers catch cod, haddock, and mackerel.

Mining is becoming increasingly important in the area. Iron ore remains plentiful in Newfoundland, Labrador, and New Brunswick. Mines on Cape Breton (BRET·uhn) Island yield coal. And offshore sites tap oil and natural gas deposits.

The region's distance from the chief population centers hampers manufacturing. Sydney, Nova Scotia, has the only iron and steel mill in the region. Tourism and the manufacture of wood pulp and paper from nearby forests also provide income.

Halifax, Nova Scotia, ranks as the largest city in the Atlantic Provinces. The Gulf Stream moderates the city's climate and makes it Canada's only eastern port that remains open during the winter.

## French Canada

Quebec Province is considered French Canada. Of all the provinces, Quebec has the largest land area and second-largest population. About 25 percent of all Canadians live there. Most people live in cities and towns along the St. Lawrence River or on the narrow lowlands nearby.

People often call Quebec City, the capital of the province, "the cradle of French civilization in North America." Many reminders of France still exist. Quaint shops line narrow, winding cobblestone streets filled with aromas of French cooking. The streets look more like streets in rural France than streets in North America.

Montreal serves as a great financial, industrial, and port city. Its harbor, one of Canada's finest, lies on the St. Lawrence River. Montreal prospers as a chief trade outlet for the Great Lakes.

## Canada's Heartland

In many ways Ontario is the Heartland of modern Canada. Home to about 36 percent of all Canadians, it has become the most populous of the 10 provinces.

The cultural landscape of the Heartland includes modern skyscrapers in the cities and fertile and productive farms in rural areas. This landscape reflects the British

*Text continues on page 262.*

Montreal lies on an island in the St. Lawrence River in Quebec Province. The city, with its sprawling suburbs, many industrial districts, magnificent skyscrapers, and rush-hour traffic, looks, on the surface, like many other large North American cities. But upon closer observation, it is soon apparent that there is something distinctive about Montreal. Two-thirds of its citizens are of French descent and speak the French language.

### Bilingual Tensions

Language differences have long created problems for the French-speaking citizens of Montreal. French Canadians form a majority in the city. Yet English is the main language of business. In addition, few of the large businesses and industries are owned by French Canadians. So most people must be able to speak English to secure the better jobs.

Frustrations over language as well as the desire to retain French culture in a largely English-speaking nation eventually led to a strong separatist movement. Its goal was to establish the province of Quebec as a separate nation. In 1976 the political party favoring separation won control of the provincial government and made French the official language of the province. This soon proved disastrous for Montreal. Many businesses moved their headquarters to Ontario or to other English-speaking provinces. Business leaders complained that restrictions on the use of languages other than French were isolating the city from its markets in the other provinces and in the United States. Unemployment increased dramatically.

After nine years of rule the separatists were swept from office in December 1985, and many of the restrictions they had imposed were lifted. A construction boom is

*Montreal's old French Quarter*

now under way, business is improving, and tourists are flocking back to this piece of France in America.

### Modern Prosperity

In the last year nearly 2.5 million people visited Montreal. They spent more than $1 billion, making tourism a major industry. Old Montreal, with its cobblestone streets, historic houses, and charming restaurants and shops, combines with a sparkling new underground shopping realm beneath the city's streets to provide a unique atmosphere. Several hundred stores and shops, restaurants, and movie theaters make the underground mall the largest such development in the world. Montreal's special quality of life helps to make it one of the most interesting and attractive urban centers in North America.

origins of a large number of the people, many of whose ancestors fled the United States after the Revolutionary War because they were loyal to Great Britain. In fact, many small towns and the older areas of large cities resemble the towns and cities of Great Britain. The Shakespearean Festival at Stratford attracts people each summer from all over the world.

Many industries have developed in Toronto and other cities along the Great Lakes. These industries produce more than half of Canada's manufactured goods. The major industry is automobile manufacturing and assembly.

Toronto ranks as Canada's largest city. It remains the leading manufacturing, financial, and communications center for English-speaking Canada. Hamilton, another large city on Lake Ontario and near Detroit, is Canada's principal iron and steel center. Ottawa (OT·tuh·wuh), in eastern Ontario, serves as the national capital.

*Learning from Pictures. The Calgary Stampede features the famous chuck wagon races. Why are rodeos popular in this part of Canada?*

## The Prairie Provinces

Vast stretches of fertile, level grasslands cover the southern parts of the Prairie Provinces—Alberta, Saskatchewan, and Manitoba. They have a landscape and climate ideal for growing wheat. The farmers of the region grow far more wheat than the country's small population needs. As a result, Canada has become the world's leading exporter of wheat, much of which it sells to the Soviet Union. Ranching also is important. Farmers raise cattle and other livestock on vast prairie ranches.

Recent discoveries of coal, oil, natural gas, and other valuable minerals have bolstered the region's economy. More than 85 percent of Canada's oil and coal comes from Alberta. Saskatchewan has large deposits of potash, a mineral used in making fertilizer. In addition, mines in northern Manitoba and Saskatchewan produce nickel, zinc, gold, and silver.

The region's largest cities include Winnipeg, Manitoba; Regina and Saskatoon, Saskatchewan; and Edmonton and Calgary, Alberta.

Although the region has several modern cities, it is farms, ranches, and wilderness that cover most of the landscape. The Calgary Stampede—the largest rodeo in the world—illustrates the importance of ranching to the region.

## The Pacific Coast

British Columbia makes up the Pacific Coast cultural region. The Rocky Mountains to the east isolate the province from the rest of Canada. The mountainous terrain and unusually mild climate make this region different from the others. Despite the mild climate, the land is too rough for large-scale farming. Tourism provides a key source of income.

About 65 percent of all British Columbians live in the southwestern corner of the

province. Vancouver ranks as the largest city and Canada's chief trade outlet on the Pacific Ocean. The city has a cultural landscape similar to that of many other large cities in North America. In addition, its Chinatown, which is second in size only to that of San Francisco, emphasizes the cultural pluralism of the city. The rest of British Columbia remains sparsely populated. Wilderness still covers much of the area.

Victoria, on Vancouver Island, is the provincial capital. It lies across the narrow Strait of Georgia from the mainland (see the map on page 253).

British Columbia has rich natural resources. Industries use wood from the dense forests along the coast to make wood pulp, paper, plywood, and other wood products. Oil and natural gas deposits underlie the Peace River Valley. Refineries in Vancouver process crude oil and natural gas. Mines yield iron ore, which is shipped overseas to Japanese steel mills. Mines also produce lead, copper, and zinc. In the north, at Kitimat, low-cost hydroelectricity powers an aluminum refinery.

## The Northlands

The Yukon Territory, the Northwest Territories, and the northern parts of Ontario, Quebec, and Labrador form Canada's Northlands region. Fewer than 1 percent of all Canadians live there. Native peoples make up a large number of these people. The region features thickly forested hills, thousands of lakes and rivers, isolated villages, and rutted dirt roads. A remote location and severe climate hamper development.

Despite the cold and isolation, the region has proved to be quite important in recent years. Mineral deposits, forests, and water-power sites draw settlers northward. Railroads and paved roads now reach mining and lumber sites in the wilderness.

*Learning from Pictures.* *A brown bear family fishes in the Yukon Territory. What is threatening the future of this wilderness home?*

Whitehorse, the capital of the Yukon, has become the center of a copper-mining and fur-trading region. Yellowknife, capital of the Northwest Territories, serves as a gold-mining center.

## SECTION 3 REVIEW

1. **Locate** Alberta, Saskatchewan, Manitoba
2. **Summarizing Ideas** What are the six cultural regions of Canada?
3. **Interpreting Ideas** (a) What are the Maritime Provinces of Canada? (b) Why are they called "maritime"? (c) What is the main economic activity of the region?
4. **Seeing Relationships** Why is Quebec City often called the "cradle of French civilization in North America"?
5. **Contrasting Ideas** How is Ontario different from the Prairie Provinces?
6. **Analyzing Ideas** What economic activities have made the most significant contributions to the economic development of British Columbia?

# CHAPTER 12 REVIEW

## Chapter Summary

The following list contains the key concepts you have learned about Canada.

1. Canada is the world's second-largest country in land area.
2. Canada's physical regions include the Appalachian Highlands, the Canadian Shield, the Great Lakes–St. Lawrence Lowlands, the Interior Plains, the Cordilleran region, the Hudson Bay Lowland, and the Arctic Islands.
3. Canada's climates are mostly colder versions of climates found in the northern United States. Climate and poor soils limit Canada's agricultural areas to the southern edge of the country.
4. An abundance of forest, mineral, and fish resources offsets the country's limited agricultural resources.
5. Climate and other factors cause most people to cluster within 200 miles (320 kilometers) of the United States border.
6. Canada is a bilingual and bicultural country of ten provinces and two territories. French Canadians form a large national minority but constitute a powerful majority in Quebec Province. English-speaking Canadians of British and other ancestries predominate in all the provinces and territories except Quebec. Native peoples form a tiny minority.
7. Canada is a compact nation with a federal system of government and a free enterprise system.
8. Geographers identify six cultural regions in Canada. They are the Atlantic Provinces, French Canada, Canada's Heartland, the Prairie Provinces, the Pacific Coast, and the Northlands.
9. The mineral-rich Canadian, or Laurentian, Shield covers a vast portion of Canada. Although the region is now sparsely populated, many Canadians are moving there to take advantage of job opportunities.

On a separate sheet of paper, complete the following review exercises.

## Reviewing Geographic Terms

Match each of the following terms with the correct definition below.

a. tree line
b. boreal forest
c. cordillera
d. peninsula
e. prime minister
f. secede
g. native peoples
h. Indian reserves

_____ 1. Narrow piece of land surrounded on three sides by water
_____ 2. To withdraw
_____ 3. Areas of Canada set aside for Indians
_____ 4. Northern limit of the forest
_____ 5. Canada's first inhabitants, including the Inuit
_____ 6. Northern needleleaf tract of pines, hemlocks, and other coniferous trees
_____ 7. Mountain system
_____ 8. Public official who runs the affairs of Canada's national government

## Developing Critical Thinking Skills

1. **Summarizing Ideas** (a) What are Canada's most important rivers and lakes, and why is each important? (b) In what way does winter affect these waterways?
2. **Synthesizing Ideas** How have French Canadians, English-speaking Canadians, and native peoples contributed to cultural pluralism in Canada?
3. **Comparing Ideas** How are the political and economic settings of Canada and the United States similar?
4. **Interpreting Ideas** Why have the Northlands, despite their cold and isolation, become important to Canada?
5. **Writing About Geography** In two clearly written paragraphs, discuss one of the following ideas. (a) What effects did the Ice Age have on the Canadian Shield, and why do Canadians today consider the shield lands an area of potential growth? (b) Given Canada's richness of natural resources, low population density, and free enterprise sys-

tem, what do you think Canada will be like in the next century? Be sure to consider any possible effects of Canada's diverse culture.

## Using Primary Sources

In the following excerpt from *Travels in North America*, Charles Lyell, a geologist who toured Canada in the 1840s, discusses the ideas of a bicultural Canada and French separation. As you study the reading, compare Lyell's impressions of the situation in the early 1840s with the later attitudes toward French separatism in Canada during the 1980s.

On approaching Montreal we seemed to be entering a French province. The language and costume of the peasants, . . . the priests with their [prayer books], the large crosses on the public roads, with the symbols of the Crucifixion, the architecture of the houses, with their steep roofs, large casement windows, and, lastly, the great Catholic cathedral rising in state, with its two lofty towers, carried back our thoughts to Normandy and Brittany, where we spent the corresponding season of last year. The French spoken in those provinces of the mother country is often far less correct, and less easy to follow, than that of Canadians, whose manners are very [favorable], much softer and more polite than those of their Anglo-Saxon fellow-countrymen, however superior the latter may be in energy and capability of advancement.

I was informed . . . at Montreal that the English language has made great progress; . . . and all agree that it would soon become still more general if the seat of government were transferred to that city. . . . I was assured by many that it was the only step towards anglicising Lower Canada that would be popular with the French party.

1. What sort of comparison does the author make between French Canadians and Anglo-Saxon (English) Canadians?
2. **(a)** According to the author, what action would help to make Montreal more English? **(b)** Would that work today? Explain.

## Practicing Geography Skills

*Before completing this activity, review Developing Geography Skills on page 257.*

**Analyzing Primary Sources**   Reread the preceding excerpt. Then answer these questions.

1. **(a)** What opinions does the author state? **(b)** What bias, if any, is present?
2. What is the cause-effect relationship between the English language and government?

## Exploring Geography

1. Study the photographs in Chapter 12. Then write a statement for each photograph explaining which of Canada's physical regions each photograph shows. Your statements should include justifications for each choice.
2. Imagine that you have $1,000 and that you are planning a one-week vacation to Canada. Write a schedule for your trip detailing how you will travel to Canada, how you will travel once you have reached Canada, where you will stay in Canada, and what you will do each day. You might want to visit a local travel agent or write to Tourism Canada, 235 Queen Street, Ottawa, Ontario K1A OH5, Canada, to ask for brochures on hotels and sights in Canada. Your schedule should also include a daily budget showing how much each day of your trip will cost. As you prepare your budget, do not forget to figure how much transportation (either by airplane, automobile, train, or bus) will cost between your home and Canada.

# UNIT 4 REVIEW

## Unit Summary

The following list contains the key concepts you have learned about the United States and Canada.

1. The United States has eight physical regions, while Canada has seven. Canada and the United States share several of these physical regions, which have contributed to the development of similar human activities in both countries.
2. Both the United States and Canada have a wealth of renewable resources such as forests, water, soils, and fish, and nonrenewable resources such as coal, oil and natural gas, iron ore, copper, gold, silver, lead, zinc, uranium, and molybdenum.
3. Both the United States and Canada have federal systems of government. Both also are developed nations with free enterprise systems that provide their citizens with two of the highest standards of living in the world.
4. The United States has 11 of the 13 subtypes of global climates. Generally, Canada's climates are colder versions of climates found in the northern United States.
5. The United States and Canada can be divided into many cultural regions, each with a unique personality.
6. The United States, with its six major groups of people, is an example of cultural pluralism. Canada is a bilingual and bicultural country in which French Canadians and English-speaking Canadians of British and other ancestries predominate.

## Checking Your Understanding

1. How do physical and cultural regions differ?
2. (a) What are the eight physical regions of the United States? (b) What are the seven cultural regions of the United States?
3. What factors have been responsible for the changes in population distribution in the United States?
4. What cultural region of the United States is the most urban?
5. Why is population density in Canada heaviest close to the United States border?

## Applying Critical Thinking Skills

1. **Summarizing Ideas** (a) What mineral and energy resources are found in each of the seven cultural regions of the United States? (b) Which of these resources are found in Canada?
2. **Organizing Ideas** (a) What major agent of erosion helped to create the extension of the Canadian Shield region in the United States? (b) What part of the United States lies on the shield? (c) What part of Canada lies on the shield?
3. **Interpreting Ideas** Describe how the social patterns that are evident in the United States and Canada are different.
4. **Comparing Ideas** (a) How are the political settings of the United States and Canada alike? (b) How are they different?
5. **Analyzing Ideas** Why is the United States an example of cultural pluralism, while Canada is predominantly bicultural?

## Reviewing Unit Features

1. **City Focus** Why is Dallas often called the most optimistic big city in the United States?
2. **City Focus** Why did a strong separatist movement develop in Montreal?
3. **Geography in the Workplace** On what types of resources do conservationists focus their attention?
4. **The Geographic Web** How have the effects of the modern world changed the wilderness areas of the United States?

## Using Map Skills

1. Study the map on pages 96–97. Identify the climates present in the northern United States that extend into Canada.

2. Study the map on page 253. What bodies of water are part of the political boundary between Canada and the United States?

## Investigating Geography

1. Identify a particular product people could use to keep comfortable in the climate zone where you live. Then write down five reasons why they should use it. Explain to members of the class why they need the product by presenting these reasons. Poll the class to find out how many students would buy your product.
2. Contact the information desk at City Hall in the city where you live or one nearby and ask what year the city was founded. Research the events that occurred around this date in the area surrounding the city. Then prepare a report outlining why you think the city may have been founded.
3. Review the information in Chapters 9 and 12 on the physical regions of the United States and Canada. Then, on an outline map of North America, color and label the physical regions of each country. Be certain that your completed map shows where the regions cross national borders.

## Further Reading

### Chapter 9

Davis, Bertha, and Susan Whitfield. *The Coal Question.* New York: Franklin Watts. Discusses coal as a fuel source and the various environmental and economic controversies surrounding its use.

*Our Continent: A Natural History of North America.* Washington, D.C.: National Geographic Society. Studies the physical forces that forged the North American continent.

Special Publications, National Geographic Society. *America's Magnificent Mountains.* Washington, D.C.: National Geographic Society. Shows the beauty and majesty of North America's mountains.

### Chapter 10

*The American Land.* Smithsonian Exposition Books. New York: W. W. Norton. Reviews the geography, resources, and people of the United States.

Anderson, Lydia. *Immigration.* New York: Franklin Watts. Reviews immigration history from colonial times to the present.

Franklin, P. A. *Indians of North America: The Eight Cultures and How Their Inhabitants Lived Before the Coming of the Whites.* New York: David McKay Company, Inc. Describes hunting, family life, and life styles of various American Indian cultures.

### Chapter 11

Cohen, David, ed. *A Day in the Life of America.* New York: Collins Publishers. Provides a pictorial essay of the United States from photos taken by 200 of the world's best photographers on May 2, 1986.

Garreau, Joel. *The Nine Nations of North America.* New York: Avon Press. Divides the United States and Canada into nine "nations" based on economic and cultural features and lists the characteristics of each.

Pierce, Neal, and Jerry Hagstrom. *The Book of America: Inside Fifty States Today.* New York: W. W. Norton. Surveys the United States as a whole and each of its 50 states.

### Chapter 12

"Acid Rain." *UNESCO Courier,* January 1985. Deals with the problems and possible solutions of acid rain in Canada and in other regions of the Northern Hemisphere.

Editors of Time–Life Books. *The Canadians.* With text by Ogden Tanner. Alexandria, Va.: Time–Life Books. Captures the flavor of the Canadian wilderness and the experiences of Canadian pioneers in developing the area's rich resources.

Harris, Jeanette. *Canada: The Land and Its People.* Morristown, N.J.: MacDonald Educational Ltd., Silver Burdett Company. Discusses the people, culture, geography, history, and economy of Canada.

# UNIT 5

# MIDDLE AMERICA

269

# PUTTING THE CHAPTER IN FOCUS

Mexico forms a major part of a Spanish-speaking cultural region called Latin America. It also makes up part of a smaller region called Middle America. Middle America includes Mexico, Central America, and the islands of the Caribbean. The region contains sharp contrasts. Mexico has the largest population in Middle America. Mexico's progress and the way it deals with its problems will set the standard for the region's development.

## Ideas to Understand

In studying about Mexico, use these ideas to give direction to your reading.

1 Mexico is a mountainous land with three upland climate zones.
2 Mexico's cultural setting blends ancient Indian and Spanish colonial ways.
3 Modern Mexico faces many problems typical of a developing nation.

## Terms to Define

The following terms are some of the key terms in the chapter. Defining them will help you understand Mexico.

| | |
|---|---|
| sierra | hacienda |
| mesa | *ejido* |
| rift valley | land reform |
| isthmus | collective |
| mestizo | subsidy |
| subsistence farmer | |

## Places to Locate

Locating the following places will add to your knowledge of geography.

| | |
|---|---|
| Latin America | Guadalajara |
| Middle America | Sierra Madre Oriental |
| Mexican Plateau | Gulf of California |
| Baja California | Colorado River |
| Yucatán Peninsula | Rio Grande |
| Mexico City | |

## 1 Mexico is a mountainous land with three upland climate zones.

Mexico, a land three times the size of Texas, features spectacular contrasts. Rugged snowcapped mountains rise from the middle of parched, semiarid grasslands. Most of the land remains unsuited for agriculture, yet it contains many mineral resources. Mexico lies in the tropics, yet its mountainous terrain gives much of the country a mild climate.

### Physical Regions

Eight physical regions cross Mexico (see the map on page 272). These regions include the Mexican Plateau, two high *sierras* (see·ER·uhs)—Spanish for "mountain ranges"—the Gulf Coastal Plain, Baja (BAH·hah) California, the Transverse Volcanic Range, the Southern Highlands, and the Yucatán Peninsula.

**Mexican Plateau.** The centrally located Mexican Plateau, a southern extension of the Interior Plains of the United States, forms Mexico's largest physical region. Few people live in the dry north. High mountains and old volcanoes divide the plateau's southern end into several very densely populated basins. The basins and surrounding **mesas,** elevated plateaus with steep sides, have rich volcanic soil suitable for farming. Mexico's largest cities—Mexico City, Puebla, and Guadalajara (gwahd·uh·luh·HAHR·uh)—occupy these basins today.

◀ *National Autonomous University, Mexico City*

271

**Two high sierras.** High mountain ranges border the Mexican Plateau on the east and west. The Sierra Madre Oriental (*oriental* means "eastern" in Spanish) form the plateau's eastern edge. The Sierra Madre Occidental (*occidental* means "western" in Spanish) make up its western edge. The mountains make east–west travel difficult in northern Mexico.

**Gulf Coastal Plain.** In eastern Mexico a coastal plain borders the Gulf of Mexico. This lowland area resembles the Gulf Coastal Plain of Texas. As it does in Texas, the coastal plain holds rich oil and natural gas deposits.

**Baja California.** *Baja*, or "lower," California extends as a long, narrow peninsula in northwest Mexico. The mountainous, dry peninsula stretches south from California in the United States and lies between the Pacific Ocean and the Gulf of California. Much of the land is barren and sandy.

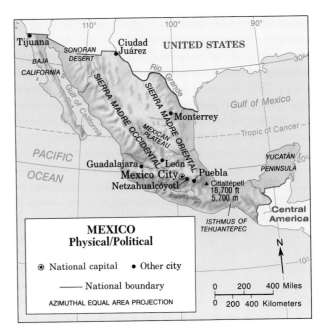

*Learning from Maps.* Most of Mexico consists of mountains and highlands with little land suitable for farming. What area forms Mexico's largest physical region?

*Learning from Pictures.* Popocatépetl last erupted in 1943. What causes the volcanic eruptions and earthquakes that pose a constant threat for the people of this region?

The Gulf of California occupies a **rift valley,** a long, narrow depression along a fault, that lies between Baja California and the Sierra Madre Occidental. A large delta at the mouth of the Colorado River fills part of the northern end of the gulf. Irrigated with river water, the fertile soils on the delta produce large agricultural yields.

**Transverse Volcanic Range.** A row of volcanoes, called the Transverse Volcanic Range, reaches from east to west at the southern end of the Mexican Plateau. Some of the volcanoes—including Citlaltépetl (see·tlahl·TAY·pet·uhl), which at 18,700 feet (5,700 meters) is Mexico's highest mountain—are now inactive. Others—such as Popocatépetl (poh·puh·KAT·uh·peht·uhl)—occasionally emit steam but rarely erupt. The mountain range rises above an area where tectonic plates meet, so earthquakes are common. A large earthquake measuring 8.1 on the Richter scale destroyed parts of nearby Mexico City in 1986.

*Text continues on page 274.*

# DEVELOPING GEOGRAPHY SKILLS
## READING ABOUT GEOGRAPHY: Understanding Descriptions

> High mountains and old volcanoes divide the plateau's southern end into several very densely populated basins.

> Rugged, snowcapped mountains rise from the middle of the parched, semiarid grasslands.

Geographers study the physical and cultural features of the earth. They observe and then describe those features. The excerpts above describe the physical setting of Mexico. In the first excerpt geographers have used adjectives such as *high* and *old* to describe the mountains around the Mexican Plateau. They also use the verb *divide* to illustrate the effect these mountains have on the plateau's surface. They use the adverbial phrase *densely populated* to describe the area's basins. In the second excerpt, geographers use adjectives such as *rugged, snowcapped, parched,* and *semiarid* to help paint a mental picture of the landscape.

Geographers use many types of modifying words and phrases to describe physical and cultural features and actions. Using such words and phrases gives you a clearer image of what a place is actually like. To get a clear mental image of what geographers are describing, you must understand the descriptive words they use and link them to what they describe.

## How to Understand Descriptions

To understand geographic descriptions, follow these guidelines.

1. **Read the description carefully.** Identify the basic information that the description contains. Note in general what basic landforms or cultural features are being described.
2. **Identify the descriptive words.** Note the adjectives, adverbs, and other modifying words and phrases in the description. Link the descriptions to the physical settings they modify. If necessary, use a dictionary to define specific descriptive terms.
3. **Form a mental picture.** Put all the information in the description together to form a mental picture of what is being described. Note how each descriptive word or phrase helps you bring the mental image of the geographic concept more sharply into focus.

## Applying the Skill

Read the excerpt below. The excerpt describes the cultural landscape of Mexico City. In the excerpt the geographer uses several descriptive words—*few, short, beautiful, squalid, steep-sided,* and others—to tell you that you will find poor families living in miserable shacks close to the cleanest parts of the city. The descriptive words help you ''see'' the conditions in the slums of Mexico City.

> So just a few short blocks from the beautiful tree-lined boulevards sit squalid slums that house 46 percent of the city's population. Thousands of the poorest families live in kitchenless shacks or lean-tos and cook along the sides of the streets. Other families occupy the roofs of factories or live in shacks that barely cling to steep-sided ravines.

*To practice this skill, see Practicing Geography Skills on page 285.*

**Southern Highlands.** To the south of the Transverse Volcanic Range the Southern Highlands cross Mexico. The high mountains known as the Sierra Madre del Sur (*del sur* is Spanish for "of the south") form the highlands. Level lands suitable for settlement occur near Oaxaca (wuh·HAHK·uh) and on the Isthmus of Tehuantepec (tuh·WAHNT·uh·pehk) between the Pacific and Atlantic oceans (see the map on page 272). An **isthmus** is a narrow piece of land that connects two landmasses.

**Yucatán Peninsula.** In eastern Mexico the Yucatán Peninsula reaches northeast between the Gulf of Mexico and the Caribbean Sea (see the map on page 272). Mexico shares this peninsula (see the map on page 288) with the Central American country of Belize. Parts of the peninsula receive up to 80 inches (200 centimeters) of rainfall each year. Nevertheless, few rivers or lakes exist because the soluble limestone underneath the peninsula allows nearly all the rain to sink into streams deep underground. This feature of the physical landscape limits agriculture on the peninsula.

## Climate

The climatic control that affects Mexico's climate the most is elevation. As elevations get higher, temperatures get cooler. The climate zone at the lowest elevation is called *tierra caliente*, which means "hot land." It occurs between sea level and 3,000 feet (900 meters). Yearly temperatures there average more than 80°F (27°C).

*Tierra templada*, or "temperate land," lies between 3,000 and 6,000 feet (900 and 1,800 meters). Temperatures there range from 50°F to 80°F (10°C to 27°C), with little seasonal change.

*Tierra fría*, or "cold land," occurs above 6,000 feet (1,800 meters). Mexico City lies in the tierra fría. It has an average January temperature of 57°F (14°C) and an average July temperature of only 63°F (17°F). In the winter the jet stream carries blasts of cold Arctic air and freezing temperatures as far south as Mexico City. Permanent snows cover mountaintops higher than 12,000 feet (3,500 meters).

Most of the precipitation falls in a summer rainy season. The winter remains dry. In southern Mexico enough rain falls for farming, but the average yearly precipitation steadily decreases to the north. Parts of the Sonoran Desert, Baja California, and other northern desert areas receive less than 4 inches (10 centimeters) of precipitation each year.

## Vegetation

When Spanish explorers first arrived in Mexico in the 1500s, they found forests covering three-fifths of the land. Today, after 450 years of haphazard cutting and burning, forested areas cover less than one-fifth of the country. Trees grow up to the tree line at about 13,000 feet (3,900 meters). Thorny desert plants provide the chief vegetation of desert areas. Grasslands cover semiarid regions on the northern Mexican Plateau.

## Resources

Much of Mexico's land remains poorly suited for farming, but it holds vast mineral resources. These minerals provide potential wealth in a generally poor country.

**Agriculture.** Despite the unsuitable land, farming remains Mexico's chief economic activity. Arable land covers only 15 percent of Mexico and farmers cultivate only 8 percent of the total land area. Unfarmed land, mostly in the north, needs irrigation to make it productive.

Most of Mexico's farms lie on the southern part of the Central Plateau. Mexico's principal food crops include corn, beans, wheat, and rice. Farms in the warm climate

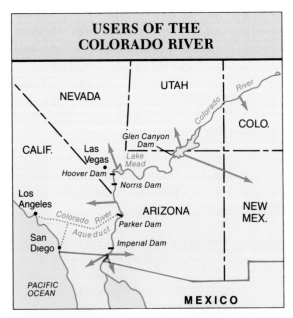

### USERS OF THE COLORADO RIVER

*Learning from Diagrams.* Several American states and Mexico compete for the limited waters of the Colorado River. Why does Mexico need the river's water?

of the Gulf Coastal Plain grow tropical crops such as bananas, cacao, coffee, pineapples, citrus fruits, and sugarcane for export. Wheat, cotton, and vegetables grow in irrigated northern areas. Under the terms of agreements with the United States, most irrigation water used today comes from the Colorado River and the Rio Grande.

**Fish.** Shrimp, caught in the Gulf of Mexico, provide Mexico's leading seafood export. Commercial fishers also fish the coastal waters of the Caribbean Sea, the Pacific Ocean, and the southern end of the Gulf of California.

**Minerals.** Oil is Mexico's chief resource and export. In the 1970s Mexico found and developed vast new oil reserves at the southern end of the Gulf Coastal Plain and offshore near Veracruz and Tampico. Besides oil, other exports include minerals such as lead, silver, zinc, and manganese.

### SECTION 1 REVIEW

1. **Define**   sierra, mesa, rift valley, isthmus
2. **Locate**   Latin America, Middle America, Baja California, Gulf of California, Yucatán Peninsula, Mexico City, Guadalajara, Sierra Madre Oriental, Colorado River, Rio Grande
3. **Summarizing Ideas   (a)** What are the eight physical regions of Mexico? **(b)** What is the highest mountain in Mexico?
4. **Organizing Ideas   (a)** What climatic control has the greatest impact on Mexico's climate?   **(b)** What are the different climate zones in Mexico?
5. **Analyzing Ideas**   Why is only 8 percent of Mexico's land farmed today?

## 2 Mexico's cultural setting blends ancient Indian and Spanish colonial ways.

A walk through the central square of almost any Mexican town or city shows the unique nature of Mexican culture—a blend of Indian and Spanish influences. On one side of the square stands a Roman Catholic church similar to those found in Spain. In front of the church, descendants of Indians and Spanish colonists sell the same foods that Indians of the region grew hundreds of years before the Spanish conquest of the 1500s.

### A Brief History

As in the United States and Canada, early people settled in Mexico centuries before the Spanish came to the region. Mexico's first inhabitants probably were descendants of the nomads who crossed the land bridge from Asia. These nomads had spread slowly south into Mexico, Central, and South America.

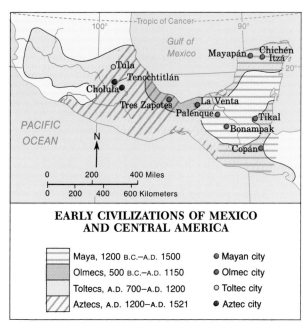

## EARLY CIVILIZATIONS OF MEXICO AND CENTRAL AMERICA

| | |
|---|---|
| Maya, 1200 B.C.–A.D. 1500 | ● Mayan city |
| Olmecs, 500 B.C.–A.D. 1150 | ● Olmec city |
| Toltecs, A.D. 700–A.D. 1200 | ○ Toltec city |
| Aztecs, A.D. 1200–A.D. 1521 | ● Aztec city |

*Learning from Maps.* *Before the Spanish conquest, Mexico's Indians created several highly developed civilizations. Which Indian group did the Spanish conquer?*

By about 1500 B.C. the people in central Mexico lived in villages. By 1000 B.C. they had built ceremonial and trading centers. Advanced cultures with sophisticated institutions, educational systems, and scientific methods grew around these centers.

The Maya had the most advanced ancient American culture. They occupied the Yucatán Peninsula and nearby areas of Central America. By A.D. 900 the Maya had declined. Some theories speculate that the slash-and-burn method of farming used up all the arable land. However, the latest archaeological findings indicate that the Maya traded to supplement their farming. They also developed a technique for farming the swamps of the Yucatán Peninsula. This new evidence challenges earlier theories that questioned the ability of the Maya to provide enough food to feed the people.

After the decline of Mayan civilization, a new group of Indians—the Toltecs—emerged as the major power in the region. Then about 1325 a new civilization, the Az-

tecs, conquered the region. In 1519 Spaniards led by Hernan Cortés invaded Mexico. Cortés conquered the Aztec empire and helped organize Mexico as a Spanish colony. Mexico remained a colony of Spain until 1821, when it gained independence.

## Population Patterns

Three major groups—Indians, mestizos, and Europeans—make up the Mexican people. Each group feels a special pride in its background.

**Indians.** Indians who trace their ancestry to ancient Mayan, Aztec, Toltec, and other

*Learning from Pictures.* *Important archaeological evidence has been found at the Plaza of Three Cultures in Mexico City. What three cultures are represented in this picture?*

Central American Indian civilizations (see the map on page 276) account for about 24.6 million Mexicans, or 30 percent of the people. Today Mexicans are classified as Indian if they speak an Indian language or live in an Indian village. Most Indians live in villages in isolated parts of the Southern Highlands. The Mexican government sponsors many educational programs that stress the important role Indians played in the development of the Mexican culture.

**Mestizos.** In Mexico people of mixed Indian and Spanish ancestry are called **mestizos** (meh·STEE·zohs). Mestizos, who number 49 million, make up about 60 percent of the Mexican people.

**Europeans.** People of European ancestry comprise about 9 percent of the Mexican people. Many trace their descent to the Spaniards who settled in Mexico before it gained independence in 1821. Most Europeans live in Mexico City and in the drier northern areas that their ancestors colonized in the 1600s and 1700s.

**Population distribution.** Mexico's population—82 million—ranks as the largest in Middle America by far. About 70 percent of the people live in towns and cities. Nearly half of all the people live at the southern end of the Central Plateau, in and around Mexico City. Northern parts of the plateau contain fewer people. Government-sponsored plans to relieve the crowded Mexico City area now encourage people to move into these sparsely populated lands. The least populated areas include dry Baja California and areas without surface water in the Yucatán Peninsula.

## Social Patterns

Mexico's social patterns reflect its Indian and Spanish past. Both cultures have contributed significant imprints.

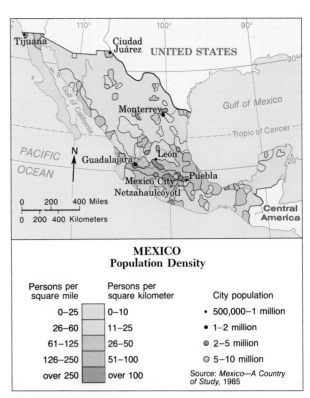

*Learning from Maps.* The Mexican government undertakes resettlement programs to relieve over-population. Where is the Mexican population the most dense?

**Indian imprint.** The Indian imprint remains evident in Mexico's farming and foods. Mexico's ancient Indians specialized in growing corn, beans, and squash—all unknown in Europe until the Spanish conquest of Mexico. These three crops remain Mexico's main food crops. Indian farmers grew many other crops unknown in Europe, such as sweet potatoes, tomatoes, potatoes, avocados, pineapples, papayas, and chili peppers. For flavoring they grew vanilla and made chocolate from cacao beans. They raised cotton and used the fibers to make cloth. Typical Indian foods included *tortillas* and *tamales*, both of which remain popular in Mexico today.

**Spanish imprint.** In many ways the Spanish imprint eventually replaced the Indian imprint in Mexico. For example, Spanish is

*Learning from Pictures. Interlaced by waterways, the Xochimilco Gardens were built on Lake Xochimilco by the Aztecs. When did the Aztecs conquer this region?*

Mexico's official language. Today about 92 percent of all Mexicans speak Spanish. The remaining 8 percent speak one of the more than 50 Indian dialects. Most members of this group, however, also speak Spanish. The most widely spoken Indian language is Nahuatl (NAH·waht·uhl).

In addition, Roman Catholicism brought by the Spanish largely replaced Indian religions. Today 97 percent of the Mexican people are Roman Catholics. Spanish-style houses, churches, and towns replaced Indian styles of architecture. The Spanish brought horses, cattle, and wheat—all unknown to the Indians—to Mexico. They also introduced many ideas that were different from traditional Indian ideas. For example, the Spanish introduced the European concept of private ownership of land. Indians had viewed land as shared by everyone in the community.

The ideas and institutions that the Spanish introduced into Mexico provide examples of cultural diffusion. So, too, do the new crops that were brought back to Europe after the Spanish conquest of Mexico.

## Political Patterns

Mexico borders the United States. The border between the two countries stretches about 2,000 miles (3,200 kilometers). Mexico, like Canada, is a compact nation. Its 31 states and the Federal District of Mexico make up a democratic federal republic. The federal district, similar to the federal district of Washington, D.C., serves as the national capital. A president leads the government. A governor with duties and responsibilities similar to those of a United States governor serves as the chief executive in each state.

## Economic Patterns

Economists classify Mexico as a developing nation with a mixed economy. The Mexican government uses a variety of methods to produce goods and services.

*Learning from Maps. Mexico is a developing nation that encourages industrialization. Where is most of Mexico's oil and natural gas located?*

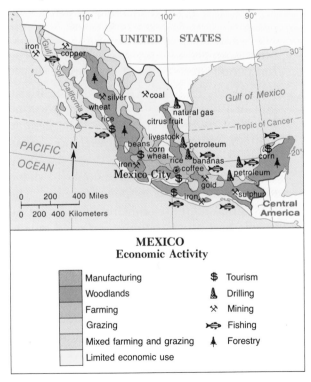

**MEXICO**
**Economic Activity**

| | |
|---|---|
| Manufacturing | $ Tourism |
| Woodlands | ⚒ Drilling |
| Farming | ✗ Mining |
| Grazing | ⇆ Fishing |
| Mixed farming and grazing | ♠ Forestry |
| Limited economic use | |

| MEXICO'S MAJOR SOURCES OF INCOME | |
|---|---|
| **Source** | **Annual Revenue*** |
| CRUDE PETROLEUM | $13,309,000,000 |
| TOURISM | $ 1,719,700,000 |
| MOTOR VEHICLE ENGINES AND PARTS | $ 1,227,000,000 |
| AGRICULTURAL PRODUCTS (Coffee, tomatoes, and cotton) | $ 772,000,000 |
| PETROLEUM PRODUCTS | $ 619,000,000 |
| FROZEN SHRIMP | $ 443,000,000 |
| COPPER | $ 148,000,000 |
| *Figures for 1986 Source: *Europa Yearbook*, 1987 | |

***Learning from Charts.*** *Mexico must expand its foreign trade and reduce its huge debt. Which of Mexico's resources generates the most income?*

**SECTION 2 REVIEW**

1. **Define** mestizo
2. **Summarizing Ideas** How is Mexican culture unique?
3. **Contrasting Ideas** **(a)** What concept of land ownership did the Spanish introduce in Mexico? **(b)** How was this idea different from the Indian idea?
4. **Seeing Relationships** How are the political patterns of Mexico and Canada similar?
5. **Analyzing Ideas** Why is the cultivation of corn, beans, and squash in Europe an example of cultural diffusion?

For example, the government owns all mineral rights. As a result, mining companies work under contracts they buy from the government.

Until the tapping of oil deposits, mining was the key to Mexico's economy. Although Mexico still mines large amounts of silver, lead, zinc, copper, sulfur, and other minerals, today oil production ranks as the most important part of the economy.

Agricultural production continues to increase, chiefly as a result of scientific farming and irrigation methods introduced in Mexico in recent years. The importance of manufacturing has grown, too. Processing of food and raw materials such as cotton, wood, oil, and minerals lead the way. In addition, the government is working to develop new industries.

Mexico's foreign trade continues to expand. Raw materials provide the chief exports and manufactured goods serve as the major imports.

## 3 Modern Mexico faces many problems typical of a developing nation.

Like other developing nations, Mexico faces problems. Among them are population pressures, a low per capita GNP, slowly modernizing economy, and a large debt.

### Population Pressures

Mexico's population grows and changes quickly. A high growth rate, a young population, and rapid urbanization cause economic, political, and social problems.

**High growth rate.** Mexico has one of the world's highest growth rates. Mexico's population has grown from 15 million in 1910 to 82 million today. And according to population experts, Mexico will have 138 million people by the year 2020.

The current rate of population growth is 2.5 percent a year. This rate is much higher than the world's average population growth rate of 1.7 percent and is nearly 4 times higher than the 0.7 percent growth rate of the United States.

# GEOGRAPHY IN THE WORKPLACE
## Population Geographers

Geographers and other social scientists frequently use the term *overpopulation.* This term reflects a problem that lies at the heart of many of the other problems facing the people of the planet Earth.

You go to a campground for a restful weekend and the ranger tells you the sites are full and that you should have reserved a campsite at least three months ago. Overpopulation! You go to the beach and there is no place to park. You look out at the water and see it filled with swimmers. Overpopulation! You have tickets to a football game across town and miss the first half because you are delayed by traffic. Overpopulation! Even headlines about overpopulation bombard us:

WORLD POPULATION EXPLODES

OVERPOPULATION THREATENS FOOD SUPPLIES

HUNGER STALKS BOOMING POPULATIONS IN AFRICA AND ASIA

Doubtless the business of counting people is important. Population geographers are among the experts studying and analyzing the population growth of the world around us. Population geographers study the locations of people, interpret the differences in birth and death rates, sex ratios, age groups, and migration patterns, and analyze what those differences mean.

Population geographers describe and analyze the relationships between spatial distributions. Important spatial relationships include the geographic links among population, economic growth, standard of living, and industrialization. Population geographers also study the relationship between population and the quality of life.

Most population geographers work for the United States Bureau of the Census or for the governments of other nations. They determine ways to improve the collection of census data and prepare maps, tables, and charts to illustrate census data.

And perhaps more importantly, population geographers predict changes in population figures. Some of their predictions show where people will probably live in the future, how age-group distributions will change, and what the probable incomes of people in different regions will be. Such data prove invaluable to people who are planning for the future. If you enjoy thinking about and planning for the future, if you like mathematics, and if you are interested in people, population geography is a challenging career.

A high birth rate and a low death rate account for Mexico's high growth rate. Mexico's birth rate measures 31 births per 1,000 people—higher than the world average of 28 and about twice as high as the United States average of 16. As a result of the government's expanded health care system, the death rate stands at an amazingly low 7 per 1,000.

**A young population.** Mexico's age distribution is typical of developing nations. This distribution adds to population pressures. Young people under 15 years of age make up about 43 percent of the population (compared with 22 percent in the United States). People over 65 account for only 4 percent of the population (compared with 12 percent in the United States). Educating and

providing future jobs for this large group of young people presents an important challenge for Mexico.

**Rapid urbanization.** Like other developing nations, Mexico is rapidly changing from a rural to an urban society. Since the 1940s large numbers of people unable to find jobs in rural areas have moved to cities in search of better opportunities. Today 70 percent of the people live in urban areas, up from only 38 percent in 1950.

Mexico City now has nearly 15 million people in its metropolitan area. It ranks as one of the largest and fastest-growing cities in the world (see page 182). Other large cities include Netzahualcóyotl (neht·zah·hwahl·COH·yoh·tuhl), Guadalajara, and Monterrey, each of which has more than 1 million people.

## Low Per Capita GNP

Mexico has a per capita GNP of $2,370. This totals much less than the per capita GNP of $16,688 in the United States. But it is close to the world average of $2,880 and higher than most other developing nations.

Mexico's greatest challenge remains to make its GNP grow faster than its population. If the government's plans prove successful, Mexico's low standard of living will rise. If the GNP does not grow as rapidly as the population, the already low standard of living will decline even further.

## A Changing Economy

Most workers in developing nations farm. But in Mexico farmers make up only about 40 percent of the labor force. Many Mexican farmers are **subsistence farmers** who only produce enough food for themselves and family members. Only about 10 percent of the GNP comes from farming, but farm production continues to grow.

Modern Mexico is more industrialized than most developing nations. About 13 percent of the laborers work in manufacturing, which provides nearly 30 percent of the GNP—much higher percentages than for most developing nations.

**Land reform.** By the late 1800s large landowners held most of Mexico's farmland. They developed large **haciendas** (hahs·ee·EN·duhz), or estates similar to plantations. Some haciendas covered as many as 100,000 acres (35,000 hectares). During the Mexican Revolution of 1910 to 1921 the government broke up the haciendas into smaller, government-owned units of about 20 acres (7 hectares) called *ejidos* (ee·HEE·dohs), which is Spanish for "public lands." The breakup was part of a **land reform**

*Text continues on page 283.*

*Learning from Pictures.* *This subsistence farm family is from the state of Chiapas in southeast Mexico. How is the Mexican government helping more people own land?*

**281**

*The Basilica of Our Lady of Guadalupe*

Mexico City presents an excellent example of a primate city (see page 179). It serves as Mexico's capital city, but is important economically as well as politically. More than 45 percent of Mexico's industrial employees work in Mexico City and the surrounding suburbs. They produce almost one-half of the country's total of manufactured goods. This importance has caused rapid growth. In 1900 only 345,000 people lived in Mexico City. Today more than 15 million people live in the sprawling metropolitan area.

## Site

Mexico City occupies a dry lake basin surrounded on all sides by high volcanic mountains. Because of its elevation of 7,350 feet (2,240 meters), frost sometimes occurs even though at 19° 30′ N latitude the city is close to the Tropic of Cancer.

## Serious Problems

Because of its beauty, people often call Mexico City the "Paris of the Americas."

But Mexico City also has major problems such as housing shortages, traffic congestion, and air pollution.

The city cannot house all of the people who have moved there. Thousands of Mexicans from rural areas flock to Mexico City each year. They seek employment and better opportunities for their children. So just a few short blocks from the beautiful tree-lined boulevards sit squalid slums that house 46 percent of the city's population. Thousands of the poorest families live in kitchenless shacks or lean-tos and cook along the sides of the streets. Other families occupy the roofs of factories or live in shacks that barely cling to steep-sided ravines. They scavenge rubbish dumps for discarded food and things to sell.

Traffic jams and air pollution afflict the city. Rapidly increasing numbers of motor vehicles clog narrow streets that were originally laid out for a much smaller city. The exhaust fumes remain trapped over the city by surrounding mountains instead of dispersing. The air in Mexico City now has the highest carbon monoxide level of any city in the world. Public health officials are concerned about the effects this pollution will have on the health of the population.

Mexico City also faces the continuing danger of earthquakes. Powerful earthquakes in 1985 and 1986 killed thousands of city residents and destroyed large parts of the city. Nearby volcanoes, so spectacular to view from the city on a sunny day, remind residents of Mexico City's location near a tectonic plate boundary (see the map on page 69).

Despite these many problems Mexican officials continue to seek ways to improve the quality of life for the city's people. Strict building codes now make new buildings less vulnerable to earthquakes, while new social programs seek to lessen the effects of poverty.

program—a program designed to allow more people to own land. In 1976, believing that ejidos were too small for profitable farming, the government grouped several ejidos together to form larger **collectives** throughout the country. The national government runs the collectives and makes the farming decisions.

**Industrialization.** Oil refining leads Mexico's industries. The Mexican government runs the entire oil industry, including the largest petrochemical industry in Latin America. Mexico refines and processes the oil rather than exporting crude oil. These operations increase the export value of oil and provide needed jobs for Mexicans. The United States buys most of Mexico's oil.

Other industries important to the Mexican economy produce iron and steel, automobiles, and textiles. Mexico City and Monterrey serve as the principal industrial centers.

In recent years many American manufacturers have built factories in Mexican towns near the United States border to take advantage of Mexico's low wage rates. In the United States the average factory worker earns more than $10 per hour, whereas the average factory worker in Mexico earns less than $3 per hour. Nevertheless, these factories attract many rural Mexicans to the border towns. These towns cannot provide the housing and other services, however, that are needed by the new residents. This forces large numbers of families to live in shacks on the outskirts of the towns. This situation also causes another problem. Many Americans complain bitterly about losing jobs to Mexican workers.

## Debt

During the early 1980s when world oil prices were high, Mexico borrowed large sums of money from international bankers. The money helped build factories and de-velop resources. Yet Mexico's debt climbed to more than $100 billion. Because income from oil has dropped since 1982, when world oil prices fell, Mexico has had trouble paying its debt. In fact, Mexico must borrow money every year from the International Monetary Fund (IMF) just to pay the interest on its debt.

The IMF lends Mexico the money it needs only on certain conditions. These conditions, called austerity measures, restrict unnecessary spending. But they also cause problems for the Mexican people. For example, one measure ended **subsidies,** the payments made to farmers to help keep food costs low. Halting the subsidies increased food prices and hurt many of the poorest citizens. Mexico also cut back spending for new factories—a cutback that led to further unemployment.

Despite problems such as a booming population and large debts, Mexico continues to modernize. New farming methods improve farm output. Improved health standards extend life expectancy and raise the general health of the people. And the government continues to build new factories, housing, and schools.

---

**SECTION 3 REVIEW**

1. **Define** subsistence farmer, hacienda, ejido, land reform, collective, subsidy
2. **Summarizing Ideas** How is population causing problems in Mexico?
3. **Interpreting Ideas** What challenge must Mexico meet so that the country's standard of living will rise?
4. **Analyzing Ideas** (a) Why is Mexico having trouble paying its debt? (b) Do you think that the austerity measures the IMF requires benefit Mexico? Why or why not? (c) In what other ways can Mexico reduce unnecessary spending?

---

# CHAPTER 13 REVIEW

## Chapter Summary

The following list contains the key concepts you have learned about Mexico.

1. Mexico has eight physical regions. Even though it is located in the tropics, a mountainous terrain gives much of Mexico a mild climate.
2. Mexico has three climate zones—tierra caliente, tierra templada, and tierra fría.
3. Much of Mexico's land is poorly suited for farming, and only 8 percent is currently being farmed. The land, however, holds vast natural resources, of which oil and natural gas are the most important.
4. The Mexican population includes three major groups of people: Indians, mestizos, and people of European ancestry.
5. The cultural pattern of Mexico combines Indian and Spanish imprints and can be seen in the Mexican way of life.
6. Economists classify Mexico as a developing nation with a mixed economy.
7. Mexico is a leading developing nation in Latin America. Like other developing nations, Mexico faces population pressures, a low per capita GNP, a slowly modernizing economy, and a large debt.
8. Since 1900 the Mexican economy has introduced land reform and collective farming. Mining was the major source of income, but in recent years manufacturing and farming have gained importance. At the present time oil is the largest source of most income.
9. Agriculture, much of it subsistence farming, is still the leading occupation. Continued industrialization is a key government aim. However, Mexico has assumed a large debt from international bankers.
10. Mexico City, a primate city, is the capital of Mexico and the center of activity in the country. Although Mexico City is one of the world's most beautiful cities, it faces serious problems. Leaders seek ways to improve the city's quality of life.

On a separate sheet of paper, complete the following review exercises.

## Reviewing Geographic Terms

Match each of the following terms with the correct definitions below.

a. subsidy  
b. land reform  
c. ejido  
d. hacienda  
e. collective  
f. subsistence farmer  
g. sierra  
h. mesa  
i. rift valley  
j. isthmus  
k. mestizo  

_____ 1. Spanish for "mountain range"
_____ 2. Elevated plateau with steep sides
_____ 3. Long narrow depression lying along a fault
_____ 4. Narrow piece of land that connects two landmasses
_____ 5. Person of mixed Indian and Spanish ancestry
_____ 6. Spanish for "public land"
_____ 7. Large estate in Mexico that is similar to a plantation
_____ 8. Ejidos grouped together
_____ 9. Farmer who only produces enough food for family members
_____ 10. Program of the Mexican government designed to break up large estates and allow more people to own land
_____ 11. Payment made to farmers to help keep food costs down

## Developing Critical Thinking Skills

1. **Summarizing Ideas** (a) What rivers provide most of the water sources that Mexico uses for irrigation? (b) Where does most of Mexican fishing take place?
2. **Interpreting Ideas** (a) Why is agricultural production in Mexico increasing? (b) How is foreign trade expanding in Mexico?
3. **Organizing Ideas** How did the government change the land reform program in 1976?

4. **Evaluating Ideas** Why might someone conclude that Mexico's attempts at modernization are improving the quality of life for the Mexican people?
5. **Analyzing Ideas** (a) Why is Mexico City a good example of a primate city? (b) Do you consider being a primate city a positive or a negative characteristic of Mexico City? Why?
6. **Writing About Geography** In two clearly written paragraphs, complete one of the following activities. (a) Explain the problems Mexico's young people face given the country's rapidly growing population. (b) Discuss how the physical setting surrounding the site of Mexico City affects the people's quality of life.

## Using Primary Sources

In the following excerpt from *Selections from the Works of the Baron de Humboldt*, Baron Alexander de Humboldt describes the geographical strengths of Mexico as the center of the Spanish Empire. As you study the reading, consider whether these same features remain Mexico's strengths today.

Mexico possesses [uncounted] advantages, if we consider it with relation to its [trade] with the rest of the civilized world. Placed on an isthmus, washed by the South Sea and Atlantic Ocean, Mexico appears destined to possess a powerful influence over the political events which agitate [give motion to] the two continents. A king of Spain resident in the capital might transmit his orders in five weeks to the Peninsula in Europe, and in six weeks to the Philippine islands in Asia. This vast empire, under a careful [management], would alone produce all that commerce collects together from the rest of the globe,—sugar, cochineal [red dye], cacao, cotton, coffee, wheat, hemp, flax, silk, oils, and wine. It would furnish every metal, without even the exception of mercury. The finest timber and an abundance of iron and copper might favour the progress of Mexican navigation, although the state of the coasts and the want of ports oppose [pose] obstacles in this respect which would be difficult to overcome.

1. Why would Mexico be a good capital for the Spanish Empire?
2. What could possibly stop the export of Mexican timber and metals?

## Practicing Geography Skills

*Before completing this activity, review Developing Geography Skills on page 273.*

**Understanding Geographic Descriptions** Reread the section entitled "Mexican Plateau" on page 271. Then complete the following activities.

1. (a) List the adjectives that describe the Mexican Plateau. (b) Define, in your own words, what each adjective means.
2. Rewrite the subsection, adding and changing descriptive words to further describe the Mexican Plateau.

## Exploring Geography

Construct a wall chart showing the three climate zones that predominate in Mexico. You may wish to use the outline of a mountain for the background of your chart and add the three climate zones at the appropriate elevation on the mountain background. Each of the zones should be accompanied by elevation and climatic information. Your chart should also include a table showing a major city in each of the three climate zones. The table should list the altitude, average January temperature, average July temperature, average yearly temperature, and average precipitation for each city. Refer to your textbook and other reference sources for this information.

# Central America

# PUTTING THE CHAPTER IN FOCUS

Seven small countries—Belize, Guatemala, Honduras, El Salvador, Nicaragua, Costa Rica, and Panama—make up Central America. They occupy an isthmus at the southern end of North America. As developing nations, these countries face many political, economic, and social problems as they modernize. Because of their relative locations, however, the nations of Central America play an increasingly important role in world affairs.

## Ideas to Understand

In studying about Central America, use these ideas to give direction to your reading.

1 Central America occupies a rugged and hazardous physical setting.
2 Central America's cultural setting closely resembles that of Mexico.
3 Central American nations face many similar problems.

## Terms to Define

The following terms are some of the key terms in the chapter. Defining them will help you understand Central America.

land bridge     literate
alluvial soil     dictatorship
floodplain     mulatto
leach     *finca*
ladino

## Places to Locate

Locating the following places will add to your knowledge of geography.

San Salvador     Belize
El Salvador     Honduras
Guatemala City     Panama
Guatemala     Belize City
Managua     Panama Canal
Nicaragua

## 1 Central America occupies a rugged and hazardous physical setting.

Imagine thick, steamy jungles full of brightly colored birds and screeching monkeys. There are no roads. You hack your way through dense vegetation with a machete (muh·SHEHT·ee). The rain forest finally thins out, and you see a spine of volcanic mountains rising in the distance. You are crossing Central America, a region that covers an area smaller than Texas. This **land bridge**—a small, twisting isthmus connecting two larger landmasses—links Mexico and South America. Its hazardous physical setting, with its volcanoes and earthquakes, often causes hardships for its people.

◀ *The mountain city of Quezaltenango, Guatemala*

## Physical Regions

Many of Mexico's rugged landforms stretch through Central America. The Central American landscape has three main features: a mountainous backbone, the Pacific lowlands, and the Caribbean lowlands.

The Sierra de Chiapas are one of Central America's dominant landforms. The region's few important rivers flow from the mountains toward the Caribbean Sea. Farmers ship their products down these rivers to Caribbean ports. The mountain chain greatly affects Central America's climate and is the location of the volcanoes and earthquakes that shake the region.

Coastal lowlands stretch along both sides of the region's mountainous spine. Narrow Pacific lowlands lie in the south-

west, and wider Caribbean lowlands lie in the northeast. Dense rain forests, so thick that only machetes and bulldozers can penetrate them, blanket both lowland areas, making settlement difficult.

## Natural Hazards

Natural hazards threaten Central America more than most other regions of the world. Three of the most destructive are violent volcanic eruptions, frequent earthquakes, and powerful hurricanes.

**Volcanic eruptions.** Central America has more than 100 active volcanoes. Many in the region's mountainous central spine rise to more than 12,000 feet (4,000 meters). More than 40 of the volcanoes, all on the Pacific side of Central America, have erupted in the last 20 years.

Eruptions often destroy crops and buildings, but the volcanoes also provide thick layers of volcanic ash. The ash from past eruptions has weathered into highly fertile soils. The volcanic soils found in the uplands of Central America produce more

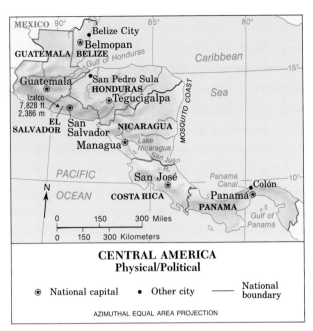

*Learning from Maps.* The people living on the land bridge called Central America face natural and political upheavals. On which coast do hurricanes do the most damage?

crops than the soils usually found throughout the tropics.

**Earthquakes.** Frequent earthquakes also plague Central America. The earthquakes generally cause far more damage than volcanic eruptions.

San Salvador, the capital of El Salvador, has been completely or partially destroyed by earthquakes and rebuilt 10 times since it was first established in 1528. Guatemala City, Guatemala's capital, has also been ruined and rebuilt several times. In 1972 a devastating earthquake toppled many buildings in the central business district in Managua, the capital of Nicaragua, and killed more than 8,000 people.

**Hurricanes.** People living on Central America's coastal lowlands face the additional hazard of hurricanes. Coastal lowlands facing the Caribbean Sea generally suffer far more damage from hurricanes than lowlands facing the Pacific Ocean.

*Learning from Pictures.* Earthquakes have caused millions of deaths over the centuries. Why does Central America have so many earthquakes?

The hurricane season along the Caribbean lowlands lasts from July through October. Hurricanes often cause great damage because people are unprepared. Poor communications give the people little warning, and poor roads give them little chance to escape the storm.

## Climate

Because of its absolute location between the Tropic of Cancer (23.5° N) and the equator (0°), Central America has a tropical climate. As in Mexico, variations in elevation create three climate zones: tierra caliente, tierra templada, and tierra fría (see page 274).

Rainfall differences cause the region's two seasons—a rainy season from May to November and a dry season from December to April. The northeast trade winds bring the rain, which is heaviest along the Caribbean coast (see the map on page 288). The east coasts of Guatemala and Costa Rica receive 120 inches (305 centimeters) or more of rain a year. The high mountains that rise inland cut off interior valleys, leeward slopes, and Pacific coast regions from the rain-bearing winds. These areas receive only 20 to 40 inches (50 to 100 centimeters) of rain each year.

## Vegetation

Vegetation patterns follow landform and rainfall patterns. Tropical rain forests blanket the Caribbean coasts. Along the sides of the mountains and in drier areas, vegetation thins out. However, throughout the region enough rain falls for many different types of trees and plants to grow.

## Resources

Central America has no large mineral deposits and only small amounts of farmland. Fertile soils usually lie in volcanic mountain areas but often erode rapidly.

Flooding rivers and streams deposit rich **alluvial soils,** soils deposited by flowing water, on floodplains in river valleys. These **floodplains** are level areas made of sediments deposited along a river or stream. When the river spills over its banks, it deposits rich, new soil. But throughout the region heavy rains and erosion **leach,** or wash out, nutrients from the soil. Farmers grow corn, beans, and rice as the principal food crops. Bananas, cotton, and coffee lead the list of exports.

---

### SECTION 1 REVIEW

1. **Define**  land bridge, alluvial soil, floodplain, leach
2. **Locate**  San Salvador, Guatemala City, Managua
3. **Summarizing Ideas**  What are the three major physical features of Central America?
4. **Interpreting Ideas**  (a) In what ways are volcanic eruptions both a disadvantage and an advantage to Central America?  (b) Why do hurricanes often cause more damage in Central America than in the United States?
5. **Analyzing Ideas**  How does elevation affect the climate of Central America?

---

## 2 Central America's cultural setting closely resembles that of Mexico.

The Indian and Spanish imprints evident in Central America's culture resemble those evident in Mexico. Central American countries and Mexico also face similar problems. Probably the greatest challenge to both is to provide the additional food, jobs, housing, and education that the growing population needs.

## A Brief History

The history of Central America, like that of Mexico, has two parts. For centuries the Indians built great civilizations (see the map on page 276.) Then, in the 1500s and 1600s, the Europeans took control of Central America. The Spanish controlled most of the region from Mexico south. The English gained territory only along the swampy Caribbean coasts of Belize (buh·LEES), Honduras, and Nicaragua. The Europeans brought their languages, religions, and customs to Central America.

El Salvador, Costa Rica, Guatemala, Honduras, and Nicaragua gained independence from Spain in 1821. Panama gained independence from Colombia in 1903. After many years as a colony called British Honduras, Belize gained independence in 1981.

***Learning from Maps.*** *Densely populated areas are located on the Pacific side of Central America. Why is the population density low along the Caribbean lowlands?*

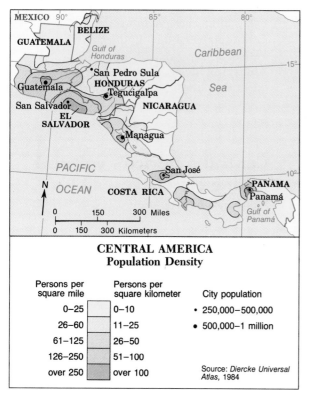

**CENTRAL AMERICA**
**Population Density**

| Persons per square mile | Persons per square kilometer | City population |
| --- | --- | --- |
| 0–25 | 0–10 | • 250,000–500,000 |
| 26–60 | 11–25 | • 500,000–1 million |
| 61–125 | 26–50 | |
| 126–250 | 51–100 | |
| over 250 | over 100 | Source: *Diercke Universal Atlas,* 1984 |

## Population Patterns

Though Central America's population patterns vary, they are similar to those of Mexico. Many of the same groups make up much of the rapidly growing and urbanizing population.

In Honduras, Nicaragua, El Salvador, and Panama mestizos comprise the largest group of people. In Guatemala Indians make up the majority group, and **ladinos**—as mestizos are called there—comprise a large minority. In Costa Rica most of the people trace their descent to Europeans, most of whom were Spanish. In Belize blacks make up 51 percent of the population. Most of their ancestors came from Caribbean islands.

Central America's rapidly growing population—27.2 million, about the same as that of California—is unevenly distributed over the land. Population geographers predict a population of 64.4 million by 2020 if current rates of increase stay the same.

The most densely populated lands are the Pacific plateaus and lowlands. These areas receive abundant rainfall and have fertile soils for farming. Fewer people live on the hot and humid Caribbean lowlands. The government in each of the six countries with Caribbean coasts—El Salvador has only a Pacific coast—encourages people in densely settled Pacific areas to resettle on less-crowded Caribbean lands. But these efforts have, for the most part, met with resistance because most rural Central Americans remain unwilling to leave familiar surroundings.

**A rapid growth rate.** A combination of high birth rates and low death rates in Central America produces one of the world's highest rates of natural increase, just as it does in Mexico. The average rate of natural increase in Central America totals 2.8 per 1,000 people, while the world average is only 1.7 per 1,000 people.

**A move to the city.** Many rural people, unable to find jobs in crowded rural areas, move to fast-growing cities. Most rural migrants move to their nation's capital city. As centers of government and industry, the capital cities offer the greatest employment opportunities. For example, Guatemala City, Central America's largest city, grew from an estimated 770,000 people in 1970 to 1.8 million in 1986. Six of the seven capital cities rank as the largest city in their nation. The exception is Belmopan, the new capital of Belize.

## Social Patterns

As in Mexico the cultural landscape of Central America has strong Indian and Spanish imprints. Indians shaped the region's first cultural landscape—great cities, widely scattered villages, and terraced fields. The Spanish drastically changed all of these.

Perhaps the most dramatic change was in the Indian population. The Indians were not immune to diseases brought by the Spanish. Within a century, smallpox, typhoid fever, measles, mumps, and influenza (flu) had reduced the Indian population from an estimated 15 to 25 million to 2.5 million.

The Spanish language and the Roman Catholic religion replaced Indian languages and religions. Spanish systems of government, architecture, and social organization took over. Today the life styles of the countries blend Indian and Spanish ways similar to the blend in Mexico. Belize, with its British influence, provides an exception.

Many of the region's social problems typify developing nations. For example, the percentage of people who are **literate,** or able to read and write, remains much lower than in developed nations. Raising literacy marks an important goal in all of the region's countries. Leaders work with the

***Learning from Pictures.*** *Panamanian folk dancing shows the influence of Spanish culture. Which Central American country reflects least the Spanish imprint?*

United Nations to build schools, train teachers, and start adult education programs.

Central America faces difficult population, political, economic, and social problems. Beginning in the 1980s there has been significant progress in solving the problems that trouble the area. With the new stability has come a determination to end even more of the troubles.

## Political Patterns

Today the countries of Central America call themselves democratic republics. All have constitutions that give the people the power to control the government through elections. However, since gaining independence, the countries have had trouble forming stable governments.

In most countries there has been little or no democracy. Wealthy businesspeople and landowners, with the help of the military, control the government. Usually **dictatorships,** governments ruled by a single powerful ruler or group of leaders, maintain power. Sometimes people rebel, throwing out one dictator only to have another take

*Text continues on page 293.*

Many of Guatemala's Indians live far from the modern bustle of Guatemala City. They live in lofty highland villages lined with dirt or cobblestone streets and stone-walled yards.

## Descendants of the Maya

In Quiché, a province in northwest Guatemala, 95 percent of the people trace their descent to the ancient Maya whose civilization existed in the area more than 1,000 years ago. They still speak the language used by their Mayan ancestors.

Like the farmers of ancient Maya times, the people of modern Quiché live in tiny villages scattered amid the volcanoes of Guatemala's highlands. The rhythm of their lives revolves today, as it did for their ancestors, around the growing of corn.

Guatemala's highland Indian farmers plant corn wherever suitable land exists. Some corn grows on almost-level floodplains along streams. Some clings to life on steep mountain slopes that farmers reach by crawling on their hands and knees.

*Marketplace in the Guatemala Highlands*

Few Indian farmers can grow enough food to feed their families. Most men must leave their villages periodically to earn money for extra food and other needs. Many work for a month or two harvesting coffee or sugarcane or weeding cotton on Guatemala's many plantations.

The women of Quiché help maintain the village by cooking, hauling water, and collecting firewood. Every spare moment, often in the shadowy light of an evening fire, they are busy at their looms weaving the intricate designs on *huipiles,* the traditional blouses that most Indians still prefer to Western clothing. The sale of these beautiful blouses in town markets brings in a little extra income.

## Civil Defense Patrols

Despite their isolation, Indians in Quiché are not far from the political troubles of modern Guatemala. As evening falls men in hundreds of small Indian villages leave home wrapped in blankets to protect them from the cold night air. Armed with ancient weapons, they trudge through the mists, seeking suspected guerrillas and terrorists opposed to Guatemala's rulers.

The nightly civil defense patrols date from the early 1980s, when Guatemala's military leaders suspected the Indians of rebelling against the government. Today every Indian man is required to join a civil defense patrol and be on duty one day each week. But the duty is often a severe economic hardship. It means losing a day's work in the fields or at another income-producing job. And the patrols have become socially harmful. Each man now feels he must spy on his neighbors. Many Indians feel they are losing that special sense of togetherness that has helped them, as it did their Mayan ancestors, survive their harsh mountain environment.

over a short time later. Only Costa Rica, a democracy since 1918, has maintained a stable government. Its democratic system remains a model for the region.

## Economic Patterns

As developing nations, all seven Central American countries remain less urbanized, less industrialized, and poorer than developed nations such as the United States and Canada. In all the countries farming ranks as the most important economic activity. Fishers in coastal areas catch fish, shrimp, and lobster for home markets and for export to the United States. Industry, however, is growing in importance. Food and mineral processing serve as the leading industries.

Central American countries depend on agricultural exports—especially bananas, coffee, and cotton—for much of their income and they trade mainly with the United

*Learning from Pictures.* *Guatemalans still harvest sugarcane by primitive means. What is the most important economic activity in Central America?*

States. However, the prices of such crops often rise and fall from year to year, which makes the economies dependent on them unstable.

*Learning from Maps.* *The Central American Common Market represents the region's economic interests. Which country on the map has petroleum resources?*

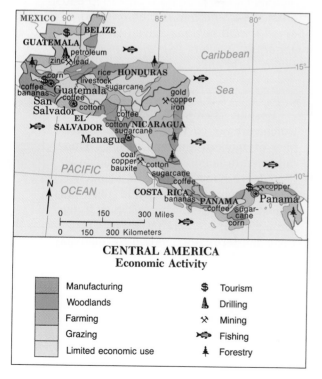

**CENTRAL AMERICA**
**Economic Activity**

| | |
|---|---|
| Manufacturing | $ Tourism |
| Woodlands | ⚒ Drilling |
| Farming | ✕ Mining |
| Grazing | ⇔ Fishing |
| Limited economic use | ♠ Forestry |

### SECTION 2 REVIEW

1. **Define** ladino, literate, dictatorship
2. **Locate** Belize, Honduras, Panama
3. **Summarizing Ideas** What is the greatest challenge facing Central American nations today?
4. **Interpreting Ideas** (a) Why are the Pacific plateaus and lowlands the most densely populated parts of Central America? (b) Why have Central Americans resisted government attempts to resettle them on the Caribbean lands?
5. **Synthesizing Ideas** How have Europeans influenced the cultural setting of Central America?
6. **Analyzing Ideas** Why does the dependence on agricultural exports cause economic problems for Central American economies?

*Text continues on page 295.*

# DEVELOPING GEOGRAPHY SKILLS
## WRITING ABOUT GEOGRAPHY: Composing Paragraphs

*A weaver working in time-honored fashion*

You have already learned the skill of recognizing main ideas (see the skill lesson on page 117). To write a paragraph, you must learn to expand on the main idea by adding an explanation, evidence, and supporting detail.

## How to Write a Paragraph

To write an effective paragraph, follow these guidelines.

1. **State a main idea.** Develop a clear statement of the information you want your readers to understand.

2. **Support your statement.** Include detail in sentences that add information or interest. These sentences should explain, support, or expand the main idea of the paragraph.
3. **Explain special vocabulary.** Define or explain any special words you use in the paragraph.
4. **Connect all the pieces.** Make sure that your paragraph has a beginning and an end. Also make sure all the information is tied logically together.

## Applying the Skill

Read the paragraph below. The main idea is stated in the first sentence: *Despite their isolation, Indians in Quiché are not far from the political troubles of modern Guatemala.* This main idea is expanded by the sentence: *Armed with ancient weapons, they trudge through the mists, seeking suspected guerrillas and terrorists opposed to Guatemala's rulers.* A third sentence adds interest: *As evening falls men in hundreds of small Indian villages leave home wrapped in blankets to protect them from the cold night air.*

> Despite their isolation, Indians in Quiché are not far from the political troubles of modern Guatemala. As evening falls men in hundreds of small Indian villages leave home wrapped in blankets to protect them from the cold night air. Armed with ancient weapons, they trudge through the mists, seeking suspected guerrillas and terrorists opposed to Guatemala's rulers.

*To practice this skill, see Practicing Geography Skills on page 301.*

# 3 Central American nations face many similar problems.

The seven Central American countries—Belize, Guatemala, Honduras, El Salvador, Nicaragua, Costa Rica, and Panama—face problems typical of developing nations. However, the seriousness of the problems and the ways in which they are solved vary from country to country.

## Belize

Belize, formerly British Honduras, lies between the Yucatán Peninsula and the Caribbean Sea. It is about the size of Massachusetts and has the region's fewest people, about 175,000.

Belize remains the exception to most general statements about Central America. It has only one coast and no high mountains, a democratic government, and uses English instead of Spanish as the official language. Most of its people are black or **mulatto**—of mixed black and European ancestry. Belize has few mestizos or Indians.

Even though Belize differs from other Central American nations, it has not escaped the problems of developing nations. Unemployment remains high in the cities, and the small rural population cannot raise enough food to feed the people. In addition, many young people in Belize leave the country in search of opportunities in other English-speaking nations.

Sugarcane, clothing, and citrus fruits lead the country's exports. Exports of shrimp and lobster go to the United States. Private businesses have built several freezing and canning factories in Belize City to process the catch. Belize also hopes to use a magnificent offshore coral reef, the world's second longest, to build a tourist industry based on boating, sport fishing, snorkeling, and scuba diving.

**Learning from Pictures.** *Technology improves the packaging of bananas on this Guatemalan plantation. On which coast do bananas grow?*

## Guatemala

Guatemala is roughly the size of Ohio and has Central America's largest population—8.6 million people. It is a country of opposites, a country whose spirit is both Mayan and modern. Although Guatemala is democratic in name, military leaders often control the country's government.

Indians make up the largest group in the population. They trace their descent to the Maya, whose civilization was at its height 1,000 years ago. Most Guatemalan Indians live as subsistence farmers on small farms in mountain areas. Many of them supplement their income by weaving beautiful fabrics or making colorful pottery (see the photograph on page 294). The Indians often trade food surpluses and crafts in lively weekly markets (see the CASE STUDY on page 292.)

Ladinos form another large group of the people. They own much of Guatemala's land. Most of the exported coffee, cotton, and bananas grows on plantations owned by ladinos. Coffee serves as the major crop grown on the Pacific slopes of the highlands. Cotton grows on the Pacific lowlands, and bananas grow mainly along the Caribbean coast. The discovery of small oil deposits in northern Guatemala in the 1980s may help the economy expand.

## Honduras

Honduras is about the size of Tennessee and has Central America's most rapidly growing population. Today's population of 4.7 million may grow to 12 million by 2020.

Ten percent of the people own most of Honduras's land and wealth. These landowners and several United States corporations have divided much of the land into plantations. Bananas and coffee grown on the plantations earn 50 percent of Honduras's export income.

The remaining 90 percent of the people each earn less than $100 a year. Most live as subsistence farmers who use machetes and hoes for planting and harvesting. They grow corn, beans, and other crops on farms that typically cover 15 to 25 acres (6 to 10 hectares). Like Guatemala, Honduras has a nominal democracy that is often controlled by military leaders. Opposition to such leaders sometimes causes severe turmoil in Honduras as it does in many of the other countries.

## El Salvador

El Salvador ranks as the smallest country in Central America—slightly smaller than Massachusetts. It also is the most crowded country, with over 618 people per square mile (1,600 people per square kilometer), and the poorest country, with a per capita income of about $710 a year. The mostly rural population grows faster than the government can provide land, food, housing, jobs, or schools.

Much of the best land lies on large plantations called *fincas* that are owned by the few landowners. Coffee grows on fincas located on hillsides above 2,000 feet (600 meters). Cotton and sugarcane grow on the fincas in the hot, humid Pacific lowlands. Most of El Salvador's export income comes from these three crops and from shrimp.

Mestizos make up nearly 90 percent of the people. Most live as subsistence farmers. Life remains so hard for these farmers that many must leave their families periodically to earn extra money. Most earn lit-

**Learning from Pictures.** *Voting in free elections is a valued privilege in Central America's democracies. What type of government often controls Honduras?*

## COMPARING CENTRAL AMERICAN NATIONS

| Nation | GNP (in millions) | Population Density | Urban Population (percent) | Literacy Rate* (percent) |
|--------|-------------------|--------------------|----------------------------|--------------------------|
| BELIZE | $ 170 | 19 per sq. mi/49 per sq. km | 66 | 80 |
| COSTA RICA | $3,500 | 135 per sq. mi/350 per sq. km | 43 | 90 |
| EL SALVADOR | $3,700 | 603 per sq. mi/1,562 per sq. km | 39 | 62 |
| GUATEMALA | $8,890 | 20 per sq. mi/52 per sq. km | 34 | 48 |
| HONDURAS | $2,900 | 104 per sq. mi/269 per sq. km | 37 | 55 |
| NICARAGUA | $2,400 | 64 per sq. mi/166 per sq. km | 55 | 87 |
| PANAMA | $4,400 | 75 per sq. mi/194 per sq. km | 49 | 87 |

*Literacy Rate is determined by each country. A person who can read and write in the official language is considered literate.

Source: *World Almanac*, 1987

**Learning from Charts.** *The small countries of Central America have a great range of population densities. Which country has the lowest population density?*

tle money, however, because they are illiterate and unskilled.

El Salvador's democratic government promotes industrialization as a way to provide jobs for its fast-growing population. Today more industries exist in El Salvador than in any other Central American nation except Costa Rica. Textiles woven from Salvadoran cotton serve as the chief products. The country's other major industries include refining imported crude oil and manufacturing petrochemicals.

## Nicaragua

Nicaragua, which is about the size of Pennsylvania, ranks as the largest country in Central America and contains about 3.5 million people. Most of these people live as subsistence farmers who raise corn and beans. Cotton, coffee, and sugarcane serve as the chief exports.

Since 1978 civil war has torn the country. Although the Sandinistas (SAN·dah·nees·tahs), who are backed by Cuba and the Soviet Union, control the government, the

Contras, who are supported by the United States, struggle to overthrow them. A peace agreement, arranged by Costa Rica and consisting of many details, has been signed. Working out the details of the agreement now stands as the major challenge. The Sandinistas have nationalized many of the industries and large estates. These actions led many wealthy and educated Nicaraguans to leave the country, creating a shortage of both capital and professional workers.

## Costa Rica

Costa Rica, like Belize, differs from the other Central American countries. Few of its people claim Indian ancestry. It has the region's highest literacy rate, the most democratic government, and the highest standard of living. Costa Rica also can claim the region's longest history of peace and economic prosperity.

The Indian civilizations of Mexico and Central America did not reach south into Costa Rica, and today only 10 percent of

*Text continues on page 299.*

*A freighter in the Miraflores locks*

Colón and Panama City have special locations. Colón lies at the Caribbean opening of the Panama Canal. Panama City lies at the canal's Pacific opening.

### Colón

Since 1953 Colón has had a free trade zone. In this zone goods can be imported and exported without payment of **duties,** or taxes on imports and exports. The free trade zone has created an economic boom for the city.

More than 300 export and import firms now operate in the free trade zone, making Colón a center of activity. Trading vessels constantly sail into and out of port. Industry also has started to grow. For example, a petroleum refinery on Las Minas Bay, just five miles east of Colón, refines crude oil imported from Venezuela. The refinery meets all of Panama's oil needs and exports petroleum products to other Central American nations.

Besides all of this activity, a steady line of ships from all over the world anchor off Cristóbal, a town just south of Colón, waiting for their turn to proceed through the canal. As a result, Colón's streets are always crowded with merchants and tourists inspecting the duty-free bargains that fill the windows of the city's shops.

### Panama City

Even though its location on the canal also brings Panama City much activity, its tone differs. As the capital of Panama, it is much larger than Colón and is marked by impressive government buildings and skyscrapers. Parks with well-tended flowerbeds and pleasant walkways stretch along its waterfront.

Panama City, like Colón, attracts visitors and business people from all over the world. Yet Panama City's role as an international urban center is not limited to its port. The Pan-American Highway links Panama City with the rest of Panama as well as with the other Central American nations and Mexico to the north. A towering bridge over the canal brings the highway into the heart of Panama City.

### Site and Situation

The sites of these two cities are special because of their ties to the canal. The canal, in turn, provides the cities with a special urban situation. The flags of ships from all over the world flutter in the tropical breezes over Colón and Panama City as the ships enter or exit one of the most important waterways on earth—the Panama Canal. Few cities located only 50 miles (80 kilometers) apart have such far-reaching influences as Colón and Panama City.

the people trace their descent to Indian ancestors. The other 90 percent consider themselves European.

In the 1970s Costa Rica became the first Central American country to earn more money from manufacturing than from farming. Leading manufactured goods include fertilizers, textiles, chemicals, and plastics. Major industries include the processing of coffee and cocoa.

Nonetheless, coffee and bananas still account for half of all Costa Rica's exports. Most of the coffee grows on small, family farms. People value it highly for its superior flavor. Bananas grow primarily on plantations located along the Pacific coast. Diseases wiped out the banana trees on the Caribbean lowlands in the 1930s.

Costa Rica and the United States maintain close ties, including active trade and various cultural exchanges.

## Panama

Panama has been more closely linked to the United States in this century than any other Central American country. A few days after Panama gained its independence in 1903, its leaders signed a treaty giving the United States control over a strip of land 10 miles wide and stretching from coast to coast on which to build and operate the Panama Canal. The Canal Zone, as it was called, was United States territory and most of its people were United States citizens.

In 1979 a new treaty returned the Canal Zone to Panamanian control. In the treaty the United States also agreed to transfer all rights to the Canal Zone to Panama in 1999. Panamanians now hold many jobs on the canal that traditionally were held by Americans before 1979.

The Panama Canal remains Panama's chief source of income. Farmers cultivate only about 17 percent of Panama's land. The chief crops and leading exports include

**Learning from Pictures.** *Spain introduced the horse—here shown in a Costa Rican fiesta—to Central America. What other cultural traits did the Spanish bring to Central America?*

bananas and sugarcane. Oil, discovered in the Gulf of Panama in the 1980s, also ranks as a leading export. Panama sends more than 55 percent of its oil to the United States. Panama maintains a nominal democracy ruled by a military leader.

---

### SECTION 3 REVIEW

1. **Define**  mulatto, finca, duty
2. **Locate**  Belize City, Colón, Panama Canal
3. **Interpreting Ideas**  How is the government of El Salvador trying to provide jobs for its people?
4. **Analyzing Ideas**  Why is the economy of Nicaragua unstable?

# CHAPTER 14 REVIEW

## Chapter Summary

The following list contains the key concepts you have learned about Central America.

1. Frequent earthquakes, volcanic eruptions, and hurricanes make the physical setting of Central America hazardous.
2. Although Central America's absolute location is in the tropics, different altitudes give the region a varied climate.
3. Central America has few natural resources to help economic development.
4. The people of Central America have high birth rates and low death rates. This combination causes populations to increase at a faster rate in Central America than in the world as a whole. Such population pressures strain the limited resources of most of the countries of the region.
5. People in the seven nations of Central America are typically rural, nonindustrialized, poor, and have little education. However, urbanization and industrialization are increasing. In addition, several of the countries have made improved economic and educational conditions their top priorities for the future.
6. Seven tiny nations occupy the Central American isthmus.
7. Life for Guatemala's highland Indians is similar in many ways to that of their Mayan ancestors.
8. Belize, until 1981 a colony called British Honduras, is unlike its neighbors in many ways.
9. Strong military leaders control Nicaragua, Honduras, and Panama.
10. El Salvador faces serious social and economic problems arising from rapid population growth.
11. Costa Rica, the most industrialized Central American country, has fewer problems than the other nations.
12. Panama benefits from the operation of the Panama Canal.

On a separate sheet of paper, complete the following review exercises.

## Reviewing Geographic Terms

Match each of the following terms with the correct definitions below.

a. ladino
b. land bridge
c. mulatto
d. leach
e. literate
f. alluvial soil
g. finca
h. floodplain
i. dictatorship

_____ 1. Government ruled by a single powerful ruler or group of leaders
_____ 2. Level areas made of sediments deposited along a river or stream
_____ 3. Wash nutrients from the soil
_____ 4. Small, twisting isthmus connecting two larger landmasses
_____ 5. Guatemalan name for mestizo
_____ 6. Soils deposited by flowing water
_____ 7. Able to read and write
_____ 8. Person of mixed black and European ancestry
_____ 9. Large plantation

## Developing Critical Thinking Skills

1. **Summarizing Ideas** (a) What three natural hazards plague Central America? (b) What type of damage does each cause?
2. **Comparing Ideas** How are the (a) climate and (b) population patterns of Central American countries similar to the climate and population patterns of Mexico?
3. **Categorizing Ideas** (a) What Central American nations are democracies or are working toward democracy? (b) What nations have dictatorships?
4. **Interpreting Ideas** There is little cultural diffusion in Central America. Why do you think this is true?
5. **Seeing Relationships** How are the people of modern Quiché like the ancient Maya?

6. **Contrasting Ideas** How are Belize and Costa Rica different from the other countries of Central America?
7. **Writing About Geography** In two clearly written paragraphs, discuss one of the following ideas. **(a)** What political problems currently plague Guatemala, Honduras, and Nicaragua? **(b)** What are the characteristics of the economies of each of the nations of Central America?

## Using Primary Sources

In the following excerpt from *I, Rigoberta Menchú*, Elisabeth Burgos-Debray describes the life on a finca in Guatemala. As you study the reading, consider what life as migrant workers would be like for your family.

Before we get into the [truck] in our village, the [labor] contractor tells us to bring with us everything we'll need for the month on the *finca*; that is, plates and cups, for example. Every worker carries his plate, his cup, and his water bottle in a bag on his back so he can go and get his *tortilla* [round thin piece of dough made from cornmeal or wheat flour] at mealtimes. Children who don't work don't earn, and so are not fed. They don't need plates. They share with their parents. The little ones who *do* earn also have plates for their ration of *tortilla*. When I wasn't earning anything, my mother used to give me half her ration. All the mothers did the same. We get *tortilla* and beans free, but they are often rotten. If the food varies a bit and we get an egg about every two months, then it is deducted from our pay. Any change in the food is deducted. . . .
The children, who are hot and tired and hungry, are always asking their parents for treats and it makes parents sad to see their children asking for things they can't give. But everything they buy is marked up on an account, and at the end when you get your pay, you always owe so much for food, so much at the shop, so much at the pharmacy. You end up owing a lot. . . . They deduct for everything and you end up having to pay debts before you can leave.

1. What happens to the children who do not work?
2. From the excerpt, what impressions do you get about working as a migrant worker?

## Practicing Geography Skills

*Before completing this activity, review Developing Geography Skills on page 294.*

**Writing Paragraphs** Study the following main idea. Then using information from the chapter, develop a paragraph that adds details and interest about the topic.

Most Central American countries have faced conflict and change in the last 20 years.

## Exploring Geography

1. Use the resources in your school or public library to find information on the worst natural disasters—volcanic eruptions, earthquakes, and hurricanes—that have struck Central America in the last 25 years. Then use this information to construct a chart. Your chart should include the type of natural disaster, when and where it occurred, and the amount of damage to property and to human life it caused.
2. Reread CITY FOCUS: Colón and Panama City, Panama, on page 298. Then use resources in your school or public library to write a similar report on another Central American city of your choice.

## CHAPTER 15

# Islands of the Caribbean

# PUTTING THE CHAPTER IN FOCUS

A vast arc of islands known as the "West Indies" stretches through the clear blue waters of the Caribbean Sea. Christopher Columbus claimed these islands for Spain in the late 1400s. Over the years other European countries also staked claims to some of the islands. Today many of the islands are independent nations. And most retain a mixture of European and African imprints.

## Ideas to Understand

In studying about the Caribbean Islands, use these ideas to give direction to your reading.

1 In the Caribbean region the physical setting varies from island to island.
2 The cultural setting blends European and African imprints.
3 The Caribbean region includes many nations and colonial possessions.

## Terms to Define

The following terms are some of the key terms in the chapter. Defining them will help you understand the Caribbean Islands.

| | |
|---|---|
| cay | overpopulate |
| archipelago | state farm |
| dependency | voodoo |
| indentured laborer | commonwealth |

## Places to Locate

Locating the following places will add to your knowledge of geography.

| | |
|---|---|
| West Indies | Dominican Republic |
| Greater Antilles | Havana |
| Bahamas | Virgin Islands |
| Lesser Antilles | Barbados |
| Cuba | Trinidad and Tobago |
| Puerto Rico | ABC Islands |
| Jamaica | Leeward Islands |
| Haiti | Windward Islands |

## 1 In the Caribbean region the physical setting varies from island to island.

Imagine that you are on a vacation cruise. Perhaps warm breezes, sparkling water, friendly people, and sandy beaches come to mind. Welcome to the Caribbean. The thousands of islands in the Caribbean region, known as the West Indies, curl in an arc 2,200 miles (3,600 kilometers) long linking the Atlantic Ocean and the Caribbean Sea.

The islands have varied physical settings. The exposed tops of an underwater mountain chain that stretches from Florida to Venezuela form many of the islands. **Cays** (KEES)—low-lying islands of coral—make up others.

*El Morro Castle in San Juan, Puerto Rico*

## Physical Regions

The Caribbean Islands can be divided into three main groups—the Greater Antilles, the Bahamas, and the Lesser Antilles (see the map on page 304). Geographers place each island in one of these groups according to the island's location.

**Greater Antilles.** The Greater Antilles account for more than 90 percent of the Caribbean region's total land area. They include the four largest islands—Cuba, Hispaniola, Puerto Rico, and Jamaica—as well as the Virgin Islands. On the islands of the Greater Antilles mountain highlands slope from each island's center to the sea. Frequent earthquakes rock the islands, a reminder of their relative locations near the boundaries of tectonic plates.

**The Bahamas.** A chain of about 700 small islands lying off the southeast coast of Florida forms the Bahamas. Another term for "chain of islands" is **archipelago.** The Bahamas feature low-lying coral and limestone islands with few rivers.

**Lesser Antilles.** The Lesser Antilles include an inner arc of mountainous islands with active volcanoes, an outer arc of islands with inactive volcanoes, and five islands off the coast of South America (see the map below). Volcanic cones, crater lakes, and bubbling hot springs attract tourists to many of the islands. The outer arc and Aruba (uh·ROO·buh), Bonaire (boh· NAYR), and Curaçao (KOOHR·uh·soh) off the coast of South America have lower elevations than the inner arc have, and are relatively flat.

## Climate and Vegetation

The West Indies have an absolute location between 10° and 27° N latitude. Except for the Bahamas, all of the islands lie between the Tropic of Cancer and the equator and enjoy a warm climate all year. In summer monthly temperatures average about 80°F (27°C), but steady northeast trade winds blowing from the ocean keep the days pleasant. In winter monthly temperatures average about 75°F (24°C).

***Learning from Maps.*** *Since the 1960s most of the smaller Caribbean countries have gained their independence. Which islands are United States possessions?*

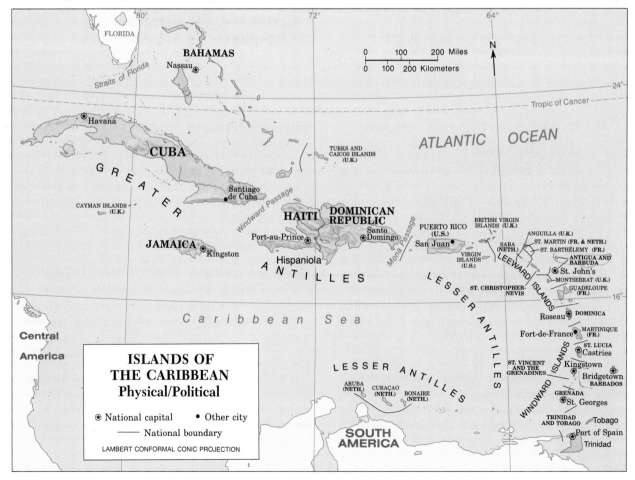

FLORIDA

**BAHAMAS**
Nassau

Straits of Florida

0   100   200 Miles
0   100   200 Kilometers

N

24°

Tropic of Cancer

Havana

**CUBA**

ATLANTIC   OCEAN

G R E A T E R

TURKS AND CAICOS ISLANDS (U.K.)

CAYMAN ISLANDS (U.K.)

Santiago de Cuba

Windward Passage

**HAITI**   **DOMINICAN REPUBLIC**

Santo Domingo

Mona Passage

PUERTO RICO (U.S.)
San Juan

BRITISH VIRGIN ISLANDS (U.K.)

ANGUILLA (U.K.)
ST. MARTIN (FR. & NETH.)
ST. BARTHÉLEMY (FR.)

**JAMAICA**   Kingston

Port-au-Prince

Hispaniola

A N T I L L E S

VIRGIN ISLANDS (U.S.)

SABA (NETH.)

L E E W A R D   I S L A N D S

ANTIGUA AND BARBUDA
St. John's
MONTSERRAT (U.K.)
GUADELOUPE (FR.)

16°

ST. CHRISTOPHER-NEVIS

*C a r i b b e a n   S e a*

L E S S E R   A N T I L L E S

Roseau   DOMINICA

Fort-de-France   MARTINIQUE (FR.)

**Central America**

ST. VINCENT AND THE GRENADINES

ST. LUCIA
Castries

Kingstown

W I N D W A R D   I S L A N D S

Bridgetown
BARBADOS

### ISLANDS OF THE CARIBBEAN
#### Physical/Political

⊛ National capital   • Other city
—— National boundary
LAMBERT CONFORMAL CONIC PROJECTION

L E S S E R   A N T I L L E S

ARUBA (NETH.)   CURAÇAO (NETH.)   BONAIRE (NETH.)

GRENADA
St. Georges

TRINIDAD AND TOBAGO   Tobago

Port of Spain
Trinidad

**SOUTH AMERICA**

80°   72°   64°

Rainfall, which varies dramatically with elevation and exposure to winds, occurs mainly between May and early November. Because the northeast trade winds sweep the entire region, rain falls mostly on the northeastern sides of the islands. For example, El Yunque (YOONG·kay)—a mountain on the northeast, or windward, side of Puerto Rico—often receives over 200 inches (508 centimeters) of rain a year. Other parts of Puerto Rico, cut off from rain-bearing winds, receive only about 30 inches (76 centimeters) of rain a year.

The location of the islands remains a key to their mild climates, but it also places them in the paths of hurricanes during late summer. These storms often bring devastating floods and destructive winds.

Landforms and climate affect the vegetation patterns of the region. Lush, tropical vegetation covers the windward sides of the islands. Vegetation thins at higher elevations and on the drier leeward sides.

## Resources

The small total land area and the mountainous terrain of the Caribbean area limit its resources. Volcanic deposits help to make the soil fertile, but there is little level land on most islands. Sugarcane ranks as the leading crop. The sides of hills and mountains provide suitable sites for raising coffee, while the valleys have the mild climate and fertile soils needed to produce citrus fruits, tobacco, and bananas.

Sport fishing attracts tourists to the Caribbean throughout the year. Local fishers catch shrimp, lobsters, and a variety of fish for local markets. But the region has little commercial fishing, because its waters are too shallow for large schools of fish.

The region's mineral resources include small deposits of bauxite, oil, iron, and chromium. Raw rather than refined ores provide most of the mineral exports.

**SECTION 1 REVIEW**

1. **Define** cay, archipelago
2. **Locate** West Indies, Greater Antilles, Bahamas, Lesser Antilles, Cuba, Hispaniola, Puerto Rico, Jamaica
3. **Summarizing Ideas** Identify the three main groups of islands in the Caribbean region.
4. **Comparing Ideas** How do the physical settings of the Greater Antilles and the Bahamas differ?
5. **Analyzing Ideas** (a) Why does rainfall differ in various areas of the same island? (b) Why do most islands have many different kinds of vegetation?

## 2 The cultural setting blends European and African imprints.

Caribbean history holds the key to the region's cultural diversity. The region's people have come from all over the world, bringing with them many cultural traits. First Indians, then Europeans and Africans settled the islands and contributed important elements to their cultural imprints.

### A Brief History

Historians estimate that at the time of Columbus's arrival in the 1490s about 1.5 million Indians lived on the Caribbean Islands. These Indians belonged to three different groups. The Arawaks (AR·uh·wahks), who lived on the Greater Antilles, were farmers. The Caribs (KAR·uhbs), who came to the region after the Arawaks, inhabited the Lesser Antilles. Adventurous traders, the Caribs traveled throughout the Caribbean in large canoes that carried 20 to 40 people. Scattered on other islands in the

region were descendants of an earlier Indian group, the Ciboney (see·boh·NAY).

Life in the Caribbean changed dramatically in October 1492 when Christopher Columbus and a small group of Europeans landed in the Bahamas. Over the next 150 years the Spanish, Dutch, English, and French colonized islands in the West Indies.

Most of the larger islands have now gained independence. Many smaller ones remain self-governing **dependencies,** territories ruled by, but not part of, another nation.

## Population Patterns

Nearly 32 million people live on the Caribbean Islands. Cuba, Haiti, the Dominican Republic, Puerto Rico, Jamaica, and Trinidad and Tobago (toh·BAY·goh) account for 94 percent of the region's total population.

Blacks constitute a majority on many islands. Most trace their heritage to Africans who were brought to the islands as slaves in the 1700s and 1800s. People of European descent form a majority only on Puerto Rico. On several other islands, mulattoes—or people descended from both blacks and whites—make up the largest population group.

Trinidad has many people of Asian descent. Their ancestors came mainly from India and China in the 1800s as **indentured laborers.** Planters anxious to find workers for their sugarcane fields after slavery was abolished made contracts with overseas workers willing to move. Under most contracts, called indentures, the laborers agreed to work for a specified time in exchange for transportation to the islands.

Dense populations cover most Caribbean Islands. Many population experts classify them as **overpopulated** because they try to support too many people with too few resources. The average rate of population increase for the region measures 1.8 percent a year, close to the world average of 1.7 percent. However, the populations of Haiti, the Dominican Republic, Jamaica, and Puerto Rico are growing rapidly.

Most of the people live in small rural villages. Many of the islands have a primate city that is at least three times larger than any other city. These cities grow rapidly as rural families move there seeking jobs and services that the cities provide.

## Social Patterns

Social patterns in the Caribbean resemble a mosaic made up of many different and distinct pieces. The region's diversity of languages illustrates this image. Spanish, English, French, and Dutch—languages of present or former colonial rulers—serve as official languages in the Caribbean. In addition, many local dialects mix European and African languages. Haitian Creole, for example, mixes words from French and African languages; Jamaican Creole mixes words from English and African languages. Papiamento (pahp·yuh·MEN·toh), spoken in some of the islands controlled by the Netherlands, mixes words from several European and African languages.

## Political Patterns

The Caribbean's political patterns also reflect the mixed heritage of the islands. The United States or European countries continue to govern certain islands that still have political ties with them. In addition, the governments of many of the recently independent countries still resemble the governments of their former rulers. The governments of the larger islands that have been independent for longer periods of time, however, vary greatly. Cuba has a totalitarian dictatorship; Haiti is working toward democracy; and the Dominican Republic and Jamaica are democracies.

*Text continues on page 309.*

Identifying cause-and-effect relationships is very important to a geographer. A *cause* is an event, person, or condition that makes something happen. An *effect* is the result or outcome of a cause. For example, the diagram below shows the cause-and-effect relationship between absolute location and climate in the Caribbean.

| CAUSE | | EFFECT |
|---|---|---|
| Islands located between 10° and 27° N | → | Warm climate all year |

The following diagram illustrates another cause-and-effect relationship—the relationship between resources and population that exists in the Caribbean region.

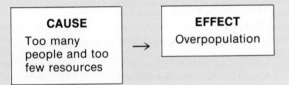

| CAUSE | | EFFECT |
|---|---|---|
| Too many people and too few resources | → | Overpopulation |

Remember that an effect may have several causes. And a cause may have several effects. You, as a student of geography, should be able to identify the main geographic cause or main geographic effect in a situation.

## How to Identify Cause-and-Effect Relationships

To identify cause-and-effect relationships, follow these guidelines.

1. **Look for the clues.** Writers often give clues that make it easy to uncover cause-and-effect relationships. *Cause* clues include *led to, brought about, produced, because,* and *the reason is. Effect* clues include *as a consequence,*

*dependent on, give rise to,* and *outcome.* But remember that geographers do not always give clues to connect cause and effect. Sometimes you will have to "read between the lines" to identify the cause-and-effect relationship.

2. **Check for complex connections.** Remember that there may be many causes or effects in a situation. After identifying the main ones, look for other links between happenings.

## Applying the Skill

Climate is one of the most important geographic factors in the physical setting of the Caribbean Islands. In studying the region's climate, you will note several cause-and-effect relationships.

Study the excerpt below. On a separate sheet of paper, use the following statement to prepare a diagram like the ones in the first column.

Because the northeast trade winds sweep the islands, rain falls mostly on the northeastern sides of the islands.

Your completed diagram should resemble the following one.

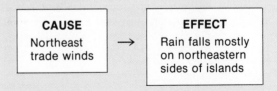

| CAUSE | | EFFECT |
|---|---|---|
| Northeast trade winds | → | Rain falls mostly on northeastern sides of islands |

In this case, the word *because* is the clue that the sentence contains a cause-and-effect relationship.

*To practice this skill, see Practicing Geography Skills on page 317.*

# THE GEOGRAPHIC WEB
## The Quality of Life

What does "quality of life" mean? Is it just another term for standard of living? Does it refer mainly to economic factors? Does it include social and political values such as freedom, equality, and democracy? How do we compare the quality of life available to people in different countries?

### The PQLI

One measure of the quality of life often used by social scientists is called the Physical Quality of Life Index, or the PQLI. The PQLI ranks countries according to their infant mortality rate, life expectancy, and literacy rate. Each country receives a score for each of the three factors. The average of the three scores is a country's PQLI.

Social scientists feel that these three measures provide some proof of the quality

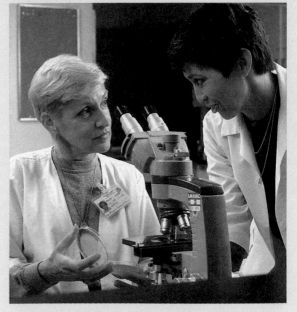

*Continuing health concerns*

*A colorful Ndbele home*

of life available to a country's people. Low infant mortality rates tell us a great deal about both the nutrition and health care available. Life expectancy rates tell us a great deal about available health care and about how safe people are from accidents, fires, crime, and war. Literacy rates tell us about the education system and the potential for economic development. The four countries with the highest PQLI are, in order, Japan, Switzerland, Canada, and the United States.

### Other Factors

But there are some things that the PQLI or any other quality of life index cannot measure. Such indexes cannot objectively measure happiness, personal interests and ambitions, or satisfying family life. And, after all, the only real measure of quality of life is what is important to the people living in each country.

## Economic Patterns

Economically, the Caribbean region is a patchwork of developing nations. Most have a low per capita GNP, a largely rural farming population, few industries, a wide income gap between the wealthy and the poor, and a low literacy rate. Most also have the problems that result when the population grows faster than food supplies, jobs, and educational facilities. However, the impact of these problems varies from island to island.

As in most developing nations, Caribbean cities have grown dramatically since the 1940s. Each island's primate city receives most of the money spent for education, health, and economic development. This spending, in turn, attracts increasing numbers of rural people to the growing cities.

Just as the political systems of the Caribbean countries differ so do their economic systems. Cuba has a Communist system and Jamaica has a socialist system. The Dominican Republic and other countries work toward capitalism.

---

### SECTION 2 REVIEW

1. **Define** dependency, indentured laborer, overpopulate
2. **Locate** Haiti, Dominican Republic
3. **Summarizing Ideas** What three Indian groups originally inhabited the Caribbean region?
4. **Comparing Ideas** How do the population patterns of Puerto Rico and Trinidad differ from the population patterns of the other islands in the Caribbean region?
5. **Analyzing Ideas** (a) In what ways do the social patterns of the Caribbean region resemble a mosaic? (b) How do the language patterns illustrate these mosaic-like social patterns?

---

## 3 The Caribbean region includes many nations and colonial possessions.

Many different nations and dependencies with a wide variety of cultural patterns make up the Caribbean region. These nations include Cuba, Haiti, the Dominican Republic, Jamaica, and Puerto Rico. The region also includes some of the world's smallest and newest nations.

### Cuba

Cuba, located about 100 miles (160 kilometers) south of Florida, has about as much land area as Pennsylvania. This size makes it the largest nation in the region. Its varied physical landscape includes mountains and hills that rise at the western end of the island and cover about 25 percent of the land. The center of the island contains the most fertile land. There, farmers raise vegetables, rice, tobacco, coffee, and produce dairy products.

With 10.3 million people, Cuba ranks as the most populous nation in the Caribbean region. Most Cubans trace their descent to original Spanish colonists or black slaves. Mulattoes make up a majority of the population today. About 69 percent of the people live in urban areas. Havana, which has nearly 2 million people, is Cuba's capital and primate city (see page 310).

Cuba was a Spanish colony until 1898, and the Spanish imprint remains strong. Spanish is the national language. Roman Catholicism, though discouraged by the present government, is the major religion.

In 1959 Fidel Castro led a successful revolution and established a totalitarian dictatorship and a Communist economy. Thousands of Cubans left the country following the takeover. Since then the government has devoted more and more land to raising sugarcane for export. Sugarcane,

*Text continues on page 311.*

*Once the capitol, now museums*

During the first half of the 1900s Havana was the most popular tourist resort in the Caribbean. Americans flocked to its sun-warmed beaches, dazzling night life, and magnificent hotels. Cars filled streets lined with shops displaying the latest tropical fashions and the finest imported foods.

## A Changed City

Havana has changed! Today Havana's beaches are virtually empty. Many of the nightclubs have closed. The hotels, in need of maintenance and repair, continue to decay. Only a few cars remain, held together and kept running by the ingenuity and skill of their owners. Since the early 1960s American automobile parts have been almost impossible to obtain. The shops along Galiano y San Rafael now have little to display. Almost no luxury goods are available and the government rations food and clothing. Some people see this once-lovely city that in years past was called "the Queen of the Caribbean" as a victim of the Communist revolution that Fidel Castro led in 1959.

Havana is a shell of its former self. Many of its residents have moved to the United States or to rural areas in Cuba. Money needed to keep the city alive is spent elsewhere. Havana, the "Queen of the Caribbean," has faded.

Today most of Havana's people, as well as residents of Cuba's other cities, are expected to spend weekends and holidays on farms. This is especially true at harvest time, when urban residents are expected to perform "voluntary" work. These government policies have added to Havana's decay. Because the Cuban government invests most of its resources in the development of rural areas, Havana suffers from housing problems. Many of the magnificent tourist hotels have been converted to public housing units. A few new public housing buildings have been constructed, but little money is available for repairs to buildings that have decayed after more than 25 years of neglect.

Since 1961, when the United States ended diplomatic relations with Cuba and placed severe restrictions on travel to Cuba, the country's tourist industry has faded. Even though Americans can once again travel to Havana, few spend their vacation dollars there. Today cities on other islands of the West Indies offer the same kinds of sights and excitement that once drew Americans to Havana. Few tourists choose to visit Havana.

## An Important City

Havana remains the capital and largest city of Cuba. It also serves as the commercial and industrial heart of the island. Almost all trade passes through Havana. And because the government now owns virtually all of the businesses and industries, the government employs most of Havana's workers.

which flourishes in Cuba's tropical wet-and-dry climate, grows on more than 50 percent of the island's farmland today. Large government-run plantations called **state farms** produce much of this sugarcane, which is a valuable export. Cuba must import much of its food.

Cuba has few major industries. The most important include food processing, oil refining, and light manufacturing. Cuba's world trade, however, is growing. While sugarcane ranks as the major export, nickel, fish, fruit, and tobacco exports boost the economy. The Soviet Union serves as Cuba's principal trading partner.

## Haiti

Haiti, at the western end of the island of Hispaniola directly east of Cuba, has more than 6 million people. It covers about the same-sized area as Maryland. Haiti gained independence from France in 1804 and became the world's first black republic.

Most of Haiti's people today are black. Although French serves as the official language, only a small, educated minority speak it. Most Haitians speak Haitian Creole, a language of African and French origins. **Voodoo,** a type of religion based on West African beliefs and ceremonies, coexists with Roman Catholicism, introduced to the island by the French.

Haiti ranks as one of the world's poorest and least-developed countries. Most Haitians earn less than $200 a year and have a life expectancy of only 45 years. Three of every four Haitians, most of whom are illiterate and live in one-room huts with thatched roofs, make a living as subsistence farmers. They farm with hand tools and raise cassava, an edible, starchy root; plantains, a banana-like fruit; and yams, or sweet potatoes. Farmers grow coffee, sugarcane, and cotton for export.

Haiti faces many problems. It is densely populated and has few mineral resources or industry. Although lush forests once covered the hillsides, they have long since been cut down to make room for farms. Such deforestation has led to severe erosion. As a result, the farmland on the mountainous island barely produces crops. Civil unrest and an unresponsive government add to the country's troubles. The end of a dictatorship in 1986 has not solved the government's problems. Many Haitians continue to come to the United States.

## Dominican Republic

The Dominican Republic, located on the eastern two-thirds of Hispaniola, has an area as large as New Hampshire and Vermont combined. It is a Spanish-speaking nation of 6.8 million people, 75 percent of whom are mulattoes. More than 50 percent of all Dominicans live in urban areas such as Santo Domingo, the nation's capital and primate city.

The Dominican Republic has had a turbulent history, both before and after gaining independence from Spain in 1844. United States Marines occupied the country from 1916 to 1924. The United States again sent troops to restore order in 1965 during a violent civil war. Since then the government has been stable. Its leaders currently are working toward democracy.

The economy of the Dominican Republic is strengthening. Agricultural products—particularly sugar—and minerals provide key exports. Tourism shows marked increases. In addition, several American companies have recently built factories in the Dominican Republic because of its low wages.

## Jamaica

Jamaica lies west of Hispaniola and south of Cuba. Less than 20 percent of this

| LEADING CARIBBEAN TOURIST DESTINATIONS | | |
|---|---|---|
| Destination | Tourists (in millions) | Tourist Revenue (in millions) |
| BAHAMAS | 2.6 | $770.0 |
| PUERTO RICO | 1.6 | $743.0 |
| VIRGIN ISLANDS | 1.3 | $360.0 |
| NETHERLANDS ANTILLES | .8 | $364.0 |
| JAMAICA | .8 | $394.0 |
| DOMINICAN REPUBLIC | .6 | $227.0 |
| BERMUDA | .6 | $356.8 |
| CAYMAN ISLANDS | .4 | $ 75.0 |
| BARBADOS | .4 | $284.2 |
| Source: *World Almanac*, 1987 | | |

**Learning from Charts.** *Cruise ship travel has become the region's leading form of tourism. Why has Cuba not shared in the tourist boom?*

mountainous island, which is slightly smaller than New Hampshire, has good farmland. As a result, farmers intensively cultivate this small portion of land.

Jamaica has about 2.3 million people and its population is growing rapidly. Most of the people crowd into the farming areas along the coast. Kingston, the capital, ranks among the Caribbean's largest cities. More than 90 percent of the island's people trace their descent to African and African and European ancestors.

Jamaica gained independence from Britain in 1962 and much of the imprint in Jamaica remains British. English is the official language, and many Jamaicans are Protestant. However, Spanish and African influences in areas such as religion and language combine to make Jamaican culture an example of cultural pluralism.

About 35 percent of all workers farm, but less than 1 percent of the people own

more than 50 percent of the agricultural land. Such inequities cause social and economic problems. Just as in Cuba, sugarcane ranks as the chief crop and export. Other export crops include coffee, bananas, coconuts, and citrus fruits.

Bauxite mining and tourism bring in most of Jamaica's income. But they do not provide enough jobs for the rapidly growing population.

## Puerto Rico

Puerto Rico is the easternmost island of the Greater Antilles. It measures about 35 miles (56 kilometers) from north to south and 110 miles (177 kilometers) from east to west. A spine of mountains reaches east and west, and a narrow coastal plain surrounds the island.

Puerto Rico was a Spanish colony until 1898 and the Spanish imprint remains. Most of the people speak Spanish and a majority are Roman Catholic.

Puerto Rico was acquired by the United States from Spain in 1898. Today it is now a self-governing **commonwealth** of the United States. This means that Puerto Ricans are United States citizens. They elect a nonvoting representative to the United States Congress, but they cannot vote in presidential elections and do not pay federal income taxes while living on the island. Some Puerto Ricans want Puerto Rico to become the 51st state of the United States. Others feel that the island should retain commonwealth status. A small, vocal group favors complete independence.

Puerto Rico is more developed than most islands in the region. Per capita income has risen from $125 in the 1940s to about $4,000 in 1986—one of the highest in Latin America. Unlike the rest of Latin America, less than half of the workers farm. Those who do grow sugarcane on much of the land along the coasts. They also grow

**312**

*Text continues on page 314.*

Pictures that travel agents use to advertise on television and in magazines show the Caribbean as an earthly paradise filled with white sand, palm trees, and a gentle sea. But behind the sun and the sand stirs the reality of poverty, unemployment, hunger, and resentment.

### Sharp Contrasts

Tourism is the leading moneymaker for the Bahamas, the Virgin Islands, Martinique, and many other islands. Each year millions of tourists step off cruise ships, yachts, and airplanes for a week or two in the sun.

However, contrasts exist almost everywhere that tourists congregate. Huge, glittering hotels, complete with swimming pools, lavish grounds, and luxurious accommodations, serve the tourists. But the hotels tower over neighborhoods where local people live without running water or many of the other basic conveniences of modern life. In restaurants magnificent meals are served in beautiful surroundings to tourists. Yet the people who work in the restaurants go home to hungry children.

### Resentment

The arrival of so many outsiders, their pockets bulging with money, often causes resentment among the island people. The contrast between the islanders' life styles and those of their guests is painfully obvious. Some islanders now refuse to work in the tourist industry.

This negative aspect of tourism has given many leaders second thoughts about the value of the industry to their nations. They worry that the resentment will flare up into violence and scare again away the tourists. Or even worst, they fear that angry citizens will rebel against the government and its leaders.

*The Straw Market in Nassau, Bahamas*

### Anger

Resentment has turned to anger for many tourist-industry employees. They direct much of the anger toward the government for failing to provide other jobs or a better education system. Islanders also direct some of the anger toward hotel chains and tour companies. These huge corporations now dominate the tourist industry. They arrange transportation, meals, accommodations, entertainment, and even shopping for the tourists. This deprives local entrepreneurs of opportunities to acquire some of the money spent by tourists. Local people also complain that the corporations control employment opportunities and keep wages low.

For these reasons, many people continue to question whether the beautiful physical setting of the Caribbean has been a blessing or a curse.

**Learning from Pictures.** *The streets of old San Juan, like the one above, show the influence of Spanish architecture. What is the political status of Puerto Rico today?*

coffee, fruits, and tobacco, often on hillsides. Attracted by an eager work force and relatively low wages, American businesses have built plants in Puerto Rico that produce petrochemicals, medicines, and electrical equipment.

### The Virgin Islands

The Virgin Islands lie to the east of Puerto Rico. Some islands belong to the United States and others belong to Britain. The islands nearest Puerto Rico—St. Thomas, St. John, and St. Croix—and more than 50 tiny coral islands belong to the United States. The United States purchased the islands from Denmark in 1917. Approximately three-fourths of the 96,000 inhabitants on the United States Virgin Islands are black.

The limestone islands have poor soil for farming and no rivers. As a result, the islands import almost all of their food.

Tourism remains the main industry. Warm sunshine, sandy beaches, and a duty-free port attract nearly a million tourists a year. Local industries include bauxite and oil processing, and textile manufacturing.

### The Bahamas

The Bahamas form an archipelago of nearly 700 low-lying islands fringed with coral reefs. Soil on these limestone islands fails to support farming and the country imports almost all of its food.

The Bahamas gained independence from Britain in 1973, but they have always been closely linked to the United States. Many Bahamians, for example, watch American television programs and read American newspapers. Their economy depends almost entirely on tourists from nearby North America. Nearly 2 million tourists a year visit the Connecticut-sized nation of less than 300,000 people.

### Barbados

Barbados (bar·BAY·dohz) is the easternmost island in the Caribbean region. The island, which is about half the size of New York City, ranks as the most densely settled country in the Americas.

The cultural imprint of Barbados is strongly British and African. The British settled Barbados in 1627 and imported African slaves to work on the sugarcane plantations. The island gained independence from Britain in 1966, but it remains the most traditionally British of the former colonies. Tourists enjoy seeing traffic moving on the left, police wearing British uniforms, and other attractions of this little bit of Britain in the Caribbean.

Tourism makes up only part of Barbados's diversified economy. Sugarcane and molasses provide important agricultural products. Factories produce chemicals, clothing, and electronics.

## Trinidad and Tobago

Trinidad and Tobago form a two-island country about the size of Delaware. The islands are located in the Atlantic Ocean only 7 miles (11 kilometers) from Venezuela's coast. Trinidad is the larger of the two islands and lies closer to Venezuela. Blacks, totaling 43 percent of the population, and Asians, totaling 40 percent, make up most of the country's 1.2 million people.

The islands gained independence from Britain in 1962. English remains the official language. But diversity highlights the country's cultural imprint. Trinidad features Hindu temples, calypso music, and offshore oil wells, while small farms cover more traditionally British Tobago.

Tourism and oil provide the chief sources of income, but the economy still struggles. The sagging world oil market has hurt the country's income. The unemployment rate averages nearly 17 percent.

Oil products, refined on Trinidad, are the leading exports. Asphalt is mined on Trinidad from the world's largest asphalt lake and is exported. Farmers grow sugarcane, coffee, cacao, and coconuts for export. Food is the leading import.

## Aruba, Bonaire, and Curaçao

Aruba, Bonaire, and Curaçao, known as the ABC Islands, form part of the Netherlands Antilles. All three islands are low-lying and have little rainfall.

There is no better example of cultural diversity than the ABC Islands. Like their language (Papiamento), their culture combines Spanish, Portuguese, Dutch, English, and African elements.

## The Leeward and Windward Islands

The Caribbean region also includes the Leeward Islands and Windward Islands. Fifteen small islands in the northern Lesser Antilles make up the Leeward Islands. The

**Learning from Pictures.** *Oil refining is one aspect of Trinidad's diverse economy. What are the chief sources of income in Trinidad?*

islands at the southern end of the Lesser Antilles make up the Windward Islands. Both island groups include several newly independent nations as well as territories of Britain, France, and the Netherlands (see the map on page 304).

(see the map on page 304).

### SECTION 3 REVIEW

1. **Define** state farm, voodoo, commonwealth
2. **Locate** Havana, Virgin Islands, Barbados, Trinidad and Tobago, ABC Islands, Leeward Islands, Windward Islands
3. **Interpreting Ideas** What effects has Cuba's emphasis on the production of sugarcane had on the economy?
4. **Comparing Ideas** (a) How are Haiti and the Dominican Republic alike? (b) How are they different?
5. **Contrasting Ideas** In what ways is Puerto Rico different from other islands in the Caribbean region?

# CHAPTER 15 REVIEW

## Chapter Summary

The following list contains the key concepts you have learned about the varied islands of the Caribbean.

1. The four largest islands in the West Indies—Puerto Rico, Cuba, Hispaniola, and Jamaica—are mountainous. Other islands include the low-lying Bahama archipelago and the partly volcanic Lesser Antilles. The Caribbean region has a predominantly tropical climate.
2. Blacks, whites, and members of other racial groups live throughout the islands. Languages reflect the European and African origins of most of the people.
3. The cultural settings vary from island to island. They include a mixture of cultural influences from more than 400 years of colonial rule by France, Britain, Spain, and the Netherlands as well as influences from the United States.
4. Cuba is the largest and most populous nation. It is a Communist nation with no economic ties to the United States.
5. Haiti, the world's first black republic, is today one of the world's poorest and most troubled nations.
6. Development in the Dominican Republic is slowed by periodic political unrest.
7. Inequities in land ownership in Jamaica cause social and economic problems for the young nation.
8. Puerto Rico is a United States commonwealth with a growing economy.
9. Most other nations in the Caribbean are small, poor, and dependent on tourism. The exception, the two-island nation of Trinidad and Tobago, have developed important oil-refining industries.
10. Tourism, the chief source of income for many islands in the region, has both benefits and costs.

On a separate sheet of paper, complete the following review exercises.

## Reviewing Geographic Terms

Supply the geographic term that correctly completes each sentence.

1. A ____ is a low-lying island of coral.
2. The Bahama ____, a chain of about 700 small islands, stretches along the southeast coast of Florida.
3. Territories ruled by but not part of another nation are called ____.
4. ____ ____ sign a contract agreeing to work for a specified time in exchange for transportation to a new location.
5. Many population experts refer to the Caribbean Islands as ____ because there are too many people to be supported by the islands' limited resources.
6. Large government-run plantations in Cuba are called ____ ____.
7. The type of religion based on West African beliefs and ceremonies and practiced by many Haitians is ____.
8. Puerto Rico is a self-governing territory, or ____, belonging to the United States.

## Developing Critical Thinking Skills

1. **Comparing Ideas** How do the physical settings of the three main island groups of the Caribbean region differ?
2. **Summarizing Ideas** (a) How does the absolute location of the West Indies influence climate? (b) What resources does the region have?
3. **Studying Maps** Study the map on page 304. What islands of the Caribbean region are still governed by European nations?
4. **Analyzing Ideas** How do the (a) population patterns and (b) social patterns of the islands of the Caribbean region reflect the mixed heritage of the islands?
5. **Interpreting Ideas** Why are the islands of the Caribbean region classified as developing nations?
6. **Writing About Geography** In two clearly written paragraphs, complete one of the fol-

lowing activities. **(a)** Compare the population, social, political, and economic patterns of Cuba, Haiti, the Dominican Republic, and Jamaica. **(b)** Discuss the ways that tourism emphasizes the differences between developing and developed nations.

## Using Primary Sources

In the following excerpt from *Diary of the Cuban Revolution*, Carlos Franqui describes the unique geography and culture of Cuba. As you study the reading, use the information it presents to help you compare the development of Cuba with that of the United States.

[Cuba's] character and destiny are those of an island crossroads: a ship. It looks toward its neighboring or distant continental shores, a tradition inherited from its founders, who never stayed long in port.

Cuba is an adventure without fear of the unexpected, the magical, the impossible, or the unknown.

Cuba is not Indian. Cuba is not white. It is neither black nor yellow. Cuba is mulatto, mixed, whitish black, and tobacco-hued. Together with Brazil, it is one of the blackest countries in white America. One of the whitest of black countries as well.

Cuba, like the United States — which is geographically so near and yet so remote and different in everything else — is one of the newest nations of the world. One is a continent, the other is an island. One is Anglo-Saxon Protestant in character, and based on the industrial revolution, power, and wealth. The other is Latin, Spanish, black, and Chinese.

If Venice was Europe's door to the Orient and Florence symbolized the end of antiquity and the coming of the Renaissance, Cuba is the beginning of America's new world, yesterday embodied in

today. There, everything began. All travelers paused there. The island was a bridge, a crossroads, and a base for continental expeditions in the New World. . . .

1. According to the author, how are the United States and Cuba different?
2. Why does the author consider Cuba to be "the beginning of America's new world"?

## Practicing Geography Skills

*Before completing this activity, review Developing Geography Skills on page 307.*

**Identifying Cause-and-Effect Relationships** Reread Section 1 of the chapter on pages 303–05. Then prepare diagrams for at least two cause-and-effect relationships mentioned in that section.

## Exploring Geography

1. Construct a table showing population information on the Caribbean region. Your table should have three columns—Greater Antilles, Lesser Antilles, and Bahamas. Each column should list such items as total population, population densities, and major cities. Then on a separate sheet of paper write a paragraph that analyzes what factors might have influenced population patterns in each of the island groups.
2. Research one of the Indian groups that inhabited the Caribbean before the arrival of Europeans. Focus your research on the ways of life followed by the Indians and the impact that the Europeans had on these ways of life. Record your findings in a brief written or oral report.
3. Using the map on page 304 or other maps, draw a map of either the Greater or Lesser Antilles. Label all the islands, capitals and major cities, water passages, and other points of interest.

# UNIT 5 REVIEW

## Unit Summary

The following list contains the key concepts you have learned about Mexico, Central America, and the Caribbean Islands.

1. The cultural regions of Middle America are Mexico, Central America, and the Caribbean Islands.
2. The physical setting of Middle America is mountainous and volcanic, and is occasionally rocked by earthquakes.
3. Middle America has a variety of climates. The tropical and subtropical climates in Mexico and Central America are influenced by elevation. The Caribbean Islands have a tropical climate.
4. Mexico is the only region in Middle America that contains abundant natural resources.
5. The high birth rate in Middle America hampers economic development.
6. Colonial rule affected the cultural setting of Middle America. Mexico and Central America have Indian and Spanish imprints. The Caribbean Islands have a variety of imprints: West African, French, British, Spanish, and Dutch.
7. Mexico is the leading developing nation of Middle America. Costa Rica is the most industrialized nation in Central America. In the Caribbean Islands, Puerto Rico's economy is growing due to its commonwealth connection with the United States.
8. The United States plays a major role in Middle America. It is one of Mexico's most important trading partners and the protector of the Panama Canal. It also has governmental authority over one of the largest islands in the Caribbean, Puerto Rico.

## Checking Your Understanding

1. (a) What climatic control do Mexico and Central America share? (b) What climate type influences the physical setting of the Caribbean Islands?
2. What is Mexico's leading industry today?
3. What is the absolute location of the West Indies?
4. What is the only country in Central America in which English is the national language?

## Applying Critical Thinking Skills

1. **Analyzing Ideas** (a) What type of government exists in Costa Rica? (b) Is this type of government unique to the region? Why or why not?
2. **Synthesizing Ideas** (a) How is Middle America's history similar to the histories of Canada and the United States? (b) What impact did European colonization have on the Indian imprint in Middle America?

## Reviewing Unit Features

1. **Geography in the Workplace** Why do population geographers study spatial distributions of populations?
2. **The Geographic Web** Why is it so hard to specifically identify what country has the best quality of life?
3. **City Focus** (a) What are some of the distinct differences between Colón and Panama City? (b) How do these cities differ from Mexico City?
4. **City Focus** (a) Why has Havana faded? (b) Why is it still the commercial and industrial heart of Cuba?

## Using Map Skills

1. Study the map on page 272. What Mexican cities lie near the border between the United States and Mexico?
2. Study the map on page 293. (a) How far from the Panama Canal is the nearest drilling site? (b) Why might a relative location near the canal be an advantage?
3. Study the map on page 304. (a) Which European powers still control territory in the Caribbean? (b) What are the names of the islands that Europeans control?

## Investigating Geography

1. Write an essay in which you consider what might happen to life in Mexico during the next 50 years if the population continued to grow at its present rate. Your essay should include both social and economic results and should pay particular attention to life in Mexico City and its metropolitan area.

2. Use the references in the library to further research the impact the Spanish had on the Indians of Middle America. Pay special attention to the arrival of Cortéz and the conquest of the Aztecs in Mexico. In a one-page essay, explain why you think the Europeans were able to conquer the Indians so easily.

3. List five ways to measure the quality of life in your school. Write them in order, beginning with the one you think is the best measure. In a written statement, explain why you ordered your choices as you did. Share your explanation with the class.

## Further Readings

### Chapter 13

Karen, Ruth. *Feathered Serpent: The Rise and Fall of the Aztecs.* New York: Macmillan Publishing Company, Four Winds. Examines the Aztec civilization and the possible reasons for its pessimistic outlook on life. Includes a fictional story of a young Aztec warrior, suggested readings on Aztec society, a glossary, and an index.

Perl, Linda. *Mexico: Crucible of the Americas.* New York: William Morrow. Describes Mexico and shows that even though it has great natural and cultural wealth, major problems hamper its efforts to become a modern, stable nation.

Riding, Alan. *Distant Neighbors. A Portrait of the Mexicans.* New York: Alfred A. Knopf. Discusses Mexico from its beginnings to the present with emphasis on current population growth, economic problems, poverty, the system of government, and the unique relationship with the United States.

### Chapter 14

Cheney, Glen Alan. *Revolution in Central America.* New York: Franklin Watts. Focuses on the social, political, and historical elements of four countries—Nicaragua, El Salvador, Guatemala, and Honduras—and explores the causes of conflict in Central America.

Dominguez, Jorge I., and Marc Lindenberg. *Central America: Current Crisis and Future Prospects.* New York: Foreign Policy Association. Reviews the present problems facing Central America and future prospects for that region, with special emphasis on United States-Central American relations.

Markun, Patricia Maloney. *Central America and Panama.* Rev. ed. New York: Franklin Watts. Introduces the seven countries of Central America and includes current information in a discussion of their culture, geography, and history.

Perl, Linda. *Guatemala. Central America's Living Past.* New York: William Morrow. Covers in text and illustrations the Mayan past of Guatemala, the Spanish conquest, Guatemala today, and Guatemala's relationships with its neighbors and the United States.

### Chapter 15

Augelli, John P., ed. *Caribbean Lands.* Grand Rapids, Michigan: The Fideler Company. Presents a text and picture journey through the various islands of the Caribbean, focusing on the history of the Caribbean, its people, and their societies. Also discusses natural resources, farming, industry, and tourism throughout the Caribbean area.

Lewis, Barry, and Peter Marshall. *Into Cuba.* New York: Alfred Van Der Marck Editions. Examines Cuba's people, geography, cities, and society as well as the island's unique relationship with the United States.

Nicholls, Colin. "The Caribbean Community." *UNESCO Courier* (October 1986). Gives a brief history of the movement toward economic integration among the nations of the Caribbean.

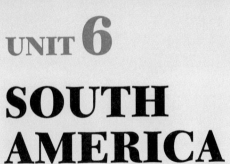

# UNIT 6

# SOUTH AMERICA

# CHAPTER 16 The Settings of South America

# PUTTING THE CHAPTER IN FOCUS

South America stretches 4,750 miles (7,640 kilometers) from north to south and almost 3,300 miles (5,300 kilometers) from east to west. As you would expect on such a vast landmass, South America includes a variety of landforms, climates, and vegetation patterns. The Isthmus of Panama links South America to Central America and the rest of North America. As in Middle America, the Spanish imprint in South America remains strong.

## Ideas to Understand

In studying about the physical and cultural settings of South America, use these ideas to give direction to your reading.

1 South America contains a vast array of physical features.

2 Cultural threads from four continents add to South America's cultures.

## Terms to Define

The following terms are some of the key terms in the chapter. Defining them will help you understand the physical and cultural settings of South America.

Altiplano          montane
selva              plantation

## Places to Locate

Locating the following places will add to your knowledge of geography.

Andes              Orinoco River
Guiana Highlands   Rio de Janeiro
Brazilian Plateau  Buenos Aires

## 1 South America contains a vast array of physical features.

Imagine that you are a time traveler. The year—1500. The place—South America. The physical setting that you survey looks much the same as it does in the 1980s. But as you move among the people you note that they differ from the South Americans of today. The Incas control a vast empire of flourishing cities and productive farms from their capital amid the jagged peaks of the Andes. Relay runners stationed at short intervals carry messages throughout the well-organized empire. Other Indians inhabit settlements scattered throughout the rest of the continent. Soon, however, the Spanish and Portuguese will conquer the region and alter its cultural setting forever.

◀ *Machu Picchu, ancient Inca city*

## Physical Regions

South America consists of three physical regions—the Andes Mountains, the Eastern Highlands, and the Central Plains.

**The Andes.** The jagged peaks of the Andes stretch along the entire west coast of South America 4,500 miles (7,200 kilometers). They form high walls of mountains from Panama in the north to Tierra del Fuego (tee·er·uh·del·FWAY·goh) at the southern tip. In Colombia the Andes break into three separate "fingers," separated by the Magdalena (mag·duh·LAY·nuh) and Cauca (KAU·kuh) river valleys. In Peru and Bolivia the Andes form two parallel mountain chains enclosing a high-elevation plateau called the **Altiplano**. Elevations of from 12,000 to 15,000 feet (4,000 to 5,000 meters) make the Altiplano one of the highest inhabited areas on earth.

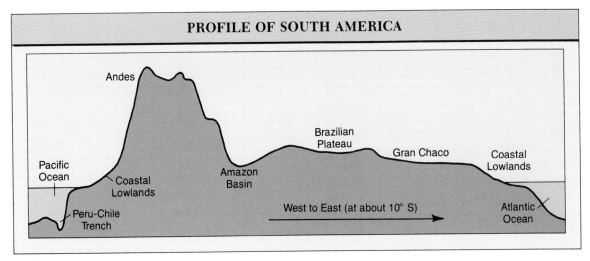

## PROFILE OF SOUTH AMERICA

Andes

Brazilian
Plateau

Gran Chaco

Coastal
Lowlands

Pacific
Ocean

Coastal
Lowlands

Amazon
Basin

West to East (at about 10° S)

Atlantic
Ocean

Peru-Chile
Trench

**Learning from Diagrams.**   *In general, the landscape of South America slopes downward from west to east. What process is forming the Andes?*

**Eastern Highlands.**   The Eastern Highlands consist of two blocks of ancient, worn-down mountains in eastern South America. Lower than the Andes, they average between 2,500 and 5,000 feet (760 and 1515 meters) in elevation. A few higher points in the Eastern Highlands reach over

**Learning from Pictures.**   *Iguaçu Falls in Brazil near the Paraguay border is one of South America's many beautiful waterfalls. What energy resource do waterfalls help provide?*

9,000 feet (2727 meters). The Amazon River divides the Eastern Highlands into the Guiana (gee·AN·uh) Highlands to the north and the Brazilian Plateau to the south.

**Central Plains.**   Between the Andes and the Eastern Highlands lie lowlands known as the Central Plains. Geographers divide the Plains into four subregions—the Llanos (LAN·ohs) in Colombia and Venezuela, the Amazon River Basin in Brazil, the Gran Chaco in Argentina and Paraguay (PAHR·uh·gwy), and the Pampas in Argentina.

### Rivers and Lakes

South America includes some of the world's great rivers. The Amazon River, second only to the Nile River in length, snakes through the rain forests of Brazil. It flows almost 3,900 miles (6,280 kilometers) from the Andes to the Atlantic Ocean. The Paraguay, Paraná (par·ah·NAH), and Uruguay (YUHR·uh·gwy) rivers form South America's next longest river system and drain southward into the Rio de la Plata estuary that lies between Uruguay and Argentina. The Cauca and Magdalena rivers flow from

the Andes through Colombia before emptying into the Caribbean Sea. The Orinoco River, which drains much of northern South America, forms part of the border between Colombia and Venezuela. The huge Van Blommenstein Reservoir occupies a depression in Suriname (soor·uh·NAM).

Shallow Lake Maracaibo (mahr·uh·KEYE· boh), located in the heart of Venezuela's oil-producing region, ranks as South America's largest lake. Lake Titicaca (tiht·ee·KAHK· uh)—12,500 feet (3,810 meters) high in the Altiplano—is the highest lake in the world that is used for transportation. Smaller lakes abound in a scenic lake district of the southern Andes on the border between Chile and Argentina.

## Climates and Vegetation

Much of the South American continent lies in the **tropics**—the area between the Tropic of Cancer (23.5° N) and the Tropic of Capricorn (23.5° S). Not surprisingly, then, tropical climates affect much of South America. The mountainous areas near the equator contain the three vertical climates—tierra caliente, tierra templada, and tierra fría—also found in Central America (see Chapter 14). The two colder zones—tierra templada and tierra fría—affect mountain areas outside the tropics.

**Tropical climates.** Areas near the equator have a tropical wet climate. A second tropical and wet area occurs in eastern Brazil, where southeast trade winds blow onshore and drop heavy rains as they cross the mountains along the coast.

Tropical rain forests flourish in tropical wet climates. In South America the rain forests are called **selva** on flat lands in the Amazon Basin and **montane** on rainy slopes in the Andes.

Two belts of tropical wet-and-dry climates occur on each side of the equator (see the map in the next column). These

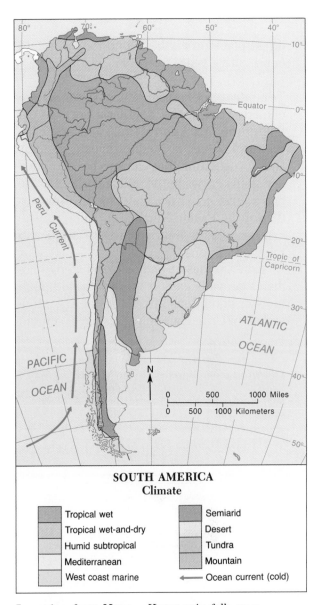

### SOUTH AMERICA
#### Climate

| | |
|---|---|
| Tropical wet | Semiarid |
| Tropical wet-and-dry | Desert |
| Humid subtropical | Tundra |
| Mediterranean | Mountain |
| West coast marine | ← Ocean current (cold) |

*Learning from Maps.* *Heavy rain falls on a large part of the South American continent. Why does the continent's tropical location affect rainfall?*

areas contain a mixture of savanna grasslands and thorny scrub forests.

Desert conditions characterize the coastal areas of Peru and northern Chile near the Atacama Desert. Temperatures remain hot all year with an average annual rainfall of less than 1 inch ( 2.54 centimeters) in some places. Arica, Chile, considered the

driest place on earth, had no rainfall for 14 consecutive years from 1958 to 1972.

**Temperate climates.** Zones of temperate climates cover the southern portions of South America. Central Chile, like southern California, has a Mediterranean climate. Hardy vegetation that can survive extended dry spells grows in the area. Southern Chile has a west coast marine climate similar to that of the Pacific Northwest. Thick forests and woodlands flourish in these mild and rainy conditions.

A belt of desert and semiarid steppe climates prevails east of the Andes, although moister conditions affect coastal Argentina and all of Uruguay. Such areas have a humid subtropical climate like that of the southeastern United States.

## Resources

South America has a wealth of natural resources. Many, however, remain undeveloped or are used less efficiently than in other parts of the Western Hemisphere.

**Agriculture.** Farming has always been the basis of life in South America. In ancient times Peruvian Indians living at bitterly cold elevations beat frozen potatoes into a pulp and ground the pulp into a powder. They stored it in this form until they reconstituted it with a little water. In other words, these ancient Indians developed freeze-dried instant mashed potatoes.

Four-fifths of South America's land is considered suitable for farming, yet large parcels of land remain forested or uncultivated. In many countries much of the land belongs to a few politically powerful landowning families. They regard land as wealth, instead of as a productive asset. Some of these private estates cover more territory than the states of Rhode Island or Delaware. A few South American countries have enacted land reform programs. The government has broken up the unused farmland into small farms and redistributed the lands to landless farmers.

**Plantations**, or very large farms, also typify South American agriculture. Many occupy the best farmlands in Brazil, Colombia, Peru, and Argentina. The plantations mainly grow cereal grains, soybeans, sugarcane, bananas, cotton, and coffee for export. Because so much land is devoted to crops for export, most countries of the region must import much of their food. In addition, plantation workers often work only a few months of the year and, in general, receive low wages. Poverty leaves them unable to buy consumer goods and slows industrialization.

*Learning from Maps.* *All four of these highlights occur in Argentina. Why does the lowest temperature for South America not occur at its southern tip?*

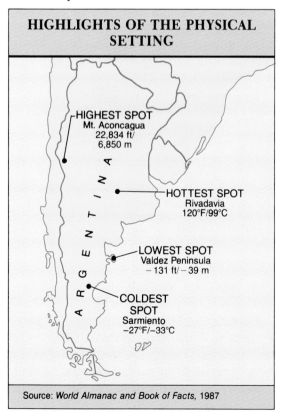

**HIGHLIGHTS OF THE PHYSICAL SETTING**

HIGHEST SPOT
Mt. Aconcagua
22,834 ft/
6,850 m

HOTTEST SPOT
Rivadavia
120°F/99°C

LOWEST SPOT
Valdez Peninsula
−131 ft/−39 m

COLDEST SPOT
Sarmiento
−27°F/−33°C

Source: *World Almanac and Book of Facts*, 1987

## MAJOR MINERAL RESOURCES OF SOUTH AMERICA

| Mineral | Country Where Found |
|---------|---------------------|
| BAUXITE | Brazil, Guyana, Suriname |
| COPPER | Bolivar, Chile, Ecuador, Peru |
| COAL | Argentina, Brazil, Chile, Peru, Venezuela |
| DIAMONDS | Guyana, Venezuela |
| GOLD | Brazil, Chile, Colombia, Ecuador, Guyana, Guyane, Peru, Venezuela |
| IRON ORE | Argentina, Brazil, Chile, Colombia, Peru, Venezuela |
| LEAD | Argentina, Bolivia, Brazil, Peru |
| MANGANESE | Brazil, Chile |

| Mineral | Country Where Found |
|---------|---------------------|
| MOLYBDENUM | Chile, Peru |
| NATURAL GAS | Argentina, Bolivia, Brazil, Chile, Peru, Venezuela |
| PETROLEUM | Argentina, Bolivia, Brazil, Chile, Colombia, Ecuador, Peru, Venezuela |
| SILVER | Argentina, Bolivia, Brazil, Colombia, Ecuador, Peru |
| TIN | Argentina, Bolivia, Peru |
| TUNGSTEN | Bolivia, Peru |
| URANIUM | Argentina |
| ZINC | Bolivia, Ecuador, Peru |

Source: *The Europa Yearbook*, 1987

***Learning from Tables.*** *South America has a variety of mineral resources. Based on the table, which country has the richest mineral deposits?*

Other South American farmers depend on subsistence agriculture. They struggle to grow enough food for their families on tiny farms they own or rent from landowners. Primitive machetes and hoes often serve as their only tools. Most subsistence farmers cannot afford the special seeds and fertilizers needed to improve crop yields using modern farming techniques.

**Forestry and fishing.** The Amazon Basin contains the world's largest expanse of tropical rain forest. However, in spite of a lack of transportation routes and the remote location of the area, some lumbering and farming projects are disturbing the forest's natural beauty. Many scientists, believing that the rain forest plays an important role in regulating world climates, want to slow down development. (See the CASE STUDY on page 367.)

South America also has vast supplies of fish. Fishing remains a leading economic activity along the coasts of Ecuador, Peru, and Chile.

**Mining.** Vast mineral deposits underlie much of South America. The long list of minerals includes iron ore in Brazil and Venezuela; tin and silver in the Andes of Peru and Bolivia; and bauxite, manganese, diamonds, gold, copper, and nitrates (for fertilizers) throughout the region.

Large oil deposits help make Venezuela wealthier than other South American nations. Smaller quantities of oil have been tapped in Brazil, Peru, Bolivia, and Colombia. Colombia, Brazil, Chile, and Peru have small deposits of coal. South American countries that lack oil and coal resources work to harness hydroelectricity to help meet their energy needs.

*Text continues on page 329.*

## EXPLORING NATURE: El Niño

*A Peruvian fishing catch*

The Peru Current, which flows northward along the western coast of South America, sometimes behaves in ways that scientists do not fully understand. Because this usually occurs soon after Christmas, it is called *El Niño* (NEEN·yoh), Spanish for "The [Christ] Child."

### Upwelling

Upwelling—a natural condition brought on by winds that persistently drive water away from the coast—is of great biological importance to the west coast of South America. When upwelling occurs the cold subsurface water of the Peru Current rises to replace the usually warm water.

The rising, cooler water is rich in nutrients for phytoplankton—microscopic ocean plants (see Chapter 6). Tiny marine animals called zooplankton feed on the trillions of phytoplankton. At the upper end of the food chain, fish thrive on the abundance of food. This process makes the coasts of Ecuador, Peru, and Chile among the world's most productive fishing areas.

Occasionally northerly winds replace the prevailing southerly winds and the cold Peru Current moves westward. In its place comes a warm current—El Niño. The warm waters of El Niño stop the upwelling and completely break down the normal ecological system. Most of the marine life moves in search of plankton-rich cooler waters and the fishing fleets follow.

### Effects of El Niño

In 1972 El Niño appeared quite suddenly. Warm water herded fish into a narrow band of cool water along the coast of Peru. Several thousand fishing vessels closed in. Together they caught as much as 180,000 tons of fish in a day.

When El Niño stopped, upwelling resumed. But most of the fish were gone. Without fish to consume the plankton, they overmultiplied and exhausted their food sources. Billions died and decomposed on the ocean floor. Decomposition used large quantities of the water's oxygen, making the ocean off Peru unable to support fish until balance was restored.

### Worldwide Influences

Scientists now recognize that El Niño's influences reach far beyond the west coast of South America. Indeed, it is now known that El Niño interacts with worldwide weather patterns. Rainfall shifts from the normally wet western Pacific toward the drier eastern Pacific. The Philippines and Indonesia experience drought. Intense heat and drought sweep Australia. Ecuador and Peru receive heavy rain and floods take heavy tolls in human lives and property losses. Record-breaking snowfalls paralyze the east coast of North America, while western Canada and Alaska experience unusually mild winters. All result from a still-unexplained change in the weather.

## SECTION 1 REVIEW

1. **Define** Altiplano, tropics, selva, montane, plantation
2. **Locate** Andes Mountains, Guiana Highlands, Brazilian Plateau, Orinoco River
3. **Summarizing Ideas** **(a)** What are the three physical regions of South America? **(b)** What makes the Altiplano unique?
4. **Contrasting Ideas** In what ways do the Andes Mountains and the Eastern Highlands differ?
5. **Interpreting Ideas** **(a)** How are South American governments working to make better use of the land? **(b)** What factor hampers these efforts?

# 2 Cultural threads from four continents add to South America's cultures.

Three major cultural threads weave in and out of the fabric of South American society. They include American Indian, European, and African heritages. Asians also contribute significantly to the cultures of some countries.

## A Brief History

American Indians occupied South America for centuries before the Spanish conquerors came in the 1500s. During these years primitive hunting and agricultural societies lived scattered throughout the sparsely settled continent.

The most advanced Indian culture and the highest Indian population densities were found in the Inca Empire high in the Andes. The Inca Empire included parts of what is today Peru, Bolivia, Ecuador, Colombia, and Chile. It developed out of much older Indian civilizations.

Spain and Portugal carved the continent into colonies during the 1500s. Other European nations later joined the scramble for colonies. France claimed French Guiana, Britain developed British Guiana, and the Netherlands controlled Dutch Guiana.

Labor was scarce in the lowlands of South America, where most of the Europeans began to farm. Many landowners brought people from Africa to work on coastal plantations as slaves.

Independence movements developed on the continent in the early 1800s. All nations except the Guianas eventually won their independence. Today only French Guiana remains under foreign control.

## Population Patterns

Population patterns throughout South America reflect Indian, European, and African imprints. Today, whites of European ancestry constitute a majority in three countries—Brazil, Argentina, and Uruguay. Indians form a majority in Bolivia and a significant minority in Peru, while most people in Chile, Colombia, Ecuador, Paraguay, and Venezuela are mestizos. Guyana, Brazil, Venezuela, and Colombia have large black populations. Mulattoes are most numerous in Brazil and Colombia.

South America's Indian population remains largely concentrated in the Andes. Concentrations of other ethnic groups including Asians occupy coastal areas, especially along the Atlantic and Caribbean.

South America's 300 million people are unevenly distributed across the continent. In general, the coastal areas have the highest population densities, while almost no people live in parts of the Andes or the Amazon Basin. Brazil remains the most populous country, with one-half of all South Americans.

As in Middle America, people under 15 years of age make up more than 35 percent

**Learning from Pictures.** *This family supplements its diet with fish from the Amazon River. What is one important nutrient that fish provide?*

of South America's population. Such high numbers of young people put a strain on governments' attempts to educate the population. Limited funds further hamper these efforts. As a result, many young people in South America face lives of chronic unemployment because of a lack of skills and a shortage of jobs.

Many South Americans leave rural areas to look for better opportunities in the cities. São Paulo (sow POW·looh) and Rio de Janeiro (REE·oh·day·zhuh·NER·oh) in Brazil and Buenos Aires (bway·nuh·SAHR·eez) in Argentina rank as the three largest cities in the region. In addition, Brazil has constructed its national capital—Brasilia (bruh·ZIL·yuh)—in the isolated center of the country.

## Social Patterns

The European conquerors imposed their languages, religion, and European ways on South America. Today Spanish or Portuguese serve as the official languages in all the countries except the Guianas. The Roman Catholic religion dominates life and unifies the people throughout the region. Many Indians, however, continue to speak their own languages and to practice traditional religions. This is particularly true of those who live in the Andes.

In general, the social patterns of South America vary according to which cultural thread dominates a country's national life. Traditional Indian ways remain strongest in four nations—Ecuador, Peru, Bolivia, and Paraguay. European ways predominate in

*Text continues on page 332.*

**Learning from Maps.** *As is true in many world regions, the densest populations line South America's coasts. What features of the physical setting help to cause this pattern?*

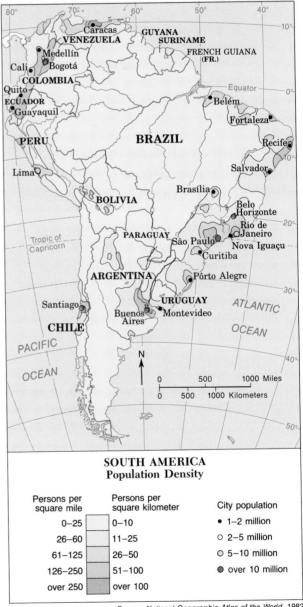

**SOUTH AMERICA**
**Population Density**

| Persons per square mile | Persons per square kilometer | City population |
|---|---|---|
| 0–25 | 0–10 | • 1–2 million |
| 26–60 | 11–25 | ○ 2–5 million |
| 61–125 | 26–50 | ◎ 5–10 million |
| 126–250 | 51–100 | ◉ over 10 million |
| over 250 | over 100 | |

Source: *National Geographic Atlas of the World,* 1983

# CITY FOCUS
## Brasilia, Brazil

Located some 600 miles (960 kilometers) northwest of Rio de Janeiro, Brasilia—the gleaming, modern capital of Brazil—lies in a region known as *sertao*. In a geographical sense the word *sertao* refers to the dry interior of northeast Brazil. Sertao also conveys a broader concept to most Brazilians. To them, sertao means the mysterious backlands or unknown areas of their country. Yet it is precisely this remote hinterland that has become a dynamic center of development because of the presence of Brasilia. The spectacular capital city was constructed between 1956 and 1960.

*Government buildings in Brasilia*

### The Plan

Seen from the air Brasilia resembles the shape of a drawn bow with an arrow. Magnificent government buildings—the Plaza of the Three Powers—house the executive, legislative, and judicial branches of government and form the tip of the arrow. Business, cultural, and recreational areas lie at the intersection of the bow and arrow. Farther along the shaft of the arrow are hotels, a sports arena, and fairgrounds. Residential areas run north and south along the curve of the bow.

### Problems

Certain political, geographical, and psychological problems have troubled Brasilia. The first problem is political. Many people felt that building an entire new capital in a wilderness was a terrible waste of government money—and some continue to feel that way. The second problem was the geographical problem of Brasilia's location in the sertao—the inaccessible interior. Today, however, new highways radiate outward from Brasilia, and the interior no longer seems quite as remote and mysterious as it did in the 1950s.

The third problem—the psychological one—was a little more subtle. Brazilians love city life. They enjoy the bustle and what they call the *movimento* of a city. However, Brasilia is not a typical Brazilian city. Its broad avenues and great open spaces lack congestion and the sense of movimento. This problem has been more difficult to solve. As a result, some Brazilians still feel that their new capital, in spite of its magnificent architecture and careful planning, is not a place for real living.

### Symbol of Pride

Nevertheless, the city stands as a symbol of national pride for most Brazilians. Further, its continuing growth marks its success in opening up the great sertao. It may lack movimento, but many of its residents are happy to live in a place where there are no transportation problems, where schools are available for their children, and where they can live inexpensively in a modern apartment. Some even confess, in non-Brazilian style, that they like the quiet life of Brasilia, far from the jangle of the big cities to the east.

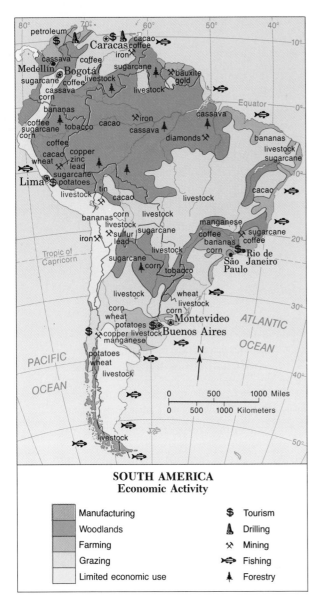

**SOUTH AMERICA**
**Economic Activity**

| | |
|---|---|
| ▨ Manufacturing | $ Tourism |
| ▨ Woodlands | 🛢 Drilling |
| ▨ Farming | ⚒ Mining |
| ▨ Grazing | 🐟 Fishing |
| ▨ Limited economic use | 🌲 Forestry |

***Learning from Maps.*** *Agriculture remains South America's leading economic activity. What is the major agricultural product of the drier lands of Argentina and Brazil?*

Brazil, Chile, Argentina, and Uruguay. Brazil also reflects important African cultural influences. Colombia and Venezuela have mixed cultural heritages.

## Political Patterns

South America includes one French *department*—French Guiana—and 12 in-dependent nations. (In the French government system, departments are political units that are represented in the French legislature.) All of these nations call them-selves democratic republics. Most, however, have long histories of political instability. Dictators and military leaders periodically seize control of governments and disrupt civilian rule.

## Economic Patterns

Economists classify all of the countries of South America as developing nations. Each country struggles to improve its economy, develop its natural resources, and industrialize. Most use the free enterprise system to accomplish this task. Some countries, however, have socialist economic systems in which the government has nationalized certain key industries.

Brazil and Argentina have the most developed and diversified economies in South America. Although both countries have several manufacturing facilities, agriculture remains the main economic activity and provides the major exports.

---

**SECTION 2 REVIEW**

1. **Locate** Rio de Janeiro, Buenos Aires
2. **Understanding Ideas** **(a)** What are the three major cultural threads that influence South America? **(b)** What fourth group now contributes to the cultural imprint?
3. **Summarizing Ideas** **(a)** Where did most Indians live before the Spanish conquerors came to South America? **(b)** Where do most live today?
4. **Interpreting Ideas** How does the large under-15 age group common in many countries strain the resources of South American governments?
5. **Synthesizing Ideas** In what ways do the social patterns of South America show European influences?

# DEVELOPING GEOGRAPHY SKILLS
## WRITING ABOUT GEOGRAPHY: Answering Essay Questions

Many of your assignments in school require you to write an *essay*—several paragraphs on a specific topic. You have already learned the first step in writing an essay—writing a paragraph (see the skill lesson on page 294).

In class you may be asked to write an essay to report on a research topic, to take sides on an issue, or even to tell what you did last summer. You may also be asked to write a different type of essay—an essay to answer a question on a test. For example, the following essay directive may appear on a test in this geography course.

> Discuss the characteristics of the South American population. Your essay should name the major groups that make up the population (5 points), explain how the characteristics of the population have changed over the years (5 points), and identify the most important aspects of the region's population patterns today (10 points).

To write such an essay, you need to know exactly what the question asks you to do. You can then draw on the information you learned from studying the chapter.

## How to Answer Essay Questions

Follow these steps to answer essay questions effectively.

1. **Note informational terms.** Look for words and phrases that give you clues to what you should include in your essay.
2. **Determine the essay's scope.** Note whether you are asked to write about one main idea or several main ideas.
3. **Note the directions.** Read the essay directive to find the key term or terms that tell you what kind of essay to write. The directive above tells you to *discuss* South America's population. This direction means to "tell in some detail." Other typical essay directions and their meanings are: *identify*—name and mention significance; *describe*—create a complete word-picture; *explain*—show cause-and-effect and other relationships; *compare*—indicate similarities and differences; *contrast*—indicate differences. Also note the point value given to each part of the question.
4. **Organize your ideas.** Once you understand what you are to write about, list the main ideas that your answer will contain. Each main idea should be developed in its own paragraph. Then add to your list all the supporting details you are planning to include in your answer. Through this process you can develop a detailed outline of your intended answer.

## Applying the Skill

Look again at the sample essay directive. In the directive the informational clues are *groups, changed, most important aspects,* and *today.* They let you know that you need to provide information about the major groups that make up South America's population. They further indicate that you need to describe how the population has changed and to identify key issues concerning the population today.

To prepare to answer the question stated in the directive you should organize your thoughts around those three main ideas. You should collect details that develop those ideas. You should also note that the first two parts are worth 5 points each and the third part is worth 10 points.

*To practice this skill, see Practicing Geography Skills on page 335.*

# CHAPTER 16 REVIEW

## Chapter Summary

The following list contains the key concepts you have learned about the physical and cultural settings of South America.

1. The three physical regions of South America are the Andes Mountains, the Eastern Highlands, and the Central Plains.
2. Tropical climates prevail in the north, temperate climates in the south. Deserts line part of the west coast and the foothills of the southern Andes.
3. Vegetation patterns closely parallel climatic patterns.
4. Resources are abundant but are, for the most part, undeveloped or used less efficiently than in some other parts of the hemisphere.
5. American Indians, Europeans, and Africans have all contributed to the cultural setting of South America.
6. A growing population strains resources in South America.
7. Most South Americans live near the coast. Interior areas are sparsely populated.
8. South America's 12 nations and one French department face many of the same problems that confront developing nations around the world. All the countries call themselves democratic republics.
9. El Niño has disastrous effects on fishing in South America and wreaks havoc on climate patterns throughout the world.

On a separate sheet of paper, complete the following review exercises.

## Reviewing Geographic Terms

In the following sentences, the underlined term is incorrect. Rewrite each sentence with the correct term.

1. In Peru and Bolivia the Andes form two parallel mountain chains that enclose a high-elevation plateau called the Highlands.

2. The rain forests that occupy the flat lands of the Amazon Basin are called jungles.
3. Savannas are rain forests found on rainy slopes in the Andes Mountains.
4. Farms are large estates that use resident laborers to grow crops.

## Developing Critical Thinking Skills

1. **Interpreting Ideas** (a) What was the ethnic background of the South American population in 1500? (b) What are the key features of the ethnic background of the population today?
2. **Identifying Ideas** What are the four subregions of the Central Plains in South America?
3. **Studying Maps** Study the maps of South America on pages 325 and 332. (a) What current runs along the west coast of South America? (b) Do you think this is a warm or cold current? Why? (c) Why is an ocean current shown on a climate map? (d) What unusual weather event is closely associated with the current? (e) What economic activity is associated with it?
4. **Comparing Maps** Examine the maps on pages 325 and 330. What part of South America has a climate similar to that of (a) southern California, (b) the Pacific Northwest, and (c) the southeastern United States?
5. **Analyzing Ideas** (a) What makes logging in the Amazon Basin difficult? (b) Why do many scientists claim it is necessary to preserve the rain forests?
6. **Seeing Relationships** What (a) political and (b) economic problems do the majority of countries in South America share?
7. **Writing About Geography** In a one-page essay, complete one of the following activities. (a) Analyze how the physical setting of South America has affected population densities in the region. (b) Describe the factors in modern South America that provide hope for future economic growth.

## Using Primary Sources

In the following excerpt from the *Journal of the Voyage of the Beagle*, Charles Darwin discusses the geography of South America. As you study the reading, compare the current geography of South America with Darwin's description.

It required little geological practice to interpret the marvelous story which this scene at once unfolded; . . . I saw the spot where a cluster of fine trees once waved their branches on the shores of the Atlantic, when that ocean (now driven back 700 miles) came to the foot of the Andes. I saw that they had sprung from a volcanic soil which had been raised above the level of the sea, and that subsequently this dry land, with its upright trees, had been let down into the depths of the ocean. In these depths, the formerly dry land was covered by sedimentary beds, and these again by enormous streams of submarine lava — one such mass attaining the thickness of a thousand feet; and these deluges of molten stone and [watery] deposits five times alternately had been spread out. The ocean which received such thick masses, must have been profoundly deep; but again the subterranean [underground] forces exerted themselves, . . . forming a chain of mountains more than seven thousand feet in height. . . . Those . . . forces . . . are always at work wearing down the surface of the land: the great piles of strata [layers of rock] . . . and the trees, now changed into silex [sand], were exposed projecting from volcanic soil, now changed into rock. . . . Now, all is utterly irreclaimable and desert. . . . Vast, and scarcely comprehensible [understandable] as such changes must ever appear, yet they have all occurred within a period, [that is] recent when compared with [other geological changes].

1. According to the author, how has the relative location of the Atlantic Ocean and the Andes changed?
2. (a) What type of landform dominates this region today? (b) What did the author claim to see springing from the volcanic soil? (c) To what underground forces does the author refer? (d) How does the author say these forces changed the landscape?

## Practicing Geography Skills

*Before completing this activity, review Developing Geography Skills on page 333.*

**Answering Essay Questions** Read the following essay directive. Then answer the questions below.

Describe the effects of the Andes on the climate, economy, and culture of South America.

1. (a) What are the informational terms in the essay directive? (b) What is the directional term? (c) What does the directional term mean?
2. (a) At least how many paragraphs should your essay contain? (b) In general, what will be the topic of each paragraph?

## Exploring Geography

1. Use maps and diagrams in this chapter, in Chapter 9, and in the Atlas, as well as references in your school or public library, to compare the physical geography of South America and North America. Then construct a chart noting similarities and differences in landforms, climates, and vegetation.
2. Use resources in your school or public library to gather information on an early Spanish explorer. Then prepare a written report on the explorer's life and expeditions.

# The Caribbean Coast Countries

# PUTTING THE CHAPTER IN FOCUS

Five countries in northern South America make up the continent's Caribbean countries. All five have strong links to the Caribbean region. Two of the five—Colombia and Venezuela—have coastlines on the Caribbean Sea and have strong ties to the rest of Latin America. The other three Caribbean nations—Guyana, Suriname, and French Guiana (Guyane)—front on the Atlantic Ocean. Often grouped together as the Guianas, these three lay outside Spanish colonial control and were originally colonized by Great Britain, the Netherlands, and France.

## Ideas to Understand

In studying about the Caribbean countries of South America, use these ideas to give direction to your reading.

1 Colombia fronts on both the Pacific Ocean and the Caribbean Sea.

2 Oil makes Venezuela South America's most prosperous nation.
3 The three Guianas have both similarities and differences.

## Terms to Define

The following terms are some of the key terms in the chapter. Defining them will help you understand the Caribbean countries of South America.

cordillera  martial law
*tierra helada*  alumina

## Places to Locate

Locating the following places will add to your knowledge of geography.

Sierra del Choco  Caracas
Llanos  Cayenne
Bogotá  Georgetown
Lake Maracaibo  Paramaribo

---

## 1 Colombia fronts on both the Pacific Ocean and the Caribbean Sea.

In the 1530s gold-hungry Spaniards, inspired by legends of a fabulously wealthy civilization called El Dorado, landed in what is today Colombia. Although the Spaniards never discovered El Dorado, they stayed on to rule Colombia as part of a colony called New Granada.

### Physical Setting

Colombia covers an area about the size of Texas and New Mexico combined. In western Colombia the deep trenches of the Cauca and Magdalena river valleys separate the northern end of the Andes into three mountain chains called **cordilleras.** The snowcapped Central Cordillera is higher and more densely populated than the cordilleras to the east and west. A fourth mountain chain called the Sierra Nevada de Santa Marta branches off from the Eastern Cordillera in northernmost Colombia. A fifth mountain chain, separate from the Andes, forms the Sierra del Choco on Colombia's Pacific coast.

The lowlands in eastern Colombia form part of South America's great Central Plains (see Chapter 16). Northern sections lie in the Llanos and are drained by the Orinoco River. Southern sections of the Eastern Lowlands lie in the Amazon Basin.

Colombia has a tropical climate in the lowlands. Rainy and dry seasons alternate throughout the year. The rainiest lands are

*Simón Bolívar Square in Caracas, Venezuela*

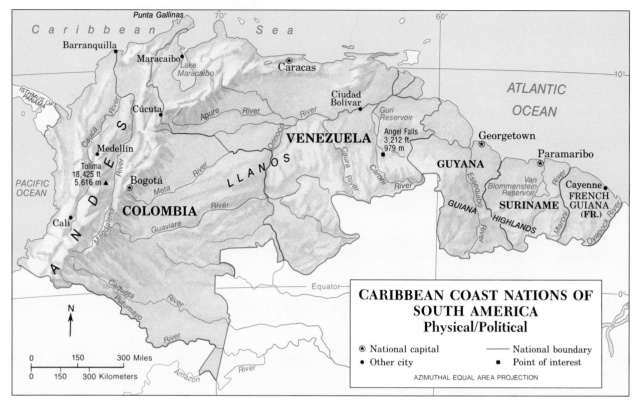

**Learning from Maps.** *South America's Caribbean countries border two other major bodies of water. What are they?*

in the Sierra del Choco, which receives 32 *feet* (384 inches or 980 centimeters) of rain a year. Vertical climate zones in the mountains range from tierra caliente to **tierra helada,** or frozen land, where snow permanently covers the ground.

Forests grow in the mountains as high as the tree line—about 12,000 feet (3,600 meters). Savanna grasslands cover the Llanos, while tropical rain forests cover the southern section of the Eastern Lowlands.

## Cultural Setting

Colombia's diverse population faces problems typical of developing nations. Colombian leaders work to overcome these problems as the 1900s draw to a close.

**Population patterns.** Colombia has perhaps the most ethnically varied population

in all of South America. Mestizos account for about 58 percent of the people. About 20 percent trace their heritage to European ancestry. Mulattoes make up about 14 percent; blacks and Indians each account for about 4 percent.

More than 90 percent of the people live in the western mountains near the Cauca and Magdalena rivers. Most mestizos and Europeans live in the cooler tierra templada and tierra fría mountain zones, while Indians tend to be concentrated at the southern end of the Colombian Andes near Popayán and Pasto. Most blacks and mulattoes live in coastal areas.

Colombia's population increases at a rate of 2.1 percent a year. About 65 percent of the people now live in urban areas such as Bogotá, the capital; Medellin; and Cali. As in other developing nations, many people move to cities in search of better op-

portunities. This urbanization strains the resources of the cities and has resulted in the growth of large slum areas that surround sprawling urban centers.

**Social patterns.** The Spanish imprint remains strong in Colombia. The vast majority of the people are Roman Catholic, and almost everyone speaks Spanish. Colombians take such pride in their language that they have a law that protects it from unnecessary changes. They consider their form of Spanish purer than that spoken in other areas of South America.

**Political patterns.** After it gained its independence from Spain in 1821 Colombia was united for a time with present-day Venezuela, Ecuador, and Panama in a short-lived federation called Greater Colombia. Venezuela and Ecuador withdrew from the federation in the 1800s to become independent countries. Panama separated from Colombia in 1903.

Political unrest has marked Colombia's recent history. The conflict has its roots in the wide income gap between the impoverished majority and the small wealthy elite who control much of the economy. Many Colombians remember with horror the civil unrest known as *La Violencia* (The Violence) from 1948 to 1958. Between 150,000 and 200,000 people died as a result of the conflict. Military officers seized control of the government and imposed **martial law,** or rule by the military, in 1953 and brutally repressed all who opposed them. Civilian rule was restored in 1957, but violence again broke out in the 1970s and 1980s.

**Economic patterns.** Although manufacturing continues to expand, Colombia's economy remains primarily agricultural. Only 20 percent of all workers earn a living in manufacturing.

Many developing nations depend on one crop (see the feature on page 343). Colombia depends on coffee. Coffee grown

*Learning from Pictures.* These Sibundoy men of Colombia wear traditional clothing. What culture's imprint now dominates Colombia's cultural setting?

**Learning from Pictures.** *Workers, rather than machines, still pick most of Colombia's coffee crop. Which of Colombia's other agricultural products are probably still tended by hand?*

**SECTION 1 REVIEW**

1. **Define** cordillera, tierra helada, martial law
2. **Locate** Sierra del Choco, Llanos, Bogotá
3. **Summarizing Ideas** Where do Colombia's major climates occur?
4. **Contrasting Ideas** How are Colombia's population patterns unique in South America?
5. **Seeing Relationships** How has rapid urbanization caused problems for Colombia's cities?

## 2 Oil makes Venezuela South America's most prosperous nation.

In 1498 Spanish explorers, seeing the Indians in canoes, named the land Venezuela, meaning "Little Venice," for the watery Italian city. Venezuela shared Colombia's history until the 1830s, when it became an independent nation.

### Physical Setting

The northernmost nation in South America, Venezuela borders the Caribbean Sea and sends an almost rectangular tail of territory south into the Amazon Basin. Venezuela is about twice the size of California. The nation includes four physical regions—the Maracaibo Basin, the Northern Uplands, the Llanos, and the Guiana Highlands.

Approximately half of Venezuela's huge oil output comes from deposits under Lake Maracaibo or the mountain-rimmed Maracaibo Basin around it. The Northern Uplands consist of the high mountains of the Andes' Eastern Cordillera that continue into northern Venezuela as snowcapped Cordillera Merida (MER·ee·uh). South of these mountains lie the Llanos, which are

on mountain slopes in the tierra templada earns about 70 percent of Colombia's total export income. Other important agricultural products include sugarcane, bananas, cotton, tobacco, corn, wheat, barley, potatoes, and livestock. Oil found along the Venezuelan border accounts for 15 percent of the country's export income.

Colombia started to industrialize in the 1940s. Today Colombian factories produce steel, chemicals, motor vehicles, and other manufactured goods. Textiles, made using Colombian-grown cotton, now rank as the second-leading export after coffee. Government programs continue to focus on increasing industrialization and diversifying the economy.

*Text continues on page 342.*

**340**

# DEVELOPING GEOGRAPHY SKILLS
## THINKING GEOGRAPHICALLY: Asking Geographic Questions

Geography is distinguished from the other social sciences by the questions it asks. Geographers explore the *where* and *why there* aspects of a physical or cultural setting.

The answers that geographers receive to these two types of questions provide them with information linked to the five themes of modern geography (see Chapter 1). Answers to where questions, for example, describe location. Answers to why there questions might provide data on several themes, such as relationships within places, movement, or regions. By asking the right questions geographers can learn a great deal of important information about a place. For that reason, geographers are constantly refining their questioning skills. As a student of geography, it is important for you to also develop such techniques.

### How to Ask Geographic Questions

To develop geographic questioning skills, follow these guidelines.

1. **Identify geographic concepts.** Note the important geographic ideas in an excerpt.
2. **Ask geographic questions.** Always ask where and why there questions to discover geographic significance.
3. **Think geographically.** Use your questions and their answers to identify relationships, understand processes, and establish significance.

### Applying the Skill

Study the chart on this page. Note that it contains information related to the climates of several South American cities. Among the geographic questions you may ask about climates in South America are: Where are the highest January and lowest July temperatures? (*Buenos Aires and Santiago, La Paz*) Where are the highest and

### TEMPERATURES AND PRECIPITATION IN SELECTED SOUTH AMERICAN CITIES

| City/Country | January Low* | July High* | Precipitation (in/cm) |
|---|---|---|---|
| ASUNCIÓN, PARAGUAY | 81°F 27°C | 64°F 13°C | 53/ 135 |
| BOGOTÁ, COLOMBIA | 67°F 19°C | 48°F 9°C | 42/ 106 |
| BUENOS AIRES, ARGENTINA | 85°F 29°C | 42°F 6°C | 37/ 95 |
| CARACAS, VENEZUELA | 78°F 26°C | 56°F 13°C | 33/ 84 |
| LA PAZ, BOLIVIA | 63°F 17°C | 33°F 1°C | 23/ 57 |
| LIMA, PERU | 82°F 28°C | 57°F 14°C | 2/ 4 |
| RIO DE JANEIRO, BRAZIL | 84°F 29°C | 63°F 17°C | 43/ 109 |
| SANTIAGO, CHILE | 85°F 29°C | 37°F 3°C | 14/ 36 |
| SÃO PAULO, BRAZIL | 77°F 25°C | 53°F 12°C | 57/ 145 |

*The seasons are reversed in South America
Sources: *World Almanac*, 1987
*The Statesman's Yearbook*, 1986–87

lowest average rainfall amounts? (*São Paulo, Lima*)

To refine your questioning further and add to your geographic knowledge, you may ask questions such as: Why does La Paz have a lower July temperature than Santiago, which is farther south? Or, Why does Lima receive so little rainfall even though it is located near the ocean? (By the time you finish this textbook, you should be able to answer these questions!)

*To practice this skill, see Practicing Geography Skills on page 349.*

drained by the Orinoco River. Venezuela's fourth physical region, the Guiana Highlands, occupies the southern half of Venezuela south of the Orinoco River. Much of the region remains forested and unexplored. Mines produce rich iron ore at El Pao and Cerro Bolívar on the northern edge of the Guiana Highlands.

Like Colombia, Venezuela has a tropical wet-and-dry tierra caliente climate in the lowlands. Cooler climates prevail in the mountains. Venezuela's rainy season lasts from June to October.

*Learning from Pictures.* *Caracas's Plaza Chacaito Sabana Grande shopping district attracts both local and foreign shoppers. Why might Venezuela be considered prosperous?*

## Cultural Setting

Venezuela, proud of its Spanish heritage, has worked hard to improve its social, political, and economic patterns. Venezuela's vast oil reserves help the nation in its drive to industrialize.

**Population patterns.** Mestizos make up about 66 percent of the Venezuelan population. About 20 percent trace their descent to Europeans. The remainder includes small numbers of Indians, blacks, and mulattoes. The Europeans, mestizos, and Indians live mainly in the Northern Uplands. Most blacks and mulattoes live along the coast.

About 76 percent of Venezuela's people live in urban areas. The largest cities include Caracas, the capital, and Maracaibo.

**Social patterns.** As in Colombia, the Spanish imprint in Venezuela remains strong. The population includes a small, well-educated elite as well as a large class of both urban and rural poor. Today the nation has a rapidly growing middle class centered in the larger urban areas.

**Political patterns.** Political instability plagued Venezuela after independence. In 1958, however, the people overthrew the dictatorship. Since then Venezuela has enjoyed a democratic government.

The government plays a strong role in the socialist economy of Venezuela. Laws allow the government to seize large estates and redistribute the land among landless farmers. The iron-mining, oil, and electrical industries were nationalized in the 1970s and are run directly by the government.

**Economic patterns.** The most prosperous country in Latin America, Venezuela has a per capita GNP of $3,110—twice as high as the average for South America as a whole. More people work in mining and industry than in agriculture.

*Text continues on page 344.*

# CASE STUDY
## EXPLORING IDEAS: Oil and Venezuela

Most experts say that a healthy economy produces a variety of products. Economists call such an economy *diversified*. Economists also believe that a one-crop economy, or an economy that is based largely on the production and sale of just one product, is weak. Unfortunately, most South American nations depend on one or two products for their prosperity. Variations in demand for these products, along with widely fluctuating prices, can cause serious economic problems.

### Venezuela's One-Crop Economy

Venezuela provides South America's most dramatic example of a one-crop economy. For more than 70 years the efficient production of oil has been the single most outstanding economic fact of life in Venezuela. With the revenues earned from the sale of its oil, the Venezuelan government has developed an excellent highway system. It makes available to its young people a free education from kindergarten through college. Venezuela has also been able to offer its people many of the social services that most other South American nations are simply too poor to afford.

These facts seem to imply that a one-crop economy may not be so bad after all. What all of this impressive data does not show, however, is how such an economy affects the people of Venezuela. Careful study reveals that the income from the petroleum reaches very few Venezuelans.

The oil industry provides by far the highest wages of any industry in Venezuela. Yet it employs only about 1 out of every 100 Venezuelan workers. In addition, inflation caused by years of huge oil profits has made the price of most everyday commodities, especially food, extremely high. To make matters worse, most of the oil revenue has gone to make a showplace of

*Oil derricks in Lake Maracaibo*

Caracas. Despite much talk by the politicians, the development of the interior has been neglected.

### An Uncertain Future

Awash in wealth for 70 years, Venezuela's one-crop economy faces an uncertain future. By early in the next century the country's oil fields may be nearing the end of production. Venezuelan wells are five times as deep as wells in other parts of the world, making them expensive to drill and maintain. Also the flow per well is a mere one tenth of that of wells elsewhere.

It is true that its nearness to markets in North America has given Venezuela a great advantage in transportation costs in the past. Today, however, the expanding use of supertankers by competing nations reduces the advantages of Venezuela's relative location. All of these factors cloud the future prospects of Venezuela if the nation cannot find ways to reduce its dependence on oil. They also point to the potential problems faced by one-crop economies.

Oil serves as Venezuela's chief source of income and principal export. The government nationalized the oil industry in 1975. Although the oil industry employs a small percentage of all workers, taxes on oil and mining account for 60 percent of all government revenues.

Other forms of industrialization were neglected until the 1950s. Today the government uses some of its oil wealth to diversify the economy. Workers are building a huge industrial complex in the Llanos. The new Guri Dam provides abundant hydroelectricity for the complex; deposits of oil, iron ore, manganese, and bauxite, the principal source of aluminum, lie nearby.

Venezuela imports more than half its food. To reduce food imports, the government sponsors programs to grow more crops and produce more meat and milk. Part of this program calls for improving, through cross-breeding with pedigreed

**Learning from Pictures.** *This iron ore mine in Venezuela taps one of the area's many mineral resources. What are the other major mineral resources of the Caribbean Coast countries?*

**Learning from Pictures.** *Cowhands round up cattle in Venezuela's growing livestock industry. In what area of the United States might this be a typical scene?*

stock from industrialized countries, Venezuelan cattle raised on the Llanos. Coffee, Venezuela's chief export before the discovery of oil in 1917, remains the chief crop.

### SECTION 2 REVIEW

1. **Locate**  Lake Maracaibo, Caracas
2. **Summarizing Ideas**  What are the four physical regions of Venezuela?
3. **Interpreting Ideas**  How does Venezuela deal with unequal land distribution among the people?
4. **Analyzing Ideas**  **(a)** What role does oil play in the Venezuelan economy?  **(b)** In what ways is the Venezuelan government trying to lower the nation's food imports?

# GEOGRAPHY IN THE WORKPLACE
## Political Geographers

Viewed from a political standpoint, the earth is an exceedingly complex place. Land makes up roughly 30 percent of the planet. This land, however, is divided into nearly 160 nations and about 50 dependent territories. The population of the earth's nations ranges from more than 1 billion in the People's Republic of China to just slightly more than 750 in Vatican City. In terms of land area, the largest country by far is the Soviet Union, with 8,650,000 square miles (22,400,000 square kilometers). The smallest nation in land area is Vatican City, whose area is so tiny that it is measured in acres, some 108 in all, instead of square miles.

The very word *political* in political geographers helps to define their work. Political geographers give special attention to nations as political regions and study their structure, internal divisions, transportation systems, and external relationships. Since the beginning of the 1900s political geographers have devoted much of their time to attempting to evaluate and estimate the degrees of power of individual nations as well as that of blocks of nations united for protection or for economic reasons.

However, most political geographers today, especially those who work for the United States Department of State or similar agencies in other nations of the world, focus primarily on problems of international boundaries. This is a very practical task because disputes over boundaries often cause hostility and even wars among nations. It is the responsibility of political geographers to determine exactly how the disputed boundary came into being, whether or not treaties dealing with the boundary exist and are soundly drawn, and how an international court might view the disputed boundary. Thus, the work of political geographers often includes legal analysis.

For students interested in the geography of political processes and the law, political geography could hold a promising, challenging, and exciting career. Detailed research involving both library work and travel often allows political geographers to have an impact throughout the world.

## 3 The three Guianas have both similarities and differences.

In addition to Portugal and Spain, three other colonial powers carved footholds in the Caribbean countries of South America. Britain, the Netherlands, and France claimed small colonies along South America's northeastern coast. In general, these European colonial powers did little to develop the economies of their Caribbean coast holdings—the Guianas.

### Physical Setting

In all three Guianas a swampy coastal plain borders the Atlantic Ocean. It widens from east to west from 15 miles (24 kilometers) in French Guiana to 60 miles (96 kilometers) in Guyana. An alluvial plain, created by ocean currents that sweep some of the alluvium along the coast from the mouth of the Amazon River, gradually extends outward into the sea. Rivers that rush down from the highlands and flood during the rainy season also deposit alluvium. The alluvium remains unusually fertile, and

farmers drain it and protect it from the sea with dikes, creating rich fields.

Farther inland elevations in the Guiana Highlands average between 1,200 and 2,000 feet (360 and 600 meters). Higher lands, reaching 9,219 feet (2,810 meters) at Mount Roraima (roh·RY·muh), form a landscape marked by rock walls along Guyana's border with Venezuela.

The ancient rocks of the Guiana Highlands contain a wealth of minerals. Mines in the highlands of Suriname and French Guiana produce bauxite. The area also contains deposits of gold, diamonds, and several other minerals.

The Guianas have a tropical wet climate with high heat and humidity throughout the year. A rainy season from May to August causes some rivers to flood. The wettest place in the region is Cayenne, French Guiana, which receives about 130 inches (330 centimeters) of rain a year.

Tropical rain forests and thick jungles cover much of the region. Occasional stretches of savanna interrupt this vegetation in parts of southern Guyana.

*Learning from Pictures.* *These Guyanese hunting and fishing families live on houseboats held afloat by empty oil drums. How does this life style differ from that of the typical Guyanese family?*

## Cultural Setting

The people of the Guianas represent a variety of ethnic backgrounds. Indians predominate in the interior forests and savannas. Blacks, many of whose ancestors were slaves and laborers in Brazil, and a large Asian population, many of whom trace their descent to Asians brought to work on plantations as indentured laborers after slavery was abolished in the 1800s, populate the coastal plain. Europeans, who administered the Guianas when they were colonies, form a small minority in the region today and live mostly in the capital cities.

European colonists left their languages and religions in each of the countries they ruled. English remains the official language in Guyana, Dutch in Suriname, and French in French Guiana. All three countries include a mixture of Roman Catholics and Protestants.

## The Guianas

Until 1966 Britain ruled present-day Guyana as a colony called British Guiana. Until 1975 the Netherlands ruled present-day Suriname as Dutch Guiana. France still controls French Guiana, which was a colony before becoming an overseas department of France in 1946.

**Guyana.** Guyana, the largest of the three Guianas in both land area and population, covers an area the size of Idaho. It gained independence from Britain in 1966. The vast majority of the population occupies the country's narrow coastal plain. The interior of Guyana remains inaccessible and almost uninhabited. Georgetown, with 72,000 inhabitants, serves as Guyana's capital and largest city.

Guyana's leaders proclaimed the nation a republic in 1970. Today the country has a socialist economy in which the government owns all major industries. The government

allows foreign investment in some industries as long as Guyanese citizens serve as the principal business partners.

Guyana ranks as one of the poorest and least developed countries in South America. Agriculture remains the leading economic activity. Bauxite, sugarcane, and rice account for more than 90 percent of Guyana's exports. Oil and consumer goods lead the list of imports. The lack of roads and railroads hampers industrial development and makes logging difficult.

**Suriname.** Suriname is slightly larger than Georgia. The country is the most ethnically diverse of the three Guianas. The population of 391,000 includes blacks, Indians, Asians, and Europeans. They or their ancestors brought to Suriname cultural traits from four different continents. Paramaribo, with about 67,000 inhabitants, is the largest city and serves as the country's capital.

Suriname gained independence in 1975 and formed a parliamentary republic. In 1980, however, military leaders overthrew the government. A civilian president was inaugurated in 1988, ending military rule. The new government has promised to restore human rights lost in recent years.

Suriname's economy, which is moving toward communism, centers on bauxite mining. Bauxite accounts for 90 percent of all export income. Traditionally the country exported unprocessed bauxite. Today plants process increasing amounts of bauxite, which is exported in a semifinished form known as **alumina.** Current plans call for the construction of new electrical plants to supply the energy needed to process alumina into finished aluminum—a more valuable product.

Rice serves as Suriname's principal crop for local use as well as for export. The country depends on imports to supply much of its other food needs.

**French Guiana.** French Guiana lies wedged between Suriname and Brazil. It is slightly smaller than Idaho. Until 1951 French Guiana was known around the world for its penal colonies for French criminals. Devil's Island was the most notorious of these colonies. Today French Guiana is an overseas department of France. A prefect, or governor, rules the area with the assistance of an elected council. French Guiana sends a representative to the French parliament. Cayenne serves as the capital for French Guiana.

The economy of French Guiana depends heavily on financial aid from France. Only small areas near the coast support agriculture. The chief crops include rice, corn, cocoa, sugarcane, and bananas. French Guiana has gained fame as the source of cayenne pepper, a potent hot pepper. Tropical rain forests produce some rosewood, but most forest resources remain undeveloped. French Guiana's gold and bauxite deposits also remain generally untouched. Shrimp and gold lead the list of exports.

---

**SECTION 3 REVIEW**

1. **Define** alumina
2. **Locate** Cayenne, Georgetown, Paramaribo
3. **Seeing Relationships** What must farmers do to take advantage of the rich alluvium along the coastal plains of the Guianas?
4. **Understanding Ideas** Under what condition does Guyana allow foreigners to invest in businesses there?
5. **Analyzing Ideas** (a) How is Suriname's government working to expand the country's role in aluminum production? (b) Why will this help the economy?
6. **Contrasting Ideas** How are political patterns in French Guiana unique in South America?

# CHAPTER 17 REVIEW

## Chapter Summary

The following list contains the key concepts you have learned about the Caribbean coast countries.

1. The five nations in South America with strong links to the Caribbean region are Colombia, Venezuela, Guyana, Suriname, and French Guiana.
2. Most of Colombia's diverse population occupies the mountainous region in the western half of the country. This population is perhaps the most ethnically varied in all of South America. Its economy relies on one crop—coffee.
3. Venezuela ranks as the wealthiest country in South America because of income from its oil production.
4. Both Venezuela and Colombia have wide income gaps between the poor and the wealthy. Both countries have long histories of political instability but have civilian leaders and are moving toward democratic rule today.
5. Venezuela uses some of its oil wealth to spur land reform programs and develop sparsely settled regions in the east.
6. Guyana, Suriname, and French Guiana are often grouped together as the Guianas. All three have small populations, similar physical settings, and common problems, but their cultures differ.
7. Guyana is the largest of the three Guianas in both land area and population.
8. Suriname gained independence as a parliamentary republic. A civilian government took over in 1988, replacing a military dictator who had ruled since 1980.
9. French Guiana remains the only part of South America still ruled by a European power.
10. Venezuela has a one-crop economy based on oil.

On a separate sheet of paper, complete the following review exercises.

## Reviewing Geographic Terms

Match each of the following terms with the correct definition below.

a. tierra helada    c. cordillera
b. alumina    d. martial rule

1. ____ Semi-finished form of bauxite from which aluminum is made
2. ____ Mountain chain in Colombia
3. ____ Government led by the military
4. ____ Frozen land where snow permanently covers the ground

## Developing Critical Thinking Skills

1. **Comparing Ideas** (a) How are social patterns in Venezuela and Colombia alike? (b) How are they different? (c) How are population patterns in Colombia and the Guianas alike?
2. **Understanding Ideas** In what ways is the government of Venezuela involved in the country's economy?
3. **Interpreting Ideas** (a) Why can both the Colombian and Venezuelan economies be classified as one-crop economies? (b) How has oil helped spur economic growth in Venezuela? (c) How has it hindered Venezuela's economic growth?
4. **Summarizing Ideas** (a) Which European nations colonized the Guianas? (b) Which European nation still governs part of the Guianas? (c) Which part does it govern?
5. **Analyzing Ideas** How are the cultural settings of the Guianas unique to the region?
6. **Studying Maps** Study the map on page 11. Why is it incorrect to call Lake Maracaibo a "lake"?
7. **Writing About Geography** In a full-page essay, complete one of the following activities. (a) Discuss how each of the Caribbean coast countries is trying to solve its economic problems. (b) If you were an investor looking for a country in which to build a new automobile plant, which Caribbean coast country would you choose? Why?

## Using Primary Sources

In the following excerpt from *South American Primer*, Katherine Carr Rodell discusses the problems caused by Colombia's geography. As you study the reading, consider whether these problems still cause serious problems for Colombia today.

Although the Equator goes through the southern part of the country, Colombia is not all tropical by any means, for the Andes run the whole length of the nation, splitting into three great ranges, with wide valleys and high table lands in between. In the high, cool part of the country lives most of Colombia's population. . . . The Pacific coast is especially hot and rainy, and Buenaventura is popularly supposed to be the hottest port in the tropics. All of Colombia's ports, on both the Caribbean and the Pacific, are cut off from the interior by the steep mountains, and communication with the interior is immeasurably difficult except by the rivers which flow from the mountains to the sea. Even so, to go the eight hundred miles from the sea up the Magdalena River to Bogotá takes a week under the best possible conditions. Goods have to be loaded and unloaded as many as thirteen times—put onto barges, taken off and put on narrow-gauge railroads to go around rapids and falls, then put back on boats again.

1. According to the author, where does the majority of Colombia's population live?
2. What does the author say cuts off Colombia's ports from the interior?
3. Why does the 800-mile trip to Bogotá take at least a week?

## Practicing Geography Skills

*Before completing this activity, review Developing Geography Skills on page 341.*

**Asking Geographic Questions.** Study the map on page 332. Focus on the information it contains about the Caribbean Coast countries. Develop six geographic questions that relate to the information about economic activities in Colombia, Venezuela, and the Guianas contained on the map. Then answer the six questions you have developed.

## Exploring Geography

1. Coffee has long played an important role in the economies of many nations of South America—particularly Colombia. Use resources in your school or public library to find information on exactly how coffee is grown and harvested in Colombia. Then write a brief report detailing the process. You might also conduct research on the price of coffee in the United States over the past 10 years and use the information to plot a simple line graph to accompany your report. At the bottom of the line graph, make a generalization about what years were probably more prosperous than other years for the Colombian economy. Then give reasons to justify your generalization.
2. Use resources in your school or public library to find information on current political, economic, and social conditions in Venezuela. Then use the information as the basis for a brief essay that considers what political, economic, and social problems Venezuela may face as the 1900s draw to a close.
3. Visit a local travel agent or write to the Colombian Government Tourist Bureau, 140 East Fifty-Seventh Street, New York, New York 10022; or the Venezuelan Government Tourist Bureau, 7 East Fifty-First Street, New York, New York 10022 to obtain brochures and information on travel to these two countries. Then prepare an illustrated report on what you would see and do during a two-week vacation to either or both of these countries. You might also prepare a collage to accompany your report.

# The Pacific Coast Countries

# PUTTING THE CHAPTER IN FOCUS

Not finding the gold they sought in their colony of New Granada, Spanish conquerors advanced southward down the Andes Mountains toward the great Inca capital at Cuzco. They conquered the Inca Empire, imposing a strong Spanish imprint on the land and its inhabitants. Today Peru, Ecuador, Bolivia, and, to a lesser extent, Chile reflect both Indian and Spanish heritages.

## Ideas to Understand

In studying about the geography of the Pacific Coast countries of South America, use these ideas to give direction to your reading.

1 Ecuador straddles the equator.
2 Indian and Spanish cultures live side by side in modern Peru.
3 Bolivia is an impoverished and land-locked country in the Andes.
4 Long and narrow Chile faces many problems.

## Terms to Define

The following terms are some of the key terms in the chapter. Defining them will help you understand the geography of the Pacific Coast countries of South America.

| | |
|---|---|
| *paramos* | *yunga* |
| oasis | social legislation |

## Places to Locate

Locating the following places will add to your knowledge of geography.

| | |
|---|---|
| Andes | La Paz |
| Guayaquil | Atacama Desert |
| Lima | Tierra del Fuego |
| Lake Titicaca | Santiago |
| Arequipa | |

## 1 Ecuador straddles the equator.

The name Ecuador comes from the Spanish word for equator. This imaginary line dividing the Northern Hemisphere and the Southern Hemisphere crosses Ecuador about 15 miles (24 kilometers) north of the city of Quito (KEE·toh).

### Physical Setting

Ecuador slices into the northwest corner of Peru. In fact, a long-standing border dispute continues to cause friction between the countries. Ecuador's territory, which includes the Galapagos Islands, is about the same size as Colorado. The country has three widely diverse physical features. They include a coastal plain, mountains, and lowlands.

◀ *Central market in El Alto, Bolivia*

The coastal plain, the economic heart of modern Ecuador, fronts on the Pacific Ocean. Tropical rain forests flourish in the tropical wet climate of the northern part of the coastal plain. Savanna and desert vegetation cover drier regions at the southern end of the coastal plain.

The Andes form two parallel cordilleras—the Eastern Cordillera inland and the Western Cordillera near the coast. Fertile and densely populated upland basins lie between the two mountain ranges. Climates in the mountains vary with altitude as they do in the rest of Latin America. Forests cover lower mountain slopes, while treeless upland plains known as *paramos* cover the higher slopes where the climate is too cold and windy for trees. Severe earthquakes jolt Andean areas from time to time as mountain-building processes caused by

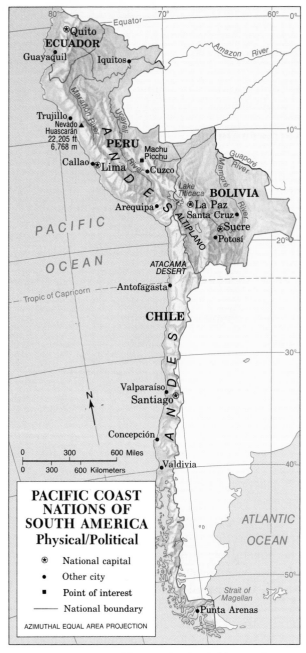

**Learning from Maps.** *On the Galápagos Islands, 600 miles (965 kilometers) west of Ecuador, scientists study the development of animal life. What landform isolates the lowlands of Ecuador?*

tectonic plate movements disturb the earth's crust.

Eastern Ecuador consists of tropical lowlands isolated from the rest of the country by the mountains. Ecuadoreans value the sparsely inhabited, densely forested lowlands as an undeveloped frontier and have taken steps to limit its development and preserve its natural beauty.

## Cultural Setting

The Incas made Ecuador part of their empire long before the Spanish conquest. Today Indians and mestizos form the largest population groups. Agriculture continued as the mainstay of life until the discovery of oil in the 1970s.

**Population patterns.** Indians make up about 35 percent of Ecuador's total population and are a majority in the higher elevations. Mestizos, who live mainly on the coastal plain and lower mountain slopes, make up about 55 percent of the population. About 10 percent of the people trace their descent to European ancestors.

**Social patterns.** Traditional life styles, often unchanged since the 1700s, persist in Indian communities throughout the Andes. The people live in small huts and eke out a minimal existence as subsistence farmers. Many speak only Quechua (KECH·wuh), the language of the Incas that today serves as an official language. Others speak Spanish, the country's other official language.

People live quite differently in the modern industrial cities. Guayaquil (gwy·uh·KEEL), with its growing industrial economy and direct connections by sea and air to the rest of the world, has replaced Quito as Ecuador's largest city. People also live differently on the modernizing cacao and banana plantations on Ecuador's coastal plain.

Church and state have been separate in Ecuador since 1895. Although the Roman Catholic church continues to play a strong role in Ecuadoran life, membership in Protestant and Mormon churches has grown. Missionaries from these religions have

made many converts among the country's Indian population.

**Political patterns.** Military rulers have often dominated the unstable political patterns of Ecuador, but democratic government resumed in 1978. The wide income gap between impoverished Indians in the mountains and wealthier mestizos and people of European descent, however, continues to cause problems.

**Economic patterns.** The discovery of vast oil resources in eastern Ecuador in the 1970s transformed the country's traditionally agricultural economy. Oil now accounts for about 60 percent of all export income. Agricultural products, which once provided 95 percent of all of Ecuador's exports, now bring in less than 20 percent. On small highland farms, working mainly with hoes and machetes, farmers grow corn, barley, wheat, and beans. On plantations and small farms on the coastal plain, they grow tropical crops such as cacao, coffee, and bananas for export. A land reform program begun in 1964 limits the amount of land individuals may own. Although industry remains at an early stage of development, Ecuador now manufactures some textiles and processes foods.

**Learning from Pictures.** *The changes brought by Ecuador's new role as an oil exporter have had little effect on Quito. What city has replaced Quito as Ecuador's largest city?*

## 2 Indian and Spanish cultures live side by side in modern Peru.

Peru, which gained independence from Spain in 1821, shares many of the challenges typical of developing nations. Peruvian society remains sharply divided between a wealthy minority of Spanish ancestry and an impoverished Indian majority.

### Physical Setting

Peru curves along South America's northwest coast. The country has a land area slightly smaller than Texas, New Mexico, and Arizona combined. Three distinct physical features characterize Peru's physical setting. They include a coastal plain, the montane, and the selva.

353

Along the Pacific Ocean Peru's narrow, dry, almost uninhabited coastal plain stretches about 35 miles (56 kilometers) inland. Only a few isolated **oases,** or fertile areas surrounded by desert, support human populations. Lima (LEE·muh), the capital of Peru, developed at one of these oases.

The Andes rise abruptly from the coastal plain to form the mountainous montane that lies in the tierra fría climate zone. Two rugged cordilleras enclose a high plateau that lies between 11,000 and 14,000 feet (3,300 and 4,270 meters) above sea level.

The selva lies to the east of the highlands and consists of forested foothills and dense rain forests. The selva covers more than half of Peru's territory and lies above vast oil reserves.

## Cultural Setting

Peru remains a land where forces for economic and social change compete with forces of traditionalism. The country, which served as the heartland of the Inca Empire and the seat of Spanish government in western South America, struggles to modernize.

*__Learning from Pictures.__ Indian farmers near Jauja, Peru, practice subsistence farming. What industries are now employing many Peruvians?*

**Population patterns.** Indians account for almost 50 percent of Peru's people. Mestizos form another large ethnic group, while people of European ancestry, blacks, and Asians make up small minorities. Indians predominate in the montane and selva, while the other ethnic groups generally live on the coastal plain.

**Social patterns.** The Indians of Peru take pride in their long heritage. Many speak only Quechua, which joined Spanish as one of Peru's two official languages in 1975. Aymara (eye·muh·RAH) Indians living near Lake Titicaca also speak Aymara, another Indian language. Other Peruvians reflect Spanish cultural imprints, speaking Spanish and practicing Roman Catholicism.

**Political patterns.** Peru's political history presents an alternating picture of unstable civilian and military governments. Small political organizations that practice violence threaten the stability of Peru's government, but political and economic power remains largely concentrated in the hands of a small number of wealthy landowners.

**Economic patterns.** Peru has developed slowly. About 40 percent of the people still earn a living as farmers, but this is far less than the 60 percent who farmed in the early 1950s. Many workers have switched from farming to better-paying jobs in manufacturing, mining, and fishing.

Most Indian farmers in the highlands are subsistence farmers, producing only enough food for their families and for sale in nearby markets. The Indian farmers chiefly grow wheat, potatoes, barley, and beans. In the upland areas they raise sheep for wool.

Farmers in oases along the coast practice commercial farming. They grow cotton, sugarcane, rice, and soybeans for export. The use of mountainous Peru's scarce farm-

land for commercial crops makes it necessary for the country to import substantial quantities of food.

Peru's government began a long-term industrialization program in 1958. The production of electricity—especially hydro-electricity—and consumer goods such as processed foods, pharmaceuticals, and clothing have increased dramatically. Lima and Arequipa (ahr·uh·KEE·puh) serve as Peru's main industrial centers. Oil and textiles rank as important exports.

---

### SECTION 2 REVIEW

1. **Define** oasis
2. **Locate** Lima, Lake Titicaca, Arequipa
3. **Analyzing Ideas** Why is Peru's coastal plain almost uninhabited?
4. **Understanding Ideas** (a) What are Peru's two official languages? (b) What other language do many Peruvians speak?
5. **Synthesizing Ideas** (a) Where is political and economic power in Peru concentrated? (b) How might this affect the stability of the Peruvian government?

---

## 3 Bolivia is an impoverished and landlocked country in the Andes.

Bolivia—one of two landlocked South American nations—ranks as one of the poorest countries in the world. A land of windswept plateaus and jagged mountains, the country is struggling to modernize.

### Physical Setting

Bolivia, which is about the size of Texas and California combined, has two major physical features—highlands in the Andes and lowlands east of the Andes. It also has great variations in climates.

The Andes extend in two cordilleras across Bolivia. The Altiplano separates the cordilleras. La Paz, the capital, lies in a valley on the Altiplano at an elevation of more than 12,400 feet (3,780 meters). Bolivia's cold and dry Antiplano is less suitable for farming than Peru's. Part of the central plains that stretch down the middle of South America east of the Andes, the lowlands cover more area than the highlands. Climates range from tropical wet-and-dry to subtropical.

### Cultural Setting

Of all the countries of South America, the Indian imprint remains strongest in Bolivia. Today economic and political problems disrupt the country, which ranks as the continent's poorest.

**Population patterns.** Three-fourths of all Bolivians live in the highlands. The most densely populated areas lie on the Altiplano near Lake Titicaca and in the *yungas,* or valleys, in the Eastern Cordillera. In the 1970s the government encouraged Indians to leave the overcrowded Altiplano and resettle in the sparsely settled lowlands. However, most who did move found it difficult to adapt physically to the lower elevations. Others were reluctant to leave the physical setting they knew. Although La Paz, Sucre (soo·kray), and Cochabamba (koh·chuh·BAHM·buh) are urban centers, most Bolivians live in rural areas.

**Social patterns.** Aymara-speaking Indians account for about 37 percent of the people. Another 24 percent of the people speak Quechua. Spanish-speaking mestizos comprise between 25 and 30 percent of the population. Inhabitants of pure European ancestry represent only a small minority.

*Text continues on page 358.*

# THE GEOGRAPHIC WEB
## The Cocaine Connection

An undeclared war is in progress. The participants are farmers in the jungles of Bolivia and Peru; powerful drug dealers in Colombia; transshippers and repackagers in Central America, Mexico, and the Caribbean; and law enforcement officials in the United States. The big winners thus far are a handful of rich and ruthless Colombian drug traffickers who supply the bulk of the $70 billion in illegal narcotics to the United States.

### The South American Thread

The geography of the cocaine connection begins on tiny farms deep in the mountains of Bolivia and Peru. Ninety percent of the cocaine that is smuggled into the United States originates in these two countries.

Peru's largest plantings of the coca leaves from which cocaine is made are in the Upper Huallaga Valley, northeast of Lima. The town of Tingo María was, for many years, the center of the valley's coca trade. Then in mid-1987 economic activity came to a halt in Tingo María because the Peruvian government had launched an expensive anti-drug campaign.

But the end of the drug trade in Tingo María did not represent a complete anti-drug success. Attacks by heavily armed drug traffickers on Peru's narcotics officers and on workers destroying the coca plants limited the anti-drug campaign to Tingo María. The drug trade was indeed virtually eliminated in Tingo María. But throughout the rest of the jungles of the Upper Huallaga Valley coca planting and harvesting continued unchecked. In fact, from 1984 through 1987 coca acreage increased by 124,000 acres (49,600 hectares) while government agents were able to destroy only 30,000 acres (12,000 hectares). And today a total of nearly 1 million acres (400,000 hectares) is under coca cultivation in Peru's Upper Huallaga Valley alone.

Coca paste, produced in small jungle clearings from the bitter leaves of the coca bush, provides the raw material from which

*Smugglers often use fast boats in attempts to outrun the Coast Guard.*

the deadly cocaine crystal is refined. Much of the coca paste is carried by truck or mule over jungle trails, as well as by small aircraft, into Colombia. There powerful drug dealers in well-protected hideouts refine the paste into pure cocaine worth billions of dollars.

## Transport

Smugglers use a great variety of air and sea routes to move the cocaine from Colombia to the United States. Three common travel routes exist. One crosses through the open waters between Cuba and Haiti. The second cuts through the Yucatán Channel between Mexico and Cuba. The third moves the cocaine through the waters that separate the Dominican Republic and Puerto Rico. Smugglers follow air routes that trace similar paths.

Traditionally, 90 percent of the cocaine shipped by these routes entered the United States at various points along the Florida coast. But as law enforcement officers began intensifying their anti-drug efforts in Florida in the mid-1980s, traffickers shifted their deliveries to other states along the Gulf Coast as well as to inland locations in the Southwest. Cocaine also moves directly from Colombia's west coast to California and other western states.

Aircraft transport nearly two-thirds of the cocaine that arrives in the United States from South America. Most planes must stop along the way. Such stops prove essential to the entire operation. Traffickers stop at various locations throughout Central America, Cuba, the Dominican Republic, and the Bahamas. From these points high-speed boats or small planes that can land on tiny unprotected airstrips carry the cocaine to the United States.

Mexico became a key transshipment point when law enforcement officers began their crackdown in Florida. The geography of Mexican transshipment shows three different geographic patterns. First, Mexican traffickers purchase cocaine in Colombia, transport it to Mexico either by ship or by

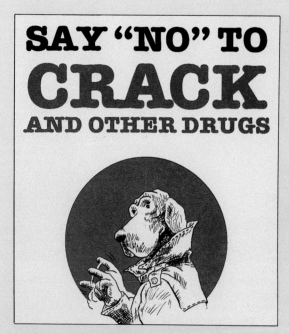

McGruff's advice: "DON'T USE DRUGS"

plane, and then carry it by car, truck, or bus into the United States. In the second pattern couriers who travel by commercial aircraft from South America to Mexico and then on to the United States carry the cocaine in their baggage. Finally, traffickers use the large number of small and isolated airstrips found throughout Mexico to refuel. They then fly the cocaine directly into the United States by routes that avoid radar detection.

## Who's to Blame?

The expansion of drug smuggling alarms police and federal drug enforcement officials. Many see it as a full-fledged national emergency. Some blame the ever-increasing supply of drugs on the Andean farmers who grow raw coca leaves. Others blame the Colombian government's inability to stop the nation's drug barons. Some say that Mexico must crack down harder on the smugglers who operate within that nation. Still others point out that if there were not drug buyers in the United States, the farmers and the drug dealers would all be out of business.

**Learning from Pictures.** *Indians on the treeless Altiplano use the papyrus plant to make boats. How do these boats illustrate the Indians' adaptation to their natural environment?*

Bolivians are predominantly Roman Catholic. However, many Indians have added elements of their ancient religions to the practice of Roman Catholicism.

**Political patterns.** Bolivia remains one of the most politically troubled countries in South America. The latest troubles date to a revolution in 1952. The revolution broke out when the government nationalized the large tin industry, previously owned by a few wealthy families, and began a program of land reform. In 1964 military leaders overthrew the government and ended the reforms. Since then Bolivia has teetered back and forth between periods of civilian and military rule.

**Economic patterns.** The lack of a coastline and the mountainous land hamper economic growth. Subsistence farming remains the chief occupation of Bolivia's Indian majority. Farms remain small and inefficient, and many farmers work in communal fashion as their Inca ancestors did. The farmers chiefly grow potatoes, corn, beans, and a grain called quinoa. On the more productive farms in the subtropical yungas farmers grow coffee, cacao, bananas, and citrus. In recent years the coca plant, from which cocaine is extracted, has become the most profitable crop (see THE GEOGRAPHIC WEB on pages 356–57). Minerals, including tin and silver, provide about 70 percent of Bolivia's export income.

**SECTION 3 REVIEW**

1. **Define** yunga
2. **Locate** La Paz
3. **Contrasting Ideas** (a) How does Bolivia's Altiplano differ from the Altiplano in Peru? (b) How are the people and the economy of Bolivia different from the rest of South America?
4. **Analyzing Ideas** In what ways is the cultural setting of Bolivia a reflection of the country's history?
5. **Interpreting Ideas** What factors hamper economic growth in Bolivia?

# 4 Long and narrow Chile faces many problems.

Remote from the center of the Inca Empire, Inca influences were weak in Chile. Today Chilean society reflects far more European imprints than do its neighbors.

## Physical Setting

Chile stretches like a thin ribbon along the western edge of the Andes but has a total land area the size of Texas. A narrow lowland runs north to south between the coastal ranges and the rugged Andes. Three different climates divide the country into Northern Chile, Middle Chile, and Southern Chile.

The Atacama Desert of Northern Chile remains extremely dry. It has no rivers, and

*Text continues on page 361.*

# CASE STUDY
## GEOGRAPHY AND PEOPLE: The Aymara

More than 13,000 feet (4,000 meters) above sea level, in the frigid reaches of the Andes, live the Aymara. No one knows how long the Aymara have inhabited the wind-swept plateau near Lake Titicaca in Peru and Bolivia. But though life there is hard, the Aymara have probably lived in the region for thousands of years.

### Conquest

Once independent, the Aymara fell victim to the Inca conquest in the 1400s. The Incas were replaced as the Aymara's rulers by the Spanish in the late 1500s. Thousands of Indians died working in mines for the Spanish. Those who could held stubbornly to their land. Their descendants still follow traditional life styles in this barren, frigid land on top of the world.

### A Harsh Environment

The land of the Aymara has only two seasons. The Aymara call them "the green time" and "the ice time." The green time lasts from October until April. The ice time comes during the South American winter, from May through September.

The coming of green time marks the beginning of the planting season. The Aymara believe that choosing exactly the right day for planting is most important. Aymara people believe that dreams tell the future. So they wait until a dream of a good harvest comes before planting crops.

When the special planting day finally arrives, the Aymara carefully plant potatoes, oca (OH·cuh), ullucu (yoo·LUH·kuh), quinoa (ki·NOH·uh), corn, beans, barley, and wheat. Because the soil in this desolate region is poor, harvests are usually meager. Through careful tending of crops and by spreading wood ashes over soil as a fertilizer, however, the Aymara grow enough to feed the people.

*An Aymaran village high in the Andes*

### An Aymaran Village

Several families make up a typical Aymaran village. And in some cases all the people in a village may be related. Aymaran villages feature tiny, one-room houses. Pounded earth with no rug or other covering serves as a floor. The houses have no windows at all. The small door always faces the morning sun. The only furnishings are low platform beds made of stone. Reeds are tied together to make a mattress. Llama-pelt blankets ward off the constant cold, for there is no fireplace. A pottery bowl filled with smoldering llama fat provides the only light and heat. A tiny shed that leans against a wall outside the house serves as a kitchen.

Although their lives are harsh, the Aymara love the open spaces of the windy plateau. They love the towering snow-capped Andes despite the struggle they face farming the infertile, stony land.

359

# DEVELOPING GEOGRAPHY SKILLS
## STUDYING ECONOMIC GEOGRAPHY: Interpreting Statistics

As you learned in Chapter 1, economic geographers study resources and resource use, agriculture and land use, and global trade interactions. Among the most important tools of economic geographers are statistics. Geographers use statistics to identify trends, study current economic settings, and predict future changes. As a student of geography, you must be able to interpret statistics in order to form hypotheses and draw conclusions about economic conditions.

Statistics are numerical data. Most statistics are presented in chart form. Charts make it possible to analyze the data easily, to see relationships among the data, and to make comparisons.

### How to Interpret Statistics

To interpret economic statistics, follow these guidelines.

1. **Identify the subject of the data.** Note all titles and subtitles, especially on charts and tables. Read all the headings and subheadings supplied on the chart or table.
2. **Examine the data's components.** Note the specific type of data given under each heading and subheading.

3. **Note quantities and values.** Check the quantities in which each category is recorded. Often a note in parentheses will indicate whether the statistics are to be read in thousands, millions, billions, tons, dollars, or other units.
4. **Read footnotes.** Statistical data often carry footnotes explaining special circumstances. A footnote may note changes in gathering or recording procedures. A footnote also may indicate when data was not available. On a chart this may be shown either by a blank space or by "NA" in the appropriate space.
5. **Look for relationships.** Note increases, decreases, and other trends, especially changes over time.
6. **Use the data.** Form hypotheses and draw conclusions based on the statistics presented.

### Applying the Skill

Study the table at the bottom of the first column. Note that the title—"Increases in Consumer Prices"—indicates it contains economic information. Vertical headings show that the data pertains to Ecuador, Peru, Bolivia, and Chile. The horizontal headings indicate that the chart includes data for 1984, 1985, and 1986. A footnote or note in parentheses may state all the numbers are percentages.

The statistics show that inflation has continued from year to year in all the countries. They also show that inflation has grown most in Bolivia and least in Chile. After you read about the economic patterns of these countries, you should be able to form hypotheses and draw conclusions about why this is true.

*To practice this skill, see Practicing Geography Skills on page 363.*

| INCREASES IN CONSUMER PRICES (in percents) | | | |
|---|---|---|---|
| Country | 1983–84 | 1984–85 | 1985–86 |
| BOLIVIA | 1,281 | 11,750 | 14,173 |
| CHILE | 20 | 31 | 21 |
| ECUADOR | 31 | 28 | 24 |
| PERU | 110 | 163 | 78 |
| Sources: *Statistical Abstract of the United States,* 1987 | | | |

thick sea fogs in winter provide the only moisture. However, every 25 years or so El Niño brings unusually heavy rains.

Middle Chile has the only Mediterranean climate in South America. Summers are hot and dry and winters mild and rainy. Snow-fed streams flowing from the Andes help irrigate crops in the Central Valley.

Southern Chile, extending south from Concepción (kuhn·sep·see·OHN) to Tierra del Fuego, has a west coast marine climate. Onshore westerly winds keep Southern Chile cool and damp in summer and chilly and rainy in winter.

## Cultural Setting

Chile's cultural setting shows a marked contrast to that of its northern neighbors. The problems that face Chile, however, are typical of all of South America.

**Population patterns.** The ethnic makeup of Chile contrasts with the ethnic makeup of its neighbors. Fewer than 7 percent of all Chileans are Indians. Mestizos account for nearly 62 percent of the people. People of European ancestry compose about 31 percent. Rather than Spaniards or Portuguese, however, Germans, Swiss, and Italians form the largest European groups.

Nine out of 10 Chileans live in Middle Chile. The Central Valley remains the most densely populated area and includes Santiago, the capital, where one-third of the Chileans live.

**Social patterns.** Chileans have a great regard for education and their literacy rate ranks high among South American nations. Chile has a long tradition of **social legislation,** or government programs to help the people. But the country finds it difficult to pay for such programs.

Spanish serves as the official language, although some people still speak German in settlements near Valdivia (vahl·DEEV·ee·uh). Most Chileans belong to the Roman Catholic church but Chile has long practiced religious toleration.

**Political patterns.** Chile's political parties worked for many years for democratic rule within a parliamentary framework. In 1973, however, the military overthrew the socialist regime and established a military dictatorship that now rules the country.

**Economic patterns.** The best farmlands and most fertile soils lie in the Central Valley of Middle Chile. Wealthy landowners, however, have carved the greater part of this land into large haciendas. The government started a land reform program in 1962 to break the haciendas into smaller farms. On these farms, farmers grow grapes, apples, and other fruits chiefly for export.

Chile ranks as the most industrialized of South America's Pacific Coast nations. In addition, Chile leads the world in the production of sodium nitrates used in fertilizers. Chile also produces about one-fourth of the world's total copper. This metal accounts for more than half the value of Chile's exports. Unfortunately for Chile's economy, world copper prices have fallen by 50 percent since the 1970s.

---

### SECTION 4 REVIEW

1. **Define** social legislation
2. **Locate** Atacama Desert, Santiago
3. **Summarizing Ideas** What climatic condition sometimes brings heavy rains to arid Northern Chile?
4. **Contrasting Ideas** How does Chile's ethnic makeup differ from that of its neighbors?
5. **Interpreting Ideas** How has Chile's government worked to ensure that more people can own land?

# CHAPTER 18 REVIEW

## Chapter Summary

The following list contains the key concepts you have learned about the Pacific Coast countries of South America.

1. Four countries make up the Pacific Coast countries of South America. They are Ecuador, Peru, Bolivia, and Chile.
2. The Andes dominate the area's landscape.
3. Dry conditions prevail over large parts of the Pacific Coast countries.
4. Several ancient Indian civilizations developed in the high Andes.
5. Indians are today an important ethnic group in all the Pacific Coast countries except Chile.
6. The Pacific Coast countries are developing nations. Currently each is at a different stage of industrialization.
7. The modern life styles of coastal Ecuador and Peru contrast with the traditional Indian life styles in the Andes.
8. The discovery of vast oil reserves in Ecuador transformed the economy.
9. Peru has two official languages—Spanish and Quechua.
10. Most people of Bolivia live near Lake Titicaca and in subtropical yungas.
11. Harvesting coca leaves for the illegal drug trade has become a major economic activity in Bolivia and Peru despite government efforts to stop it.
12. Because of Chile's physical features, its people are concentrated in Santiago and the Central Valley of Middle Chile.
13. The Aymara continue to live on the windy plateaus surrounding Lake Titicaca as their ancestors have for centuries.

On a separate sheet of paper, complete the following review exercises.

## Reviewing Geographic Terms

Supply the geographic term that correctly completes each sentence.

1. Treeless upland plains in South America are called ____.
2. An ____ is a fertile area surrounded by desert.
3. Valleys in the Eastern Cordillera of Bolivia are called ____.
4. Chile has a tradition of ____ ____, or programs to help the people.

## Developing Critical Thinking Skills

1. **Synthesizing Ideas** (a) What natural hazard plagues Andean communties in Ecuador? (b) Why is this so? (c) Where else in South America do you think this natural hazard occurs?
2. **Interpreting Ideas** What has the government of Ecuador done to change patterns of land ownership?
3. **Contrasting Ideas** How are population patterns in Ecuador, Peru, and Bolivia different from population patterns in the other countries of South America that you have studied?
4. **Comparing Ideas** (a) How are political patterns in Ecuador, Peru, Bolivia, and Chile similar? (b) How do Chilean social patterns differ from social patterns in Ecuador, Bolivia, and Peru?
5. **Analyzing Ideas** (a) How do you think Bolivia's dependence on mineral exports might hurt the country's economy? (b) How is this typical of one-crop economies?
6. **Determining Cause and Effect** An earthquake in 1822 permanently added 100,000 square miles (259,000 square kilometers) of beach to Chile's coast. How does this give evidence that Chile lies in the Ring of Fire?
7. **Writing About Geography** In a full-page essay, discuss one of the following ideas. (a) What similarities and differences exist in the population patterns of Ecuador, Bolivia, Peru, and Chile? What are some of the reasons for these similarities and differences? (b) What might each of the nations you have studied in this chapter do to help ensure political and economic stability?

## Using Primary Sources

In the following excerpt from *The Old Patagonian Express*, Paul Theroux describes the physical and cultural landscapes of Bolivia. As you study the reading, consider whether Bolivia has changed since the author wrote this description in 1978.

The mountain was soon far behind us; we were sprinting toward an irregular wall of rain clouds and hills, past wheat fields and pepper patches. The eastern horizon was white and domed, like the skyline of an Arabian city idealized in a fable; it was the far edge of the high plains, this range of mosquelike peaks buried to their domes and squat minarets, and it was so thin and yet so marvelously shaped that at times it appeared as oddly beautiful as a mirage. Nearer the railway line—but very far apart—were small mud huts. They had mud-block courtyards and some had corrals, but none of them had any windows. They were shut; there were no lights; they were no more than hovels, and they looked forlorn. . . .

There were no cars in the villages, no roads, no trees; only mud huts and cows, and Indians wrapped up against the cold. Except for the llamas, which frisked when they saw the train, and the very shaggy mules, which took no notice, traveling across the high plains was a bit like traveling through Texas. The hills were distant and slightly rounded—rain poured on one, the sun was setting on another—and the sky was enormous.

1. With what two other landscapes does the author compare the mountains and clouds of Bolivia?
2. According to the author, what feature dominates the cultural landscape of a Bolivian village?
3. Reread the CASE STUDY on page 359. What evidence in the excerpt indicates Theroux viewed an Aymaran village when traveling through Bolivia?

## Practicing Geography Skills

*Before completing this activity, review Developing Geography Skills on page 360.*

**Interpreting Economic Statistics.** Study the data for Ecuador, Peru, Boliva, and Chile found in the *Geodata Files*, pages 720–33. Then answer these questions.

1. Which headings indicate data of specific interest to economic geographers?
2. **(a)** Which country has the highest per capita GNP? **(b)** Which has the lowest? **(c)** How is land use in Bolivia and Peru similar? **(d)** Which country seems the most industrialized? Explain your answer. **(e)** How can you tell that Ecuador is industrializing?
3. Why is food a more important import to Bolivia than to Ecuador?

## Exploring Geography

1. Study the diagram "Profile of South America" on page 324. Then draw a similar profile of Ecuador. Your profile should include the following labels: Pacific Ocean, Coastal Plain, Andes, Quito, and Eastern Lowlands. Also include elevations for the highest and lowest points in the country.
2. Chile's political problems have made the headlines of newspapers and magazines in the United States in the last few years. Use the *Readers' Guide to Periodical Literature* and newspaper indexes in your school or public library to find recent articles about political unrest in Chile. Make notes about the articles you read, and use your notes to prepare a five-minute oral presentation describing political unrest in Chile during the past five years. You might also construct a time line showing particular events that you describe in your presentation.

# The Atlantic Coast Countries

# PUTTING THE CHAPTER IN FOCUS

The Atlantic Coast countries of South America include Brazil, Argentina, Uruguay, and Paraguay. Brazil, the largest nation in South America and the fifth-largest nation in the world, differs from other nations on the continent because of its strong Portuguese imprint. Argentina, second in size to Brazil, extends to the southern tip of the continent. Uruguay, east of the Rio de la Plata, ranks as one of the continent's most prosperous nations and landlocked Paraguay as one of its poorest.

## Ideas to Understand

In studying about the Atlantic coast countries of South America, use these ideas to give direction to your reading.

1 Brazil is the largest and most populous country in South America.
2 Argentina ranks as one of the world's great food producers and exporters.

3 Uruguay and Paraguay are slowly developing.

## Terms to Define

The following terms are some of the key terms in the chapter. Defining them will help you understand the geography of the Atlantic Coast countries of South America.

leach                    *pampa*
cultural hearth          gaucho

## Places to Locate

Locating the following places will add to your knowledge of geography.

Amazon Basin             Córdoba
Brasilia                 Buenos Aires
Rio de Janeiro           Rio de la Plata
São Paulo                Montevideo
Chaco                    Asunción
Patagonia

## 1 Brazil is the largest and most populous country in South America.

Brazil occupies about half of South America and contains about half of the continent's total population. Brazil is so large that it borders all but two of the other South American countries. Brazil's size makes it the fifth-largest nation in the world.

### Physical Setting

Despite its vast size, Brazil lacks the varied physical setting of some South American nations. It has only two physical regions—lowlands in the Amazon Basin and highlands in the Brazilian Plateau—and no great climatic extremes.

◀ *Copacabana Beach in Rio de Janeiro, Brazil*

The Amazon Basin, one of the world's last great "empty" spaces, covers about 40 percent of Brazil's territory. The enormous Amazon River and its tributaries drain the lowlands, which extend inland to the foot of the Andes. The area's vast tropical rain forests contain few human settlements.

The Brazilian Plateau makes up part of South America's ancient shield. As on the Canadian Shield, soils are generally thin and infertile, but minerals abound. Ancient lava flows cover the Paraná Plateau at the southern end of Brazil. The fertile volcanic soils help to make this Brazil's chief farming region.

The Brazilian Plateau tilts up toward the east coast, giving the east higher elevations than the *sertao*, a Portuguese word meaning "interior." Like the Appalachians in the

365

eastern United States, these uplands obstructed movement inland, keeping early colonists close to the coast.

The Amazon Basin and the northeast coast have a hot and rainy tropical wet climate, while semiarid and desert conditions prevail farther inland in the sertao. Other parts of Brazil have a humid subtropical climate similar to that of Washington, D.C. Snow often falls in the highlands in winter,

*Text continues on page 368.*

**Learning from Maps.** *Argentina plans to follow Brazil's example and build a new capital in the interior. Why did Brazil move its capital?*

**ATLANTIC COAST NATIONS OF SOUTH AMERICA**
**Physical/Political**

⊛ National capital   • Other city

——— National boundary

AZIMUTHAL EQUAL AREA PROJECTION

# CASE STUDY
## EXPLORING PLACES: The Rain Forest

In 1985 Extrema, Brazil, was only a wide place in a dirt road in the Amazon rain forest. A few wooden buildings marked the only visible break in the surrounding tropical wilderness. Just 15 months later Extrema had become a boom town. At least five new settler families arrived daily.

### Why the Boom?

Ask anyone on the streets of Extrema why all of this hustle and bustle has suddenly occurred and there is one universal answer, "*a estrada*—the road." The road is paved, all-weather, two-lane BR-364, the newest and best Amazon highway. BR-364 stretches nearly 1,300 miles (2,090 kilometers) from the scrublands of Mato (MAT·uh) Grosso, west of Brasilia, into the tropical rain forests of the states of Rondônia and Acre (AHK·ruh).

Since the completion of BR-364, more than 12,000 colonos, or settlers, have arrived in the rain forest every month in search of free land and easy credit. The settlers, most of whom do not understand how fragile the rain forest really is, pose a terrible threat to the forest ecology as they clear the land to make way for farms. Burned, cut, knocked down, scooped out— acre by acre—the Amazon rain forest rapidly falls to the hands of humans seemingly bent on tearing this huge wilderness to shreds. According to the latest estimates, during every minute of the day people destroy at least 100 acres (40 hectares) of tropical forest.

### Worldwide Disaster?

This destruction may have a potential long-term impact on plants, animals, and people living far beyond the rain forest. Many scientists believe, for example, that the Amazon rain forest normally produces about half of its own rainfall through the

*Building a road in the Amazon*

process of evaporation. As the trees disappear, however, so does the abundant rainfall that characterizes a tropical rain forest. In some cleared areas along the forest's eastern and southeastern edges, rainfall has already dropped drastically.

Many scientists also express the concern that the disappearance of the rain forest will bring serious oxygen losses to the world beyond the forest. Their concern stems from a scientific fact—vegetation is the major contributor to the atmosphere's oxygen component. In addition, the large-scale burning of tropical forests increases the amount of carbon dioxide in the atmosphere. This adds to the greenhouse effect, or the heating of the lower atmosphere (see Chapter 4). This process could result in dangerous climatic changes. The climates of the most important agricultural areas could become significantly drier. Even more frightening, a few added degrees of temperature might result in a breakup of parts of the Antarctic ice sheet. With such an occurrence, the oceans could easily rise high enough to swamp coastal cities. All these negative effects could be triggered by the destruction of the rain forest.

which comes in June and July throughout the Southern Hemisphere.

Forests cover Brazil's rainiest areas. In the humid Amazon Basin the lushness of the tropical rain forests deceived early European settlers, who were used to the fertile soils of Europe's forests. When the settlers cleared an area for farming, heavy rains quickly **leached,** or washed out, the soil's nutrients. The settlers soon realized that farming the area would be difficult.

Deciduous forests (see Chapter 4) grow in a narrow belt to the west of the rainy east coast. Farmers till the soils formed on the drier edge of this forest because they remain fertile. Drier lands in the sertao generally support savannas of tropical grasslands and scattered trees.

## Cultural Setting

Brazil's cultural setting differs from its South American neighbors because its European heritage is linked to Portugal, rather than Spain. Its racially mixed population have all contributed to Brazil's unique culture.

**Population patterns.** Brazil's rapidly growing population includes a mixture of people who trace their descent to Indians, Brazil's original inhabitants; Portuguese, who ruled the land from 1500 to the 1820s; and Africans, who were brought to Brazil as slaves. After Brazil became an independent monarchy in 1822, people from many different countries settled in southern Brazil.

Most of Brazil's people live within 200 miles of the Atlantic coast. To encourage settlement and development in the country's vast interior, however, the government built a new capital—Brasilia—far inland.

**Social patterns.** Brazil's **cultural hearth,** where colonial settlement began and many cultural institutions and attitudes developed, lies in the coastal Northeast. Years ago the Portuguese brought people from Africa to the area to work as slaves on sugar plantations. The Africans and their descendants contributed African words, music, traditions, and cooking styles that now enrich Brazilian culture.

A different colonial society developed inland on the sertao of the Northeast. The land, too dry for sugarcane, was divided into vast cattle ranches. Southern Brazil also differs from the Northeast. European colonists who arrived there in the 1800s largely shaped its society.

Most of the people throughout Brazil speak Portuguese. Most Brazilians belong to the Roman Catholic church, although significant numbers of Protestants live in southern areas. African beliefs also play an important role in the lives of many Brazilians.

**Political patterns.** The flag of Brazil carries the national motto, "Order and Progress." The recent political history of Brazil reflects the effort by the country's leaders to achieve both goals. Military leaders ruled the nation from 1964 to 1985. They borrowed heavily to build Brasilia and to stimulate industrialization. Civilian leaders now must find ways to repay a huge foreign debt of more than $100 billion and to curb rapid inflation.

**Economic patterns.** Brazil's economy is the most industrialized in South America and leads in terms of development. The southern half of the country, including Rio de Janeiro and São Paulo, long ago replaced the Northeast as the economic heartland of modern Brazil.

A focus on farming has made Brazil largely self-sufficient in agriculture. The country imports only one major food product—wheat. Moreover, the agricultural

frontier is steadily moving inland, bringing new lands under cultivation.

Soybeans and coffee head the list of exports but account for less than 20 percent of all export earnings. Coffee, once Brazil's most important crop, has declined in importance. Brazilian farmers also produce cacao, sugarcane, and citrus. High-quality cattle survive the heat of the interior and provide good meat.

Industrial goods produced in São Paulo and Rio de Janeiro now earn about 60 percent of the country's export income. Brazil ranks as one of the world's leading shipbuilding nations. In addition, its automobile and steel industries rank as the largest in South America. Because it lacks coal and has only small oil supplies, Brazil uses hydroelectricity to supply more than 80 percent of its energy needs.

Brazil's huge foreign debt clouds its prospects for growth. Other major economic problems include its lack of investment money to sustain economic growth and its large numbers of jobless and poor.

**Learning from Pictures.** *Brazil's farmers in the state of Paraná have used the fertile soil to grow fields of soybeans. What is Brazil's other leading agricultural export?*

## SECTION 1 REVIEW

1. **Define** leach, cultural hearth
2. **Locate** Amazon Basin, Brasilia, Rio de Janeiro, São Paulo
3. **Summarizing Ideas** (a) Where is Brazil's chief farming region? (b) Why is this area favorable for farming?
4. **Analyzing Ideas** Why is farming on lands cleared from rain forests usually unproductive?
5. **Interpreting Ideas** Why do social patterns in the sertao and southern Brazil differ from social patterns in the northeast?
6. **Determining Cause and Effect** (a) Why are people being attracted to the Amazon rain forest? (b) How does the destruction of the rain forest affect the environment?

## 2 Argentina ranks as one of the world's great food producers and exporters.

In South America only Brazil is larger than Argentina, which is four times the size of Texas. Until the 1960s Argentina was the continent's most developed country, but it now lags behind Brazil.

### Physical Setting

Geographers divide Argentina into four physical regions—the Andes, Northern Argentina, the Pampas, and Patagonia.

The Andes form Argentina's boundaries with Chile and Bolivia. In northwestern Argentina the Andes are dry and barren. People live only in the few river-fed oases of the piedmont at the eastern edge of the mountains. Although colder than the mountains in the northwest, the Andes in the southwest receive more precipitation.

**Learning from Pictures.** *Because Argentina has few forest resources, grass from the Pampas is used to make paper. To what region of the United States is the Pampas similar?*

Northern Argentina includes three distinct subregions—the Argentine Chaco, which is part of South America's Central Plains (see Chapter 16); part of the lava-covered Paraná Plateau of the Brazilian Highlands; and a lowland between the Paraná and Uruguay rivers called "Entre Ríos." The climate of Northern Argentina features characteristics of the continent's tropical wet-and-dry climates in the north and more temperate conditions farther south. The Chaco ranks as one of the hottest places on earth.

The lowland Pampas region, one of the largest level areas in the world, remains the economic heart of Argentina. The word *pampa* is Spanish for "grassy plains." Prairie grasses covered much of the Pampas before farming began in the 1800s.

Cold and windy conditions characterize Patagonia, a plateau in southern Argentina. Located on the leeward side of the Andes, Patagonia also is very dry because the prevailing winds drop most of their moisture over the Andes to the west.

## Cultural Setting

The cultural imprint left by Spain remains strong in Argentina. Compared to the Indian cultures found in the Andes, Argentina seems quite European. Like Brazil, Argentina faces a high rate of inflation and bears a staggering foreign debt. Its fragile democratic government struggles to survive following years of military dictatorship.

**Population patterns.** An estimated 85 percent of all Argentines trace their descent to Europeans, principally Spanish and Italian immigrants who arrived after the 1850s. Mestizos and a few Indians in the Andes make up most of the other 15 percent of the country's population. Unlike Brazil, Argentina has very few blacks.

A highly urbanized nation, about 84 percent of Argentina's population live in cities clustered in two main settlement zones. One cluster consists of the old cities of Tucumán (too·kuh·MAHN), Mendoza, and Córdoba in the oases at the foot of the Andes. Founded in the late 1500s by Spanish colonists crossing the Andes from arid Pacific coastal regions, these cities are the oldest settlements in Argentina. The Pampas, housing two-thirds of all Argentines, contains the country's second population cluster. This cluster is centered in Buenos Aires (bway·nuh·SAHR·eez). Approximately 10 million people live in and around Buenos Aires, Argentina's capital (see the CITY FOCUS on page 372). In 1987 the Argentine government approved a plan to move the nation's capital to help reduce crowding in Buenos Aires and spur development of Patagonia (see the map on page 366).

**Social patterns.** Over 90 percent of Argentina's people practice Roman Catholicism and the country maintains strong ties with the Roman Catholic church. The nation's constitution requires that the presi-

*Text continues on page 373.*

# DEVELOPING GEOGRAPHY SKILLS
## WRITING ABOUT GEOGRAPHY: Making Comparisons

- Describe the similarities and differences in the settings of Brazil and Paraguay.
- Compare the sites and situations of Buenos Aires and Mexico City.

Each of these directives requires you to compare geographic information. To compare means to identify the similarities or similarities and differences among items.

### How to Make Comparisons

To make geographic comparisons, follow these guidelines.

1. **Read the directive carefully.** Note what it is you are asked to compare.
2. **List the key aspects of each item to be compared.** Include important details.
3. **Note similarities (or similarities and differences).** Identify things that are alike and those that are different.

### Applying the Skill

Read the following directive.

- Compare the cultural settings of Brazil and Argentina.

The chart below highlights the key aspects of the two countries' cultural settings contained in this chapter.

You can see from the chart that there are several similarities. For example, both have a Roman Catholic majority, are largely urbanized, have relatively high literacy rates, now have civilian leaders, and rank among South America's leading economies. You can also note several differences. For example, Brazil has a more mixed population than Argentina, and Brazil's economy is more diversified.

*To practice this skill, see Practicing Geography Skills on page 377.*

| COMPARING THE CULTURAL SETTINGS OF BRAZIL AND ARGENTINA | | |
|---|---|---|
| | BRAZIL | ARGENTINA |
| POPULATION PATTERNS | Mixed population includes Indians; people of Portuguese, other European, and African ancestry; and Japanese<br>Urbanized<br>Most live near coast | Most people with European ancestry; few Indians, mestizos, or blacks<br>Urbanized |
| SOCIAL PATTERNS | Most people Roman Catholic; some Protestants and African religions<br>Portuguese official language<br>High literacy rate<br>African imprints | Most people Roman Catholic; few Protestants<br>Spanish official language<br>High literacy rate<br>Some French imprints |
| POLITICAL PATTERNS | Civilian rule recently replaced military government | Civilian rule recently replaced military government |
| ECONOMIC PATTERNS | Among leading South American economies<br>Exports many farm products<br>Industrial goods now lead exports<br>Shipbuilding, automaking, iron and steel industries<br>Large debt | Among leading South American economies<br>Among world leaders in food production and exportation<br>Most industry processes farm products |

# CITY FOCUS
## Buenos Aires, Argentina

Water laden with mud washes out of the heart of South America and flows as a great river toward the Atlantic Ocean. The yellowish water laps against the grassy banks and moss-covered concrete walls of the waterfront of Buenos Aires. Yet on summer nights, when the moon is full, the water appears to take on a silvery sheen. It dances in the moonlight with such a luster that it almost speaks the river's name, Rio de la Plata, or River of Silver.

### Site

Buenos Aires, along with its suburbs, sits on the banks of the Rio de la Plata in a great half-circle whose radius measures nearly 20 miles (32 kilometers). Located inside this sprawling metropolitan region is the 70-square-mile (182-square-kilometer) Federal District, an area that serves the

*The Casa Rosada, site of the president's office*

same function as the District of Columbia in the United States.

### Primate City

The primate city of Argentina, Buenos Aires is home to 10 million people—more than one-third of Argentina's entire population. More than 80 percent of Argentina's foreign trade pours across Buenos Aires' docks. Highways and railroad tracks reach outward from the docks like a giant spiderweb to tap the resources of the countryside and to carry goods back to it. Within the metropolitan area are more than half of the nation's industrial plants, employing two-thirds of all its workers and producing more than seven-tenths of the nation's industrial products.

Few cities in the world so dominate a nation as does this proud city on its river of silver. Because of its dominance, every year thousands of Argentines move to Buenos Aires, dreaming of finding work and success. Since the 1940s the city's population has grown from 4.5 million to more than 10 million. But in spite of the presence of the nation's largest assemblage of industries, there simply are not enough jobs to meet the demand. Widespread unemployment has resulted and thousands of poverty-stricken families live in miserable shacks in the slums of the western and southern suburbs.

Argentina has recently focused attention on the problems of Buenos Aires' people. Social programs aimed at providing training and medical care have helped many. But as happens to so many great cities, the attraction of the city draws in more people than it can serve. Future plans call for development of outlying areas. Until that happens, people from throughout South America will continue to crowd beautiful Buenos Aires in search of opportunity.

dent of the republic be Roman Catholic and guarantees protection to the church.

Argentina provides its people free education up to the college level. The nation has a high literacy rate and a large middle class. Despite its Spanish heritage and language, many Argentines also have close cultural ties to France.

**Political patterns.** Argentina has faced political unrest since the 1950s. Over the years the country teetered between military rule and democracy. Military rulers held control of the government from 1976 to 1983. Many abuses occurred under this dictatorship, resulting in a continued public outcry. In 1982 the military tried to deflect public criticism by attacking the British-held Falkland Islands, called the Malvinas Islands by the Argentines and long claimed by Argentina. Argentina suffered a humiliating defeat in the war that followed. Shortly thereafter a civilian government took over and restored democracy.

**Economic patterns.** Argentina ranks as one of the world's leading producers and exporters of food. Argentina's chief exports include grain and livestock products from the Pampas. In the 1850s the Pampas were cattle country, where Argentine cowhands called **gauchos** (GOW·chohs) tended the herds much as American cowhands did in the West. Hides and skins were the principal products. Later, farmers fenced the open range to grow wheat for export to Europe. With the invention of refrigeration, meat joined the list of exports. In time a corn-and-livestock type of farming similar to that in the American Plains developed on the Pampas.

Farmers grow cotton in the Gran Chaco and sugarcane and fruit at the eastern foot of the Andes. Farmers in Patagonia, where the frigid, dry climate makes raising cattle almost impossible, raise millions of sheep.

*Learning from Pictures.* One of Córdoba's growing industries is the production of automobile engines. What other city in Argentina is an industrial center?

Buenos Aires and Córdoba serve as Argentina's major industrial centers. Leading industries include food processing and leather tanning. Tanneries transform cattle hides into leather. A large textile industry also uses the country's wool and cotton supplies to make clothing and other goods.

### SECTION 2 REVIEW

1. **Define** pampa, gaucho
2. **Locate** Chaco, Patagonia, Córdoba, Buenos Aires
3. **Summarizing Ideas** (a) Where is the economic heart of Argentina? (b) Why do dry conditions prevail in Patagonia?
4. **Understanding Ideas** What factors have hampered Argentina's development since the 1950s?

## 3 Uruguay and Paraguay are slowly developing.

Uruguay and Paraguay, both developing nations, offer great contrasts. Uruguay is one of the region's most prosperous nations, and Paraguay its poorest.

### Uruguay

Uruguay lies wedged between its much larger neighbors, Argentina and Brazil. It gained independence from Spain in 1812 as a part of Argentina and became a separate nation in 1828. The country long served as a model of stability but now faces problems.

**Physical setting.** The only South American nation located entirely outside the tropics, Uruguay lies north of the Rio de la Plata and east of the Uruguay River at the southern end of the Brazilian Plateau. Flat plains similar to the Pampas of Argentina cover the area along the Rio de la Plata, with more rolling landscapes inland. The country, which is about the same size as the state of Washington, boasts highly fertile soils for ranching and farming.

**Cultural setting.** Uruguay ranks as one of the most prosperous South American nations. Although agriculture dominates the economy, about half the people live in urban areas.

Uruguay's population numbers fewer than 3.1 million. Nine out of 10 Uruguayans trace their descent to European ancestors. Mestizos and blacks each make up about 5 percent of the population. An estimated 85 percent of Uruguayans live in urban areas. More than one-third of these reside in and around Montevideo (mahnt·uh·vuh·DAY·oh), Uruguay's capital and primate city.

Uruguay has a large and well-educated middle class. The country places a great emphasis upon education, even paying college tuition for its citizens. Uruguayans speak Spanish, and more than two-thirds belong to the Roman Catholic church. Uruguay does not have the wide gap between rich and poor found in many South American nations, in part because of social legislation begun in the early 1900s.

While Uruguay has had a long history of peace and prosperity, it has faced such serious modern problems as terrorism, unemployment, and inflation. In addition, the country has been ruled by a military dictatorship since 1973.

Uruguay's economy centers on livestock farming. Grazing accounts for more than 75 percent of the nation's land use. Crops used for livestock feed grow on another 11 percent of the land. Not surprisingly, meat and wool lead Uruguay's exports. The temperate climate allows cattle and sheep to graze outdoor all year.

Uruguay lacks exploitable mineral deposits. Food processing remains the chief manufacturing activity. Other factories produce textiles, electronics, and other items chiefly for local consumption.

### Paraguay

Paraguay, the poorest of the Atlantic Coast countries, gained independence from Spain in 1811. Most of the modern changes of this century have bypassed Paraguay.

**Physical setting.** Landlocked Paraguay is about the size of California. The Paraguay River divides Paraguay into two physical regions—the Chaco and Eastern Paraguay. Hot, rainy summers and extremely dry winters characterize the nearly uninhabited Chaco. Eastern Paraguay lies on the fertile lava soils of the Brazilian Plateau and has a more reliable rainfall pattern.

**Cultural setting.** Mestizos make up the majority of Paraguay's population. Spanish

and the Indian language of Guarani (gwahr·uh·NEE) both serve as official languages. The country remains poor economically and lacks mineral resources.

Nearly 95 percent of Paraguay's people live in the eastern half of the country. People of European descent make up only about 1 percent of the population and Guarani Indians make up 4 percent. Mestizos account for the overwhelming majority. Asunción (uh·soon·see·OHN) founded in 1537, serves as the nation's capital and largest city.

Over half of Paraguay's people live in the countryside, where they work as subsistence farmers. The government guarantees freedom of religion but recognizes the Roman Catholic church as the state church. Almost all of the people practice Roman Catholicism. In the schools teachers instruct their pupils only in Spanish, but Guarani has a rich tradition and most Paraguayans are bilingual.

Authoritarian rule by a succession of dictators characterizes Paraguay's political history. A military leader who seized power in 1954 still heads the government. The undemocratic system remains the cause of mounting social and political unrest.

Paraguay's lack of useful mineral deposits and manufacturing industries makes it one of the poorest countries in South America. Cattle raising, farming, and forestry serve as the principal economic activities. Cotton ranks as the chief crop, but farmers use primitive methods to till the soil and productivity remains low. Most small farms lie along the Paraguay River, which is widely used for transportation and irrigation purposes.

In recent years Paraguay's leaders have worked to develop hydroelectric resources along the Paraná River and its tributaries. The giant Itaipu (ee·TY·puh) power project, built jointly with Brazil, ranks as the largest hydroelectric project in the world. The na-

***Learning from Pictures.*** *The art of making lace by hand was brought from Europe by the Spaniards. What are some other European imprints in Paraguay?*

tion has planned other hydroelectric projects with Argentina. Paraguay hopes to use some of the energy to help stimulate local manufacturing industries.

## SECTION 3 REVIEW

1. **Locate** Rio de la Plata, Montevideo, Asunción
2. **Summarizing Ideas** **(a)** What makes Uruguay's physical setting unique? **(b)** What are Paraguay's two physical regions?
3. **Understanding Ideas** What is the chief **(a)** agricultural and **(b)** manufacturing activity in Uruguay? **(c)** What is the major economic activity in Paraguay?
4. **Interpreting Ideas** How is Paraguay attempting to stimulate economic growth?

# CHAPTER 19 REVIEW

## Chapter Summary

The following list contains the key concepts you have learned about the Atlantic Coast countries of South America.

1. The Atlantic Coast countries of South America include Portuguese-speaking Brazil and Spanish-speaking Argentina, Uruguay, and Paraguay.
2. Among the regions, the Atlantic Coast is South America's most developed, most diversified, and most prosperous.
3. Brazil takes up about half of South America's land area and contains about half the continent's total population. The country includes the Amazon Basin—one of the world's last great empty spaces.
4. The Pampas are the agricultural and economic heartland of modern Argentina. The country is one of the world's great food producers and exporters.
5. The Pampas's development from ranching to wheat and corn-and-livestock farms parallels a similar transformation in the Great Plains and American Middle West.
6. Buenos Aires, Argentina's capital and primate city, faces problems similar to those faced by Mexico City. Large numbers of newly arrived people place added strain on the city resources.
7. Uruguay is the most prosperous Atlantic Coast country.
8. Paraguay is the poorest and least developed of the Atlantic Coast countries.
9. Rapid settlement in the rain forest of Brazil is threatening to alter world climate patterns.

On a separate sheet of paper, complete the following review exercises.

## Reviewing Geographic Terms

In the following sentences, the underlined term is incorrect. Rewrite each sentence with the correct term.

1. When farmers clear lands in the tropical rain forest, heavy rains soon drain, or wash out, nutrients from the soil.
2. Northeast Brazil is the development region of the country because that is where colonial settlement began and where many cultural institutions and attitudes developed.
3. Cowhands on the South American Pampas are called sertaos.
4. The Spanish name for grassy plain is chaco.

## Developing Critical Thinking Skills

1. **Interpreting Maps** Study the map of South America on page 11. **(a)** How are the physical settings of Bolivia and Paraguay similar? **(b)** How do they differ?
2. **Summarizing Ideas** What are Brazil's physical regions?
3. **Interpreting Ideas** How and why did Brazil's eastern highlands influence early patterns of settlement?
4. **Contrasting Ideas** **(a)** How does Brazil's cultural setting differ from that of its neighbors? **(b)** How are Argentina's population patterns different from those of other South American nations? **(c)** How is Uruguayan society different from that found in many South American countries? Why is this so?
5. **Analyzing Ideas** **(a)** Why did the Brazilian government move the national capital to Brasilia? **(b)** What other South American country is moving its capital?
6. **Synthesizing Ideas** Why does Brazil's economy face an uncertain future?
7. **Understanding Ideas** What is the major economic activity in Uruguay?
8. **Seeing Relationships** Why is Paraguay one of the poorest countries in South America?
9. **Writing About Geography** In a full-page essay, complete one of the following activities. **(a)** Describe the political patterns of Brazil, Argentina, Uruguay, and Paraguay. **(b)** Analyze the impact that settlement is having on the rain forest and offer suggestions to safeguard the environment there.

## Using Primary Sources

In the following excerpt from *Brazil: The Infinite Country*, William Lytle Schurz describes the geography of Brazil. As you study the reading, compare the geography of Brazil to that of the United States.

Brazil ranks fifth in size among the nations of the world. Only the Soviet Union, Canada, China, and the United States have a larger area. But of these, Brazil is bigger than continental United States or China proper. It is larger than Australia, and, with one-sixth the population, has 2,000,000 more square miles [5,180,000 square kilometers] than India. It occupies nearly half the surface of South America, and its 14,000-odd miles [22,400 kilometers] of land frontier adjoin every nation of the continent except Chile and Ecuador. Its single coast is nearly 4,600 miles [7,360 kilometers] long. It is, indeed, a spacious land.

Like the two other "United States" of the Western Hemisphere [the United States of America and Mexico], Brazil is a federal republic. It is composed of 21 states, four territories, and a federal district, in which the new capital, Brasilia, is situated. The former federal district is now the state of Guanabara [gwahn·uh· BAR·uh]. One of the 21 states, Amazonas, is bigger than Alaska. Three are larger than Texas and six are larger than California. Bahia, sixth in size, is almost as big as France. The adjoining country of Bolivia would fit into the state of Mato Grosso, with room enough left over for Uruguay.

1. According to the text, which countries in the world have a larger land area than Brazil?
2. Why does the author claim Brazil "is, indeed, a spacious land"?
3. What political units comprise the United States of Brazil?

4. In what ways is Brazil geographically similar to the United States?

## Practicing Geography Skills

*Before completing this activity, review Developing Geography Skills on page 371.*

**Making Comparisons.** Reread the subsections on the physical settings of Brazil and Argentina. Then follow this directive.

Compare the physical settings of Brazil and Argentina in terms of landforms, climate, and other aspects of the environment.

## Exploring Geography

1. Review the material in the chapter. Then construct a chart entitled "Comparing the Atlantic Coast Countries." Your chart should include brief descriptions comparing economic, social, political, and population patterns in each of the countries you have studied in Chapter 19.
2. One of the most popular pastimes in all of South America is soccer. The Atlantic coast countries in particular have achieved considerable success in international soccer competitions over the years. Use resources in your school or public library to find information on the history of soccer in the Atlantic coast countries. In doing your research, pay close attention to the records of each country in such international soccer competitions as the World Cup. Then use the information you have gathered to prepare a brief report on soccer for the rest of the class.
3. Reread the CITY FOCUS on Buenos Aires on page 372. Then write an essay that provides similar information on the capital city of one of the other Atlantic Coast countries that you have studied in this chapter. Your essay should also include a paragraph on the meaning and origin of the city's name.

# UNIT 6 REVIEW

## Unit Summary

The following list contains the key concepts you have learned about South America.

1. The three physical regions of South America are the Andes Mountains, the Eastern Highlands, and the Central Plains.
2. Tropical climates dominate in the north, while temperate climates influence the south. Deserts line parts of the west coast and the foothills of the southern Andes.
3. Large deposits of a variety of minerals underlie South America. In general, however, the continent's abundant natural resources remain undeveloped.
4. The cultural imprint of South America reflects contributions from Indians, Europeans, and Africans.
5. South America's 12 nations and one French department face many of the same problems confronting developing nations around the world. All the countries claim to be democratic republics.
6. Colombia, Venezuela, Guyana, Suriname, and French Guiana are closely linked to the Caribbean.
7. The Pacific Coast countries include Ecuador, Peru, Bolivia, and Chile.
8. Portuguese-speaking Brazil and three Spanish-speaking countries—Argentina, Uruguay, and Paraguay—lie on the Atlantic coast.
9. El Niño has disastrous effects on fishing in South America and wreaks havoc on climate patterns throughout the world.
10. Brazil and Argentina have relocated their capitals to encourage settlement and development of those areas.

On a separate sheet of paper, complete the following review exercises.

## Checking Your Understanding

1. Identify the countries of South America by geographic region.
2. Identify and describe the physical regions of South America.
3. Identify and give the locations of South America's major rivers.
4. Which three groups contributed to South America's cultural imprint?
5. What is the most common type of political system in South America?
6. What are the chief (a) food and (b) commercial crops grown in South America?
7. (a) In what areas does Indian culture remain strongest? (b) Why?

## Applying Critical Thinking Skills

1. **Interpreting Ideas** (a) What is South America's relative location with regard to the rest of the Western Hemisphere? (b) Why does its relative location make South America important to the United States?
2. **Determining Cause and Effect** In what ways do (a) elevation and (b) latitude affect South America's climate?
3. **Analyzing Ideas** (a) What is a one-crop economy? (b) Why is it dangerous for a country to depend on a single product as the basis of its economy?
4. **Seeing Relationships** How does the continent's physical setting directly influence the economic development of the countries of South America?
5. **Contrasting Ideas** (a) In what ways is Brazil different from the other countries of South America? (b) In what ways does Paraguay differ from the other Atlantic Coast countries?
6. **Comparing Ideas** How are the social patterns of Uruguay and Argentina similar?

## Reviewing Unit Features

1. **City Focus** (a) What problems hampered the development of Brasilia? (b) What problems still remain?
2. **Geography in the Workplace** (a) Why and how do political geographers solve

boundary disputes? **(b)** How might political geographers help solve an international political problem?

3. **The Geographic Web** Describe the routes cocaine typically takes from the coca fields in South America to the streets of the United States.

4. **City Focus** **(a)** Why is Buenos Aires considered a primate city? Give specific examples to support your answer. **(b)** What has the government of Argentina done to help solve problems in Buenos Aires?

## Using Map Skills

1. Study the map on page 332. What is the major economic activity in **(a)** a central Argentina, **(b)** central Chile, **(c)** near Lake Maracaibo, Venezuela. **(d)** What minerals are mined in the Guianas?
2. Examine the map on page 330. **(a)** What is South America's largest city? **(b)** What other cities have more than 2 million people?
3. Study the map on page 325. What type of climate prevails along South America's west coast?

## Investigating Geography

1. Select a South American country to research. Draw a large map that illustrates the major physical regions and the largest cities of the country. Find out information about current life styles, political patterns, and economic activities. Collect photographs or draw pictures that show life in the country you have selected. Post your report on the bulletin board or otherwise share it with the class.
2. Using the *Geodata Files* for South America, prepare a series of pie or bar graphs that illustrate the geographic and economic data for each country. Then write several generalizations that reflect the comparisons you see in the graphs you have developed. Post your graphs on the bulletin board.

## Further Reading

**Chapter 16**

Brooks, John, ed. *South American Handbook.* New York: International Publications Service. Provides a wealth of useful information for the student as well as the traveler.

Carter, William E. *South America.* Rev. ed. New York: Franklin Watts. Explores the geography, history, and civilization of the countries of South America.

Clark, James I. *Latin America.* Revised edition. Evanston, Illinois: McDougal, Littell. Surveys life in Latin America from pre-Columbian times to the present day.

Morris, Arthur S. *South America.* New York: Barnes & Noble. Studies the physical, cultural, and economic geography of the South American continent.

**Chapter 17**

Carpenter, Allan, and Jean Lyons. *Surinam.* Chicago: Childrens Press. Presents a view of the multiethnic culture of Suriname and focuses on life and work in the country.

**Chapter 18**

Hints, Martin. *Chile.* Chicago: Childrens Press. Covers the multicultural and geographical aspects of Chile and focuses on how the people live. Also illustrates how the different ethnic groups have adapted to the country.

**Chapter 19**

Cross, Wilbur, and Susanna Cross. *Brazil.* Chicago: Childrens Press. Provides a cultural and geographic view of the giant country of Brazil.

Lyle, Gary, and John C. Caldwell. *Let's Visit Argentina.* London: Burke Publishing Company. Covers the geography, people, and culture of Argentina and describes how the people live day to day.

Robb, Patricia. *We Live in Brazil.* New York: The Bookwright Press. Provides a look at the people, geography, and culture of Brazil through the words of various members of Brazil's large and diverse population.

# PUTTING THE CHAPTER IN FOCUS

Politically fragmented Western Europe contains 24 small nations, none of which covers as much territory as the state of Texas. Some of the smallest nations cover less area than a large American farm or a small city. Despite their small sizes, the countries of Western Europe have a combined population that is larger than that of the United States. Their economies also rank among the world's most productive.

## Ideas to Understand

In studying about the countries of Western Europe, use these ideas to give direction to your reading.

1 Western Europe has a maritime physical setting.
2 A diversity of cultural traditions characterizes Western Europe.
3 The United Kingdom, France, and West Germany rank as leading world economies.

4 Many other important nations lie in Western Europe.

## Terms to Define

The following terms are some of the key terms in the chapter. Defining them will help you understand Western Europe.

| | |
|---|---|
| fjord | constitutional |
| mistral | monarchy |
| sirocco | geyser |
| alpine meadow | polder |
| moor | neutral |
| nationalism | canton |

## Places to Locate

Locating the following places will add to your knowledge of geography.

| | |
|---|---|
| Alps | Rhine River |
| Massif Central | Norden |
| Pyrenees | Benelux |
| Apennines | Low Countries |

## 1 Western Europe has a maritime physical setting.

Paris, Rome, London, Vienna, Madrid—the very names bring to mind beautiful cities, rich histories, and vibrant cultures. But much more than Western Europe's great cities characterize the region.

The varied landscape includes the majestic beauty of the Alps, the eerie silence of the sparsely populated British uplands, the almost desolate stretches of the northern tundra, and the flat plains that have been reclaimed from the sea. Thousands of small towns and villages dot this urban and industrial region. Its people speak many different languages and have many different cultures.

◀ *Sidewalk cafe along the Champs Elysées in Paris*

### Physical Regions

Western Europe lies on a peninsula of Eurasia bordered by the Mediterranean Sea in the south, the Atlantic Ocean in the west, and the North Sea, Baltic Sea, and English Channel in the north. No part of the region lies more than a few hundred miles from these surrounding seas, which stay open for trade all year despite cold winters.

Landforms divide Western Europe into four physical regions—the Northwest Uplands, the North European Plain, the Central Uplands, and Alpine Europe.

**Northwest Uplands.** The Northwest Uplands consist of the low but rugged remnants of an ancient, worn-down mountain

383

**Learning from Pictures.** *Norway's peaceful fjords were once the home of Vikings who raided the coast of Western Europe. How are fjords formed?*

chain in northwest Europe. The uplands cover Norway and Sweden on the Scandinavian Peninsula, Finland, Iceland, northwestern sections of the British Isles, the Plateau of Brittany in France, and part of the Iberian Peninsula.

Glaciation during the Ice Age left most of Western Europe with thin soils and steep slopes unsuitable for settlement or farming. In Norway the glaciers carved coastal areas into spectacular, steep-sided inlets called **fjords** (fee·OOHRDS) and created many waterfalls and lakes. Features of the landscape in Britain's Scottish Highlands include long lakes called **lochs** (LAWKS) and sheltered valleys called **glens.**

**North European Plain.** A broad lowland called the North European Plain extends across northern Europe directly south of the Northwest Uplands. It stretches from western France and southeastern Great Britain eastward to Denmark on the Jutland Peninsula and the southern tip of Sweden.

Elevations of less than 500 feet (150 meters) characterize this region.

**Central Uplands.** A mixture of small uplands lies just south of the North European Plain. Parts of a worn-down mountain chain that broke apart and then rose upward over time formed this upland region. The Central Uplands include France's Massif (ma·SEEF) Central, which literally means "central mountain block"; the Jura (JOOR·uh) Mountains in Switzerland; and West Germany's Black Forest. The Ardennes (ahr·DEN) and Vosges (VOHZH) mountains form upland blocks in eastern France. Elevations in the Central Uplands generally reach less than 8,000 feet (2,400 meters).

**Alpine Europe.** Much higher and younger mountain chains, all part of the alpine mountain system, stretch across southern Europe. The Alps, located in France, Switzerland, West Germany, Austria, and northern Italy form the highest alpine chain. They rise to a high point of 15,771 feet (4,810 meters) at France's Mont Blanc.

Related mountain ranges to the west include the Sierra Nevada in southern Spain and the Pyrenees (PIR·uh·nees) between Spain and France. Mountain ranges to the east include the Pindus and Rhodope (RAHD·uh·pee) mountains on the Balkan Peninsula. Italy's Apennines (AP·uh·nyns) form a lower offshoot of the alpine mountain system on the Italian Peninsula. The North Italian Plain, nestled between the Alps and Apennines, forms the only large lowland in Alpine Europe. Earthquakes and occasional volcanic eruptions in Italy serve as reminders that the young alpine mountain system continues to form (see Chapter 3).

## Rivers

The Rhine forms Western Europe's major river system. Because of its heavy boat

and barge traffic, it serves as one of the world's great trading arteries. The Rhine crosses or forms parts of the borders of Switzerland, France, West Germany, and the Netherlands before emptying into the North Sea.

A network of canals connects the Rhine with many other rivers in France, including the Seine (SAYN), Loire (luh·WAHR), Rhône, and Saône (SOHN) rivers. The Po performs a vital function in Alpine Europe—it carries melted snow from the Alps to lands in the North Italian Plain for use in irrigation. The Tagus, Ebro (AY·broh), and other rivers in Spain help irrigate its land, but their flows diminish in the hot, dry summer.

## Climates

Geographers identify three principal types of climate in Western Europe—west coast marine climate, mountain climate, and Mediterranean climate. In general, the climate types remain milder than those in places located at the same latitudes in North America and Asia.

Prevailing westerly winds carry marine influences from the sea far inland across low-lying northern Europe. This gives northern Europe comparatively mild winters, cool summers, and a succession of damp, rainy, and cloudy days. A warm ocean current called the North Atlantic Current (see the map on page 130) flows offshore. The current keeps seas from freezing and moderates coastal climates as far north as Iceland and Scandinavia on the Arctic Circle. Subarctic conditions prevail inland in those northern areas, while northern Finland and Norway have a tundra climate similar to northernmost Canada.

Higher elevations in the mountain system have a mountain climate. Climatic conditions vary in the mountains with changes in elevation. The coldest, most extreme conditions prevail at higher elevations.

Southern Europe has the hot, dry summers and mild, occasionally rainy winters typical of a Mediterranean climate. Days usually remain pleasant but strong winds from bordering regions occasionally sweep the area. In winter the **mistral** (MIS·truhl)—a cold, dry wind that brings blasts of cold air down the Rhône River Valley to southern France—often damages sensitive crops. In summer hot winds called **siroccos** (suh·RAHK·ohs) bring hot, dry, and dusty air to the region from North Africa's deserts.

*Learning from Diagrams.* *Western Europe contains a mixture of plains, uplands, and mountains. Which mountains divide Spain from France?*

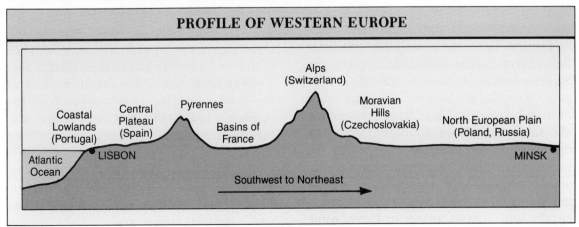

## PROFILE OF WESTERN EUROPE

Alps (Switzerland)

Pyrennes

Coastal Lowlands (Portugal)

Central Plateau (Spain)

Basins of France

Moravian Hills (Czechoslovakia)

North European Plain (Poland, Russia)

Atlantic Ocean

LISBON

MINSK

Southwest to Northeast

385

| TEMPERATURES AND PRECIPITATION IN SELECTED WESTERN EUROPEAN CITIES | | | |
|---|---|---|---|
| City/Country | January Low | July High | Precipitation (in/cm) |
| AMSTERDAM, NETHERLANDS | 34°F 1°C | 69°F 21°C | 26/ 65 |
| BERLIN, GERMANY | 26°F −3°C | 74°F 23°C | 23/ 59 |
| DUBLIN, IRELAND | 35°F 2°C | 67°F 19°C | 30/ 75 |
| GENEVA, SWITZERLAND | 29°F −2°C | 77°F 25°C | 34/ 86 |
| LONDON, ENGLAND | 35°F 2°C | 73°F 23°C | 23/ 58 |
| MADRID, SPAIN | 33°F 1°C | 87°F 31°C | 17/ 42 |
| PARIS, FRANCE | 32°F 0°C | 76°F 24°C | 22/ 57 |
| ROME, ITALY | 39°F 4°C | 88°F 31°C | 30/ 75 |

Source: *World Almanac and Book of Facts*, 1987

**Learning from Charts.** *The North Atlantic Current warms Western Europe despite the region's northerly location. Which city has the coldest temperature in January? in July?*

## Vegetation

Forests once covered Western Europe. Over the years, however, people cleared most of the forests so that the land could be farmed. The few remaining forests lie in the subarctic areas of Finland, Norway, and Sweden and in mountain and upland regions. Tundra (see Chapter 4) covers much of interior Norway and Iceland, where the climate is too cold or windy for trees. Tundra also covers high, open areas in the mountains. These tundra-covered fields above the tree line are known as **alpine meadows.** A treeless vegetation of hardy shrubs and grasses grows in rainy, wind-swept uplands known as **moors** in northern and western Great Britain.

## Resources

People are Western Europe's greatest resource. Their skill and creativity have made the region productive.

**Agriculture.** Western Europe's small land area limits its farming activities. Nevertheless, northern European farmers use intensive farming and modern technologies to produce some of the world's highest grain, meat, and dairy yields per acre. Southern European farmers grow winter wheat, olives, citrus fruits, grapes, and summer rice and sugarcane on irrigated lands.

**Forestry and fishing.** Because the remaining forests cover generally inaccessible areas, lumbering is important in only a few countries. Operations remain limited elsewhere. Although overfishing in some areas has affected supplies, fish remain plentiful in most Western European waters. The principal fishing areas lie near Iceland in the cold waters of the North Sea and in the Mediterranean Sea.

**Mining.** Western Europe contains large deposits of coal, oil, and natural gas, and many of these deposits have been tapped. The principal coal field is located in the Ruhr (ROOHR) Valley in West Germany. Offshore rigs in the North Sea provide supplies of oil and natural gas. Great Britain and Norway rank among the world leaders of these valuable energy resources (see the graph on page 465). Western Europe also has important iron ore reserves in Sweden and France and hydroelectric resources in many mountain areas. Despite these resources, countries in Western Europe still must import energy supplies to fuel their vast industrial complexes.

## 2 A diversity of cultural traditions characterizes Western Europe.

In the early 1900s the populations of Western Europe completed the demographic transition to low birth rates, low death rates, and slow or zero rates of natural increase (see Chapter 7). This transition brought about by industrialization exists within an even older framework of national and cultural diversity.

### A Brief History

Western Europe nurtured Western civilization. Through cultural diffusion this culture spread from Greece and Rome throughout Europe and much of the world.

**Early beginnings.** Ancient Greeks laid the foundations of Western European culture about 900 B.C. Romans inherited and extended that culture throughout the lands of the Roman Empire between 200 B.C. and A.D. 400. After the Roman Empire collapsed in 476, members of many ethnic groups began to form their own countries. The Roman Catholic church was the only unifying force in the politically fragmented region.

**Renaissance, Reformation, and exploration.** In the 1300s the Renaissance, or "rebirth," of Western culture sparked a period of great social, economic, and cultural change. In time religious life, too, changed as Protestants broke away from the Roman Catholic church in what came to be known as the Reformation.

By the 1500s Europeans had sailed around the world. The strongest nations, including France, Great Britain, and Spain, built large overseas empires and extended European culture around the world.

**Industrialization.** Beginning in the mid-1700s and continuing during the 1800s, the Industrial Revolution transformed Western Europe from an agricultural to an industrial society. Industrialization brought increases in food supplies as farmers adopted scientific and mechanized technologies. Nutritional and health standards rose and, in turn, populations increased. Living standards also rose as industry and trade offered new job opportunities and made more goods available.

**Wars.** Rivalries among Western European nations led to many wars, including two world wars. World War I began in 1914 and ended in 1918. World War II began in Europe in 1939 and ended in 1945. The wars resulted in the deaths of millions of people and the destruction of property and cities throughout Western Europe.

**Moves toward unity.** Efforts to unify Western Europe began after World War II. In 1957 six nations—France, West Germany, Belgium, Italy, the Netherlands,

*Text continues on page 390.*

*Druggist's tools from the 1800s*

Some 650 years ago little was known about effective ways to cure diseases or to check epidemics. In just three years, for example, from 1348 through 1350, one-fourth of the entire population of Europe died from a devastating plague. Known as the black death, the bubonic plague was one of the greatest disasters in European history.

## The Black Death

Modern researchers discovered that fleas, especially fleas carried by black rats, can transmit the dread disease to humans. The plague causes high fever, agonizing pain, and within five or six days, death. The name "black death" comes from the dark blotches that appear on the victim's skin.

The plague began early in the winter of 1348 in port cities in Italy. Scholars have theorized that rats that came ashore from merchant ships arriving from ports on the Black Sea brought the disease with them. But whatever its origins, the disease quickly spread throughout Italy. By June it had reached Hungary, Austria, Switzerland, France, and Spain. By December it had reached England. During the next two years it swept across the entire continent, finally reaching Norway and Sweden by December 1350.

The black death was most deadly in crowded, unsanitary cities. Summer was the worst time because the warm weather provided ideal conditions for fleas to thrive. In the winter, when most fleas died, the disease slowed. With the coming of spring it would break out anew.

Although most deaths from the plague occurred between 1348 and 1350, deaths continued during the remainder of the 1300s. The total number of deaths eventually rose to include more than one-third of the entire population of Europe. In the city of Florence, Italy, the population dropped from 90,000 to 45,000. Hamburg, Germany, lost two-thirds of its people. Marseille, France, lost 40,000 people. England's population fell from 3.8 million in 1348 to 2.1 million in 1374. And in France the losses were even greater.

The black death caused panic. Doctors could not explain it, let alone cure it. Four out of five people who got the disease died.

*An early electrocardiograph to monitor heart rates*

increasing in size. As cities developed, the prosperity of rural areas increased because of the growing demand for food.

Following the plague the economies of rural areas virtually collapsed. There were far fewer people to buy food in the urban areas, and the price of grain and other foods dropped. As the prices of farm goods fell, rural people began moving to the towns, seeking work. Thousands of farms were deserted. In central Germany, for example, 70 percent of all of the farm settlements were abandoned following the black death. After the black death had passed, Europe sank into a long period of depression. More than two centuries passed before Europe's population finally reached pre-plague levels. It was this population growth, along with the rise and spread of the Industrial Revolution, that finally brought stability once again to the nations of Europe. But not until the 1800s did real economic prosperity return.

*A pharmacist's scales and kit, 1700s*

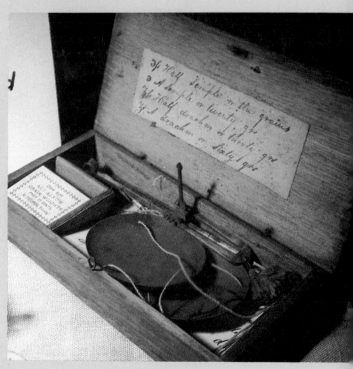

In an attempt to slow the spread of the disease, troops were sent to surround any town struck by the plague. They were ordered to allow no one to enter or leave. They chained off streets and left the sick and dying to fend for themselves. Corpses lay unburied because people were afraid to go near them. Country roads swarmed with people rushing away from the cities. Those who got away boarded themselves up in houses in the country. England's Queen Elizabeth locked herself in Windsor Castle.

## A Slow Recovery

Before the arrival of the black death, Europe had been experiencing a period of great prosperity. There had been a steady growth in population. Cities were rapidly

and Luxembourg—formed the European Economic Community (EEC). The United Kingdom, Ireland, Greece, Spain, Portugal, and Denmark later joined the EEC, also known as the Common Market.

The EEC is now one of three organizations in the European Community (EC) aimed at promoting European unity. Six other Western European nations—Austria, Finland, Iceland, Switzerland, Sweden, and Norway—have formed a separate alliance called the European Free Trade Association (EFTA). All trade barriers between EFTA nations were removed by 1979, but each nation continues to follow separate trade policies.

Most Western European nations also belong to the North Atlantic Treaty Organization (NATO), a military alliance formed in 1949 to protect Western Europe. The European members of NATO are Belgium, Denmark, France, Greece, Iceland, Italy, Luxembourg, the Netherlands, Norway, Portugal, Spain, Turkey, the United Kingdom, and West Germany. The United States and Canada also belong to NATO.

## Population Patterns

Many ethnic groups live in Western Europe. In many nations almost all the citizens belong to one ethnic group, giving the people a strong sense of national identity. This sense of national identity, usually reinforced by a common language, history, and culture, creates a force called **nationalism.** Some nations contain two or more ethnic groups. These groups often live peacefully within a country, but in a few countries constant tension reflects the divisions among the people. The Basques of northern Spain, for example, have repeatedly attempted to break away from Spain and organize their own nation.

With a population of more than 355 million, Western Europe has more people than the United States. West Germany ranks as the most populous nation in the region with 61 million inhabitants. France, Italy, and the United Kingdom have more than 57 million people each. Spain ranks fifth with 40 million people.

As you read in Chapter 7, Europe is one of the three areas of the world with the highest population density. Europe's population densities are highest in the heavily industrialized Rhine Valley and in southeastern Great Britain. They remain lowest in the mountainous areas of the Alps and

*Learning from Graphs.* *European towns and cities—and urbanization in general—have been growing since the 1400s. What might explain Portugal's relatively low rate?*

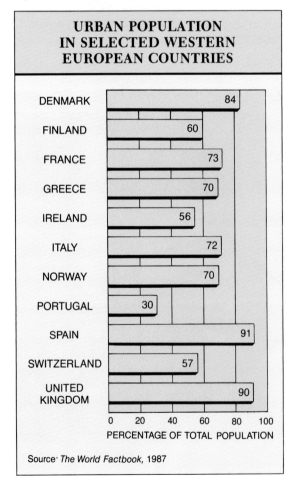

**URBAN POPULATION IN SELECTED WESTERN EUROPEAN COUNTRIES**

| Country | Percentage |
| --- | --- |
| DENMARK | 84 |
| FINLAND | 60 |
| FRANCE | 73 |
| GREECE | 70 |
| IRELAND | 56 |
| ITALY | 72 |
| NORWAY | 70 |
| PORTUGAL | 30 |
| SPAIN | 91 |
| SWITZERLAND | 57 |
| UNITED KINGDOM | 90 |

PERCENTAGE OF TOTAL POPULATION

Source: *The World Factbook,* 1987

*Text continues on page 393.*

**EUROPE\***
**Population Density**

| Persons per square mile | Persons per square kilometer |
|---|---|
| 0–25 | 0–10 |
| 26–60 | 11–25 |
| 61–125 | 26–50 |
| 126–250 | 51–100 |
| over 250 | over 100 |

City population

- 1–2 million
- ◎ 5–10 million
- ● 2–5 million

ICELAND

Arctic Circle

SWEDEN

FINLAND

NORWAY

SOVIET UNION

UNITED

IRELAND

KINGDOM

North Sea

Baltic Sea

• Birmingham

DENMARK

○ London

Hamburg •

NETH.

Berlin •

BELGIUM

WEST

EAST

Warsaw ●

POLAND

○ Paris

LUX.

GERMANY

GERMANY

Prague •

ATLANTIC

OCEAN

Munich •

CZECHOSLOVAKIA

FRANCE

SWITZ.

LIECH.

Vienna ●

○ Budapest

AUSTRIA

HUNGARY

ROMANIA

● Milan

Turin ●

PORTUGAL

ANDORRA

SAN MARINO

Bucharest ●

MONACO

Madrid •

ITALY

YUGOSLAVIA

BULGARIA

● Barcelona

VATICAN

● Rome

Sofia •

SPAIN

CITY

ALBANIA

TURKEY

Naples ●

Adriatic Sea

GIBRALTAR
(U.K.)

Mediterranean

Sea

GREECE

ASIA

AFRICA

N

MALTA

| 0 | 150 | 300 Miles |
|---|---|---|
| 0 | 150 | 300 Kilometers |

\*Excluding Soviet Union

# DEVELOPING GEOGRAPHY SKILLS
## THINKING GEOGRAPHICALLY: Drawing Conclusions

- The world's largest population clusters lie near fertile farmlands.

- Larger cities tend to grow even larger because the variety of services and opportunities they offer attract migrants from other urban and rural areas.

The statements above are conclusions. A conclusion is a reasoned judgment arrived at by studying evidence.

Geographers often draw conclusions from data. For example, population geographers draw conclusions about where people live and why they live there. As evidence they use tools such as the map of population density on page 391. They also use data provided by a census, such as the rate of population growth and the percentage of people who live in urban areas. As a student of geography, you should be able to draw conclusions from evidence as well.

*Overlooking the Alhambra in Granada*

## How to Draw Conclusions

Follow these steps to draw conclusions.

1. **Study the evidence carefully.** Note relationships among the evidence, especially unstated relationships.
2. **Use your own reasoning abilities.** Look for information and relationships that are merely implied or suggested to discover new meanings.
3. **Treat all inferences with caution.** Because inferences are unstated, they may not always be true.
4. **Continually test your conclusions.** Conduct additional research. The more supporting facts you gather, the more likely it is that your conclusion is correct.

## Applying the Skill

Study the map on population density on page 391 and focus on the Iberian Peninsula (Spain and Portugal). You can draw the following conclusions from the map.

- The physical setting along the coast of Portugal is habitable and probably lacks deserts, jagged mountains, and dense forests.

- Large parts of Spain are poorly suited for settlement.

- Spain is fairly urbanized.

To further research this last conclusion, study the picture of Granada, Spain and the plain beyond to the left, and the graph on page 390. The graph shows that over 90 percent of Spain's people live in urban areas. This supports the last conclusion. (You may want to further compare the graph's data with that on the map.)

*To practice this skill, see Practicing Geography Skills on page 441.*

Pyrenees and in the colder Northwestern Uplands.

Most of the people throughout Western Europe live in urban areas. Parts of the United Kingdom, Portugal, and southern Italy, however, remain primarily rural and agricultural. The only nomadic peoples in the region are Lapps, who earn their living as reindeer herders in the tundra lands of northernmost Sweden and Norway.

## Social Patterns

The many languages and religions of Western Europe reflect the cultural diversity of its people.

**Language.** Most of the languages and dialects spoken in Western Europe belong to either the Romance or the Germanic family of languages. Romance languages originally developed from Latin, the language of the Roman Empire. The principal Romance languages include Portuguese and Spanish, which are quite similar, and French and Italian. Members of minority groups in Spain, Italy, and Switzerland speak other Romance dialects. The Germanic languages include English, Danish, Dutch, German, Icelandic, Swedish, and Norwegian.

Years ago Celtic languages were widely spoken in Western Europe. Today, however, the use of these languages is declining. People in parts of Ireland and Scotland still speak a Celtic language call Gaelic. People in parts of Wales speak Welsh, another Celtic language.

**Religion.** Most Western Europeans are Christians. In general, Roman Catholics predominate in Ireland, France, Spain, Italy, Portugal, Belgium, and Austria. Protestants predominate in Scandinavia and the United Kingdom. Nearly equal numbers of Protestants and Roman Catholics live in the Netherlands, Switzerland, and West Germany. Many Greeks follow the Eastern Orthodox

*Learning from Pictures.* St. Peter's Basilica in Vatican City in Rome is the center of Roman Catholicism. Which countries of Western Europe are predominantly Catholic?

religion, which separated from the Roman Catholic religion after 1054. Jews and Muslims make up small minorities in many Western European nations.

## Political Patterns

All 24 Western European nations have democratic forms of government. Many are **constitutional monarchies** in which the rulers, whose powers are limited, share the powers of government with elected or appointed officials. The monarchies include kingdoms, such as the United Kingdom; principalities, such as Monaco and Liechtenstein; and the Grand Duchy of Luxembourg.

## Economic Patterns

The nations of Western Europe have highly industrialized and developed economies. Until it was replaced by oil in the

*Text continues on page 395.*

# EUROPE: Economic Activity

ATLANTIC OCEAN

Arctic Circle

**ICELAND** — livestock

livestock — iron, gold

**NORWAY** — copper, iron, livestock, lead copper barley, nickel titanium, sugar beets, barley, potatoes

**SWEDEN** — wheat, iron copper, oats, zinc, Stockholm

**FINLAND** — wheat barley, cobalt nickel, zinc lead, oats wheat, zinc iron copper

North Sea

**UNITED KINGDOM** — oats livestock, coal, petroleum, potatoes, livestock, Newcastle, coal, Manchester, livestock wheat, Birmingham, coal barley, sugar beets, Bristol, London, wheat

**IRELAND** — livestock, barley

Amsterdam, **NETH** — livestock, natural gas

petroleum

natural gas

**DENMARK** — barley, wheat sugar beets potatoes, livestock, Copenhagen

Baltic Sea

**SOVIET UNION**

**EAST GERMANY** — coal, potatoes, Berlin, coal, uranium, wheat, coal, silver

**WEST GERMANY** — Hamburg, natural gas, wheat potatoes, Brussels, **BELGIUM**, Lille, coal, wheat, sugar beets, **LUX**, iron, grapes, Nancy, barley, oats, Bern, Munich, iron

**POLAND** — Gdańsk, oats, sugar beets, Poznań, Warsaw, potatoes, oats, Katowice, Kraków, rye, wheat, magnesium iron

**CZECHOSLOVAKIA** — Prague, silver, Vienna

**FRANCE** — Paris, potatoes, livestock, barley, uranium, oats, grapes, Bordeaux, grapes, corn, wheat, Bilbao

**SWITZ.** — coal silver bauxite uranium, Lyon, livestock, **LIECH.**, iron, livestock corn wheat, Turin, Milan, rice, Venice, livestock, grapes, Genoa, **SAN MARINO**

**AUSTRIA** — grapes, magnesium lead, **HUNGARY** — corn, petroleum, bauxite, wheat grapes

**ROMANIA** — potatoes, sugar beets, sunflower seeds, livestock, grapes, sugar beets, Bucharest

**PORTUGAL** — coal tungsten, cork, wheat, sugar beets, natural gas, grapes, livestock, iron uranium, Lisbon, livestock, Madrid, olives, Barcelona

**SPAIN** — copper tungsten, iron coal, zinc iron, olives, mercury, rice, grapes, grapes, citrus fruit, silver lead zinc, livestock

**ANDORRA**, Marseille, **MONACO**, mercury, grapes

**ITALY** — Rome, grapes, Naples, potatoes, olives, tobacco

**YUGOSLAVIA** — magnesium chrome, grapes, livestock, magnesium gold silver, sunflower seeds, livestock, tobacco, lead, rice

Adriatic Sea

**BULGARIA** — grapes, **TURKEY** — cotton

**ALBANIA** — livestock

**GREECE** — bauxite chromium aluminum, Athens, olives, grapes, olives, grapes

citrus fruit, olives, petroleum

**MALTA**

Mediterranean Sea

**AFRICA**

**ASIA**

## EUROPE: Economic Activity

| Legend | |
|--------|--------|
| Manufacturing | $ Tourism |
| Woodlands | ⛏ Drilling |
| Farming | ⚒ Mining |
| Grazing | 🐟 Fishing |
| Limited economic use | 🌲 Forestry |

N

0 — 150 — 300 Miles
0 — 150 — 300 Kilometers

**394**

1950s, coal was the principal source of industrial energy. As a result, countries with coal fields industrialized first. The largest coal fields lie around the Pennine (PEN·eyn) Chain in Great Britain, in the Ruhr and Saar areas of West Germany, along the Meuse (MYOOS) and Namur (nah·MOOHR) river valleys of Belgium. Because they developed first, many have aging industrial centers. Others, destroyed in World War II, have been rebuilt.

Countries without coal industrialized more slowly. Hydroelectricity from swift-flowing mountain streams in the Alps helped Switzerland and Italy to industrialize, but both nations now need far more energy than hydroelectricity can provide. Tourism is a major component of the economy in many Western European countries.

Most Western European countries have mixed economies, and most combine elements of capitalism and socialism. Many countries, such as the United Kingdom and Sweden, have economic systems based on democratic socialism (see Chapter 7).

**Learning from Pictures.** *In the 1930s Germany built superhighways called autobahns to move troops and supplies. How do such superhighways contribute to the economy?*

**SECTION 2 REVIEW**

1. **Define** nationalism, constitutional monarchy
2. **Interpreting Ideas** What did the Industrial Revolution accomplish in Western Europe?
3. **Identifying Ideas** How have Western European nations tried to unify since World War II?
4. **Organizing Ideas** (a) What are the major language groups in Western Europe? (b) How has the use of the Celtic language changed? (c) Where is Celtic spoken today?
5. **Analyzing Ideas** (a) Why did countries with coal fields industrialize first? (b) In what ways has early industrialization affected the modern economies of nations?

## 3 The United Kingdom, France, and West Germany rank as leading world economies.

Although Western European nations have become more unified since World War II, each retains its own government and economic system. Three of these nations—the United Kingdom, France, and West Germany—rank as leading world economic powers.

### The United Kingdom

The islands of Great Britain and Ireland make up the British Isles. England, Scotland, and Wales lie on Great Britain. Tiny

Northern Ireland occupies the tip of Ireland. Together England, Scotland, Wales, and Northern Ireland make up the nation of the United Kingdom of Great Britain and Northern Ireland, often called Britain.

**Physical setting.** Geographers divide Britain into two regions—the lowlands and the highlands. The southeastern one-third of Great Britain covers the lowlands, which are separated from the rest of the North European Plain by the narrow English Channel. The northern and western parts of Britain lie in the highlands. Rugged, rocky landscapes, the result of glaciation, limit farming in the highlands. Cattle and sheep grazing lead the list of economic activities in the area. The rushing rivers in the highlands provide hydroelectricity for industry throughout Great Britain.

**Cultural setting.** Level land and fertile soil have attracted many people to the British lowlands. Today most of the 56.8 million Britons live in the southeast lowlands and

**Learning from Pictures.** *The gala wedding of Prince Charles and Lady Diana Spencer shows the British tradition of royal pageantry. Why is the United Kingdom a constitutional monarchy?*

on industrialized coal fields along the edge of the Pennines. About 90 percent of the British people live in urban areas. London and Birmingham rank as Britain's two largest cities. Although English is the official language, some people in parts of Scotland and Ireland speak Gaelic, while people in parts of Wales speak Welsh. Large groups of people from Britain's former colonies now live in the United Kingdom, giving the country a multiethnic dimension.

Though farming employs less than 1.5 percent of the workers, British farmers rank among the most productive and advanced in the world. Despite limited farmlands and relatively cool growing seasons, Britain is 63 percent self-sufficient in food. Farmers grow wheat, barley, potatoes, and sugar beets. Livestock and livestock products, especially dairy products, account for 62 percent of farm income.

Britain was the first nation in the world to industrialize. Industries fueled by coal produced almost every type of good imaginable. Britain remained the world's leading industrial nation until the 1930s, prospering for over 100 years as a supplier of industrial goods to a vast empire. But as time passed, British methods and equipment lagged behind more recently developed nations.

Most of Britain's former colonies have gained independence. But many retain loose political and economic ties to the United Kingdom as part of the Commonwealth of Nations. In recent years, however, Britain's trade with its former colonies has declined, and the British economy has begun to stagnate. Government leaders have revitalized the sagging economy through closer ties with the European Community as well as by tapping the vast mineral deposits that have been discovered under the territorial waters of the North Sea. Further industrialization will be fueled by oil and natural gas from the submarine deposits rather than by coal.

**WESTERN EUROPE**
**Physical/Political**

⊛ National capital
• Other city
— National boundary

AZIMUTHAL EQUAL AREA PROJECTION

*Learning from Maps.* Nations at war in the past often work together on common problems today. Which nation in Western Europe has the largest area?

# France

France, one of only two Western European nations with coastlines on both the Atlantic Ocean and the Mediterranean Sea, ranks as the second-largest country in Europe. Next to the Soviet Union in size, it is about four-fifths as large as Texas. Like most other Western European nations, France is a democratic republic.

**Physical setting.** Mountain barriers range across southern and eastern France.

**397**

The Pyrenees separate France from Spain in the south. The Alps form the boundary between France and Italy in the southeast. And the Jura, Vosges, and Ardennes mountains separate it from Switzerland and West Germany in the east. North and west of these barriers stretches the rolling North European Plain. Though mostly level and ideal for farming, hills, plateaus, and low mountains interrupt the plain in places.

A mild, wet marine climate affects most of France. Coupled with expanses of fertile soil, this climate makes the country ideal for farming. Only south France along the Mediterranean Sea has a different climate. Lands along that coast have a Mediterranean climate—very hot and dry summers with mild and wet winters.

**Cultural setting.** Although French culture reflects a combination of Celtic, Roman, and Germanic influences, the French language and the Roman Catholic religion unify the people. Most of the 55 million people live in urban areas such as Paris, the capital and primate city; Marseille (mahr·SAY); Lyon (lee·OHN); Bordeaux (boohr·DOH); and Lille (LEEL).

Agriculture and industry are both well developed in France. Much of the French countryside is suitable for farming, and farms cover more than 35 percent of the country. Farming employs about 8 percent of the workers. Some farmers grow wheat, potatoes, grapes, and citrus fruits. Other farmers raise cattle for beef and dairy products. French farmers produce enough to make the country self-sufficient in food. In addition, France exports more than 25 percent of its farm output.

Rich iron ore deposits in northeast France and scattered coal deposits serve as leading industrial resources. The country exports some of the iron to steel mills in West Germany and Belgium and uses other supplies to manufacture steel, automobiles, machinery, and ships. France also specializes in producing fashionable clothing, fine china, cosmetics, and other high-quality consumer items.

International trade, especially trade with other parts of the European Community, forms an important part of France's economy. The country has an excellent relative location for trade. Outlets on three bodies of water—the English Channel, the Atlantic Ocean, and the Mediterranean Sea—provide trade links in all directions. In addition, several large rivers—the Seine, Loire, Garonne, Rhône, and Rhine—serve as highways from interior France. Canals link many of the rivers, and a modern rail system helps ease transportation throughout the nation. The country's ultrafast TGV trains, for example, whisk passengers and freight at speeds over 200 miles (320 kilometers) per hour between Paris and cities in southeastern France.

## West Germany

After Germany's defeat in World War II the victorious allies divided the nation into four zones. Three of the military zones—occupied by troops from France, Britain, and the United States—were combined in 1949 to form a new country now called the Federal Republic of Germany, or West Germany. West Germany is about the size of Wyoming. The Soviet Union occupied the fourth military zone, now called East Germany (see Chapter 21), which is about the size of Virginia. The city of West Berlin, although surrounded by East German territory, is an integral part of West Germany.

**Physical setting.** Together the countries of West and East Germany feature three physical regions. The North European Plain extends through northern and central Germany. The Central Uplands reach into Bavaria and the Rhineland. And the Alps tower

**398**

*Text continues on page 400.*

# CITY FOCUS
## Paris, France

Few cities receive the worldwide acclaim for beauty and culture that people bestow on Paris, the capital of France. Its parks burst with flowers and its broad avenues, sheltered by ancient chestnut trees, have ample room for lovely sidewalk cafes. At night floodlights illuminate the city's many cathedrals, monuments, and government buildings. Its luster has earned Paris the title "City of Light."

### An Ancient City

No one knows precisely when Paris was founded, but it is known that the Romans established a colony on its current site in 52 B.C. and that the city soon spread out on both banks of the Seine. Its location on the river and astride the major north-south overland trade routes was ideal for the growth of a city.

Like London, which also was developed by the Romans, Paris remained small throughout the Middle Ages. Its first wall, built between 1180 and 1210, enclosed only 675 acres (270 hectares). Unlike London, however, which began to expand much earlier, it was nearly 1800 before Paris stretched beyond its original walls.

Even the earliest inhabitants of Paris recognized the many advantages of its location. The city lies in the heart of a large and productive agricultural region. The Seine, which is navigable by barge traffic, joins several navigable tributaries near Paris. Thus, water connections combined with ancient overland trade routes to provide Paris with all of the attributes of a great central city. Railroads and highways have added to this primate city's central situation.

### A Crowded Center

More than 2 million people live in Paris, and another 7 million people live in the

*The Eiffel Tower, a Paris landmark*

suburbs surrounding the city. In addition, Paris welcomes more than 2 million visitors annually.

The 185-square-mile (479-square-kilometer) metropolitan area includes a variety of landscapes, some of which seem curiously alien to the typical images of Paris.

The great open spaces of the Bois de Boulogne (bwahd uh boo·LOHN) in the west and the Bois de Vincennes in the east, for example, seem so peaceful and remote that it is difficult to believe that nearly 9 million people crowd close at hand. But the intense bustle of the city's great boulevards and the jam-packed tenement slums of the East End serve as reminders that Paris actually is one of the most densely populated cities in the world.

Indeed, the city's dominant feature, and certainly its most overwhelming problem, is congestion. Officials are studying ways to ease the city's overcrowding. Despite such problems, Paris remains one of the most beautiful cities in the world.

***Learning from Pictures.*** *A BMW worker helps make automobiles for which West Germany is famous. What may determine West Germany's future industrial growth?*

along Germany's southern edges, with the highest peaks forming the Austrian border.

Germany contains many large, navigable rivers. In the south the Danube flows through southern Germany on its journey to the Black Sea. In the north the Oder empties into the Baltic Sea and the Rhine, Weser (VAY·zuhr), and Elbe (EL·buh) rivers flow to the North Sea. As in France a series of canals connects smaller rivers with larger ones to form a network of waterways, especially in West Germany.

**Cultural setting.** With a population of 61 million, West Germany is Western Europe's most populous country. Germans make up a large majority, while people from Denmark, known as Danes, form the largest minority group. About 45 percent of the people practice Roman Catholicism and about 45 percent follow one of the Protes-

tant religions. The remainder belong to one of many other religious groups.

A well-educated and highly urbanized population has given West Germany the vitality to recover from the ashes of war and rank once again among the world's leading industrial nations. Machinery, ships, cars, and airplanes lead the country's many manufactured products. The Rhine Valley and Ruhr and Saar coal fields rank among the world's most industrialized regions. However, further industrial growth may hinge on acquiring increased energy sources. Refineries import and process crude oil and natural gas. The oil flows through pipelines from North Sea deposits, and natural gas comes through pipelines from the Netherlands and the Soviet Union.

Much of Germany has ideal farming conditions. A mild, wet climate and fertile, level lands cover much of the country. Farmers grow wheat, barley, oats, potatoes, and sugar beets and raise livestock for meat and dairy products. Although West German agriculture is mechanized and technologically advanced, farmers meet only about 75 percent of the country's food needs. For this reason, trade—especially the importation of food—remains essential.

**SECTION 3 REVIEW**

1. **Locate**   United Kingdom, Ireland, British Isles, England, Scotland, Wales, Northern Ireland, London, France, Paris, West Germany
2. **Seeing Relationships**   **(a)** In what way is the landscape of France ideal for farming?   **(b)** Why do you think that West Germany must import more food than France?
3. **Analyzing Ideas**   How have **(a)** location and   **(b)** internal transportation networks helped Britain, France, and West Germany become trading leaders?

## 4 Many other important nations lie in Western Europe.

Though Britain, France, and West Germany rank among the world's economic powers, several other European countries have great historic, social, and economic importance as well.

### Norden or Scandinavia

Five nations in northernmost Europe—Norway, Sweden, Finland, Denmark, and Iceland—share similar cultures. Geographers sometimes group these countries together as Norden, or "Northlands," because of their northerly location. The countries are also known as Scandinavia.

**Norway.** A rugged landscape covers fingerlike Norway, which is slightly smaller than New Mexico. Because less than 3 percent of the land is suitable for farming, Norwegians have traditionally looked to the sea for their livelihood. Today abundant fishing catches along the long and irregular coast make Norway Western Europe's leading fishing nation. Oil from under the North Sea is Norway's principal resource today and Norway is a world leader in oil production.

Norway's leading industries include forestry, chemicals, and metals. Most are near Oslo, the capital, and Bergen and Stavanger on the west coast.

**Sweden.** Sweden, which is larger than California, is another finger-shaped country east of Norway. Climate and mountainous terrain limit agriculture in Sweden to the southern lowlands near the Swedish capital of Stockholm. Although less than 7 percent of Sweden's land is suitable for farming, Swedish farms supply 80 percent of Sweden's food needs.

Iron ore deposits near Kiruna (KIR·ooh·nah) support the manufacture of precision steel, automobiles, and machinery. Forest resources provide the raw materials for producing wood pulp, paper, and modern Scandinavian-style furniture.

The Swedish people enjoy one of the world's highest standards of living. They have a democratic socialist economic system. The government also provides many social services, including day care, old-age

**Learning from Maps.** *Though a Scandinavian country, Denmark is often more closely linked with the other countries of Western Europe. How would location explain this?*

**SCANDINAVIA**
**Physical/Political**

⊛ National capital      • Other city      —— National boundary

AZIMUTHAL EQUAL AREA PROJECTION

pensions, and low-cost medical care. To pay for these social programs, however, the Swedes pay very high taxes.

**Finland.** Located east of Sweden, Finland forms the third stubby finger of Norden. Glaciers scoured Montana-sized Finland, creating a rugged plateau with more than 50,000 beautiful lakes.

First Sweden, then Russia, ruled Finland. Russia granted Finland independence in World War I, but the Soviet Union reclaimed a large area in the east during World War II. Many Finns left the eastern territories to resettle in western Finland. Finland is a bilingual country recognizing both Finnish and Swedish as official languages.

Forests serve as Finland's principal resource. The nation's most important products include lumber, wood pulp, and paper. With the help of hydroelectric power, factories produce ships, textiles, and chemicals. The severe climate and glaciated land restrict farming, most of which is located near the capital of Helsinki. Dairying ranks as the chief farming activity.

**Denmark.** Denmark stretches across the Jutland Peninsula and several small islands to the east. Together its lands cover about the same area as Massachusetts and New Hampshire combined. In the past the country grew rich charging tolls on ships using the Kattegat and Skagerrak (SKAG·uh·rak) waterways to get to and from the Baltic Sea.

More than 60 percent of Denmark's land is suitable for farming. An intensive and scientific form of livestock farming obtains some of the world's highest milk and meat yields per animal and per acre. Danish butter, cheese, bacon, and veal have gained worldwide fame.

Manufacturing expanded rapidly after World War II and now earns more money for Denmark than farming. The Danes produce machinery, with farm machinery a leading export. Other products include textiles, furniture, and electronics.

**Iceland.** Isolated Iceland, with about as much land as Virginia and only 250,000 people, attracts attention from geologists around the world because of its location atop the Mid-Atlantic Ridge (see pages 134–35). According to the theory of plate tectonics, the continents of Europe and North America have been steadily drifting apart along this ridge for millions of years. Numerous active volcanoes and hot springs, called **geysers,** serve as reminders of continuing seafloor spreading. Icelanders use the hot water of the geysers for heating homes and greenhouses.

Fishing remains Iceland's major economic activity, and the country ranks among the world's top fishing nations. Other key occupations include sheep farming and tourism. Icelandic sweaters made from the wool of hardy Icelandic sheep are world-famous.

## Ireland

Because green vegetation dominates its landscape, the Irish Republic is often called the "Emerald Isle." Farms with stone fences divide the rolling countryside that forms the central part of the island. Tiny fishing villages hug the steep cliffs that surround the island. A mild and wet marine climate affects Ireland.

Today Ireland is officially bilingual. Almost all of the people speak English. Irish, or Gaelic, promoted by Irish nationalists as Ireland's traditional language, also remains an official language.

For hundreds of years chiefly Roman Catholic Ireland chafed under the rule of chiefly Protestant Britain. The nation won independence from Britain in 1922, and the Republic of Ireland was formed in 1949. Terrorism and fighting in Northern Ire-

land—still part of the United Kingdom—is a source of tension throughout Ireland.

The Irish economy remains largely agricultural. Farmers use more than 70 percent of the farmland to grow hay or as pasture for livestock. Cattle and dairy products lead its list of exports. Though the agricultural economy of Ireland is much less prosperous than that of highly industrialized Britain, Irish farmers provide about 85 percent of the country's food needs.

Industry in Ireland remains quite limited. The leading products include food products, textiles and clothing, and chemicals. Workers produce these goods almost entirely for local markets. Joining the Common Market is helping Ireland industrialize. Since Ireland joined, foreign companies have begun to build factories in the country.

## The Benelux Nations

Geographers often call Belgium, the Netherlands, and Luxembourg the Benelux nations, a term derived from the first letters of their names. The three small nations form a borderland between West Germany and France.

**Belgium.** Tiny Belgium extends between France and the Netherlands and is slightly larger than Maryland. Much of the coastal country lies below sea level, protected from the sea by dikes, seawalls, and sand dunes. The Schelde (SKEL·duh) and Meuse rivers cut a small central plateau through the country.

In the 1830s Roman Catholics in the southern parts of the Netherlands, who were supported by the French, separated from the Protestant country and founded Belgium. Since then Belgium has retained a dual personality—part Dutch, from the influence of the Netherlands, and part French. For example, Belgium recognizes two official languages. People in the northern half of the country speak Flemish, which is writ-

***Learning from Pictures.*** *The world's continuing search for energy sources includes harnessing energy from geysers. In what ways do Icelanders use hot geyser water?*

ten in the same way as Dutch but spoken differently. People in the southern half of Belgium speak Walloon, a French dialect. Although the two groups are rivals, Roman Catholicism serves as a unifying force in the country.

Coal provides Belgium's chief industrial resource. It supports aging industrial centers located near the coal fields in the Meuse and Namur river valleys. Newer industrial centers surround Antwerp, the chief port, and Brussels, Belgium's capital and the administrative center for the European Community.

**The Netherlands.** Along the curving coast of the North Sea between Belgium and West Germany lies the Netherlands. Its lands are about the size of Massachusetts, Connecticut, and Rhode Island combined.

More than half of the land in the Netherlands, which means "low lands," lies below sea level. Together Belgium and the Netherlands are known as the Low Countries. The name fits well because much of the Netherlands consists of **polders,** or drained lands, that once lay beneath the sea. Along the coast, high sand dunes and dikes shelter the polders from the North Sea, and canals and pumps keep them dry. Although windmills did the pumping in the past, electrical pumps do the job today.

Two ambitious drainage projects continue to add farmland to the Netherlands. One drains Lake Ijssel (EYE·suhl), an extension of the North Sea once known as the Zuider Zee (ZYD·uhr ZAY). The other drains swampy lands at the mouth of the Rhine River. Along the southeastern tip of the country, rolling hills and forest cover provide a sharply contrasting landscape.

The Netherlands has about 14.6 million people, who are known as the Dutch. Dutch farmers use intensive farming methods and advanced farming technologies to produce high-value farm items. Tulips and other flower bulbs, for example, grow near the city of Haarlem. Farmers scientifically breed dairy cows and feed them special diets to make them produce more milk. Some of the milk is converted into butter and cheese. Farmers use the waste milk products left over from processing to fatten livestock.

The Netherlands remains one of the world's great trading nations. Because of its location at the mouth of the Rhine River, Western Europe's chief waterway, imports and exports for much of West Germany, Switzerland, and eastern France pass through the Netherlands.

The country's chief industrial resources lie in huge natural-gas deposits beneath the North Sea and in the northeast corner of the country. These deposits provide a source of energy for heating, cooking, and industry. The Netherlands also exports natural gas by pipeline to West Germany, France, Belgium, and Switzerland.

Although it lacks most mineral resources, the Netherlands has built a strong industrial economy using imported raw materials. Major industries include oil refining, diamond cutting, and the manufacture of electrical equipment and chocolate. Many of these industries are located in Amsterdam and Rotterdam, the chief port for the European Community. A new port city called Europort has been built nearby to handle increasing traffic. As in many of the countries of Western Europe, large rivers—the Rhine, Meuse, and Schelde—connected by canals provide a key transportation network in the Netherlands.

**Luxembourg.** Luxembourg, smaller than Rhode Island, lies nestled between Belgium, France, and West Germany. The hilly Ardennes Plateau dominates its landscape.

Most of the 366,000 people in Luxembourg practice Roman Catholicism and speak French, German, or a dialect known as Luxembourgish. They enjoy one of the highest standards of living in Europe.

Landlocked Luxembourg draws special trading benefits from being part of the European Economic Community. Iron ore and steel rank as its principal exports, while coal remains its chief import.

## Switzerland

Landlocked and mountainous Switzerland is about the same size as the Netherlands. The Alps cover southern Switzerland and the Jura Mountains extend through the northwest. Between the mountain

ranges lies the Swiss Plateau, which stretches from Lake Geneva to Lake Constance.

Meadows and farms cover the plateau, along with the major Swiss cities and industries. Most of Switzerland's 6.6 million people also live and work there. Zurich is the principal city.

To avoid conflicts with its more powerful neighbors, Switzerland has a long tradition of staying **neutral,** or not taking sides, in European wars. Because it did not take part in World War I or World War II, the nation suffered none of the damage that disrupted the economies of the other European nations.

Today Switzerland remains a confederation of 23 political units called **cantons.** Each canton joined the republic at a different time and each retains its own traditions and language. People in western cantons speak French; people in eastern and central cantons speak German; and people in southern cantons speak Italian and Romansh. Both French and German serve as official languages.

Switzerland's per capita GNP of $16,380 ranks as the highest in Western Europe. The Swiss economy is largely industrial, emphasizing the manufacture of watches, clocks, expensive precision instruments, chocolates, and chemicals. By exporting such small, high-value items that cost little to transport and require few raw materials, Switzerland compensates for its inland location. A productive dairy industry provides milk for making many types of cheese. Banking and tourism also play important roles in the prosperous Swiss economy.

## Austria

Austria, which is slightly smaller than Maine, extends east amid the Alps from Switzerland. Its landscape and climate closely resemble those of Switzerland.

***Learning from Pictures.*** *Villages such as Tulfes, Austria, dot the alpine valleys of Western Europe. How might a mountain chain such as the Alps affect economic development?*

As in Germany, Allied troops divided Austria and its capital, Vienna, into four military zones after World War II. The four Allied forces—Britain, France, the United States, and the Soviet Union—withdrew from Austria in 1955 after the country's leaders agreed to remain neutral in future European conflicts.

About 95 percent of Austria's 7.5 million people speak German, and almost 25 percent of the people live in Vienna. Once the capital of a great empire, Vienna remains the cultural center of Austria.

The Austrian economy depends on manufacturing. Steel, machinery, automobiles, electrical equipment, and chemicals lead Austria's many manufactured goods. Extensive forests in the mountains provide exports of lumber, pulp, and paper. Although agriculture is declining in importance, farmers meet 90 percent of Austria's food needs and provide exports of dairy products.

**405**

## Four Nations in the South

Four nations of Western Europe occupy three peninsulas in the south. Spain and Portugal occupy the Iberian Peninsula, Italy the Italian Peninsula, and Greece part of the Balkan Peninsula.

**Spain.** Separated from France by the Pyrenees Mountains, Spain extends from southwestern Europe on the Iberian Peninsula. Its lands cover about the same area as Arizona and Utah combined. A high plateau covers most of the country.

Spain grew rich in the 1600s and 1700s from its colonies in Latin America, but it declined after the colonies were lost in the 1800s. Today the Spanish people have a generally lower standard of living than northern Europeans.

Castilian Spanish serves as Spain's official language. However, the government also recognizes several regional languages in self-governing, autonomous regions. For example, people in Catalonia around Barcelona speak Catalan, a language related to both French and Spanish. Another regional language is Basque, spoken in northern Spain near the Pyrenees. Galician, a Romance language spoken in northwest Spain, resembles Portuguese.

In the 1950s Spain's economy began changing from predominantly agricultural to predominantly industrial. A lack of industrial resources hampered this transition, although Madrid, Barcelona, and Bilbao (bil·BAH·oh) have become industrial centers. Spain's leaders hope that joining the Common Market will open markets and will stimulate manufacturing. Officials also hope to expand Spain's tourism industry.

**Portugal.** Long, narrow Portugal lies next to Spain on the southwest corner of the Iberian Peninsula. Low mountains slope westward to meet the coastal lowlands of this Indiana-sized country.

Portugal ranks as Western Europe's poorest and least developed nation. Only 30 percent of the 10.3 million people live in urban areas. Agriculture, fishing, and tourism support the economy. Wine serves as Portugal's chief export. In addition, the country leads the world in the production of cork, which comes from the bark of cork oak trees. Lisbon, the capital, and Oporto are Portugal's major cities.

**Italy.** A boot-shaped peninsula, Italy extends from southern Europe. Mountains form a rugged backbone down the center of the country, which is slightly larger than Arizona. Plains reach to the east and west of the mountainous spine.

Most of the 57.4 million Italian people live in cities and towns near the coasts. More than 72 percent live in urban areas. Italians make up a vast majority of the population, although small clusters of French-Italians, German-Italians, and others live in various border areas.

Italy was a collection of independent city-states until it was unified in the 1870s. Strong regional differences persist, especially between north and south.

Northern Italy includes the nation's largest industrial centers and its most productive farmlands. Factories in large industrial cities such as Milan, Turin, and Genoa produce precision machinery, automobiles, and textiles for export. The alluvial soils in the Po Valley make especially rich farmland. Farmers there cultivate rice, corn, wheat, sugar beets, and hemp. Because of the highly developed economy, northern Italians have a fairly high standard of living.

Southern Italy lags behind the north in industrial and agricultural development. Only Naples has developed as an industrial center. The rugged Apennines, dry climate, and a scarcity of water for summer irrigation limit farm output. Winter wheat grown in the rainy season provides the chief food

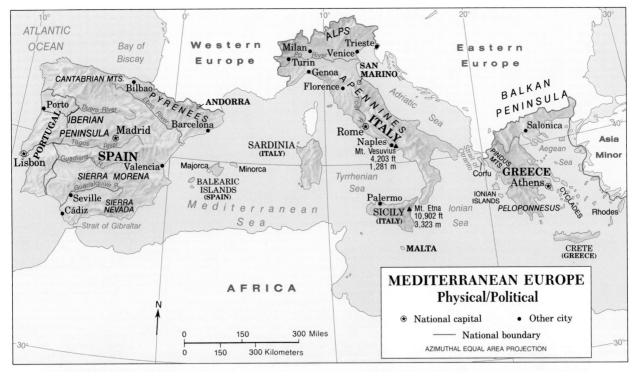

 map content:

10°  0°  10°  20°  30°

ATLANTIC OCEAN

Bay of Biscay

Western Europe

ALPS

Eastern Europe

BALKAN PENINSULA

CANTABRIAN MTS.

Bilbao

PYRENEES

Porto

Duero River

IBERIAN PENINSULA

Madrid

ANDORRA

Barcelona

Milan • Turin • Po River Venice Trieste

Genoa

SAN MARINO

Florence

APENNINES

ITALY

Adriatic Sea

Salonica

PINDUS MTS.

Asia Minor

Aegean Sea

PORTUGAL

Lisbon

Tagus River

SPAIN

Guadiana R.

Valencia

SIERRA MORENA

Guadalquivir R.

Seville

Cádiz

SIERRA NEVADA

Strait of Gibraltar

Ebro River

SARDINIA (ITALY)

Majorca  Minorca

BALEARIC ISLANDS (SPAIN)

Mediterranean Sea

Rome

Naples

Mt. Vesuvius 4,203 ft 1,281 m

Tyrrhenian Sea

Palermo

SICILY (ITALY)

▲ Mt. Etna 10,902 ft 3,323 m

Strait of Otranto

Corfu

IONIAN ISLANDS

Ionian Sea

GREECE

Athens

PELOPONNESUS

CYCLADES

Rhodes

40°

AFRICA

N

MALTA

CRETE (GREECE)

30°

**MEDITERRANEAN EUROPE**
Physical/Political

⊛ National capital   • Other city

——— National boundary

AZIMUTHAL EQUAL AREA PROJECTION

0    150    300 Miles
0    150    300 Kilometers

***Learning from Maps.*** *The Mediterranean, the world's largest inland sea, has great commercial importance. Which country on the map lacks a Mediterranean coast?*

crop, while grapes and olives grow well in hilly areas. Because many of the people in southern Italy cannot find employment, they migrate to other countries, to the industrial cities, or to Rome.

**Greece.** Greece juts southward from eastern Europe. It is about the size of New York State. Its strategic location between Europe and the lands to the east have made Greece an important focus of attention.

Although it lies close to southeastern Europe, Greece remains culturally tied to Western Europe. It was in the city-states of ancient Greece that Western ideals of democracy and Western styles of art first appeared.

The southern part of Greece, which extends four fingers of land into the Mediterranean Sea, is called the Peloponnese (PEL·uh·puh·neez). The nation also includes the island of Crete and dozens of small islands in the Aegean (i·JEE·uhn) Sea.

Most of Greece's 10 million people live in small towns that dot the hillsides. Most Greeks are Christians who belong to the Greek Orthodox church, which is the national church and part of the Eastern Orthodox church. Modern Greek—different from the classical Greek used in ancient times—is the official language. Athens serves as the principal city; Piraeus (py·REE·uhs) serves as the chief port.

Rugged mountains cover four-fifths of the land. In isolated valleys and on steep hillsides Greek farmers raise olives, citrus fruits, and tobacco in the south and sheep and cattle in the north.

Industry in Greece remains less developed than in most Western European nations, although food processing, textiles, and chemical manufacturing continue to expand. In general, Greeks have a lower standard of living than most other Western Europeans. Many Greeks leave their homeland to find work overseas.

**407**

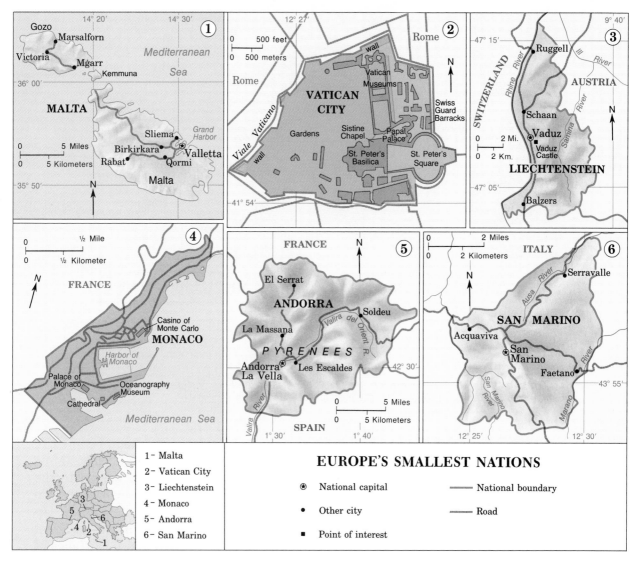

**Learning from Maps.** *Europe was once broken into hundreds of microstates such as the six that remain. Why are these countries called "microstates"?*

As in Spain, Greek leaders hope that joining the EEC will boost sales of Greek products and increase industrialization. Tourism and shipping add to the economy.

### Europe's Microstates

Six tiny nations, among the world's smallest, lie scattered throughout Europe. You will learn more about these six countries—Andorra, Malta, Liechtenstein, San Marino, Monaco, and Vatican City—in the CASE STUDY on page 409.

**SECTION 4 REVIEW**

1. **Define** geyser, polder, neutral, canton
2. **Locate** Norden, Benelux, Low Countries
3. **Identifying Ideas** How does the Netherlands benefit from its location at the mouth of the Rhine River?
4. **Contrasting Ideas** How do the economies of Greece and Portugal differ from others in Western Europe?

# CASE STUDY
## EXPLORING PLACES: Europe's Microstates

Imagine six nations whose *combined* areas occupy less that 375 square miles (975 square kilometers), approximately the area of New York City. Each of these nations is an independent country with its own government, economy, and history.

### Andorra and Malta

Andorra, by far the largest of these microstates, covers 188 square miles (487 square kilometers). Sandwiched between Spain and France in the Pyrenees Mountains, the 43,000 Andorrans depend on tourism to provide between 80 and 90 percent of their income.

Malta, an island nation in the Mediterranean Sea, covers 122 square miles (316 square kilometers). An economy based on tourism and textile manufacturing supports the population of 355,000.

### Liechtenstein

Wedged between Switzerland and Austria, Liechtenstein has a population of only 28,000. Most Liechtensteiners live in tiny rural villages and work in small factories or businesses. The nation itself depends on two major sources of income—the sale of postage stamps, which are highly prized by collectors all over the world, and taxes levied on foreign businesses. Liechtenstein's business and income taxes are quite low when compared with those in most other nations of the world. As a result, about 5,000 foreign companies use the nation for their corporate headquarters.

### San Marino

San Marino, completely surrounded by Italy, is barely one-third the size of Liechtenstein. Yet it traces its independence back more than 1,600 years. Its 24,000 people pride themselves on being citizens of the oldest republic in the world.

*A key income source for some microstates*

San Marino's picturesque capital, also named San Marino, sits at the very peak of the country's highest mountain. The entire setting, with its magnificent vistas, fortress walls, and numerous festivals, makes it a favorite spot for tourists. Indeed, tourism provides the major source of income for San Marino. Like Liechtenstein, San Marino also is noted for its postage stamps.

### Monaco and Vatican City

Perhaps more well known than the other microstates are the two smallest nations in the world, Monaco and Vatican City. Monaco occupies 0.73 square mile (1.9 square kilometers) of land. Famed for its resortlike atmosphere on the Mediterranean coast, Monaco ranks as one of the favorite vacation spots in the world.

Vatican City's total area is just 108.7 acres (44 hectares). Vatican City, ruled by the Pope, serves as the spiritual and governmental headquarters of the Roman Catholic church. Vatican City lies entirely within the city of Rome. Yet its area is recognized as the territory of an independent nation.

# CHAPTER 20 REVIEW

## Chapter Summary

The following list contains the key concepts you have learned about Western Europe.

1. The four physical regions of Western Europe are the Northwest Uplands, the North European Plain, the Central Uplands, and Alpine Europe.
2. Western Europe's major rivers include the Rhine, Seine, Loire, Rhône, and Saône.
3. Europe's location gives it a variety of climates—west coast marine, Mediterranean, subarctic, tundra, and mountain.
4. People remain Western Europe's greatest resource.
5. Since World War II Western European nations have attempted to unify the region.
6. Western Europe is divided into 24 nations, most of which are highly industrialized.
7. Britain was the first nation to industrialize.
8. France is the largest nation in Western Europe and has well-developed agricultural and industrial systems.
9. West Germany rose from the ashes of defeat to become one of the world's great economic powers. It is the most populous nation in Western Europe.
10. Five nations in northernmost Europe— Norway, Sweden, Finland, Denmark, and Iceland—share a common history and similar cultures.
11. Largely rural Ireland has begun efforts to industrialize.
12. Belgium, the Netherlands, and Luxembourg are often called the Benelux nations. Belgium and the Netherlands are known as the Low Countries.
13. Switzerland has the highest per capita GNP in Europe. Austria shares Switzerland's alpine setting.
14. Spain, Portugal, and Greece are less industrialized than the other nations of Western Europe.
15. Agriculture and industry are productive in northern Italy. Southern Italy is less developed than northern Italy.
16. Western Europe includes six microstates— Andorra, Malta, Liechtenstein, San Marino, Monaco, and Vatican City.

On a separate sheet of paper, complete the following review exercises.

## Reviewing Geographic Terms

Match each of the following terms with the correct definitions below.

a. constitutional monarchy
b. mistral
c. neutral
d. fjord
e. nationalism
f. canton
g. alpine meadow
h. moor
i. polder
j. sirocco
k. geyser

_____ 1. Hot spring
_____ 2. Steep-sided inlet in Norway
_____ 3. Windswept upland in northern and western Great Britain
_____ 4. Cold, dry wind that brings air down the Rhône River Valley to southern France
_____ 5. Wind that brings hot, dry, and dusty air from North Africa's deserts
_____ 6. Political unit in Switzerland
_____ 7. Tundra-covered fields in the mountains above the tree line
_____ 8. Not taking sides
_____ 9. Drained land that once lay beneath the sea
_____ 10. Government in which rulers have limits on their power and share power with elected or appointed officials
_____ 11. Sense of national identity reinforced by a common language and culture

## Developing Critical Thinking Skills

1. **Summarizing Ideas** (a) In which countries are the Alps located? (b) What is the only large lowland in Alpine Europe?
2. **Interpreting Ideas** What had European exploration accomplished by the 1500s?

3. **Identifying Ideas** (a) What gives Europeans a strong sense of national identity? (b) Why do the Basques want to set up their own nation?
4. **Analyzing Ideas** (a) Why do Swedes pay very high taxes? (b) Do you think the government should provide social programs? Why or why not?
5. **Writing About Geography** In a full-page essay, complete one of the following activities. (a) Evaluate the size of West Germany's population and explain how it helped West Germany become a leading world economic power. (b) Evaluate the food resources of Western Europe and discuss how the region is able to produce one of the world's highest agricultural yields.

## Using Primary Sources

In the following excerpt from *Paris Journal 1944–1965*, Janet Flanner (Genêt) describes the state of French agriculture. As you study the reading, compare the situation of French farmers with that of American farmers.

French farmers, who are nature's conservatives—the perfect producers of perfect rich-tasting produce by nineteenth-century methods, on farms still as lovely-looking as landscape gardens—are way behind the times in living standards and are outraged that factory workers can buy the best they raise when they themselves cannot afford to buy even the average of whatever the factory workers manufacture. What drives the farmers really mad is to read in the local-newspaper produce quotations that the Paris housewife pays three hundred francs for a kilo [2.2 pounds] of leeks when the farmer has sold four kilos [8.8 pounds] for half that—the difference going largely to the Halles' great central-market middlemen, France's most hated locusts. Farmers here want land mortgages at

three per cent interest, like their neighbors in other countries, instead of at the twelve per cent the French pay, and want government money loans at one per cent, instead of three and four per cent, which is unheard of beyond their borders. Briefly, they want to get out of debt; want to modernize, because government technocrats assure them that it pays; and, most of all, simply want to make money again.

1. What does the author conclude about the state of technology in French agriculture?
2. (a) What are the major demands of French farmers? (b) What are the motivations behind the demands?

## Practicing Geography Skills

*Before completing this activity, review Developing Geography Skills on page 392.*

**Drawing Conclusions.** Study the Physical/Political map of Europe on pages 12–13 and answer the following questions.

1. State conclusions you can draw about the population densities of (a) northern Sweden and (b) central Switzerland.
2. What economic activities will you most likely find there?

Check the map of population density on page 391. Were your conclusions about the population patterns of northern Sweden and central Switzerland correct? Refer to the economic activity map on page 394 to check your conclusions about economic activities in those places.

## Exploring Geography

Use this textbook, atlases, and encyclopedias to locate the areas where the three Western European language groups—Romance, Germanic, and Celtic—are found. Then illustrate these areas on an outline map of Europe.

# CHAPTER
# 21 Eastern Europe

# PUTTING THE CHAPTER IN FOCUS

Eastern Europe lies between the maritime nations of Western Europe and the Soviet Union. Before 1945 all eight nations of Eastern Europe—East Germany, Poland, Czechoslovakia, Hungary, Bulgaria, Romania, Yugoslavia, and Albania—had strong political and cultural ties to Western Europe. Today all have Communist, or authoritarian socialist, economic systems and totalitarian dictatorships. As a result, some of these nations have limited contacts with Western Europe.

## Ideas to Understand

In studying about the countries of Eastern Europe, use these ideas to give direction to your reading.

1 Eastern Europe has limited access to world sea-lanes.
2 Eastern Europe is a patchwork of cultural settings.
3 The countries of Eastern Europe face many problems.

## Terms to Define

The following terms are some of the key terms in the chapter. Defining them will help you understand Eastern Europe.

moraine
loess
balkanization
satellite nation

collective farm
state farm
nationalized industry

## Places to Locate

Locating the following places will add to your knowledge of geography.

North European
  Plain
Sudetic Mountains
Dinaric Alps
Carpathian
  Mountains
Transylvanian Alps
Balkan Mountains
Hungarian Plain
Walachian Plain

Danube River
Elbe River
Silesia
Estonia
Latvia
Lithuania
Bohemia
Dobruja
Tirane

## 1 Eastern Europe has limited access to world sea-lanes.

Eastern Europe's eastern boundary has long been a matter of debate among geographers. Some geographers identify the Ural Mountains (see the map on pages 12–13) as the eastern extent of the region. Others take a more cultural view, claiming that the border of the Soviet Union marks the division between regions.

Economically and politically the eight countries of Eastern Europe differ greatly from the countries of Western Europe. However, the two regions have similar physical landscapes.

*Beautiful Dubrovnik on Yugoslavia's Adriatic coast*

## Physical Regions

Three of the four physical regions of Western Europe (see pages 383–84) continue eastward to form the physical regions of Eastern Europe. They are the North European Plain, the Central Uplands, and Alpine Europe.

**North European Plain.** Northern parts of East Germany and Poland lie on the North European Plain. Low, rolling hills and scattered lakes cover the plain in the north. They are part of the **moraine** (muh·RAYN), or combination of earth and stone left by glaciers as they melted and retreated at the end of the Ice Age. Strong winds picked up the finer soils of the moraines and

dropped them as **loess** (LES), fine soil deposited by the wind, on the southern edge of the plain in Germany and Poland.

As in Western Europe, the North European Plain in Eastern Europe serves as a great highway for human movement. People have migrated by way of the plain and armies have marched across it. Today highways and rail lines crisscross the plain.

**Central Uplands.** Three distinctive uplands lie south of the North European Plain (see the map on page 422). They include the Saxon Uplands in southern East Germany, the Bohemian (boh·HEE·mee·uhn) Upland in western Czechoslovakia (chek·uh·sloh·VAHK·ee·uh), and the Polish Uplands in southern Poland.

The Saxon and Polish uplands are fairly low and covered with fertile loess deposits. The Bohemian Upland is more rugged. It consists of an inner lowland surrounding Prague (PRAHG) and four outer mountain ranges that form the shape of a diamond. The Bohemian Forest in the southwest, the Ore Mountains in the northwest, the Sudetic (soo·DET·ik), or Sudeten, Mountains in the northeast, and the Moravian (muh·RAY·vee·uhn) Hills in the southeast are the diamond's sides.

**Alpine Europe.** The alpine mountain system extends eastward into Eastern Europe as two separate mountain ranges. The two ranges swing across Eastern Europe in the shape of the letter R (see the map on page 422). The Dinaric (duh·NAR·ik) Alps in Yugoslavia and the Pindus Mountains in Albania form the long stroke of the R in the west. The Carpathian (kahr·PAY·thee·uhn) Mountains in eastern Czechoslovakia and Romania form the top of the loop of the R. The Carpathians continue as the Transylvanian Alps that form the bottom of the loop of the R in Romania. The Balkan Mountains and the Rhodope Mountains in Bulgaria form the short stroke of the R.

The Hungarian, or Transylvanian, Plain, which occupies the center of the mountainous R, covers all of Hungary and parts of Yugoslavia. The Walachian Plain lies between the Transylvanian Alps and the Balkan Mountains in southern Romania and northern Bulgaria. South of the Danube (DAN·yoob) River in Bulgaria lies the Danubian Plain.

## Rivers

The Danube ranks as Eastern Europe's longest river and one of the world's great

*__Learning from Diagrams.__ Despite its rugged mountains, Eastern Europe has been repeatedly invaded. What landform has made invasion easy?*

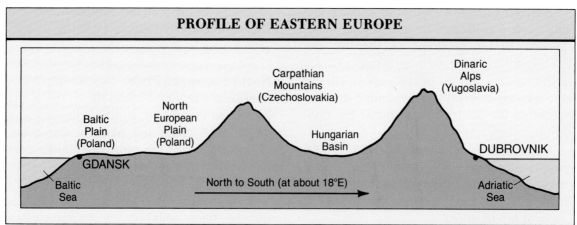

### PROFILE OF EASTERN EUROPE

trade arteries. It begins in West Germany and crosses or forms parts of the boundaries of Austria, Hungary, Yugoslavia, Romania, and Bulgaria. It flows generally southeast for 1,776 miles (2,858 kilometers) before breaking up into a swampy delta at the Black Sea.

The second most important river in Eastern Europe—the Elbe—served as a great trade outlet for eastern Czechoslovakia and the eastern part of Germany before 1945. Since that time, however, politics have interrupted trade on the river. The mouth of the Elbe is in West Germany and the river serves as an important outlet for that country. However, the mouth receives little trade from areas along most of the Elbe, located in Communist-controlled East Germany and Czechoslovakia.

## Climates

Five types of climate occur in Eastern Europe (see the map on pages 96–97). East Germany, Poland, and Czechoslovakia have climates that range from a west coast marine climate in the west to a humid continental with cool summers climate in the east. In general, these climates feature sunnier and colder winters, sunnier and hotter summers, and less rainfall than do similar types of climates in Western Europe.

Southern Bulgaria and coastal Yugoslavia experience the dry summers and rainy winters typical of a Mediterranean climate. A humid subtropical climate with rainier summers than usual prevails inland from the Mediterranean climate, while the upper elevations of the alpine mountain system have a mountain climate.

## Vegetation

Eastern Europe's original natural vegetation consisted of steppe grasslands in the Hungarian Plain and forests and woodlands elsewhere. Although much of the grass-

**Learning from Pictures.** *Polish farmers have turned the level land of the North European Plain into productive farms. What type of vegetation probably once covered this plain?*

lands and forests have been cleared for farming, extensive forests and woodlands remain in mountainous regions (see the map on pages 100–01).

## Resources

The nations of Eastern Europe have limited natural resources, especially fuels. The resources generally have been used less productively than natural resources have been used in Western Europe.

**Agriculture, forestry, and fishing.** Fertile black soils cover most of the Hungarian Plain and parts of Poland. The loess in the North European Plain in East Germany and Poland also provides fertile soil that is easy to farm with modern equipment. However, farmers use less modern machinery and fewer scientific methods than in Western Europe, resulting in generally lower yields.

**415**

*Learning from Pictures.* The Czerwona Gwardia coal mine in Katowice, Silesia, helps fuel Poland's industry. Which countries in Eastern Europe have large oil and gas deposits?

## SECTION 1 REVIEW

1. **Define** moraine, loess
2. **Locate** North European Plain, Sudetic Mountains, Dinaric Alps, Carpathian Mountains, Transylvanian Alps, Balkan Mountains, Hungarian Plain, Walachian Plain, Danube River, Elbe River, Silesia
3. **Summarizing Ideas** What three physical regions of Western Europe extend into Eastern Europe?
4. **Identifying Ideas** **(a)** What are the two most important rivers of Eastern Europe? **(b)** Why has trade on one of these two rivers been interrupted?
5. **Analyzing Ideas** Why are the yields on Eastern European farms lower than on Western European farms?

Food shortages remain common in some of the Eastern European countries.

The forests that have not been cleared lie in inaccessible locations. For this reason, forestry makes only limited contributions to regional economies. Fishing, too, contributes little, primarily because of the lack of coastal waters in the region.

**Mining.** Only Poland has abundant coal supplies. The Silesian (sy·LEE·zhun) coal field on the Poland-Czechoslovakia border near Katowice (kaht·uh·VEET·suh) ranks as one of the world's richest (see the map on pages 110–11). Other sections of Yugoslavia, Romania, Bulgaria, and Hungary also have coal deposits. Most of the coal in these fields, however, is low-quality coal unusable in heavy industry. Large oil and natural gas deposits underlie Romania, but they are being rapidly exhausted. Because Eastern European nations lack energy resources, they import coal, oil, and natural gas from the Soviet Union.

## 2 Eastern Europe is a patchwork of cultural settings.

Eastern Europe's relative location helps explain why the region remains fragmented and developing. To the east lies the powerful Soviet Union, which now controls much of the region's political and economic life. To the west lies developed and wealthy Western Europe, which traditionally had close links to the region. The forces of these two cultural regions pull at Eastern Europe, which seems to be caught in the middle.

The cultural setting of Eastern Europe reflects a mixture of many different peoples and cultures. Differences in history, language, religion, and politics create a culturally diverse population.

### A Brief History

Eastern Europe has long been politically unstable. Its history has been dominated by the rise and fall of powerful empires, each

# DEVELOPING GEOGRAPHY SKILLS
## READING ABOUT GEOGRAPHY: Using Geodata Files

As you have learned, statistics are often presented in tables, charts, and graphs (see Interpreting Statistics on page 360). One such table in this textbook presents statistical data in what are called the *Geodata Files.*

The *Geodata Files* categorize each country by the region under which it is discussed in the textbook. Countries are listed alphabetically within each region. The files contain geographic information on population, economics, and much more. To fully understand the geography of a country and a region, it is important to be able to use the *Geodata Files.*

### How to Use the Geodata Files

To use the *Geodata Files,* follow these guidelines.

1. **Read the headings.** Note that files present information on population, urbanization, land area and use, economics, and trade.
2. **Study the files.** Identify the specific information given under each heading.
3. **Analyze the information.** Look for relationships among data. Note relationships among world regions. Also note trends and relationships within regions.
4. **Put the information to use.** Draw conclusions and state hypotheses, which can be confirmed or denied by data in the files.

### Applying the Skill

Study the information in the Geodata Files for Bulgaria on page 725. Note that Bulgaria's population is nearly 9 million, that 66 percent of the people live in urban areas, that 52 percent of the land is suitable for farming (41 percent arable and 11 percent agricultural), and that the per capita GNP is $2,920. Also notice that fuel ranks among the country's main imports—reflecting the lack of energy resources and the abundant amount of farmland found in Bulgaria. To study relationships among the countries of Eastern Europe, turn to the Geodata Files on pages 724–725.

*To practice this skill, see Practicing Geography Skills on page 429.*

---

of which left a strong cultural imprint on the region. Nationalism took hold in Eastern Europe during the early 1900s, and its strong pull contributed to the region's political fragmentation and instability. Though the presence of the Soviet Union dominates the region today, its countries retain their individual personalities.

**Changes after World War I.** When World War I began in 1914, Germany and Austria-Hungary controlled much of Eastern Europe. The Balkan Peninsula in the southeast consisted of many small nations that had gained independence from the Ottoman Empire a few years earlier.

After the defeat of Germany and Austria-Hungary in World War I, the political map of Eastern Europe was totally redrawn. Three new nations emerged—Czechoslovakia, Yugoslavia, and Poland, which had disappeared from the map in 1795. Germany, Hungary, and Bulgaria were reduced in size. Romania was enlarged.

When redrawing the boundaries in 1919, politicians followed United States President

***Learning from Pictures.*** *This girl in Moravia, Czechoslovakia, wears a traditional Slavic costume. What cultural differences exist among the Slavs?*

Woodrow Wilson's idea of "self-determination." In other words, they tried to create nations based on similarities in language, culture, and traditions. They were unable to do so, however, because of Eastern Europe's great cultural complexity. Several groups of people were divided by boundaries that split their traditional homelands. Many found they were now minorities on the wrong side of new national boundaries. Large numbers chose to migrate to join others of similar cultures. The process of breaking up a large area into many small states introduced a new term into the language—**balkanization**—named after the Balkan Peninsula where these changes chiefly occurred.

**World War II and its aftermath.** Many of the new nations were still struggling to establish their national identities when World War II began in Europe in 1939. After that war the political map of Eastern Europe was again redrawn. The Soviet Union took over lands to its west, claiming the former Eastern European nations of Estonia, Latvia, and Lithuania and parts of Poland, Czechoslovakia, and Romania. It also set up Communist economic systems and totalitarian dictatorships in other nations that it had occupied during the war, such as Hungary and Bulgaria.

## Population Patterns

The people of Eastern Europe have many different origins. Slavs migrated into the region from the east about 1,500 years ago. Poles, Czechs, and Slovaks are among the Slavic peoples who settled in the north. Other Slavs—including Serbs, Croatians, Slovenes, Macedonians, Bosnians, and Montenegrins—settled in Yugoslavia, which means "the Land of the Southern Slavs."

Hungarians trace their descent to the Magyar (MAG·yahr) people, who entered Hungary from the east about A.D. 900. Romanians claim descent from the Romans who entered Eastern Europe from the west between 200 B.C. and A.D. 200. Germanic peoples also settled throughout Eastern Europe during the Middle Ages.

Eastern Europe has a total population of about 130 million people, equal to just over one-half the population of the United States. Poland remains the most populous nation with 37.8 million people. Romania and Yugoslavia are next, each with 23 million people. East Germany and Czechoslovakia rank fourth and fifth, each with about 17 million people.

Most of Eastern Europe's people live in urban areas, but the region is less urbanized than Western Europe. Birth and death rates remain generally low. The highest population densities occur in southern Poland and in southern areas of East Germany.

## Social Patterns

Members of many different cultural groups live in Eastern Europe. They have different languages, religions, and traditions. In many of the countries several of these groups live side by side. This arrangement often causes rivalry and tension, and hinders development of a national identity.

**Language.** The language mosaic of Eastern Europe illustrates both its cultural diversity and its problems. In only a few nations, such as Poland, does a large majority speak the same language. In the others, such as Yugoslavia, members of different ethnic groups speak their own languages.

Polish, Czech, and Slovak make up the northern Slavic languages. Serbs, Croatians, and Montenegrins speak Serbo-Croatian, one of the southern Slavic languages. Serbs, however, write the language using the Cyrillic alphabet. Croatians use the Roman alphabet with extra consonants. Slovene, another southern Slavic language spoken in multiethnic Yugoslavia, resembels Serbo-Croatian. Other southern Slavic languages spoken in Eastern Europe include Bulgarian and Macedonian.

Romanian is a Romance language. It traces its origin to Latin. But Romanian now reflects many Slavic influences. Magyar, written in a modified Roman alphabet, serves as the language of the Hungarians.

Turkish, a language spoken in the days of the Ottoman Empire, still survives in isolated areas in the Balkan Peninsula. An estimated 10 percent of all Bulgarians spoke Turkish before the government launched a campaign in the 1980s to discourage its use.

**Religion.** Official government policy in all eight countries of Eastern Europe discourages religious affiliations. In Poland, however, which is traditionally Roman Catholic, ties to the church remain especially strong for many people. Hungary and Czechoslovakia also have historic ties to the Roman Catholic church.

In East Germany most of those who practice a religion belong to a Protestant denomination. Many of the southern Slavs are Eastern Orthodox Christians, as their ancestors had been since the days of the Byzantine Empire. Islam, brought to Eastern Europe by the Ottoman Empire, ranks as the dominant religion in Albania and among the Bosnian peoples of Yugoslavia.

## Political Patterns

Since the end of World War II the Soviet Union has dominated the governments of six nations—Poland, East Germany, Hungary, Czechoslovakia, Romania, and Bulgaria. Political geographers often call these six nations **satellite nations,** or nations that are controlled by a powerful nation. All six nations have totalitarian dictatorships. Although elections are held, only Communist party candidates may seek office.

The Warsaw Pact coordinates military matters throughout the region. The countries of Eastern Europe created the Warsaw Pact in 1955 to rival the NATO alliance in Western Europe. Under an agreement similar to NATO's, if one member of the Warsaw Pact is attacked or threatened, other members will send military assistance.

Totalitarian dictatorships run by the Communist party also control Yugoslavia and Albania. These two nations, however, do not maintain the close ties with the Soviet Union that the satellite nations do.

## Economic Patterns

The countries of Eastern Europe have reached varying stages of industrialization. East Germany is the most industrialized nation, and Albania is the least industrialized. All have Communist, or authoritarian socialist, economic systems. CMEA, the

*Text continues on page 421.*

# CASE STUDY
## GEOGRAPHY AND PEOPLE: The Gypsies

*Gypsy wagon train in Granada, Spain*

Brightly painted wagons, colorful costumes, and wild violin music are part of a culture unique in the world. The culture belongs to bands of nomads who owe allegiance to no national government. This is the culture of the Gypsies, also called Romanies. Although Gypsies live on every continent except Antarctica, they remain concentrated in the nations of Eastern Europe. Population geographers (see GEOGRAPHY IN THE WORKPLACE on page 280) have had a difficult time taking a census of the Gypsies. They estimate that 300,000 Gypsies live in Yugoslavia, 400,000 in Czechoslovakia, 500,000 in Hungary, and 800,000 in Romania.

### Gypsy Origins

Gypsy origins remain shrouded in mystery. The Gypsy language, Romany, is an offshoot of Sanskrit, the ancient language of India. Because of this link, scholars have theorized that Gypsies trace their descent to people who originally lived in India. For unknown reasons the Gypsies began migrating throughout the Middle East and Europe thousands of years ago. By the 1600s Gypsies lived in Europe and North Africa, and even the Americas.

### Gypsy Society

Gypsies usually live in bands of from 10 to several hundred families. A chief, elected for life, heads each band and governs with the help of a council of elders. The entire band shares the responsibility of raising the group's children. Such an upbringing gives the children a sense of loyalty to the band and helps to explain why Gypsies seldom leave the band into which they were born. Gypsies depend on cooperation among band members. Taking advantage of another Gypsy is considered dishonorable.

### A History of Discrimination

As have many nomads, the Gypsies have suffered discrimination from people through whose domains they pass. They have been accused of bringing bad luck, being the source of disease, and of lying and cheating. Persecution reached its height during World War II when German Nazis imprisoned and executed more than 500,000 Gypsies.

### Gypsies Today

Although some Gypsies have given up their nomadic life style and settled in various countries, many still follow traditional ways. As they travel through the countryside, they earn their living as migrant agricultural workers, circus workers and performers, fortune-tellers, or entertainers.

However, the traditional life style of the Gypsies is rapidly disappearing. Increasing urbanization, political tensions, and the policies adopted by many national governments are forcing Gypsies to give up their nomadic life style and find permanent jobs.

Council for Mutual Economic Assistance (formerly referred to as COMECON), mirrors the activities of the European Economic Community. Established in 1949, this organization coordinates planning and economic development in the satellite nations. While economic relations between members and the Soviet Union are close, relations among members remain weak. Bulgaria, Romania, Hungary, Czechoslovakia, Poland, and East Germany have joined CMEA. But despite the efforts of CMEA, the economies of member nations remain generally less prosperous than the economies of Western Europe.

---

### SECTION 2 REVIEW

1. **Define** balkanization, satellite nation
2. **Locate** Estonia, Latvia, Lithuania
3. **Summarizing Ideas** (a) Which new nations emerged on the political map of Eastern Europe after World War I? (b) What forces did the politicians consider when they redrew the boundaries?
4. **Interpreting Ideas** Why was Eastern Europe unstable after each of the world wars?
5. **Comparing Ideas** (a) How are the political patterns of Albania and Yugoslavia similar to those of the other nations of Eastern Europe? (b) How are they different?

---

## 3 The countries of Eastern Europe face many problems.

The eight Communist nations of Eastern Europe have distinctive economies, languages, and ways of life. In general, however, the Eastern European nations remain less developed than the countries of Western Europe.

## East Germany

Between West Germany and Poland lies the German Democratic Republic, better known as East Germany. Soviet troops occupied the eastern half of Germany at the end of World War II and declared East Germany, which is about the size of Virginia, a separate nation in 1949. Although the government now has close ties to the Soviet Union, the country is linked both culturally and historically to West Germany.

In the late 1940s and 1950s many East Germans opposed to communism left their homeland to live in democratic West Germany. To prevent further population losses the government built a barbed-wire fence along East Germany's entire border with West Germany. The army patrols the border at all times.

In the city of Berlin a concrete wall separates Communist-controlled East Berlin from democratic West Berlin, which is entirely within East Germany. The Berlin Wall consists of two thick walls over 10 feet (3 meters) high. Broken glass and barbed wire top the walls and heavily armed guards patrol it. Vehicles and pedestrians may travel between the two Berlins only at designated checkpoints.

About 77 percent of the 16.6 million East Germans live in urban areas. The country has the highest standard of living of the six Soviet-controlled European nations.

In East Germany major crops include sugar beets, wheat, barley, rye, oats, and potatoes. The government owns all of the country's farmland, which is organized into either collective farms or state farms. On a **collective farm,** farmers rent the land from the government and work it cooperatively. The government sets output targets for the farmers, who earn wages and receive a share of the farm's profits. The government runs **state farms** more directly. Farm workers on state farms receive wages, but the government keeps the

*Text continues on page 423.*

## EASTERN EUROPE
### Physical/Political

- ⊛ National capital
- ● Other city
- — National boundary

AZIMUTHAL EQUAL AREA PROJECTION

0    75    150 Miles

0    75    150 Kilometers

N

*Learning from Maps.* Before 1914 most of the nations of Eastern Europe were part of the German, Austro-Hungarian, or Russian empires, none of which exist today. What two forces contributed to the breakup of these empires?

profits. In general, state farms are larger than collectives.

In East Germany, as in most Communist countries, the government has nationalized all industries. A **nationalized industry** is an industry owned by the government. Government experts decide what factories to build and what products to manufacture within the priorities set by CMEA. Steel, machinery, transportation equipment, precision tools, and cameras lead East Germany's many manufactured goods. The Soviet Union serves as East Germany's principal trading partner.

## Poland

Poland, which is about the size of New Mexico, borders East Germany on the west and the Soviet Union on the east. Poland is Eastern Europe's largest country in both land area and population. An extension of the North European Plain called the Baltic Plain occupies most of the country. Throughout Polish history armies have used this plain as an invasion route. These invasions often resulted in the conquest of Poland, which even disappeared from the map of Europe at times.

Along the Czechoslovakian border in the south rise the foothills of the Carpathian and Sudetic mountains. These hills contain rich mineral deposits that supply raw materials for Poland's heavy industries.

Although a totalitarian dictatorship rules Poland, the Polish people have fought to maintain their rights and traditional ways of life. When the government tried to collectivize agriculture, for example, farmers resisted. Today 75 percent of all farms remain privately owned. Rye and potatoes rank as the major crops.

In the early 1980s industrial workers formed an independent trade union called Solidarity to demand greater freedoms. Members of Solidarity took part in anti-

*Learning from Pictures.* Berliners can cross their divided city only at places like Checkpoint Charlie, shown above. Why is East Germany separated from West Germany?

Soviet and anti-government demonstrations. Government leaders eventually banned Solidarity and arrested its leaders. Although the leaders were released, the ban only increased Polish nationalism and stirred international support for the outlawed union.

After World War II the Communists transformed Poland's agricultural economy to one based primarily on industry. They also rebuilt the nation's cities that had been destroyed during the war, including the capital and primate city of Warsaw. Warsaw lies amid rich farmlands near the center of the country. The city originally developed on the banks of the Vistula River. Roads and rail lines link it with the rest of the country. The city also remains the cultural, political, and historical heart of Polish culture.

Today steel, chemicals, metals, ships, and cement rank as the principal manufactured goods. The government developed these industries at the expense of industries that produce consumer goods. As a result, people often wait in long lines to buy what consumer goods are available.

**Learning from Pictures.** *The Solidarity trade union began among workers in the port of Gdansk, Poland. What effects did the government's ban of Solidarity have?*

## Czechoslovakia

Czechoslovakia is located south of East Germany and Poland. Mountains, valleys, and high plateaus cover the landscape of this country, which is about the size of New York State. Czechoslovakia shares much with its northern neighbors.

Czechoslovakia is a landlocked federal republic consisting of two parts—the Czech Socialist Republic on the west and the Slovak Socialist Republic on the east. Czech and Slovak, closely related Slavic languages, serve as the two official languages.

Bohemia, the western part of Czechoslovakia, has been traditionally linked to Western Europe. The Elbe River, which flows west through Germany to the North Sea, carried goods and ideas into and out of Bohemia. As a result, this region developed more quickly than others. It was, for example, the first part of the heartland of Eastern Europe to industrialize. And because Prague, the capital, was located there, Czechoslovakia always looked westward.

Like Warsaw, Prague is a primate city. Its site is ideal for city growth. The Vltava (VUHL·tuh·vuh) and Elbe rivers provided early transportation routes. The surrounding mountains held valuable ore deposits for industry. So Prague quickly became the heart of the country.

About 74 percent of all Czechoslovakians live in urban areas such as Prague and the industrial cities of Plzen (PUHL·zen), Brno (BUHR·noh), Ostrava, and Bratislava. About 77 percent of the people belong to the Roman Catholic church.

Most Czechoslovakians dislike living under Soviet control. In 1968 government leaders tried to introduce greater political freedoms, but Soviet troops invaded the country and put an end to the reforms. Soviet policies have been strictly enforced in Czechoslovakia ever since.

Czechoslovakia is highly industrialized and the people enjoy a relatively high standard of living. In addition, Czechoslovakia has always been a leader in science and technology. Bohemia continues to serve as the principal industrial region. Manufactured goods include machinery, iron, steel, glass, chemicals, motor vehicles, and cement. Farms are organized as collectives. Although soils are poor output is relatively high.

## Hungary

Western influences and development decrease in Eastern Europe from west to east and from north to south. While Poland and

Czechoslovakia show marked links to the west, Albania, much farther southeast, shows few. Midway along this line of diffusion lies Hungary.

Flat and fertile Hungary is surrounded by Czechoslovakia, Austria, Yugoslavia, and Romania. A sliver of the Soviet Union also forms an eastern border. Hungary, which is slightly smaller than Indiana, makes up part of the breadbasket of Eastern Europe. Hungary shows true cultural diversity. The Hungarians, or Magyars, trace their origins to Asians who arrived in the A.D. 800s. The country was a stronghold of the Turkish Ottoman Empire for more than 100 years. In addition, Hungary has long been a refuge for people fleeing unsettled conditions in their homelands.

About 56 percent of Hungary's 10.6 million people live in urban areas. Budapest, with more than 2 million inhabitants, serves as Hungary's capital and primate city. Despite government disapproval, many of the people practice Roman Catholicism.

As with Poland and Czechoslovakia, Hungary dislikes its Soviet-dominated government. In 1956 the independent-minded Hungarians rebelled against Soviet control but were brutally crushed by Soviet forces. Many of the leaders of the rebellion were executed. In time Hungary's government allowed increased freedoms. In 1968, for example, Hungary adopted the New Economic Mechanism (NEM) that reduced the government's role in the economy. Under the NEM the government allows people to own small businesses. Today such freedoms have helped boost productivity and the Hungarians have one of the higher standards of living in Eastern Europe.

Hungary's economy depends on both agriculture and industry. Iron, steel, machinery, transportation equipment, textiles, and precision instruments lead Hungary's many manufactured goods. Bauxite, the ore used to produce aluminum, ranks as the princi-

pal resource. However, coal and iron ore, transported on the Danube to steel plants, have increased in importance in recent years. Hungary now trades with countries outside CMEA, although the Soviet Union remains its principal trading partner.

## Bulgaria

Ohio-sized Bulgaria lies at the northeastern end of the Balkan Peninsula. The Balkan and Rhodope mountains run through the country. Between them lies the fertile Maritsa (muh·REET·suh) River Valley. To the north stretch the Danubian Plains.

Bulgaria's cultural diversity resembles Hungary's. A long history of Turkish rule

*Learning from Pictures.* In 1956 Soviet tanks surged into Budapest, shown below, to crush a revolt against communism. What are some of the reasons that Hungarians dislike Soviet control?

***Learning from Pictures.*** *Bulgaria's Black Sea coast at Varna is a favorite vacation spot of East Europeans. Why is the tourist industry less developed in Eastern Europe than in Western Europe?*

brought Turkish and Byzantine imprints to the culture.

Bulgars form the dominant ethnic group among the country's 9 million people. A campaign to coerce minority Turkish Bulgarians to speak Bulgarian and take Slavic names began in the 1980s. Although two-thirds of the people live in urban areas, Sofia, the capital, remains the only large city.

Bulgaria's still-developing industries produce processed foods, steel, and machinery. Its collective farms make Bulgaria mainly self-sufficient in food. Leading crops include grain, tobacco, fruits, and vegetables. The traditionally weak economy has strengthened considerably in recent years.

### Romania

Romania stretches east of Yugoslavia toward the Soviet Union and the Black Sea. A varied landscape covers the country, which is twice the size of Ohio. The Hungarian Plain extends into Transylvania, as the central part of the country is called.

The Transylvanian Alps rise to the south of the plain. A high plateau reaches to the east and joins the Carpathian Mountains. The Walachian Plain leads south to the Black Sea.

Romanians make up more than 85 percent of the 23 million people. Hungarians form the largest minority group and generally live in the north and west. Only about half the people live in urban areas; most of them live in and around Bucharest, the capital and primate city.

Romania doubled in size by the boundary changes following World War I, but lost parts of its territory to the Soviet Union after World War II. The region called Dobruja (DAW·bruh·jah), once part of Bulgaria, stretches to the Black Sea.

Romania has sizeable oil and natural gas fields in the southern and eastern foothills of the Transylvanian Alps. The Soviet Union remains Romania's leading customer for oil and natural gas, but much is also transported to other Eastern European countries by pipeline. Pipelines now link Bucharest and Budapest.

Farmers on collective farms raise wheat, corn, barley, oats, fruits, vegetables, and livestock. The standard of living remains low, even by Eastern European standards.

### Yugoslavia

Three landscape regions divide Yugoslavia, which is about the size of Wyoming. A narrow coastal strip borders the Adriatic Sea. The rugged Dinaric Alps rise directly behind the coast. The Hungarian Plain, which is part of the Danube Basin, stretches far into the country on the north and east and forms Yugoslavia's heartland.

Yugoslavia was created after World War I as a homeland for Serbs, Croatians, and other Slavic groups. It was first ruled by Serbian monarchs, but the monarchy collapsed during World War II. The country

was reborn as a republic with a Communist economic system under the leadership of Marshal Tito in 1945.

Yugoslavia has three official languages—Serbo-Croatian, Slovenian, and Macedonian. About 50 percent of the 23.4 million people are Eastern Orthodox Christians, 30 percent Roman Catholics, and 10 percent Muslims. Only 46 percent of the Yugoslavian people live in urban areas such as Belgrade, Ljubljana (lee·oo·blee·AHN·uh), and Zagreb (ZAHG·reb).

Unlike the satellite nations, Yugoslavia relies less heavily on the Soviet Union and follows its own special brand of communism. Yugoslavia is a federal state consisting of six republics and two autonomous provinces. Each of the six republics is associated with one of Yugoslavia's principal ethnic groups. Serbs predominate in Serbia, Croatians in Croatia, Slovenes in Slovenia, Bosnians in Bosnia-Herzogovina (hert·suh·goh·VEE·nuh), Montenegrins in Montenegro, and Macedonians in Macedonia. Albanians, Hungarians, Gypsies, and Turks also live throughout the country. Albanians make up more than 80 percent of the population of Kosovo (KAW·suh·voh) province.

Farming remains Yugoslavia's major economic activity. Farmers raise wheat, corn, grapes, olives, oats, and barley. Yugoslavia also has deposits of lead, bauxite, antimony, oil, and natural gas. Tourism on the Adriatic coast is increasingly important.

## Albania

Albania lies between Yugoslavia and Greece at the extreme southern end of Eastern Europe. The Adriatic Sea forms Albania's western border. Only slightly larger than Maryland, Albania is the smallest and poorest country in Eastern Europe. Only about 3.1 million people live in Albania, and only about 35 percent live in urban areas, making it the least urbanized country of Eastern Europe. Many people live in isolated villages. Tirane (ty·RAHN·uh), the capital, ranks as the largest city but has only about 100,000 residents and few factories. Reflecting its location near Turkey and the Middle East, most of the people are Muslims. But as with many totalitarian and Communist dictatorships, the government discourages all religious practice.

As with Yugoslavia, Albania now follows its own brand of communism. For many years Albania's leaders maintained close ties with Communist leaders in the People's Republic of China. Today, however, leaders emphasize a policy of political independence and economic self-reliance.

Albania remains the least-developed country in Eastern Europe. Subsistence farmers grow corn, wheat, and potatoes. Commercial farmers produce tobacco and cotton. The nation has few natural resources and little industry or foreign trade. Small exports of oil, tobacco, and chrome ore provide the only outside income.

### SECTION 3 REVIEW

1. **Define** collective farm, state farm, nationalized industry
2. **Locate** Bohemia, Dobruja, Tirane
3. **Summarizing Ideas** **(a)** Why did many East Germans leave their homes to go to West Germany? **(b)** What was the response of the East German government to this migration?
4. **Interpreting Ideas** How does a collective farm differ from a state farm?
5. **Determining Cause and Effect** What effect did the Baltic Plain have on Poland's history?
6. **Analyzing Ideas** What have the Polish people done to resist the totalitarian Communist dictatorship?
7. **Evaluating Ideas** **(a)** How have the Czechs and Hungarians reacted to life under communism?

## Chapter Summary

The following list contains the key concepts you have learned about Eastern Europe.

1. The three physical regions of Eastern Europe are the North European Plain, the Central Uplands, and Alpine Europe.
2. The Danube and the Elbe are Eastern Europe's principal rivers.
3. Eastern Europe has five types of climate—west coast marine, humid continental with cool summers, Mediterranean, humid subtropical, and mountain.
4. The nations of Eastern Europe have limited natural resources, especially much-needed fuels.
5. The people of Eastern Europe include descendants of Slavs, Magyars, Romans, and Germanic peoples.
6. All eight countries of Eastern Europe have Communist economic systems and totalitarian dictatorships. Yugoslavia and Albania follow their own styles of communism while the Soviet Union controls the others.
7. Although the governments of Eastern Europe discourage religion, most people still belong to an organized religion.
8. Of the six Soviet-controlled European nations, East Germany ranks as the most industrialized and has the highest standard of living.
9. Although Poland is a totalitarian dictatorship, the Polish people have fought collectivization and have formed an independent trade union to demand greater freedoms.
10. Czechoslovakia is a landlocked federal republic consisting of two separate parts.
11. In recent years Hungary has begun to permit a degree of economic freedom, including private ownership of small businesses.
12. Bulgaria, Romania, and Albania have lower standards of living than the other nations of Eastern Europe.
13. Yugoslavia is a federal state consisting of six republics and two provinces.
14. Gypsies are nomads who are thought to have migrated from India long ago. Today Gypsies live throughout the world.

On a separate sheet of paper, complete the following review exercises.

## Reviewing Geographic Terms

In the sentences below, the underlined terms are incorrect. Rewrite each sentence using the correct term.

1. The Dobruja is a combination of earth and stone left by the glaciers as they melted and retreated.
2. Moraine is a fine soil blown by the winds and deposited along the southern edge of the North European Plain.
3. The process of dividing a region or country into several smaller states is called nationalization.
4. The six Eastern European nations most closely associated politically, economically, and militarily with the Soviet Union are called associated states.
5. The form of agricultural organization in which farmers rent the land from the government and work it cooperatively is called a cooperative farm.
6. A principal farm is a form of agricultural organization run directly by the government.
7. An industry owned by the government is called a socialized business.

## Developing Critical Thinking Skills

1. **Determining Cause and Effect** (a) What energy resources does Eastern Europe have? (b) What energy resources must Eastern European nations import?
2. **Organizing Ideas** What geographical and political features promote trade within Eastern Europe?
3. **Synthesizing Ideas** One hundred years ago three large empires occupied the land

area of Eastern Europe. In 1919 politicians redrew the map of the region and created many new countries. **(a)** How has this division helped the peoples of the region? **(b)** How has it caused problems?

4. **Studying Maps** Study the map on page 422. For centuries the Danube River served as a key route for the diffusion of ideas from Western to Eastern Europe. Why?
5. **Analyzing Ideas** How is the political organization of Yugoslavia designed to lessen tensions among the nation's many ethnic groups?
6. **Interpreting Ideas** How does the Soviet Union dominate the governments of the satellite nations?
7. **Writing About Geography** In a full-page essay, complete one of the following activities. **(a)** Compare the different relationships that Eastern European nations have with the Soviet Union. **(b)** Trace the differences that exist among the political systems of the Eastern European nations.

## Using Primary Sources

In the following excerpt from *The Ottoman Impact on Europe*, Paul Coles describes the impact of geography on the emergence of the Hungarian economy. As you study the reading, consider if there are other cases where geography influenced the development of an economy in the same manner.

The characteristics of the large Hungarian state which emerged during the late Middle Ages were a consequence of its situation at the western terminus [end] of the Eurasian steppe, in an area traversed by rivers (notably the Danube system) and protected by mountain ranges (notably the great arc of the Carpathians). This geographical configuration allowed the nomad, pastoral economy of the steppe to be supplemented in this region by some primitive agriculture, forestry and mining. The development of these alternative sources of wealth produced a settled class of small cultivators and scattered and rudimentary urban populations. These, however, lay always at the mercy of nomadic conquerors enjoying superior mobility and sustained by warlike practices and traditions. The Magyar horsemen . . . were the origins of the Hungarian aristocracy.

The feudal society and attitudes of the medieval west offered this ruling class of free warriors a cultural model infinitely more attractive and better suited to their purposes than the caesarism and centralization of the Byzantine world.

1. How did geography affect the development of the Hungarian economy?
2. What group caused the settled rural and urban classes so many problems?

## Practicing Geography Skills

*Before completing this activity, review Developing Geography Skills on page 417.*

**Using Geodata Files** Turn to the *Geodata Files* for Eastern Europe on pages 724–25 and answer these questions.

1. **(a)** Which Eastern European country has the most urbanized population? **(b)** Which has the highest per capita GNP? **(c)** Which has the highest rate of natural increase?
2. Study the lists of major industries, imports, and exports for all the countries in Eastern Europe. Then state two generalizations about Eastern European industry.

## Exploring Geography

Construct a chart comparing the physical geography of Eastern Europe and Western Europe. Your chart should have the following headings: "Physical Features," "Climate Types," "Natural Vegetation," and "Natural Resources."

# The Soviet Union

# PUTTING THE CHAPTER IN FOCUS

The Union of Soviet Socialist Republics, or U.S.S.R., is a giant nation made up of 15 republics. One of the world's superpowers, the Soviet Union—another commonly used name and the one used in this textbook—covers a vast territory—8,649,512 square miles (22,402,236 square kilometers). Few places on the earth have as many natural resources and such a varied physical landscape. Only the People's Republic of China and India have more people. The population of the Soviet Union includes almost 100 different ethnic groups, each with its own distinctive culture and way of life.

## Ideas to Understand

In studying about the Soviet Union, use these ideas to give direction to your reading.

1 The Soviet Union covers more territory than any other nation.
2 The cultural setting of the Soviet Union is diverse.

3 The centrally planned economy of the Soviet Union faces many problems.

## Terms to Define

The following terms are some of the key terms in the chapter. Defining them will help you understand the Soviet Union.

| | |
|---|---|
| permafrost | multinational state |
| taiga | centrifugal force |
| steppe | centripetal force |
| chernozem | soviet |
| *glasnost* | |

## Places to Locate

Locating the following places will add to your knowledge of geography.

| | |
|---|---|
| Ural Mountains | Transcaucasia |
| Kara Kum | Volga River |
| Dzungarian Gate | Fertile Triangle |
| Siberia | Gor'kiy |
| Caucasus Mountains | Novosibirsk |

## 1 The Soviet Union covers more territory than any other nation.

The frigid late-September air holds the promise of snow as you board your train amid the bustle of one of the world's busiest railroad stations. On the train you see people representing all races and speaking many languages as they sway in the narrow corridor. You have boarded the legendary Trans-Siberian Express that will take you across 5,600 miles (9,000 kilometers) and seven time zones on your seven-day journey from Moscow to Vladivostok (vlad·uh·vuh·STAHK). You are about to cross the world's largest nation—the Soviet Union.

◀ *The Kremlin, along the Moscow River*

## Physical Regions

Geographers divide the vast expanse of the Soviet Union, which is nearly two and one-half times the size of the United States, into seven physical regions. They are the East European Plain, the Ural (YOOHR·uhl) Mountains, the Aral-Caspian Lowland, the West Siberian Lowland, the Central Siberian Upland, the Kazakh (kuh·ZAK) Upland, and various border mountains.

**East European Plain.** The North European Plain widens as it reaches the Soviet Union and takes the name East European Plain. Elevations generally rise less than 500 feet (150 meters). Rich coal and iron ore deposits underlie southern parts of the

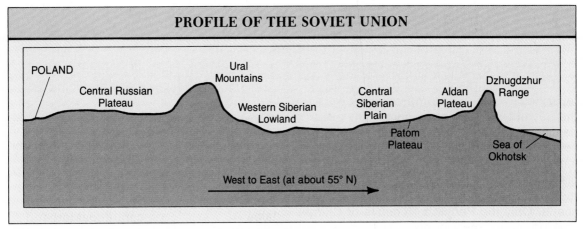

## PROFILE OF THE SOVIET UNION

POLAND

Central Russian Plateau

Ural Mountains

Western Siberian Lowland

Central Siberian Plain

Patom Plateau

Aldan Plateau

Dzhugdzhur Range

Sea of Okhotsk

West to East (at about 55° N)

**Learning from Diagrams.** *Level land dominates the landscape of the Soviet Union. Which landforms on the diagram reflect this generally level topography?*

plain around the Black Sea. Numerous lakes and hilly moraines of glacial origin cover northern areas. One of these enormous moraines runs from Warsaw all the way across the Soviet border to Moscow.

**Ural Mountains.** On the eastern edge of the East European Plain lie the Urals, an old, eroded mountain range. The Urals, which contain rich deposits of iron ore and other metals, mark the traditional dividing line between Europe and Asia. The mountains average less than 3,000 feet (915 meters) in height and are easily crossed by the Trans-Siberian Railroad and other east-west transportation routes.

**Aral-Caspian Lowland.** Lowlands border the Aral (AR·uhl) and Caspian seas in central Asia south of the Urals. Much of the lowland lies below sea level. The surface of the Caspian Sea, for example, lies 92 feet (28 meters) below sea level. Two deserts, the Kyzyl Kum (kuh·ZIL KOOHM), meaning "red sands," and the Kara Kum, meaning "black sands," occupy much of the Aral-Caspian Lowland. Eventually the whole region may become a desert. Farmers have drained off much of the water from the region's two

major rivers—the Amu Darya (AHM·OO DAHR·yuh) and the Syr Darya (*darya* means "river")—for irrigation. The dry climate with its high rate of evaporation removes much of the remaining water.

**Kazakh Upland.** The Kazakh Upland forms a grassy plateau northeast of the Aral-Caspian Lowland. The treeless landscape extends east to a low pass on the China-Soviet border known as the Dzungarian (zuhng·GAR·ee·uhn) Gate.

**West Siberian Lowland.** Siberia occupies the lands east of the Urals. Lowlands in West Siberia form one of the world's largest and flattest plains, where drainage is poor and elevations rise to no more than 500 feet (150 meters). Sluggish rivers flow across the lowland to mouths on the Arctic Ocean. In early summer, when ice still blocks their northern mouths, the rivers back up and overflow, transforming the region into a huge, mosquito-infested swamp.

**Central Siberian Upland.** Higher lands form the Central Siberian Upland (see the map on page 434). Elevations average more than 2,000 feet (610 meters), and rivers

*Text continues on page 434.*

# CASE STUDY
## EXPLORING IDEAS: Transcontinental Railroads

Although sleek jet aircraft crisscross the Soviet Union and the United States today, barely 100 years ago these nations had no transcontinental surface links at all. In the United States the transcontinental railroad was completed in 1869, and in 1916 the world's longest transcontinental rail line, the Trans-Siberian, finally linked Moscow with the Pacific Ocean.

### The Need for Transportation Links

For a large nation transcontinental links are essential. They help unite the nation. They keep one language in use and one set of political ideals alive. They bind the nation into a single economic network. And, perhaps most important, they link the people psychologically.

### The United States

By the 1850s most Americans recognized the need for a transcontinental railroad. People were pouring into the Oregon Territory, and California had already become a state. Finally, on July 1, 1862, Congress passed a law launching the first railroad to the Pacific. Two companies agreed to take on the job. The Central Pacific Railroad began in the west and tackled the difficult task of bridging the Sierra Nevada in California. The Union Pacific built westward across the Great Plains and spanned the Rockies near South Pass, Wyoming.

At Promontory, Utah, a short distance from Ogden, in mid-May 1869, a small group of workers and a handful of officials watched as dignitaries drove in the final spike, made of gold, that completed North America's first intercontinental rail line.

### The Soviet Union

In 1860 the Russians founded the port of Vladivostok on the Pacific Ocean in terri-

*Nearing the end of the line in California*

tory recently taken from the Chinese. After five centuries of expansion the Russian Empire stretched across the entire Asian continent. It soon became clear to Russian leaders that a transcontinental railroad was essential to bind together their broad country. In 1892 the Russians began constructing the Trans-Siberian Railway. It was finally completed in 1916.

To appreciate the immensity of this undertaking, it helps to gain some sense of the time that is involved, as well as the number of miles that must be traveled, to cross the Soviet Union. The journey between Moscow and Vladivostok takes seven full days. Passengers and freight that start at the Polish border travel 6,284 miles (10,110 kilometers). No other train trip in the world even comes close to this distance. The mileage equals that from San Francisco to London. It is this tremendous distance that makes the Trans-Siberian Railway such an essential link in the political, economic, and cultural life of the Soviet Union.

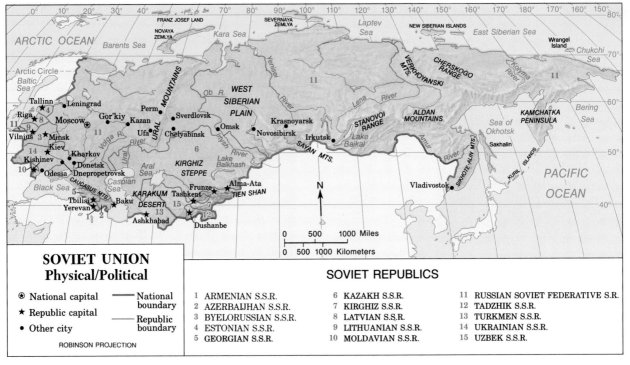

***Learning from Maps.*** *The Soviet Union is organized as a federated state. How many different republics make up the Soviet Union?*

flow swiftly through deep U-shaped valleys. The region's volcanic rocks hold many minerals, including gold and diamonds.

**Border Mountains.** High mountains form a protective "fence" along much of the Soviet Union's long border with 12 neighboring nations. In the west a small section of the Carpathian Mountains rises to more than 6,000 feet (1,830 meters). Farther east the Yaila (YEYE·luh) Range cuts across the Crimean (kry·MEE·uhn) Peninsula on the Black Sea.

The Caucasus (KAW·kuh·suhs) Mountains, in the southwestern region called Transcaucasia, form the Soviet boundaries with Turkey and Iran. The mountains rise to 18,481 feet (5,637 meters) at Mount Elbrus. Farther east The Pamirs and Tien Shan (tee·EN SHAHN) separate the Soviet Union from neighboring Afghanistan, Pakistan, and northwest China. Communism Peak, which rises to 24,590 feet (7,500 me-

ters) in The Pamirs, is the Soviet Union's highest peak. Other high mountains form the Soviet boundary with Mongolia. The border mountains then continue northeast along the nation's Pacific edge as the East Siberian Uplands.

### Rivers and Lakes

The Lena (LEE·nuh) in central Siberia is the Soviet Union's longest river. Other long rivers include the Ob and Yenisei (yen·uh·SAY). All three flow north across Siberia into the Arctic Ocean. Frozen at their mouths for seven to nine months of the year, these rivers remain almost useless as transportation routes.

The Volga, draining into the Caspian Sea, carries one-half of all river traffic in the Soviet Union and also provides hydroelectricity and water for irrigation. Canals link the Volga to the Don and Dnieper (NEE·puhr) rivers and to the Black Sea.

The salty Caspian Sea stands as the largest inland body of water in the world. The Aral Sea, which also is salty, lies to the east. Both the Caspian and Aral seas were once part of an ancient seabed connected to the Mediterranean Sea. Today, however, both lakes are shrinking. The Aral Sea has dropped almost 9 feet (3 meters) since 1961 and the lake is in danger of drying up completely. Lake Balkhash and Lake Baikal, two lakes farther east, are freshwater lakes.

## Climates

A continental climate that features long, frigid winters and brief, but warm summers affects most of the Soviet Union. About half of the nation has either a tundra or a subarctic climate (see the map on pages 96–97). Temperatures in Siberia typically range from 50°F (10°C) in summer to −50°F (−45°C) in winter. **Permafrost,** or perma-

nently frozen subsoil, causes many problems for people trying to live in such cold regions. Permafrost makes houses, factories, highways, and rail lines difficult to build. All need special foundations to prevent them from tilting when their warmth causes the upper layers of soil to thaw.

Mild winters and hot summers occur only in two small southwestern regions where mountains protect the land from the cold winds that prevail farther north. Transcaucasia—Georgia, Azerbaijan (az·uhr·by·JAHN), and Armenia (ahr·MEE·nee·uh)—has a humid subtropical climate. The southern part of the Crimean Peninsula has a Mediterranean climate. The mild climates make both areas popular Soviet vacation spots.

Yearly precipitation averages 20 to 40 inches (50 to 100 centimeters) over most of the Soviet Union. Amounts generally diminish inland. The Caucasus Mountains receive as much as 100 inches (250 centimeters) of

*Learning from Maps.* The Soviet Union covers one-seventh of the earth's surface. What are the advantages and disadvantages of such a large size?

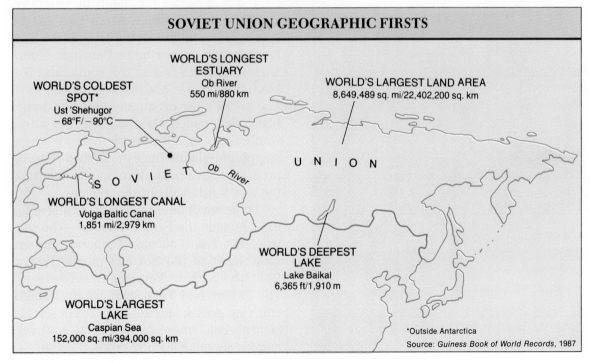

### SOVIET UNION GEOGRAPHIC FIRSTS

WORLD'S COLDEST SPOT*
Ust 'Shehugor
−68°F/−90°C

WORLD'S LONGEST ESTUARY
Ob River
550 mi/880 km

WORLD'S LARGEST LAND AREA
8,649,489 sq. mi/22,402,200 sq. km

WORLD'S LONGEST CANAL
Volga Baltic Canal
1,851 mi/2,979 km

WORLD'S DEEPEST LAKE
Lake Baikal
6,365 ft/1,910 m

WORLD'S LARGEST LAKE
Caspian Sea
152,000 sq. mi/394,000 sq. km

*Outside Antarctica
Source: *Guiness Book of World Records,* 1987

precipitation a year. But the Kara Kum and Kyzyl Kum deserts in the Aral-Caspian Lowland receive as little as 4 inches (10 centimeters of rain in places.

## Vegetation

Six great vegetation belts extend from east to west across much of the Soviet Union (see the map on pages 100–01). Tundra predominates near the Arctic Ocean where conditions remain too cold for trees. Hardy needleleaf forests known as **taiga** (TY·guh) cover areas with a subarctic climate. South of the taiga in the western Soviet Union lies a wedge-shaped belt of mixed forests, much of which has been cleared for farming. To the south the natu-

*Learning from Pictures.* Soviet farmers harvest grain on a state farm in the Rostov region near the Black Sea. What is the primary farming region in the Soviet Union called?

ral flat grasslands known as **steppes** also have been largely replaced by farms. The steppes border the desert region of central Asia. A subtropical vegetation of evergreens and fruit and nut trees flourishes in the mild and rainy lowlands of Transcaucasia.

## Resources

The Soviet Union's vast size gives the nation a wealth of natural resources. That size, however, also makes the costs of building roads and railroads to reach the resources unusually high. In general, most of the resources used today lie close to existing transportation lines. Only the richest of resources found in more remote areas can justify the high construction costs needed to develop them.

**Agriculture.** Only about 10 percent of the Soviet Union is suitable for planting crops and another 10 percent for grazing. Because of the limited farmlands and poor yields, the Soviet Union must import food, particularly grains and sugar.

The best Soviet farmlands lie in a "Fertile Triangle" in the western part of the country. The points of the triangle lie near Leningrad in the north, the Caucasus Mountains and Black Sea in the south, and Novosibirsk (noh·voh·suh·BIRSK) in the east. The area's most productive soils are fertile black soils called **chernozem.** They cover southern areas of the Fertile Triangle where steppe grasslands once flourished. Special programs have been developed to improve the less fertile soils of this region.

Three small but important farming areas exist outside the Fertile Triangle—the subtropical Transcaucasia, where farmers grow most of the Soviet Union's tea and fruit; the narrow Fergana Basin between The Pamirs and Tien Shan, where farmers cultivate grains; and the irrigated deserts in central Asia, where cotton, fruits, and vegetables serve as leading crops.

**Forestry and fishing.** The Soviet Union contains vast forest resources. The taiga alone contains an estimated one-third of the world's total forest resources.

The Soviet Union ranks second only to Japan among the world's leading fishing nations. Large, factory-like fishing vessels operating in the Pacific and Atlantic oceans catch most of the fish. Smaller amounts come from other inland bodies of water, including the Caspian Sea, which is famous for caviar (sturgeon eggs).

**Mining.** The Soviet Union leads the world in oil and natural gas production. It ranks second to the United States in coal production. It also ranks high among the world's leading producers of iron ore, chromium ore, manganese, nickel, tungsten, and many other industrial metals. Other abundant mineral resources include phosphates, diamonds, gold, bauxite, uranium, copper, zinc, molybdenum, and mercury.

---

**SECTION 1 REVIEW**

1. **Define** permafrost, taiga, steppe, chernozem
2. **Locate** Ural Mountains, Kara Kum, Dzungarian Gate, Siberia, Caucasus Mountains, Transcaucasia, Volga River, Fertile Triangle
3. **Summarizing Ideas** What are the seven physical regions of the Soviet Union?
4. **Interpreting Ideas** (a) What advantages are provided by the Eastern European Plain? (b) What advantages are provided by the Ural Mountains?
5. **Organizing Ideas** What types of climates are found in the Soviet Union?
6. **Synthesizing Ideas** (a) What impact does the Soviet Union's size have on the availability of natural resources? (b) Why does the Soviet Union have to import food?

---

## 2 The cultural setting of the Soviet Union is diverse.

The Soviet Union contains many different ethnic groups. Although the Soviet government has attempted to bind this diverse population into a unified nation, it has met with limited success.

### A Brief History

According to legend, in the 800s warring Slavs living east of the Urals invited Scandinavians called *Rus* to rule over them. In the 1200s Mongols swept across the steppes from Asia and conquered the Russian states. While under Mongol rule Moscow developed as the leading Russian state. Moscow's leaders eventually led the Russians to victory over the Mongols in 1480.

**The Russian Empire.** In 1547 Moscow's Grand Prince Ivan IV, also known as Ivan the Terrible, was crowned the first Russian **tsar** (ZAHR), or emperor. He and later tsars greatly increased the size of the Russian Empire. Russian troops crossed the Urals and conquered Siberia. The Russians also took control of once-independent states in the Ukraine, Transcaucasia, central Asia, Byelorussia, and western Poland.

**The Russian Revolution.** Under tsarist rule Russia remained very traditional and fell behind the rest of Europe in technological, educational, and social advances. The country was ill-equipped to fight in World War I (1914–1918) and suffered many hardships and losses of territory.

In March 1917 the people overthrew the last of the tsars in the Russian Revolution. The Duma (DOOH·muh), or parliament, set up a provisional democratic government that proclaimed Russia a republic. In November, however, Communist leaders known as Bolsheviks ended democratic

A visit to a doctor's office and the study of geography may, at first thought, seem remote from one another. Yet medical geography is a specialized field of study that attracts the interest of geographers.

Medical geographers analyze the spatial, or locational, aspects of health. They seek clues to the relationships between people and their environments.

Maps, the geographer's primary tool, can bring special insights to the medical geographer. By mapping the distribution of a disease, for example, medical geographers may trace a disease to its origin and find a way to stop it.

One of the most famous cases in medical geography involved such mapping. In the year 1854 London suffered a devastating siege of cholera. A physician, Dr. John Snow, began mapping the locations of the deaths. The pattern of deaths clearly illustrated that many of the fatalities occurred within a few blocks of pumps used as sources of drinking water by nearby residents. Dr. Snow theorized that the outbreak of cholera must be related to contaminated water drawn from the neighborhood wells. City officials could clearly see from Snow's map that cholera fatalities did, indeed, cluster around municipal pumps. The pumps were quickly shut off. Almost immediately the number of new victims of cholera dropped to zero.

Studies of the spread of disease have concerned medical geographers ever since Dr. Snow's time. Today, for example, many medical geographers busily map the worldwide incidence and spread of acquired immune deficiency syndrome (AIDS), a deadly disease that attacks the immune system and is virtually 100 percent fatal.

Almost as important to medical geographers as determining the patterns and causes of disease is determining the most effective pattern for the delivery of medical care. Medical geographers have found a tremendously uneven spatial distribution of people looking for care and doctors who provide it. Research in both industrialized nations and developing nations shows clearly that patients least able to afford care must bear high travel costs or simply do without medical assistance.

These are just a few of the concerns of medical geographers today. If being a medical detective interests you, medical geography can offer an interesting, challenging, and lifesaving career.

---

rule and made V. I. Lenin the nation's leader. Although Lenin's New Economic Policy (NEP) permitted some free enterprise, his successor, Joseph Stalin, outlawed capitalism and gave the Communist party total control over the government and economy.

After Stalin died in 1953 he was denounced as a tyrant. Later governments, however, continued the tradition of totalitarian dictatorship and kept strong control over all aspects of Soviet life. Today a new policy called **glasnost,** meaning "openness," promises greater political and economic freedoms. However, it is too early to know if any lasting changes will occur.

## Population Patterns

The Soviet Union ranks as the world's third most populous nation (after the People's Republic of China and India) with 284 million inhabitants. Although many people refer to all citizens of the Soviet Union as Russians, Russians actually make up only

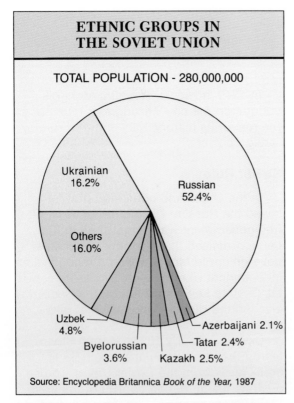

## ETHNIC GROUPS IN THE SOVIET UNION

TOTAL POPULATION - 280,000,000

Russian 52.4%

Ukrainian 16.2%

Others 16.0%

Uzbek 4.8%

Byelorussian 3.6%

Kazakh 2.5%

Tatar 2.4%

Azerbaijani 2.1%

Source: Encyclopedia Britannica *Book of the Year*, 1987

**Learning from Graphs.** *Members of many of the ethnic groups in the Soviet Union live in autonomous republics. How does this arrangement help avoid ethnic conflicts?*

one of more than 100 different nationalities living in this huge **multinational state.**

People of Slavic origins predominate in Soviet lands west of the Urals. Russians, who form the nation's largest ethnic group, are one of the Slavic peoples. Ukrainians comprise the second-largest Slavic group. Other Slavic peoples include Byelorussians, sometimes called White Russians, and Poles, who live mostly in the Ukraine.

Turkic peoples predominate in Soviet Central Asia. Uzbeks are the most numerous of the Turkic peoples. Other Turkic peoples include Kazakhs, Kirghiz (kir·GEES), and Azerbaijani.

Georgians and Armenians predominate along the Soviet border with Iran in Transcaucasia. Finns and Karelians inhabit So-

viet lands taken from Finland in World War II. Estonians, Latvians, Lithuanians, and Moldavians are other major ethnic groups.

More than 90 percent of the Soviet people live west of the Urals and in Soviet Central Asia. Siberia is home to less than 10 percent of the nation's population.

Birth rates remain low among Soviet Slavic nationalities and high among Turkic peoples. As a result, the Slavic share of the total population has dropped from 79 percent in 1959 to 72 percent today. Population geographers predict that it will drop to 65 percent by the year 2000.

About 65 percent of the Soviet people today live in urban areas. Moscow, the capital, and Leningrad rank as the largest cities. Other large Soviet cities west of the Urals include Kiev, Kharkov, and Gor'kiy. Baku and Tbilisi (tuh·BIL·uh·see) are chief cities in Transcaucasia. Tashkent is the chief city in Soviet Central Asia. Novosibirsk is the largest city east of the Urals in Siberia.

*Text continues on page 441.*

**Learning from Pictures.** *This woman lives in Tashkent, the capital of the Uzbek Socialist Republic in south-central Soviet Union. Why are such republics considered the Soviet Union's frontier?*

# CITY FOCUS
## Kiev, Soviet Union

*St. Sophia Church in Kiev*

In the days of the tsars people often said, "Moscow is the heart of Russia, St. Petersburg [Leningrad] is its head, but Kiev is its mother." In some ways these three cities, ranking first, second, and third in size in the Soviet Union, continue to provide those functions. But it is in Kiev that the past reaches out to touch the present.

### An Ancient City

Kiev, capital of the Ukraine, stands as one of the oldest urban centers in the Soviet Union. No one really knows exactly how ancient it is. Archaeological research has uncovered the wooden streets and remains of ancient buildings. Evidence indicates it was already a trading post, situated on a high bank of the Dnieper River, in the 700s. By the early 1100s Kiev had become a cultural and economic center.

In 1240, however, invading Mongols conquered the city. Throughout much of the rest of its history, Kiev endured rule by foreign powers.

### Soviet Rule

In the chaos and confusion that followed the Russian Revolution of 1917, a free government was established in Kiev. Lenin promised that the new Communist government in Moscow would recognize an independent Ukraine with Kiev as its capital. Despite Lenin's promises, the Red Army invaded the Ukraine. By 1920 Kiev was tightly locked inside the Soviet Union.

During the early 1930s Joseph Stalin feared that the Ukrainians would try to break away from the Soviet Union. To demonstrate his tightened control of the area, Stalin imposed impossibly high production quotas on Ukrainian farmers, even though they already produced much of the country's food. Communist troops sealed the Ukraine's borders and famine swept the land. Kiev almost ceased to function. The totals will probably never be known, but many scholars believe that at least 5 million people died in the area in 1932 and 1933.

### Kiev Today

In time Kiev recovered. Today the old and the new mix with a charm that is largely absent from many Soviet cities. The golden domes of the Cathedral of St. Sophia, built in the 1000s, seem in harmony with the forested hills of the city. Even the dullness of huge apartment buildings appears softened by the pots of flowers at every window and the vines that tumble from the balconies. Along the shores of the Dnieper and on its many islands, Kiev's citizens sun themselves on hot summer Sundays. Kievians take pride in living in one of the world's great historical cities.

## Social Patterns

The Soviet government uses language as the principal basis for identifying nationality. Varying religions, histories, and other aspects of Soviet society also contribute to the cultural mosaic that makes up the Soviet Union.

Russian, one of the Slavic languages, serves as the Soviet Union's official language. Nevertheless, many Soviet citizens continue to speak other languages, such as Ukrainian, Byelorussian, Lithuanian, Latvian, Estonian, Finnish, Karelian, Moldavian, Tadzhik (tah·JIK), Azerbaijan, Kazakh, Kirghiz, and Georgian. To advance in the Soviet Union, however, a citizen must speak Russian fluently.

Although Communist ideology does not forbid religion, it discourages religion as old-fashioned and unscientific. Nonetheless, about one-fourth of all Soviet citizens consider themselves Russian Orthodox Christians. Many of the people in Soviet Central Asia and in Azerbaijan follow Islam. Soviet Jews form a small but vocal minority.

**Cultural differences.** Geographers often speak of **centrifugal forces** that tend to divide people within a country. Such forces of disunity may include differences in language, culture, or racial background. In contrast, successful national unity requires **centripetal forces** that bind a nation together. Examples of these forces would be a common language, a shared history, or even a good network of transportation.

The Soviet Union experiences a tug of war between its centrifugal and centripetal forces. While the central government uses the term "Soviet people," most citizens identify themselves first with local groups, such as Ukrainians or Uzbeks. These centrifugal forces often cause resentment of the Russians, who are the most powerful ethnic group.

**Learning from Pictures.** *The architecture of Registan Square in Samarkand reflects Middle Eastern influences. Why is the Soviet Union's great cultural diversity to be expected?*

## Political Patterns

The Soviet Union is a federal state made up of 15 republics governed by **soviets,** or councils of Communist party members. Each republic was set up for a particular ethnic group. In addition, a few of the republics have **autonomous republics** within their borders. The autonomous soviet socialist republics (ASSRs) offer small minorities a chance at self-government.

Each republic and autonomous republic governs itself to some extent. Each has a separate constitution and government and elects delegates to the Supreme Soviet, the Soviet Union's legislative body. Real political power at all levels, however, rests with the leadership of the Communist party. Only about 10 percent of all Soviet citizens belong to the Communist party.

Despite the constitutional guarantees of **human rights,** or the basic rights of all people, Soviet society remains a totalitarian dictatorship. The government controls all aspects of the people's lives. The only political party is the Communist party. Those who strongly oppose the government may

**441**

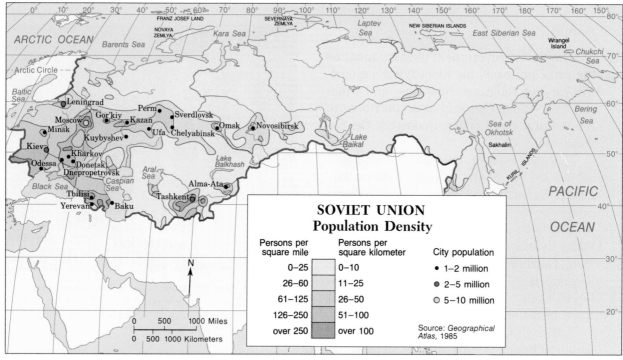

**Learning from Maps.** *Wide stretches of the Soviet Union are sparsely settled. What physical and cultural factors might explain this pattern?*

receive stiff sentences in labor camps or be forced to move to isolated areas.

Internationally the Soviet Union ranks with the United States as a superpower. Relations between the two rivals often fluctuate. Attempts at **détente** (day·TAHNT), or a gradual relaxing of tensions, began in the early 1970s. President Richard Nixon and Secretary of State Henry Kissinger held discussions with Soviet leaders on key issues separating the two countries. Relations continued to improve until Soviet troops invaded Afghanistan in late 1979. President Jimmy Carter warned that such actions posed a serious threat to world peace and détente lagged. Despite discussions between President Ronald Reagan and Soviet leaders, human rights violations and Soviet aggressions blocked further détente.

## Economic Patterns

The Soviet Union was the first nation in the world to adopt a Communist, or authoritarian socialist, economic system. Today the government owns and directs all aspects of the economy. Some recent reforms allow private enterprise. However, these businesses make up only a tiny fraction of the economy.

---

**SECTION 2 REVIEW**

1. **Define** tsar, glasnost, multinational state, centrifugal force, centripetal force, soviet, autonomous republic, human rights, détente
2. **Locate** Gor'kiy, Novosibirsk
3. **Contrasting Ideas** How did the policies of Lenin and Stalin differ?
4. **Interpreting Ideas** How and why is the ethnic composition of Soviet society changing?
5. **Analyzing Ideas** In what ways is the Soviet Union an example of
   (a) a totalitarian dictatorship and
   (b) a Communist economic system?

---

*Text continues on page 444.*

Imagine that you are an explorer. You arrive in a new setting. As you study the people and the activities they pursue, you ask *where* and *why there* questions (see the skill lesson on page 341).

## How to Analyze Land Use

To analyze land use you must apply several of the skills that have already been introduced. You may wish to review the skill lessons on reading economic maps (page 163), understanding descriptions (page 273), and identifying cause and effect (page 307). Using these and many other critical thinking skills will help you understand why people use their land as they do.

## Applying the Skill

Study the map below. Note that the legend (key) contains colors and symbols marking categories of land use. Intense manufacturing, marked in orange, exists near the cities of Moscow, Donetsk, Tbilisi, and Novosibirsk; east of the Aral Sea; west of Lake Balkhash; and near Lake Baikal. Forestry takes place throughout the country, even on Sakhalin Island.

People use large expanses of the southern and western parts of the country for farming. This area is marked in green. Land used for grazing, marked in light green, occurs mostly in the central and southern Soviet Union. Three areas—in the extreme north, the southwest, and the southeast—are of limited economic use. This category includes lands that are not used for manufacturing, lumbering, farming, or grazing but that still have some economic use. Note the types and locations of the other activities shown on the map.

*To practice this skill, see Practicing Geography Skills on page 447.*

## 3 The centrally planned economy of the Soviet Union faces many problems.

Communist leadership has transformed the Soviet Union from an agricultural nation to the world's second leading industrial power. The transformation occurred after 1928 under ambitious five-year plans directed by the government. These plans, however, have entailed high social costs.

Government planners guide economic development through an agency called "Gosplan." Gosplan decides what crops will be grown and what industrial products will be made. It also sets production targets and the prices at which most goods will be bought and sold.

A centrally planned economy stands as the opposite of the free, or market, economies found in the United States and other non-Communist nations. In a market economy individuals or privately owned corporations decide what crops to grow and what goods to produce.

### Agriculture

All farmland in the Soviet Union was nationalized in the 1920s. Although private plots of land now supply some important products, two types of communal farms still dominate Soviet agriculture.

**Collective farms.** On collective farms, which operate on one-third of all farmland, farmers pay rent to the government and work together to meet crop output goals set by the government. The farmers earn a small wage from the government and receive a share of the farm's income. Each farm family on a collective also uses a small private plot of land for raising vegetables and livestock. Output from these plots can be sold by individual farmers.

**State farms.** Averaging more than 100,000 acres (40,000 hectares), state farms are much larger than collective farms. Farmers on state farms earn higher wages than collective farmers but do not share in the management or the profits of the farm. As on collective farms, farmers on state farms may use small plots of land.

### Industry

The largest concentrations of industries lie west of the Ural Mountains. Labor shortages and inadequate transportation limit industrial development east of the Urals.

*Learning from Pictures.* Markets selling farm products and craft goods are becoming increasingly popular in the Soviet Union. Why is this unusual in a Communist economy?

At first Soviet planners concentrated on building heavy industries. Heavy industries provide the iron and steel, chemicals, and machinery needed to support industrialization. Light industries producing consumer items were largely neglected until the 1970s. As a result, consumer items such as automobiles, clothing, electronics equipment, and refrigerators remain in short supply.

Industry in the Soviet Union developed in four main regions. Factories in Leningrad, Moscow, and Gor'kiy manufacture automobiles, clothing, and electronics. In the Ukraine factories located near rich coal fields and iron ore deposits produce iron and steel. Industries in the Urals, particularly in the cities of Sverdlovsk (sferd·LOOHFSK) and Chelyabinsk (chel·YAH·buhnsk), use rich ores found in the old, worn-down mountains to supply iron, copper, nickel, manganese, and chromium for industrial use. Plants in Siberia manufacture steel and machinery for more populous areas of the nation.

## Foreign Trade

The Soviet Union's principal trading partners are other members of CMEA. You will remember from Chapter 21 that CMEA, formerly COMECON, stands for Council for Mutual Economic Assistance. Today, however, the Soviet government seeks more trade with non-Communist nations.

The Soviet Union exports a large variety of goods and materials. Oil, natural gas, and gold rank as the most important exports. In fact, the country exports large quantities of natural gas by pipeline to countries in Eastern and Western Europe.

## Soviet Life

Although the standard of living for Soviet citizens has improved, it lags far behind that of the people of Western Europe and the United States. The government's emphasis on heavy industry often leads to shortages of consumer goods. As is true in Eastern Europe, few consumer goods are available and they are often of poor quality.

Officially the Soviet Union is a classless society in which all people are equal. In reality, however, Communist party members make up a privileged class. Party members are likely to own large apartments and automobiles, to vacation in summer homes in the countryside, and to dine in the best restaurants.

Life for the vast majority of Soviet citizens is very different. Most must stand in long lines to buy food or consumer goods. Often many people share a tiny apartment. Although education is free, the best schools are reserved for Communist party members and their families.

Soviet leader Mikhail Gorbachev has announced plans to improve life in the Soviet Union. So far, however, the changes have been few and have not affected most Soviet citizens.

### SECTION 3 REVIEW

1. **Contrasting Ideas** (a) How does a centrally planned economy, such as that in most Communist countries, differ from a free, or market, economy, such as that in much of Western Europe? (b) Which type of economy does the Soviet Union have? (c) Which type of economy does the United States have?
2. **Seeing Relationships** (a) Who are the Soviet Union's major trading partners? (b) Why do you think this is so?
3. **Interpreting Ideas** How has the Soviet emphasis on heavy industries affected life for Soviet citizens?

# CHAPTER 22 REVIEW

## Chapter Summary

The following list contains the key concepts you have learned about the Soviet Union.

1. The seven physical regions of the Soviet Union are the East European Plain, the Ural Mountains, the Aral-Caspian Lowland, the West Siberian Lowland, the Central Siberian Upland, the Kazakh Upland, and various border mountains.
2. The Volga carries half of all river traffic in the Soviet Union and is linked to the Don and Dnieper rivers and to the Black Sea by canals.
3. About half of the Soviet Union has either a tundra or subarctic type of climate. Mild winters and hot summers are found only in two small southwestern regions, where mountains protect the land from the cold winds that prevail farther north.
4. Six great vegetation belts extend generally from east to west across much of the Soviet Union. These vegetation belts include tundra, taiga, mixed forests, steppes, deserts, and subtropical vegetation.
5. The Soviet Union is the world's third most populous nation. Geographers classify it as a multinational state because it has people from more than 100 different nationalities living within its borders.
6. The Soviet Union is a federal state consisting of 15 republics, each of which was set up for a particular ethnic group. The nation is a totalitarian dictatorship.
7. The Soviet Union has a Communist, or authoritarian socialist, economic system in which the government owns almost all the means of production and directs all economic development.
8. In the late 1800s and early 1900s the United States and Russia constructed transcontinental railroads.

On a separate sheet of paper, complete the following review exercises.

## Reviewing Geographic Terms

Supply the geographic term that correctly completes each sentence.

1. The fertile black soils that cover southern areas of the Fertile Triangle are called ____.
2. Hardy needleleaf forests known as ____ cover the areas of the Soviet Union that have a subarctic climate.
3. The ____ are the natural grasslands of the Soviet Union.
4. A ____ is a council of Communist party members.
5. Permanently frozen subsoil that causes many problems for people trying to live in very cold regions is called ____.
6. The Soviet Union, with its more than 100 different nationalities, is an example of a ____ ____.
7. ____ ____ are elements of disunity, such as different cultures that tend to divide people within a country.
8. ____ is a new Soviet policy meaning "openness" that promises greater political and economic freedoms.
9. The basic rights and privileges of all people are called ____ ____.
10. The hereditary ruler of Russia, or ____, was deposed during the Russian Revolution.
11. President Nixon and his Secretary of State, Henry Kissinger, led efforts at ____, the lessening of tensions, between the United States and the Soviet Union.

## Developing Critical Thinking Skills

1. **Summarizing Ideas** (a) Which physical region does the Soviet Union share with Western and Eastern Europe? (b) What is the Dzungarian Gate?
2. **Interpreting Ideas** (a) How much of the Soviet Union is suitable for farming? (b) What are the four major agricultural areas of the Soviet Union?
3. **Understanding Ideas** Why are transcontinental links essential to large nations?

4. **Synthesizing Ideas** What are the major political patterns in the Soviet Union?
5. **Comparing Ideas** **(a)** How are collective farms and state farms similar? **(b)** How are they different?
6. **Writing About Geography** In a full-page essay, complete one of the following activities. **(a)** Compare life in the Soviet Union to life in the United States by examining politics, economics, and standards of living. **(b)** Explain how the Soviet leadership has transformed the Soviet economy from an agricultural to an industrial economy. What social costs has this transformation entailed?

## Using Primary Sources

In the following excerpt from *Memoirs 1950–1963*, former United States Ambassador George Kennan describes the Soviet Union. As you study the reading, compare Kennan's descriptions to what you have just read about the Soviet Union in the 1980s.

It was summer—the marvelous summer of central Russia, with its deep blue skies, its fields and ravines, its evergreens and birches and poplars, its straggling villages and onion-domed churches, its far horizons with always the dark dim line of distant forests. The common people, beginning now to recover to some extent from the horrors and privations of the war, and animated, in these final months of the Stalin era, by a fear of all political involvement and a revulsion to all thought and talk of internal politics, were digging in again, so to speak, with their characteristic patient, [irrepressible] vitality— creating a life for themselves, such as they could, within the rigid limits prescribed by the system. The collective farmers were permitted now to sell, at open outdoor markets, such surplus produce as they could grow on their own small private plots. The city suburbanites had likewise their kitchen gardens and sometimes even an animal or two. These various private activities tended to merge; and in this way there was growing up, particularly on the outskirts of Moscow, . . . a form of petty free enterprise—a free enterprise strictly limited . . . but active, busy and, in its way, hopeful. There was, therefore, something old-Russian about these suburban communities . . . an atmosphere of health and simplicity and subdued hope.

1. What does the author say animated the Russian people in the final months of the Stalin era?
2. What is the author's general opinion of Russia and its people?

## Practicing Geography Skills

*Before completing this activity, review Developing Geography Skills on page 443.*

**Analyzing Land Use** Study the map on page 434 again and reread Section 1 of the chapter on pages 431–37. Then answer the following question.

What aspects of the physical setting of the Soviet Union explain the land use patterns indicated on the map?

## Exploring Geography

Obtain an outline map of the Soviet Union. Then use information in Chapter 22 and in atlases, almanacs, and encyclopedias to locate the Soviet Union's major transportation routes. Color these routes in on your map. Your final map should have a key showing what symbols stand for highways, railroads, canals, and any other transportation routes you choose to include. On the back of your outline map write a brief paragraph describing what parts of the Soviet Union are still far from transportation routes.

# UNIT 7 REVIEW

## Unit Summary

The following list contains the key concepts you have learned about Europe and the Soviet Union.

1. Europe's physical regions are the Northwest Uplands, the North European Plain, the Central Uplands, and Alpine Europe.
2. Europe's major rivers include the Seine, Loire, Rhône, Saône, Danube, and Elbe.
3. Europe has seven types of climate: west coast marine, humid continental with cool summers, Mediterranean, humid subtropical, subarctic, tundra, and mountain.
4. Western Europe is divided into 24 nations, most of which are highly industrialized. Eastern Europe is divided into 8 nations, all of which, like the Soviet Union, have Communist economic systems and totalitarian dictatorships.
5. Britain was the first nation to industrialize.
6. The nations of Eastern Europe lack natural resources.
7. Technological and social advances moved from Western Europe eastward, reaching the Eastern European countries that are the farthest east last.
8. The Soviet Union has seven physical regions. Many of its rivers freeze in winter and are useless as transportation routes. The Volga, however, serves as an important transportation route and is linked to the Don and Dnieper rivers and to the Black Sea by canals.
9. Much of the Soviet Union has either a tundra or subarctic type of climate. The nation includes six great vegetation belts. Nearly one-third of the world's forests lie in the Soviet Union.
10. The Soviet Union reflects great cultural diversity. Its political and economic patterns are much different from those of the United States.

On a separate sheet of paper, complete the following review exercises.

## Checking Your Understanding

1. In what ways have Western European nations become more unified since the end of World War II?
2. How are the foreign policies of Switzerland and Austria different from those of other Western European nations?
3. How do political patterns among the eight nations of Eastern Europe differ?
4. Describe the major characteristics of the economic system of the Soviet Union.

## Applying Critical Thinking Skills

1. **Contrasting Ideas** How are the political patterns of Western European nations different from those of Eastern European nations and the Soviet Union?
2. **Analyzing Ideas** Both Western Europe and the Soviet Union are highly industrialized and have many natural resources, yet the standard of living in Western Europe is much higher than that in the Soviet Union. Why do you think this is the case?
3. **Interpreting Ideas** How has the map of Eastern Europe changed since World War I?
4. **Seeing Relationships** (a) How is the ethnic composition of the Soviet Union different from that of any of the nations of Western or Eastern Europe? (b) How has the Soviet government tried to minimize the divisive effect that this ethnic composition tends to cause?
5. **Evaluating Ideas** (a) What is détente? (b) What actions have hindered the most recent efforts at détente? (c) Why is détente important to world politics?

## Reviewing Unit Features

1. **Geography in the Workplace** What are the major questions that medical geographers ask?
2. **The Geographic Web** What were the long-term effects of the black death on Europe?

**3. City Focus** What are the advantages of Paris's site and situation?

**4. City Focus** Why did Stalin tighten control over Kiev in the 1930s?

## Using Map Skills

1. Study the maps on pages 397 and 407. What rivers flow through **(a)** London, **(b)** Paris, and **(c)** Rome?

2. Study the map of the Soviet Union on page 443. What is the major economic activity in the region around Kiev?

## Investigating Geography

1. Use references in the library to further research one of the nations of Western or Eastern Europe. Prepare a written report in which you explain the quality of life, the social structure, and the culture of the nation you have chosen. Conclude your report by examining the social problems that the nation is currently facing and the steps the government is taking to solve these problems.

2. Prepare a chart that compares the population, political, and economic patterns of the nations of Western and Eastern Europe and the Soviet Union. Your chart should list the population, the type of government and economic system, and per capita GNP. Excellent resources for your chart are the *Geodata Files* on pages 720–33 of this textbook, encyclopedias, and almanacs.

3. Use resources in your school or public library to find information on the government of the Soviet Union. Then construct a wall chart showing the main branches of the Soviet government and the ways in which these branches are related.

## Further Readings

### Chapter 20

Barzini, Luigi. *The Europeans.* New York: Simon and Schuster. Provides a thorough examination of how and why Europe is so culturally diverse today.

Editors of Time-Life Books. *Scandinavia.* Amsterdam, Holland: Time-Life Books. Covers the climate, geography, and culture of Denmark, Iceland, Norway, Finland, and Sweden.

Green, Carol. *England.* Chicago: Childrens Press, Regensteiner Publishing Enterprise, Inc. Discusses England's geography, history, art, industry, and people.

Knight, Max. *Return to the Alps.* New York: The Seabury Press. Explores the geographical and climatic areas of the Alps.

Stein, R. Conrad. *Italy.* Chicago: Childrens Press, Regensteiner Publishing Enterprises, Inc. Presents a pictorial history of Italy and discusses the country's future.

### Chapter 21

Dornberg, John. *Eastern Europe: A Communist Kaleidoscope.* New York: The Dial Press. Describes the different approaches to communism in Eastern Europe.

Krok-Paszkowski, Jan. *Portrait of Poland.* New York: Thomas and Hudson Inc. Explores the past and present of Poland.

Sharman, Tim. *We Live in East Germany.* New York: The Bookwright Press. Describes East Germany as seen through the eyes of a cross-section of its people.

### Chapter 22

Binyon, Michael. *Life in Russia.* New York: Berkley. Studies life in the Soviet Union by focusing on such subjects as the status of women, religion, crime, health care, leisure activities, and teenage life styles.

Editors of Time-Life Books. *The Soviet Union.* Amsterdam, Holland: Time-Life Books. Covers various aspects of the Soviet Union—its culture, life styles, and history.

Mikhailov, Nikolai Nikolaevich. *Russia—The Land and People of the Soviet Union.* New York: Harry N. Abrams Publishers. Explores the land, natural resources, industries, science, and people of the Soviet Union.

# UNIT **8**

# NORTH AFRICA AND THE MIDDLE EAST

# CHAPTER 23 The Settings of the Region

# PUTTING THE CHAPTER IN FOCUS

Geographers have long been interested in North Africa and the Middle East as the "cradle of civilization." The first agriculture, cities, writing, and early science began there and diffused throughout the world.

Geographers group North Africa and the Middle East together because they share many common physical traits including landscape and climate, and common cultural traits. Yet there are as many differences among the countries of this vast region as there are similarities.

## Ideas to Understand

In studying about the settings of North Africa and the Middle East, use these ideas to give direction to your reading.

**1** A difficult physical setting influences life in the region.

**2** Contrasting life styles form the cultural setting of this two-part region.

## Terms to Define

The following terms are some of the key terms in the chapter. Defining them will help you understand the settings of North Africa and the Middle East.

subregion    monotheism
exotic river    absolute monarchy
prehistory    desertification

## Places to Locate

Locating the following places will add to your knowledge of geography.

North Africa   Euphrates River
Middle East    Fertile Crescent
Tigris River    Dead Sea

## 1   A difficult physical setting influences life in the region.

Brown deserts of burning sands and rock stretch as far as the eye can see. Broad rivers edged with green fields snake through the deserts. Camel caravans and flocks of sheep pass only a few miles from beaches lined with palm trees. All of these contrasts and many more characterize North Africa and the Middle East. At the same time, all the countries face a common problem—the scarcity of water.

### Physical Regions

North Africa and the Middle East cover nearly 5 million square miles (13 million square kilometers), extending from the Atlantic Ocean to Afghanistan. The region spans the Sahara and the Arabian Desert and reaches into the Sahel (suh·HAYL), a dry grassland south of the Sahara. Throughout the region water is the key element of the physical setting. The uneven distribution of this vital resource has influenced growth and development for centuries.

Two distinctive **subregions,** or smaller parts of a whole area, form the region. One subregion—North Africa—includes Egypt, Libya, Tunisia (tooh·NEE·zhuh), Algeria, Morocco, Western Sahara, and Mauritania (mowr·uh·TAY·nee·uh). The countries of Turkey, Cyprus, Syria, Lebanon, Israel, Jordan, Saudi Arabia, the Yemen (YEM·uhn) Arab Republic (North Yemen), the People's Democratic Republic of Yemen (South Yemen), Oman, the United Arab Emirates, Qatar (KAHT·uhr), Bahrain, Kuwait, Iraq, Iran, and Afghanistan make up the subregion of the Middle East.

◀ *Desert oasis in Algeria*

453

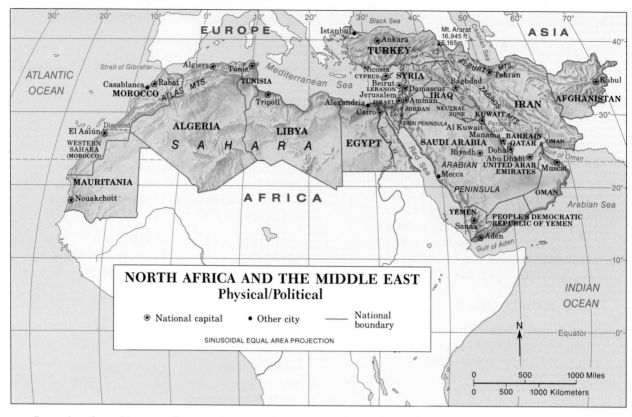

**Learning from Maps.** *The driest parts of the region lie in the low latitudes. How does location affect the amount of moisture the area receives?*

**Mountains and highlands.** Mountain ranges stretch across many of the region's northern areas. The Atlas Mountains reach across northern Africa from Morocco to Tunisia, the Pontic Mountains across northern Turkey, and the Elburz (el·BUHRZ) Mountains across northern Iran. Mountains and highlands cover most of the Middle East north of the Arabian Peninsula. Just north of the Turkey–Iran border rise the high Caucasus Mountains.

These mountain ranges have influenced the region in many ways. They feature extremely rugged terrain, making communication and transportation difficult. They also help wring out what little moisture there is in the dry desert air.

**Deserts.** Varied desert landscapes cover much of North Africa and the Middle East,

*Text continues on page 456.*

**Learning from Tables.** *The world's largest deserts lie in North Africa and the Middle East. In what ways does the wide expanse of desert affect transportation?*

### DESERTS OF NORTH AFRICA AND THE MIDDLE EAST

| Name | Location | Size (sq. mi/sq. km) |
|------|----------|----------------------|
| ARABIAN | Egypt/Sudan | 70,000/ 112,000 |
| RUB 'AL KHALI | South Arabian Peninsula | 250,000/ 400,000 |
| SAHARA | North Africa | 3,500,000/ 5,600,000 |
| SYRIAN | Saudi Arabia, Jordan, Syria, and Iraq | 100,000/ 160,000 |

Source: *World Almanac,* 1987

# CASE STUDY
## EXPLORING NATURE: Desert Landscapes

Most dictionaries define a desert as "a wilderness," "a barren place," or "a place without people." But these definitions could apply equally well to polar areas or to many mountain regions. What, then, makes a desert distinctive among physical settings?

### Geographic Definitions

When geographers use the word desert, they have something special in mind. A geographer's desert may be crowded with people. For example, Cairo and Alexandria, Egypt, both lie in a desert, yet millions of people live in these two cities. So "wilderness," "barren," and "place without people" really do not provide a useful geographic definition of desert.

To the geographer, lack of water is the fundamental factor that defines a desert. Deserts have little surface water, limited ground water, and unreliable rainfall.

*The fertile Nile Valley and bordering desert*

### Unreliable Precipitation

Annual average precipitation figures for deserts often are almost meaningless. Although statistics may say that a desert area receives 5 inches (12.5 centimeters) of rain a year, the figure does not mean that 5 inches of rain falls every year. This is because averages are calculated by adding all the precipitation received over a period of years and then dividing the total by the number of years. So in one year, for example, a place may receive 10 inches (25 centimeters) of rain. The next year it may receive no rain at all. The yearly average for those two years would be 5 inches (12.5 centimeters), or 10 (inches) ÷ 2 (years). Such averages are misleading because all the precipitation for a given year may fall in one or two heavy showers. Such heavy rains usually pelt the hard, dry earth and run off rather than penetrating the surface.

### Colors of the Desert

Two colors symbolize life and death in many desert areas. The primary desert color—brown—illustrates the lack of water. Often this color stretches as far as the eye can see. And even though the brown desert may burst into bloom after a rain, the colorful outburst is short-lived and brown soon returns.

The other desert color—green—identifies the few arable areas. Here life-giving water is available from rivers such as the Nile or from underground reserves. People can be found, often in large numbers as in Cairo, living on these green ribbons in the world's deserts.

The line between green and brown is often sharp in desert regions. The rich green of an irrigated oasis or river valley suddenly ends. Beyond is the vast, dry emptiness of brown terrain.

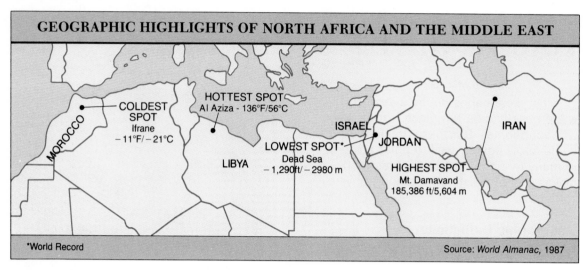

COLDEST SPOT
Ifrane
−11°F/−21°C

MOROCCO

HOTTEST SPOT
Al Aziza - 136°F/56°C

LOWEST SPOT*
Dead Sea
−1,290 ft/−2980 m

LIBYA

ISRAEL

JORDAN

HIGHEST SPOT
Mt. Damavand
185,386 ft/5,604 m

IRAN

*World Record

Source: *World Almanac*, 1987

**Learning from Maps.** *The world's hottest spot—Al Azizia, Libya—actually lies more than 30° north of the equator. Why is the region so hot?*

the world's largest desert area. In southern Saudi Arabia, huge sand dunes called **ergs** dot the land. In the Sahara, rocky, dry plateaus called **hammadas** stretch for hundreds of miles, broken only by small oases. Many valleys cut through the plateaus, especially in the western Sahara. These dry valleys, or **wadis,** have steep sides and narrow floors. Soil and gravel deposits and the existence of water near the surface of the ground make wadis farmable. The oases and wadis produce an interesting desert pattern of widely spaced ribbons of green in the brown desert landscape (see the CASE STUDY on page 455).

A fourth type of desert landscape—the **basin and range**—covers the eastern parts of the region. Basin and range landscapes consist of steep, rugged mountain chains with dry basins between. Like wadis, the basins have enough soil and water to support limited farming.

## Climate

North Africa and the Middle East span the world's most extensive dry area. Most of the region receives less than 10 inches (25 centimeters) of rain a year. Often many years pass with no rainfall. The little rain that does fall quickly evaporates. Constantly rising warm air in the equatorial low-pressure belt causes the dry climate.

Despite vast areas of dryness, the region's climate patterns do vary somewhat. A Mediterranean climate dominates the area along the Mediterranean coast. Rains are plentiful in winter but summers are hot and dry. Just south of the Mediterranean a semiarid climate affects a narrow band of land in North Africa and a large area inland in the Middle East.

One of the most noticeable characteristics of the region's climate is the heat. Many areas with continental and desert climates reach temperatures of 110°F (44°C) at least one day a year. The world's highest measured temperature—136.4°F (58°C)—was recorded at Al Azizia (ahl ahz·ee·ZEE·yah), Libya. Yet temperatures in the same area cool at night, often dropping to 60°F (15°C).

## Rivers

Several broad rivers cross the region. These rivers serve as lifelines throughout

456

the region. They also are the focus of many current regional conflicts and problems. They are called **exotic rivers** because they are found where they are least expected— in dry desert areas. The rivers get their waters from rainy mountains or from more humid areas outside the desert. The major rivers of the region include the Nile, Tigris, Euphrates, and Jordan.

Formed by two large tributaries—the Blue Nile and White Nile—that join at Khartoum (kahr·TOOHM), Sudan (soo·DAN), the Nile is the world's longest river. It flows 4,145 miles (6,670 kilometers) from its source to the Mediterranean Sea.

The Tigris and Euphrates rivers begin in the mountains of Turkey and flow through Iraq and Syria. Heavy winter rains in Turkey cause the rivers to flood between September and May. Over the years these floods

created a rich valley that was the home of some of the earliest civilizations.

The Jordan River flows through Syria and forms the border between Israel and Jordan. A river of key religious significance, the Jordan River flows into the Dead Sea.

## Resources

Despite the world's largest reserves of oil and natural gas, the region lacks adequate resources. Limited farmland and water has hampered growth for centuries.

**Agriculture.** The region's rugged landscape and scarce water supply make farming difficult. Only areas near rivers, along the Mediterranean coast, and in a few oases have the fertile soil and adequate rainfall needed for farming. Unfortunately, misuse

***Learning from Maps.*** *Wide areas of North Africa and the Middle East have only limited economic use. In what ways are these lands probably used?*

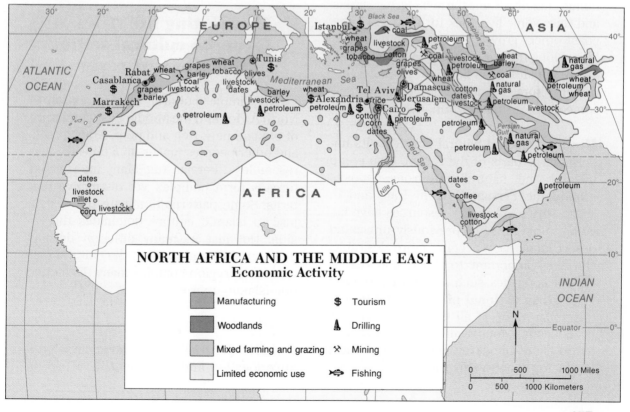

**NORTH AFRICA AND THE MIDDLE EAST**
Economic Activity

- Manufacturing
- Woodlands
- Mixed farming and grazing
- Limited economic use
- $ Tourism
- Drilling
- Mining
- Fishing

***Learning from Pictures.*** *Berber farmers tend a field high in the Atlas Mountains of Morocco. Why are many farms in the region located in mountain or river valleys?*

for centuries has reduced the productivity of many of these areas.

Despite these difficulties, subsistence farming remains the region's leading economic activity. Some farmers grow grains and raise some livestock for food. Near the coast others grow fruit, olives, and vegetables. Along the edges of the deserts and the Sahel, nomads raise flocks of goats, sheep, camels, horses, and cattle. Farmers sell some crops, usually cotton, commercially.

**Mining.**  Oil and natural gas deposits underlie large parts of the region. Rigs pump the oil and natural gas from deposits around the Persian Gulf, in Iran, and in North Africa. As energy resources have become more valuable, previously unwanted desert lands have become more desirable. Oil is so important to the region that it causes countries such as Kuwait to have huge **gross national products** (GNPs), or the dollar value of all goods and services produced in a country in a year. Oil has also led to economic development and political power for countries that have it.

Other than oil, the region has few mineral resources. Turkey has deposits of coal, iron ore, and chromium, and Morocco mines phosphate. Mines also produce salt and chemicals from the area around the Dead Sea. Few other mineral deposits contribute to regional economies.

**SECTION 1 REVIEW**

1. **Define**  subregion, erg, hammada, wadi, basin and range, exotic river, gross national product
2. **Locate**  North Africa, Middle East, Sahara, Arabian Desert, Atlas Mountains, Elburz Mountains, Al Azizia
3. **Evaluating Ideas**  **(a)** What natural resource has been the key to development in the region over the centuries? **(b)** What resource has risen to great importance recently?  **(c)** Which do you consider the most important resource today? Why?

## 2 Contrasting life styles form the cultural setting of this two-part region.

No simple cultural pattern exists in North Africa and the Middle East. A mixture of old and new, rich and poor, Arab, Israeli, and other peoples makes up a tapestry that resembles a Persian rug. Many intertwined threads form complex yet distinctive patterns. Some patterns dominate the design, just as Islamic culture dominates the region. But just as many different designs make up the total pattern, the cultural pattern of the region contains many distinctive non-Islamic imprints.

### A Brief History

In North Africa and the Middle East, relative location and movement have had an

458

especially important impact for centuries. Many of the world's earliest civilizations began here. These civilizations added skills and knowledge to human culture.

**Ancient civilizations.** About 10,000 years ago people began to settle in the fertile valley between the Tigris and Euphrates rivers. This area, in what is today Iraq, was called Mesopotamia (mehs·uh·puh·TAY·mee·uh), or "land between the rivers." This valley and the Mediterranean coast to the west form the Fertile Crescent.

Historical geographers often call the region the cradle of civilization. Between 3500 B.C. and 600 B.C. several great civilizations rose and fell. The first recorded civilization — Sumer (SOO·muhr) — arose in Mesopotamia. The Sumerians expanded clusters of mud huts into villages and developed the first form of writing, called cuneiform. The development of writing marked the end of **prehistory,** the time before written records were kept. Other great civilizations included the Egyptians; the Phoenicians, in what is today Syria and Lebanon; and the Persians, in what is today Iran.

**World religions.** The Middle East, as the birthplace of three great religions—Judaism, Christianity, and Islam—has had a lasting impact on the world. First to develop, Judaism was unique among early religions because it is based on **monotheism,** or the belief in only one god. Later another monotheistic religion, Christianity, developed in the same area. Christianity, based on the teachings of Jesus Christ, slowly spread around the world. The third great religion to begin in the region was Islam. Founded by Muhammad, Islam stresses the belief in one god, Allah. It is called Islam, which means "submission," because followers—called Muslims—submit to the will of Allah. Islam began in the 600s in what is today

*Text continues on page 462.*

*Learning from Maps.* Islam has become the dominant religion in widespread areas. How is Islam an example of cultural diffusion?

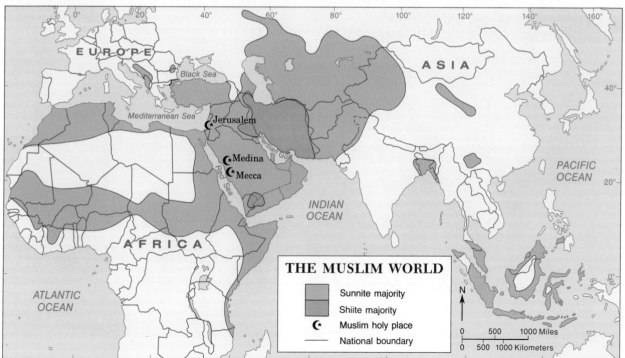

THE MUSLIM WORLD

Sunnite majority
Shiite majority
☪ Muslim holy place
— National boundary

459

# THE GEOGRAPHIC WEB
## Treasures from the Past

Starting as an inconspicuous stream east of Lake Tanganyika, the Nile River commences a 4,000-mile (6,400-kilometer) journey through mountains and deserts, finally fanning out in a great marshy delta and flowing into the Mediterranean Sea. Within its narrow valley the land of the Nile is alive with people, livestock, and crops. One step beyond lies the windswept emptiness of the Sahara.

Until the construction of the Aswan Dam, the flood-swollen river would drown the floodplain every summer with another layer of mineral-rich silt. In this fertile setting the Nile nourished one of the world's great civilizations—a civilization that lasted nearly 3,000 years.

### A Protective Barrier

Nature was kind to Egypt in the past. Deserts on both sides of the Nile Valley discouraged invaders and the people lived in comparative security. The villages that shared the life-giving waters of the river learned that cooperation was essential in controlling the annual flood. Rather than fighting among themselves, they found that cooperation allowed abundant harvests.

Cooperation meant organization. Perhaps more than any other factor, the organizational ability of the Egyptians enabled them to create and maintain a strong and enduring nation. This special quality of Egyptian civilization began to appear under the very earliest pharaohs, as their rulers were called. The social structure that developed lasted with few interruptions throughout the following 27 centuries.

### Social Structure

Basic to the Egyptian system was the concept that all power lay in the hands of the pharaoh, who played a dual role—both monarch and god. The pharaoh was at the

*Ancient monuments at Abu Simbel, Egypt*

*Gold pendant of Egyptian god Horus*

The concept that the pharaoh's life was everlasting motivated all of this construction. The pharaoh's tombs and temples were constructed with the intention that they would last forever. A common term for tomb meant "house of eternity." Egyptian workers willingly struggled to build these houses of eternity for their dead rulers because they believed that their rulers, as gods, should have ample provisions for eternal life.

Although the pharaohs did not live forever, a vast number of their tombs and shrines survive to the present. These monuments ensure that the names of those ancient rulers are still household words—over 3,000 years later—in societies and cultures they could never have imagined.

very top of society. Beneath the pharaoh were high officials, and below them was a vast bureaucracy that supervised the labor of the workers and peasants.

### Egyptian Achievements

Stability was accompanied by learning. Over time the people developed writing, which allowed them to keep records. Methods of calculation developed along with writing. Now taxes could be computed, land surveyed, and weights, measures, distances, and time recorded with accuracy.

With increased learning, architecture flourished. Within a century after the first pharaoh assumed the throne, Egyptian builders had graduated from building with sun-dried bricks to using sophisticated stone masonry. Large numbers of laborers were available to quarry huge blocks of stone and transport them to building sites. In just 200 years Egyptian builders had so mastered the use of stone that they were able to engineer the pyramids at Giza (GEE·zuh), regarded to be among the greatest of all wonders of the ancient world. In succeeding centuries, hundreds of massive stone monuments were constructed. They dot the landscape from the Nile Delta to lower Nubia, 800 miles (1,280 kilometers) south.

*Gold sarcophagus (coffin) of Tutankhamen*

Saudi Arabia, and spread rapidly throughout the Middle East and North Africa.

Various Muslim rulers and empires controlled the region until the Europeans established colonies throughout the area in the late 1800s. Soon after World War II, however, most of the region's countries gained independence. Nationalism remains strong in each of these nations.

## Population Patterns

Scattered unevenly throughout the millions of square miles of North Africa and the Middle East are about 300 million people. The densest populations line the banks of the Nile River, where an average of nearly 2,000 people per square mile (772 per square kilometer) live. People also crowd along the Mediterranean coast and other river valleys. However, in many desert areas you might travel for days without seeing a single person or village.

Although some of the first and greatest cities—Alexandria, Carthage, and others—began here, today nearly two-thirds of the region's people live in rural areas. But as in other developing lands, more people are moving to the cities. Nearly 6 million people crowd each of the region's two largest cities—Cairo, Egypt, and Tehran, Iran. Other large cities include Alexandria, Egypt; Ankara, Turkey; Baghdad, Iraq; Casablanca, Morocco; and Istanbul, Turkey.

## Social Patterns

The region's function as a crossroad between east and west brought many people to North Africa and the Middle East over

***Learning from Maps.*** *Physical surroundings and settlement are closely linked in North Africa. Why do people cluster along the Nile and the coast?*

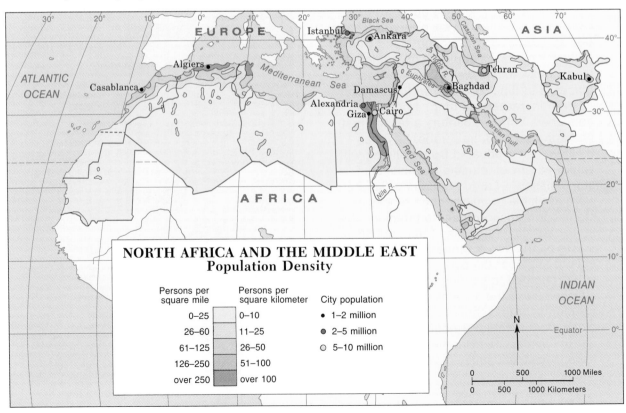

### NORTH AFRICA AND THE MIDDLE EAST
#### Population Density

| Persons per square mile | Persons per square kilometer | City population |
|---|---|---|
| 0–25 | 0–10 | ● 1–2 million |
| 26–60 | 11–25 | ● 2–5 million |
| 61–125 | 26–50 | ○ 5–10 million |
| 126–250 | 51–100 | |
| over 250 | over 100 | |

the years. Today most of the region's people are Arabs, a term that refers to people whose cultures are marked by Arab influences. Other important groups in the region include Jews; Turks; and Persians, or Iranians. These groups represent a majority of the people in some countries of the region.

Despite the dominance of Arab culture, the region's social patterns remain complex. Although Arabs form the largest population group, religious and regional differences often divide the Arabs. Over 90 percent of the people are Muslims. Yet among Muslims there are different religious sects, such as the Sunnites and the Shiites (SHEE·yts) (see the map on page 459). Arabs also speak many different **dialects,** or language variations, of Arabic. In addition, many Jews and Christians live amid Arab majorities and many people speak Turkish, Armenian, Iranian, Hebrew, French, or English, rather than Arabic.

## Political Patterns

The region's political patterns also reflect wide diversity. Nearly every type of political system exists in Northern Africa and the Middle East.

**Absolute monarchies,** in which the rulers have no restrictions on their powers, control Bahrain and Oman. Morocco and Jordan have **constitutional monarchies,** in which the powers of the rulers are limited and shared with elected or appointed officials. Several countries, such as Mauritania and North Yemen, are ruled by Communist leaders. Others, such as Egypt, Israel, and South Yemen, are democratic republics.

Some countries in the region fit none of these categories. Iran, for example, is a **theocracy,** or a government led by a religious leader. Soviet troops back Afghanistan's government. The government of Cyprus represents only a minority of the

***Learning from Pictures.*** *Camels, shown in the distance, are the most important commodity at this livestock market in Morocco. Why are camels so valuable in this region?*

people. And in many North African countries, **Bedouins,** or Arab nomads, wander across national borders and live only by tribal laws

## Economic Patterns

The countries of North Africa and the Middle East reflect various stages of economic development. Many oil-rich countries such as Saudi Arabia, Kuwait, and Bahrain have greater incomes and development programs than the region's other nations.

The countries of the region have various economic systems. Socialism, set up by the Soviets, guides Afghanistan, while Israel and other countries have a free enterprise system. Algeria and many others have socialist-style economies.

Regardless of its economic system, each country has serious economic problems to solve. Two-thirds of the region's people farm for a living. For centuries these farmers grew enough food to feed their families. Today, however, worn-out soil and increasing populations make this difficult. Nearly

**463**

all the countries of the region must import food. Although oil-rich countries can afford to do this, the other countries are building a huge debt.

Throughout North Africa and the Middle East new techniques for farming and irrigation help to increase farm output. Many countries, for example, follow Algeria's example by planting trees to hold valuable topsoil against desert winds. This plan is aimed at stopping **desertification** (di·zuhrt·uh·fuh·KAY·shuhn), the process by which fertile land becomes desert. Although such measures have created new farmland and have led to greater farm production, they will fail unless farmers take better care of the land.

Oil was discovered in the Middle East in the 1930s and by the 1950s had changed the area's economic patterns. In 1960 the leaders of Iran, Iraq, Kuwait, Saudi Arabia, and Venezuela formed OPEC—the Organization of Petroleum Exporting Countries. OPEC sought to control oil prices by regulating the amount of oil on world markets. Since OPEC's founding, Algeria, Ecuador, Gabon (ga·BOHN), Indonesia, Libya, Nigeria, Qatar, and the United Arab Emirates have joined the organization. Billions of dollars now flow into OPEC countries, changing the lives of the countries' people.

Oil income has brought both problems and progress to the region. It sharply divides the region into rich and poor countries. It also divides the population in oil-rich countries into rich and poor groups. And it focuses worldwide attention and political pressure on OPEC members. But in most countries, the government spends its petro dollars, or the money earned from oil profits, on services for the people such as telephone service, medical care, and education. Many countries also use the income to build roads, ports, and factories. Recent declines in oil income and feuds among OPEC members, however, have begun to affect the value of oil production.

*Learning from Pictures.* *Even oil exploration has proceeded slowly in the empty expanses of the Arabian Desert. Why are international borders in this region often undefined?*

**SECTION 2 REVIEW**

1. **Define**   prehistory, monotheism, dialect, absolute monarchy, constitutional monarchy, theocracy, bedouin, desertification
2. **Locate**   Tigris River, Euphrates River, Fertile Crescent, Dead Sea
3. **Analyzing Ideas**   How does the region reflect different   **(a)** social patterns,   **(b)** political patterns, and   **(c)** economic patterns?
4. **Evaluating Ideas**   **(a)** What problems has the discovery of oil in the region caused?   **(b)** What benefits has the discovery of oil brought?   **(c)** Do you think the benefits outweigh the costs? Defend your answer.

# DEVELOPING GEOGRAPHY SKILLS
## INTERPRETING VISUALS: Reading Pie Graphs

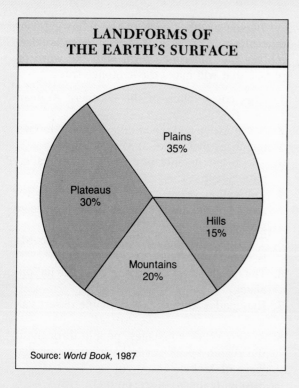

### LANDFORMS OF THE EARTH'S SURFACE

Plains 35%

Plateaus 30%

Hills 15%

Mountains 20%

Source: *World Book,* 1987

A pie graph (or pie chart) is a graphic that presents two pieces of information. First, a pie graph breaks a subject down into its various components. Second, a pie graph indicates what part of the whole each component represents.

The pie graph above, for example, illustrates the proportions of the earth's surface covered by each of the four major landforms (see Chapter 3). The graph lists the four landforms—plains, plateaus, hills, and mountains. It also indicates what percentage of the earth's surface each landform covers—plains cover about 35 percent of the surface, plateaus about 30 percent, mountains about 20 percent, and hills about 15 percent.

### How to Read a Pie Graph

Review the steps for reading graphs that are listed in the skill lesson on page 213.

Apply those steps to a pie graph such as the one below.

### Applying the Skill

Study the pie graph below. Note that the title is "Crude Oil Production, 1987." The labels list the leading oil producers in 1987 and give the percentage of total oil production each producer contributed. You will notice that OPEC produced the largest percentage of the world's oil. OPEC is an oil cartel, a group that is formally bound together to regulate the production and sale of oil. The "slices" of the graph illustrate the relative amounts of oil each contributor produced.

*To practice this skill, see Practicing Geography Skills on page 467.*

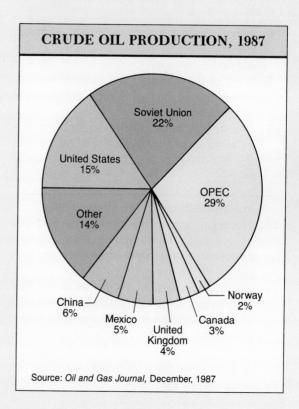

### CRUDE OIL PRODUCTION, 1987

Soviet Union 22%

United States 15%

OPEC 29%

Other 14%

China 6%

Mexico 5%

United Kingdom 4%

Canada 3%

Norway 2%

Source: *Oil and Gas Journal,* December, 1987

## Chapter Summary

The following list contains the key concepts you have learned about the settings of North Africa and the Middle East.

1. Two distinct subregions—North Africa and the Middle East—make up the region. Despite certain differences, they share common physical and cultural features.

2. A narrow lowland rims the Mediterranean Sea, but plateaus cover most of both North Africa and the Middle East.

3. Desert climates influence most of both North Africa and the Middle East. Several different types of desert landscapes cover the vast expanses of dry areas.

4. Great exotic rivers flow through many of the desert areas.

5. Most natural resources are scarce. Water, forests, good farmland, and mineral deposits are limited. Deposits of oil and natural gas, however, provide great wealth for many of the region's countries.

6. Three major world religions—Judaism, Christianity, and Islam—developed in the region.

7. Many of the countries are sparsely and unevenly settled. Few people live in vast areas of the deserts.

8. Due in part to its location as a crossroads between east and west, North Africa and the Middle East have a complex cultural setting.

9. Nearly every kind of political system exists in North Africa and the Middle East.

10. The region's countries are in various stages of economic development. Many oil-rich nations use oil income to provide services for their citizens.

11. Geographers define deserts as areas that lack water. The color pattern—brown and green—illustrates the differences in water availability.

On a separate sheet of paper, complete the following review exercises.

## Reviewing Geographic Terms

Decide whether each of the following sentences is true or false. If the sentence is false, replace the underlined term with the word or phrase that will make the sentence true.

1. Ergs cover much of the southern Arabian Desert.

2. North Africa and the Middle East are the two countries that make up the region.

3. The belief in only one god is often called nationalism.

4. Cultivation occurs when vegetation is removed, farmland is overused, and the desert spreads.

5. The time before people kept written records is called prehistory.

6. The development of cuneiform ended nationalism.

7. Hammadas are dry but farmable desert valleys.

8. Among other languages, people throughout the region speak several variations, or dialects, of Arabic.

9. Strong feelings of resentment drive each country to maintain its independence.

## Developing Critical Thinking Skills

1. **Interpreting Ideas** (a) Why are North Africa and the Middle East grouped together as one region? Give specific examples to support your answer. (b) Why might some geographers separate the two subregions for study?

2. **Summarizing Ideas** (a) What are the four major rivers of the region? (b) Why are rivers particularly important to the people of this region?

3. **Analyzing Ideas** (a) Why might it be considered misleading to state that North Africa and the Middle East receive an *average annual* rainfall of 10 inches (25.4 centimeters)? (b) Do you think that average rainfall statistics for any region are misleading? Explain your answer.

4. **Writing About Geography** In a full-page essay, complete one of the following activities. **(a)** Evaluate the impact of oil production on the region's social and economic patterns. **(b)** Explain why so many early civilizations developed in this region compared to elsewhere.

## Using Primary Sources

In the following excerpt from *Caravan: The Story of the Middle East*, Carleton S. Coon describes the Arabs' keen understanding of geography. As you study the reading, consider the importance of understanding geography in the modern world.

The good geographer is a philosopher.

The medieval Arabs, who wrote some of the finest geographical treatises [essays] ever penned, knew this. They knew that the culture of a people bears an intimate relationship to the landscape on which they live. They knew that the geography of a region shapes the way of life of its inhabitants, as the bones and muscles of a healthy man shape his skin. Scholars . . . realized that if one is to understand the civilization of a people, one must start with the geography of the land they inhabit.

Geologically speaking, the world's oldest civilizations arose in some of the world's youngest lands. During Mesozoic and early Cenozoic times, most of North Africa . . . [was] under water. When these lands finally rose to the surface they were covered with sea-deposited layers of sandstone and limestone. Sandstone and limestone are easily worked and make excellent building material. . . .

In the Middle Eastern countries it is only where the mountains have folded and faulted, exposing older layers, that . . . desirable minerals are to be found.

. . . The scarcity of these substances and the long distances between known deposits have kept Middle Eastern peoples on the move since the dawn of the age of metal.

1. What, according to medieval Arabs, shapes the way of life of a people?
2. What examples does the author provide in the excerpt to illustrate this geographic idea?

## Practicing Geography Skills

*Before completing this activity, review Developing Geography Skills on page 465.*

**Reading Pie Graphs** Study the graph on page 60. Then answer the following questions.

1. **(a)** What are the major divisions of the earth's land surface? **(b)** Which continent covers the largest land area? **(c)** Which covers the smallest?
2. What percentage of the earth's total land area lies in **(a)** North America, **(b)** Europe, **(c)** Africa, and **(d)** Antarctica?

## Exploring Geography

1. Use resources in your school or public library to find information on the life and work of one of the great Arab scholars of the past. Your research should focus on what the scholar's work contributed to Western learning. Present your findings in a brief oral report as you study the next chapter.
2. Almost every aspect of life in North Africa and the Middle East is dominated by the landscape—desert. Look through magazines and newspapers to find illustrations of the different types of deserts described in Section 1. Then prepare a collage illustrating these desert types. Your collage should also identify which desert type each illustration shows.

# PUTTING THE CHAPTER IN FOCUS

An Arab culture dominates North Africa, which includes the developing nations of Egypt, Libya, Tunisia, Algeria, Morocco, Mauritania, and the territory of Western Sahara. Most of the people in the region live near sources of water—along the Nile River in Egypt or along the Mediterranean coast. Harsh desert conditions make development difficult elsewhere in the region.

## Ideas to Understand

In studying about North Africa, use these ideas to give direction to your reading.

1 Egypt, a leading Arab nation, follows an independent course.
2 Many obstacles slow the development of other North African countries.

## Terms to Define

The following terms are some of the key terms in the chapter. Defining them will help you understand North Africa.

| | |
|---|---|
| bazaar | free port |
| silt | zone of transition |
| depose | coup d'etat |
| balance of trade | guerrilla |

## Places to Locate

Locating the following places will add to your knowledge of geography.

| | |
|---|---|
| Sinai Peninsula | Algeria |
| Suez Canal | Morocco |
| Cairo | Mauritania |
| Libya | Western Sahara |
| Tunisia | |

## 1 Egypt, a leading Arab nation, follows an independent course.

The waters of the Nile River, providing relief from the desert's unforgiving heat and arid conditions, nurtured one of the world's oldest civilizations—Egypt. The pyramids stand as a symbol of this ancient civilization. Today Egypt's rich cultural heritage and strategic location give it a unique place in North Africa and the Middle East.

### Physical Setting

Egypt, which is about the size of Texas and Oregon combined, lies at the eastern edge of North Africa. Egypt borders the Red Sea on the east, Libya on the west, and Sudan on the south. The Mediterranean Sea washes Egypt's northern coast.

A thin strip of lowland extends along Egypt's coast between the Sinai (SY·ny) Peninsula and the Libyan border. This thin band receives Egypt's greatest annual rainfall—4 to 8 inches (10 to 20 centimeters). Very little rain falls on the rest of the country. In some years southern and eastern Egypt get no rain at all.

Just south of the coast lie Egypt's seemingly endless deserts. East of the Nile, hammadas rise to between 1,000 and 2,000 feet (305 and 610 meters) to form the edge of the Arabian Desert. To the west of the Nile lies the Libyan Desert. In the northern part of the Libyan Desert the land actually dips 436 feet (133 meters) below sea level to form the Qattara (kuh·TAHR·uh) Depression, which covers more than 10,000 square miles (25,900 square kilometers). Numerous small oases dot the Libyan Desert, although their waters can only be tapped by drilling shallow wells.

◄ *Feluccas sailing on the Nile near Aswan, Egypt*

Egypt has long been called "the gift of the Nile." The Nile, which ranks as the world's longest river, flows northward through Egypt's dry landscape to a massive delta that reaches far into the Mediterranean Sea. Each year heavy rains in the highlands of Ethiopia cause the Nile to flood between June and October.

The Sinai Peninsula lies on the eastern edge of Egypt. A mountainous desert, the Sinai Peninsula has served as a crossroad between the subregions of North Africa and the Middle East for centuries. One of the world's major transportation links—the Suez Canal—cuts through the Sinai to connect the Red and Mediterranean seas.

## Cultural Setting

Egypt's rich cultural heritage dates back thousands of years. Today Egypt's growing population and urban development, against

*Learning from Pictures.* *Air pollution is one of the forces causing monuments such as the Great Sphinx and the pyramids to decay. Why does Egypt's dry climate help slow the decay?*

### TEMPERATURES AND PRECIPITATION IN SELECTED NORTH AFRICAN CITIES

| City/Country | January Low | July High | Precipitation (in/cm) |
|---|---|---|---|
| ALGIERS, ALGERIA | 49°F 9°C | 83°F 28°C | 30/ 76 |
| CAIRO, EGYPT | 47°F 8°C | 96°F 36°C | 1/ 3 |
| CASABLANCA, MOROCCO | 45°F 7°C | 79°F 26°C | 16/ 40 |
| TRIPOLI, LIBYA | 47°F 8°C | 85°F 29°C | 15/ 38 |
| ALEXANDRIA, EGYPT | 58°F 14°C | 79°F 26°C | 7/ 18 |
| TUNIS, TUNISIA | 48°F 9°C | 79°F 26°C | 16/ 41 |

Source: *Statesman's Yearbook*, 1987

*Learning from Charts.* *The most striking statistic on this chart is the low precipitation received by Cairo. Why does Algiers receive more precipitation than Cairo?*

the backdrop of this ancient history, gives the country a unique cultural setting.

**Population patterns.** More than 90 percent of Egypt's 51.9 million people live within a few miles of the Nile River. This already crowded ribbon of land gets more crowded every year. With an annual growth rate of 2.6 percent, more than 1 million people are added to the population each year.

Today about 46 percent of Egypt's people live in cities and towns. The capital and largest city—Cairo (KY·roh)—has more than 6 million residents. Another 4 million crowd the slums that surround Cairo for miles in all directions. Other major cities include Giza (GEE·zuh) and Alexandria.

**Social patterns.** Nubians comprise about 90 percent of Egypt's population. People of Greek, Italian, Syrian, and Lebanese de-

*Text continues on page 472.*

# CITY FOCUS
## Cairo, Egypt

Cairo, Egypt's capital and the African continent's largest city, sits on the east bank of the Nile River at the entrance to the fertile Nile Delta. It is a magnificent site, lying in the shadows of ancient pyramids. Yet it is also fast becoming one of the most overcrowded cities in the world.

### A Crowded City

Those who remember the Cairo of old, when it was known as "The Jewel of the Arab World," can only shake their heads. Some now call it "The Calcutta of the Middle East," a place where rich and poor fight for living space in a jam-packed metropolitan area of 10 million people. In 1965, with a population of 2.5 million, the city was already regarded as having too many people for its water supply, sanitation facilities, and transportation system.

Cairo's suburbs now reach all the way to the edge of the pyramids, more than 9 miles (14.5 kilometers) from the center of the city. Seepage from an ancient and inadequate sewer system is beginning to undermine the Great Sphinx, a monument that has guarded the pyramids for more than 4,000 years. And with summer temperatures that soar to a daily average of 96°F (36°C), unbelievable noise, and life-threatening atmospheric pollution, Cairo is fast becoming an urban disaster area. Yet people by the thousands continue to pour into the city from the countryside, hoping to find jobs and a better way of life.

### A City of Contrasts

Few cities reflect such stunning contrasts in ways of life as Cairo. The wealthy live along the banks of the Nile in elegant apartment buildings surrounded by beautifully landscaped gardens. Neon signs of fashionable skyscraper hotels, casinos, and nightclubs flash along the Nile's waterfront.

*Modern buildings lining the Nile in Cairo*

But beyond this facade lies a maze of festering ghettos, decaying buildings, filthy alleys, and the hovels of the very poor.

And the contrasts go even deeper. Despite the grinding poverty and massive unemployment, Cairo ranks as the cultural center of the Arab world. Its great university, a renowned symphony orchestra, a national theater and opera, and various museums support this distinction. At the same time some 50,000 Egyptians make their homes in tombs in the City of the Dead, a cemetery of crumbling vaults near downtown Cairo. Even worse off are the thousands who dwell amid the stench and smoke of Cairo's garbage dumps. Forced to share their shacks with their livestock, they scrounge for a living beside decaying mounds of refuse and great clouds of flies and fleas.

Many Cairo residents claim that the growing problems of their city are a result of Western influences. Around the city's mosques people are beginning to demand that Egypt return to the basic teachings of Islam. These people hope that such a change will restore Cairo's greatness.

scent make up most of the other 10 percent. Most of the people speak Arabic, the official language, although many also speak English and French. About 94 percent of the people are Muslims. Most of the remaining 6 percent are Coptic Christians—descendants of Egyptians who first practiced this form of Christianity in the 600s.

**Political patterns.** Egyptian civilization began more than 8,000 years ago. At that time the people lived in small farming villages along the Nile. About 3100 B.C. Menes (MEE·neez)—thought to be the first pharaoh—united the country. Egypt remained united and independent until Alexander the Great conquered it in 333 B.C. From then until 1953 a series of foreign groups, including Romans, Persians, Arabs, Turks, French, and British, ruled Egypt. In 1953 Egypt won complete independence from Britain and established a republic. Today the country struggles to maintain its fragile democracy.

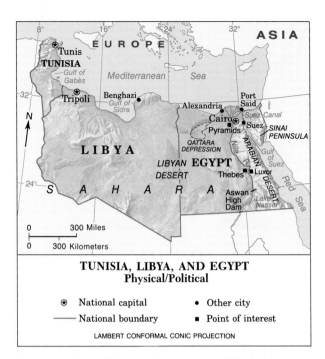

*Learning from Maps.* This corner of North Africa is among the world's driest places. How do the low-pressure belts in the low latitudes help to create the dry climate?

**Economic patterns.** Egypt remains a developing nation. Most Egyptians lead difficult lives, farming small fields along the Nile. They rent farmland and struggle to grow enough food to feed their families and to pay the rent. They sell or trade any extra crops they grow at the village **bazaar,** or marketplace.

Many Egyptian farmers continue to use ancient tools and methods. Some still use basin irrigation, the traditional method that relied on the Nile's annual floods. Before construction of the Aswan Dam ended yearly floods, the Nile's waters would sweep over the fields, bringing with them rich, moist soil, or **silt,** carried as sediment in the river's waters. Today, without the floods, workers carry water to fields from irrigation canals. Water is fed to the canals from dams to the south.

In recent years many Egyptian farmers have turned to perennial, or year-round, irrigation that makes it possible to grow two crops a year. Huge dams store the Nile's

*Learning from Pictures.* This Egyptian farmer near Luxor relies on oxen to plow his fields. What techniques have Egyptian farmers used to increase productivity?

waters for use throughout the year. The Aswan (ah·SWAHN) Dam, 364 feet (111 meters) high and 2 miles (3.2 kilometers) long, holds enough water to irrigate over 2 million acres (800,000 hectares) of farmland and provides hydroelectricity for industry. Despite its benefits, however, the dams rob the Nile's waters of its rich silt, which is trapped by the dams. For this reason, Egyptian farmers must now use huge amounts of artificial fertilizers to replenish the soil's nutrients.

Farmers along the Nile grow rice, onions, wheat, corn, barley, and peanuts for food. Nevertheless, food still leads the list of Egypt's imports, accounting for nearly two-thirds of the value of the country's total yearly imports. Raw cotton and cotton yarn and fabric rank behind oil as the country's leading exports.

Although Egypt has few major industries, food, chemical, and oil processing and light manufacturing contribute to the economy. Mines tap deposits of iron ore, phosphate, and manganese. Deposits of oil and natural gas have also been tapped. Tourism, the sale of hydroelectricity, and fees for the use of the Suez Canal also serve as sources of income.

---

### SECTION 1 REVIEW

1. **Define**  bazaar, silt
2. **Locate**  Egypt, Sinai Peninsula, Suez Canal, Cairo
3. **Summarizing Ideas**  **(a)** What are Egypt's major physical features?  **(b)** What is Egypt's climatic setting?
4. **Interpreting Ideas**  How is the distribution of Egypt's people related to its physical setting?
5. **Comparing Ideas**  **(a)** How has farming in Egypt changed recently?  **(b)** What are the benefits of the change?  **(c)** What are the costs?

---

## 2 Many obstacles slow the development of other North African countries.

West of Egypt lie the countries of the western Sahara. The western Sahara, sometimes called the Arab West, extends from Egypt westward to the Atlantic Ocean and from the Mediterranean Sea across the Sahara and the Sahel. The region includes the countries of Libya, Tunisia, Algeria, Morocco, and Mauritania, and the territory of Western Sahara.

### Physical Setting

The countries of the western Sahara share a similar landscape. A narrow lowland lines the coast of the Mediterranean Sea. The coastal lowland widens from east to west. The vast Sahara, with its harsh, dry conditions, reaches south from the lowland.

Rising between the coastal lowland and the desert, the high Atlas Mountains stretch east to west from Tunisia to Morocco. The windward sides of these mountains receive heavy rainfall. But the drying effects of the pressure belt and mountain barrier result in desert conditions beyond these mountain ranges.

In the south the lower Ahaggar (uh·HAHG·uhr) and Tibesti (tuh·BES·tee) mountains interrupt the desert plateaus. Farmable wadis stretch from the mountains far into the desert.

### Cultural Setting

The cultural setting of the western Sahara has undergone many changes over the years. Black farmers and Berber shepherds first inhabited the area. In the late 600s Arabs arrived with camels—the "ships of the desert"—and a fruit known as dates. The Arabs later established caravan routes that carried cargoes of gold, gems, ivory, and

slaves across the desert. The Arabs also converted the Berbers to Islam. Eventually, the religion spread deep into the Sahara. The spread of Islam throughout this area is an excellent example of cultural diffusion.

Europeans came to the western Sahara in the 1830s. They quickly conquered the coastal towns. But it took them years to gain control of the Berber settlements scattered throughout the Sahara. Although the colonies of the western Sahara eventually won independence from the nations of Europe, the European imprint **remains strong** in many areas.

## Countries of the Western Sahara

The nations of the western Sahara share many similarities—especially in terms of their physical setting. Culturally, however, the nations reflect diverse social, political, and economic patterns.

**Libya.** Libya, a country larger than Alaska, occupies the Sahara west of Egypt. A very narrow lowland rims the coast. This lowland receives the country's only mea-

*Learning from Pictures. These "walking" irrigators bring water to a field in the Kufra Desert in Libya. What source of income allows Libya to develop irrigation projects?*

surable rainfall—10 to 20 inches (25 to 50 centimeters) a year. The Libyan Desert, one of the driest places on earth, covers more than 90 percent of the country.

Although a few people live near oases or in mountain valleys, most of Libya's 3.8 million people live near the Mediterranean coast, where the country's two largest cities—Tripoli and Benghazi (ben·GAHZ·ee)—are located. With a growth rate of 3.2 percent a year, coastal areas are becoming increasingly crowded.

Arabs and Berbers comprise over 90 percent of the people. People from southern Europe, Pakistan, India, and the Middle East make up most of the rest. Nearly 97 percent of the people are Muslims and almost everyone speaks Arabic. Many of the people in the cities also understand Italian and English.

Once ruled by the Ottoman Empire and then by Italy, Libya won its independence in 1951. A monarchy ruled the country for 19 years, but in 1969 the king was **deposed,** or removed from office, and a military dictatorship took control. Today Colonel Muammar al-Qaddafi (kuh·DAHF·ee) leads the Islamic government, which is politically active throughout the region.

Nomadic herding and subsistence farming remain the country's leading economic activities. Herders raise sheep, cattle, and camels on scanty pasturelands. Farmers grow wheat, barley, olives, peanuts, and tobacco on small fields along the coast and dates and fruit at oases. Libya must import about 65 percent of its food.

Oil serves as Libya's only major export, adding $10 billion a year to its socialist economy. The government uses the income to supply an army and support terrorists, as well as to build roads and factories.

Though still a developing nation, Libya has benefited enormously from its oil resources. Since 1963 the total value of Libya's exports has exceeded the total value

*Text continues on page 477.*

# CASE STUDY
## EXPLORING NATURE: Desertification

To understand the events that have occurred in recent years along the southern edges of the Sahara, you must know two key terms—*Sahel* and *desertification*. Sahel refers to a place; desertification refers to a process.

### The Sahel

Located south of the Sahara, the semiarid Sahel covers large parts of Burkina Faso, Chad, Gambia, Guinea-Bissau, Mali. Mauritania, Niger, and Senegal (see the map on page 511). Today the loss of valuable soil threatens to transform the entire Sahel into desert.

### Desertification

A combination of human activities and continued drought cause desertification—the spread of desert conditions. Desertification began to engulf the Sahel in 1968. No rains came and though drought persisted, nomadic herders continued to graze their livestock. Pastures became increasingly eroded. Soon vast areas were so desperately overgrazed that no pastures remained.

In addition to overgrazing the land, the nomads cut the few trees and shrubs for firewood. This deforestation leaves the soil bare and open to devastating winds that sweep the soil away. But wood provides 80 to 90 percent of the region's energy and cutting the trees is a necessity. As a result, deforestation is extremely rapid. Each year Sahelian residents strip trees from 1,000 to 1,500 square miles (2,600 to 3,900 square kilometers) of woodland and reforest only one-tenth of that. And always the winds come to sweep away the soil.

Although the nations of the region recognize the dangers of deforestation and have established tree-planting campaigns, the programs have had limited success.

*Shepherds tending a flock of sheep in the Sahel*

The people of the Sahel think of trees in terms of firewood, not as protection against the relentless march of the desert.

### Effects of Desertification

Desertification has had disastrous effects on the region. Hundreds of thousands of people and millions of animals have died of starvation. And as the Sahara relentlessly gobbles up the Sahel at the rate of 4 miles (6 kilometers) per year, more and more people flee to the region's impoverished cities. Having lost their herds—their traditional source of livelihood—nomads now crowd into wooden and tin shacks and depend on assistance from others to survive. Nouakchott (noo·AHK·shaht), Mauritania, for example, has absorbed more than 500,000 desert refugees since the drought began. Meanwhile, a reddish-orange cloud of sand and soil blocks the sun from view as the Sahara continues to expand.

475

# DEVELOPING GEOGRAPHY SKILLS
## INTERPRETING VISUALS: Interpreting Landsat Imagery

For centuries geographers have wished they could climb a mountain and view the earth from above. They were finally offered that chance in 1972 when the first Landsat satellite was launched. As you read in Chapter 2, geographers today receive tremendous amounts of information from scanners aboard Landsat satellites that circle the earth 14 times a day in an orbit 570 miles (920 kilometers) high. The image of the Nile Delta below was produced by a Landsat's thematic scanner.

Landsats scan the earth electronically. The electronic signals are sent to a communications satellite, which transmits the signals to a receiving station on earth. A computer translates the electronic signals into colors—blue, green, red, and several infrared bands. For this reason, Landsat imagery is known as a false-color image.

Each color on a Landsat image reveals something different. Blue indicates bare soil and shallow water. Red marks harvested croplands and cultural features such as cities and highways. Green identifies forests. Combinations of infrared, which show as red, indicate intensive farm use.

### How to Interpret Landsat Imagery

Review the steps for gathering data from photographs that are listed on page 141. Remember, however, that you are working with a false-color image.

### Applying the Skill

Study the image below. Note that two streams of the Nile snake through the delta. Along the banks of each stream are patches of red, indicating villages and intensively farmed fields. Scattered here and there are spots of light blue, identifying barren lands. The very light blue at the top of the image indicates the shallow water at the edge of the Mediterranean Sea.

*To practice this skill, see Practicing Geography Skills on page 481.*

of its imports, giving the country a favorable **balance of trade**—the difference in the value between a nation's imports and its exports.

**Tunisia.** Tucked between Libya and Algeria lies Tunisia, which is about the size of Missouri. Tunisia has two distinct physical regions. In the northwest half of the country a plateau rises westward to the Atlas Mountains. Small streams flow across the plateau and rain occasionally falls. The Sahara spreads southeastward.

Most of Tunisia's 7.6 million people live in the northwest or along the coast. Small villages occupy some oases, but very few people live in the southern one-third of the country. Tunis, the capital and main port, ranks as the country's only large city.

Tunisia won its independence from France in 1956, but ties between the two countries remain strong. Arabs make up 98 percent of the people and Arabic serves as the official language. Many people, however, also speak French. France remains Tunisia's leading trading partner.

Tunisia is a democratic republic and, unlike in most other Arab countries, women can vote in the country's national elections. A national school system set up in colonial days educates most children and the literacy rate has risen to more than 62 percent.

Although somewhat diversified, Tunisia's economy still depends on farming. Farmers grow barley, wheat, olives, fruit, and vegetables. Deposits of phosphate, oil, and natural gas support growing industries that process minerals, food, and textiles. Oil accounts for 40 percent of Tunisia's exports. Tourism adds more than $500 million a year to the economy.

**Algeria.** Directly west of Tunisia lies Algeria. Desert covers 80 percent of this huge country, which is more than three times the size of Texas.

***Learning from Pictures.*** *The Opera House in Oran, Algeria, was built when Algeria was a French colony. Why did colonists bring opera and other aspects of their culture to the colonies?*

A narrow coastal strip that receives moderate rainfall runs along Algeria's Mediterranean coast. A few miles inland from the coast rise the Atlas Mountains. To the south, beyond the mountains, lie the dry plateaus of the Sahara. The Tibesti and Ahaggar mountains jut from desert plateaus in extreme southern Algeria.

More than 85 percent of Algeria's 23 million people live within 50 miles of the coast. Nearly 4 million people crowd the port of Algiers, the capital and largest city. The rapidly growing population—at 3.2 percent a year—threatens to further crowd the settled areas.

Today Arabs and Berbers comprise 99 percent of the people. Ninety-nine percent also practice Islam, the country's official religion. Most of the people speak Arabic, although many also speak French. France remains Algeria's chief trading partner.

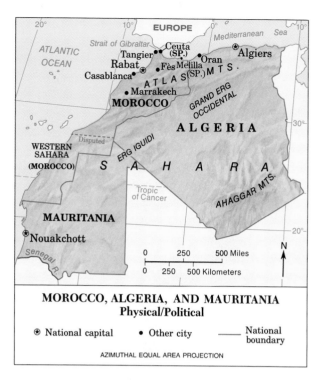

MOROCCO, ALGERIA, AND MAURITANIA
Physical/Political

⊛ National capital    • Other city    —— National boundary

AZIMUTHAL EQUAL AREA PROJECTION

***Learning from Maps.*** *Unlike the eastern Sahara, which is covered by dry plateaus, large ergs cover the western Sahara. What are ergs?*

Algeria's battle for independence from France led to a devastating civil war. After years of bloody warfare Algeria became independent in 1962. An authoritarian dictatorship run by military leaders has guided the country since then.

Most Algerians farm in a continuing struggle to grow enough food to feed the country's people. Most years crops of wheat, barley, and oats yield barely enough to avoid widespread hunger. Food accounts for 20 percent of Algeria's imports.

Oil and natural gas make up 98 percent of Algeria's exports. Tapping vast oil reserves has brought surplus income, which the country's socialist leaders use to build schools, roads, and hospitals and to train teachers and medical personnel.

**Morocco.** Morocco, which is larger than California, lies wedged in the northwest corner of North Africa, facing both the Mediterranean Sea and the Atlantic Ocean. The coastal lowland widens considerably in Morocco to the foothills of the interior highlands, making nearly 50 percent of the country's land livable. The Atlas Mountains separate the lowland from the Sahara, which extends through the southern part of the country.

Nearly 24 million people live in Morocco. Many people live in coastal cities such as the capital of Rabat (ruh·BAHT), Casablanca, or the ancient port of Tangier (tan·JIR). Tangier serves as a **free port** where the government levies little taxes on imports and exports. Other people live in inland towns such as Marrakech that grew along caravan routes.

Moroccan culture blends Arabic, French, and Spanish elements. Nearly 98 percent of the people trace their descent to Arab and Berber ancestors. Islam remains the dominant religion. Most people speak Arabic, the official language, although French is used in government and business.

In 1956 the colonies of French Morocco and Spanish Morocco and the International Settlement of Tangier—a free city governed by an international council—combined to form Morocco. The new country established a constitutional monarchy. Spain continues to control two **enclaves,** or territories enclosed within a foreign country, on Morocco's coast—Ceuta (SAY·oot·uh) and Melilla (muh·LEE·uh).

Still a developing nation, Morocco's people remain quite poor. Farmers grow wheat, barley, fruit, and vegetables, while herders raise goats, sheep, and some cattle. Fishers haul in moderate catches in both the Mediterranean and the Atlantic. However, Morocco must import most of its food.

Though it lacks large oil reserves, Morocco has rich deposits of other minerals. Phosphates make up 25 percent of the value of the country's exports. Mines also produce iron ore, manganese, lead, and zinc.

**Mauritania.** Mauritania lies southwest of Morocco, between North Africa and West Africa. Geographers often categorize the country with the North African nations because it shares several common physical and cultural traits with those countries.

The sparsely populated Islamic Republic of Mauritania has a land area larger than Texas and California combined. Rocky plateaus, large ergs, and sparse vegetation cover the landscape, which is almost 90 percent desert.

Almost all of Mauritania's 2 million people live in settlements scattered on the coastal plain and the southern plateau. Only 35 percent of the people live in towns and cities. Mauritania's ethnic composition reflects its relative location between North and West Africa. An area that lies between cultures is called a **zone of transition.** Moors, the descendants of Arab and Berber ancestors, make up about 30 percent of the people. Blacks make up another 30 percent. People of mixed heritage make up the largest group—about 40 percent. Nearly all Mauritanians are Muslims.

Mauritania's political situation since its independence has been stormy. The military first seized power in the republic in 1978. Another **coup d'état** (KOOD ay·TAH), or overthrow of the government, took place in 1979. According to the constitution of 1979, the Military Committee for National Salvation rules by decree, or direct order.

Nomadic herding and subsistence farming lead the economic activities. The chief farm products include livestock, grains, vegetables, and dates. Despite these products and some catches of fish, food accounts for more than half the imports.

In recent years Mauritania has begun to develop its mineral potential. Today iron ore leads the country's exports. The mining of gypsum, a mineral used in making fertilizer and plaster, and the processing of fish add to the economy.

**Western Sahara.** Western Sahara, formerly called Spanish Sahara, lies between Morocco and Mauritania. Because Western Sahara is virtually all desert, droughts continually plague the country. Only about 100,000 people live scattered along the coast and at a few oases. Arabs and Berbers make up most of the population. Almost everyone is Muslim and speaks Arabic.

The current legal status of Western Sahara remains uncertain. When Spain left the territory in 1976, the area was divided between Morocco and Mauritania. When Mauritania withdrew from its newly acquired lands in the south in 1979, Moroccan officials occupied the area and took administrative control. **Guerrillas,** members of organized opposition groups that use violent methods to oppose the existing government, seek to drive the Moroccans out of the southern territory.

Herders raise camels, goats, and sheep, while farmers grow a few vegetables, dates, and, in "wet" years, small crops of barley. Fishers catch some fish, but fuel shortages keep them from better fishing grounds. As a result, Western Sahara imports more then 90 percent of its food. The territory has no industry, but mineral deposits yield phosphate, the leading export, and iron ore.

---

### SECTION 2 REVIEW

1. **Define** depose, balance of trade, free port, enclave, zone of transition, coup d'etat, guerrilla
2. **Locate** Libya, Tunisia, Algeria, Morocco, Mauritania, Western Sahara
3. **Summarizing Ideas** What physical and cultural features do the countries of the western Sahara share?
4. **Contrasting Ideas** (a) How is Mauritania's policy toward Western Sahara different than Morocco's? (b) What are Saharans doing to change this policy?

# CHAPTER 24 REVIEW

## Chapter Summary

The following list contains the key concepts you have learned about North Africa.

1. Egypt's climate and landscape are very hot and dry. The life-giving Nile River winds through the country and its fertile valley, keeping Egypt from being completely covered by desert.
2. An advanced civilization developed in Egypt in ancient times. But from 333 B.C. to 1953 foreign powers ruled Egypt.
3. Egypt is a developing nation, and most Egyptians are very poor. New irrigation methods are increasing farm output, but they have changed ways of life that have existed since ancient times.
4. The western Sahara, also called the Arab West, includes the countries of Libya, Tunisia, Algeria, Morocco, and Mauritania and the territory of Western Sahara.
5. The countries of the western Sahara have narrow coastal lowlands and vast deserts beyond.
6. Population distribution reflects the physical setting. Most of the people live within a few miles of the coast or along rivers.
7. Arab culture dominates North Africa. Most of the people are Muslims and most speak Arabic. But European imprints remain strong in many places.
8. Political systems in the region range from Egypt's democratic republic to Libya's totalitarian dictatorship.
9. The countries of North Africa are developing nations. Limited water, farmland, and resources hinder development, although a few countries have benefited from discoveries of oil. Most have adopted socialist economic systems.
10. The discovery of oil in several of the countries has had a major impact on social, political, and economic patterns.

On a separate sheet of paper, complete the following review exercises.

## Reviewing Geographic Terms

Match each of the following terms with the correct definition below.

a. free port     e. zone of transition
b. depose     f. coup d'etat
c. bazaar     g. guerrilla
d. silt

1. City where little or no taxes are charged on imports or exports
2. Marketplace where villagers and farmers sell farm products and crafts
3. Area with a relative location between cultures that reflects elements of each of the cultures
4. Rich soil carried as sediment in water
5. Overthrow of the existing government, often by the military
6. Removal of the monarchy from power
7. Member of an organized group that uses violent methods to oppose the government

## Developing Critical Thinking Skills

1. **Comparing Ideas** (a) How is Egypt similar to the other countries of North Africa? (b) How is it different?
2. **Organizing Ideas** Considering Egypt's history from 333 B.C. to 1953, why is it unusual that one group of people makes up 90 percent of its population?
3. **Determining Cause and Effect** Why are many of the interior parts of the western Sahara so dry?
4. **Evaluating Ideas** (a) Which is a more important resource to the people of North Africa, oil or water? (b) How has the discovery of oil changed life in some of the countries of North Africa? (c) How would the discovery of large pools of water change life in North Africa?
5. **Analyzing Ideas** (a) What European country had a strong impact on North Africa? (b) Why did this impact occur? (c) What relationship still exists between this Euro-

pean country and the nations of North Africa?

6. **Writing About Geography** In a full-page essay, discuss one of the following ideas. **(a)** Why do you think most North African countries have some form of dictatorship? **(b)** What might the governments of the North African countries do to ensure economic growth? Defend your suggestions.

## Using Primary Sources

In the following excerpt from *In Morocco*, Edith Wharton describes the different groups brought together at a Moroccan oasis. As you study the reading, consider the cultures represented by these different groups.

The men were lean and weatherbitten, . . . all muscular and fierce-looking. Some were wrapped in the black cloaks worn by the Blue Men of the Sahara [because the blue dye of their cloaks leaves a permanent stain on their skin], with a great orange sun embroidered on the back; some [dressed] like the Egyptian fellah, under a rough striped outer garment trimmed with bright tufts and tassels of wool. The men of the Rif [hilly, coastal region of Morocco] had a braided lock [of hair] on the shoulder, those of the Atlas [Mountains] a ringlet [of hair] over each ear, and brown woolen scarfs wound round their temples, leaving the shaven crown bare.

The women, squatting among their kids [young goats] and poultry and cheeses, glanced at us with brilliant . . . eyes. . . . Their thin faces were painted in stripes and patterns of indigo. Silver necklets covered their throats, long earrings dangled. . . .

They seemed abler bargainers than the men, and the play of expression on their dramatic and intensely feminine faces as they wheedled the price of a calf out of a fierce hillsman, or haggled over a heap of dates . . . showed that they knew their superiority and enjoyed it.

1. What differences did the author note between the men of the Rif and those of the Atlas?
2. What did the author notice about the bargaining abilities of the women?

## Practicing Geography Skills

*Before completing this activity, review Developing Geography Skills on page 476.*

**Interpreting Landsat Imagery** Study the Landsat image on page 49. Then complete the following activities.

1. List the dominant colors in the image.
2. Explain what the tiny specks of white scattered across the image represent.
3. Describe in a well-written paragraph what the Landsat image of the Mekong Delta illustrates about land use and economic activity in that area.

## Exploring Geography

The Mediterranean coast of North Africa is a popular vacation area for many people. To gather information on some of the more popular tourist destinations, visit a local travel agent or write to the embassy or government tourist office of a North African country of your choice, asking for recommendations for tourist attractions. Your letter should also ask for information on what travel documents, such as passports, visas, and vaccination certificates, the country requires. Then make a presentation to the class detailing your findings. You might also use any brochures that you receive to make a collage showing the major tourist attractions found in the country.

# PUTTING THE CHAPTER IN FOCUS

The 17 countries of the Middle East share many physical and cultural characteristics. Unlike North Africa, however, they also reflect several striking differences. These differences make the area very complex. Because conditions vary so much, it is useful to group the countries into three parts: the eastern Mediterranean, the Arabian Peninsula, and the eastern borderlands. Political and economic problems trouble many of the countries.

## Ideas to Understand

In studying about the Middle East, use these ideas to give direction to your reading.

1 Religious and political conflicts plague the eastern Mediterranean.
2 Saudi Arabia and seven small countries share the Arabian Peninsula.
3 Warfare disrupts life on the eastern edge of the Middle East.

## Terms to Define

The following terms are some of the key terms in the chapter. Defining them will help you understand the Middle East.

| | |
|---|---|
| strait | kibbutz |
| international city | emir |
| water table | desalinization |

## Places to Locate

Locating the following places will add to your knowledge of geography.

| | |
|---|---|
| Dardanelles | Rub'al Khali |
| Bosporus | Mecca |
| Anatolia | Shatt-al-Arab |
| West Bank | Persian Gulf |
| Haifa | Strait of Hormuz |

## 1 Religious and political conflicts plague the eastern Mediterranean.

The lands at the eastern end of the Mediterranean Sea attract many different types of people. Archaeologists visit the area to investigate the ruins of ancient civilizations found there. Religious pilgrims visit holy sites of Christianity, Judaism, and Islam. Soldiers come to keep the peace or defend their beliefs. Business people come to keep appointments at company offices. Thousands of tourists come to sightsee throughout the area every year.

### Physical Setting

Landforms in the eastern Mediterranean rise from a narrow coastal plain facing the sea to high mountains and rocky highlands in interior regions. Coastal areas enjoy Mediterranean climates. Climates farther inland become increasingly dry. The Syrian Desert east of the mountains has a desert climate.

The region also contains a strategic waterway that connects the Black and Mediterranean seas. The Sea of Marmara and two **straits,** or narrow bodies of water that connect larger bodies of water, form this waterway. The Dardanelles (dahrd·uhn·ELZ) links the Sea of Marmara and the Aegean Sea. The Bosporus (BAHS·puh·ruhs) links the Sea of Marmara and the Black Sea. This waterway separates European Turkey from Anatolia, or Asia Minor, the Asian part of Turkey. Turkey's control of this vital link contributes to the country's strategic importance as a member of NATO (see Chapter 20).

◀ *The Triumphal Arch at the Palmyra ruins, Syria*

The Dead Sea lies 1,302 feet (390 meters) below sea level—the lowest point on the earth's crust. Located between Israel and Jordan, the Dead Sea is fed by the Jordan River but has no outlet. As does the Great Salt Lake in the United States, the Dead Sea has a high salt content. Its waters remain too salty for common marine life—hence the name Dead Sea.

## Cultural Setting

As in North Africa, the principal religion in the eastern Mediterranean is Islam. Jews form a majority in Israel. Christians make up a significant minority in Lebanon.

Geographers classify most of the countries of the region as developing nations. The people continue to struggle to modernize their economies and to industrialize. Only Israel ranks as a developed nation.

## Countries of the Eastern Mediterranean

Six countries—Turkey, Cyprus, Syria, Lebanon, Jordan, and Israel—curve in an arc around the eastern end of the Mediterranean Sea.

***Learning from Maps.*** *Asia Minor is the land bridge between Europe and Asia. Why is control of the straits also of interest to the Soviet Union?*

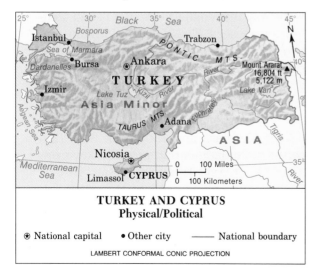

**TURKEY AND CYPRUS**
Physical/Political

⊛ National capital　　• Other city　　—— National boundary

LAMBERT CONFORMAL CONIC PROJECTION

**Turkey.**　Turkey, which is twice as large as California, benefits from its location in both Europe and Asia. It occupies a sliver of Europe and the Anatolian Plateau. Mountains and plateaus stretch inland from a rugged coastline of inlets. Numerous small islands lie along the coast of Anatolia. The Pontic Mountains extend along the coast in the north and the Taurus Mountains reach along the coast in the south. Mount Ararat, which rises to more than 16,800 feet (5,100 meters), towers along the border Turkey shares with Iran and the Soviet Union.

Climates in Turkey range from Mediterranean along the coast to continental in the interior. The extreme west coast is one of the wettest spots in the Middle East.

More than 53 million people live in Turkey. Most of them are concentrated in the western third of Anatolia and along the coast of the Black Sea. Slightly less than 50 percent of the people reside in urban areas. Most live in small farming villages. Istanbul, located on the Bosporus in European Turkey, is the largest city and port. Nearly 5 million people live in its metropolitan area. The capital city of Ankara has about 2 million residents.

Turks comprise about 85 percent of the nation's people. Kurds, a mountain people scattered from Turkey to Afghanistan, make up about 12 percent. Armenians once comprised a large part of the population, but were brutally oppressed. Today they form a small minority in northeastern Turkey. Nearly 98 percent of the people follow the Sunni branch of Islam. Most of the people speak Turkish, the official language. Others speak Kurdish, Arabic, and English.

Turkey was a focal point of ancient world culture. Constantinople, now Istanbul, was the center of eastern Christianity and, later, the source of Byzantine culture.

For centuries Turkey was part of the Ottoman Empire, ruled by religious leaders called **sultans.** This empire controlled

areas as far west as Yugoslavia and Bulgaria. In 1923 Turkey became a republic. Today it struggles to maintain a fragile parliamentary democracy.

Although Turkey has advanced economically, it remains a developing nation. More than half of the people engage in subsistence farming, but the rugged landscape and dry climate limit farm output. Farmers rely on water from the many rivers, such as the Euphrates, that begin in the mountains. However, control of these rivers is a major source of tension between Turkey and Syria. Subsistence farmers throughout much of Turkey grow grains and sugar beets and raise livestock. Commercial farmers grow cotton, tobacco, hazelnuts, and fruit along the wetter west coast. These commercial crops lead Turkey's list of exports. Some farmers in Turkey also produce opium poppies for the international drug trade despite periodic crackdowns by the government.

For years Turkey has been slowly building a foundation for industrialization. Its factories, roads, and railroads rank among the subregion's best. The chief industries produce textiles and processed foods for local markets. Mining companies work deposits of coal, chromium, copper, and iron ore. In addition, recent discoveries of oil in the eastern mountains hold great potential.

**Cyprus.** Less than 50 miles (80 kilometers) south of Turkey and 80 miles (128 kilometers) west of Syria lies the island of Cyprus. The island is smaller than the state of Connecticut. A broad plain separates two jagged mountain chains that cross the island from west to east.

Most of the 700,000 people of Cyprus live on the plain or the coast. Nicosia (nik·uh·SEE·uh), in the center of the island, is the capital and the largest city.

Cyprus is a politically divided island. About 75 percent of the Cypriots trace their

**Learning from Pictures.** *Nicosia, Cyprus, is the capital of a land divided by ethnic differences. What two peoples inhabit the island nation?*

ancestry to Greeks and follow the Greek Orthodox religion. The other 25 percent are of Turkish descent and follow Islam. Greek Cypriots speak Greek and Turkish Cypriots speak Turkish. Fighting between the two groups has continued off and on since Cyprus gained its independence from Britain in 1960.

Because of the nation's political unrest, economic progress in Cyprus has slowed, and the economy continues to depend on farming. Potatoes and other vegetables, grapes, and wheat lead farm output and exports in the Greek sector, while fruits and potatoes lead output and exports in the Turkish sector. The mining and export of copper, pyrites, asbestos, gypsum, and marble add to the economy. Small factories process minerals and produce food products, clothing, footwear, and building materials for local markets. The widespread conflict, however, blocks economic development.

**Syria.** Roughly diamond-shaped, the Syrian Arab Republic extends inland from the Mediterranean Sea directly south of Turkey and east of Cyprus. It covers about the same amount of territory as North Dakota. Its varied landscape includes low mountains and valleys in the north and the Syrian Desert in the south. The Euphrates River flows northwest to southeast across the center of the country. The western third of Syria has a Mediterranean climate; a desert climate affects the rest of the country.

More than 11 million people live in Syria, which has the Middle East's most rapidly growing population—3.8 percent per year. Most people live along the west coast and in the fertile valley along the Euphrates River. Arabs make up more than 90 percent of the people. Kurds and Armenians form the largest minorities. Most of the people belong to the Sunni sect of Islam. About 10 percent of the people practice Christianity.

Syria's leaders opposed the creation of Israel in 1948. They joined other Arab countries in Arab-Israel wars in 1948, 1956, 1967, and 1973. Israel occupied Syria's Golan Heights in the 1967 war and annexed this area in 1981. Border clashes continue.

Since 1963 military leaders have operated an authoritarian dictatorship in Syria. Involvement in Lebanon's civil war, and tensions with Turkey and Iraq add to Syria's political unrest. Syria maintains ties with the Soviet Union.

Syrian farmers grow vegetables and citrus fruits in the nation's wetter coastal areas. In drier western areas they grow wheat, barley, and cotton on lands irrigated by waters from the Euphrates. Herders raise sheep and goats on western and central pastures. Deposits of oil have recently been tapped and mines produce phosphates, chromium and manganese ores, iron, marble, and gypsum. Limited manufacturing includes textiles, food processing, and local crafts. An oil refinery and a huge dam on the Euphrates, to be used for irrigation and hydroelectricity, promise increased industrial output.

**Lebanon.** Tiny Lebanon, smaller than Connecticut, occupies 140 miles (225 kilometers) of coastline at the eastern end of the Mediterranean Sea. Desert covers more than 60 percent of the mountainous country. A Mediterranean climate prevails in the rest of the country. There, farmers grow fruits, wheat, corn, barley, and potatoes.

Arabs make up more than 90 percent of Lebanon's population. For years Christian Arabs formed a majority. In recent years, however, many Christians have left the unstable country. Today about 57 percent of the people are Muslims. Tensions between Muslims and Christians have wracked Lebanon for years. Although an uneasy truce prevailed in the 1960s, sporadic civil wars erupted in the 1970s and 1980s.

Political problems have completely disrupted Lebanon's former economic importance as an international banking and trade center for the Middle East. Pipelines to Sidon (SYD·n) and Tripoli, once great oil-refining and shipping centers, no longer carry any oil. Lebanon's beautiful capital, Beirut (bay·ROOT), once called "the Paris of the Middle East," lies in ruins.

**Jordan.** Jordan, slightly larger than Minnesota, occupies territory in the Syrian Desert south of Syria and east of the Jordan River. A fragmented nation, Jordan's territory is interrupted by territory controlled by Israel. Dry, rocky plateaus cover 90 percent of the country.

Jordan's 3 million people are scattered in villages in west and central Jordan. The rapidly growing population severely strains this arid country's limited farming capabilities. Nearly all the people are Arabs and more than 95 percent are Sunni Muslims. These people include thousands of Palestin-

ian Arabs who formerly lived in what is today Israel and fled to Jordan when Israel was declared a Jewish state (see below). About 250,000 Palestinians still live in refugee camps throughout the country. The Palestinian Liberation Organization (PLO) leads the fight to reestablish a Palestinian homeland.

Since it adopted its constitution in 1952, Jordan has been a constitutional monarchy. King Hussein rules the nation with the help of a parliament.

Jordan began developing its economy following World War II. Workers built irrigation canals and established mines throughout the Jordan valley. Farmers grew vegetables, fruit, and wheat and herders tended large flocks of sheep and goats. In 1967, however, Israel took control of much of Jordan's farmland and pastures, as well as many of its mines. Today most Jordanian workers raise livestock, but not enough to feed the nation's people. As a result, Jordan must rely on the United States, Western Europe, and even Communist countries for food and financial assistance.

**Israel.**   Israel lies on the Mediterranean coast, wedged between Syria, Lebanon, Jordan, and the Sinai Peninsula. Israel also occupies the West Bank to the east and the Gaza Strip to the south (see the map on this page). Israel's total territory is about the size of Massachusetts.

A thin strip of fertile land with a Mediterranean climate lines Israel's coast. This landscape gradually merges with the rolling hills of central Israel. Farther east lie the Jordan River Valley, the Dead Sea, and the Negev Desert. A warm, dry desert climate dominates in this eastern area.

Israel has had a short but turbulent history. After World War I, the British controlled Palestine. In 1948, however, the United Nations mandated that the territory be granted independence as the Jewish

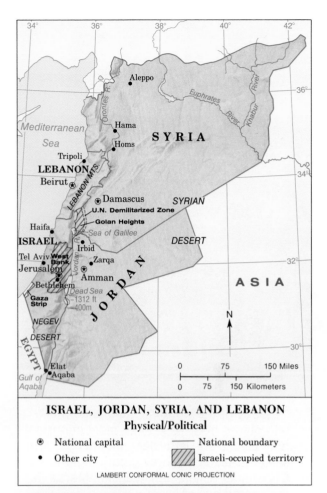

**ISRAEL, JORDAN, SYRIA, AND LEBANON**
**Physical/Political**

⊛  National capital          —— National boundary
•  Other city               ⧄ Israeli-occupied territory

LAMBERT CONFORMAL CONIC PROJECTION

***Learning from Maps.***   *The eastern Mediterranean has been a battleground since the founding of Israel in 1948. Why has Israel taken control of areas such as the West Bank?*

state of Israel. Neighboring Arab countries immediately invaded Israel and bitter fighting erupted. By 1949 Israel had taken control of the fighting. Eventually an armistice, or cease-fire, was signed and national borders were established. The peace was a troubled one, however, and wars again erupted in 1956, 1967, and 1973.

The status of Jerusalem—holy city to Jews, Christians, and Muslims—remains a source of conflict (see the CASE STUDY on page 488). When Israel was founded, its government leaders agreed to divide Jerusalem. Jordan claimed the older, eastern section of the city. The newer part became

*Text continues on page 489.*

**487**

*Jerusalem's famous Wailing Wall*

Many of the world's religions hold certain places holy. Two of the most important holy places are Jerusalem and Mecca. Jerusalem is sacred to three great religions—Christianity, Islam, and Judaism. Mecca is the sacred city of Islam.

### Jerusalem

For 2,000 years Christian pilgrims have flocked to Jerusalem's Church of the Holy Sepulchre (SEHP·uhl·kuhr), erected near the site of Jesus' crucifixion. Beyond this site lies the Via Dolorosa, or the Way of the Cross, the route that Jesus followed on the way to his crucifixion. The city also holds many other sites sacred to Christians.

For the Muslim faithful Jerusalem contains the magnificent golden Dome of the Rock, Islam's oldest religious building. Muslims believe that Muhammad ascended into heaven from the mosque's site. Nearby stands the silver-domed El Aqsa Mosque, the third holiest mosque in Islam.

Followers of Judaism find faith and unity in another sacred symbol—the Wailing Wall, or Western Wall. The wall marks the remains of the Jewish Temple that Roman soldiers destroyed in A.D. 70. The wall's name comes from the tears and prayers that Jewish pilgrims offer as they remember the sad events in their proud history and mourn the destruction of the Temple.

Jerusalem today is the capital and largest city of Israel. The Israeli government is very conscious of the city's special place in the world. To protect its holy places Israel imposes a seven-year prison sentence on anyone who attempts to damage any religious site. In addition, anyone who tries to prevent someone from entering a holy place can be imprisoned for five years.

### Mecca

Quite unlike Jerusalem, which has holy significance to three of the world's great religions, Mecca has religious significance mainly for Muslims. Only Muslims may enter Mecca, the holiest city of Islam.

Muhammad was born in Mecca. Also the city is the site of the Kaaba, the shrine toward which all Muslims turn during their prayers. Islam requires all Muslims to make the *hajj*, or pilgrimage to Mecca, at least once in their lifetime if they are able to do so. A hajj must be made between the eighth and thirteenth days of the last month of the Muslim year. During those five days more than 1 million pilgrims pour into the city. Approximately half of the pilgrims come from Saudi Arabia. The other faithful come from all over the world.

Since the 1950s the Saudi government has spent great sums to modernize Mecca. Today modern hotels house the pilgrims, and hospitals and clinics provide health care.

The special importance of Jerusalem and Mecca gives each a vitality. Visitors and residents alike feel the unique energy of these two holy cities.

Israel's capital. Though Israel chose Jerusalem as its capital, the United States and other countries refuse to accept it as such. Because of Jerusalem's importance to so many different groups, many countries outside the Middle East believe Jerusalem should remain an **international city,** governed by an international council.

Most of Israel's 4.2 million people live along the coast and in towns along the Jordan River and Dead Sea. Few people live in the arid south. Three-fourths of the people live in urban areas such as Tel Aviv (tel uh· VEEV) and Haifa (HY·fuh). Israel's relatively slow growth rate—1.7 percent—keeps the settled areas from becoming extremely overcrowded. About 83 percent of Israel's people are Jewish and follow Judaism. Arabs make up most of the remaining people. Eleven percent of the people are Muslims, while 4 percent are Christians. Hebrew serves as the official language, but members of the Arab minority speak Arabic.

Israel is a representative democracy with strong democratic traditions. Uniting people who have immigrated from Europe, the Soviet Union, and North Africa and the Middle East has proved difficult. Limited jobs, farmland, and irrigation water cause problems. So do differing customs and traditions. In addition, Arab guerrillas constantly threaten the nation's security.

Israel faces the difficult task of developing productive economic patterns in a land of few natural resources. Dry climates and lands ruined by poor farming methods limit Israel's agricultural potential. The narrow coastal strip contains the most fertile farmland. Farmers grow oranges and other citrus fruits, vegetables, wheat, oats, and barley, and raise poultry as well as cattle for beef and dairy products there. They also have begun to grow peanuts and cotton. Farmers widely use irrigation, especially during the dry summer months. Unfortunately, more water is being pumped from

wells to irrigate fields than rainfall replaces. As a result, the **water table,** or level of underground water, is dropping near Tel Aviv and Haifa. In some areas salt water from the sea seeps in as the water table drops, making the underground water unusable for drinking or irrigation.

Many Israeli farmers live on large collective farms called **kibbutzim.** All the kibbutz members own each kibbutz and work it cooperatively. Israeli farmers use fertilizers, machinery, and modern farm technologies. Using these methods, they harvest three crops a year of some products.

The Israeli people also recognize that land must be properly managed. Herders preserve pastures by alternating sheep and cattle, because sheep eat grass to the roots and kill it. Farmers maintain fields by rotating crops. Wherever possible, forests have been replanted. Such reforestation projects help hold land and water.

Mineral resources are as limited in Israel as is fertile farmland. The few mining operations produce small amounts of copper,

*Learning from Pictures.* Israelis make the desert fertile by irrigation at En-gedi kibbutz near the Dead Sea. How does the kibbutz system help increase Israel's farm output?

# GEOGRAPHY IN THE WORKPLACE
## Historical Geographers

Geography and history are closely related social sciences. The essential difference between the two subjects can be most easily understood by comparing the outlook of each. As you study history, you gain an orientation in time. As you study geography, you gain an orientation in space. In other words, historians base their study on time. Geographers study spatial arrangements and distributions on the earth's surface. Historical geography, which is concerned with both space *and* time, combines both fields.

The central task of historical geographers is to reconstruct the geography of past times. Rarely, however, do historical geographers study the past for the past's sake. Instead they study the past geographies of a region in order to better understand the region's geography today. The historical geographer takes into account both natural and human history, for virtually every place has natural and human imprints.

Interpreting these imprints helps us gain a better understanding of the earth's surface today. For this reason, historical geographers must understand the methods of history *and* geography. Today's historical geographers also must be familiar with advanced technologies, such as the high-altitude photography and satellite imagery that are used to uncover landscape patterns that evolved in the past. Ancient irrigation channels not easily seen on the ground, for example, show up clearly on satellite images of the Nile Delta.

Historical geographers also rely on field work. They bring the research methods of historians and the field-work methods of the geographer to the sites of ancient civilizations. There, they seek to unlock mysteries that the natural and human imprints hold and to find new understandings about how people of the past used the earth and its resources. If investigating the past interests you, historical geography could hold a fascinating career.

---

phosphate, and manganese. The Dead Sea and surrounding lands yield potash, sulfur, bromide, and other salts.

With few heavy industries, Israel has developed high-technology industries instead. Israel's factories produce optical instruments, military weapons, medicines, precision tools, and other high-tech manufactured goods. Diamond-cutting, which turns raw diamonds into polished jewels, accounts for nearly one-third of the value of the country's exports. Tourism adds significant income to the economy. In addition, the United States contributes more money and goods to Israel than it does to any other country.

## SECTION 1 REVIEW

1. **Define**   strait, sultan, international city, water table, kibbutz
2. **Locate**   Dardanelles, Bosporus, Anatolia, Dead Sea, Istanbul, Beirut, West Bank, Gaza Strip, Jordan River, Tel Aviv, Haifa
3. **Summarizing Ideas**   Why is there conflict between Arabs and Israelis in the Middle East?
4. **Comparing Ideas**   In what ways are Israel and Lebanon   **(a)** different and **(b)** similar?
5. **Distinguishing Ideas**   How does modern irrigation affect Israel?

## 2 Saudi Arabia and seven small countries share the Arabian Peninsula.

A few years ago empty deserts with few animals and little vegetation covered the Arabian Peninsula. Only nomads and explorers ventured into the silent emptiness. Today pipelines crisscross the barren landscape and clusters of derricks rise from the sand. Scattered settlements sprout in the desert, providing shelter for technicians who tend the pipelines and derricks.

### Physical Setting

Windswept, barren deserts, dotted here and there with jagged mountains, dominate the landscape of the Arabian Peninsula. A dry climate prevails and no lakes or permanent rivers exist. The only water lies far below the ground and there are only widely scattered oases. A giant erg desert—called the Rub'al Khali (ruhb·al KAHL·ee), or "Empty Quarter"—stretches across much of southeast Saudi Arabia, while the Nafud (nuh·FOOD) and Syrian deserts lie farther north. Only sections of the southwest and southeast coastal areas receive enough rain to support farming.

### Cultural Setting

Although the physical landscape remains forbidding and desolate, the Arabian Peninsula holds some the world's largest oil reserves. These reserves have enriched the economies of many of the peninsula's countries. Today sleek skyscrapers and multilane highways coexist with Bedouin villages. The income from oil, however, has not benefited all of the people, and not all of the countries have oil reserves. Many of the people continue to farm or tend herds just as their ancestors have done for centuries. Great differences separate a small minority of wealthy people from an impoverished majority.

Just as oil dominates many of the area's economies, Islam dominates its social patterns. The Muslim influence helps to unite the almost entirely Arab population.

### Countries of the Arabian Peninsula

Saudi Arabia and seven small independent countries—North Yemen, South Yemen, Oman, the United Arab Emirates, Qatar, Bahrain, and Kuwait—share the dry and barren Arabian Peninsula.

**Saudi Arabia.** Saudi Arabia occupies the largest part of the Arabian Peninsula. Desert covers more than 95 percent of the country, which is one-third the size of the United States. Saudi Arabia's dry plains reach from coastal lowlands along the

*Learning from Maps.* *Nations on the Arabian Peninsula have some of the world's highest per capita gross national products. Which countries on the peninsula do not border the Persian Gulf?*

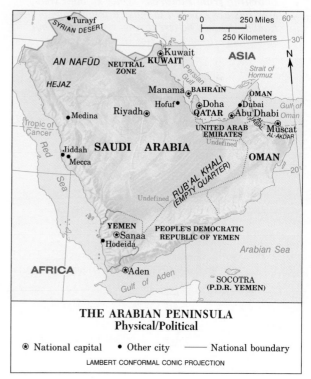

**THE ARABIAN PENINSULA**
Physical/Political

⊛ National capital    • Other city    —— National boundary

LAMBERT CONFORMAL CONIC PROJECTION

**491**

Persian Gulf to a chain of mountains along the Red Sea. Some mountain peaks rise to heights of 10,000 feet (3,000 meters).

The territory that is now Saudi Arabia was part of the Ottoman Empire until World War I ended, and for a while afterward was two separate nations—Nejd and Hejaz. The Saud (sah·OOD) family founded modern Saudi Arabia in 1932. As the birthplace of both Islam and the Arabic language Saudi Arabia remains the heart of the Muslim world. Mecca (see the CASE STUDY on page 488) and Medina serve as Islam's holiest cities. All Muslims hope someday to visit them as part of their religious duties.

About 15 million people live in this thinly occupied country. Much of the landscape remains unknown to anyone but Bedouin herders. Most people live around Mecca and Medina. A second, more recent area of settlement has developed near the oil fields along the Persian Gulf. A single large oasis surrounds Riyadh (ree·YAHD), the capital. Because of the vast expanse of

**Learning from Pictures.** *Once in their lives, Muslims are expected to make a pilgrimage to the Kaaba—Islam's holiest shrine—in Mecca. What other holy city of Islam lies in Saudi Arabia?*

uninhabitable landscape, three-fourths of the people now live in urban areas. The growth of the oil industry attracts more settlers to cities each year.

Arabs make up more than 90 percent of Saudi Arabia's people. Small numbers of Africans in the west and Asians in the east comprise the rest of the population. Virtually everyone speaks Arabic and follows Islam. The ruling Saud family has built a country based on traditional Islamic law.

Before the development of the oil industry, most Saudis relied on subsistence farming and nomadic herding. Farming and herding remain important. The main crops include dates, wheat, and barley. The country's leaders hope that large desalinization projects will increase usable farmland and attract people back into farming. Herders graze camels, sheep, and goats. However, the number of farmers and nomads dwindles yearly as people give up their difficult traditional life styles and move to the cities in search of better job opportunities. Because of this migration and the lack of water for irrigation, Saudi Arabia must import large amounts of processed foods.

Petrodollars have changed Saudi Arabia from an impoverished wasteland to one of the wealthiest countries in the world. Saudis have invested large amounts of money in banks around the world and have bought land and businesses in many other countries. At home, the government uses the new wealth to build schools, hospitals, and roads. Modern industries have been started. Petrochemical plants process crude oil and natural gas into more valuable products for export. Construction also has begun on a steel mill and an aluminum smelter. Mines produce iron ore, gold, and copper. New ports are being built on the Persian Gulf and the Red Sea and old ports are being modernized. Pipelines carry oil and natural gas from the oil fields to processing plants and ports.

*Text continues on page 494.*

# DEVELOPING GEOGRAPHY SKILLS
## WRITING ABOUT GEOGRAPHY: Composing an Essay

An essay is a short composition that deals with a specific topic. It should always contain three components—an introduction, a body of information, and a conclusion. Just as geographers do when they prepare reports, you compose an essay when you write a report.

You have already learned about the two preliminary steps to composing an essay: summarizing information (see page 178) and composing a paragraph (see page 294). You also have learned about answering an essay question (see page 333), which requires you to write one type of essay. The next step is the actual writing of an essay.

### How to Write an Essay

To write an essay, follow these guidelines.

1. **Select a topic.** Unless a topic is assigned, you need to select a topic. Make sure the topic is broad enough to provide enough material for an essay but not too broad to be dealt with in a brief composition.
2. **Organize your ideas into an outline.** Remember that an essay should have three parts. Organize your thoughts accordingly.
3. **Compose your essay.** Clearly state your topic in the introduction. Present your evidence and supporting details in the body. Your conclusion should briefly sum up what you have said in the essay.

### Applying the Skill

Read and respond to the following directive.

Write an essay in which you describe the religious conflicts that plague the eastern Mediterranean area.

*Muslim faithful at prayer*

Since the topic—religious conflicts that plague the eastern Mediterranean area—has already been selected for you, the next step is to gather information and prepare an outline. Reread the information in Section 1 of the chapter on pages 483–90. Remember (from the skill lesson in Chapter 1—Using This Textbook) to use the headings as your guide. Your outline should resemble the following one.

I. Introduction
II. Religious Conflicts
  A. Greek Orthodox and Muslims on Cyprus
  B. Muslims and Christians in Lebanon
  C. Muslim conflicts—Shiites and Sunnites
  D. The problem of Israel
  E. Jerusalem—holy city for Christians, Jews, and Muslims
III. Conclusion

*To practice this skill, see Practicing Geography Skills on page 503.*

**North Yemen.** The Yemen Arab Republic, or North Yemen, is slightly smaller than South Dakota. The country lies along the Red Sea in the Arabian Peninsula's southwestern corner. In the west coastal lowlands are very dry, but in the east low mountains receive enough rain to allow farming without irrigation. Farmers grow grains, fruits, and vegetables. Coffee and cotton serve as leading exports. Along the coast of the Red Sea herders graze sheep, goats, and camels.

More than 6.5 million people live in North Yemen. Nearly all are Muslims. North Yeman lacks industry and ranks among the world's poorest countries. Although oil deposits probably exist in both Yemens, they have not been developed. North Yemen's military dictatorship has failed to solve the country's economic problems.

**South Yemen.** The People's Democratic Republic, or South Yemen, is about the size of Nevada and extends between North Yemen and Oman. The country has a strategic location at the entrance to the Red Sea and has close ties to the Soviet Union. A lack of defined borders (see the map on page 491) causes problems for both Yemens.

The port city of Aden (AHD·n) is the country's capital. Most of the 2.5 million people live in coastal villages near Aden.

Like North Yemen to the northwest, South Yemen ranks among the world's poorest developing nations. Farmers grow small amounts of wheat, oats, and dates; herders graze small herds of livestock; and a small fishing industry has begun.

**Oman.** Oman, about the size of New Mexico, wraps around the southeastern corner of the Arabian Peninsula. Dry lowlands in the west rise to a ridge of mountains near the east coast. A hereditary sultan with absolute power rules Oman, a former British territory that retains many British traditions.

Oman has a more diverse population than its neighbors. The 1.5 million people are mostly Arabs and Muslims. Subsistence farming and herding remain the leading economic activities. Farmers raise small amounts of fruits, dates, wheat, barley, cattle, and camels. Fishers add small amounts to the food supply, but Oman imports most of its food.

Oman lacks manufacturing, but it is rich in oil and natural gas. Though still a developing nation, Oman's per capita GNP now tops $7,000. The country has begun to put its petrodollars to work to improve life for its people.

**The Persian Gulf states.** Strung along the Persian Gulf coast between Oman and Saudi Arabia lie three small countries—the United Arab Emirates, Qatar, and Bahrain. Farther north, sandwiched between Saudi Arabia and Iraq, lies Kuwait.

Desert covers most of the land in each of these countries. Almost all food is im-

*Learning from Pictures.* Saudi Arabia is building pipelines to Red Sea ports. What conflict might these pipelines help prevent?

ported, although farmers grow small crops of dates, vegetables, and grains at oases and fishers haul in small catches.

All four countries are rich in oil and use their petrodollars to build schools, hospitals, roads, and factories. Because of oil, modernization has come quickly.

Seven small emirates form the federation known as the United Arab Emirates or UAE, the southernmost country. All seven emirates are absolute monarchies governed by hereditary rulers called **emirs.** Abu Dhabi (AHB·oo DAHB·ee), the most influential emirate, serves as the federation's capital. Nearly 50 percent of the UAE's 2 million people are non-Arabs, although virtually all are Muslims. Vast oil wealth gives the UAE a per capita GNP of $19,120, the highest in the world.

Qatar lies north of the United Arab Emirates. Large groups of Pakistanis, Indians, and Iranians give Qatar a diverse population of 350,000 people. Qatar also has one of the world's highest per capita GNPs—more than $15,000.

Bahrain is a fragmented nation consisting of a small mainland and 32 islands in the Persian Gulf. Together they make up a tiny country covering less territory than New York City. The diverse population of 475,000 people is ruled by an emir.

Diamond-shaped Kuwait occupies the northwestern end of the Persian Gulf. A constitution limits the powers of the emir.

*Learning from Maps.* Numerous pipelines highlight the abundance of energy resources in the Middle East. Between what two bodies of water do the longest pipelines extend?

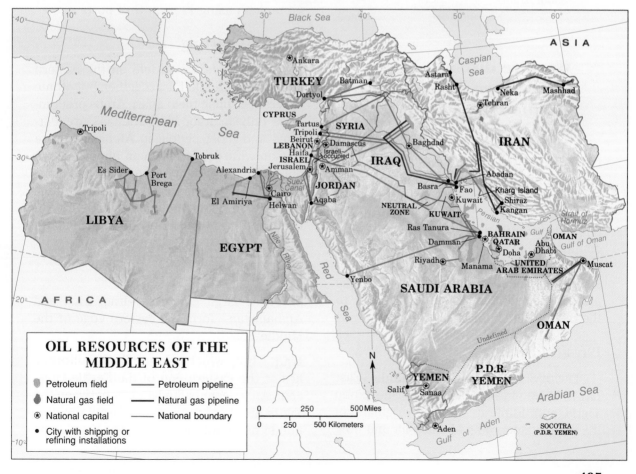

495

Kuwait's 2 million people benefit from oil income, as the country has rapidly modernized and built roads and schools. Kuwait also is experimenting with **desalinization,** or the removal of salts from seawater so that it can be used for irrigation.

---

### SECTION 2 REVIEW

1. **Define**  emir, desalinization
2. **Locate**  Rub'al Khali, Mecca, Riyadh
3. **Comparing Ideas**  **(a)** In what ways are the countries you studied in this section similar?  **(b)** In what ways do they differ?
4. **Summarizing Ideas**  What changes has the discovery of oil brought to Saudi Arabia?
5. **Contrasting Ideas**  How are North Yemen and South Yemen different from the other countries that ring Saudi Arabia?

---

## 3 Warfare disrupts life on the eastern edge of the Middle East.

In many ways the countries on the eastern edge of the Middle East differ from other Middle Eastern countries you have studied in this chapter. The people have different ethnic backgrounds and speak different languages than people in the other countries, for example. In terms of the Islamic religion, the importance of oil, and slow economic development, however, this part of the world remains very similar to the rest of the Middle East.

### Physical Setting

The eastern edge of the Middle East has a varied physical landscape. The exotic Tigris and Euphrates rivers originate in the wetter mountains of Anatolia and flow through the dry western portion of the region. Fertile plains border the river valleys. The plains were the birthplace of cities about 8,000 years ago and have been important ever since. Towering mountain ranges, desolate desert basins, and arid plateaus cover much of the rest of the region.

Two geographic features of the area have strategic importance. One is the Shatt-al-Arab (shat·al·AR·uhb)—the river formed by the joining of the Tigris and the Euphrates. The river forms the part of the Iran-Iraq border. Navigation rights and control of the river is vital to Iraq, which has no other outlet to the Persian Gulf. A strait provides the area's second strategic feature. The Strait of Hormuz lies between Oman, which owns the southern side, and Iran, which owns the northern side and several islands in the straight. This international waterway serves as the only route for oil tankers using Persian Gulf ports.

### Cultural Setting

Islam draws the people on the eastern edge of the Middle East together, but ethnic differences push them apart. Arabs predominate only in Iraq. Most Iranians are Persians and most people in Afghanistan are Afghans. Kurds also form an important minority in the mountains of Iraq and Iran. Languages spoken throughout this culturally diverse region include Arabic, Farsi (in Iran), and Pashto and Dari (in Afghanistan).

### Countries of the Eastern Middle East

Three large countries—Iraq, Iran, and Afghanistan—form the eastern edge of the Middle East.

**Iraq.**  Iraq, which is larger than California, lies at the eastern end of the Fertile Crescent. An irrigated alluvial plain between the Tigris and Euphrates rivers forms the economic heartland of the country. Fertile soil

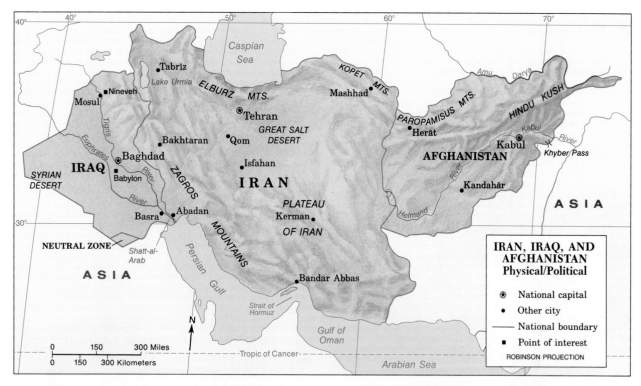

IRAN, IRAQ, AND
AFGHANISTAN
Physical/Political

⊛   National capital
•   Other city
—   National boundary
■   Point of interest

ROBINSON PROJECTION

**Learning from Maps.**  *War engulfs all three nations of the eastern Middle East. Which nation was invaded by the Soviet Union?*

on the plain provides the basis for a productive agricultural system. To the north lies the mountainous homeland of the Kurds, a rugged mountain people. The Kurds seek an independent country of their own. To the south the Shatt-al-Arab flows to the Persian Gulf. The international boundary between Iraq and Iran traditionally runs along the east bank of the river, rather than down the middle as is customary. The placement of the boundary gives all of the Shatt-al-Arab to Iraq and is a frequent source of conflict and war with neighboring Iran. Marshes stretch to the east of the Shatt-al-Arab. The dry lands of the Syrian Desert lie to the west.

More than 17 million people live in Iraq. Most live in farming villages that line the river valleys. The densest cluster of people—more than 2 million—live in and around Baghdad, the capital. Arabs comprise three-fourths of the population and

Kurds and Turks account for the rest. Nearly 95 percent of the people follow Islam, but 55 percent belong to the Shia sect rather than the larger Sunni sect.

Iraq's current government has been responsible for several democratic reforms, including nationwide elections held in 1984. Still, numerous political problems slow progress. The Kurds continue to seek their own homeland. Also Iraq has been at war with Iran for much of the 1980s. The war has been costly—in money and in human lives—for both countries.

Farming was the basis of the Iraqi economy until the development of the country's oil industry in the 1930s. Nevertheless, farming remains a major economic activity. Wheat and barley continue to lead farm output. Farmers also grow apricots, peaches, and nuts. Two-thirds of all the world's dates grow in the alluvial soils along the Shatt-al-Arab. Herders graze sheep and goats.

*Text continues on page 499.*

*Baghdad on the banks of the Tigris*

People who live in Baghdad, the capital of Iraq, say that you can feel thousands of years of civilization around you. Indeed, people have lived there since 4000 B.C. when the site of Baghdad was part of ancient Babylonia. But Baghdad was only a small village when in 762 Abu Jafar al-Mansur (al·mahn·SOOR), leader of the Arab Empire, selected its site for his capital. More than 100,000 workers labored to construct the circle-shaped city at his command.

### A Troubled History

Within 38 years of its founding more than 1 million people lived in Baghdad. By 900 it was among the world's largest and richest cities and a renowned center of learning. But in 1258 Mongols swept out of Central Asia and virtually destroyed Baghdad. Wars, fires, and floods plagued the remnants of the city through the succeeding centuries. By the 1700s only about 15,000 people lived in the once-fabled city.

As recently as 1970 Baghdad was little more than a sprawling mass of shanty-towns. Sanitation facilities were ancient and generally nonoperable. The city's streets were unpaved. Baghdad had only its name to recall its mighty past as the city of Sindbad, Aladdin, and Ali Baba.

### Rebirth

Rich with oil money, Iraq began to rebuild Baghdad in 1979. Costs were disregarded. Some of the world's best architects were hired to make Baghdad once again the center of the Arab world.

Today luxurious hotels and expensive apartment complexes dot the 1,200-year-old, walled section of the city. New underground sewer and water lines underlie the huge city of 4 million residents. A network of multilaned, high-speed freeways cuts through the city and around it. Twelve bridges cross the Tigris as it meanders through the city. A new international airport lies to the southwest of the city. Several government buildings of unique design and five Western-style shopping centers have been constructed.

Even a new University of Baghdad, long ago the center of Arab learning, is being built. Its new 860-acre (348-hectare) campus lies along the Tigris, will cost nearly $2 billion, and will have 273 buildings including a great domed structure housing the university mosque.

But more is modern in Baghdad than its architecture. The city has a vibrant nightlife. And, even more surprising in the conservative Middle East, the Iraqi government accords women full equality with men. In Baghdad women dress in the latest fashions; attend the universities; and work as engineers, doctors, lawyers, and architects. In fact, women make up one-fourth of Iraq's labor force. The ancient city of Baghdad now reflects Iraq's rapidly modernizing society.

Despite its huge oil income, Iraq remains a developing nation. Oil revenues, however, have made progress possible. Petrodollars have been used to build roads and airfields, to improve transportation and communication, and to fund schools. Farm improvement tops the list of development priorities. Oil income has financed irrigation projects and the building of several large dams on the Tigris and Euphrates rivers. In addition, a government project drained the lands along the Shatt-al-Arab south of Basra (bahs·RAH), creating thousands of acres of rich farmland. Government-funded agricultural schools teach new farming methods and the use of mechanized equipment to young farmers. In the 1980s, however, the Persian Gulf War closed Iraq's oil port and drained most of its financial resources.

**Iran.** North of the Persian Gulf, south of the Caspian Sea, and east of Iraq lies Iran. The large country is slightly smaller than the states of Alaska and Washington combined. Towering mountain ranges and a high plateau in the center of the country make up much of Iran. The high Elburz Mountains, with peaks above 18,000 feet (5,486 meters), extend along the Caspian Sea. In the west, parallel to the Persian Gulf, rise the Zagros Mountains. Though dry desert climates affect most of the country, mountain streams provide enough water for irrigation in many places.

An absolute monarch called the shah ruled Iran from the 1950s until 1979. In that year the people revolted and a theocracy, or a state headed by religious leaders, was established. The top religious leader, the Ayatollah Khomeini (eye·uh·TOH·luh koh·MAY·nee) became the head of the country's government.

Iran leads a movement aimed at the global diffusion of fundamental Islamic values. Iran's theocracy has tried to rid the country of all foreign influences. Shortly after the shah's departure, anti-American sentiments led to the seizing of American hostages from the United States embassy. Though the hostages were freed in 1981, bitter feelings remain. At about the same time the Persian Gulf War with Iraq erupted. The war escalated as Iran's Shiite Muslims sought to dominate Iraq's Sunni Muslims. In 1987 the Iranian navy began to attack ships of all nations passing through the Persian Gulf and the Strait of Hormuz. These attacks in international waters once again brought Iran into conflict with the United States and many other countries.

Iran's population—more than 50 million people—is the second largest in the Middle East. The two most densely settled areas are near the Caspian Sea and just east of the Zagros Mountains along the Persian Gulf. About half the people live in urban areas. Tehran, the capital and largest city, has more than 4.5 million residents.

Iran's population differs ethnically from that of most of the other countries of the Middle East. Persians make up the largest

*Learning from Pictures.* Iran's Islamic theocracy requires women to wear veils in public. In what ways do women's rights in Iranian society differ from those in Iraqi society?

group of people—more than 70 percent of the population. Virtually everyone speaks Farsi, or Persian, rather than Arabic. And although 98 percent of the people are Muslims, 93 percent belong to the Shiite sect rather than the larger Sunnite sect.

Oil serves as Iran's chief resource. Oil deposits underlie only a small part of Iran along the eastern edge of the Zagros Mountains near the Persian Gulf. Still, it has been

**Learning from Pictures.** *Foreign help enabled these Afghan guerrillas to fight the Soviet-controlled government. How has war affected Afghanistan's economy?*

estimated that this deposit holds more than 8 percent of the world's known oil supply. Iran's oil refineries such as those at Abadan on the Shatt-al-Arab produce more than 1 billion barrels of crude oil each day. Oil accounts for 96 percent of Iran's export value; in 1986 oil contributed nearly $12 billion to the economy. However, Kharg Island, Iran's chief oil terminal, frequently has been bombed by Iraq. Iran also has deposits of phosphate, sulfur, coal, iron ore, copper, lead, and manganese but these deposits have yet to be fully developed.

Despite Iran's rich oil deposits, more than 80 percent of the people still eke out an existence by farming or herding animals. Land-reform programs begun during the shah's reign have improved the people's lives somewhat. Before the reforms almost all the farmland was owned by a few wealthy people who rented small plots to farmers. By the mid-1960s most of the large farms had been broken into smaller ones and distributed to peasant farmers.

On the many small mountainside farms farmers grow wheat, barley, sugar beets, tea, and tobacco. In the valleys they raise rice, dates, grapes, and cotton. Shepherds tend sheep and goats on dry pastureland.

The shah also began a series of industrial programs. As a result, Iran has several small manufacturing plants, auto assembly plants, and a nuclear power plant. However, due to the disruption caused by the Persian Gulf War in the 1980s, these plants now produce few manufactured goods. Trade also has been disrupted because many of the country's ports are closed due to war. Until the fighting ends, Iran's economic development will remain at a standstill.

**Afghanistan.** To the east, surrounded by Iran, Pakistan, and the Soviet Union, lies landlocked Afghanistan. Either mountains or deserts cover three-fourths of the country, which is about the size of Texas. The

majestic Hindu Kush mountain range extends through the northeast. On the west the plateau of Iran crosses into Afghanistan. This plateau dips to a desert basin so dry it has almost no permanent inhabitants. Set amid this rugged landscape are several fertile valleys where irrigation produces excellent crops. Dry continental and desert climates characterize Afghanistan. Summers are often very hot, while winters bring freezing temperatures.

One physical feature in Afghanistan has long had geopolitical importance—the Khyber (KY·buhr) Pass. This narrow ravine in the northeast provides the only relatively easy passageway through the mountains. Often the route of armies invading India, the pass remains strategic in Afghanistan's battle with the Soviet Union.

Only about 15 percent of Afghanistan's 18.5 million people live in urban areas. Many live around Kabul (KAHB·uhl), the capital and only large city. Most other people live in towns in the foothills of the Hindu Kush. Afghanistan has one of the world's lowest literacy rates. Less than 15 percent of the men and less than 10 percent of the women are literate.

As does Iran's, Afghanistan's ethnic makeup differs from that of most other countries in the Middle East. Members of the Pathan tribe, among Afghanistan's first inhabitants, make up about half the people. Russian, Pakistani, and Turkish minorities make up much of the rest of the population. In addition, few people speak Arabic. About half the people speak Pashto, and most other people speak Dari—or Afghan Persian—and Turkish dialects. Though 99 percent of the people are Muslims, about 25 percent belong to the Shiite sect.

Warfare and political unrest continue to plague Afghanistan. In 1979 a pro-Soviet Communist economic system was set up, but a power struggle developed among the new leaders. Fighting soon broke out between Communists and opposing Islamic guerrillas. In 1979 the Soviet army invaded Afghanistan to defeat the guerrillas and support the government. Afghan rebels opposed to Soviet domination have carried on a war to free their homeland ever since. Nearly 25 percent of the people have fled the country since the conflict began. In 1988 the Soviets began to withdraw some troops and promote a neutral Afghanistan.

Afghanistan remains one of the poorest developing nations, with a per capita GNP of only $214. Most of the workers herd animals or farm on a subsistence level. Herders graze cattle and sheep in mountain valleys, while farmers grow small crops of wheat, barley, cotton, sugar beets, and sugarcane in small irrigated fields. Despite its troubles, Afghanistan is self-sufficient in food.

The Communist system has failed to significantly improve Afghanistan's economy. The government has also failed to develop the country's mineral potential. Deposits of natural gas, oil, coal, sulfur, lead, zinc, and iron ore wait to be tapped, but their locations make mining very difficult. And warfare continues to disrupt economic patterns throughout the country.

## SECTION 3 REVIEW

1. **Locate**  Shatt-al-Arab, Persian Gulf, Strait of Hormuz, Baghdad, Tehran
2. **Comparing Ideas**  **(a)** How does the physical setting of Iraq differ from the physical settings of Iran and Afghanistan?  **(b)** How are the cultural settings of these three countries similar?
3. **Analyzing Ideas**  How do Iran's political problems block modernization?
4. **Interpreting Ideas**  How are Afghanistan's physical setting and traditional life style related?

501

## Chapter Summary

The following list contains the key concepts you have learned about the Middle East.

1. Turkey, Cyprus, Syria, Lebanon, Jordan, and Israel arc around the eastern edge of the Mediterranean Sea. Political turmoil hampers economic progress in most of these countries.
2. Israel's social, political, and economic patterns differ widely from those of its Arab neighbors. Israel has faced continued threats to its existence from these neighbors since its beginning after World War II.
3. Saudi Arabia includes most of the thinly settled Arabian Desert and its widely scattered oases. Seven small independent countries—North Yemen, South Yemen, Oman, the United Arab Emirates, Qatar, Bahrain, and Kuwait share the peninsula with their large neighbor.
4. All the countries that occupy the Arabian Peninsula have similar physical settings and all but the two Yemens benefit from the production of oil. However, social and polit-

5. Iraq, Iran, and Afghanistan form the eastern borderlands of the Middle East. Though landscapes and life styles differ, recent political conflict and warfare plague all three.
6. Iraq has used much of its oil income to help improve the lives of its people.
7. Revolution in Iran deposed the shah and established a theocracy.
8. Soviet troops back the government of Afghanistan. Soviet aggression has been condemned by the United States and many other countries. In 1988 the Soviets began to withdraw their troops.
9. Historical geographers are concerned with both space and time. They use the methods of history and geography as they seek to reconstruct the geography of the past.

On a separate sheet of paper, complete the following review exercises.

## Reviewing Geographic Terms

Decide whether each of the following sentences is true or false. If the sentence is false, replace the underlined term with the word or phrase that will make the sentence true.

1. Because of Jerusalem's importance to three major religions, many people feel it should remain a holy city.
2. Many of Israel's farming villages are kibbutzim where families share farming and other work.
3. In the Middle East recent attention has been focused on the bay connecting the Persian Gulf and the Gulf of Oman.
4. Heavy pumping of water for irrigation has seriously reduced the level of the mineral deposits in many Middle Eastern countries.
5. Several countries are attempting to increase water supplies through the desalinization of seawater.
6. Hereditary monarchs on the Arabian Peninsula include kings and emperors.

## Developing Critical Thinking Skills

1. **Comparing Ideas**   In what ways are Turkey, Iran, and Afghanistan similar?
2. **Summarizing Ideas**   Why is the Shatt-al-Arab a source of conflict between Iraq and Iran?
3. **Charting Information**   Develop a chart listing the name of each country in the Middle East and its type of government.
4. **Seeing Relationships**   How are physical setting, population distribution, and economic activity related   **(a)** in Saudi Arabia? **(b)** on the rest of the Arabian Peninsula?
5. **Organizing Ideas**   What are the main causes of political trouble that plagues Lebanon?
6. **Analyzing Ideas**   What benefits has the development of oil industries had for the countries of the Arabian Peninsula?
7. **Writing About Geography**   In a well-written essay, complete one of the following ac-

tivities. **(a)** Discuss the relationship between the development of oil industries in the Middle East and the growth of nationalism. **(b)** Explain why Turkey and Afghanistan developed differently in this century.

## Using Primary Sources

In the following excerpt from *The Middle East: Oil, Conflict, and Hope*, Albert H. Hourani discusses the development of Iraqi society. As you study the reading, determine how this development affects modern-day Iraq.

> In Iraq once more we find a different social and political structure inherited from the past. . . . In the river-valleys, and particularly in the great alluvial plain of the south, there has always been the possibility of the existence of large cities controlling fertile hinterlands, but this has depended on the maintenance of large and complicated irrigation works, and Iraq entered the modern age after a long period during which the irrigation system had broken down, [and] the social control of cities over hinterland had been weakened. . . . The territories incorporated into the modern state of Iraq had formed part of several different Ottoman provinces, and their population was deeply divided: ethnically, they were Arabs or Kurds (with some smaller groups); in religion, Sunni or Shi'i [Shiite] Muslims (again with some smaller groups). Of the total population of some ten millions today, roughly 55 percent are Shi'is [Shiites], 20 percent Arab Sunnis, and 20 percent Kurdish Sunnis. But Arab Sunnis are dominant in the cities of the river-valleys which were the centers of Ottoman rule.

1. What system in Iraq gave cities the potential to control farmland?
2. Which group in Iraq controlled the cities of the river valleys?

## Practicing Geography Skills

*Before completing this activity, review Developing Geography Skills on page 493.*

**Composing an Essay** Read the essay directive below. Develop an outline from material in the chapter. Then write your essay.

Explain how nationalism is the source of many of the conflicts threatening the Middle East today.

## Exploring Geography

1. Use resources in your school or public library to find information on the history of the Turkish city of Istanbul. Then write an essay that outlines Istanbul's history and describes the city's major geographical features.
2. Construct charts or graphs comparing life expectancy, infant mortality, and literacy rates for the Arabian Peninsula countries in 1970 and in 1985. You might find it useful to refer to such sources as *The World Almanac and Book of Facts* and the *United Nations Statistical Yearbook* to find the information that you will need to construct your charts or graphs.
3. As you have read, all Muslims are expected to make a *hajj* to Mecca once during their lifetimes. Use resources in your school or public library to prepare a short speech explaining what a *hajj* is and why Muslims are expected to make one. You might also mention what roles pilgrimages play in Christianity and Judaism.
4. Use the information in this chapter to construct a table comparing the countries at the eastern edge of the Middle East with the other Middle Eastern countries. Your table should include information on landforms, climate, culture, and economic and political structure. Your completed table should be large enough to be displayed on the bulletin board.

# UNIT 8 REVIEW

## Unit Summary

The following list contains the key concepts you have learned about North Africa and the Middle East.

1. The two distinct subregions of North Africa and the Middle East are grouped together because they share many physical and cultural features.
2. Most of the region is desert, but exotic rivers flow through many of the areas.
3. Natural resources are limited except for deposits of oil and natural gas, which provide great wealth for some of the region's countries.
4. The region's complex cultural setting includes many religions and many types of political and economic systems.
5. Arab culture dominates the region. Most of the people are Muslims, although they belong to different sects, and most of the people speak Arabic.
6. Egypt, Libya, Tunisia, Algeria, Morocco, Mauritania, and the Western Sahara make up the dry lands of North Africa.
7. Population distribution reflects the physical setting. Most of the people live within a few miles of the coast.
8. The Middle East can be divided into three parts: the eastern Mediterranean; the Arabian Peninsula; and the eastern borderlands.
9. Religious and political conflicts plague the eastern Mediterranean.
10. Saudi Arabia and seven small countries share the Arabian Peninsula.
11. Warfare disrupts life on the eastern edge of the Middle East.

On a separate sheet of paper, complete the following review exercises.

## Checking Your Understanding

1. (a) List the countries of North Africa. (b) List the countries of the Middle East.

2. List five words or phrases that describe the general physical setting of North Africa and the Middle East.
3. What event, which started in the late 600s, gave the Middle East much of its cultural imprint?
4. What are the two most precious resources of the region?
5. What are the leading economic activities of the region?

## Applying Critical Thinking Skills

1. **Seeing Relationships** What are four ways that most of the countries of this region are alike?
2. **Comparing Ideas** (a) In what ways are the physical and cultural settings of Egypt and Iraq alike? (b) In what ways are they different? (c) In what ways are Libya and Iran alike?
3. **Interpreting Ideas** (a) What effect do you think nationalism has had on the political patterns of the region's countries? (b) In what ways has nationalism especially affected Cyprus, Israel, and Iran?
4. **Analyzing Ideas** Why is Iran's relative location so important today?
5. **Evaluating Ideas** (a) What are Egypt, Israel, and Iraq doing to solve their water problems? (b) Which country do you think will be the most successful? Why?

## Reviewing Unit Features

1. **Geography in the Workplace** (a) What is the primary task of historical geographers? (b) What techniques do they use to accomplish this task?
2. **The Geographic Web** What principle was the underlying idea behind Egyptian monument-building?
3. **City Focus** What are some of the contrasts that exist in Cairo today?
4. **City Focus** In what ways has Baghdad modernized since 1979?

## Using Map Skills

1. Study the map entitled "The Muslim World" on page 459. What countries have the largest numbers of Shiite Muslims?
2. Examine the map entitled "Oil Resources of the Middle East" on page 495. **(a)** What countries have the largest oil deposits? **(b)** What country has no oil deposits?

## Investigating Geography

1. Research the social changes that have accompanied the development of oil industries and the flow of oil revenue. Identify the beliefs, traditions, economic activities, and other characteristics that have changed.
2. Prepare a report on the Suez Canal. Include information on the ancient and recent history of the canal.
3. Identify and report on the contributions of the Muslims in language, science, astronomy, mathematics, literature, medicine, and agriculture.
4. Prepare illustrations of the unique clothing of the region, such as the *yarmulke*, or skullcap, and the *keffiya*, or headdress. Share your drawings with the class.

## Further Readings

### Chapter 23

Aroian, Lois A., and Richard P. Mitchell. *The Modern Middle East and North Africa.* New York: Macmillan. Studies the geography, history, and peoples of North Africa and the Middle East.

*Atlas of the Arab World.* Compiled by Michael Dempsey. New York: Facts on File. Gives an overview—in map form—of the geography, history, and economy of the Arab nations.

Drysdale, Alasdair, and Gerald H. Blake. *The Middle East and North Africa: A Political Geography.* New York: Oxford University Press. Examines the political changes taking place in North Africa and the Middle East, viewed from a geographical perspective.

Peters, Stella. *Bedouin.* Morristown, N.J.: Silver Burdett. Presents a cultural and historical view of the bedouins of Arabia, showing where and how they survive in the desert.

### Chapter 24

Lhote, Henri. "Oasis of Art in the Sahara." *National Geographic.* Volume 172, Number 2. August 1987. pp. 181–91. Describes the pictorial art and paintings left by early peoples on rock formations in the Sahara thousands of years ago.

McDowall, David. *Let's Visit Algeria.* London: Burke Publishing Co. Covers Algeria's history, culture, and economy, and the effect of the Islamic faith on attempts to blend Algeria's ancient culture with the modern world.

### Chapter 25

Eban, Abba. *Promised Land.* New York: Thomas Nelson Inc., Publishers. Depicts ancient and modern Israel in pictures with text by Abba Eban, former Israeli Foreign Minister.

Ellis, William S. "The New Face of Baghdad." *National Geographic.* Volume 167, Number 1, January, 1985. pp. 80–109. Presents a photo essay on Baghdad, from its ancient greatness to its modern style.

Gilfond, Henry. *Afghanistan.* New York: Franklin Watts. Provides a look at Afghanistan with a focus on the history, religion, and culture of the Afghan people.

———. *Syria.* New York: Franklin Watts. Presents a pictorial essay on the history, people, tribes, and town and village life in Syria. The author concludes the text with a chapter on Syria's confrontations with its neighbors, particularly Israel.

Shapiro, William E. *Lebanon.* New York: Franklin Watts. Studies this troubled country and provides historical background and explanations of the recent turmoil.

Thesiger, Wilfred. *Arabian Sands.* New York: Penguin Books. Looks at the geographic environment and way of life of the bedouins of Saudi Arabia.

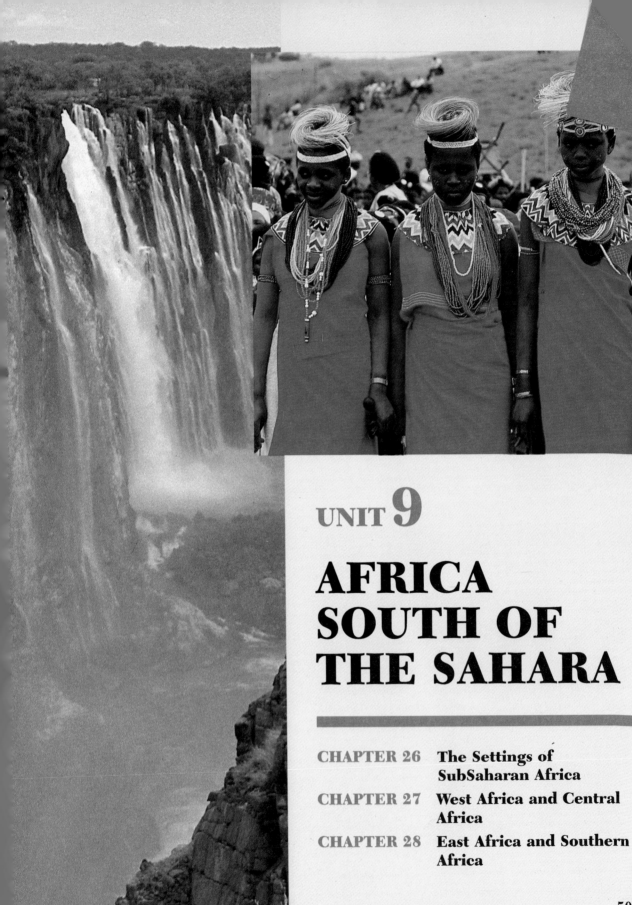

# The Settings of SubSaharan Africa

# PUTTING THE CHAPTER IN FOCUS

Basins, valleys, and mountain peaks add diversity to the flat plateau that covers most of Africa south of the Sahara. The people of the region also reflect a wide diversity. Though most are black, they come from hundreds of different tribes and cultures. Descendants of both Europeans and Asians from many countries now call Africa home as well. This diversity of setting, both physical and cultural, causes problems for many of Africa's governments as they try to create a sense of national identity.

## Ideas to Understand

In studying about the physical and cultural settings of Africa south of the Sahara, use these ideas to give direction to your reading.

1 Most of Africa south of the Sahara rests on a high plateau.

2 Unique cultural patterns characterize modern Africa.

## Terms to Define

The following terms are some of the key terms in the chapter. Defining them will help you understand the physical and cultural settings of Africa south of the Sahara.

safari                  jungle
basin                   tribe
tropical rain forest

## Places to Locate

Locating the following places will add to your knowledge of geography.

Cape Agulhas            Tombouctou
Mount Kilimanjaro       Zambezi River
Lake Victoria           Zaire River
Red Sea                 Kalahari Desert
Niger River             Olduvai Gorge

## 1 Most of Africa south of the Sahara rests on a high plateau.

Imagine that you are on a **safari**—Swahili for "journey"—through Africa south of the Sahara. Sweltering jungles, broad grasslands, and an endless variety of animals undoubtedly come to mind. Bright birds screech and big cats roar. You can feel the ground vibrate as elephants and rhinoceroses rumble past. This is SubSaharan Africa—this and much more.

### Physical Regions

The shifting sands and eerie emptiness of the Sahara, the world's largest desert, separate the Mediterranean region from the lands south of the Sahara, or SubSaharan Africa. Wide expanses of water—the Indian Ocean on the east and south and the Atlantic Ocean on the west and south—form the region's other borders.

SubSaharan Africa stretches for vast distances north and south. It reaches northward to the Sahara beyond 20° N and southward to Cape Agulhas (uh·GUHL·uhs) at nearly 35° S. The region can be divided into four subregions—West, Central, East, and Southern Africa. (You will learn more about each of these subregions in Chapters 27 and 28.) In general, the subregions lie on a high plateau that is broken here and there by basins and deep valleys.

**The plateau.** The plateau of Africa south of the Sahara resembles a tall table. Steep

*Mount Kilimanjaro, Kenya*

slopes rise from the coast in the east and much of the west. The slope is especially steep in southeastern Africa, between Lesotho (luh·SOH·toh) and South Africa. Only in Liberia, Ghana (GAHN·uh), and Ivory Coast—on Africa's western bulge—and in Mozambique (moh·zuhm·BEEK)—in the east—does the slope rise more gently.

Lowlands occur only in narrow strips along the coast. No mountain ranges cross the plateau. Individual mountain peaks, however, dot the eastern portion of the tableland. Some peaks, such as Mount Kilimanjaro (kil·uh·muhn·JAHR·oh), soar thousands of feet above the plateau.

**The basins.** Five deep **basins,** broad dips in the earth's surface, dent Africa's plateau. These basins, each more than 600 miles (960 kilometers) wide, sink more than 5,000 feet (1,525 meters) below the top of the plateau.

Three of the basins reach southward from the Sahara. From west to east along the southern edge of the Sahara lie the Al-Juf, Chad, and Sudan basins. The fourth basin, the Congo Basin, dips below the plateau in Zaire (ZYR) in Central Africa. The plateau also dips in Southern Africa to form the Kalahari (kal·uh·HAHR·ee) Basin, which spans Botswana (baht·SWAHN·uh). In this basin lies the Kalahari Desert.

**Rift valleys.** Perhaps the most remarkable landform of SubSaharan Africa is the Great Rift Valley. This great structural crack along a fault in the earth runs north and south near the eastern edge of the plateau. Steep sides line the edges of the rift valley, which formed thousands of years ago when a block of the plateau dropped down to form what is now the narrow valley floor. Rainwater has since filled parts of the valley, creating several long and narrow lakes.

Lake Malawi (muh·LAH·wee) in Malawi is one such lake (see the map on page 511).

Other lakes stretch northward, tracing the valley floor to the west of Lake Victoria and far into Uganda (ooh·GAN·duh). Another series of lakes extends eastward of Lake Victoria to Lake Turkana. The Great Rift Valley then continues north to include the Red Sea and the Dead Sea.

**The Sahel.** The Sahel, a semiarid to arid plain, borders the Sahara on the south. It stretches from Mauritania and Mali (MAHL·ee) on the west through Niger (NY·juhr), Chad, and Sudan to Kenya on the east. In recent years unwise land use and changes in rainfall have caused desertification. The Sahara has taken over an estimated 250,000 square miles (647,500 square kilometers) of the Sahel in the last five years.

Short-grass savannas, dotted with a few trees and thorny bushes, cover the Sahel. Annual rainfall averages between 4 and 20 inches (10 and 50 centimeters). Some areas, however, get no rainfall for years, creating severe droughts.

The environment of the Sahel is especially fragile. Famines that plague the area illustrate the delicate relationship between people and their habitat. The famine cycle begins when herds increase during wetter years. The animals quickly overgraze the dying grass in drier years. Soon the ground cover disappears and the soil turns to dust and blows away. Massive droughts in the 1980s killed pastures, crops, and livestock and led to widespread famine.

### Rivers

The many rivers of SubSaharan Africa form unique patterns (see the map on page 511). In western Africa the Niger begins in the highlands of Guinea (GIN·ee). Curiously, it flows northward, away from the ocean and into the Sahara. Near Tombouctou (tohn·book·TOO), the river turns sharply back and empties into the Atlantic. In northeastern Africa the White Nile spreads into a

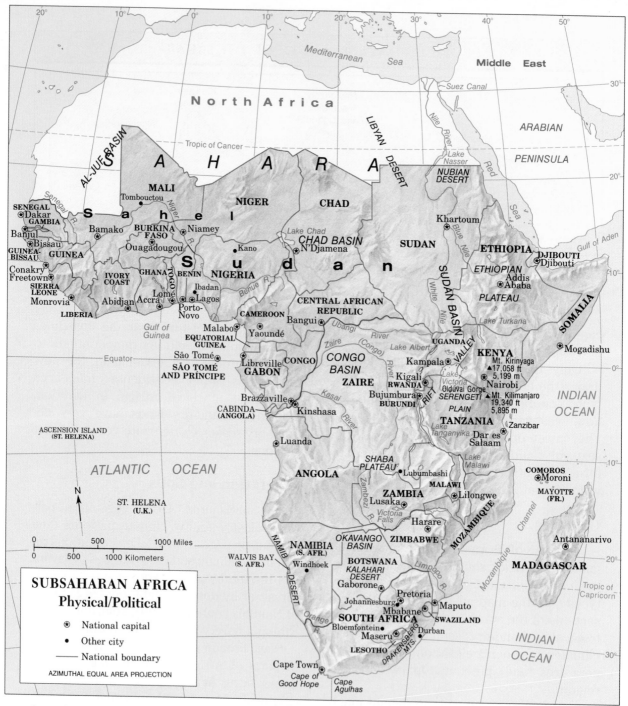

**Learning from Maps.** *Most European colonies in Africa became independent countries in the 1950s and 1960s. Which country is not yet independent?*

huge swamp before reforming and flowing northward into the Nile. In south-central Africa the Zambezi (zam·BEE·zee) River flows eastward from Angola into Zambia.

As the Zambezi changes course, it is joined by streams that formerly flowed into the Limpopo (lim·POH·poh) River. Thousands of years from now, the Zambezi probably will

**511**

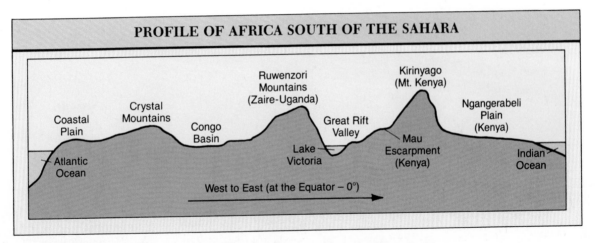

**PROFILE OF AFRICA SOUTH OF THE SAHARA**

*Learning from Diagrams.* Faulting formed the Great Rift Valley. What theory explains faulting?

capture the upper parts of the Limpopo and take on a new course.

Only the Zaire (Congo) River, which drains the heart of the continent, follows a typical course. The Zaire and its tributaries flow westward from the Shaba Plateau. They meet upstream from Kinshasa (kin·SHAHS·uh) and Brazzaville (BRAZ·uh·vil) to form a mighty waterway that carries fresh water far into the Atlantic.

## Climates

Because of its vast expanse and unique landforms, Africa south of the Sahara contains many different climate types and subtypes (see the map on pages 96–97). Large sections of the continent have tropical wet, tropical wet-and-dry, semiarid, and desert climates. In general, elevation modifies temperatures and precipitation within the region.

Dry conditions prevail throughout much of the African continent. In fact, greater portions of Africa have a desert climate than any other continent. A look at a world map will tell you why. First, the rising air of the equatorial low-pressure belt causes dry conditions. Second, winds blowing across the vast continent from the oceans

release their moisture near the coastlines or a few miles inland. As they continue to cross hundreds of miles of land, the now dry winds bring continental influences throughout much of Africa. In addition, tropical wet-and-dry lands have very defined dry seasons, often with very brief wet seasons.

## Vegetation and Soils

In SubSaharan Africa vegetation patterns closely follow climate patterns (see the map on pages 100–01). Dry conditions result in seemingly endless stretches of savannas broken by an occasional tree, a scrub forest, or by desert vegetation. Large areas of Namibia (nuh·MIB·ee·uh), Mauritania, and Ethiopia have very little vegetation.

Vast broadleaf evergreen forests thrive in parts of Africa where tropical wet climates bring heavy rainfall of 100 inches (254 centimeters) or more a year. Such forests are called **tropical rain forests.** Often, however, people mistakenly call the rain forests jungles. A **jungle** is a thick growth of plants found in a tropical rain forest wherever sunlight penetrates the dense umbrella of tall trees and reaches the forest floor—usually along rivers.

Much of the soil of the region lacks nutrients. Shifting sands cover desert areas such as the Kalahari, while leaching produces soils in Central Africa that are generally unproductive. Only thin strips of land along rivers and in a few areas in Southern Africa contain rich, alluvial soils.

## Resources

Africa south of the Sahara has abundant resources. Many areas, however, have not yet developed the technology to use these resources efficiently.

**Learning from Pictures.** *Rivers often provide the only transportation networks for the people in parts of Gabon. What kind of vegetation surrounds the canoeist?*

**Learning from Maps.** *Many of the African countries south of the Sahara must import food. What are the major food products grown by the farmers of the region?*

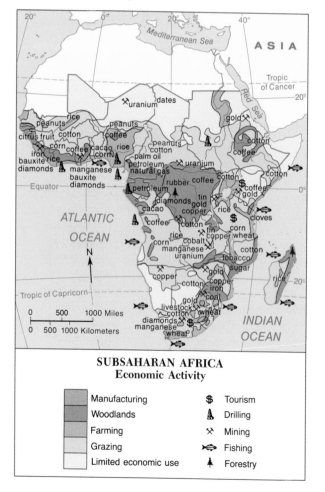

**SUBSAHARAN AFRICA**
**Economic Activity**

| | | | |
|---|---|---|---|
| Manufacturing | | $ | Tourism |
| Woodlands | | ⚲ | Drilling |
| Farming | | ✕ | Mining |
| Grazing | | ⇄ | Fishing |
| Limited economic use | | ♠ | Forestry |

**Agriculture.** Most of the farming in SubSaharan Africa remains subsistence farming. Small farms and farming villages are the rule. Farmers grow cassava, grain, bananas, and sugarcane in areas with enough rainfall. Coffee grows in highland areas of West, Central, and East Africa, while tea grows in the highlands of East Africa. Sheep and goats graze the short grasses of the savannas, while cattle and sheep graze the broader grasslands in East and Southern Africa.

Despite the efforts of African farmers, Africa does not produce enough food to feed its growing population. Farmers actually cultivate less than 25 percent of the estimated 2 billion acres (809 million hectares) suitable for farming. In Central Africa dense rain forests, a lack of roads, and tropical diseases that affect both humans and livestock hinder farming. The tsetse fly, whose bite can give both humans and animals sleeping sickness, infests 6.2 million square miles (16 million square kilometers) of Central Africa—an area larger than the United States. Other areas of SubSaharan

*Text continues on page 515.*

**513**

*Masai herders in the N'gong Hills of Kenya*

A vast tropical grassland covers southwestern Kenya and the adjoining countryside of north-central Tanzania. Nomadic herders known as the Masai have lived on this expanse of grassland for hundreds of years.

### The Masai

The Masai believe that they have always been cattle herders. According to their legends, God gave them cattle as a gift when the earth and sky separated. Today the Masai rely almost totally on their herds of cattle for subsistence. They milk the cattle, make butter and cheese, and bleed the animals periodically. Though it sounds unappetizing to us, they drink the blood, which serves as an important source of protein. As a last resort, when an animal is too old or weak to graze, the Masai slaughter it for food.

In addition to their cattle, the Masai graze sheep and goats on pastures too poor to support cattle. They also use donkeys to haul their goods from place to place as they follow their herds.

### Masai Society

The Masai live in small groups of four to eight families. The elders of each group serve as authority figures for all the group's members. The families stay in camps made of flat-roofed, straight-walled mud houses. Beside the houses is an area surrounded by thick, thatched fences where the cattle—the measure of each family's wealth—are kept at night. Each group lives in a dozen such camps throughout the year. The Masai tear down their camps and rebuild them from scratch as they move their cattle from place to place according to the season and the need for water for the animals.

### An Uncertain Future

The Masai population grew from 115,000 in 1958 to more than 300,000 in 1988. But as more people compete for grazing lands, there is less room to wander. And the Masai must continue to compete for grazing lands and water with the many wild animals of Africa. The Masai realize that to survive they must guard against overgrazing, which is increasingly difficult.

To reduce the pressure on the pastures, the governments of Kenya and Tanzania have encouraged the Masai to settle down as farmers. Few of these efforts have been successful, however, for the Masai prefer to wander through the grasslands that have been their home for centuries. They feel no loyalty to national governments and no obligation to abandon their way of life. Instead they remain loyal to the elders of their group and their traditional way of life.

Africa remain too dry to farm each year and can be planted with crops only every five or six years.

**Forestry.** Forests blanket nearly 45 percent of the region's total land area. In fact, forests cover almost 78 percent of Gabon (gah·BOHN), 76 percent of Zaire, and more than 50 percent of the land in the Congo, the Central African Republic, Senegal, Cameroon, and Botswana. Most of these forests contain tropical hardwoods, which are among the world's most valuable trees.

Despite the vast forests, the region supports few commercial lumbering projects. Roads rarely reach beyond towns into the forests, making it difficult to transport workers and equipment into the forest and to transport products out. In addition, traditional methods and primitive tools make lumbering inefficient. Squabbles between local groups and national governments over who owns the forests also discourage commercial interests.

**Fishing.** By studying the map of major fishing grounds on page 138, you can see that several limited fishing areas ring the African coast. Most of these areas, however, are small and produce few fish. Very warm waters, like those found in most of the region, attract far fewer fish than cooler waters. In addition, African fishers use old-fashioned methods and tools, which further reduces potential yields.

**Mining.** Abundant and rich mineral deposits underlie much of SubSaharan Africa (see the map on page 513). African mines produce more than 59 percent of the world's cobalt, 35 percent of its uranium, 26 percent of its manganese, and 25 percent of its copper. Several countries, notably South Africa, Zimbabwe (zim·BAHB·way), and Zaire, have modern mining industries. In addition, companies from many foreign countries have joined local businesses to tap the region's mineral reserves.

---

**SECTION 1 REVIEW**

1. **Define** safari, basin, tropical rain forest, jungle
2. **Locate** Cape Agulhas, Mount Kilimanjaro, Lake Malawi, Lake Victoria, Lake Turkana, Red Sea, the Sahel, Niger River, Tombouctou, White Nile River, Zambezi River, Limpopo River, Zaire River, Kalahari Desert
3. **Summarizing Ideas** Describe the **(a)** plateau, **(b)** basins, **(c)** rift valley, and **(d)** rivers that characterize SubSaharan Africa.
4. **Analyzing Ideas** Why are African farmers unable to produce enough food to feed the African people?
5. **Evaluating Ideas** **(a)** How important are the contributions of fishing and mineral resources to the overall economic health of SubSaharan Africa? **(b)** How can the contributions of each be improved?

---

## 2 Unique cultural patterns characterize modern Africa.

As you continue your safari across SubSaharan Africa, you will see many different people and many different cultures. You will see tall herders striding across the dry plains of northern Uganda, their heads protected from insects by large, mud headdresses. You will see children in Ghana wearing hundreds of glass beads. You will see a tribal king in Benin (buh·NIN) crouching under an umbrella held by one of his many granddaughters. You also will see men and women dressed in Western business clothes hurrying along car-filled streets.

## A Brief History

Evidence gathered by paleoanthropologists (PAY·lee·oh·an·thruh·pawl·uh·juhst), scientists who study the fossil remains and artifacts of early people, suggests that people have lived continuously in East and Southern Africa longer than anywhere else on the earth—more than 2 million years. Two of the scientists, Louis and Mary Leakey, unearthed the bones and tools of these early people in the Olduvai (OHL·duh·vy) Gorge in northern Tanzania (tan·zuh·NEE·uh; see the map on page 511).

Unfortunately, scholars know little of the early history of SubSaharan Africa. Few early written records, especially those written by Africans, exist. Most groups kept their history alive orally. Storytellers, who have always held an honored place in African society, helped to pass down the history of their people from one generation to another.

**Early civilizations.** Scholars do know that several advanced civilizations blossomed and faded in the region before A.D. 1500. Most Africans lived in **tribes,** groups of people who share a common language and culture. Each tribe lived on traditional tribal lands—lands that had been controlled by the tribe for centuries. Over the years many of the tribes established great tribal kingdoms.

The kingdoms of Kush and Aksum, for example, grew along the Nile River in what is today southeastern Sudan. Several other important civilizations arose in West Africa. Between 500 and 1900 the successive empires of Ghana, Mali, Songhai (SAWNG·hy), and Kanem-Bornu had risen and fallen between the upper parts of the Senegal and Niger rivers in present-day Mali. These empires maintained trade with North Africa and the Middle East. Streams of camel caravans brought goods to West African merchants.

Great civilizations such as the kingdom of Zimbabwe and the empire of the Mwanamutapa (mwah·nuh·MOO·tuh·puh) also grew far to the south.

**European control.** In the 1400s European countries began setting up trading posts along the African coasts. The Europeans rarely traveled into the interior of the continent because dense vegetation, rugged landscape, and rapids in the rivers blocked their paths. Along the coasts the Europeans traded manufactured goods for ivory, gold, and silver. In the 1500s, however, the main trade item was slaves. By the time the slave trade ended in the mid-1800s, about 10 million Africans had been sent to the Americas against their will.

*Learning from Pictures. Much of West Africa's early art focused on masks worn in tribal ceremonies. What West African civilizations dominated trade between 500 and 1900?*

*Text continues on page 518.*

# CITY FOCUS
## Tombouctou, Mali

Tombouctou is a crumbling, mud-brick town in central Mali with fewer than 20,000 people. Yet from the 1200s to the 1500s it was one of Africa's wealthiest trading cities. It was also a famous cultural center whose university was renowned throughout the Arab world for its scholarship in history, law, and Islamic religious studies. Today, however, much of the site of the fabulous city lies buried beneath the ever-shifting sands of the Sahara.

*Trade in Tombouctou today*

### A Strategic Location

Tombouctou's past prosperity as a center of trade hinged directly on its situation—a location between the vast empty reaches of the Sahara to the north and the more populous and wetter lands to the south. In such a location Tombouctou served as a center of exchange for the different goods produced by the two regions. In addition, its site near the Niger River, which turns sharply to the south toward the coast just beyond Tombouctou, gave the city the advantage of relatively easy access to the more productive southern region.

Tombouctou would have been a far smaller city than it actually became if there had been only desert to the north. A desert produces so little for exchange. But beyond the desert was the highly developed coast of the Mediterranean Sea, an area that produced far different products than the areas south of Tombouctou. Some of these Mediterranean products included salt, cloth, dates, figs, and metal goods, as well as cowrie shells that were used for money in tropical Africa.

The route from the Mediterranean coast to Tombouctou required an exceptionally long haul through the desolate Sahara. The major carriers—camels—were an expensive means of transportation and their carrying capacity was limited. Because the costs of transport on the trans-Sahara route were so high, only the most valuable goods were carried. Goods transferred at Tombouctou to be carried back to the Mediterranean coast included such valuable items as gold and ivory. Slaves also were taken on the route, but they had to provide their own transportation—by foot.

### Decline of Tombouctou

Over time the invention of the steam engine improved ocean shipping. Africa's commerce soon began to reach the entire world. The goods that formerly moved by camel and canoe through Tombouctou on their way to market began to move instead by oceangoing freighters through the ports of West Africa.

Tombouctou slowly declined as a trading post. It suffered numerous attacks by invading armies and its population declined. Today there is little of the past glory in its all-but-deserted ruins—ruins that have gradually fallen victim to that cruelest conqueror of all, the winds and the sands of the Sahara.

Although the Europeans had come to Africa as traders, they eventually began to carve the entire continent into colonies. The new national boundaries often cut across tribal lands with little regard to the traditions of their inhabitants. By 1914 only Ethiopia and Liberia remained independent countries.

**Nationalism and independence.** Over the years Africans chafed under colonial rule and worked toward independence. In 1956 Sudan gained its independence from Britain. It became the first former colony in Africa to be recognized as independent. Many other countries soon followed. Today SubSaharan Africa contains more than 50 independent countries. Only Namibia, which is administered by South Africa, has yet to gain independence.

## Population Patterns

Population characteristics in SubSaharan Africa reflect unique patterns. Many factors contribute to the region's distinct composition and distribution.

**Population composition.** Blacks comprise about 95 percent of the people living in SubSaharan Africa. Although as a group they form the vast majority, black Africans are divided into hundreds of different language and ethnic groups.

About 5 million people in SubSaharan Africa are whites of European descent. About 60 percent of the whites live in South Africa. Many trace their descent to Dutch colonists known as Boers. Other white Africans trace their descent to British, French, and Portuguese settlers. These groups live mainly in South Africa, Zimbabwe, and Kenya.

Africans of Asian origin number nearly 1 million. Many of their ancestors came to Africa from India and Pakistan in the 1800s to work on plantations. In the last 30 years many others have come from East Asia. Arabic influences remain particularly strong in West Africa and along the coast of East Africa.

**Population distribution.** Over 450 million people live in SubSaharan Africa. These people are distributed unevenly over the vast region. Many countries have large populations, while others have relatively few people. In general, the most densely populated areas lie in the volcanic highlands

*Learning from Maps.* *Despite growing populations and urbanization, there are few large cities in SubSaharan Africa. What city in the region has more than 2 million people?*

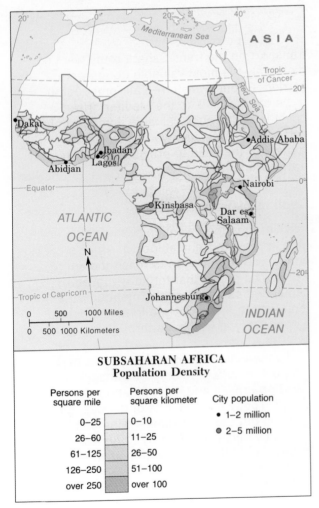

### SUBSAHARAN AFRICA
#### Population Density

| Persons per square mile | Persons per square kilometer | City population |
|---|---|---|
| 0–25 | 0–10 | • 1–2 million |
| 26–60 | 11–25 | ● 2–5 million |
| 61–125 | 26–50 | |
| 126–250 | 51–100 | |
| over 250 | over 100 | |

along the Great Rift Valley and along the coasts.

**Growth rates.** SubSaharan Africa has the world's fastest regional population growth rate—over 3.0 percent a year. This rate is nearly double the world average of 1.7 percent a year. The population of the region increases by more than 1 million people each *month*. If the present growth rate continues, the number of Africans living in Africa south of the Sahara will double in less than 25 years. Such statistics reveal the serious challenges that African leaders face as they try to find ways to support such rapidly growing populations.

**Urbanization.** While several large cities dot the African coast south of the Sahara, most of the region's people live in small villages. As elsewhere around the world, however, large numbers of people move to the cities each year. And, as in other regions, the number of new residents in the cities exceeds the jobs, housing, and services the cities can provide. Kinshasa, Zaire; Lagos, Nigeria; and Johannesburg, South Africa rank as SubSaharan Africa's three largest cities.

## Social Patterns

A mixture of peoples of African, European, and Asian origins inhabits Africa today. This cultural diversity presents special problems. The many different languages spoken in the region often make it difficult for governments and educational systems to function effectively. Religious differences also can be divisive.

**Language.** Different languages abound in SubSaharan Africa. English, French, Portuguese, Spanish, and Arabic all serve as official languages in different areas of the region. So do Amharic, a mixture of an

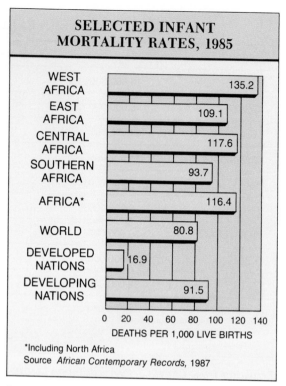

**SELECTED INFANT MORTALITY RATES, 1985**

| | DEATHS PER 1,000 LIVE BIRTHS |
|---|---|
| WEST AFRICA | 135.2 |
| EAST AFRICA | 109.1 |
| CENTRAL AFRICA | 117.6 |
| SOUTHERN AFRICA | 93.7 |
| AFRICA* | 116.4 |
| WORLD | 80.8 |
| DEVELOPED NATIONS | 16.9 |
| DEVELOPING NATIONS | 91.5 |

\*Including North Africa
Source *African Contemporary Records*, 1987

***Learning from Graphs.*** *Even though the infant mortality rate in SubSaharan Africa is 114 per 1,000 live births, the growth rate remains over 3 percent. What is the world's average growth rate?*

ancient African language, Arabic, and Bantu; Afrikaans, a blend of Dutch, English, and African languages; and Malagasy, a mixture of Arabic, African, and East Asian languages. Somali, Swahili, Kurinidi, Iswana, Kunyarwanda, Chichewa, and Crioulo, which are mixtures of several African languages, are also used. In addition to the official languages, Africans speak hundreds of other traditional languages and thousands of dialects.

**Religion.** Religions also vary widely in the region. Animism, traditional religions involving belief in spirits, prevails in some areas, as do many other local religions. One of the dominant religions in the region, however, is Islam. Long before European

**519**

## HEALTH CARE IN SELECTED AFRICAN NATIONS

| Nation | Population* | Number of Hospitals** | Number of Beds* | Number of Doctors* |
|---|---|---|---|---|
| CAMEROON | 10,600,000 | 1,003 | 25,541 | 640 |
| CHAD | 5,000,000 | 33 | 3,353 | 90 |
| KENYA | 23,000,000 | 1,328 | 28,108 | 2,057 |
| MADAGASCAR | 11,000,000 | 749 | 20,625 | 901 |
| MALI | 8,700,000 | 12 | 3,200 | 319 |
| RWANDA | 6,900,000 | 170 | 9,015 | 164 |
| SOUTH AFRICA | 36,600,000 | 595 | 156,245 | 18,003 |
| TOGO | 3,300,000 | 69 | 3,655 | 168 |
| ZAIRE | 32,800,000 | 942 | 79,244 | 1,900 |
| ZAMBIA | 7,600,000 | 636 | 20,638 | 821 |

*1987 estimates
**Includes clinics

Source: *Statesman's Yearbook*, 1987-88

**Learning from Charts.** *Poor sanitation and inadequate health care contribute to widespread disease. Which country on the chart has the poorest health care? the best?*

**Learning from Pictures.** *Large Muslim minorities have great influence in Nigeria. What group of people introduced Islam to the west coast of Africa?*

explorers arrived, Arab traders spread Islam along trade routes across the Sahara and down the east coast of Africa. Some Africans practice Christianity, which also spread from the Middle East. Ethiopians follow one of the oldest forms of Christianity. After the 1400s European colonists and missionaries introduced Protestantism and Roman Catholicism to the region.

## Political Patterns

Most of the countries of SubSaharan Africa struggle with political problems. For the most part, the independent countries retain their colonial boundaries. These boundaries continue to cause conflicts. Governments throughout the region find it difficult to build a national identity among people who speak so many different languages and have such different cultural backgrounds. In fact, civil wars sometimes arise because hostile tribes live within the

*Text continues on page 522.*

# DEVELOPING GEOGRAPHY SKILLS
## INTERPRETING VISUALS: Comparing Maps

One of the most important ways that geographers acquire information is from comparing maps of the same area that contain different information. Such comparisons often make it possible to see new relationships among the data.

You have already been introduced to the skills you will need to compare maps. Review the steps for reviewing map basics (page 44), interpreting physical maps (page 63), reading economic maps (page 163), and analyzing land use (page 443).

### How to Compare Maps

To effectively compare maps, follow these guidelines.

1. **Select the maps to be compared carefully.** Note the areas covered by the maps, dates of the information (if appropriate), and other important pieces of information.
2. **Note similarities and differences.** Examine locational patterns.
3. **Look for relationships.** Identify relationships among the data contained on the maps.
4. **Apply critical thinking skills.** Make inferences, state generalizations, and draw conclusions from the evidence.

### Applying the Skill

Compare the map on this page with the map on page 518. Notice that you are comparing a map containing data on the population density of SubSaharan Africa with one containing rainfall information for Africa. A close look at the patterns reveals that in several places, such as northern Mali, both population density and rainfall are limited. Elsewhere, such as along Nigeria's coast, the opposite pattern exists—high population density and heavy rainfall. By closely examining the maps, you can discover more similarities and differences in their patterns.

From the evidence on the maps, you can form several generalizations, conclusions, and inferences. For example, you can conclude that population density and rainfall are related. You can generalize that people settle in areas that receive abundant rainfall. You can infer that people settle where rainfall is sufficient to support agriculture. Think of other generalizations, conclusions, and inferences you can apply to the maps.

*To practice this skill, see Practicing Geography Skills on page 525.*

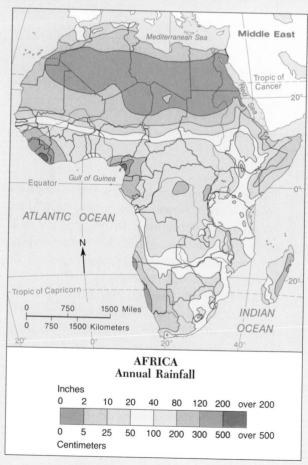

**AFRICA**
**Annual Rainfall**

Inches
| 0 | 2 | 10 | 20 | 40 | 80 | 120 | 200 | over 200 |

| 0 | 5 | 25 | 50 | 100 | 200 | 300 | 500 | over 500 |
Centimeters

# GEOGRAPHY IN THE WORKPLACE
## Economic Geographers

Economic geography is important because it deals with the geographic distribution of the economic activities of people. The economic maps in this text show you that the economic activities of people occur unevenly over the earth's surface. This distribution is of great interest to economic geographers.

In general, economic geographers study one of six major types of economic activities. In the first—production—economic geographers focus on commodities that are obtained in natural form from the land, seas, mines, forests, and farms. The second category of study—secondary production—focuses on the ways in which products are changed in manufacturing. The third field—retailing—analyzes the consumption of products. The fourth area—the consumer sector—considers consumer goods and services. The fifth area—services—includes services provided to the first three productive sectors and to the consumer sector of the economy. This area includes services provided by hair stylists, lawyers, doctors, teachers, and many others. The final area of study by economic geographers focuses on transportation.

Because economic geographers are primarily concerned with the locational aspects of economics, most economic geographers become experts at evaluating the relative assets of different locations for a particular activity. For example, some economic geographers specialize in locating the best possible site for a factory. They must take into account the location of the raw materials required in manufacturing. They must learn what kind of labor will be needed and if this labor is readily available. And they must find the best and least expensive transportation routes for sending the products to market.

Economic geography offers a variety of opportunities for a student with interests in both geography and business.

---

borders of the same country. Other disputes result from a single tribe being split apart by two and sometimes three national borders. For example, battles between the government and groups of Somalis seeking to move or drive out "foreigners" have rocked Ethiopia, Chad, Nigeria, and Zaire.

Because of such problems, the political patterns of the region change constantly. Though most African leaders claimed to believe in democracy, many set up dictatorships soon after independence. Since then, some countries have moved toward democracy. Others have not, often because their leaders worry that tribal infighting will destroy national unity.

## Economic Patterns

Economists classify all of the countries of SubSaharan Africa except South Africa as developing nations. Each has serious economic problems. African nations rank among the poorest in the world. Of the 34 countries of the world with per capita GNPs below $400, 21 are in Africa. Only 7 of the 46 countries in Africa south of the Sahara—Congo, Gabon, Angola, South Africa, Mauritius (mooh·RISH·uhs), Namibia, and Seychelles (say·SHELZ)—have annual per capita GNPs over $1,000. Poverty adds to the region's other problems—inadequate nutrition, sanitation, and health care. Millions of

**Learning from Pictures.** *Lagos's site and situation make it an excellent break-of-bulk point. What remains the main economic activity in SubSaharan Africa?*

people suffer from malnutrition, and in some areas medical care is unavailable. Education programs that focus on proper sanitation and health care procedures often lack funding. The spread of AIDS—acquired immune deficiency syndrome—in the region takes an especially high toll in lives. AIDS is an as-yet-incurable disease that attacks the body's immune system.

Subsistence farming remains the most common economic activity in SubSaharan Africa. Most countries of the region lack the money to industrialize. Many rely heavily on foreign assistance and on loans from the World Bank and the International Monetary Fund. In order to receive the loans, however, these organizations often require that the countries enact economic reforms such as those enacted in Mexico (see Chapter 13). Such "belt-tightening" is never popular and sometimes leads to political and social unrest.

Despite this gloomy picture, SubSaharan Africa has the potential for economic growth. The region's abundant natural resources hold the key to that growth. In order to improve their economies, African leaders have adopted a variety of economic systems to take advantage of their nations' natural gifts. Today the region is a patchwork of socialism and capitalism.

---

### SECTION 2 REVIEW

1. **Define** tribe
2. **Locate** Olduvai Gorge
3. **Interpreting Ideas** **(a)** Why is little known about the early history of Sub-Saharan Africa? **(b)** How was history passed on from one generation to another?
4. **Analyzing Ideas** Why have colonial boundaries created continuing problems for modern African nations?
5. **Evaluating Ideas** What factors give SubSaharan Africa the potential for economic growth?

# CHAPTER 26 REVIEW

## Chapter Summary

The following list contains the key concepts you have learned about the physical and cultural settings of Africa south of the Sahara.

1. Most of the countries in SubSaharan Africa lie on a high plateau, which is broken by several basins. In the east the Great Rift Valley slices deeply into the plateau.
2. The many rivers of SubSaharan Africa form unique patterns. They include the Niger in western Africa, the White Nile in northeastern Africa, the Zambezi and the Limpopo in south-central Africa, and the Zaire in Central Africa.
3. SubSaharan Africa includes many climate types and subtypes, but much of the region is very dry. Deserts are expanding in several places throughout the region. Soils in Central Africa are leached by the rains and generally unproductive.
4. SubSaharan Africa has abundant natural resources but at present lacks the technology to fully use them. Agriculture in particular has failed to keep pace with the technological advances required to meet the food needs of the people.
5. A succession of great civilizations once flourished in ancient Africa. In the 1800s Europeans colonized the region and divided it, with little regard to tribal boundaries or traditions. By 1914 only Ethiopia and Liberia remained independent.
6. The vast majority of Africans are black. Europeans and Asians form small minorities.
7. The world's fastest regional population growth rate puts tremendous pressure on the resources of the region.
8. Most of the countries of SubSaharan Africa struggle with political problems. All except South Africa are developing nations.
9. The Masai live on the tropical grassland that covers parts of Tanzania and Kenya.

On a separate sheet of paper, complete the following review exercises.

## Reviewing Geographic Terms

Supply the geographic term that correctly completes each sentence.

1. Members of each ____ share a common language, religion, and customs.
2. In Africa, depressions called ____ dip 5,000 feet (1,525 meters) below the surface of the plateau.
3. African forests are often mistakenly called ____, which are actually dense undergrowth in rain forests.
4. Swahili for "journey," ____ have long been associated with trips across Africa.
5. Vast broadleaf evergreen forests are called ____ ____ ____.

## Developing Critical Thinking Skills

1. **Summarizing Ideas**  What are the major landforms of SubSaharan Africa?
2. **Understanding Ideas**  How was the Great Rift Valley formed?
3. **Identifying Ideas**  (a) Where is the richest soil in SubSaharan Africa?  (b) Why are soils in other places not as fertile?
4. **Analyzing Ideas**  Why did Europeans rarely travel to the interior of the continent during colonial times?
5. **Evaluating Ideas**  (a) Why has rapid urbanization strained resources in the region's cities?  (b) Which three cities rank as the largest in SubSaharan Africa?
6. **Analyzing Ideas**  (a) What factors limit economic growth in SubSaharan Africa?  (b) Why might African leaders be reluctant to request loans from the International Monetary Fund?
7. **Writing About Geography**  In a one-page essay, complete one of the following activities.  (a) Evaluate colonialism in Africa south of the Sahara and describe how it affected the region.  (b) Evaluate the region's potential for development given its population setting, political setting, and resource base.

## Using Primary Sources

In the following excerpt from *Africa to 1875—A Modern History*, Robin Hallett describes the geography of Central Africa. As you study the reading, consider if the geography favors any particular type of industry.

Central Africa is . . . that great bloc of territory whose bounds are the tropical forest to the north, the line of great lakes to the east, the northern frontier of South Africa and Botswana to the south and the Atlantic Ocean to the west. . . .The geography of Central Africa is less varied than that of any other region of the continent. Here are no mountain ranges, though most of the land lies three thousand feet above sea level and there are highlands in southern Angola and eastern Rhodesia [Zimbabwe]; no deserts except a small coastal strip in southern Angola; only the rolling stretches of "bush"—vegetation of varying density, part savannah grasslands, part woodland—broken by lines of great rivers or by occasional swamp-fringed lakes. No part of Africa is so rich in waterways—the Congo and the Zambezi with their tributaries and the numerous rivers of Angola, most of them broken by falls or rapids, but some easily navigable for long stretches.

Rainfall is sufficient for agriculture over most of the region, but much of the soil is poor and the bush infested with tsetse fly [an insect that carries disease, especially sleeping sickness]. Basically, then, one may think of Central Africa as reproducing many of the environmental features found over large parts of West Africa. And indeed, one can trace a certain similarity in historical development of the two . . . with the rise and fall of substantial kingdoms. . . .

1. How does the author define the term *bush*?

2. Sketch a profile similar to the one on page 512 for Central Africa, using the author's description as your guide.
3. What does the author say that the area of Central Africa seems to be rich in?
4. What factors make Central Africa unsuitable for farming and livestock herding despite sufficient rainfall?

## Practicing Geography Skills

*Before completing this activity, review Developing Geography Skills on page 521.*

**Comparing Maps**  Compare the data on the maps on pages 513 and 521. Then complete the following activities.

1. Describe three similarities and two differences you observe on the maps.
2. Write one inference you can draw, one generalization you can state, and one conclusion you can form by comparing the data on the maps.

## Exploring Geography

1. As you have read, the world's largest rift valley—the Great Rift Valley—is located in SubSaharan Africa. Use resources in your school or public library to write an illustrated report on how rift valleys are formed. Include in your report the dimensions and major features of some of the world's larger rift valleys.
2. Choose one of the major European explorers—such as Mungo Park, John Hanning Speke, David Livingstone, Henry Morton Stanley, Georg Schweinfurth, or Mary Kingsley—who explored Africa during the 1800s. Then use resources in your school or public library to prepare a written or oral biographical sketch on the explorer. Although your sketch should include information on the explorer's early life, it should focus on the explorer's work in Africa.

# PUTTING THE CHAPTER IN FOCUS

Differences in habitat and life style distinguish West Africa from Central Africa. Yet amid the great diversity, the regions possess many cultural similarities. Most of the countries of West and Central Africa rank among the world's poorest and least developed. Today the many small, newly independent countries of these two African regions struggle as they face social, political, and economic problems.

## Ideas to Understand

In studying about West and Central Africa, use these ideas to give direction to your reading.

**1** West Africa has a rich cultural heritage but faces serious problems.

**2** Despite small differences, Central Africa is similar to West Africa.

## Terms to Define

The following terms are some of the key terms in the chapter. Defining them will help you understand West and Central Africa.

secede                                capital resource
trade surplus

## Places to Locate

Locating the following places will add to your knowledge of geography.

West Africa                           Central Africa
Gulf of Guinea                        Cabinda
Niger River

## 1 West Africa has a rich cultural heritage but faces serious problems.

The ruins of West Africa's great ancient kingdoms dot the West African landscape, recalling many past glories. Today, however, the region bears little resemblance to those ancient civilizations. It is divided into many small countries, all of which must deal with serious problems.

### Physical Setting

West Africa lies between the Atlantic Ocean on the west and Lake Chad on the east (see the map on page 528). It extends from the Sahara on the north to the Gulf of Guinea on the south. Much of the region lies along the bulge of Africa's west coast. Narrow, swampy lowlands with few natural harbors line the Atlantic coast. Inland the land rises to high plateaus topped with rugged hills and highlands.

Although West Africa lies between the Tropic of Cancer and the equator, its climate and vegetation vary greatly. Along the northern edge of the region, near the Sahara, little rain falls and vegetation grows only at scattered oases. South of the Sahara lies the Sahel, an area of limited rainfall, short grasses, and a few drought-resistant trees. Subtropical, tropical wet-and-dry, and tropical wet climates characterize the areas farther south toward the equator. Savanna woodlands and rain forests cover this zone of tropical and subtropical climates.

### Cultural Setting

As many as 500 different ethnic groups live in West Africa. Bantu-speaking people make up the largest ethnic groups. Much of the region's cultural imprint originated

*Ashanti chief on throne in Ghana*

from the Bantus' life style and from that of the Arabs with whom they traded. More recently Europeans from several different countries—most notably Britain, France, and Portugal—have contributed to the region's cultural imprint.

The ethnically diverse population of West Africa is unevenly distributed over the region. Dense populations mark many parts of the region, especially along the coast. Population densities generally decrease inland from the coast to the Sahara (see the map on page 518).

Nutrition and health care remain major concerns for people throughout the region. Diets lack necessary protein and carbohydrates. To make matters worse, farm production has fallen, causing food shortages. Most of the region's diseases, such as malaria, yellow fever, and sleeping sickness, could be greatly reduced by modern medical techniques. Tragically, a lack of funds and a severe shortage of doctors make this impossible. AIDS has had an especially devastating impact on the area's people. In general, life expectancies in the region are low,

**Learning from Maps.** *Portions of the West African coast have names such as the Ivory Coast, Gold Coast, and Slave Coast. To what do these names refer?*

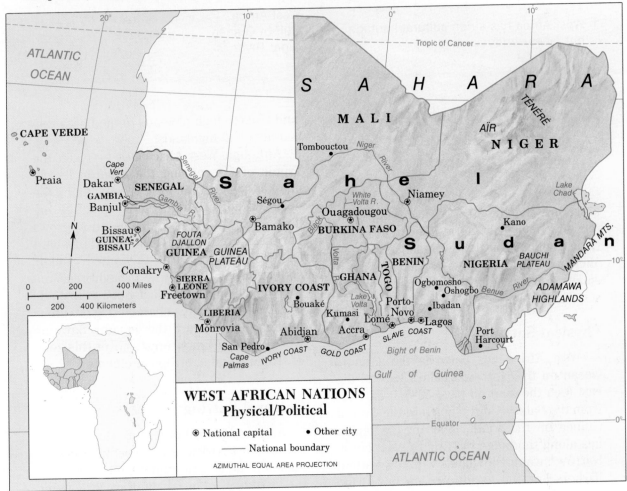

ranging between 42 and 49 years. In addition, infant mortality rates, the number of infants per 1,000 live births that die in the first year of life, are the highest in Africa and in the world (see the statistics on the charts on pages 519 and 520).

## Atlantic Coast Countries

Senegal, Gambia, Guinea-Bissau (GIN·ee bis·AOOH), Sierra Leone (lee·OHN), and Liberia span West Africa's Atlantic coast. Cape Verde (VUHRD) Islands, an island nation, lies in the Atlantic about 400 miles (640 kilometers) northwest of Senegal.

**Senegal and Gambia.**  Much of northern Senegal lies in the Sahel. The rest of Senegal, which is the size of South Dakota, and all of Gambia, which is about twice the size of Delaware, are located on the savanna.

The Walaf comprise the major ethnic group in Senegal and Gambia, but outside influences have changed their cultural imprint. Gambia, once a British colony, reflects British influences. With the arrival of the Europeans Senegal became the center of French West Africa, and Dakar was its major city. The French imprint on Senegal remains strong. French still serves as the official language. However, the majority of the people are Muslims, as were their ancestors since long before the Europeans arrived.

Senegal and Gambia illustrate the effects of unusual colonial boundaries. Senegal surrounds the tiny strip of land along the Gambia River that forms Gambia. Small nations such as these result from balkanization (see Chapter 21). Balkanization tends to separate related cultural groups and hinder progress.

In both Senegal and Gambia, peanuts and cotton grow along the coast and livestock grazes inland. Industry developed by the French during colonial times and now

**Learning from Pictures.**  *A Senegalese mother and child prepare a typical meal of fried grain patties. Why do grains make up the major part of the African diet?*

managed by Senegalese gives Senegal a diversified economy. Factories in and around Dakar process peanuts and cotton from farms in Senegal and Gambia, as well as phosphate ore from Senegal's mines.

**Guinea-Bissau.**  Guinea-Bissau, a former Portuguese colony, is about the size of New Hampshire and Connecticut combined. It became independent in 1974. Unlike in Senegal, however, European colonists did little to develop the local economy. Few roads and no railroads exist to this day. Most farming remains at the subsistence level, with cassava and rice the main crops.

Following independence the leaders of Guinea-Bissau adopted a socialist economic system. Today they still struggle to develop the economy. Deposits of gold and diamonds await the technology needed to take full advantage of these valuable resources. In the meantime the country exports peanuts, cacao, and palm oil.

**529**

**Guinea.** Guinea, a country about the size of Oregon, has both fertile farmland and valuable mineral resources. It also has a proud heritage. In the 700s Guinea was a major trading kingdom called Ghinea. Later it was a French colony. Guinea became independent in 1958.

After independence Guinea adopted an authoritarian socialist economic system and maintained close ties to the Soviet Union. Today, however, the nation welcomes investments from non-Communist as well as Communist countries.

Guinea's cash crops include coffee, peanuts, bananas, palm oil, and fruit. In addition, the country has about one-third of the world's known reserves of bauxite, as well as supplies of iron ore, gold, and diamonds.

**Sierra Leone and Liberia.** Sierra Leone and Liberia each had unique beginnings. Both were established as areas where freed slaves could settle.

In 1788 the British Society for the Abolition of Slavery bought land from the Temne people and founded Sierra Leone. Slaves who were freed or who escaped from the American colonies were welcomed to the area. Thousands of slaves freed by the British navy from slave ships also settled there. In the 1800s Sierra Leone became a British crown colony.

Sierra Leone's unique beginning contributes to its diverse culture. Today Africans from 13 tribes comprise most of the population. The descendants of freed slaves form a small, well-educated upper class. Most of the people rely on subsistence agriculture. The nation exports coffee and cacao. Mineral resources include iron ore and diamonds.

Liberia traces its beginnings to 1817, when the United States Congress granted the American Colonization Society a charter to return freed slaves to Africa. The first settlers arrived in 1822. Never a colony, Liberia became a republic in 1847 with a constitution and government modeled after those of the United States.

Today only about 5 percent of the 2.4 million Liberians trace their descent to freed slaves. Many members of this group are better educated than other Liberians and hold most of the professional jobs. Most people, however, remain subsistence farmers, growing rice and cassava to feed themselves and their families.

Liberia's leaders continue to struggle with economic problems. The Firestone Rubber Plantation, set up in 1926, long represented the major economic enterprise. The development of synthetic rubber, however, severely reduced its economic importance. Today the mining of vast deposits of high-grade iron ore has greatly spurred Liberia's economy. Iron ore now leads the country's exports. Liberia also exports coffee and cacao as well as rubber.

**Cape Verde Islands.** Ten islands scattered in the Atlantic 400 miles (640 kilometers) off Senegal form the tiny nation of Cape Verde Islands. Rugged, barren, and heavily eroded, the islands are actually the tops of submarine volcanoes.

Uninhabited when the Portuguese first arrived in 1456, the islands now have about 315,000 people and have been independent since 1975. Most of the people are of mixed European and African ancestry. Most speak Portuguese and Crioulo, a blend of Portuguese and West African languages, and practice Roman Catholicism mixed with local traditions. Scarce farmland and water resources have forced the nation to import much of its food.

## Guinea Coast Countries

Of the five countries that line the northern shores of the Gulf of Guinea, Nigeria is by far the largest. It also ranks as the

most populous nation in Africa. Four small countries—Ivory Coast, Ghana, Togo, and Benin—share the Guinea coast with Nigeria.

**Nigeria.** Nigeria stretches from the Gulf of Guinea in the south to the Sahel in the north. Its population of 95 million accounts for more than 20 percent of all the people in SubSaharan Africa. And with a population growth rate of 3.4 percent—double the world average—Nigeria ranks as one of the world's fastest-growing countries. Population experts predict that by the year 2100 Nigeria may have the world's third-largest population—500 million.

Although Lagos (LAY·gahs), the largest city, has more than 1 million people, and nine other cities each have more than 250,000 people, only about 23 percent of Nigerians live in urban areas. The majority of the people live in tribal villages.

Most Nigerians trace their ancestry to one of the more than 250 language and ethnic groups that live in Nigeria. The four major tribal groups are the Hausa, Falani, Yoruba (YOOHR·uh·buh), and Ibo (EYE·boh).

Nigeria always has reflected great cultural diversity. Early contact with the Arabs left a distinct imprint on the country, and by 1400 Islam was firmly rooted in Nigeria. Today more than 47 percent of the people are Muslims. The city of Kano in northern Nigeria serves as the major Muslim cultural center in West Africa. As a former British colony, Nigeria also reflects European influences. For example, 34 percent of the people today practice Christianity, and English remains the official language.

As with many African nations, Nigeria's boundaries, which follow colonial lines, have been a source of tension. A civil war erupted in 1967 when the Ibo **seceded,** or withdrew from the country, and set up the republic of Biafra along the southeastern coast. The war ended in 1970 with Biafra's defeat. Today Nigerian leaders work to cre-

**Learning from Pictures.** *Vendors line the side streets of Lagos, Nigeria, as they do in many African cities. Why are African cities growing so rapidly?*

ate a sense of national unity in the diverse population.

More than two-thirds of all Nigerian workers farm. They grow yams, cassava, millet, corn, and rice. Though most of the country's agriculture is subsistence farming, cash crops include cacao, rubber, and palms for oil. In the drier north farmers raise peanuts, cotton, and soybeans and graze cattle. The sleeping sickness caused by the tsetse fly limits farming activities in central Nigeria.

Nigeria has abundant natural resources. Important waterways include the Niger River and its main tributary, the Benue (BAYN·way). In addition, Nigeria has supplies of coal, manganese, and iron ore, as

*Text continues on page 533.*

# CITY FOCUS
## Lagos, Nigeria

*The fragmented city of Lagos*

Lagos, the capital and largest city of Nigeria, is one of tropical Africa's busiest and most Westernized urban centers. Fishers cast their nets within sight and sound of the traffic-filled highway that skirts Lagos. Towering skyscrapers soar above ancient mud-walled houses built in traditional West African style. On the side streets shopkeepers and customers haggle over prices. Street vendors, with their goods perched on top of their heads, maneuver their way in and out of the crowds. The office buildings, hotels, and university and hospital towers give one a feeling of being in a Western European or North American city.

### Site

Lagos's site is unusual. The city lies partially on the African mainland and partially on four islands in the Gulf of Guinea. All of the islands are connected by bridges. The islands are low-lying and before drainage canals were dug, almost always flooded after a heavy rain. And because Lagos lies just 6° north of the equator, rainfall averages 72 inches (183 centimeters) annually. Such terrain and rainfall conditions hardly seem to provide a likely site for the development of one of Africa's largest and most modern urban centers. To understand this development requires a trip back in time.

Hundreds of years ago, long before Europeans had arrived in tropical Africa, Yoruba fishers chose this site quite deliberately. The lagoons, swamps, and forests offered protection from their neighbors.

Portuguese merchants arrived at Lagos in 1472, 20 years before Columbus set sail for the Americas. Lagos's site was on the best-sheltered harbor on the West African coast. Trade with Europe soon developed. Unhappily, the most important items of trade in West Africa were people who were sold as slaves.

### Problems and Prospects

Today rapidly growing Lagos suffers from some of the same problems that typify other large and rapidly growing urban areas. Its rush-hour traffic snarls can compete successfully with the worst traffic jams in Europe, the Americas, and Japan. Given its low and swampy site, Lagos also faces serious problems of water pollution.

In spite of the problems of its urban site, however, Lagos continues to grow. This growth can be largely attributed to its situation. Its connections with the rest of Nigeria are excellent. Nigeria's road network focuses on Lagos, funneling both goods and people into the city. Its airport is Nigeria's largest. Almost all flights within Nigeria either begin or end in Lagos. Air and water routes also connect Lagos with the rest of the world. Its harbor handles several million tons of cargo annually. Today Lagos stands as one tropical African city that has managed to successfully blend the traditions of its past with a modern outlook.

well as half the world's columbite, a metal used to harden stainless steel. Nigeria also ranks sixth in the world in oil production.

Despite the contributions of several farm and mineral products, Nigeria has a one-crop economy based on oil, which accounts for more than 90 percent of the value of the country's exports. Other exports include cacao, palm oil, tin, and rubber. While manufacturing increases steadily, the country still imports most manufactured goods, including iron and steel products, transportation equipment, medicines, and chemicals.

In the early 1980s the high price of oil helped give Nigeria a **trade surplus**—the value of its exports was greater than the value of its imports. Nigeria invested much of this surplus in its growing educational system. When the price of oil dropped in the mid-1980s, however, Nigeria's economy suffered and the government was forced to borrow money and goods. As a result, Nigeria's foreign debt quickly grew to alarming proportions.

**Ivory Coast.** East of Liberia lies Ivory Coast, which is slightly larger than New Mexico. The population of Ivory Coast numbers about 10.8 million, and the country has one of the world's highest growth rates—4 percent a year. A former French colony, Ivory Coast—also called Cote d'Ivoire—has enjoyed political stability since gaining independence in 1960.

Ivory Coast ranks as one of the most prosperous West African countries. It bases its economy on cacao, coffee, and lumber. It leads the world in cacao production, is third in coffee production, and leads Africa in the production of tropical hardwoods. Ivory Coast also exports fruit and cotton.

Manufacturing strengthens the country's diversified economy. Its manufactured goods include chemicals, aluminum, and automobiles. Abidjan (ahb·ih·JAHN), Ivory Coast's modern capital, is a major port and has numerous industries.

**Ghana.** About 13.9 million people live in Ghana, which is east of Ivory Coast. Modern Ghana, slightly smaller than Oregon, traces its roots to the Kingdom of Ghana that flourished along the Niger River between 400 and 1100. The country became a British colony and gained its independence in 1957. Since then Ghana has alternated between military and civilian rule.

Blacks comprise more than 99 percent of Ghana's population. The official language is English, but most people speak one of four African languages.

Attempts to diversify the country's economy include tapping and exporting bauxite, manganese, gold, and diamonds. A huge hydroelectric plant on the Volta River—one of Africa's largest energy projects—produces electricity. This has led to the growth of manufacturing.

*Learning from Pictures.* Modern rigs tap oil deposits offshore and in swamplands along Nigeria's coast. How has oil helped improve the quality of life in Nigeria?

*Learning from Pictures. Huge new dams, such as this one on the Volta River in Ghana, now bring hydroelectricity to many African countries. How does this energy source help industrialization?*

More than half the people of Ghana farm. Most grow rice, grains, and cassava for their own use. In addition, Ghana ranks second in the world in cacao production. In fact, about 60 percent of Ghana's money from exports is from cacao. As in other countries with one-crop economies, Ghana's dependence on a single product creates serious economic problems when bad weather ruins the crop or world prices fall.

**Togo and Benin.** Two small developing nations, Togo and Benin, lie tucked between Ghana and Nigeria. The size of West Virginia, Togo has about 3.1 million people and lies west of Benin. Blacks from 37 different tribes make up most of its population. Benin is slightly smaller than Pennsylvania. Blacks representing 42 different African tribes comprise 99 percent of its 4.2 million people.

Togo, once a German colony, was seized by British and French troops during World War I. After the war Britain ruled the western half of the country while France ruled the eastern half. In 1957 the people of British Togo voted to become part of Ghana. French Togo became independent in 1960. Phosphates lead Togo's exports.

During the early 1900s Benin was a French protectorate called Dahomey. French colonists developed little of the country beyond its coast. Frequent political unrest since independence in 1960 has further blocked progress. The country's socialist economy relies on palm oil, peanuts, and cotton for income.

## Countries of the Sahel

The landlocked West African countries of Mali, Burkina Faso, and Niger occupy the Sahel. Each gained independence from France in 1960. Sparse populations, dry conditions, nomadic herding, and the threat of famine characterize these three developing nations.

**Mali.** Because two-thirds of Mali lies in the Sahara and northern Sahel, most of its 7.9 million people live in the south, an area of savannas. More than half of the people belong to the Mande tribes, and 90 percent are Muslims. Farmers in the south raise corn and sorghum for local use. They also grow small quantities of peanuts and cotton for export. Nomads in the north herd sheep, goats, cattle, camels, donkeys, and horses.

Mali, which is larger than Texas and California combined, faces severe problems typical of the region. Unproductive land, a short life expectancy (45 years), an annual per capita income of $140, and a low literacy rate (10 percent) slow growth. Malians lack the technology to tap gold, phosphate, bauxite, and other mineral deposits discovered in their country. Attempts to increase farm productivity through irrigation from the Niger River and through completion of a dam and hydroelectric plant proceed slowly for lack of money and equipment.

**Burkina Faso.** Burkina Faso, formerly called Upper Volta, lies between Mali and Niger to the north and Ivory Coast to the south. About the size of Colorado, Burkina Faso has areas that are nearly uninhabited. Nomads roam the dry northern edges of the country. Sleeping sickness and other diseases plague much of the southern part of the country, which lies in the more humid savanna zone.

Burkina Faso has 7.1 million people. Members of more than 50 African tribes make up more than 99 percent of the people. Though French serves as the official language, more than half the people speak one of the many tribal languages. Most of the people live in the few healthful and fertile areas to the south, where they eke out an existence as subsistence farmers. Major crops include sorghum, corn, and rice. In addition, the country exports small amounts of peanuts, shea nuts, and sesame. Small manufacturing plants process farm products and make building materials, especially bricks.

Burkina Faso faces the same problems as Mali. Government programs aimed at economic development lack money, and the nation depends almost completely on money and goods from Western Europe and the United States.

**Niger.** Mali and Burkina Faso share their problems with Niger, the third West African country of the Sahel and the easternmost. The Hausa is the largest of the country's 10 tribes. Most of the 6.8 million people speak French, the official language, and more than 80 percent are Muslims.

Niger's government leaders, relying on mining income to finance development, hope eventually to make the country self-sufficient in food production. Uranium now leads Niger's exports. Mining companies also have begun to tap deposits of coal, iron ore, tin, and phosphate.

## 2 Despite small differences, Central Africa is similar to West Africa.

Picture dark tunnels of vegetation under torrents of rain that fall from the sky. Feel the soggy ground. Hear the mighty Zaire River roar past you and crash over falls. These images tell you much about the natural landscape of Central Africa.

### Physical Setting

Central Africa forms the world's largest equatorial region. Although the region extends north to Chad, population densities are greatest near the equator.

Much of Central Africa's physical setting resembles that of West Africa. Marshy lowlands rim coastal areas on the Gulf of Guinea (see the map on page 538), while inland areas rise to a plateau. A large river system, the Zaire, drains the region.

Central Africa lies entirely in the tropics and, with few exceptions, has a hot and rainy tropical wet climate. The tall, green

umbrella of the rain forest dominates the equatorial region. Little sunlight penetrates the thick growth to reach the ground, which remains soggy. The heavy rains leach the soil, robbing it of humus and nutrients and leaving it unproductive.

## Cultural Setting

Central Africa is sparsely populated. Disease and malnutrition create enormous problems, and life expectancy, literacy rates, and income levels remain among the world's lowest.

Several hundred ethnic or language groups, mostly Bantus, contribute to Central Africa's cultural setting. Added to the mixture are a variety of cultural traits brought by Europeans who colonized the area in the late 1800s. Today social, political, and economic patterns illustrate the diversity of Central Africa.

## Countries of Central Africa

Zaire, Chad, the Central African Republic, Cameroon, Equatorial Guinea, São Tomé (saooht·uh·MAY) and Principe (PREHN·sih·peh), Gabon, Congo, Angola, and Zambia occupy Central Africa. Together, they share its problems as well as its potential.

**Zaire.** Zaire, the largest Central African country, is more than one-fourth the size of the United States. With a population of only 31.5 million spread across this vast land, Zaire has a low population density. The highest densities occur in the western parts of the country, where the temperatures are cooler, and in its river valleys, where farming is better.

More than 200 African ethnic and language groups make up the diverse population. Zaire's former rulers, the Belgians, left European imprints on the nation's culture. After Zaire gained its independence, however, government leaders changed the country's name from the Belgian Congo to Zaire. They also renamed cities, provinces, and even rivers to erase the reminders of the colonial past.

Zaire's colonial leaders did little to prepare the Africans for self-government. At the time the colony became independent in 1960 no Congolese had ever held office.

Since then the country's leaders have faced many political hurdles. At first few people felt loyalty to the new nation. Their loyalty lay instead with their tribes, ethnic groups, and local regions. Rivalries among these groups led to a civil war when leaders in Katanga (now Shaba) Province tried to secede and set up a separate country. The

*Learning from Pictures. Zairian fishers brave dangerous rapids to catch fish in their traps. Why is fishing not a major economic activity in most African countries?*

*Text continues on page 538.*

To help young adults cope with their changing role in life, society develops special ceremonies or events called rites. Perhaps the most important of these rites are rites of passage.

### Rites of Passage

Of the many role changes you undergo, the change from youth to adulthood is one of the most important. You take on the responsibilities and rights reserved for the adults in your society. Rites of passage signify to you that change is taking place and new things are expected of you.

In the United States a variety of ceremonies accompany the change to adulthood. Some, such as your confirmation or bas or bar mitzvah, carry religious meanings. Others, such as getting a driver's license or graduating from high school, are civil matters. Still others, such as marriage, can have both religious and legal significance. But all have the same purpose—to let you know you are entering adulthood.

*Fezzi wedding costume*

### Rites in Africa

In Africa life revolves around family and tribal traditions. African traditions usually feature more rites of passage for boys than for girls, partly because in earlier times boys had to prove they were ready for the adult responsibilities of being a hunter or warrior.

How boys prove their manhood varies from tribe to tribe. One tribe may require a boy to prove his hunting skill, another his bravery, and still another his endurance. A young Masai boy in Kenya, for example, must prove his courage by grabbing a wild lion by the tail.

Many of these rituals remain a vital part of African culture. Boys in many West African tribes must prove they are ready to protect their families and their tribes. To

prove this, a boy must kill a wild beast without help from anyone. Warriors escort the boy to the edge of the dense jungle, but he enters it alone. He carries only a bow, one arrow, and a knife dipped in poison. On his own he must select a worthy animal as his quarry, track it, and kill it. He returns to the tribe as a man only if he brings proof of his kill. The more dangerous the animal he kills, the greater is his prestige.

Such a test of manhood is dangerous. Some boys never return. Yet tribal members have accepted such a test for centuries. They believe that it is better to die fighting than never to know you are brave. And when the time comes, all boys are eager to prove themselves.

uprising was eventually put down by the national army, but thousands lost their lives in the fighting.

In 1965, after several political attempts to end the rivalries and calm the disorder, General Mobutu Sese Seko (muh·BOO·too SAY·say SAY·koh) seized control of the government. He established a socialist economy and nationalized many of the foreign-owned businesses.

Despite the government's efforts to industrialize the country, nearly 80 percent of

**Learning from Maps.** *The Great Rift Valley forms the eastern boundary of Central Africa. What features on the map mark the valley's location?*

CENTRAL AFRICAN NATIONS
Physical/Political

⊛ National capital    ■ National Park
• Other city          — National boundary

AZIMUTHAL EQUAL AREA PROJECTION

all Zairian workers are farmers. They grow cassava, corn, and bananas as food crops. Cash crops include coffee, rubber, and palms for oil. However, the rising importance of mineral exports has reduced the importance of farm exports.

Zaire has abundant natural resources, including copper, cobalt, iron ore, manganese, gold, tin, industrial diamonds, zinc, silver, uranium, bauxite, and petroleum. Mining, along with mineral, textile, and food processing, lead the list of Zaire's expanding industries. Output from Zaire's industries, however, fails to meet the people's needs and wants. As a result, the nation must import consumer goods, mining and transportation equipment, and fuels.

**Chad.** The northernmost country of Central Africa—Chad—was once part of French Equatorial Africa. For this reason, many geographers categorize it in Central Africa, though people also associate it with West Africa.

The northern two-thirds of Chad, which is the size of Texas, Oklahoma, and New Mexico combined, lies in the Sahara and the Sahel. The southern third lies in the savanna zone. Most of Chad's 5.3 million people, who belong to more than 200 different ethnic groups, live in the southern part of the country.

Divisions between north and south are evident in all aspects of life in Chad. French serves as Chad's official language in the south; Arabic, in the north. In southern Chad most people practice African and Christian religions and are better educated and wealthier than the Muslims of northern Chad. Southerners also control the national government. For these reasons, the people of northern Chad from time to time have worked to secede from the nation and form a separate nation.

In the south farmers grow food crops such as millet, sorghum, rice, yams, and

*Learning from Pictures.* Farmers in Chad must often bring water by hand to the drought-stricken fields. What major problems threaten residents of the Sahel?

cassava. They also grow small quantities of cotton and peanuts for export. In the north nomads tend herds of scrawny animals. Few mineral resources and little manufacturing limit development and make Chad one of the poorest countries in the world.

**Central African Republic.** Slightly smaller than Texas, the Central African Republic lies mostly in the savanna zone. Rain forests cover an area along the southern edge of the country.

The tsetse fly infests many areas of the Central African Republic. However, most of the 2.8 million people live in towns and villages unaffected by the diseases that the fly carries. About 80 ethnic and language groups—mostly Bantus—make up the population. The nation's religions are about as diverse as its languages. About one-fourth of the people are Roman Catholics; one-fourth, Protestants; and one-tenth, Muslims. The rest of the people practice traditional African religions.

Since gaining independence from France in 1960 the people have worked hard to stimulate their underdeveloped economy. With few resources and little technology, however, the economy continues to sag. Today the only industries include a few mines and sawmills. More than 90 percent of the people farm, growing cassava, corn, peanuts, rice, and potatoes for local markets. Commercial farmers raise small amounts of cotton, coffee, and sesame. These crops, along with diamonds and timber, are the country's leading exports. Leading imports include textiles, fuels, machinery, chemicals, and medicines.

**Cameroon.** Cameroon lies along the Bay of Biafra in the curve of Africa's west coast. Mountains and dense rain forests cover much of the country, which is somewhat larger than California. The western slopes of Mount Cameroon, the country's highest peak, receive more than 400 inches (1,016 centimeters) of rainfall a year, making them one of the world's rainiest places.

Cameroon's 10 million people are among the most diverse in the region. People from widely varying backgrounds representing more than 200 tribes make up the population. Much of this diversity stems from Cameroon's location—at the crossroad of routes along Africa's west coast.

Cameroon's economic future looks bright when compared to the economies of the other countries of the region. About 75 percent of the people farm. They grow cassava, yams, potatoes, millet, rice, and sorghum and raise livestock for local consumption. They also raise coffee, cacao, cotton, rubber, bananas, peanuts, tobacco, and tea for export. Industries include bauxite and food processing, light manufacturing, lumbering, and the production of crude oil. Further development of commercial farming and mineral resources promises continued economic growth for Cameroon.

**Equatorial Guinea.** Rio Muni on the mainland and two offshore islands—Bioko (bee·OH·koh) and Annobón (an·uh·BAHN), or Pagalu—make up fragmented Equatorial Guinea, a country about the size of Maryland. Of the country's 360,000 people, 270,000 live on the mainland.

Equatorial Guinea is very poor, even by African standards. No railroads and only 115 miles (185 kilometers) of paved roads link the country. Although almost everyone practices subsistence farming, food remains the leading import. The tropical climate supports cacao, coffee, and tropical hardwoods, which serve as the leading exports. Money from Spain and other Western nations supplements the weak economy.

**São Tomè and Principe.** São Tomè and Principe consists of two islands in the Gulf of Guinea that were once colonized by the Portuguese. The islands, united as a republic in 1975, lie about 125 miles (200 kilometers) off the coast of Gabon and have an area about the size of New York City. During the 1800s the islands served as an important link on slave trade routes. Today their 108,000 inhabitants are a mixture of mestizos and the descendants of freed slaves and indentured laborers. Farmers grow cacao, coffee, and coconuts for export. Food leads the list of imports.

**Gabon.** Gabon is Central Africa's wealthiest country with a per capita GNP of $3,340. Roughly the size of Colorado, Gabon has about 1 million people. Bantus make up about 90 percent of the people. People of European ancestry account for the other 10 percent.

Gabon's thriving economy results from political stability and the development of abundant resources. The country has a wealth of valuable mineral deposits and timber. Farmers grow cacao and coffee for export. Gabon also exports oil, timber,

*Text continues on page 542.*

# DEVELOPING GEOGRAPHY SKILLS
## THINKING GEOGRAPHICALLY: Analyzing Viewpoints

Issues in geography are often very complex. As a result, geographic problems rarely have simple solutions. Many different variables must be taken into account and many possible alternatives must be considered. As a student of geography, you must be able to analyze geographic viewpoints by distinguishing fact from opinion and assessing supporting evidence. By carefully examining a viewpoint, you can evaluate its validity and reasonableness.

### How to Analyze Viewpoints

To effectively analyze viewpoints in geography, follow these steps.

1. **Identify the main idea.**  Separate the main idea from supporting details.
2. **Assess the supporting evidence.**  List the details and examples used to support the main idea. Distinguish between fact and opinion. Remember that a viewpoint's strongest support usually comes from clearly stated facts.
3. **Evaluate the viewpoint.**  Decide whether the supporting evidence is used logically. Consider if the person has the proper background or experience to speak or write with authority on the subject. Detect any bias.

### Applying the Skill

Read the except below.

> Throughout the African Sahel one of the most disruptive storms of social and environmental upheaval of all time is now occurring. At its worst there is famine when tens of thousands of persons die, but always there is erosion of the family structure and a severance of the bonds of tribal traditions. As for the land, much of that is dying and being buried in shrouds of sand.

*Nomads in Mauritania*

The main idea of the excerpt is stated in the first sentence of the passage: *Throughout the African Sahel one of the most disruptive storms of social and environmental upheaval of all times is now occurring.* As evidence to support the main idea the author states that *tens of thousands of persons die,* that there is *erosion of the family structure and a severance of the bonds of tribal traditions,* and that *much of [the land] is dying and being buried in shrouds of sand.*

The evidence provided by the author seems to support the excerpt's main idea that a major upheaval is occurring in the Sahel. The supporting evidence is clearly stated and logically presented. The author, William S. Ellis, speaks with some authority. He is a senior writer for *National Geographic* and has spent considerable time on assignment in the Sahel. The author demonstrates no bias or faulty reasoning in this excerpt.

*To practice this skill, see Practicing Geography Skills on page 545.*

manganese, uranium, and gold. Leading industries include food, mineral, and petroleum processing. The leading import is food. Gabon has a trade surplus, which it invests to improve schools and communication and transportation networks.

**Congo.** The People's Republic of the Congo, which has a one-party system with a socialist economy, lies sandwiched between Gabon and Zaire. About the size of Montana, the Congo extends northeastward nearly 800 miles (1,287 kilometers) inland from the Atlantic Ocean.

The Congo has struggled economically since the country gained its independence from France in 1960. About 75 percent of the people farm, growing potatoes, cassava, rice, and corn for food and small amounts of sugarcane, coffee, and cacao as cash crops. Despite oil, potash, and timber resources, the country remains poor. Poorly organized communication and transportation networks block progress.

*Learning from Pictures.* *Beautiful Victoria Falls lies at the southern end of the Great Rift Valley. What bodies of water lie at the northern end of the valley?*

**Angola.** Angola, which is larger than Texas and California combined, stretches southward from Zaire for more than 1,000 miles (1,600 kilometers) along Africa's west coast. Savanna covers much of the country, while the barren Namib Desert blankets the southwest corner. In Cabinda, a sliver of Angola cut off by an edge of Zaire that surrounds the mouth of the Zaire River, rain forests cover most of the land.

Life for the 8.2 million Angolans, most of whom come from only a few tribes, is harsh. A short life expectancy (40 years), poor health care, a low literacy rate (20 percent), and an undeveloped school system characterize Angolan life. Political unrest constantly disrupts the country. The totalitarian government, which maintains close ties with the Soviet Union and Cuba, fails to provide consumer goods or services. Profits from exports are only now being invested in **capital resources,** the money, tools, machinery, equipment, and inventory needed to industrialize.

Most Angolans engage in subsistence farming. They grow cassava, vegetables, corn, and plantains. Drought and disruptions caused by war, however, require Angola to import much of its food. Angola has abundant mineral resources. A major oil deposit in Cabinda has been tapped, and other large deposits have been located offshore. The country has manganese, diamond, iron ore, phosphate, copper, and gold deposits as well. Leading industries include mineral and food processing and mining.

**Zambia.** Located inland to the east of Angola is Zambia. The size of Texas, Zambia covers a high plateau that extends from Angola's border. Grassy savannas stretch across the plateau. Tropical wet-and-dry and highland climates dominate. The Zambezi River drains the western parts of the country and cascades over spectacular Victoria Falls along the southern border.

**Learning from Pictures.** *Zambia produces industrial materials, such as copper wire. Why did independence cause economic problems for many African countries?*

Formerly the British protectorate of Northern Rhodesia, Zambia has 7.1 million people. Africans from 70 different tribes make up nearly 99 percent of the people.

About 85 percent of Zambia's people farm. Because the country is largely free of the tsetse fly, ranchers use the broad savannas where giraffes, elephants, and lions once roamed to graze large herds of cattle. Farmers with access to roads and railroads grow corn, peanuts, cotton, and tobacco for export. However, Zambia also imports many food products.

Zambia's wealth comes from its mineral deposits. It is a major producer of copper, zinc, and cobalt. It also exports vanadium, a gray powder used to harden steel; emeralds; lead; and uranium. Money from these mineral exports supports a growing economy. Africans trained by European mining companies fill most industrial jobs.

Zambia's government has adopted socialist economic measures. Government-run dairy farms and cattle ranches dot the savannas, and many industries have been nationalized. Government leaders invest money in economic and educational programs to help ensure continued growth.

### SECTION 2 REVIEW

1. **Define**  capital resource
2. **Locate**  Central Africa, Bay of Biafra, Mount Cameroon, Cabinda
3. **Summarizing Ideas**  What are the major landforms of Central Africa?
4. **Contrasting Ideas**  How does Central Africa's cultural setting differ from that of West Africa?
5. **Analyzing Ideas**  What problems have plagued Zaire since its independence from Belgium?
6. **Interpreting Ideas**  Why have regional differences within the country caused tension in Chad?

## Chapter Summary

The following list contains the key concepts you have learned about West and Central Africa.

1. West Africa's physical setting is characterized by narrow, swampy lowlands that rise to a broad, high plateau.
2. Arabs and Europeans as well as hundreds of African tribal groups have contributed to West Africa's cultural setting.
3. The Atlantic Coast and Guinea Coast countries struggle to overcome problems linked to their colonial past, while countries of the Sahel battle famine and drought.
4. Nigeria is Africa's most populous nation.
5. Dense rain forests dominate Central Africa's natural landscape, while its cultural setting is as diverse as West Africa's.
6. Zaire is a huge country, rich in minerals, that is struggling to modernize.
7. Most Central African countries face problems similar to those faced by West Africa.
8. Many African tribes observe traditional rites of passage.
9. Lagos successfully has adapted to its site and faces a promising future.

On a separate sheet of paper, complete the following review exercises.

## Reviewing Geographic Terms

In the sentences below, the underlined term is incorrect. Rewrite each sentence with the correct term.

1. In a few African countries the value of exports is greater than the value of imports, giving the country a famine.
2. Trade surpluses include the money, tools, machinery, equipment, and inventory used in the production process.
3. Areas that want to balkanize from a country want to withdraw from the country.

## Developing Critical Thinking Skills

1. **Summarizing Ideas**  Describe the major features of West Africa's natural landscape.
2. **Organizing Ideas**  (a) Why did European colonization lead to balkanization of West Africa?  (b) How has balkanization affected political stability?
3. **Comparing Ideas**  (a) In what ways are West Africa and Central Africa similar?  (b) In what ways are they different?
4. **Interpreting Ideas**  How has the tsetse fly affected life in Central and West Africa?
5. **Analyzing Ideas**  Why have natural resources been important to West and Central Africa?
6. **Writing About Geography**  In a full-page essay, complete one of the following activities.  (a) Explain why most of the nations of West and Central Africa have been unable to develop their many natural resources.  (b) Develop and outline a plan to help the poor nations of West and Central Africa develop economically.

## Using Primary Sources

In the following excerpt from *Africa's Sahel: The Stricken Land* William S. Ellis describes the physical and social changes the region is undergoing. As you study the reading, consider what can be done to help the families of the Sahel.

For most of his life he was a herdsman, a pastoralist who drove his cattle to distant places in search of grass and water. But when rains failed and the desert sands swept in, he went home. With death by starvation snapping at his heels, Omar Mahmoud went home to stay.

In the Republic of Chad, in central Africa . . . it is there, in the place where he was born, that Mahmoud now tends a

small garden, growing tomatoes, onions, and okra. He finds little joy in scraping a hoe over the dirt left gray and powdery after 19 years of drought.

"I don't know much about this work," he said. "My life is being with my animals, but now they are all gone. Forty head of cattle, forty sheep. Sixty goats."

Throughout the African Sahel one of the most disruptive storms of social and environmental upheaval of all times is now occurring. At its worst there is famine when tens of thousands of persons die, but always there is erosion [breakdown] of the family structure and a severance [cutting] of the bonds of tribal traditions. As for the land, much of that is dying and being buried in shrouds of sand. . . .

The first long siege of the current drought lasted from 1968 to 1973. Estimates of drought-related deaths during that time range as high as 250,000. The toll in cattle is believed to have reached 3.5 million head. . . . Rivers dried and lakes pulled back from their shores, and the specter of famine touched millions of lives in villages. . . .

And there are few, if any, adult males, for they have all left to seek work in the towns. Some have been gone a long time. . . .

Because of drought and overuse of the lands, winds had blown the sandy topsoil of the area into piles, or dunes. In the village itself the sand rose against some of the structures to roof level.

"Once there was a green belt around this place, but the sand started accumulating [building up] about five years ago, and there were lots of trees. . . . I was a herdsman, but when my sheep died I became a cultivator. Now I'm hungry all the time."

1. **(a)** How is the physical setting of the Sahel changing? **(b)** How has the cultural setting changed?
2. Why has the change in the physical setting caused a change in the cultural setting?

## Practicing Geography Skills

*Before completing this activity, review Developing Geography Skills on page 541.*

**Analyzing Viewpoints** Reread the excerpt in Using Primary Sources. Then complete the following activities.

1. Restate the excerpt's main idea in your own words.
2. List the details the author uses to support his belief that the people of the Sahel face great social and environmental upheavals.
3. Answer the following questions and explain your answers. **(a)** Does the author show bias? **(b)** Is the main idea and supporting evidence logical? **(c)** Is the evidence adequate to support the main idea?
4. In a brief paragraph, evaluate the geographic viewpoint stated in the excerpt.

## Exploring Geography

1. Use resources in your school or public library to discover what cassava is, why it grows so well in Central Africa, where else in the world it is found, and how the people of Central Africa prepare it for food. Then prepare a brief written report detailing your findings.
2. The ancient kingdom of Benin was famous for its beautiful metal art work. Many of these objects were made by a process called lost-wax casting. Use resources in your school or public library to prepare a speech that provides a step-by-step description of this process.

# East Africa and Southern Africa

# PUTTING THE CHAPTER IN FOCUS

Physical and cultural influences have played key roles in the development of the countries of East Africa and Southern Africa. Dry conditions, rugged landscapes, and traditional life styles hamper economic growth. Years of colonial rule also have affected economic and political development. Since gaining independence, countries such as Kenya and South Africa have experienced notable economic growth. Others have progressed economically and politically far more slowly.

## Ideas to Understand

In studying about East Africa and Southern Africa, use these ideas to give direction to your reading.

1 East Africa has varied natural and cultural landscapes.
2 Racial tensions hinder economic progress in Southern Africa.

## Terms to Define

The following terms are some of the key terms in the chapter. Defining them will help you understand East Africa and Southern Africa.

cataract
homogeneous
  population
ujamaa
race

apartheid
homelands
heterogeneous
  population

## Places to Locate

Locating the following places will add to your knowledge of geography.

East Africa
Mount Kilimanjaro
Nile River
Red Sea
Nubian Desert
Addis Ababa

Djibouti
Zanzibar
Southern Africa
Namib Desert
Namibia
Harare

## 1 East Africa has varied natural and cultural landscapes.

East Africa is a land of spectacular contrasts. Along the coast, **escarpments,** sheer rock cliffs, tower above the narrow beaches and the sparkling blue waters of the Indian Ocean. Inland, highland forests, deserts, and grasslands stretch to the horizon.

### Physical Setting

East Africa extends nearly 3,400 miles (5,470 kilometers) from Sudan in the north to Mozambique and Madagascar in the south. The equator runs through the middle of the region.

Variety characterizes East Africa's physical landscape. Narrow coastal lowlands border the Indian Ocean. Most of the region, however, lies on high plateaus. The Great Rift Valley you read about in Chapter 26 dominates the physical setting. Magnificent mountains, such as Mount Kilimanjaro (19,340 feet; 5,895 meters), Mount Kirinyaga (17,058 feet; 5,199 meters), and Mount Elgon (14,176 feet; 4,321 meters), soar above the plateaus.

The climate and vegetation of East Africa vary as much as its landforms. East Africa has some of Africa's wettest rain forests and driest deserts. In general, more rain falls near the equator than elsewhere. Of course, landforms and high elevations strongly influence the climate throughout East Africa.

◀ *Zebras on the Serengeti Plain in Kenya*

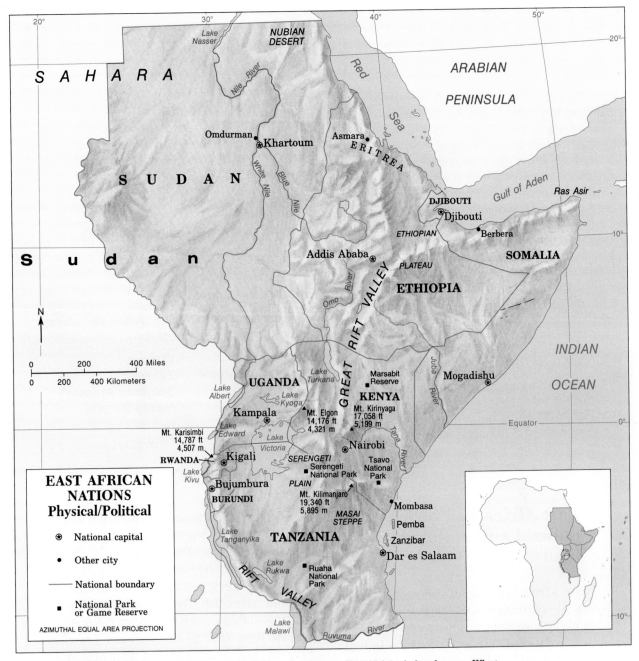

**Learning from Maps.** *The Great Rift Valley dominates East Africa's landscape. What problem does location cause for Uganda, Rwanda, and Burundi?*

## Cultural Setting

East Africa has relatively few people. Most live in the rift valleys, rather than along the coast. Even the cities scattered throughout the region remain fairly small compared to other world cities.

As in West Africa, people representing many different ethnic groups live in East Africa. However, three major groups dominate the population. Nilotic groups, or people from the Nile Basin, live in an arc that reaches from northwestern Sudan to northern Tanzania. The Kushites inhabit a trian-

gular area between the Nile River, the Red Sea, and Kenya. Bantu tribes make up the majority of the people in the southern part of the region. Thousands of people of European descent also live in many of the East African countries.

## Countries of East Africa

Of the nine nations of East Africa, Kenya has experienced the most economic growth since gaining its independence in 1963. In many ways the eight other nations of the region—Sudan, Ethiopia, Djibouti (juh·BOOT·ee), Somalia, Tanzania, Uganda, Rwanda, and Burundi—look to Kenya for leadership.

**Kenya.** Kenya, which stretches from the Indian Ocean to the rift valley, is slightly smaller than Texas. It includes marshy coastal lowlands; dry, grass-covered central plains; and western highlands consisting of two mountain ranges divided by the Great Rift Valley.

More than 21 million people live in Kenya, and the country's annual growth rate—4.1 percent—ranks as the world's highest. Improvements in nutrition and health care have bolstered this high growth rate by dramatically reducing deaths.

Kenya's people are unevenly distributed throughout the country. Because the northern part of Kenya has a shortage of water supplies, more than 80 percent of the people live in the south, where they crowd onto less than 20 percent of the country's land. Today about 15 percent of the people live in towns of 10,000 people or more.

Most Kenyans trace their heritage to one of the nearly 40 African tribes that live in Kenya today. The largest tribe, the Kikuyu, makes up 21 percent of the people. Other Bantu tribes—the Luhya, Luo, Kalenjin, Masai, and Kamba—each make up more than 10 percent of the people.

***Learning from Pictures.*** *Kenya now has automobile assembly plants such as the Leyland plant in Thika. Why does Kenya lead East Africa in terms of development?*

Both Europeans and Arabs, with their diverse religious beliefs and languages, contribute to Kenya's diverse cultural imprint. About 66 percent of the people are Christians and 6 percent are Muslims. Swahili serves as the official language, although it is not the language of any one African tribe. Swahili incorporates a mixture of words from Bantu languages, Arabic, Portuguese, and English.

Kenya has made notable progress since gaining its independence from Britain in 1963, and the nation has become a model for other African countries. After a brief period of adjustment its political stability began to attract foreign investments. These investments have helped the nation develop its industries, including oil processing. Today oil products lead Kenya's exports. Other key industries include textiles, paper, plastics, furniture, soap, processed foods, and tourism.

Despite tremendous economic growth in recent years, Kenya remains a developing nation. More than 80 percent of all Kenyans

**Learning from Pictures.** *Modern buildings in Nairobi house the headquarters of many international businesses. Why has Nairobi become East Africa's major city?*

are farmers or herders. Unlike farmers from many other African countries, however, Kenyan farmers raise enough food to feed the population. About half the farm output is for subsistence and half for export. Farmers grow subsistence crops—mainly corn, wheat, rice, sugarcane, and cassava—on small, privately owned farms. Farmers also raise coffee; tea; cotton; and sisal, a strong fiber used to make rope and twine, as cash crops on larger farms. Nomadic tribes herd cattle on Kenya's broad grasslands, providing meat as well as dairy products (see the CASE STUDY on page 514).

Unlike many other African countries, Kenya lacks large mineral supplies. Only sodium carbonate, or soda, exists in large quantities. Kenya exports the soda as soda ash, an important agent in many chemical processes. Mines also produce silver, zinc, and lead for use by local industries.

**Sudan.**  Sudan, with an area more than one-fourth the size of the United States, is the largest country in Africa. Much of Sudan lies on a high plateau. The country includes deserts in the north, plains dotted with marshes and short grasses on the central plateau, and tall grasses and trees in the wetter southern part of the country.

The Nile River snakes through Sudan, separating the Libyan Desert on the west from the Nubian Desert on the east. Four **cataracts,** or waterfalls, interrupt the river. Most of Sudan's 23 million people live in the Nile Valley, which contains almost all of the country's fertile land.

The Kushites, Arabs, and British have all added to the cultural diversity of Sudan. About 70 percent of the people are Muslims. Arabic serves as the official language, but large groups speak other languages as well. Blacks comprise about 52 percent of the Sudanese population; Arabs, 39 percent; and Beja (BAY·juh), 6 percent. Beja tribes are nomadic herders.

Nearly 80 percent of the Sudanese workers farm. They grow sorghum, millet, and wheat for food. Bedouin herders raise sheep, goats, and camels near oases in the dry north. Cash crops include cotton, peanuts, and sesame. Cotton and gum arabic lead the list of the country's exports. Cotton accounts for 30 percent of the country's export value. Gum arabic comes from the sap of the acacia tree and is used in medicine, candy, and chewing gum.

Sudan's economy has grown rapidly since the 1960s. Modern irrigation projects use water from the rivers to cultivate more land and increase farm production. Recent technology has also helped tap small deposits of oil, iron ore, gold, copper, chromium, and mica.

**Ethiopia.**  About the same size as Texas, New Mexico, and Oklahoma combined, Ethiopia includes very dry lowlands along its borders and a central plateau crisscrossed by mountains. Abundant rain and fertile soil make the plateau, home to most Ethiopians, ideal for farming.

About 44 million people—East Africa's largest population—live in Ethiopia, one of the world's oldest independent countries. Ethiopia has never been under foreign rule, except for a brief period from 1935 to 1941 when Italy controlled the nation's government. Despite the outward appearance of peace, however, internal fighting has troubled the nation for years. First quarreling among the tribes and then quarreling among the classes caused unrest. In 1974 military leaders took control of the country, declaring Ethiopia a Communist state a few years later. Political unrest has troubled the country, resulting in numerous refugee camps and massive starvation.

Nearly 90 percent of the workers farm or herd animals. Although farmers struggle to produce enough food, droughts occur often and result in famines. Geographers believe that coffee was first used as a beverage in Ethiopia. Today it ranks as a major export. In fact, agriculture in the highlands accounts for 61 percent of the country's export income. Herders also raise livestock on grasslands and mountain slopes.

Most farmers still use traditional methods; few farmers rise above subsistence levels. Cattle pull wooden plows, and farmers use primitive hoes and digging sticks to till the ground. Workers pick much of the coffee by hand from wild trees. Ethiopia's few industries include a sugar refinery, an oil refinery, cement plants, and textile mills.

**Djibouti.** The tiny nation of Djibouti lies wrapped around a natural harbor at the southern entrance to the Red Sea. A land of rocky deserts, Djibouti includes only about 10 percent pastureland and less than 1 percent farmland. The climate is extremely dry.

After gaining its independence from France in 1977, Djibouti was called the French Territory of the Afars and Issas (EE· sahs). Those two ethnic groups, the Afars

of Ethiopian origin and the Issas of Somali origin, make up most of the nation's 306,000 people. Cultural ties with these two groups have led to conflicts between Ethiopia and Somalia for control of Djibouti. For now, however, Djibouti remains independent.

A port city, also called Djibouti, is the capital and center of economic activity. The port Djibouti has traditionally served as Ethiopia's outlet to the sea. Today railroads link the port to Addis Ababa, Ethiopia's capital. More than half of Ethiopia's trade passes through Djibouti.

**Somalia.** Slightly smaller than Texas, Somalia is a land of dry savannas and desert. It occupies the Horn of Africa, which juts out into the Indian Ocean at the southern end of the Red Sea.

Unlike the populations of other African countries, Somalia's 8 million people come mostly from one ethnic group—the Somalis. And more than 90 percent are Muslims. This **homogeneous population,** a

*Learning from Pictures.* *Primitive farms such as this sorghum compound are typical in Sudan. What are the main factors limiting farming in Africa?*

population drawn from one ethnic group, gives Somalia stability. Yet it also has caused problems. The original colonial borders divided the Somali people, placing many of them in separate nations. The Somali people believe that all areas with large Somali populations should be a part of Somalia. For many years they have fought to control such areas in Djibouti, Ethiopia, and Kenya.

Most of Somalia's workers are nomadic herders. Meat and animal hides remain the chief exports. Rain sufficient for farming falls only in the extreme southern part of the country. On limited lands there, farmers grow bananas for export and corn, sorghum, beans, and peanuts for food.

**Uganda.** Wedged between Zaire on the west and Kenya on the east lies Uganda, a nation of lakes. In fact, lakes cover nearly one-third of the country's area. Lake Victoria, Lake Albert, Lake Kyoga, Lake George, and Lake Edward all fall partially or completely within Uganda.

Most of Uganda's 16 million people trace their heritage to the numerous tribes that have occupied the area for centuries. Today most people live along the shores of Lake Victoria as their ancestors did. They work as herders and subsistence farmers, raising livestock and growing sweet potatoes, cassava, corn, and beans for food. Leading cash crops include coffee, tea, cotton, and bananas. Coffee accounts for 98 percent of Uganda's export income. More than half of landlocked Uganda's imports and exports travel through Tanzania.

**Tanzania.** Tanzania consists of two separate areas that merged in 1964—Tanganyika (tan·guhn·YEE·kuh) on the mainland and the island of Zanzibar. A land of contrasts, Tanzania includes swampy marshes along the coast of the mainland that gradually rise to a high plateau. Above this pla-

teau on the northern border of the country towers snowcapped Mount Kilimanjaro.

Over 100 tribes contribute to Tanzania's ethnic makeup. Bantus account for the majority of the country's 23.5 million people, although most of the people along the coast and on the islands are of Arabic descent. One large nomadic group, the Masai, herd cattle, sheep, and goats along a strip of highland that extends from Kenya far into Tanzania. In this area, Masai herders burned the original vegetation to create open grasslands to graze their herds (see the CASE STUDY on page 514).

Once a German and then a British colony, Tanzania reflects a strong European imprint. Christians account for about one-third of the people. Muslims account for another third. The rest of the people practice traditional religions. Swahili and English serve as the nation's official languages.

About 90 percent of Tanzania's workers are subsistence farmers and herders. Despite poor soils, they grow corn, beans, and wheat for food. Many also raise cash crops. The main cash crops and the country's chief exports include coffee, cotton, and sisal. Zanzibar exports cloves and coconuts that grow there. In spite of the efforts of farmers, food is Tanzania's leading import.

Mines produce diamonds, iron ore, coal, gold, nickel, and natural gas for local use. Industries include oil refining, food processing, and the manufacturing of building materials and textiles. Dar es Salaam serves as the nation's capital, manufacturing center, and chief port.

Tanzania has undertaken an experiment in African socialism. Led by President Ali Hassan Mwinyi (MWIN·yee), the government promotes a program of **ujamaa** (oo·jah·MAH), which in the Swahili language means "working together for the good of all." Under this program people in the villages farm collectively—sharing farm work and output. People of all ages go to school

*Text continues on page 554.*

# CASE STUDY
## EXPLORING PLACES: Wild Animal Reserves

On any given day in the wild animal reserves in Kenya and Tanzania, tourists catch glimpses of lions, buffalo, elephants, zebras, wildebeests, and birds in their unspoiled, natural habitats. These reserves, which stretch on either side of snowcapped Mount Kilimanjaro, provide important sources of tourist revenues to the two nations. In Kenya alone more than 1 million tourists visit the reserves annually.

### Population Pressures

Protected by the governments of Kenya and Tanzania, millions of wild animals thrive in the reserves. Since 1978, when Kenya abolished the hunting and sale of game trophies, many wildebeest and zebra herds have increased by 50 percent. Water buffalo herds have doubled and the number of elephants has risen by 45 percent in some areas. In fact, of all the wild animals only the rhinoceros population has diminished. In Tanzania's huge Serengeti (ser·uhn·GET·ee) Park, for example, only 20 rhinoceroses survive. The horn of the black rhinoceros remains highly prized. The horns bring such high prices that poachers, or people who hunt illegally, kill rhinoceroses in spite of the threat of heavy fines and long prison sentences.

The increasing number of wild animals has caused some problems. Because the animals often roam over wide areas, they compete with domesticated animals for food and pastures. The pressure on the limited grazing lands results in overgrazing. This causes the soil to become drier and the grass to become thinner. In addition, wild animals sometimes attack domesticated livestock. One farmer in Kenya, for example, reported losing 38 cattle and 14 horses to lions in recent years.

As pressures mount, many of the area's herders, especially the Masai (see the CASE

*White rhinoceroses and a ranger in Kenya*

STUDY on page 514), have come to favor hunting. They claim that only by reducing the wild herds will there be sufficient pastures and water for their cattle. For humanitarian and income reasons, however, the national governments continue to protect the parks. They want the Masai to settle down on farms. This would open lands to the wildlife that the tourists spend millions of dollars to see.

### An Uncertain Future

Most conservationists agree that the problem of competition among people, livestock, and wild game remains unresolved. Yet many see a promising future. They note that each year more and more people move to Africa's cities. This movement allows more space for wildlife. In addition, African city dwellers may, in time, want to become tourists inside their own countries. Like the tourists who now arrive from Europe and North America, they will want to see lions, elephants, and zebras. Instead of resenting wildlife as competition for land, Africans will want to preserve wildlife as a part of their natural landscape.

to learn to read and write and to learn modern farming methods. The government owns and operates the banks and businesses in the towns and cities.

Ujamaa has had both positive and negative results. The literacy rate has risen to 79 percent, health care has improved, and farm production has increased. Yet in some cases whole villages have been abandoned. People have moved to cities for better opportunities. Farmers and workers often quarrel over wages and prices set by the government. And the government itself has accumulated a heavy foreign debt to finance its projects.

**Rwanda and Burundi.**   Rwanda and Burundi—each about the size of Maryland—are covered by volcanic mountains that line the western edge of the Great Rift Valley. Rwanda, which lies to the north of Burundi, has 6.8 million people. Burundi has about 5 million. Both countries have relatively homogeneous populations in which 85 percent of the people belong to one tribe.

*Learning from Pictures.*   *The Ruwenzori Mountains extend along Uganda's western border. How are the locations of this mountain chain and the rift valley related?*

Because both countries are landlocked, Rwanda and Burundi rely on Tanzania for the passage of their imports and exports. High altitudes give the countries cool climates. Unlike several other African countries, Rwanda and Burundi have unusually fertile volcanic soils.

First Germany and then Belgium once ruled both countries. Today Rwanda and Burundi are independent, but they remain developing nations that are overcrowded and very poor. Both countries have few towns and no large cities. There is little industry and there are few roads. Subsistence farmers make up more than 92 percent of the workers. They grow cassava, corn, bananas, and yams. Herders tend cattle and sheep that graze on the savannas. The chief cash crops include coffee, tea, and cotton. Coffee leads the exports. Because farm output does not meet the needs of the people, food ranks as a major import. Both Rwanda and Burundi remain economically and politically unstable.

## SECTION 1 REVIEW

1. **Define**   escarpment, cataract, homogeneous population, ujamaa
2. **Locate**   East Africa, Mount Kilimanjaro, Nile River, Red Sea, Nubian Desert, Addis Ababa, Djibouti, Zanzibar
3. **Seeing Relationships**   Describe the major physical features of East Africa.
4. **Analyzing Ideas**   (a) What aspects of Kenya's development make it a model for other African countries? (b) What is the goal of ujamaa and how does it work?
5. **Contrasting Ideas**   (a) What are the unique features of Somalia's population patterns?   (b) Why has Somalia often had conflicts with Djibouti, Ethiopia, and Kenya?
6. **Comparing Ideas**   What similarities do Rwanda and Burundi share?

# 2 Racial tensions hinder economic progress in Southern Africa.

Southern Africa contains an amazing variety of physical features. In the eastern part of the region, a sheer rock cliff called the Drakensberg Escarpment rises more than 11,000 feet (3,400 meters) above the Indian Ocean. In the west, jagged mountains cross beautiful, grassy plains. Desolate deserts lie in the central part of the region and along the Atlantic coast. The area also reflects a diversity of cultural features—a diversity that has led to both political and economic problems.

## Physical Setting

Southern Africa occupies the southern tip of the African continent, stretching between the Atlantic and Indian oceans. It extends south from the borders of Angola and Zambia to Cape Agulhas in South Africa. Its landforms include deserts, swamps, and high mountains.

A very narrow lowland rims the coasts of Southern Africa. In the Republic of South Africa, the lowland contains several good natural harbors. Highlands cover the rest of the region. Rugged mountains stretch along the eastern edge of the region, and lower mountains run through Namibia to the west. The central part of the region lies on a high plateau that tilts gently downward toward the west. The Kalahari Desert covers much of the plateau. Areas throughout the region contain large deposits of many different minerals.

Southern Africa has a wide range of climate and vegetation zones. The southern tip has a Mediterranean climate. A narrow strip along the east coast has a humid subtropical climate, while a marine climate occurs along the mountains. The central part of the region and the west coast have desert climates that are dotted with a few trees and hardy bushes. Many of the driest areas—such as the Namib Desert—completely lack vegetation.

## Cultural Setting

Southern Africa has a relatively small population. Unlike other parts of Africa south of the Sahara, many descendants of Europeans live in the region. In fact, descendants of Europeans control the government and economy of South Africa. Until recently they also controlled Zimbabwe—then called Rhodesia. This situation has led to clashes between blacks and whites throughout the region.

## The Countries of Southern Africa

The countries of Southern Africa include the Republic of South Africa; Malawi; Mozambique; the island nations of Madagascar, Comoros, Seychelles, and Mauritius; Zimbabwe; Namibia; Botswana; Swaziland; and Lesotho. Each has a unique setting and each faces special problems.

**The Republic of South Africa.** At the southern tip of Africa is the Republic of South Africa, nearly three times the size of California. Even though deserts (Namib and Kalahari) cover nearly 80 percent of the country, it is the richest and most developed country in Africa.

Racial policies strictly identify the population groups of South Africa's 34.2 million people. Laws group together people of the same **race**—people with similar physical traits such as skin color. Blacks known as Bantus comprise about 70 percent of the population. About 18 percent of the people are white. Afrikaners, descendants of Dutch colonists known as Boers, make up about 60 percent of the white population of South Africa, while descendants of British settlers make up most of the rest. About 9 percent

*Text continues on page 557.*

# DEVELOPING GEOGRAPHY SKILLS
## READING ABOUT GEOGRAPHY: Using Gazetteers

- Togo
- Tsaratanana Massif
- Tsavo National Park

Do you know exactly where each of the places mentioned above is located? If not, it may be difficult to find out without some organized listing. One of the first places you should look is in a gazetteer.

A **gazetteer** is a geographic index of place names. Depending on the purpose of the gazetteer, it may contain several different types of information. The *Gazetteer* in this textbook (see pages 734–49) includes the names of all the places that appear on the textbook's maps, a phonetic respelling of the more difficult names, the latitude and longitude of the place, and the page in the textbook on which the map may be found.

### How to Use a Gazetteer

To effectively use a gazetteer, follow these steps.

1. **Find the place name in the listing.** Note that names in a gazetteer are listed in alphabetical order.
2. **Read the pertinent information.** Find the absolute location and page references to maps that contain further information about the place.

Study the excerpt from the gazetteer below. Note that Togo has an absolute location of 8° 00′ N, 0° 45′ E and appears on the map on page 528. Tsaratanana (sahr·uh·TAHN·uh·nah) Massif has an absolute location of 20° 00′ S, 48° 00′ E and appears on the map on page 557. The Tsavo (SAHV·oh) National Park has an absolute location of 3° 30′ S, 38° 00′ E and appears on the map on page 548. By checking the maps, you will find that all three are in Africa.

*To practice this skill, see Practicing Geography Skills on page 565.*

| | | | |
|---|---|---|---|
| Tobago (toh·BAY·goh) | 11° 15′N | 60° 30′W | 304 |
| Tobruk (toh·BROOHK) | 32° 00′N | 24° 00′E | 495 |
| Togo (TOH·goh) | 8° 00′N | 0° 45′E | 528 |
| Tokelau Islands | | | |
| (toh·kee·LAH·ooh) | 8° 00′S | 176° 00′W | 699 |
| Tokyo (TOH·kee·oh) | 35° 45′N | 139° 45′E | 642 |
| Tokyo Bay | 34° 00′N | 140° 00′E | 642 |
| Toledo (toh·LEE·doh) | 41° 45′N | 83° 30′W | 231 |
| Tolima (toh·LEE·muh) | 4° 45′N | 75° 15′W | 338 |
| Tombouctou (tawm·book·TOO) | 16° 45′N | 3° 00′W | 528 |
| Tonga (TAWNG·guh) | 18° 45′S | 175° 15′W | 699 |
| Tongariro National Park | | | |
| (tahn·guh·RIR·oh) | 37° 15′S | 175° 30′E | 699 |
| Tonkin, Gulf of (TANG·kin) | 20° 30′N | 108° 15′E | 680 |
| (toh·REEK·uh) | 39° 00′N | 95° 45′W | 233 |
| Trinity | 43° 45′N | 79° 30′W | 253 |
| Tripoli, Lebanon (TRIP·oh·lee) | | | 498 |
| Tripoli, Libya | 32° 45′N | 13° 15′E | |
| Tromsø (TRAWM·suh) | 69° 45′N | 19° 15′E | 401 |
| Trondheim (TRAWN·haym) | 63° 30′N | 11° 30′E | 401 |
| Trujillo (troo·HEE·yoh) | 8° 15′N | 79° 00′W | 352 |
| Trust Territory of the Pacific Islands | 10° 00′N | 135° 00′E | 698 |
| Tsaratanana Massif | | | |
| (sahr·uh·TAHN·uh·nuh) | 15° 00′S | 48° 00′E | 557 |
| Tsavo National Park (SAHV·oh) | 3° 30′S | 38° 00′E | 548 |
| Tuamotu Archipelago | | | |
| (too·ah·MOH·too) | 19° 00′S | 141° 15′W | 699 |
| Tucson (TOO·sawn) | 32° 15′N | 111° 00′W | 237 |
| Tula (TOO·lah) | 20° 00′N | 99° 15′W | 276 |

| | | | |
|---|---|---|---|
| Uppsala (OOP·suh·lah) | 60° 00′N | 17° 45′E | 401 |
| Ural Mountains (YOOHR·uhl) | 56° 30′N | 58° 15′E | 434 |
| Ural River | 46° 30′N | 52° 00′E | 434 |
| Urewera National Park | | | |
| (oo·ruh·WER·uh) | 38° 30′S | 177° 00′E | 699 |
| Urmia, Lake (OOHR·mee·uh) | 38° 00′N | 45° 15′E | 497 |
| Uruguay (oo·roo·GWY) | 32° 45′S | 56° 00′W | 366 |
| Uruguay River | 33° 00′S | 58° 00′W | 366 |
| Utah (YOO·tah) | 39° 30′N | 112° 45′W | 239 |
| Uzbek S. S. R. (OOZ·BEK) | 42° 45′N | 60° 00′E | 434 |
| | | | |
| **V** | | | |
| Vaal River (VAHL) | 29° 45′S | 22° 45′E | 557 |
| Vaduz (vah·DOOHTS) | 47° 15′N | 9° 30′E | 408 |
| Valdez (VAL·deez) | 61° 15′N | 146° 15′W | 241 |
| Valdivia (vahl·DEEV·ee·uh) | 39° 45′S | 73° 15′W | 352 |
| (·LEN·thee·uh) | 39° 30′N | 0° 30′W | 407 |
| Vanuatu (van· | 42° 30′N | 1° 30′E | 408 |
| Varna (VAHR·nuh) | | | 408 |
| Västeras (VES·ter·aws) | 59° 45′N | 16° 30′E | |
| Vatican City (VAT·i·kan) | 42° 00′N | 12° 15′E | 408 |
| Vatnajökull (VAHT·nuh·yoo·kool) | 64° 30′N | 16° 45′W | 401 |
| Venezuela (ven·uh·ZWAY·luh) | 8° 00′N | 65° 00′W | 338 |
| Venice (VEN·is) | 45° 30′N | 12° 15′E | 407 |
| Veracruz (vayr·uh·KROOZ) | 19° 15′N | 96° 00′W | 10 |
| Verkhoyansk Mountains | | | |
| (vyer·koh·YANSK) | 67° 45′N | 128° 00′E | 434 |
| Vermont (ver·MAWNT) | 43° 45′N | 72° 45′W | 224 |

of South Africa's people are "coloreds," people of mixed black African, white, and Asian ancestry. Asians account for the remaining 3 percent of the people.

Each group in South Africa's population has had an important effect on the country's cultural imprint. More than 90 percent of the whites and coloreds and about 60 percent of the blacks practice Christianity. The rest of the blacks follow traditional religions, while most Asians are Hindus or Muslims. Though English serves as the official language, most Afrikaners speak Afrikaans, a language based on Dutch. Many South African blacks speak traditional tribal languages.

South Africa, which gained its independence from Britain in 1931, is a politically troubled land. Although blacks form a majority of the people, whites control the government. This government strictly separates the races according to a policy called **apartheid** (uh·PAHR·tayt) (see THE GEOGRAPHIC WEB on pages 560–61). Although the stated aim of apartheid is to allow each racial group to develop and improve its culture, apartheid has been used to ensure white power, status, and wealth. Blacks and coloreds have had little access to the resources of South Africa and, therefore, have had little chance to improve their standard of living.

*Learning from Maps.* *Walvis Bay is South African territory. Why might Namibia's independence cause a political problem concerning Walvis Bay?*

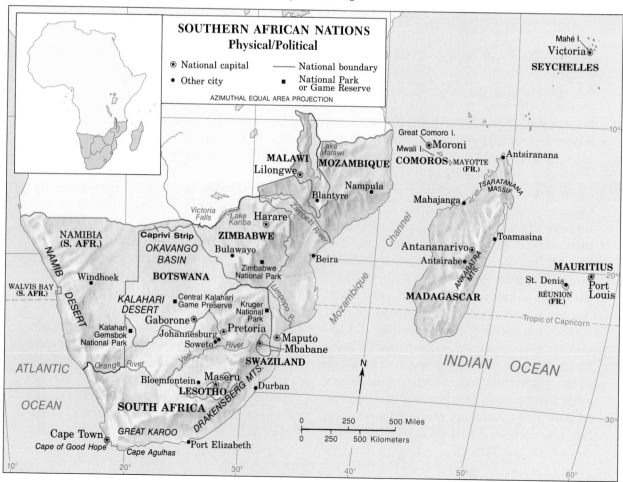

***Learning from Pictures.*** *Johannesburg, South Africa's largest city and leading industrial center, is a modern city. What cultures have contributed most to South Africa's cultural imprint?*

Many countries, including the United States, have protested against apartheid. These protests, as well as continued pressure from South Africa's blacks, have brought about some reforms. Several laws requiring the separation of the races have been repealed and other progress has been made. In general, however, apartheid remains a source of tension and violence.

Nearly 75 percent of South Africa's black workers farm. A few work on farms owned by whites, but most are subsistence farmers in specially designated areas called **homelands.** Although homelands are not recognized as countries by other nations, South Africa has given them their independence. This independent status means that blacks in South Africa are citizens of their assigned homeland, rather than of the Republic of South Africa. They cannot vote in South African elections, and blacks living in the homelands are considered foreigners even if they have lived in South Africa all of their lives. Recently many farmers have left the homelands to take jobs in white-run mines and factories.

About 20 percent of the whites farm. Major food crops include corn, wheat, fruits, vegetables, and dairy products. Wool, cotton, sugarcane, and tobacco lead the cash crops. Herders also tend cattle and sheep. South Africa raises enough food to feed its people, but uneven distribution causes certain groups to go hungry from time to time.

Tremendous mineral resources underlie South Africa. With the exception of oil, South Africa has deposits of nearly every useful mineral. South Africa leads the world in the production of gold, which accounts for nearly 40 percent of the country's export income. South Africa also ranks among the world's leading producers of copper, platinum, uranium, chromium, manganese, diamonds, and iron ore. South African mines also produce nickel, titanium (ty·TAY·nee·uhm), and vanadium (vuh·NAYD·ee·uhm).

**Malawi.** Malawi, which is about the size of Pennsylvania, lies sandwiched between Zambia on the west and Mozambique on the east. Lake Malawi fills much of the scar of the rift valley and forms most of Malawi's eastern border. Cool climates and plentiful rainfall make conditions in Malawi ideal for farming.

Bantu tribes make up 95 percent of Malawi's population. A former British colony that became independent in 1963, Malawi continues to reflect a strong British imprint. About 75 percent of the people practice Christianity. English and Chichewa, a traditional African language, serve as the official languages.

Malawi has about 7.5 million people. Most farm, raising corn, grains, cassava, and sweet potatoes for food. Cash crops include coffee, tobacco, tea, and sugarcane. Malawi lacks mineral resources, and manufacturing remains limited. Like all landlocked countries, Malawi depends on its neighbors for the safe passage of its imports and exports.

**Mozambique.** Mozambique, which is larger than Texas, stretches for 1,500 miles (2,400 kilometers) along the east coast of Africa, between Tanzania and South Africa. The Zambezi River and several other smaller rivers cut through Mozambique. Along with the country's railroad lines, these rivers form a transportation network that carries much of Southern Africa's trade.

About 20 African tribes and people of Portuguese, Dutch, British, or Asian descent make up Mozambique's 14.6 million people. Portuguese is the official language.

Mozambique has abundant natural resources for development. Good farmland covers about one-third of the country, and water resources are plentiful. There are deposits of coal, iron ore, natural gas, copper, asbestos, bauxite, and possibly petroleum. Fishing areas offshore contain abundant fish and shellfish.

Mozambique's Communist economic system has been unable to take advantage of the nation's abundant resources. Nearly 85 percent of the workers are subsistence farmers. It relies heavily on fees from other nations for the use of railroads and ports. Cash crops include cashews—the leading export—sugarcane, tea, cotton, and copra—the meat of coconuts. Infestation by the tsetse fly makes herding hazardous.

**Indian Ocean islands.** Four island nations—Madagascar, Comoros (KAHM·uh·rohz), Seychelles, and Mauritius—lie off the east coast of Africa. These islands form a zone of transition between Africa and South Asia. Both regions have had great influence on the islands' cultural imprints. People of the islands trace their descent to a variety of ancestors—Bantu, Asians, Europeans, Arabs, or a mixture of these. This has given the islands one of the world's most **heterogeneous populations,** a population made up of people from a variety of backgrounds.

All four island nations are poor. Most workers on each island engage in subsistence farming. Only mountainous Mauritius has a more developed economy based on commercial farming and tourism.

**Zimbabwe.** Landlocked Zimbabwe lies tucked between Mozambique to the east, Botswana to the west, Zambia to the north, and the Republic of South Africa to the south. This nearly round country has a land area about as large as California. Zimbabwe's population—currently about 9.4 million—is growing at an annual rate of 3.5 percent, twice the world rate. Urbanization remains less rapid in Zimbabwe than elsewhere. Only about 25 percent of the people live in urban areas. Most of those live in the large or moderate sized cities strung north and south down the center of the country. Harare, the capital and largest city, has about 660,000 people.

*Text continues on page 562.*

**Learning from Tables.** *Colonial boundaries drawn by Europeans divided many of these tribes among several countries. To what language group do most tribes of Southern Africa belong?*

| MAJOR TRIBES OF SOUTHERN AFRICA | |
|---|---|
| **Tribe** | **Members** |
| ZULU | 5,244,000 |
| XOSHA | 4,872,000 |
| TSWANA | 2,644,000 |
| NORTH SOTHO | 2,037,000 |
| SOUTH SOTHO | 1,686,000 |
| TSONGA-SHANGSAN | 788,000 |
| SWASI | 611,000 |
| NDEBELE | 579,000 |
| VENDA | 466,000 |
| Source: *World Almanac*, 1987 | |

# THE GEOGRAPHIC WEB
## The Question of Apartheid

Apartheid, the Afrikaans word meaning "apartness," is the South African government's policy of racial segregation. It has as its goal a separate development for each of the nation's official racial categories. Laws are designed to isolate each of these groups—in education, employment, housing, and politics—and to let each develop in its own way.

### Racial Classifications

At birth everyone in South Africa is classified into one of the official racial categories. A person's ancestry determines into which of the four major classifications— Bantu, or black; white; colored, or mixed; and Asian—he or she is placed. The colored and Asian categories are further broken down into several subcategories. The only way a person can change racial classification is to prove that he or she was put in the wrong group. The result is a kind of apartheid musical chairs. In 1987, for example, 506 coloreds, 14 Malays, 7 Chinese, and 9 Indians were officially declared white; 2 whites and 6l Indians became Malay; 10 blacks became Indian; 2 blacks became "other Asian;" and 1 "other colored" became black.

### Injustices of the System

Few people question that apartheid has limited the human rights and economic opportunities for nonwhites in South Africa. For the blacks who make up more than 70 percent of South Africa's population,

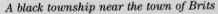
*A black township near the town of Brits*

CITY/STAD DURBAN

UNDER SECTION 37 OF THE DURBAN
BEACH BY-LAWS, THIS BATHING AREA IS
RESERVED FOR THE SOLE USE OF
MEMBERS OF THE WHITE RACE GROUP.

HIERDIE GEBIED IS, INGEVOLGE ARTIKEL
37 VAN DIE DURBANSE
STRANDVERORDENINGE, UITGEHOU VIR
DIE UITSLUITLIKE GEBRUIK VAN LEDE
VAN DIE BLANKE RASSEGROEP.

NGAPHANSI KWESIGABA 37 SOMTHETHO
WAMABHISHI ASETHEKWINI. LENDAWO
IGCINELWE UKUSETSHENZISWA
WOAMALUNGU OHLANGA OLUMHLOPHE
KUPHELA.

*A Durban beach recently opened to nonwhites*

apartheid is a constant source of frustration. Many have become militant in seeking justice, and their militancy has made many whites fearful. In many cases more restrictions have resulted.

Apartheid prohibits blacks from participating in South Africa's national government. In addition, the national government has established separate political regions for blacks. The government insists that South Africa's black people belong to one of 10 separate "nations." Each of these nations, according to the national government, has its own ancestry and culture. The government has assigned each nation a block of land within the national boundaries of South Africa. These blocks, called "homelands," represent about 13 percent of South Africa's total national territory.

## White South African Attitudes

Almost every nation of the world, including the United States, has criticized the South African government's racial policies. This criticism has spurred some reforms in the system. But most white South Africans

deeply resent what they consider to be interference from other nations in the internal affairs of their nation. They claim that South Africa is the most modern, the most stable, and the most prosperous nation in Africa. They also claim that apartheid gives blacks ample opportunity to participate actively in the government of their cultural homelands. Furthermore, some white South Africans insist that South Africa is the continent's only genuinely strong defense against communism.

## Black South African Attitudes

Despite the South African government's attempt to emphasize group or tribal loyalties in the homelands, many black South Africans are not affiliated with a tribe and do not think along tribal lines. About 65 percent of black South Africans live in cities and have lived there all their lives. The homelands have no meaning for them. Their political focus is national, not tribal, and their demands for greater participation in national government are not likely to disappear because they belong to a homeland. It seems that the future of South Africa is sure to hold further protests until the system is changed to accommodate all of the country's people.

*White suburban housing near Cape Town*

**Learning from Pictures.** *Mines such as the Orangemund diamond mine, run by South Africans, tap Namibia's mineral resources. What are Namibia's chief minerals?*

free of the tsetse fly, so herders raise cattle and sheep for meat.

**Namibia.** Namibia, which is twice the size of California, stretches for nearly 1,000 miles (1,600 kilometers) along the Atlantic Ocean to the west of Zimbabwe. Only the dry savannas in the north and central parts of Namibia receive reliable rainfall. Namibia's desert areas rank among the driest in the world.

Namibia's population numbers about 1.3 million. The country's population density is only 3.3 people per square mile (8.5 per square kilometer). Most of the people, however, live close together in the few habitable spots, especially in and around towns. More than half live in urban areas. Windhoek (VINT·hoohk) is the capital and largest city.

Blacks comprise more than 76 percent of Namibia's people. More than half belong to the Ovambo tribe. Whites, mostly the descendants of German and white South African settlers, make up about 7 percent of the people.

Namibia's political situation is unique in Southern Africa. Although the United Nations declared Namibia's independence in 1968, South Africa refuses to recognize the declaration and continues to administer the area, calling it Southwest Africa, as it has since the early 1900s.

Namibia must import almost all of its food. Dry conditions place severe limits on farm production. Most of the land is used for grazing sheep and cattle. In the wetter north farmers grow corn, millet, sorghum, and some peanuts. The country's few industries provide some goods for export. Namibia's mines produce the country's leading exports—copper, diamonds, lead, and zinc. Namibia also has the world's largest uranium mine.

**Botswana.** Botswana, slightly smaller than Texas, lies north of South Africa be-

Blacks make up nearly 96 percent of Zimbabwe's people. Most come from four Bantu tribes, the largest being the Mashona. Descendants of British settlers make up most of the small white minority. The British brought to the country their language, religion, and customs, which became official during white rule. Today English remains the official language. Many people, however, speak only traditional African dialects. About half the people follow a religion that combines Christianity and traditional African practices. About one-fourth practice Christianity and about one-fourth practice African religions.

For a time Zimbabwe was the British colony of Rhodesia. After independence Zimbabwe had a white minority government similar to that of South Africa. After years of political unrest, however, a black majority government took power in 1979.

About 78 percent of Zimbabwe's people farm its fertile land, raising tobacco, tea, sugarcane, cotton, and corn. Zimbabwe is

tween Namibia and Zimbabwe. Much of the country lies on a high plateau covered by the Kalahari Desert. In the northwest lies the Ngami Swamp, an area infested with the tsetse fly.

About 1.2 million people live in Botswana, which is very sparsely settled. Almost everyone lives in the east where the most rain falls. Members of the Bantu-speaking Botswana tribe make up nearly 95 percent of the people. This homogeneous population gives Botswana unity and national identity. English remains the official language, but only one-fourth of the people speak it. Almost everyone speaks Tswana, the Botswana tribal dialect.

About 75 percent of Botswana's workers farm or raise cattle. The main food products include corn, sorghum, millet, cowpeas (black-eyed peas), and cattle. However, Botswana depends heavily on imported food. Small mining operations produce diamonds, copper, nickel, and coal. Small food processing plants serve as the only industries, although tourism is a growing source of income. Diamonds and cattle products lead the country's exports.

**Swaziland and Lesotho.** Two small countries—Swaziland and Lesotho—occupy lands in southeastern Africa. Location, tradition, and economics closely link both countries to South Africa.

Independent since 1968, Swaziland, which is smaller than New Jersey, lies between Mozambique and South Africa. It stretches across a series of plateaus that rise from east to west. Most of its 700,000 people live in the high, cooler elevations in the west.

A homogeneous population gives Swaziland internal stability. Black Africans make up 96 percent of the people. Almost all are Swazis. Leaders hope this unity will allow the country to develop rich farmlands and forests and mineral deposits.

Subsistence farmers make up about half the work force. Major food crops include corn and rice. Cash crops include cotton, fruits, and sugarcane. Sugarcane leads the country's exports. Farms, mines, and businesses in South Africa employ about one-third of Swaziland's workers. Most workers spend at least six months a year working in South Africa. The rest of the labor force works in small local mining and lumbering operations.

Lesotho, completely surrounded by the Republic of South Africa, lies near the southeastern tip of Southern Africa. Most of its 1.6 million people live in small villages that dot the few level areas.

Lesotho, which is slightly larger than Maryland, has perhaps the most homogeneous population in the world. More than 99.7 percent of the people are black Africans, and virtually all are members of the BaSotho tribe.

Lack of level land and resources hampers the country's economy. More than 87 percent of the local workers practice subsistence farming. Using extremely primitive methods, farmers grow corn, wheat, and barley. Low production levels require Lesotho to import food.

---

**SECTION 2 REVIEW**

1. **Define** race, gazetteer, apartheid, homelands, heterogeneous population
2. **Locate** Southern Africa, Namib Desert, Namibia, Harare
3. **Seeing Relationships** What have been the major effects of apartheid?
4. **Interpreting Ideas** Why do Mozambique's prospects for future development seem good?
5. **Comparing Ideas** (a) How are population patterns in Botswana, Swaziland, and Lesotho similar? (b) How are they different?

# CHAPTER 28 REVIEW

## Chapter Summary

The following list contains the key concepts you have learned about East Africa and Southern Africa.

1. Most of the land in East Africa and Southern Africa lies on high plateaus, and most of the climates are dry.
2. For centuries tribal groups lived in East Africa and Southern Africa. Later colonized by several European countries, the nations of the subregions eventually gained their independence.
3. Kenya is East Africa's leader and serves as a model for other developing nations.
4. Sudan, Ethiopia, and Djibouti share similar physical and cultural settings along the northern edge of East Africa.
5. Uganda, Rwanda, Burundi, and Malawi struggle with low farm output, lack of industries, and political unrest.
6. Tanzania has adopted ujamaa, a socialistic system aimed at spurring development.
7. South Africa today is characterized by racial tensions. Recent reforms have been made, but apartheid continues to create dissent and violence.
8. Mozambique contains vast resources that are as yet untapped.
9. The four island nations of Southern Africa lie in a zone of transition with unique cultural settings and problems.
10. In 1979 Zimbabwe's black majority took control of the government.
11. Namibia's political situation is unusual. Although the United Nations declared Namibia independent, South Africa refused to recognize the declaration and continues to administer the area.
12. Botswana, Swaziland, and Lesotho face development problems caused by low farm production and weak economies.

On a separate sheet of paper, complete the following review exercises.

## Reviewing Geographic Terms

Match each of the following terms with the correct definition below.

a. apartheid
b. homeland
c. ujamaa
d. race
e. cataract
f. homogeneous population
g. heterogeneous population

_____ 1. Independent "nation" set aside for blacks in South Africa
_____ 2. Waterfall that interrupts a river's flow
_____ 3. Group of people drawn from one ethnic or racial group
_____ 4. African program in which villagers share farm work and output, and the government owns and operates the banks and businesses
_____ 5. South Africa's policy of keeping the races apart
_____ 6. People with similar physical traits such as skin color
_____ 7. Group of people drawn from several different backgrounds

## Developing Critical Thinking Skills

1. **Summarizing Ideas** What one physical feature dominates East Africa's landscape?
2. **Contrasting Ideas** (a) How is the cultural setting of East Africa different from that of West Africa? (b) How is the cultural setting of Southern Africa different from that of the other subregions?
3. **Understanding Ideas** What factors have bolstered Kenya's high growth rate?
4. **Evaluating Ideas** (a) What is the stated aim of the apartheid policy of South Africa's government? (b) What has been the practical effect of apartheid on South Africa's people?
5. **Comparing Ideas** (a) How were political patterns in South Africa and Zimbabwe similar in the 1970s? (b) How are they different today?

6. **Analyzing Ideas** How and why are the cultural settings of the four island countries different from those of the other countries in Southern Africa?
7. **Determining Cause and Effect** (a) How is Namibia's political pattern unique? (b) How might this pattern have affected its development?
8. **Writing About Geography** In a one-page essay, complete one of the following activities. (a) Identify and explain what you consider to be the four main problems facing Africa's developing nations. (b) Evaluate the countries in the region to decide which hold the greatest potential for economic growth, and discuss the ways in which these countries can achieve this growth.

## Using Primary Sources

In the following excerpt from *Out of Africa*, Isak Dinesen discusses the Kenyan countryside. As you study the reading, consider the beauty of the geography of Kenya and how the country currently handles its game problem.

The hill-country itself, when you get into it, is tremendously big, picturesque and mysterious; varied with long valleys, thickets, green slopes and rocky crags. . . .

In my day, the Buffalo, the Eland [an African antelope] and the Rhino lived in the Ngong Hills [an area southwest of Nairobi],—the very old Natives remembered a time when there were Elephants there,—and I was always sorry that the whole Ngong Mountain was not enclosed in the Game Reserve. Only a small part of it was Game Reserve, and the beacon on the Southern peak marked the boundary of it. When the Colony prospers and Nairobi [Kenya], the capital, grows into a big city, the Ngong Hills might have made a matchless game park for it. But during my last years in Africa many young Nai-

robi shop-people ran out into the hills on Sundays, on their motor-cycles, and shot at anything they saw, and I believe that the big game will have wandered away from the hills, through the thorn-thickets and the stony ground further South.

1. According to the author, what are some of the animals that once lived in the Ngong Hills?
2. Why does the author feel that the entire area of the Ngong Hills should have been included in the Game Reserve?

## Practicing Geography Skills

*Before completing this activity, review Developing Geography Skills on page 556.*

**Using Gazetteers** Using the *Gazetteer* (pages 734–49) and the maps in the textbook, complete the following activities.

1. Give the absolute locations of (a) San Antonio, (b) Yellowknife, (c) Machu Picchu, (d) Jerusalem, (e) Victoria Falls, and (f) Tokyo.
2. List the page number of the map or maps on which each of the following appears: (a) San Diego, (b) Bitterroot Range, (c) Padre Island National Seashore, (d) Vaduz Castle, (e) Transylvanian Alps, and (f) Masai Steppe.
3. Using the appropriate map, describe the locations of (a) Door Peninsula, (b) Monterrey, (c) Mosquito Coast, (d) Strait of Magellan, (e) Funafuti, (f) Bikini Atoll, and (g) Big Bend National Park.

## Exploring Geography

Choose one of the great African civilizations and use resources in your school or public library to write an essay detailing its history, location, and achievements.

# UNIT 9 REVIEW

## Unit Summary

The following list contains the key concepts you have learned about SubSaharan Africa.

1. The distinctive features of SubSaharan Africa's physical setting are a high plateau broken by several basins, the Great Rift Valley, many rivers that form unique patterns, and many types of climates.
2. The four subregions of SubSaharan Africa are West Africa, Central Africa, East Africa, and Southern Africa.
3. Africa has abundant resources but at present lacks the technology to fully use them. Farming, in particular, has failed to keep pace with the people's needs.
4. A succession of great civilizations once flourished in ancient Africa. By 1914, however, European nations had carved most of the region into colonies.
5. Black Africans, Arabs, Europeans, and Asians all have added to the cultural diversity of SubSaharan Africa.
6. Most of SubSaharan Africa struggles with political and economic problems. All except the Republic of South Africa are developing nations.

On a separate sheet of paper, complete the following review exercises.

## Checking Your Understanding

1. **(a)** Describe the major landforms of Africa south of the Sahara. **(b)** What factor keeps temperatures in SubSaharan Africa lower than would be expected so near the equator?
2. **(a)** Where is the Great Rift Valley? **(b)** What landscape features dominate the area between the rift valleys? **(c)** What features mark the northern end of the rift valley?
3. Identify and give the location of four ancient African kingdoms or civilizations.
4. What are the four subregions of SubSaharan Africa?

5. **(a)** Identify three major food crops grown in each subregion. **(b)** Identify three major cash crops produced in each region.
6. **(a)** How are the early histories of Sierra Leone and Liberia unique? **(b)** How are the political settings of Ethiopia and Namibia unique?
7. **(a)** What are the descendants of the Boers called? **(b)** In what country are they primarily found?

## Applying Critical Thinking Skills

1. **Summarizing Ideas** What are four factors that influence farm production in East and Southern Africa?
2. **Analyzing Ideas** Why might a large number of language groups within a country hinder the development of national unity?
3. **Determining Cause and Effect** **(a)** Describe the life style of the Masai. **(b)** How will development affect their life style? **(c)** Is this change positive or negative? Explain.
4. **Interpreting Ideas** Why are the four island countries of Southern Africa considered to be a zone of transition?
5. **Evaluating Ideas** In general, has Africa south of the Sahara benefited or suffered from its colonial past? Defend your answer.

## Reviewing Unit Features

1. **Geography in the Workplace** What six major types of economic activities do economic geographers study?
2. **The Geographic Web** Why do many white South Africans resent international protest of apartheid?
3. **City Focus** **(a)** How did Tombouctou's site help it grow into a large trading city? **(b)** How did this site eventually lead to the city's decline?
4. **City Focus** What features of Lagos's site make it unusual for the development of a major city?

## Using Map Skills

1. Study the maps on pages 511, 518, and 521. Then state a generalization that you infer from the maps' data about landforms and climate to explain the population distribution in Africa south of the Sahara.
2. Study the maps on page 528, 538, 548, and 557. Then develop a chart that lists the countries of SubSaharan Africa by subregion. Do further research to include the following information on your chart: each country's official name, former colonial ruler, date of independence, official language(s), and chief natural resources.

## Investigating Geography

1. Research the ancient African civilizations. Then on a map of Africa, illustrate the location, extent, and dates of existence of each civilization.
2. Prepare an oral or written report on one of the following topics: African wildlife preserves and the current threats they face; the discovery of diamonds in Africa, their preparation and uses, famous diamonds and legends surrounding them, and the uses of industrial diamonds; or the history and culture of the Bushmen, Masai, Zulus, or other tribe (see the table on page 559) and how the life styles of its members have changed.

## Further Readings

### Chapter 26

Brooks, Lester. *Great Civilizations of Ancient Africa.* New York: Four Winds Press. Provides a historical overview of the emergence of African civilizations such as the Cush, Ghana, Mali, and Songhai and a discussion of life in each civilization.

Campling, Elizabeth. *Africa in the Twentieth Century.* London: Batsford. Studies the history of Africa from colonial rule through independence movements to recent events.

Ellis, William S. "The Stricken Land." *National Geographic* (August 1987). Examines the expansion of the Sahara and the devastating effects of desertification on the people who live in the Sahel.

### Chapter 27

Barker, Carol. *A Family in Nigeria.* Minneapolis: Lerner Publishing Company. Focuses on the daily life of a typical family in Nigeria as seen through the eyes of a family member.

Carpenter, Allan, and James Hughes. *Ivory Coast.* Chicago: Childrens Press, Regensteiner Publishing Enterprises, Inc. Depicts in text and photographs the geography of Ivory Coast, its history, and its modern-day reemergence as a West African country.

### Chapter 28

Kristensen, Preben, and Fiona Cameron. *We Live in South Africa.* New York: The Bookwright Press. Provides a view of the culture and daily life of South Africans as described by the country's own citizens.

McCuen, Gary E., ed. *The Apartheid Reader: Ideas in Conflict.* Hudson, WI: GEM Publications. Presents many perspectives on the debate on South African apartheid.

Murphy, E. Jefferson. *The Bantu Civilization of Southern Africa.* New York: Thomas Y. Crowell. Provides a history of the Bantus.

Shachtman, Tom. *Growing Up Masai.* New York: Macmillan Publishing Co., Inc. Presents a pictorial view of the Masai, including their culture, their traditions, and their system of raising children.

Stein, R. Conrad. *Kenya.* Chicago: Childrens Press, Regensteiner Publishing Enterprises, Inc. Describes the land and people of Kenya.

Woods, Harold, and Geraldine Woods. *The Horn of Africa. Ethiopia, Sudan, Somalia, and Djibouti.* New York: Franklin Watts. Describes the geography, climates, cultures, histories, and independence movements of the countries in one of the most strategic areas of the modern world.

# UNIT 10

# SOUTH ASIA

# The Settings of South Asia

# PUTTING THE CHAPTER IN FOCUS

South Asia is a part of the continent of Asia. It covers so large an area geographically that it is known as a subcontinent of Asia (see the map on pages 14–15). Seven countries share this vast region. India, Bangladesh, and Pakistan rank as the largest. The smaller countries of South Asia include the Himalayan countries of Nepal and Bhutan and the island nations of Sri Lanka and the Maldives.

## Ideas to Understand

In studying about the physical and cultural settings of South Asia, use these ideas to give direction to your reading.

1 South Asia is a subcontinent of Asia.
2 The people of South Asia have an ancient heritage.

## Terms to Define

The following terms are some of the key terms in the chapter. Defining them will help you understand the physical and cultural settings of South Asia.

subcontinent          deforest
pass                  doubling time
monsoon               indigenous

## Places to Locate

Locating the following places will add to your knowledge of geography.

The Himalaya          Punjab
Mount Everest         Deccan Plateau
Khyber Pass           Western Ghats
Indus River           Calcutta
Ganges River          Kashmir

---

## 1 South Asia is a subcontinent of Asia.

North of India's windswept plains rises the highest landform on earth—The Himalaya. Towering nearly 6 *miles* (10 kilometers) above sea level, these mountains wind along India's northern border. The Himalaya cradle some of the oldest cultures of the world. Elephants, rhinoceroses, tigers, and leopards still roam the jungles that blanket their foothills. Over the years these mountains have had a major physical and cultural impact on South Asia.

### Physical Regions

South Asia occupies such a large area that geographers classify it as a **subcontinent,** or a landmass smaller than a continent but still of great size. The subcontinent of South Asia juts out like a peninsula from the Asian mainland. The Himalaya joins it to the rest of the continent in the north. The Indian Ocean, Arabian Sea, and Bay of Bengal form the seaward edges.

Because India ranks as the largest of the seven South Asian nations, the subcontinent often is called the Indian subcontinent. The other countries of the Indian subcontinent are Pakistan, Bangladesh, the island countries of Sri Lanka (SREE LAHNG·kuh) and the Maldives, and two small landlocked countries—Nepal and Bhutan.

Geographers divide South Asia into four physical regions from north to south—the Northern Mountains, the Indo–Gangetic Plain, the Deccan Plateau, and the Coastal Plain. Study the map on page 572 to find the locations of these four regions.

**Northern Mountains.**  High mountains link the subcontinent of South Asia to the rest of continental Asia. These Northern

◀ *Elephants and The Himalaya in Nepal*

Mountains include The Himalaya—the highest mountain range in the world. Mount Everest, the world's highest mountain peak, lies in The Himalaya on the Nepal–China (Tibet) border. One group of scientists remeasured Mount Everest in the 1980s, calculating that it stands 29,108 feet (8,878 meters) above sea level—some 80 feet (24 meters) higher than was previously thought. To the west of The Himalaya are the Karakoram (kar·uh·ᴋᴏʜʀ·uhm) Range and the Hindu Kush Mountains.

***Learning from Maps.*** *Much of South Asia's fertile land lies along its many rivers. How does South Asia's location affect farming?*

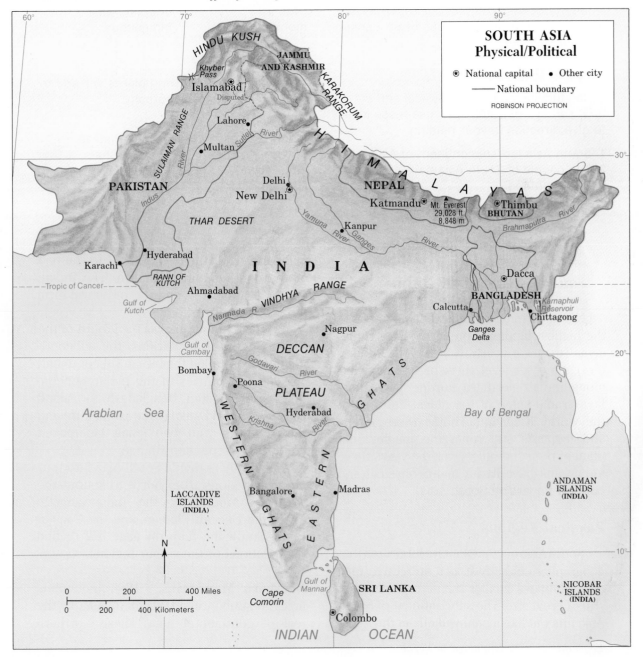

According to the theory of plate tectonics, The Himalaya formed during the collision of two crustal plates millions of years ago (see the diagram on page 69). Fossils of seashells once located on the ocean floor have been found high atop the mountains' peaks. Frequent earthquakes in the mountains serve as reminders that the mountain-building process continues. Forces continue to lift the mountains at a rate of 2 inches (5 centimeters) a year.

The majestic Himalaya and other Northern Mountains form a wall between the subcontinent and the rest of Asia. Only a few **passes,** or routeways, lead through the rugged mountain wall. The most important pass, the Khyber (KY·buhr) Pass, links Pakistan and Afghanistan. Throughout history people have poured through the Khyber Pass from the arid lands in the north to the fertile lowlands in the south.

**Indo–Gangetic Plain.** A vast alluvial lowland stretches across the subcontinent south of the Northern Mountains. Geographers call this lowland, drained by the Indus River in the west and the Ganges (GAN·jeez) River in the east, the Indo–Gangetic Plain. A third great river, the Brahmaputra (brahm·uh·PYOO·truh), drains the western end of the plain. The Ganges and Brahmaputra rivers share a vast delta, the largest in the world, on the Bay of Bengal. All three rivers on the Indo–Gangetic Plain begin in the snowcapped Northern Mountains. In the Punjab (puhn·JAHB), astride the India–Pakistan border, five rivers join to form the westward-flowing Indus River. The name *Punjab* means "land of the five rivers." The five rivers flow across the plain, depositing silt during floods and providing water for irrigation.

**Deccan Plateau.** The triangular southern part of the subcontinent of South Asia is known as Peninsular India. The flat and

***Learning from Pictures.*** *The Himalaya separated the cultures of India and China for thousands of years. Why are the mountains a less formidable barrier today?*

ancient uplands of the Deccan Plateau, often known simply as the Deccan, are at the center. Rocks from India's ancient shield form the Deccan. Like shields around the world, the Deccan holds rich minerals.

The low Vindhya (VIN·dyuh) Mountains form the northern edge of the Deccan Plateau and set it apart from the Indo–Gangetic Plain. Two more prominent mountain ranges—the Western Ghats (GOOHTS) and the Eastern Ghats—form the seaward edges of the Deccan Plateau. In the Hindi language, *ghats* means "stairs" or "elevated places." The Deccan Plateau extends south to form the uplands on the offshore island of Sri Lanka at the southern tip of Peninsular India.

**Coastal Plain.** A Coastal Plain of varying widths occupies the seaward edges of the South Asian peninsula. The Coastal Plain is narrow along the west, or Malabar, coast facing the Arabian Sea. It widens along the east, or Coromandel, coast facing the Bay of Bengal (see the map on page 572). Lowlands found on Sri Lanka are a continuation of the Coastal Plain.

**573**

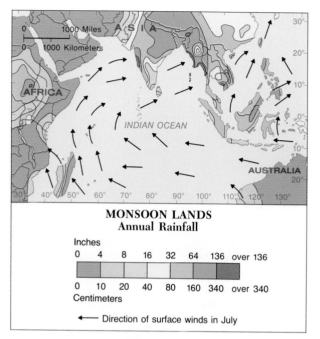

**MONSOON LANDS**
Annual Rainfall

Inches
0   4   8   16   32   64   136   over 136

0   10   20   40   80   160   340   over 340
Centimeters

← Direction of surface winds in July

*Learning from Maps. Summer monsoon winds blow across the Indian Ocean and its extensions. In what areas might you expect the most flooding from the summer monsoons to occur?*

## Climates

Winds called monsoons dominate the climates of the subcontinent. **Monsoons** are seasonal winds named for the direction in which they blow or the season in which they occur.

The northeast monsoon occurs in winter (see the map above). The northeast monsoon blows out from central Asia to the sea. It remains a dry wind unless its path takes it over areas of open sea. Winter, therefore, is a dry season in South Asia except in places where the northeast monsoon winds blow across water.

Summer is the time of the southwest monsoon. The southwest monsoon blows inland toward the Punjab and central Asia. It brings abundant moisture from the ocean, making summer the rainy season throughout most of South Asia. The rainiest areas lie in the Western Ghats and The Himalaya, which stand in the path of the moisture-bearing winds from the ocean.

Temperatures in South Asia vary because of the size of the subcontinent. The Coastal Plains, the Ganges Delta, and the islands have a tropical climate. These areas remain warm all year and the summer monsoon brings heavy rainfall. The Deccan Plateau is drier because the rain-bearing winds give up some of their moisture over the Ghats before reaching the Deccan. The Ganges Valley and most of the Punjab have hot summers and cool winters with less rain inland from the Bay of Bengal. Arid conditions prevail in Pakistan's Sind Desert at the mouth of the Indus River in the western end of the plain.

## Vegetation

Very little original vegetation remains in the lowlands after thousands of years of human settlement. Mangrove forests grow along the swampy edge of the Ganges–Brahmaputra Delta. Other forests cover parts of the Ghats and The Himalaya. Many of the mountain areas, however, have been **deforested,** or cleared of their forests, by people who still use wood as fuel for cooking and heating. Because the deforested mountains cannot control runoff, floods threaten the nearby lowlands.

## Resources

South Asia boasts a wealth of agricultural resources. Although industrial resources also are abundant, in many cases they remain undeveloped by the predominantly agricultural societies of the region.

**Agriculture.** The Indo–Gangetic Plain is sometimes called the "breadbasket" of South Asia. Many different kinds of grains grow in its fertile alluvial soils. Rice grows in the hotter and wetter end of the plain near the mouth of the Ganges. Wheat, barley, and millet, which need less heat and water, grow in cooler and drier regions such

*Text continues on page 576.*

# CASE STUDY
## EXPLORING NATURE: Monsoons

Nowhere in the world do so many people depend so much on wind patterns as they do in the monsoon regions of South Asia. Meaning "season" in Arabic, monsoon is synonymous with life-giving rain. Though it technically refers to a change in winds, the monsoon marks the semiannual rhythm of rainfall and drought.

### Seasonal Variations

Three seasonal variations occur in South Asia. From October through February clear skies, low humidity, and mild temperatures mark harvest time and a relief from the worst of the region's heat. From March through May the land becomes increasingly hot and dusty. Relative humidity increases and the air seems stifling. In June the skies suddenly open, dropping torrents of rain. The wet season, which often lasts well into September, sometimes turns into a nightmare of flooding. In India and Bangladesh thousands may drown, die from diseases caused by polluted floodwaters, or be bitten by cobras flooded out of their nests. But still the people welcome the rains brought by the monsoon winds because they are essential to life.

### Monsoon Winds

The different heating rates of land and water cause the winds (see Chapter 4). As autumn approaches, the sun's most direct rays shine farther south, warming the Indian Ocean and forming a low pressure area. Far to the north on the Asian continent cold temperatures cause a high pressure area to develop. Because air flows from centers of high pressure toward centers of low pressure (see Chapter 4), beginning in the fall air flows from the Asian mainland toward the Indian Ocean. It brings cool, dry weather to South Asia.

*Flooding of a Bangladeshi village*

By late March the sun's most direct rays reach central India. The land warms and temperatures over the Indian Ocean drop. This process creates a low pressure area over the land and a high pressure area over the ocean. By June warm, moisture-laden air from the ocean begins to blow onto the land and rains begin.

### A World Record

The town of Cherrapunji (cher·uh·POOHN·jee) provides an example of the power of the monsoon winds. Cherrapunji receives an average annual rainfall of 425 inches (1,080 centimeters). The area set rainfall records with 869 inches (2,207 centimeters) measured in one 12-month period and 41 inches (104 centimeters) measured in one day.

But while Cherrapunji's average July rainfall is 109 inches (277 centimeters), its December rainfall averages only 0.2 inch (0.5 centimeter). Cherrapunji's rainfall patterns further illustrate the marked seasonal rhythm in monsoon lands.

# GEOGRAPHY IN THE WORKPLACE
## Biogeographers

Biogeographers study the distribution, or spatial patterns, and the life cycles of plants and animals. Biogeographers are also called biophysical geographers (see page 28). Their study is no simple task because the life patterns of even the simplest living organisms are unbelievably complex. Thus a biogeographer setting out to learn about a particular organism, whether it is a butterfly or a buttercup, a tiger or a tangerine, undertakes a complicated study.

The biogeographer's principal goal is not only to understand a single plant or animal but also to understand where it is located and why it is there. Biogeographers also attempt to understand the relationships of organisms sharing the same habitat.

Biogeographers study a broad range of information. Some focus on the geography of one animal species, such as the Florida panther, while others look for global patterns of vegetation, such as savannas. Some create world vegetation maps that rely on satellite imagery. Others use microscopes to study minute organisms. Still others explore the land, seeking plant species that might help reduce world hunger.

The search by biogeographers for nourishing food plants led to the development of a plant called quinoa (ki·NOH·uh), a staple food among South American highland Indians. Quinoa interests biogeographers because it is an almost perfect protein and a particularly nourishing food for people who cannot afford to eat meat. Quinoa thrives at high altitudes where most other grains wither. Biogeographers believe farmers can grow large quantities of quinoa in the Rocky Mountains and other highland areas that today produce little food.

Biogeography offers challenging careers to students who have interests in both biology and geography. Because it involves two fields of study, an aspiring biogeographer must be prepared for considerable training. The rewards of saving an animal from extinction, protecting an especially fragile natural habitat, or finding a plant that could feed millions of people, however, certainly compensates for the effort.

---

as the Punjab. Farmers grow two and sometimes three crops a year along the warmer Coastal Plain. The availability of water—from monsoon rains or from rivers—largely determines the success of agriculture throughout South Asia. Crops shrivel in the fields if water is unavailable.

**Forestry and fishing.** Because the forests that remain generally are found only on mountainsides and in swampy areas, forestry adds little to regional economies. In some barely accessible areas loggers use elephants to push or pull over the trees and haul them out of the forest.

Fishing adds to local economies along the coast and on the islands. But old-fashioned methods keep fishing from contributing more to national economies.

**Mining.** India contains numerous energy and mineral resources. The country boasts large coal deposits on the Deccan and large oil deposits offshore from Bombay, as well as abundant deposits of iron ore and manganese, used in making steel. Pakistan also has valuable mineral resources. Hydroelectricity serves as an important energy resource in Himalayan countries and also in fuel-deficient Bangladesh.

*Learning from Pictures.* *Farmers harvest wheat in traditional ways near Jodhpur, India. Why do grains such as wheat account for such a large part of India's farm output?*

## 2 The people of South Asia have an ancient heritage.

All along the river in Varanasi (Benares), India, steps cascade to the water. Waves of people pour down these steps into the river. To Hindus, this is the sacred Ganges River, visited daily by countless pilgrims who come to bathe and pray in its holy waters.

South Asia ranks as one of the world's most densely populated places. Its many people are extraordinarily diverse. Language, religion, customs, and life styles divide the people of the region into many different cultural groups.

### A Brief History

South Asia's culture reflects thousands of years of influence by outsiders. Over the years a constant stream of people brought ideas and knowledge into the region through the Khyber Pass and across the surrounding seas.

**Early beginnings.**   South Asia is one of the oldest continuously inhabited regions in the world. Many of the people share common cultural roots in an ancient civilization that began in the Indus River Valley between 5,000 and 6,000 years ago. Archaeologists have learned much about this ancient civilization from the ruins of two of its cities—Harappa (huh·RAP·uh) and Mohenjo–Daro (moh·hen·joh–DAHR·oh).

**Aryans.**   Aryan invaders first came through the Khyber Pass and into the Indus River Valley around 1500 B.C. They brought with them the Sanskrit language, from which many of today's languages derive. They also laid the foundations of the religion called Hinduism. Many Hindu kingdoms rose and fell in the course of the next 2,000 years.

**Muslim invasions.**   The first of several waves of Muslim invaders swept through South Asia in the 700s, bringing Islam to the

**Learning from Pictures.** *A memorial to a Mogul emperor's beloved wife, India's Taj Mahal is one of the world's most beautiful buildings. Can architecture be an example of diffusion?*

subcontinent. The Muslims reached the height of their power in South Asia under Mogul rulers in the 1600s. The Taj Mahal at Agra, built by one of the Muslim Mogul emperors, stands as one of the great architectural wonders of the world.

**European colonialism.** South Asia vied with China in the 1500s as one of the wealthiest regions in the world. Europeans arriving from preindustrial Europe marveled at the spices that enriched the foods, the metalworking skills of Asian craftspeople, and the delicate weaves of handmade cotton and silk textiles. First the Portuguese then the British, French, and Dutch built profitable trade links between South Asia and Europe.

At the time of the Seven Years' War (1756–63) the British and French were also engaged in a battle over India. The British generals sent their best-trained troops to India, which they considered more valuable than America. Though they lost America, the British won India and stayed on to rule South Asia until 1947.

**Independence.** In 1947 the British withdrew from India after dividing it into Hindu India and Muslim Pakistan. Pakistan was broken into two parts—East Pakistan (now Bangladesh) and West Pakistan (now Pakistan)—interrupted by some 1,000 miles (1,600 kilometers) of India. Sri Lanka gained independence from Britain in 1948 as the country of Ceylon (suh·LAHN). Ceylon changed its name to Sri Lanka in 1972. The Maldives gained independence in 1965.

## Population Patterns

More than 1 billion people now live in South Asia. India's population of more than 800 million ranks as one of the highest in the world—second only to the People's Republic of China. Bangladesh and Pakistan each have more than 100 million inhabitants. The other countries of South Asia have much smaller populations.

**Rapid population growth.** All of the countries of South Asia have rapidly-growing populations. A useful way to understand the problems arising from rapid population growth is to look at the doubling time of a region. **Doubling time** is the number of years it will take for the population of a country or region to double in size if its current rate of growth continues. Doubling time also helps to pinpoint how quickly an economy must double to keep living standards at about the same levels. Unless food, jobs, schools, and other services double as quickly as the population, the standard of living will decline. To improve living conditions, of course, an economy must grow faster than its population.

South Asia as a whole has a doubling time of 30 years. In other words, South Asia will have 2 billion people 30 years from now instead of today's 1 billion. Sri Lanka has the slowest doubling time—38 years. The Maldives has a doubling time of only 18

*Text continues on page 580.*

# DEVELOPING GEOGRAPHY SKILLS
## THINKING GEOGRAPHICALLY: Recognizing Diffusion

Answering the geographic question "why there" often requires detective work! The solution to the mystery sometimes lies in discovering patterns of diffusion.

As you learned in Chapter 1, diffusion is the process by which things spread. Geographers study the process of diffusion for two main reasons. First, an understanding of diffusion helps geographers reconstruct movements that happened centuries ago. For example, the spread of Islam to North and West Africa indicates to geographers certain connections between those two areas. Geographers seek to reconstruct those connections. Second, understanding the process of diffusion helps geographers predict future diffusion. Understanding how a disease spreads, for example, might allow scientists to slow it down. Geographers trace diffusion by studying maps and collecting and charting other forms of data.

Geographers classify diffusion in two broad categories. The spread of Islam is an example of *expansion diffusion* because Islam remained strong at its point of origin and spread over wide areas. The spread of the scientific knowledge developed by the Aztecs is an example of *relocation diffusion* because it spread from its point of origin and then disappeared there.

### How to Recognize Diffusion

Review the steps for reading maps and graphs and the guidelines for recognizing main ideas and identifying cause and effect. Applying these and other critical thinking skills will help you trace the process of diffusion.

### Applying the Skill

Study the chart on this page. The chart provides an excellent example of cultural diffusion. It lists the major religions of the world and gives the primary locations of each. Note that Christianity spread from its point of origin—the Middle East—throughout Europe and on to North and South America. Buddhism has spread throughout Asia. Both of these religions illustrate expansion diffusion because they spread over wide areas yet remain strong at their points of origin—Christianity in the Middle East and Buddhism in Asia. Study the other religions listed on the chart. You may wish to do further research to trace their diffusion patterns.

*To practice this skill, see Practicing Geography Skills on page 585.*

| MAJOR RELIGIONS OF THE WORLD | | |
|---|---|---|
| **Religion** | **Followers** | **Areas of Concentration** |
| CHRISTIANITY | 1.1 billion | |
| *Roman Catholic* | | North and South America and Western Europe |
| *Eastern Orthodox* | | Eastern and Southern Europe |
| *Protestant* | | North America and Western Europe |
| ISLAM | 555 million | Middle East, Africa, Pakistan, Indonesia |
| HINDUISM | 464 million | India |
| BUDDHISM | 248 million | Asia |
| CONFUCIANISM | 151 million | China and Japan |
| SHINTO | 32 million | Japan |
| DAOISM | 21 million | Japan and China |
| JUDAISM | 17 million | Israel and the United States |

Source: *The World Almanac,* 1987
*The 1987 Information Please Almanac*

years. India, with its huge population of 800 million, has a doubling time of 33 years.

Most South Asian countries have reduced their death rates to modern levels. Birth rates, however, remain at high premodern rates. This continuing gap between low death rates and high birth rates has led to the region's rapid population growth.

**Population distribution.** The distribution of South Asia's population is extremely uneven. Lowlands on the Coastal and Indo–Gangetic plains remain among the most densely populated places in the world (see the map on page 589). By contrast, few people live in the Sind Desert in Pakistan and on the Himalayan slopes. Some sections of the Deccan also are too dry or too rugged for settlement.

**Urbanization.** Most of the people of South Asia still live in rural settings. Only 25 percent of India's huge population, for example, live in cities. In other South Asian nations even fewer people live in cities. The largest cities in South Asia include Bombay, Calcutta, Delhi, Karachi (kuh·RAHCH·ee), Madras (muh·DRAS), Lahore (luh·HOHR), and Bangalore.

## Social Patterns

The diversity of cultural traditions often makes it difficult for governments in South Asia to create a sense of national identity. In India, for example, languages change from state to state. Religious differences also divide the population.

**Language.** The languages spoken in South Asia often stretch across national boundaries, making it difficult for countries to choose an official language. India is one of the world's most linguistically diverse nations. Hindi serves as India's official language, but only about 40 percent of the people speak it. The country also recognizes 14 other languages as official regional

*Text continues on page 582.*

***Learning from Graphs.*** *South Asia's three largest countries are more different than alike. What generalizations can you state about Bangladesh, based on the graph?*

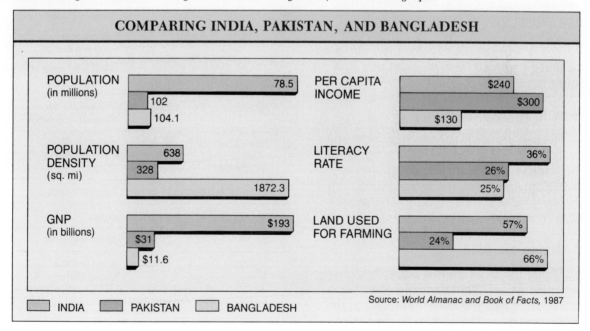

**COMPARING INDIA, PAKISTAN, AND BANGLADESH**

| | INDIA | PAKISTAN | BANGLADESH |
|---|---|---|---|
| POPULATION (in millions) | 78.5 | 102 | 104.1 |
| POPULATION DENSITY (sq. mi) | 638 | 328 | 1872.3 |
| GNP (in billions) | $193 | $31 | $11.6 |
| PER CAPITA INCOME | $240 | $300 | $130 |
| LITERACY RATE | 36% | 26% | 25% |
| LAND USED FOR FARMING | 57% | 24% | 66% |

Source: *World Almanac and Book of Facts*, 1987

# CITY FOCUS
## Delhi and New Delhi, India

In 1912 the British, then rulers of India, moved the capital of the nation from Calcutta to Delhi, a more central location. The British planned to build an entirely new capital city—New Delhi—just outside crowded Delhi as part of their long-range goal. A British architect prepared the design for New Delhi and construction began in 1912. The city was completed and became the national capital in 1931. New Delhi remained the capital after India gained independence from Britain in 1947.

### Spacious New Delhi

In sharp contrast to India's older and more crowded urban centers, New Delhi is open and spacious. It has broad avenues and beautiful gardens. Large government buildings dominate the center of the city. India's government is the city's principal employer. New Delhi has no factories. Elegant shops that appeal to wealthy Indians as well as to many foreign residents of New Delhi surround the business center. Most foreigners living in the capital are diplomats.

But New Delhi does not really stand apart from larger Delhi. In fact, the two cities have grown together. The two cities were originally 3 miles (5 kilometers) apart. Today the two cities are for all practical purposes one city.

### Crowded Delhi

Narrow streets and decaying slums mark old and crowded Delhi. The city serves as a major industrial center, producing automobiles and television sets as well as the traditional handicrafts of textiles and jewelry. Many industries occupy the most heavily populated residential areas, adding to the city's congestion, noise, and air pollution.

In spite of its apparent chaos, Delhi, like New Delhi, is a planned city. Delhi's master plan is based on a fundamental principle of

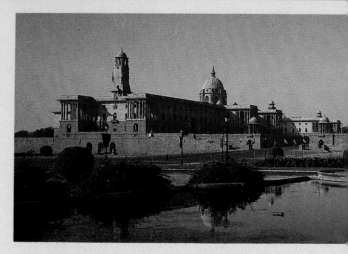

*The beautiful Secretariat in New Delhi*

Indian life, which states that the ideal Indian city combines residences, schools, shops, and workplaces in a space that can easily be traveled on foot or by bicycle. Attempting to follow this ideal, urban planners developed the concept of having 15 districts around Delhi's city center. Each district would have all of the facilities required to support a population of from 300,000 to 500,000 people.

Unfortunately, the plan never materialized. Rather than being held for city planners to develop according to the master plan, the best residential land was sold to the highest bidder. Public housing was built on the least desirable sites—those farthest from the workplaces. And the population of Delhi continued to grow.

The planners of the merged cities of Delhi and New Delhi now forecast that their cities' total population will reach 12 million by the year 2001. Limited housing already forces squatters to live on empty government land. As the population grows and resources are stretched even further, some solution to housing shortages and other urban problems will be needed.

languages. In addition, people speak hundreds of other languages and dialects. The fact that many Indian languages sound alike but are written in different scripts, or writing systems, further complicates the country's language patterns. Often Indians who speak different languages can communicate only by speaking English, which is taught in India's schools and serves as an "associate" official language.

Multiple languages also trouble Sri Lanka. Most people in Sri Lanka are Sinhalese and speak Sinhala, their traditional language. However, about one-fifth of the Sri Lankans are Tamils (TAM·uhls) who speak Tamil. The majority Sinhalese have attempted to enforce the exclusive use of Sinhala as Sri Lanka's official language. Many Tamils protest this form of discrimination. Because of language and other disputes, the Tamils are fighting to secede from Sri Lanka and form a separate nation.

**Religion.** Two of the religions practiced in South Asia are **indigenous,** or native, to the region. One is Hinduism, the religion of 80 percent of the Indian people and most Nepalese. The other indigenous religion is Buddhism. Buddhism developed in India and later spread throughout the Asian continent. Buddhism remains an important religion in Sri Lanka and Bhutan. Hinduism prevails elsewhere.

The third major religion of South Asia—Islam—was brought to South Asia by Muslim traders and invaders beginning in the 700s. Today Islam serves as the principal religion in Pakistan and Bangladesh.

People in South Asia also practice a variety of other religions. Sikhism (SEEK·iz·uhm) and Jainism (JY·niz·uhm) are minority religions in India. The subcontinent also supports an ancient Jewish community in Bombay and small groups of Christians.

**Learning from Pictures.** *Sikhs guard their religion's holiest place, the Golden Temple in Amritsar, India. What problems do small religious or ethnic minorities face?*

## Political Patterns

A variety of political systems makes up South Asia's political mosaic. Nominal democratic republics include India, the Maldives, and Sri Lanka. Monarchs rule Nepal and Bhutan. A military dictatorship controls Bangladesh. Pakistan is an Islamic republic currently ruled by a military dictatorship.

Over the years political disputes and outbreaks of violence have threatened the peace in South Asia. For example, the People's Republic of China and India disagree on certain boundary lines between the two countries. Since 1947 India and Pakistan

have disagreed over control of Kashmir. In fact, they have fought several wars in the area, which is now divided. Sikkim, once an independent kingdom, was taken over by India in 1975. India's Assam province in the northeast has been the scene of ethnic fighting between Hindus and Muslim immigrants from neighboring Bangladesh. Violence also wracks Sri Lanka following efforts by the Tamil minority to become self-governing. India, which has a small Tamil population of its own, has now become involved in that conflict.

## Economic Patterns

South Asia remains one of the world's poorest regions. Geographers classify all of the countries of the region as developing nations. The regional per capita GNP averages only $250 a year. Pakistan and Sri Lanka have GNPs above the regional average, but less than $400 a year. The GNPs of Bangladesh, the Maldives, and Nepal fall below $200. Most of the South Asian people face lives of extreme poverty.

As in other developing regions, most of the people in South Asia farm the land. The majority eke out a living as subsistence farmers. Most farmers cannot afford the special seeds and fertilizers needed to increase output. Sikh farmers in the fertile Punjab are an outstanding exception. Their investments in irrigation and modern farm technology make the Punjab one of the great food-producing areas of South Asia.

All the South Asian countries are slowly industrializing. Most South Asians benefit little, if at all, from industrialization, however, because population growth outdistances industrial expansion. Increasing numbers of people must share the meager benefits. India has the highest level of industrialization. But even the majority of the Indian people remain desperately poor farmers.

***Learning from Pictures.*** *Workers remove husks from corn in a farming village near Coimbatore in southern India. Why might working together increase the output of South Asian farmers?*

### SECTION 2 REVIEW

1. **Define**   doubling time, indigenous
2. **Locate**   Calcutta, Kashmir
3. **Identifying Ideas**   **(a)** Who were the peoples who invaded India around 1500 B.C.?   **(b)** What did they contribute to civilization on the Indian subcontinent?
4. **Organizing Ideas**   **(a)** Why did Europeans first travel to India?   **(b)** Which European people stayed on to govern India?   **(c)** What happened to the subcontinent after the Europeans left?
5. **Synthesizing Ideas**   Explain why it is so difficult for Indians to achieve a sense of national identity.

583

# CHAPTER 29 REVIEW

## Chapter Summary

The following list contains the key concepts you have learned about the physical and cultural settings of South Asia.

1. South Asia covers such a large area that geographers classify it as a subcontinent, or a landmass smaller than a continent but still of great size.
2. The subcontinent of South Asia juts out like a peninsula from the Asian mainland. The Himalaya join it to the rest of the continent in the north, and the Indian Ocean, Arabian Sea, and Bay of Bengal form the seaward edges.
3. The nations of South Asia are India, Pakistan, Bangladesh, Sri Lanka, the Maldives, Nepal, and Bhutan.
4. Four distinct physical regions occupy South Asia from north to south—the Northern Mountains, the Indo–Gangetic Plain, the Deccan Plateau, and the Coastal Plain.
5. Water from the monsoon rains and the river systems is critical for successful South Asian agriculture.
6. Most of the South Asian people have cultural roots in the ancient Indus River Valley civilization. Traditions from later invaders were added to this cultural base.
7. Buddhism and Hinduism are indigenous religions, but many other religions are also found in South Asia.
8. A variety of languages adds to South Asia's cultural diversity.
9. Rapid population growth outdistances the region's capacity to expand food supplies, jobs, schools, and other services.
10. A variety of political systems is found in South Asia, including democratic republics, monarchies, a military dictatorship, and an Islamic republic.
11. Most people in South Asia are poor farmers.

On a separate sheet of paper, complete the following review exercises.

## Reviewing Geographic Terms

Supply the geographic term that correctly completes each sentence.

1. A landmass smaller than a continent but still of great size is called a ___.
2. The best way for travelers to get over rugged mountains is through a mountain ___.
3. The seasonal wind that determines the climate of a region is called a ___.
4. ___ land is often subject to flooding because all the trees have been removed.
5. The number of years it takes for the population to double in size at current growth rates is called ___ ___.
6. Hinduism and Buddhism are said to be ___ to South Asia because the two religions first developed there.

## Developing Critical Thinking Skills

1. **Summarizing Ideas** (a) How does the northeast monsoon affect the Indian subcontinent? (b) How does the southwest monsoon affect the region?
2. **Analyzing Ideas** How do you think The Himalaya have influenced the physical and cultural development of the nations of South Asia?
3. **Distinguishing Ideas** What elements contribute to political instability in South Asia?
4. **Interpreting Ideas** Explain why the English language remains important on the Indian subcontinent 40 years after British colonial rule ended.
5. **Determining Cause and Effect** (a) Why has South Asia experienced such rapid population growth? (b) What effect does this growth have on the nations of South Asia?
6. **Writing About Geography** In a full-page essay, discuss one of the following ideas. (a) Why is the Indo–Gangetic Plain so important to the people of South Asia? (b) In what ways does language cause problems in South Asia?

## Using Primary Sources

In the following excerpt from *The Story of India*, Jean Bothwell describes the importance of the monsoon rains to India. As you study the reading, consider whether monsoons are as important to the country today.

The monsoon, a seasonal wind, is India's life line. Blowing from the southwest at the end of June, across the Indian Ocean and the Bay of Bengal to the east, it melts the cooler air from the Himalayas. The rain thus caused falls back on the Indian plain. . . .

The coming of the monsoon is watched for anxiously by many people. If there is a heavy rainfall the farmer knows he will have good crops and he will be able to raise enough grain to feed his family during the coming year, as well as to pay his share to the landlord. The merchant watches for it because the rate of rainfall affects prices in the bazaar. If there is a poor rainfall and the rice and wheat left from the preceding year are not enough to feed all the people, then there will be famine. Several times in India's long history there have been periods of severe food shortage when thousands of people have died because they couldn't get enough to eat. . . . But the rain is the great factor, kind one year and cruel another.

1. According to the author, why does the farmer want a heavy rainfall during the summer monsoon?
2. In what way does the rate of rainfall affect the merchant?

## Practicing Geography Skills

*Before completing this activity, review Developing Geography Skills on page 579.*

**Recognizing Diffusion** Reread Section 2 of the chapter, beginning on page 577. Then complete the following activities.

1. List the examples of cultural diffusion discussed in the section.
2. Write a brief paragraph describing cultural diffusion in South Asia. Your paragraph should mention the sources of cultural diffusion and its most common elements that spread to the region.
3. Using encyclopedias and other reference books, research the examples of diffusion you listed in the first question. Then develop a map that illustrates these diffusions.

## Exploring Geography

1. Use information in this chapter as well as resources in your school or public library to construct a time line that shows the major events of South Asia's history from the earliest civilizations to the present day.
2. Use resources in your school and public library to find photographs that illustrate the four physical regions of South Asia. Then prepare a brief report detailing how each photograph illustrates the particular physical region.
3. The Mogul Empire was renowned for its delicate styles of art and architecture. Prepare a short speech detailing the special features of the Mogul styles of art and architecture. If possible, find illustrations showing some of the Moguls' more distinctive works and use these illustrations as you deliver your speech.
4. Reread the CITY FOCUS on Delhi and New Delhi on text page 581. Then use information in the feature and in atlases and encyclopedias to construct a map of the two cities. Your map should include such items as major streets, important government buildings, and places of interest for tourists in both Delhi and New Delhi.

# India, Sri Lanka, and the Maldives

# PUTTING THE CHAPTER IN FOCUS

India's modern history began in 1947. Though one of the world's youngest modern countries, India has one of the world's longest histories. And while the country has modernized, many of its people continue to struggle with problems that troubled their ancestors. Sri Lanka maintains strong historical and cultural ties to India. Sri Lanka, too, is young, having gained independence in 1948. The Maldives ranks as one of the world's least populous countries.

## Ideas to Understand

In studying about India, Sri Lanka, and the Maldives, use these ideas to give direction to your reading.

1 India is a huge and populous nation.
2 Modernization is slowly changing traditional patterns in India.
3 Sri Lanka and the Maldives boast beautiful tropical settings.

## Terms to Define

The following terms are some of the key terms in the chapter. Defining them will help you understand India, Sri Lanka, and the Maldives.

| | |
|---|---|
| passive resistance | nonaligned nation |
| boycott | staple crop |
| caste system | cottage industry |
| reincarnation | atoll |
| separatism | |

## Places to Locate

Locating the following places will add to your knowledge of geography.

| | |
|---|---|
| Indo–Gangetic Plain | Bombay |
| Calcutta | Jamshedpur |
| Ganges River | Sri Lanka |
| Deccan Plateau | the Maldives |
| Punjab | |

## 1 India is a huge and populous nation.

Using remote sensing equipment, planes and satellites that pass over India send remarkable images to the earth. The high-altitude cameras glimpse India's amazing settlement patterns. Throughout the countryside lights wink at the cameras. Cities, towns, and villages seem to be everywhere. And in India they are! More than 750,000 villages lie scattered across this populous country.

### Physical Setting

The Himalaya and other high mountain ranges serve as a protective barrier along the entire northern border of India. South

*Hindu faithful along the Ganges in Varanasi, India*

of The Himalaya, fertile alluvial lowlands stretch across the Indo–Gangetic Plain. The Ganges, Yamuna (YAH·muh·nuh), Brahmaputra, and other rivers flow across the Indo–Gangetic Plain into the Bay of Bengal near Calcutta. The mountains and Indo–Gangetic Plain make up about 55 percent of India's territory. To the south the Deccan Plateau and bordering Coastal Plain make up the rest of India.

Monsoons dominate India's climate. The summer monsoons bring heavy rains to coastal areas and diminishing amounts inland. The rains turn the parched land muddy and green after a long dry season caused by the winter monsoon. Cool or cold winters affect the north, but temperatures remain mild in the south. The mild southern winters suit growing a winter crop where

water is available from monsoon rains, rivers, or wells.

## Cultural Setting

The site of many great civilizations, India fell under British rule in the 1700s. The British never ruled India as a unified country, however. Instead they focused attention on areas important to trade. Over 600 "native states" ruled by maharajas (mah·hah·RAHJ·ahs) made up the rest of India.

After World War I, Indians began to demand independence. A Hindu lawyer named Mohandas Gandhi led India's independence movement. Gandhi—who came to be called *Mahatma,* meaning "Great

*Learning from Pictures.* *Crowded cities such as Bombay are common in India, which has 10 cities of at least 1 million people. What problems does India's large population cause?*

Soul"—urged his followers to use **passive resistance,** or nonviolent protests, to drive out the British. Passive resistance took the form of protest marches and refusals to obey British laws that the Indians considered unjust. It also included **boycotts** in which Indians refused to buy British goods.

Immediately after World War II a weary Britain was ready to grant independence to India. But Indian Muslims demanded their own country. As a minority, they feared Hindu rule. At the time about 95 million Muslims and 250 million Hindus shared the subcontinent. Despite Gandhi's opposition, in 1947 Britain divided the territory into India—under Hindu control—and Pakistan—under Muslim control.

As a result of the division, great movements of people took place. Millions of Hindu families who had lived in the area given to Pakistan fled to India. And millions of Muslims moved from India to Pakistan. Thousands were killed by mobs before peace was restored in the two new countries.

**Population patterns.** More than 810 million people, or one out of every six people in the world, live in India. Only the People's Republic of China has more people than India.

Two different groups make up the Indian people—the Indo–Aryans in northern India and the Dravidians in the south. Differences in religion and language continue to divide these two groups of Indian people.

Since 1951 India's population has increased from 356.8 million to 810 million. The annual rate of increase remains relatively high at 2.1 percent. At this rate, India gains an additional 16.8 million people to feed every year! That breaks down to 47,191 additional people every *day,* or 1,966 every *hour!* Experts predict that more than 1 billion people will live in India by the year 2000 and 1.3 billion by 2020. This rapid rate

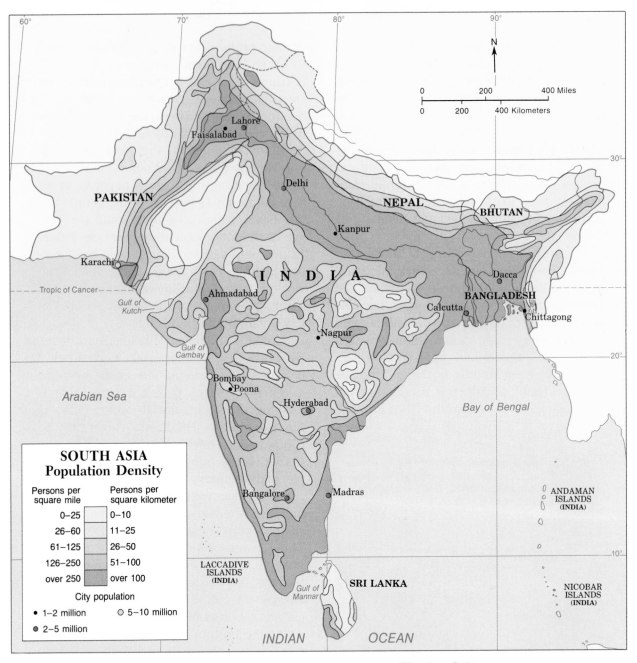

**SOUTH ASIA**
**Population Density**

| Persons per square mile | Persons per square kilometer |
|---|---|
| 0–25 | 0–10 |
| 26–60 | 11–25 |
| 61–125 | 26–50 |
| 126–250 | 51–100 |
| over 250 | over 100 |

City population
• 1–2 million     ○ 5–10 million
• 2–5 million

*Learning from Maps.* Pakistan has a striking population pattern. Why does Pakistan's population tend to cluster along a line down the center of the country?

of population growth strains India's food supplies and other resources.

India's huge population is unevenly distributed across the country. The Himalaya in the north have the lowest population densities. The highest densities lie along the Coastal Plain and in the crowded Ganges River Valley, where two out of every three Indians live.

Hundreds of thousands of villages dot the Indian countryside, but most are very small. Although only about 25 percent of

the people live in urban areas, India's cities hold great importance as the main centers of change. Modern technologies and ideas spread slowly outward from the cities to the rural areas.

**Social patterns.** India has one of the world's greatest mixtures of cultural groups. More than 1,600 different languages, three principal religions, and several other religions reflect the diversity of the people.

Before independence in 1947, Indians debated about what language their multicultural nation should choose as its official language. Some supported English because it was taught in India's schools and favored no particular ethnic group. Others favored Hindustani, which had been India's language under the Moguls. In the end Indians selected Hindi, a dialect of Hindustani and the language of the important Uttar Pradesh

*Learning from Pictures.* *Hindus believe cows are sacred and allow them to roam undisturbed, even in downtown New Delhi. How do common religious beliefs unite a country?*

(UT·uhr pruh·DAYSH) state. Hindi is similar to other Indo–Aryan languages spoken in northern India, but very different from the Dravidian languages spoken in southern India. In addition to Hindi, the Indian constitution recognizes 14 official languages.

Hinduism dominates religious life in India. Hindus make up about 80 percent of the population and form a majority in all regions. About 12 percent of the people follow Islam. Although only a small percentage of the total population practices Islam, 12 percent of 810 million people is 97 million people, which makes India one of the world's largest Muslim countries. The remaining 8 percent of the Indian people follow a variety of other religions.

Unlike Christians, Muslims, and Jews, Hindus believe in many gods. Such a belief is called **polytheism.** The **caste system,** a system in which people are placed into life-long hereditary social classes, also is fundamental to Hinduism. According to Hindu beliefs, birth puts a person into one of four castes, or *varnas.* Traditionally people had to marry within their caste and could never change their caste within their lifetime. Brahmans, who form the priestly caste, occupy the top of the class structure. Three lower castes, in decreasing order of prestige, are the warriors of the *Kshatriya* (SHA·tree·uh) caste, the merchants of the *Vaisya* (VYSH·uh) caste, and the craftsworkers and laborers of the *Sudra* caste.

At the bottom of traditional Hindu society were people without a caste, called the **untouchables.** The untouchables were barred from Hindu worship and forced to live apart from other castes. The government officially outlawed discrimination against untouchables in 1950.

Two other aspects of Hinduism—*dharma* and *karma*—affect daily life. Dharma is a person's duty to live according to one's station in life. This means a person should work hard and honestly at the jobs

*Text continues on page 592.*

# CASE STUDY
## EXPLORING IDEAS: The Role of Caste in India

The Hindu caste system originated with the Aryan invasion of India some 3,500 years ago. The invaders wished to guarantee their control over the conquered peoples, so they created a system of classes. The top three castes were reserved for Aryans. At the top were Brahmans—the priests, teachers, and judges. Next came the warriors called Kshatriyas. Below the Brahman and Kshatriya castes were the farmers and merchants in a caste called Vaisyas. Slaves drawn from the Sudra, or conquered people, made up the lowest caste. Below the castes were the "untouchables."

*A young Bengali woman in traditional dress*

### A Rigid Social System

In time the castes became rigid social divisions and the four major castes were further divided into more than 3,000 sub-castes, or *jatis*. Each jati had its own special status and occupation. Though the system was intended to stabilize and strengthen society, it began to hinder India's progress.

Enlightened Hindu leaders tried to break down the caste system, and the Indian Constitution of 1950 even outlawed the category of untouchable. Such laws, however, rarely affect the thousands of small Indian villages where most of India's huge population live. There the traditional beliefs and life styles keep the system alive.

### Caste and Marriage

Caste deeply affects the lives of many people. According to custom, the system forbids marriage between people with different social status. This practice, however, limits possible marriage partners. Because most villages have many jatis and each jati has few members, marriage between jatis has taken place for generations.

Still there are rules that must be followed. No daughter, for example, can marry anyone descended from the same family as her father. And all the boys and girls of the same generation in the father's line of descent (what we would call cousins) are regarded as brothers and sisters.

Because so many rules apply, marriages often require prolonged negotiations between the parents of the boy and the girl, who may be only six or seven years of age at the time. Once a bargain is reached, an elaborate ceremony is held at the bride's home. The wedding, however, will not take place for several years.

### Taboos

Besides influencing marriage, caste also determines what Hindus eat. Each caste and jati has certain dietary taboos. The higher the status, the greater the number of taboos. Brahman priests, for example, remain strict vegetarians and never touch meat of any kind. Salt makers, who earn little money but have high caste status because of their past importance, cannot eat mutton. But lower-caste leatherworkers can. And so in India, rules established long ago still guide many aspects of life for many people.

open to that person's caste and not struggle against strict caste rules. Karma is the belief that every action in a person's life will have consequences in the future. Karma is important to Hindus because they believe that souls go through a series of births, deaths, and rebirths, or **reincarnations.** The ultimate goal is to attain *moksha*, or perfection of the soul, which releases a person from the constant process of rebirth.

Jains and Sikhs make up two important religious minorities in India. Jains will not kill any living thing, no matter how small. They even take precautions so that they will not accidentally kill an insect. The Sikh religion combines elements of Hinduism and Islam. But Sikhs believe in only one god and have no caste system. A small number of Sikhs favor **separatism,** or breaking away from the current government, to form their own national government.

**Political patterns.** The Republic of India is a federal union of 24 states and 7 union republics. Each state has its own elected officials, but the central government can redraw boundaries at will. Many state boundaries have been drawn and redrawn since independence to avoid political disputes. Appointed officials govern the union republics.

India faces the problem of establishing a national identity. Most people tend to identify with their local state, rather than with the nation as a whole. For example, most people in the Punjab consider themselves Punjabis first and Indians second. Many countries succeed in unifying diverse groups, but language and religious differences complicate the problem for India.

The nations of the world recognize India as a leader of the **nonaligned nations.** Nonaligned nations refuse to join alliances that take sides in the political struggles between nations with Communist and non-Communist systems.

## SECTION 1 REVIEW

1. **Define**   passive resistance, boycott, polytheism, caste system, untouchable, reincarnation, separatism, nonaligned nation
2. **Locate**   Indo–Gangetic Plain, Calcutta, Ganges River, Brahmaputra River, Deccan Plateau, Indus River, Punjab
3. **Analyzing Ideas**   (a) Why did India remain a collection of independent states under British rule?   (b) How did Gandhi contribute to unification?
4. **Generalizing Ideas**   Write a generalization that describes India's population growth.
5. **Determining Cause and Effect** (a) Where are the highest population densities in India?   (b) Why do more people live in these areas?

## 2 Modernization is slowly changing traditional patterns in India.

Economists consider India to be a developing nation. Although its GNP now ranks as the tenth largest in the world, India's per capita GNP of $250 obscures the nation's overall economic strength. Raising the per capita income for 810 million people is a great challenge for modern India.

### Agriculture

Much of India's modernization effort focuses on agriculture because farming remains the most important economic activity in the country. Although only about 40 percent of India's total land area can support farming, about 70 percent of the workers earn a living as farmers. On this limited amount of land Indian farmers constantly strive to boost the food supply.

In recent years farmers have adopted several methods to increase output. They now use irrigation, chemical fertilizers, and high-yield seeds. Government loans help farmers afford modern technologies.

In general, wheat serves as the **staple crop,** or main food crop, in northern India. Rice serves the same function in the south. Typical farms are inefficient and small, sometimes covering less than half an acre (1 hectare). Nonetheless, since the 1950s India has changed from a country that imports food to one that is self-sufficient in food. India ranks among the world's leading producers of wheat, rice, peanuts, tea, tobacco, sugarcane, and cotton. Farmers also grow beans, peas, and lentils as important sources of protein in Indian diets. Many Indians need these vegetable sources of protein because, as vegetarians, they eat no meat—the most common source of protein worldwide.

Village life remains the center of Indian culture, although life in the villages slowly began changing in 1952. Land reform programs broke up large estates and redistributed the land to the tenants who worked it. The government sponsored irrigation projects and other farm improvement programs. Electricity and television also have begun to reach even remote villages.

Despite modernization efforts, however, some of rural India's older ways persist. Many farmers still plow the fields with oxen. Rural families still use cow dung as a fuel for cooking. Crops still fail and people still go hungry when the summer monsoon does not come or when it brings too little rain.

## Industry and Trade

Industrialization began in India in the middle of the 1800s. Progress was slow until India's newly independent government began using five-year economic development plans to spur industrialization. Today textiles, steel, chemicals, and machinery lead the list of manufactured products. Indian factories also produce bicycles, automobiles, radios, refrigerators, televisions, sewing machines, and fertilizers for local markets and computers, space satellites, and advanced communications equipment for export.

Calcutta and Bombay serve as India's traditional industrial centers. Another industrial area thrives at Jamshedpur (JAHM·shed·puhr), located on the Deccan Plateau near the country's principal coal, iron ore, manganese, and bauxite deposits.

India has a mixed economy. There is both public and private ownership of factories. The government owns and operates some of the businesses, while individuals

*Text continues on page 595.*

*Learning from Pictures.* *Industries such as the steel foundry at the Tata truck plant in Jamshedpur reflect India's industrialization. Why did Jamshedpur develop as an industrial center?*

# CITY FOCUS
## Calcutta, India

*A flower market in Calcutta*

When students of urban geography get together to talk about city problems, Calcutta inevitably rises to the center of the discussion. Probably no city in the world today has a worse reputation. Squalid slums, overcrowding, unemployment, inadequate sewage disposal, chaotic public transportation, and widespread corruption threaten its existence. Yet with all of its problems, Calcutta continues to attract impoverished farmers.

### Port and Manufacturing Center

Founded in 1690 by the East India Company, Calcutta grew to be the most important port and manufacturing center in India. Oceangoing vessels traveled up the Hooghly (hoog·LEE) River 90 miles (144 kilometers) to Calcutta's waterfront. There workers loaded and unloaded the cargo of smaller river craft that moved upstream to the Ganges.

By the end of the 1800s, manufacturing industries lined both banks of the Hooghly, and their products were shipped out of the port. The major industry was jute spinning and weaving. Jute is a plant fiber used to make burlap and rope. The agricultural lands of the lower Ganges had a virtual monopoly on growing, manufacturing, and exporting jute and jute products.

### Calcutta Today

Today's Calcutta no longer enjoys the many advantages of the past. Following World War II the creation of East Pakistan—later known as Bangladesh—deprived the Calcutta region of its prime agricultural land. Calcutta lost its jute monopoly to East Pakistan's new mills and ports. Because it no longer stands as the world's leader of jute processing, Calcutta's port has declined in importance. Although it still ranks as a center for foreign banking and as the management headquarters for several Indian industrial companies, Calcutta faces stiff competition from Bombay as India's leading city.

The creation of the predominantly Muslim nation of East Pakistan sent millions of Hindu refugees into Calcutta. The arrival of poor, displaced persons in such vast numbers intensified the inadequate housing and other facilities that were already strained to the breaking point.

Today more than three-fourths of Calcutta's families live in squalid single rooms that have no indoor plumbing. Many other people rent the beds in double or triple shifts. At least 50,000 people live without shelter of any kind and sleep on the open sidewalks.

To most observers, overcrowding in Calcutta has gone beyond the limits of human tolerance. Yet with an average monthly income of less than $30 for two-thirds of Calcutta's population, hopes for improvement look bleak. Until major changes take place it will be impossible for Calcutta to recapture its former greatness.

and private corporations own and operate others. **Cottage industries,** workshops run by craftspeople in their homes, form a third type of business enterprise. Weaving is the largest cottage industry in India today, accounting for about 40 percent of all of India's cotton textile goods. Cottage industry workers also produce pottery, copper and brass items, gold and silver jewelry, and leather goods.

Until the 1940s India's trading patterns were typical of a developing nation. It exported raw materials in exchange for manufactured items. Since that time the country's trading patterns have changed. Today India exports machinery and textiles. But because it imports more than it exports, India's balance of trade is not favorable. India's chief trading partners include Japan, Britain, the Soviet Union, and the United States.

## Coping with Population Growth

India has encouraged families to have fewer children as a way to slow population growth and raise living standards. Certain social factors, however, hinder this effort. For example, Indian families have traditionally valued large numbers of children. In rural areas families need many children to help them with farm chores. But officials hope efforts that stress education and information about how to limit family size will prove successful.

---

**SECTION 2 REVIEW**

1. **Define** staple crop, cottage industry
2. **Locate** Bombay, Jamshedpur
3. **Summarizing Ideas** What steps has India taken to modernize its **(a)** agriculture and **(b)** industry?
4. **Synthesizing Ideas** Why do government officials believe that reducing population growth is a key to India's development?

---

## 3 Sri Lanka and the Maldives boast beautiful tropical settings.

The island nation of Sri Lanka and a collection of small islands known as the Maldives lie south of Peninsular India. Both countries boast tropical settings.

### Sri Lanka

Sri Lanka, an island about half the size of North Carolina, lies within 22 miles (35 kilometers) of the Indian coast. It was known as Ceylon until 1972, when it adopted the Sinhalese name Sri Lanka. Since 1978 the official name has been the Democratic Socialist Republic of Sri Lanka.

Hills and mountains dominate the center of the island. A narrow coastal plain widens in the north and west. A tropical, monsoon climate affects the island. Sea breezes keep temperatures comfortable. Summer monsoon rains drench the southwestern plains and hills, an area known as the Wet Zone. The winter monsoon picks up moisture from seas separating India and Sri Lanka. Eastern and north-central areas, known as the Dry Zone, benefit from the lighter rains that this weaker monsoon brings.

About 16.5 million people live in Sri Lanka. Because its birth rate is the lowest in South Asia—about 25 per 1,000 people—Sri Lanka's population is growing at a rate of only 1.8 percent a year.

The Sinhalese ethnic group—made up of people who trace their descent to North Indian Aryans and a local people known as Veddhas—makes up about 74 percent of the population. Tamils make up about 18 percent of the population. Several smaller ethnic groups trace their descent to Muslim and European traders.

Religious and language differences divide Sri Lanka's population. The majority Sinhalese are Buddhists and speak Sinhala.

*Text continues on page 597.*

- developing nation
- debt
- balance of trade

All of these terms have already appeared in this textbook. And by now you realize that the study of a country's geography includes an analysis of its economy. Understanding economic terms is a key first step in relating geography and economics.

## How to Understand Economic Terms

Follow these guidelines to recognize and understand economic terms.

1. **Be alert for economic terms.** Skim the headings and subheadings for terms related to economics when previewing each chapter. Make a mental note to pay special attention to these terms.
2. **Analyze context clues.** Look for clues in the sentence in which the term appears or in the surrounding sentences that might help you understand the term's meaning.
3. **Expand your understanding.** Consult the textbook's *Glossary* (pages 750–58) or use a dictionary to clarify difficult terms. Note illustrations, such as maps, charts, and graphs, that contain economic information.
4. **Develop your own economic glossary.** Keep a list of economic terms as part of your study of geography. Write the definitions in your own words. Note terms that appear time and time again.

## Applying the Skill

Read the following excerpt. Note that the underlined terms and phrases contain key economic information about India and Sri Lanka. Analyzing this information gives you an idea of what the economies of these two South Asian countries are like.

> Economists consider India to be a developing nation. Although its GNP now ranks as the tenth largest in the world . . .
>
> India has a mixed economy. There is both public and private ownership of factories. The government owns and operates some of the businesses, while individuals and private corporations own and operate others. . . .
>
> Economists classify Sri Lanka as a developing nation with a socialist economic system. . . . Sri Lanka exports tea, rubber, coconuts, coffee, cacao, pepper, cinnamon, cloves, nutmeg, and other spices. . . .

As you have learned, most developing nations have agricultural economies and their people follow traditional life styles. These countries generally have little industry. Often they must depend on developed nations to help them meet their needs. GNP, or gross national product, refers to the value of all the goods and services produced by a nation each year.

You also have learned that a mixed economy combines a variety of methods to produce and distribute goods and services. The context clues indicate that India's economy mixes public and private ownership of the means of production. Sri Lanka has a socialist economic system. As you have read, that means the government owns or controls the means of production to varying degrees. The list of Sri Lanka's exports—tropical agricultural products—indicates that farming is the basis of the economy.

By understanding the use of economic terms, you can greatly expand your knowledge of the world's countries.

*To practice this skill, see Practicing Geography Skills on page 601.*

The Tamils are Hindus and speak Tamil. Since Sinhala was adopted as the official language in 1957, the Tamils have bitterly opposed it. In 1978 their protests persuaded the government to recognize Tamil as a second official language. Still not satisfied, the Tamils want to secede from Sri Lanka and become a separate nation. Fighting between the two groups continues to disrupt the country.

Economists classify Sri Lanka as a developing nation with a socialist economic system. Farming employs about 80 percent of the workers and farm products lead the exports. Sri Lanka exports tea, rubber, coconuts, coffee, cacao, pepper, cinnamon, cloves, nutmeg, and other spices. Colombo serves as the chief port and capital city.

Rice ranks as the staple food crop in Sri Lanka. Farmers grow rice on flooded fields. Bananas, mangoes, avocados, and other tropical fruits round out the Sri Lankan diet. Other occupations on the island include fishing and mining. Sri Lanka leads the world in graphite mining, most of which is exported. Sri Lanka also produces blue sapphires, moonstones, rubies, and other gems.

## The Maldives

An archipelago of about 2,000 small islands makes up the Maldives. The archipelago extends southward from the tip of India to the equator. The Maldive islands are formed by 12 atolls. An **atoll** (A·tawl) is a ring of coral surrounding an inner body of water called a lagoon. Most atolls develop atop submarine volcanoes. The Maldive islands have a hot climate all year. Most rain comes in September.

A mixture of Sinhalese, Dravidian, Arab, and African blacks make up the population of 178,000. Islam is the dominant religion, and the official language of the Maldives is Divehi, a dialect of Sinhala. An independent republic since 1965, the country's constitu-

***Learning from Pictures.*** *Many Sri Lankan laborers work on tea plantations, which produce much of the world's tea output. Why is Sri Lanka's climate ideal for tropical crops?*

tion provides civil rights and freedoms within the provisions of Islam.

Fishing employs 80 percent of the Maldivian workers. Some of the fish they catch is canned; the rest is dried. The country has little industry and depends on imports for virtually all manufactured goods. Important agricultural products include coconuts, millet, corn, pumpkins, and sweet potatoes. The warm climate and sandy beaches attract a growing tourist industry.

---

### SECTION 3 REVIEW

1. **Define** atoll
2. **Locate** Sri Lanka, the Maldives
3. **Analyzing Ideas** Explain how the economic patterns of both these countries reflect the interactions of humans with their environment.
4. **Synthesizing Ideas** How can you tell that the Maldives are a zone of transition?

# THE GEOGRAPHIC WEB
## Plants for the Future

The world is entering the age of bio-technology, where scientists can alter the genes that carry the biological codes controlling heredity in living things. Scientists at more than 200 companies and universities in the United States work to develop plants with traits such as larger size or resistance to disease. Scientists believe these new ventures will lead to the beginning of an era of custom-designed agriculture.

### Biotechnology at Work

In a matter of weeks scientists can grow the plants that take years to produce in nature. And by controlling the growth environment, they can cause the plants to grow in specific ways. Using this method, one company has developed corn containing high levels of protein-producing amino acids, which are essential to human nutrition. Scientists are also experimenting with other protein-rich crops, such as soybeans. Grown on a large scale these crops could dramatically improve the world's supply of protein.

Another research group has created several healthy snack foods that should reach grocery shelves soon. These biotech-nologically developed snacks include extra-sweet and crunchy carrots, varieties of both common and exotic fruits, and popcorn so flavorful that popcorn lovers will enjoy it without adding salt or butter.

*A winged bean*

*Tamarugo trees in Chile*

## Increasing Food Supplies

Other plant scientists work to make tropical plants grow faster so that they will grow during the shorter summer growing season of cooler regions. Similarly, scientists are trying to develop a corn that has the soybean's ability to produce fertilizer from the nitrogen in the air. The potential annual savings in fertilizer bills for corn could amount to millions of dollars.

While some plant scientists seek to increase the world's food supply through biotechnology, others look to the past for plants that may once again become important. One such plant—amaranth (AM·uh·ranth)—was the principal grain of the Aztecs and Incas. After the Spanish conquered those civilizations, they prohibited the growing and eating of amaranth because it had been used in Indian ceremonies. However, amaranth survived in a few remote highland villages. Today several research centers in the United States work to develop its use again.

Amaranth is a particularly exciting food possibility for the future because it requires little water or fertilizer and will grow almost anywhere. Even more importantly, amaranth seeds are richer in protein than any

other grain now cultivated. They look much like sesame seeds, have a pleasant nutty taste, and can be popped like corn or steamed and flattened into flakes.

Some plant scientists believe that a plant called the pepino will gain popularity in the 1990s. It, too, is an ancient South American plant. It grows a tomato-like foliage, and the fruit tastes like a cross between a strawberry and a melon. The first North American fields of pepino were planted in California in 1985. The first people to taste pepino predicted enormous success. Now researchers are working to develop a pepino that grows in cooler climates and that will be easy to pick, pack, and store.

## The Future Is Now

Plants for the future will be here soon! Watch your supermarket for amaranth, pepino, and other new and old food plants. These plants offer hope for adding significantly to the world's food supply. Biogeographers and biotechnicians continue to have success. Within just a few years a wide variety of custom-designed products will be ready for use.

*Guayule plant*

# CHAPTER 30 REVIEW

## Chapter Summary

The following list contains the key concepts you have learned about India, Sri Lanka, and the Maldives.

1. The Republic of India is the largest and most important country in South Asia.
2. India has more than 810 million inhabitants.
3. India includes two major ethnic groups—the Indo-Aryans in north India and the Dravidians in the south. Differences in religion and language divide these groups.
4. Hinduism is a major influence on daily life. Hindus believe that people go through a series of lives in their quest for perfection. Jains and Sikhs are religious minorities.
5. India is the recognized leader of the nonaligned nations that refuse to join an alliance or take sides in the political struggles between countries with Communist and non-Communist systems.
6. Although India ranks as a developing nation, the government is attempting to spur economic growth and modernization. India is now self-sufficient in food production. The nation also has adopted a series of five-year economic development plans that have speeded industrialization.
7. India's leaders believe that the country's future depends on successfully controlling population growth.
8. Tropical Sri Lanka is an island nation with historical and cultural ties to India. The nation has about 16.5 million people.
9. Sri Lanka is struggling to maintain a democratic government, but disputes between the majority Sinhalese and the minority Tamils wrack the island nation.
10. Sri Lanka is one of the world's leading producers of tea.
11. The Maldives are an island nation dependent on fishing.

On a separate sheet of paper, complete the following review exercises.

## Reviewing Geographic Terms

In the sentences below, the underlined term is incorrect. Rewrite each sentence with the correct term.

1. The Maldives are formed by 12 copras, or rings of coral surrounding lagoons.
2. About 40 percent of India's cotton textiles are made in homes by mixed economies.
3. According to Hindu's class network, people are born into one of four classes.
4. In India people without a caste are referred to as castaways.
5. Hindus believe that people go through many lives in a process called relife.
6. India, which refuses to join alliances or take sides in controversies between Communist and non-Communist systems, is a leading developing nation.
7. The main food crop of an area is called its atoll crop.
8. To convince the British to grant Indian independence, the people began a resistance of British goods.
9. Mahatma Gandhi advocated nonviolent protest marches and refusals to obey British laws that the Indians considered unjust as guerrilla activities.

## Developing Critical Thinking Skills

1. **Contrasting Ideas** How do The Himalaya and the Indo–Gangetic Plain differ in their contributions to India's landscape?
2. **Interpreting Ideas** Explain the influence of Gandhi's ideas of passive resistance on India's independence movement.
3. **Summarizing Ideas** Identify the two ethnic groups that make up India's population.
4. **Understanding Ideas** What political problems are caused by India's diverse **(a)** language and **(b)** religious patterns?
5. **Analyzing Ideas** How might Hinduism help a ruler guide a country peacefully?

6. **Seeing Relationships**  What is the relationship between India's physical setting and its population patterns?
7. **Synthesizing Ideas**  **(a)** Why has it been so difficult to reduce India's population growth rate?  **(b)** How are India's problems with population growth similar to those of Kenya?  **(c)** How are they different?
8. **Comparing Ideas**  What problems do  **(a)** Sri Lanka and India and  **(b)** Sri Lanka and the Maldives share?
9. **Writing About Geography**  In a full-page essay, complete one of the following activities.  **(a)** Suggest ways in which India might sustain a higher economic growth rate.  **(b)** Suggest measures the Sri Lankan government might take to lessen the political turmoil that is wracking the nation.

## Using Primary Sources

In the following excerpt from *The Essential Gandhi: His Life, Work, and Ideas*, Gandhi writes about India's struggle to develop its own place in the modern world. As you study the reading, consider whether modern India is following Gandhi's suggestions.

I am humble enough to admit that there is much we can profitably assimilate from the West. Wisdom is no monopoly of one continent or one race. My resistance to Western civilization is really a resistance to its indiscriminate and thoughtless imitation based on the assumption that Asiatics are fit only to copy everything that comes from the West. I do believe that if India has patience enough to go through the fire of suffering and to resist any unlawful encroachment upon its own civilization, which imperfect though it undoubtedly is, has hitherto stood the ravages of time, [India] can make a lasting contribution to the peace and solid progress of the world. . . .

There is nothing to prevent me from profiting by the light that may come out of the West. Only I must take care that I am not overpowered by the glamor of the West. I must not mistake the glamor for the true light.

1. As described in this excerpt, what is the West's incorrect assumption about India?
2. Why did Gandhi believe that India could make a lasting contribution to world peace and progress?

## Practicing Geography Skills

*Before completing this activity, review Developing Geography Skills on page 596.*

**Understanding Economic Terms**  Turn to the *Glossary* on pages 750–58. Then complete the following activities.

1. Skim the Glossary and identify 10 economic terms you think appear several times in this textbook. List those 10 terms.
2. Write a definition for each of these economic terms in your own words.
3. Turn to the page upon which each of the terms you identified is defined in context. Does your definition match the one given in the textbook? If not, adjust your definition.

## Exploring Geography

1. Reread the CITY FOCUS on Calcutta on page 594. Then write a report containing similar information on Colombo.
2. Use such sources as the *United Nations Demographic Yearbook* to find the population growth projections for India and those for one country from each of the following regions: Southeast Asia, Africa, and Latin America. Then construct a graph comparing projected population growth over the next 20 years.

# Pakistan, Bangladesh, Nepal, and Bhutan

# PUTTING THE CHAPTER IN FOCUS

Religious and ethnic differences play a major role in the cultural settings of Pakistan, Bangladesh, Nepal, and Bhutan. Pakistan and Bangladesh were both originally created as homelands for members of India's Muslim minority. Buddhism and Hinduism dominate traditional life styles in Bhutan and Nepal.

## Ideas to Understand

In studying about Pakistan, Bangladesh, Nepal, and Bhutan, use these ideas to give direction to your reading.

1 The partitioning of India created the nation of Pakistan in 1947.
2 Bangladesh faces many of the problems typical of developing nations.
3 Nepal and Bhutan are two landlocked countries high in The Himalaya.

## Terms to Define

The following terms are some of the key terms in the chapter. Defining them will help you understand Pakistan, Bangladesh, Nepal, and Bhutan.

cease-fire line     mercenary
distributary     buffer state
mangrove forest

## Places to Locate

Locating the following places will add to your knowledge of geography.

Punjab     Bangladesh
Indus River     Brahmaputra River
Sind Desert     Dacca
Karachi     Nepal
Lahore     Katmandu
Islamabad     Bhutan

# 1 The partitioning of India created the nation of Pakistan in 1947.

The name *Pakistan* provides an interesting study of the naming of a country. The name was first used around 1933. In Hindi and Urdu, the languages of the area, *Pakistan* can be interpreted to mean "land (*stan*) of the religiously pure (*pak*)." However, the name may have come from South Asian students studying in Cambridge, England. They composed an acronym—a word or name made by combining the letters of other words—from the first letters of the area's regions: *P* for Punjab, *A* for Afghania, *K* for Kashmir, and *S* for Sind. In 1947, when the new country was formed, the search for a name went no further than the acronym devised years earlier in Cambridge.

◄ *Harvesting rice in the Katmandu Valley*

## Physical Setting

Slightly larger than Texas, Pakistan is wedged between Afghanistan and India. When India was partitioned, Pakistan was left with the western half of the rich alluvial plains of the Punjab. Today these plains make up about one-third of the country and form its heartland. The Indus River and four of its five great tributaries flow through the Punjab, providing water for the plains. Without irrigation much of the Punjab would be too dry for settlement.

Arid deserts and rocky mountains cover the remaining two-thirds of Pakistan. The lower Indus River crosses the Sind Desert. To the southwest stretch the rugged and sparsely settled plateaus of Baluchistan. The Himalaya and Karakoram mountains form Pakistan's northern border with Afghanistan. The Khyber Pass cuts through

**603**

the mountains, providing the principal route to the west.

Pakistan receives sparse and erratic rainfall from the summer monsoon. Up to 60 inches (150 centimeters) of rain fall in the mountains, but only about 15 inches (38 centimeters) fall in the Punjab. The Sind gets less than 10 inches (25 centimeters) of rain a year. Temperatures are extreme, ranging from below freezing in the mountains to over 120°F (50°C) in the desert and plains.

## Cultural Setting

Once a part of India, Pakistan shares its early history with the rest of the area. Since gaining its independence, however, Pakistan has developed a distinct culture of its own.

**Population patterns.** Punjabis, who live on or near the Indus plains, make up about

*Learning from Pictures. Farming villages dot the rugged landscape of Baluchistan, Pakistan. How is Baluchistan more like Iran and Afghanistan than the rest of Pakistan?*

60 percent of Pakistan's 105 million people. Pathans, nomadic herders who live in the north and northwest, comprise about 30 percent of the people. The Baluchis and Sindhis, small minorities who live mainly in sparsely populated western Pakistan, make up the rest of the population.

Nearly 60 percent of all Pakistanis crowd onto the Punjab plains. The rest of the people live scattered throughout other parts of the country. Pakistan's urban population remains low—28 percent. Karachi, the chief port, and Lahore, in the Punjab, rank as the largest cities. The planned city of Islamabad, built in 1961, serves as the national capital.

Pakistan's population is growing even faster than India's. At current rates the nation's doubling time stands at just 24 years. Every year Pakistan must find enough extra food to feed an additional 3 million people.

**Social patterns.** The people of Pakistan are predominantly Muslims. Many found themselves on the wrong side of the border when the British partitioned India in 1947. Millions left their homes in India to start new lives among other Muslims in Pakistan. At the time of the partition fierce fighting erupted between Hindus and Muslims, both of whom wanted to remain on their traditional lands, and thousands died.

Pakistanis had difficulty selecting their official language. In the end leaders chose Urdu. Urdu is similar to the Hindi spoken in northern India except that it is written in Arabic rather than Roman script. Large groups of people speak other languages. Punjabis in the Punjab speak a language similar to Urdu. The Sindhis also speak a language similar to Urdu, except that it is written in a modified Persian script.

**Political patterns.** At the time of partition government leaders found it difficult to decide which areas should go to India and

which to Pakistan. It was impossible to find any section of the subcontinent that was inhabited solely by Muslims or Hindus. This mixed pattern caused serious problems. In Kashmir, for example, the Hindu ruler wanted the state to be part of India even though most of the people were Muslims. This dispute eventually led to a war that ended only when the United Nations intervened. The United Nations persuaded both sides to accept a **cease-fire line** that divides Kashmir into Pakistani and Indian sections.

After the partition Pakistan was a fragmented, two-part country. More than 1,000 miles (1,600 kilometers) of Indian territory separated the two sections (see the map on page 572). Although the people were Muslims, political differences between East Pakistan and West Pakistan led the people of East Pakistan to seek independence. After an armed struggle East Pakistan, supported by India, became the independent nation of Bangladesh. Pakistan lost 15 percent of its territory and more than half of its people to Bangladesh. West Pakistan survives as the compact country of Pakistan.

The secession of Bangladesh fanned separatist feelings among some of Pakistan's other ethnic groups. Pathans in the northwest, for example, sought to form an independent nation called Pushtunistan. Baluchis in the west wanted to join neighboring Iran. As disorder increased in the 1970s Pakistan's military leaders seized control of the government. A military dictatorship has been in effect since 1977, although its leaders promise an eventual return to democracy.

**Economic patterns.** Once Pakistan gained independence in 1947 it faced the colossal task of providing services it had previously shared with India. The government had to create new postal services, build new government offices, and plan new

**Learning from Pictures.** *Merchants display their goods at a traditional bazaar in Pakistan. Why is textile manufacturing often a main industry in the world's drier lands?*

transportation routes. The country also had to resettle and provide housing, food, and other basic necessities to vast numbers of immigrants who had fled from India.

Pakistan remains a developing nation. Despite limited farmland, more than 50 percent of all Pakistani workers earn a living as farmers. Farms in the Punjab, the most important farming area, produce wheat, rice, and cotton. Wheat serves as the staple food throughout Pakistan. Farmers also grow other grains, such as corn, millet, sorghum, and barley. Chickpeas add protein to Pakistani diets.

Farmers raise cotton, the chief cash crop, for export. In addition, opium poppies are illegally grown in isolated areas of the northwest. Since the late 1970s the government has made occasional but unsuccessful attempts to stamp out the area's profitable opium and heroin trade.

Manufacturing employs only 13 percent of Pakistan's work force. Nonetheless, the output of steel, chemicals, cotton textiles,

and machinery has increased significantly in recent years. Oil from rich fields near Islamabad contribute to Pakistan's industrialization. Dams in the Punjab produce hydroelectricity for industrial use. Karachi serves as the chief industrial center.

SECTION 1 REVIEW

1. **Define** cease-fire line
2. **Locate** Punjab, Indus River, Sind Desert, Karachi, Lahore, Islamabad
3. **Summarizing Ideas** Why is the Indus River so important to Pakistan?
4. **Interpreting Ideas** Why did the partition of the Indian subcontinent prove so difficult?
5. **Analyzing Ideas** What great problems did Pakistan face following the partition of India?

## 2 Bangladesh faces many of the problems typical of developing nations.

After Bangladesh gained its independence from Pakistan in 1971, it faced many problems. Not only did its leaders have to develop a completely new national government, they also had to devise ways of coping with an often hostile physical environment and a rapidly growing population.

### Physical Setting

From the air it appears as though a giant spiderweb covers Bangladesh. The country lies almost entirely on alluvial lowlands and the deltas of the Brahmaputra and Ganges rivers. Distributaries of the two rivers crisscross the watery plains (see the map on page 572). **Distributaries** are smaller streams that carry water away from the main stream of a river. Distributaries give a river many paths to the sea.

The Brahmaputra enters the northeast corner of the country and joins the Ganges in central Bangladesh. The combined rivers form a huge delta that extends far inland from the Bay of Bengal. No part of the delta is higher than 150 feet (46 meters) above sea level. Devastating floods frequently spill over the low-lying land, drowning people and animals, ruining crops, and threatening famine for survivors. The only advantage of the location is the rich alluvium left behind when the floodwaters recede.

Bangladesh's tropical and monsoonal climate resembles that of India. Summers tend to be hot and rainy, while winters remain mild and relatively dry. Rainfall averages 75 inches (191 centimeters) a year at Dacca (also spelled "Dhaka") and up to 250 inches (635 centimeters) a year in the few hilly areas in the northeast and extreme southeast. The summer monsoon brings nearly 80 percent of the rain. In addition to floods, devastating tropical storms often sweep in from the Bay of Bengal in April and May. In 1970 one such storm killed 200,000 people.

Somewhat unusual vegetation patterns cover Bangladesh. The principal forests are marshy Sundarbans, or **mangrove forests,** along the coast. The mangrove trees grow in the salty water and protect the coast from erosion. The shallow waters of the Sundarbans, as in all mangrove forests, provide a special **ecosystem,** or environmental community, for a wealth of marine life. An international effort seeks to keep the Sundarbans from being cleared for farmland.

### Cultural Setting

Bangladesh faces severe population and economic problems. Progress has been slow and may take many years.

**Population patterns.** More than 107 million people live in Bangladesh, making it

one of the most densely populated countries in the world. An average of 1,775 people crowd each square mile (685 per square kilometer). To make matters worse, the annual population growth rate—a high 2.7 percent—adds an additional 3 million Bangladeshis every year. The population's doubling time is a short 26 years. Many people consider Bangladesh overpopulated because it lacks the resources to accommodate the people.

**Social patterns.** More than 9 of every 10 Bangladeshis are Bengalis. The Bengalis reflect a mixture of Aryan and Dravidian traits. Other ethnic groups live in the northeast and southeast. Conflicts sometimes arise when the Bengalis try to settle in these border areas.

Islam remains the dominant religion in Bangladesh. Hindus who chose to stay in the area after the 1947 partition make up about 12 percent of the population. Other religious groups represent less than 1 percent of the total population.

Bengali serves as the official language of Bangladesh. In fact, the unsuccessful effort to make Pakistan accept Bengali as the equal of Urdu was one of the reasons the Bengalis fought for independence and established Bangladesh.

**Political patterns.** Today Bangladesh copes with internal problems that include flooding and famine. Continuing conflicts with neighboring India concerning jute also trouble the country. Partition left many jute mills on the Indian side of the boundary, while most of the jute fields went to Bangladesh. Both countries have spent money to duplicate facilities the other already has (see the CITY FOCUS on page 594).

Occasionally violence breaks out in India's nearby Assam (uh·SAM) state. Many Bangladeshis fled to Assam in the 1980s to escape floods and now face discrimina-

**Learning from Pictures.** *Many Bangladeshis live in houseboats on the rivers that wind through the countryside. Why is land so valuable in Bangladesh?*

tion from Assam's Hindu majority. Unable to return to their flood-ruined lands, the Bangladeshis seek help from their government. Bangladesh's military dictatorship has thus far been unable to solve these and many other problems that plague the young country.

**Economic patterns.** Bangladesh ranks as one of the poorest countries in the world. Its per capita GNP—$150—stands as the lowest in all of impoverished South Asia.

Most of the workers in Bangladesh earn a living by farming. Rice serves as the staple food crop. Foreign money helps farmers buy the high-yield rice seedlings and fertilizers they need to benefit from modern farming technology. Jute, which grows best in wet areas, remains the principal crop grown for export and industrial use.

**607**

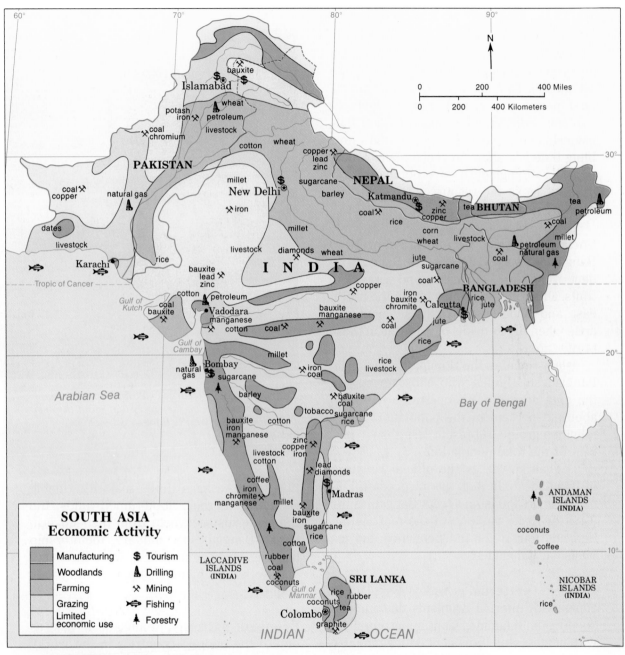

**SOUTH ASIA**
**Economic Activity**

| | |
|---|---|
| Manufacturing | $ Tourism |
| Woodlands | Drilling |
| Farming | Mining |
| Grazing | Fishing |
| Limited economic use | Forestry |

***Learning from Maps.*** *Bangladeshi farmers face a problem different from that faced by most farmers—too much water. From where does all the water come?*

Farmers do not raise much livestock because land in crowded Bangladesh is too valuable to use for livestock farming, although cattle kept for plowing provide some meat and milk. Peas, beans, and fish provide protein in Bangladeshi diets.

Bangladesh remains one of the world's least industrialized nations. The jute industry is the most important industry. A small textile industry based on imported cotton also exists. Dacca, the capital and largest city, and Chittagong serve as industrial cen-

ters. The government hopes to use new discoveries of natural gas to stimulate more industrial development.

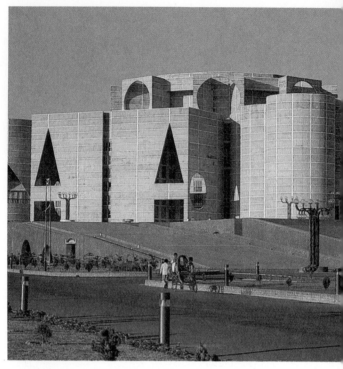

*Learning from Pictures.*   *The National Parliament building, funded by foreign money, gives Dacca a modern look. Why must Bangladesh rely on foreign money and help?*

## 3   Nepal and Bhutan are two landlocked countries high in The Himalaya.

Nepal has always been shrouded in myth and mystery. According to legend Nepal was once a huge lake that was drained by the Buddhist saint Manjushri. While on a religious pilgrimage from China, Manjushri struck the earth with his sword and opened up the gorge of Chobar—meaning "sword cut"—through which the Baghmati River flows today. The lake waters drained away and the lands became Nepal.

Nepal also is the home of the *yeti*, or Abominable Snowman, called the "bearman" by the Nepalese. Sherpas claim the creature lives high in the mountains, but it has eluded discovery.

### Nepal

Nepal stretches generally northwest to southeast along the southern edge of The Himalaya. It separates India in the south from Tibet, which is presently controlled by the People's Republic of China, in the north.

**Physical setting.**   Four roughly parallel zones run east to west through Nepal, a country slightly smaller than Wisconsin. Nepal's best farmlands lie in the lowest foothills of The Himalaya, known as the *Terai*. Thick jungles filled with elephants, tigers, leopards, wild boars, and rhinoceroses still cover some of the Terai. Next to the Terai lies a narrow highland zone called the Siwalik (si·WAHL·ik) Range. Beyond the highlands stretches the Valley of Nepal, or the Valley of Katmandu, where most Nepalese live. Katmandu, the capital of Nepal, dominates this valley. To the north tower the snowcapped Himalaya.

*Text continues on page 611.*

# DEVELOPING GEOGRAPHY SKILLS
## WRITING ABOUT GEOGRAPHY: Expressing Viewpoints

*Typical village in Nepal*

Until recently, to make a visit to Katmandu, Nepal's capital, was to take a step back in time. Unfortunately the modern world is catching up with the mystical city high in The Himalaya. Katmandu's population has doubled since 1960 and continues to boom. Industries geared to the surge of construction now pollute the formerly clean atmosphere.

The people are changing as much as their environment. In the last 10 years many young residents have abandoned their traditional clothing in favor of Western-style clothes imported from Hong Kong and Bangkok. Many of these same people lounge in "videos," shops that show Western videotapes. In addition, the younger generation rejects the ceremonies and rituals that give Nepal its special flavor. And perhaps more alarming, city officials estimated 10 years ago there were fewer than 50 drug addicts in Katmandu. Today they estimate there are 15,000— nearly one in every 25 young men.

Being informed about and able to express a point of view is important to a citizen in today's society. You will be concerned with and may wish to express your viewpoint on a variety of issues.

As a student you are also called upon to express your viewpoint—in class discussions, essay tests, and research projects.

### How to Express a Viewpoint

To effectively express your viewpoint, follow these guidelines.

1. **Research the topic.** Make sure you know what you are talking about. Find out what the opposing viewpoints are.
2. **Determine your position.** Study the evidence and evaluate the situation. Collect data to support your position.
3. **State your position clearly.** Write an introduction that identifies the issue and states your viewpoint.
4. **Support your position.** Develop additional paragraphs that provide support for your point of view. End with a concluding paragraph in which you clearly restate your position and reasoning.

### Applying the Skill

Reread the excerpt on this page. It states one geographer's view of the changes that Nepal is experiencing. The second sentence states the excerpt's main idea: *Unfortunately the modern world is catching up with the mystical city high in The Himalaya.* (Note that the geographer expresses regret by using the word *unfortunately.*) The writer supports the main idea with details of the population boom, increased pollution, and change in life styles taking place in Katmandu.

*To practice this skill, see Practicing Geography Skills on page 615.*

Monsoons influence Nepal's climate, but the effects vary greatly with elevation. The low-lying Terai has a subtropical climate—hot in summer, humid during the monsoons, and pleasantly cool in winter. The hills and valleys have mild summers and cold winters with heavy snowfalls on the higher slopes. The rainfall varies from one valley to the next depending on elevation.

**Cultural setting.** Modern ways have largely bypassed Nepal. The country's 18 million people live in one of the world's most traditional societies.

Sherpas (SHER·puhs) form Nepal's best-known ethnic group. The Sherpas, or "people from the east" (*sher* means "east" and *pa* means "people"), entered Nepal from Tibet and today live south of Mount Everest. Sherpas are noted for their mountain-climbing skills. Many work as guides and porters for mountain-climbing groups (see the CASE STUDY on page 612).

A second group, the Newars, dominate the Katmandu Valley. Newars control much of Nepal's agriculture and trade. Many are talented carvers, architects, painters, sculptors, and metalworkers.

Another group of Nepalese are the Gurkhas. The Gurkhas make up an occupational group rather than an ethnic group. The original term *Gurkhas* referred to those Nepalese claiming descent from Indian Rajputs, who took over the Nepalese throne in the 1100s. Later the British applied the name to all Nepalese soldiers serving in the British army in India. The Gurkhas distinguished themselves by their courage and skill. Today many Gurkhas find employment as **mercenaries,** soldiers who serve for pay in the armies of other countries.

The people of Nepal have religious and language ties to both Tibet and India. Although Hindus make up the largest group, Buddhism and Tantrism have Nepalese followers as well. Buddhism was founded by an Indian Hindu named Siddhārtha Gautama (GOWT·uh·muh) in the 500s B.C. Gautama—now known as Buddha, or the "Enlightened One"—taught that anyone, regardless of caste, could reach nirvana, or heaven. Although Buddhists do not believe in the caste system of Hinduism, they do believe in reincarnation and in karma.

Tantrism comes from a body of religious writings called the Tantras and influences both Buddhism and Hinduism in Nepal. Today the different religious groups often share the same temple and take part in each other's festivals.

Nepali serves as the official language of Nepal. It has similarities to Hindi and is spoken by about 50 percent of the people. Nepali also serves as the language of instruction in Nepal's schools.

Nepal serves as a **buffer state,** or country lying between two potential rivals. It separates India from Chinese-controlled Tibet. A monarch who serves as the country's sole leader governs Nepal.

Nepal remains a developing nation. Its per capita GNP of $160 ranks nearly as low as that of Bangladesh. Nepal has few roads, lacks industry, and depends almost entirely on herding and subsistence agriculture. Tourism, based on Nepal's unique culture, adds significantly to the economy.

Rice and grains make up most of the people's diet. Mild winters in the valleys usually allow farmers to harvest two rice crops. Yaks carry heavy packs along steep mountain paths and provide wool, meat, and milk.

## Bhutan

Slightly smaller than Delaware, Bhutan lies in The Himalaya directly north of Bangladesh. The narrow Indian state of Sikkim separates Bhutan from Nepal. Like Nepal, Bhutan serves as a buffer state separating India and the People's Republic of China.

*Text continues on page 613.*

*Passing on a narrow mountain bridge*

From a great distance mountains appear easy to climb. Their jagged slopes seem smooth and the treacherous crevasses in their icy peaks look like tiny cracks in a sidewalk. Only when you have experienced the staggering, exhausting agony of treading through oxygen-thin air when climbing a mountain does the majesty of a high mountain become a reality.

The reality becomes more clear in The Himalaya than anywhere else. Rising nearly 5 miles (8 kilometers) into the sky, these great mountains form the most magnificent range on earth.

### Creation of The Himalaya

The Himalaya and their neighboring ranges rank among the youngest mountains on earth. Present-day scientists use the theory of plate tectonics to explain their creation. But Hindu legend has quite a different explanation. The legend says that the Hindu god Vishnu lived on the shore of a great sea. His only companions were a pair of sea gulls. Each year the female sea gull laid her eggs near the shore. But each year the waves washed the eggs away. Although the sea gull kept building her nest farther inland, the sea continually destroyed the eggs. Eventually the birds cried out to Vishnu for help. Vishnu responded by swallowing the sea. In its place lay Mother Earth. Exhausted, Vishnu then fell into a deep sleep. While he slept the demon Hiranyanksha attacked and savagely beat Mother Earth. Her broken bones formed The Himalaya.

### Guides to The Himalaya

In the vast and snowy kingdom of The Himalaya live 30,000 Sherpas. They have become famous as the world's greatest high-mountain guides.

The Sherpas are a hearty people with a reputation for courage and physical strength. They can carry heavy loads in the thin air of The Himalaya. They developed this ability over generations as traders, guides, and porters for merchant caravans traveling between Tibet and India.

Mountain climbing in The Himalaya began in the early 1900s. The Sherpas' experience as porters and guides suited them ideally for work with the big expeditions up the Himalayan peaks.

A Sherpa guide, Tenzing Norgay, became one of the first two people to reach the top of Mount Everest and return. With Sir Edmund Hillary, a New Zealand mountaineer and explorer, Norgay stood on the summit of the world's highest mountain on May 29, 1953.

Since that date a steady flow of tourists has visited the region. The Sherpas are proud of the area's inspiring natural landscapes and of their cultural heritage. They welcome visitors. They are now increasingly involved in opening up their mountainous homeland to people from far beyond the snowy ranges of "the roof of the world."

**Physical setting.** Three zones closely resembling Nepal's are found in Bhutan. The southern foothills contain dense tropical forests, scattered savanna grasslands, and few people. Most of the people live in the central zone, which features several narrow, fertile river valleys. Thimbu, one of the main valleys, also gives its name to Bhutan's capital. In the north The Himalaya rise to elevations of 20,000 feet (6,100 meters) and more.

Because Bhutan lies relatively close to the Bay of Bengal, it gets more rain from the summer monsoons than Nepal does. However, moisture varies according to altitude and exposure. Slopes facing into the rain-bearing winds receive more rain than slopes facing away from them. Mountain barriers stop rain-bearing winds from reaching some of the dry interior valleys.

**Cultural setting.** Bhutan has a population of 1.5 million people, almost all of whom are Buddhists. Like Nepal, Bhutan is sparsely populated except in the central valley zone.

Most Bhutanese have cultural ties to people in Tibet. In general, people in eastern Bhutan trace their descent to Tibetans who immigrated centuries ago, while people in western Bhutan are descendants of more recent arrivals from Tibet. In addition, some Nepalese came to Bhutan as laborers.

The languages of Bhutan are related to Tibetan. Most people speak a Tibetan dialect called Dzongkha (zong·KUH), the official language of Bhutan.

Bhutan is governed by a limited monarchy. The legislature selects the monarch from the royal family and has the power to remove the monarch at any time.

Bhutan's economic patterns closely resemble those of Nepal. Few modern ways have reached Bhutanese society. Most people survive through subsistence agriculture, growing the staple food—rice.

***Learning from Pictures.*** *Craftspeople in Nepal and Bhutan weave sturdy matting for roofs and floors. Why do Nepal and Bhutan lack enough wood for building purposes?*

**SECTION 3 REVIEW**

1. **Define** mercenary, buffer state
2. **Locate** Nepal, Katmandu, Bhutan
3. **Summarizing Ideas** What are the effects of the monsoons on **(a)** Nepal and **(b)** Bhutan?
4. **Identifying Ideas** **(a)** What is Nepal's best-known ethnic group? **(b)** What are its members noted for?
5. **Relating Past to Present** **(a)** Which Nepalese people did the British employ in the Indian army? **(b)** How are many employed today?
6. **Organizing Ideas** What are the major economic activities in Nepal and Bhutan?

## Chapter Summary

The following list contains the key concepts you have learned about Pakistan, Bangladesh, Nepal, and Bhutan.

1. Religious and ethnic differences led to the partitioning of India and the creation of Pakistan in 1947.
2. The Indus River Valley in the Punjab forms the heart of present-day Pakistan.
3. Nearly 60 percent of all Pakistanis crowd into the Punjab plains. The rest of the people live scattered throughout the sparsely populated areas of the country.
4. After the creation of East Pakistan and West Pakistan, political differences and problems caused by fragmentation led the people of East Pakistan to seek independence. After an armed struggle, East Pakistan became the independent nation of Bangladesh in 1971. West Pakistan survives as the independent nation of Pakistan.
5. Most of the people in Pakistan and Bangladesh are Muslims.
6. Feeding a large and fast-growing population is the chief problem facing low-lying and overcrowded Bangladesh.
7. Several different ethnic and linguistic groups make their homes in Nepal.
8. Sherpas have gained fame as the guides to The Himalaya.
9. Buddhism was founded by an Indian Hindu named Siddhārtha Gautama in the 500s B.C.
10. Bhutan has historical ties to Buddhism and to Tibet.

On a separate sheet of paper, complete the following review exercises.

## Reviewing Geographic Terms

Match each of the following terms with the correct definition.

a. distributary
b. cease-fire line
c. buffer state
d. mangrove forest
e. mercenary

___ 1. Smaller streams that branch off from a river's main stream and provide several paths to the sea
___ 2. Vegetation that grows in salt water and provides an important ecosystem for marine life
___ 3. Soldier hired to serve in the army of another country
___ 4. Area, such as a country, that lies between two potential rival areas or countries
___ 5. Area marking the division between two hostile groups that have agreed to stop fighting

## Developing Critical Thinking Skills

1. **Summarizing Ideas** (a) What are South Asia's three major religions? (b) How has the existence of large groups of followers of different religions affected the history of the region?
2. **Comparing Ideas** (a) How are the political problems within Pakistan similar to those that led to the creation of the country? (b) How are they different?
3. **Interpreting Ideas** (a) What major force divides the people of India from the people of Pakistan? (b) Why did this force require the establishment of separate countries?
4. **Contrasting Ideas** How do the (a) physical settings and (b) cultural settings of Pakistan and Bangladesh differ? (c) How do the settings of both these countries differ from those of Nepal and Bhutan?
5. **Organizing Ideas** (a) What steps has India taken to modernize? (b) Why do you think that Bangladesh has failed to take similar steps toward modernization?
6. **Seeing Relationships** (a) What are the major features of the economic patterns of Nepal and Bhutan? (b) How has the physical setting of the two countries influenced their economic patterns?
7. **Analyzing Ideas** What cultural ties do the people of Nepal have with India?

**8. Writing About Geography** In a full-page essay, discuss one of the following ideas. **(a)** How was the Indian independence movement both a unifying and a dividing force for the people living in colonial India? **(b)** What was the relative location of the original Pakistan and how did it contribute to civil war and the creation of two separate countries?

## Using Primary Sources

In the following excerpt from *The New India*, Ved Mehta describes the cultural problems that caused East Pakistan to break away from West Pakistan and become the independent country of Bangladesh. As you study the reading, consider those problems and compare them with similar ones in other parts of the world.

> From the very beginning, Pakistan had been an uneasy alliance of two distinct cultural, economic, and linguistic entities . . . the richer Punjabis in the west and the poorer Bengalis in the east, separated by a thousand miles of Indian territory. The Punjabis of West Pakistan and the Bengalis of East Pakistan had much more in common with the Punjabis and Bengalis across the border in India than with each other; they were divided not only by geography but also by differences in language, in economic and social systems, in dress, and in diet. In fact, the only real bond between East Pakistan and West Pakistan was Islam, but, as other Muslim countries had discovered, religion alone could not bind together politically [different] entities. From the start, the Punjabis, who were much more prosperous than the Bengalis, ran Pakistan's Army, civil service, and industry. They strengthened and extended their advantage through the years until the nation's power and wealth became concentrated almost entirely in the west.

**1. (a)** Of the two different cultural groups mentioned by the author in the excerpt, which is the wealthier and more powerful? **(b)** How might this cause problems in a two-part country?

**2. (a)** According to the author, can the same religion bind different political groups together? **(b)** Do you agree? Explain your answer.

## Practicing Geography Skills

*Before completing this activity, review Developing Geography Skills on page 610.*

**Expressing Viewpoints** Select one of the topics below. Research the topic and determine your position. Then express your viewpoint in a clearly written essay.

- The Pakistani government should outlaw all languages except Urdu.
- Laws should be written to limit development and promote conservation of mangrove forests in Bangladesh.
- To ease overcrowding, families in Bangladesh should be limited to one child as are families in the People's Republic of China.
- The United States should send money and advisers to Nepal and Bhutan to help them modernize.

## Exploring Geography

1. Use resources in your school or public library to research the foundation, structure, and work of the Muslim League. Then prepare a five-minute oral presentation detailing your findings.
2. Use the *Readers' Guide to Periodical Literature* in your school or public library to find newspaper and magazine articles on recent floods in Bangladesh. Use these articles to prepare a written report detailing the damage to both people and property that the flood caused.

# UNIT 10 REVIEW

## Unit Summary

The following list contains the key concepts you have learned about South Asia.

1. South Asia covers such a large area that geographers classify it as a subcontinent. It extends out from the Asian mainland. The Himalaya reach across the northern extent, and the Indian Ocean, Arabian Sea, and Bay of Bengal form the southern edges.
2. South Asia includes India, Sri Lanka, the Maldives, Pakistan, Bangladesh, Nepal, and Bhutan.
3. Geographers divide South Asia into four distinct physical regions—the Northern Mountains, the Indo–Gangetic Plain, the Deccan Plateau, and the Coastal Plain.
4. Successful farming in the region relies on monsoon rains and rivers for water.
5. Most of the South Asian people have cultural roots in the ancient Indus River Valley civilization. Cultural traits from later invaders added to the ancient cultural base. Buddhism and Hinduism developed in South Asia, but many other religions also are found there.
6. Rapid population growth presents the region's greatest challenge.
7. A unique caste system that is an integral part of Hinduism continues in India. Though in many places the system's effects have faded, they remain strong in other places.

On a separate sheet of paper, complete the following review exercises.

## Checking Your Understanding

1. What are the main problems facing (a) India, (b) Pakistan, and (c) Bangladesh?
2. What is one way that Jainism differs from other religions?
3. Describe the population distributions in (a) India, (b) Pakistan, (c) Bangladesh, and (d) Nepal and Bhutan.
4. How are the economies of Sri Lanka and Bangladesh similar?

5. Why was it difficult for East Pakistan and West Pakistan to be governed as a united country?

## Applying Critical Thinking Skills

1. **Synthesizing Ideas** (a) How are the cottage industries of India similar to rug-making operations in Iran? What are the advantages of such industries to (b) developing countries and (c) the workers?
2. **Comparing Ideas** (a) How are the climates of the Maldives and Bhutan similar? (b) How have similar climates influenced life in these countries?
3. **Determining Cause and Effect** (a) What is India's annual growth rate? (b) Is that rate considered high, moderate, or low by world standards? (c) Why does India continue to have a population problem?
4. **Analyzing Ideas** (a) What is the basic idea behind Gandhi's doctrine of passive resistance? (b) How is that somewhat contrary to the Hindu principle of dharma?
5. **Contrasting Ideas** (a) How do water problems in Pakistan and Bangladesh differ? (b) How is this difference reflected in each country's economic patterns?
6. **Relating Past to Present** (a) What are the main political problems facing South Asia today? (b) Using the region's past as your guide, what steps would you take to settle these problems?

## Reviewing Unit Features

1. **Geography in the Workplace** Why is the work of biogeographers particularly important to the people of South Asia?
2. **City Focus** (a) Why can New Delhi and Delhi be considered one city? (b) How does New Delhi differ from Delhi and many other Indian cities?
3. **City Focus** How did the creation of East Pakistan affect Calcutta?

4. **The Geographic Web** Which of the plants mentioned in the feature on page 598 do you think holds the most promise for increasing the food supply in South Asia? Why?

## Using Map Skills

1. Study the map entitled "Monsoon Lands" on page 574. **(a)** Why is rainfall on the Western Ghats so heavy in July? **(b)** Why is rainfall significantly less on the Eastern Ghats than it is on the Western Ghats?
2. Examine the economic activity map on page 608 and the physical/political map on page 572. **(a)** In what countries is tea grown? **(b)** What do you notice about the locations of the tea-growing areas of South Asia?

## Investigating Geography

1. Select one of the religions of South Asia—Hinduism, Islam, Buddhism, Jainism, or Sikhism—for study. Prepare a written or oral report that answers the following questions. **(a)** How and by whom was it founded? **(b)** What are its basic beliefs? **(c)** How many people in South Asia belong to the religion you studied? **(d)** How has it influenced social, political, and economic patterns in the region?
2. Prepare a report on Indian life styles. Study the dress, food, religion, customs, and traditions of the people. Present pictures and drawings, recipes, and other forms of information to accompany your report. Besides various encyclopedias, *Through Indian Eyes*, Vol. 1 and 2, by Donald and Jean Johnson, *I Shall Not Hear the Nightingale* by Khushwant Singh, and *India Yesterday and Today* by Clark Moore and David Eldredge are excellent sources.
3. Investigate Gandhi's use of passive resistance in India's movement for independence. Then, in a written essay compare his use of passive resistance to that used by famous Americans to achieve their political goals.

## Further Readings

### Chapter 29

Hodgson, Bryan. "Mirror of India: New Delhi." *National Geographic.* 167, April 1985. Provides a view of India's capital through pictures and text.

Johnson, Donald, and Jean Johnson. *Through Indian Eyes*, Vol. 1, *The Wheel of Life.* Rev. ed. Center for International Training and Education. Describes childhood, education, and other aspects of Indian life through the writings of India's people.

### Chapter 30

Caldwell, John C. *Let's Visit Sri Lanka.* Rev. ed. London: Burke Publishing Company Limited. Discusses the history, geography, religions, and culture of Sri Lanka.

Edwards, Mike. "'Paradise on Earth.' When the Moguls Ruled India." *National Geographic.* 167, April 1985. Provides a pictorial and historical view of the Moguls (Mughals) in India as well as their modern day descendants. Also investigates the impact of the Islamic religion on India.

Johnson, Donald, and Jean Johnson. *Through Indian Eyes.* Vol. 2, *Forging a New Nation.* Rev. ed. Center for International Training and Education. Examines contemporary Indian issues through selections from historical documents, memoirs, and fiction.

### Chapter 31

Lang, Robert. *The Land and People of Pakistan.* Rev. ed. Philadelphia: J. B. Lippincott Company. Reviews the history, religion, cities, and political processes of Pakistan from the occupation by the British to the turmoil surrounding the independence of Pakistan and other recent events.

Tames, Richard. *India and Pakistan in the Twentieth Century.* London: Batsford Academic and Educational. Traces India's history, including the partition of India into India and Pakistan. Also describes the modern problems facing each country.

# UNIT 11

# EAST ASIA

# China, Mongolia, and Taiwan

# PUTTING THE CHAPTER IN FOCUS

For centuries China remained a nation apart, far removed from the changes that swept the rest of the world. Isolated by oceans, towering mountains, and windswept deserts, China developed a unique civilization. No other nation in the world has been settled for so long and by so many people sharing the same values and culture.

Mongolia and Taiwan, distinct nations located near the People's Republic of China, have at times been overshadowed by their giant neighbor. Both nations have distinctive cultures, life styles, and political and economic patterns.

## Ideas to Understand

In studying about China, Mongolia, and Taiwan, use these ideas to give direction to your reading.

1 China's physical setting reflects great contrasts.
2 The People's Republic of China is the world's most populous country.
3 China's Four Modernizations help the country industrialize.
4 Today Mongolia and Taiwan are independent countries.

## Terms to Define

The following terms are some of the key terms in the chapter. Defining them will help you understand China, Mongolia, and Taiwan.

| | |
|---|---|
| loess | mandarin |
| arable land | commune |
| abdicate | contract responsibility |
| autonomous | system |
| region | physiological density |

## Places to Locate

Locating the following places will add to your knowledge of geography.

| | |
|---|---|
| North China | Chang Jiang |
| Gobi | Taiwan |
| Huang He | Mongolia |
| South China | Taipei |

## 1 China's physical setting reflects great contrasts.

Home to one out of every five persons, the People's Republic of China ranks as a giant among the world's nations. This country covers more land area than any other nation except the Soviet Union and Canada. From snowcapped mountains to coastal rice paddies, the People's Republic of China stands as a nation of contrasts.

Different histories divide modern China into two major parts. In the east is a densely populated cultural core called China Proper. To the north and west stretches a sparsely populated borderland called Outer China. Geographers often divide these two parts into six regions. Climate and the Qin (CHIN) Ling Shan divide China Proper into North China and South China. (*Shan* means "mountain range" in Chinese.) Four other regions located in Outer China include the Northeast, Inner Mongolia, Xinjiang Uygur (SHIN·jee·AHNG wee·GUHR), and Tibet (see the map on page 622).

### North China

North China, the heartland of Chinese culture, lies north of the Qin Ling Shan. Chinese culture and civilization developed there almost 7,000 years ago.

◀ *The Shanghai oil field in China*

The Loess Uplands occupy the western portion of North China. The uplands get their name from **loess,** a fine-grained soil carried by strong winds from the Gobi (GOH·bee)—the huge desolate desert to the northwest. Over the centuries the loess settled on the uplands. The yellow-colored loess is fertile, easy to farm, and holds moisture well. For these reasons, Chinese agriculture began in this part of North China about 5000 B.C. Fertile loess silt carried from the west and deposited by one of China's great rivers, the Huang He (HWAHNG HUH), covers the other major part of North China—the gently sloping North China Plain. This plain contains the world's largest expanse of **arable land,** or land suitable for cultivation.

Most of North China has a monsoonal version of a semiarid climate. In winter the monsoon winds bring blinding dust storms, parching droughts, and bitterly cold temperatures from central Asia. In summer the winds, blocked by the Qin Ling Shan, bring sparse and unpredictable rains from the sea. The Shandong Peninsula, which points like a finger toward Korea, has a monsoonal version of a humid continental with hot

*__Learning from Maps.__* *High and rugged mountains form most of China's western border. How might these mountains have both helped and hindered China's development?*

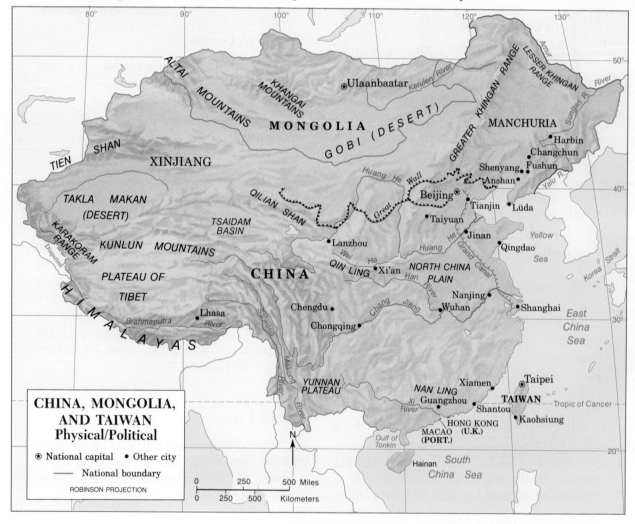

CHINA, MONGOLIA, AND TAIWAN
Physical/Political

⊛ National capital    • Other city

—— National boundary

ROBINSON PROJECTION

0   250   500 Miles

0   250   500 Kilometers

summer climate. The peninsula receives more annual precipitation than the rest of North China.

North China's principal resources include rich soils along with sufficient water for agriculture. Wheat and millet rank as the staple crops. In addition, immense coal and oil deposits aid industrialization. Beijing (BAY·jing), the capital of the People's Republic of China, is North China's largest city and one of the world's largest cities.

## South China

South China, which lies south of the Qin Ling Shan, is more mountainous, greener, wetter, and milder than dry and dusty North China. The best farmlands and highest population densities lie along the Chang Jiang (CHAHNG jee·AHNG) and Xi (SHEE) river valleys. (*Jiang* means "river" in Chinese.)

South China's climate is a monsoon version of a humid subtropical climate. Hot and rainy summers contrast with dry and mild winters. The island of Hainan (HY·NAHN) (see the map on page 622) has a tropical wet climate with average monthly temperatures above 80°F (26°C).

South China's large population and arable land serve as its leading resources. Farmers grow rice in flooded paddy fields as the main summer crop. Wheat, barley, and rice grown with irrigation lead the winter crops. Other agricultural products include tea and silk.

Shanghai (shang·HY), on the Chang Jiang Delta, ranks as one of the world's largest cities and China's leading textile center. Other large cities in the Chang Jiang Valley include Nanjing, Wuhu, Wuhan, and Chongqing (CHOONG·CHING). Guangzhou (KWANG·JOH), also known as Canton (KAN·tahn), is the largest city on the Xi River.

Close neighbors of South China and traditionally linked to the region are the British colony of Hong Kong and the Portu-

**Learning from Pictures.** *Lush valleys line many of China's great rivers. What generalization can you state about China's river patterns and population patterns?*

guese colony of Macao (muh·KOW). These colonies occupy former Chinese lands that were leased to Europeans. Macao is now largely self-governing. Both Hong Kong and Macao will revert to Chinese control in the late 1990s.

## Northeast China

The Northeast was known as Manchuria until the 1950s. The Manchurian Plain, drained by the Songhua (SOONG·HWA) River, forms Northeast China's farming region. The entire region has a cool summer, humid continental climate.

A major agricultural and industrial region, the Northeast produces wheat, barley, and soybeans. Rich coal, oil, and iron ore resources support industrialization. Shenyang (SHUHN·YANG), once called Mukden, ranks as the Northeast's largest city.

## Inner Mongolia

Inner Mongolia, a dry and sparsely settled plateau, has a climate that ranges from semiarid to arid. The region occupies traditional Mongol grazing lands north of China's Great Wall, which was originally built

*Text continues on page 625.*

# CITY FOCUS
## Shanghai, People's Republic of China

*Busy Shanghai harbor*

Urban geographers often argue about which city is the world's largest city. A city determines its population by counting the number of people who live within its political boundaries. The argument about which is largest arises because cities of the world define their city limits differently.

Some population statistics include only the city proper, while others include surrounding metropolitan areas. No matter how a city defines its limits, however, Shanghai is certainly one of the world's largest cities. With 12 million residents, it ranks first among cities that do not count the residents of surrounding areas. It ranks fifth among all cities, including those that do include people living in adjacent towns and the surrounding countryside.

### East Meets West

Shanghai is truly an international city that reflects both European and Chinese imprints. The pattern of streets and the architecture look more like those of a European than a Chinese city. The life of the city, however, is distinctly Chinese.

The design of Shanghai developed in the 1800s when people from Britain, France, the United States, and many other foreign nations settled there. They made the city one of the world's most important banking and trading centers.

With their great wealth the foreigners built magnificent two-story stuccoed houses, Western-style churches, and art deco office complexes along the waterfront. They also laid out broad, sycamore-shaded streets. All of these landscape alterations converted Shanghai, which had earlier been nothing more than a small Chinese port community, into a Western-looking metropolis. It became the wealthiest city in Asia and its "made in Shanghai" label established for the city the title of "the Paris of the East."

In 1949 the Westerners fled for their lives as the Communists marched into the city. Since that time Shanghai has belonged exclusively to the Chinese.

### Shanghai Today

The pressures that 12 million people create for a city are beyond imagination. During rush hour 3.5 million bicycles and 200,000 motorbikes jockey for position with thousands of buses, taxis, and trucks as pedestrians fill the sidewalks.

Buying and selling remain the way of life in Shanghai. Shops and carts laden with merchandise line the city's streets. Shanghai's people, too, reflect the energy of a city filled with optimism for the future.

Visual evidence of the currently more relaxed and open policies of the People's Republic of China can be seen everywhere in Shanghai. New hotels and office buildings seem to open daily, standing as glistening giants of steel and glass among the older buildings that have for so long given Shanghai its Western appearance.

in the 200s B.C. to keep the nomadic Mongolian herders out of China Proper.

Today Chinese farmers outnumber Mongolians in Inner Mongolia, and farming proves more important than herding. Fields of newly developed strains of wheat and millet cover the better-watered areas in the south. Herding continues mostly on dry lands in the north.

Coal mining and farming make up Inner Mongolia's major economic activities. Baotou (BAOO·TOH) is the region's principal city and industrial center.

## Xinjiang Uygur

Xinjiang Uygur—a region of semiarid steppes, desert basins, and snowcapped mountains—lies in northwest China. The Tien Shan divides Xinjiang Uygur into two parts—the Takla Makan Desert to the south and the semiarid steppe called Dzungaria (dzuhng·GAR·ee·uhj) to the north.

Xinjiang Uygur has long, dry, bitterly cold winters. Summers are hot and dry. Nomadic herding is the principal occupation. Some farming also takes place at the foot of the mountains where snow-fed streams provide water for irrigation.

## Tibet

High mountains isolate Tibet, or Xizang as the Chinese call it, from the rest of China. The Plateau of Tibet is the principal landform. With an average elevation of 12,000 feet (4,000 meters), the plateau has earned Tibet the nickname "Roof of the World." Peaks rise to more than 20,000 feet (6,100 meters) in the surrounding Himalaya, The Pamirs, and Kunlun Shan.

Tibet's isolation allowed the people to develop a culture distinct from that of China. Tibetans have their own language and until a Chinese invasion in 1959 had their own national government headed by a Buddhist religious leader known as the

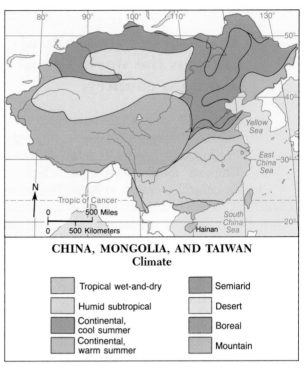

**CHINA, MONGOLIA, AND TAIWAN**
Climate

- Tropical wet-and-dry
- Humid subtropical
- Continental, cool summer
- Continental, warm summer
- Semiarid
- Desert
- Boreal
- Mountain

*Learning from Maps.* *Large countries such as China often have several climate types. How might having different types of climates cause different cultural traits?*

Dalai Lama. Conferences between the Dalai Lama and world leaders and riots in Tibet in 1987 reaffirmed Tibetan desires for their independence.

Tibet's climate is cold and dry. Most Tibetans work as farmers in sheltered valleys. Lhasa serves as Tibet's principal city.

### SECTION 1 REVIEW

1. **Define** loess, arable land
2. **Locate** North China, Gobi, Huang He, South China, Chang Jiang, The Himalaya
3. **Summarizing Ideas** What are the six main regions of China?
4. **Identifying Ideas** Where is the heartland of Chinese culture?
5. **Analyzing Ideas** What physical features allowed Tibet to develop a culture distinct from that of China?

**625**

## 2 The People's Republic of China is the world's most populous country.

Traditionally the Chinese have called their nation Zhong Guo (ZONG GOH)—the Middle Kingdom. The name expresses two key Chinese ideas. One idea refers to China's central location in Asia. The other is the Chinese belief that China is the nation in the middle of all happenings. Both of these ideas give us insight into the nature of Chinese culture.

### A Brief History

Unlike many other nations, China developed with limited outside influence. Isolation helped the Chinese people create and preserve a unique culture.

*Learning from Pictures.* *The Great Wall of China, which extends more than 1,500 miles (2,413 kilometers), was visible from the space shuttle. What was the wall's purpose?*

Until the early 1900s **dynasties**—successions of rulers from the same family—ruled China. Under these dynasties the Chinese developed a distinctive language, several philosophies and religions, advanced medical and technical knowledge, and many beautiful artforms that reflected the Chinese appreciation of nature.

Thousands of years of dynastic rule ended in 1911 when Sun Yat-sen (SOON·YAHT·SEN) led a revolt against the Qing (CHING) dynasty. When the Qing emperor **abdicated,** or gave up the throne, Sun helped set up the Republic of China.

After World War I Chinese Communists, who formed their own party in 1921, challenged Sun Yat-sen's Nationalist government. Chiang Kai-shek (CHANG KY·SHEK), Sun's successor, and Mao Zedong (MOW DZUH·DOONG), the Communist leader, vied for power. In 1949 the Communists defeated the Nationalists and created the People's Republic of China. Chiang Kai-shek and other Nationalist leaders fled to Taiwan, an island off China's coast. There they set up the Republic of China, which they claimed was the true government of China.

### Population Patterns

Many different ethnic groups live in the People's Republic of China today. Some have adopted aspects of Chinese culture. Others retain their traditional cultures and life styles.

**Ethnic groups.** The Han, who get their name from the Han Dynasty that ruled China from 206 B.C. to A.D. 220, form the country's largest ethnic group. They make up more than 90 percent of China's huge population.

The Chinese refer to the country's 55 other ethnic groups as minority nationalities. The minorities make up less than 10 percent of the total population but consti-

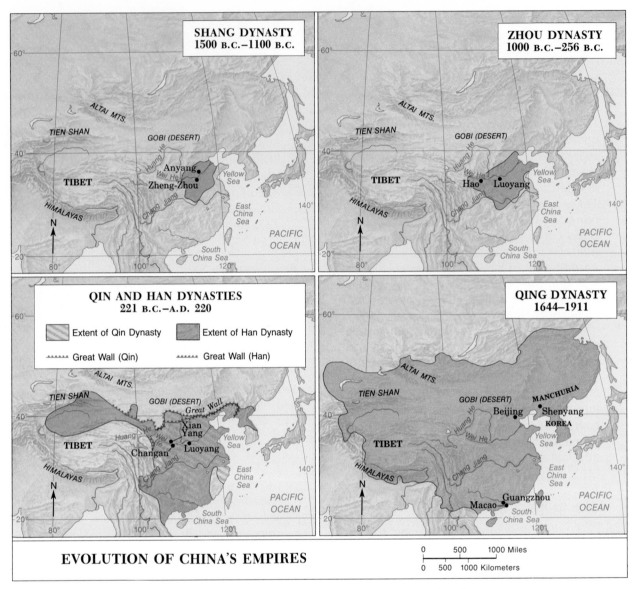

EVOLUTION OF CHINA'S EMPIRES

**SHANG DYNASTY**
**1500 B.C.–1100 B.C.**

**ZHOU DYNASTY**
**1000 B.C.–256 B.C.**

**QIN AND HAN DYNASTIES**
**221 B.C.–A.D. 220**

Extent of Qin Dynasty    Extent of Han Dynasty

Great Wall (Qin)    Great Wall (Han)

**QING DYNASTY**
**1644–1911**

*Learning from Maps.* Although China had many powerful dynasties, the five shown here were among the most important. When did dynastic rule end?

tute majorities in many border areas. Five **autonomous regions,** political units set up by the government, allow the minorities limited self-government.

**Population pressures.** The population of the People's Republic of China, much of which is concentrated in China Proper, doubled from just over 500 million in 1950 to over 1 billion today. This increase—500 million people—equals more than the entire population of Europe and is double the population of the United States.

China's large population strains the nation's resources and is a major source of concern for the government. To slow population growth, the government encourages people to marry late and to have only one child. Men are forbidden to marry until they are 22 years old; women until they are 20. Couples who agree to have only one child receive monthly bonuses and the best

Geographers divide areas into regions so they can study the land and people more closely. To a geographer, regions are areas of any size on the earth's surface that are defined by unifying characteristics. These characteristics may be physical. The generally level land of the central United States, for example, forms the Plains region. Or the characteristics may be cultural. Large farms of similar crops in several states in the United States Middle West form the Corn Belt, a cultural as well as a physical region.

Dividing a large area into regions helps geographers to study the landscapes and people on the earth. Geographers focus their study of a region on the physical processes that formed and are forming it, the human activity taking place within it, and how it has changed or is changing. The information they gather provides clues to the physical and human history of the earth.

## How to Identify Regions

To identify geographic regions, follow these guidelines.

1. **Determine criteria.** Decide whether you are planning to study the physical or cultural characteristics of an area.
2. **Gather information.** Find out what you can about a variety of physical or cultural aspects of an area. Physical aspects might include landforms, climate, and vegetation. Cultural aspects might include history and social patterns.
3. **Identify similarities.** Note the areas that can be grouped according to the similarities. Also note where one region ends and the next region begins.

## Applying the Skill

Read the following excerpt. In it the author explains that cultural features such as history determine some regions. Physical features such as climate variations and the presence of the Qin Ling Shan characterize other regions. Using the same criteria, geographers can divide an area of any size—a subcontinent, a country, or a city—into regions according to similar characteristics.

> Different histories divide modern China into two major parts. In the east is a densely populated cultural core called China Proper. To the north and west stretches a sparsely populated borderland called Outer China.... Climate and the Qin Ling Shan divide China Proper into North China and South China.

*To practice this skill, see Practicing Geography Skills on page 639.*

---

jobs and houses. Couples who have more than one child are fined, have their paychecks reduced, and receive few benefits.

## Social Patterns

The Chinese people were creating a unique culture more than 3,000 years before Columbus sailed to the Americas. The Chinese language, scientific investigation, the accumulation of knowledge, and Confucianism represent aspects of this culture.

**The Chinese language.** The Chinese language has hundreds of distinct dialects. In general, people who speak one dialect can-

not understand people who speak another dialect. In addition, the minority groups of China have their own languages. Seeing the need to establish an official language so that the different groups in China could communicate, in 1955 the government declared the Chinese dialect spoken in Beijing as China's official language. This dialect is often called Mandarin Chinese because it was the language that **mandarins,** or Chinese officials, used under the emperors.

**The impact of Confucius.** Throughout the centuries many philosophies have influenced the Chinese view of life. China's most influential philosopher and teacher was Gongfuzi (GONG·FOO·ZEE), or Master Gong, whose Westernized name is Confucius.

Confucius, who lived from 551 to 479 B.C., taught that a society in which people lived together in peace was the natural way of life. To preserve this way of life, people must have "right action," or proper behavior, and perform specific obligations and duties. Confucius also taught that differences among people are basically the result of differences in the environment and in educational training.

Confucius's teachings influenced Chinese education, government, laws, literature, religion, and morality. Confucianism also spread to Japan, Korea, and Southeast Asia.

Later philosophies such as Daoism, from a word meaning "the Way," and Legalism differ from Confucianism. These and other philosophies had varying impacts on Chinese life. The teachings of Confucius, however, dominated philosophy in China until the coming of communism.

## Political Patterns

Except for the island of Hainan, which lies a few miles south of the mainland, the People's Republic of China is a compact nation (see the map on page 622). Its government is a totalitarian dictatorship that controls all aspects of the people's lives. For administrative purposes, the government has divided the country into 21 provinces, 5 autonomous regions, and 3 municipalities. The 3 municipalities include Beijing, Shanghai, and Tianjin.

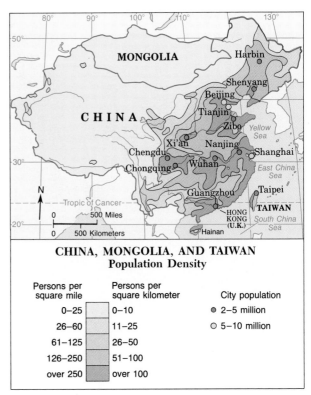

**CHINA, MONGOLIA, AND TAIWAN**
**Population Density**

| Persons per square mile | Persons per square kilometer | City population |
|---|---|---|
| 0–25 | 0–10 | ● 2–5 million |
| 26–60 | 11–25 | ○ 5–10 million |
| 61–125 | 26–50 | |
| 126–250 | 51–100 | |
| over 250 | over 100 | |

***Learning from Maps.*** *Most of China's population of over 1 billion people live in the eastern half of the country. Why is western China so sparsely settled?*

## Economic Patterns

Despite Chinese factories that make steel, automobiles, space satellites, and nuclear weapons, the country is far from being one of the world's developed nations. Agricultural workers account for more than 75 percent of the labor force (see the CASE STUDY on page 631), while fewer than 11 percent work in industry. In addition, under China's authoritarian socialist, or Communist, economic system, the government

**629**

**Learning from Pictures.** *Workers harvest sugar-cane near Kweilin in southern China. Why is it difficult to get many of the farmers in developing nations to modernize?*

owns almost all of the means of production and distribution and controls the entire economy. Although the government has relaxed some of this control in the 1980s, such centralized decision making has often hampered economic growth.

### SECTION 2 REVIEW

1. **Define** dynasty, abdicate, autonomous region, mandarin
2. **Locate** Taiwan
3. **Comparing Ideas** How was the cultural development of China different from the cultural development of most other countries?
4. **Interpreting Ideas** How has Confucius influenced Chinese life?
5. **Analyzing Ideas** Why does the Chinese government discourage population growth?

# 3 China's Four Modernizations help the country industrialize.

In 1978 China's government began a development program called the "Four Modernizations." It was designed to make China a world superpower by upgrading four areas of the economy—agriculture, industry, science and technology, and military defense. While there is little information on defense modernization programs, information about the other three modernizations indicates great advances.

## Agriculture

After the Communist takeover, the government organized Chinese farmland into **communes,** or large collective farms for which officials made all economic decisions. Because communal farming never reached desired output levels, the government adopted a system known as the **contract responsibility system.** Under this system the government leases land to each family, which decides what to plant. Farmers have a production contract with the government and are paid according to their output. After farmers satisfy the terms of their contract, they may sell the surplus to the government for a high price or at one of the 60,000 "free markets" not controlled by the government. These free markets now offer everything from dried sausages to blue jeans to pots and pans. The chance to sell surpluses provides an incentive to grow more food. The plan has helped increase farm production throughout China.

The new freedom to profit from hard work also encourages farm families to earn extra money by making goods at home for sale. Such families are called "specialized households" in China. The Chens of Pingnan, for example, are a specialized household that manufactures a popular brand of

*Text continues on page 632.*

# CASE STUDY
## GEOGRAPHY AND PEOPLE: Chinese Farmers

Few aspects of Chinese life have changed so dramatically as farming. Before the Communist revolution of 1949 most Chinese farmers were debt-laden tenants who did not own the land they worked. Wealthy landlords owned the land and received a large portion of the crops as rent.

Mao Zedong's great appeal to the impoverished Chinese farmers was his promise that the Communist revolution would sweep out the landlords and redistribute the land to the tenant farmers. Millions of peasants believed that they would be free to farm their own fields. For this reason, they supported the successful Communist revolution.

*Fertilizing a rice paddy in Yunnan Province*

### Collectivization of Agriculture

Mao's actions, however, soon proved otherwise. The government, not individual farmers, took control of the land. Farmers would work together to produce the kinds and amounts of crops that the government determined.

In 1958 the government started farm communes. Commune leaders controlled life in the villages. They supervised farm production. Communal kitchens and dining rooms fed everyone. Some communes even broke up families. Husbands were forced to live in separate dormitories from their wives and children. No farmer in a commune could earn more money than any other.

Traditionally China's population was too large for the farmers to support. The record shows that production did increase for a time under the commune system. But production barely kept ahead of population growth. Mao's philosophy of "let everyone eat from the same rice pot" offered little incentive to most farmers. For the ambitious Chinese farmer, life and work on the commune took the pleasure of working the land away.

### A Little Free Enterprise

Recent changes are slowly allowing the traditional Chinese farmer, the master at getting every ounce of production out of the land, to emerge again.

By 1980 some 3,000 communes had been abolished. Workers willing to sign production contracts received land to farm. The government allowed cooperatives to raise and sell whatever crops they contracted to produce. Everything produced above the quota belonged to the producer. Farmers also were permitted to raise ducks or fish for the market. Such free enterprise freed many farmers from a subsistence-level existence.

This change does not mean that life in rural areas has suddenly become easy. Good land remains scarce, individual plots are small, and the water supply is uncertain. Farmers living in remote areas have difficulty transporting their crops to market, and many farmers still till the fields by hand with heavy hoes. Few, however, are discouraged because they know that the opportunities for a better life are possible under the new system.

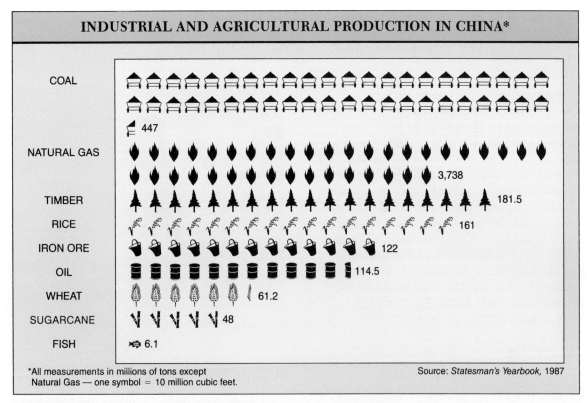

**INDUSTRIAL AND AGRICULTURAL PRODUCTION IN CHINA\***

COAL

NATURAL GAS 447

3,738

TIMBER 181.5

RICE 161

IRON ORE 122

OIL 114.5

WHEAT 61.2

SUGARCANE 48

FISH 6.1

*All measurements in millions of tons except
Natural Gas — one symbol = 10 million cubic feet.

Source: *Statesman's Yearbook, 1987*

***Learning from Graphs.*** *The People's Republic of China ranks among the world's leaders in the production of many goods. Why is China classified as a developing nation?*

shoes. Most of the men in the family make shoes while the women take care of the one-acre (half-hectare) farm.

## Industry

Today in China the government controls all industry, including light manufacturing, heavy manufacturing, metal refining and production, and petroleum refining. The main light industries produce cement, chemicals, textiles, and tires and rubber. Much of the light industry is located in the countryside, often near sources of raw materials. Most fertilizer plants, for example, are located in farming regions. Heavy industries, which are usually located in the major cities, produce agricultural machinery, aircraft, engineering tools, and ships.

China's metal industries produce iron, steel, and lead. Many of the smelting and iron and steel plants developed in northeastern China near large iron and coal deposits. Oil fields lie scattered throughout northern and south-central China. Pipelines carry the petroleum to refineries in nearby cities.

The Four Modernizations program calls for less direct government control of industry than in the past. Local managers can use pay raises, bonuses, and other incentives to encourage hard work. Factories also win cash rewards for increasing industrial output and efficiency.

## Science and Technology

The People's Republic of China lags far behind other industrial nations in science

and technology. In order to catch up, the government is buying computers, aircraft, and mining and agricultural equipment from other countries. It also hopes to buy entire oil refineries, nuclear power stations, and other technically advanced factories from foreign businesses and governments.

After many years of hostility the People's Republic of China again welcomes foreigners to invest in Chinese industries. Japanese experts have drawn up plans for 120 large factories they expect to open in China by 1990. Many American technicians and researchers have helped modernize the country's mining and metal industries. The People's Republic of China also has set up free trade zones where foreign companies receive tax incentives to build factories and to invest.

The People's Republic of China now presents a large, untested market for world products. At the same time, the Chinese government needs the foreign money that joint ventures bring to the nation. Chinese

***Learning from Maps.*** *Less than 30 percent of the land produces food to support China's huge population. Why does the Grand Canal appear on an economic map?*

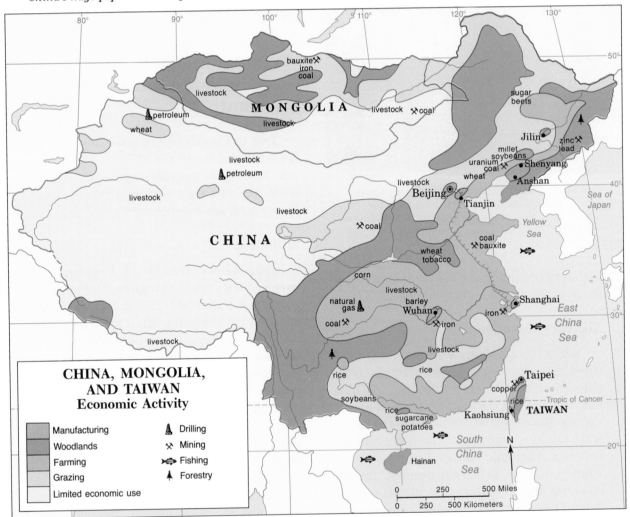

633

***Learning from Pictures.*** *China, which may have launched the world's first rockets in the 1300s, now has several satellites in orbit. How do such satellites help China modernize?*

planners predict that China will be a major force in world trade by the year 2000.

## Military Defense

While most military information is classified as secret, some information is available. First, the People's Republic of China has the world's largest army. Recent advances have helped to provide the army with modern equipment. In addition, the People's Republic of China has tested atomic devices. The government insists, however, that its efforts are aimed only at defending the country's long borders.

### SECTION 3 REVIEW

1. **Define**   commune, contract responsibility system
2. **Summarizing Ideas**   What areas of the Chinese economy are the Four Modernizations designed to improve?
3. **Identifying Ideas**   **(a)** How has the contract responsibility system helped increase farm production?   **(b)** What is a "specialized household"?
4. **Interpreting Ideas**   How does the Four Modernizations program reward increased industrial output?
5. **Analyzing Ideas**   Why do planners predict that China will be a major force in world trade by the year 2000?

## 4 Today Mongolia and Taiwan are independent countries.

Two of China's neighbors—Mongolia to the north and the island of Taiwan less than 120 miles (190 kilometers) to the east—were part of China earlier in this century. Today both are independent countries.

### Mongolia

Geographers usually distinguish between China's physical region of Inner Mongolia (see pages 623–25) and Outer Mongolia. Outer Mongolia, often known simply as Mongolia, gained its independence from China in 1911, but fighting between the two countries continued for several years. Support by the Soviet Union helped Mongolia maintain its independence. Mongolia adopted a Communist economic system in 1921. A land of distinctive physical characteristics, Mongolia, officially known as the Mongolian People's Republic, lies along the northern edge of the Gobi between China and the Soviet Union.

**Learning from Pictures.** *Huge ergs form the Singing Mountains of the Gobi Desert between Inner and Outer Mongolia. What other desert is covered by huge ergs?*

**Learning from Pictures.** *Mongolian nomads, who are among the world's best riders, live in yurts made of animal hides. Why is the nomadic life style ideal for Mongolia?*

**A harsh environment.** Mongolia is a land of dry, cold winds and little rain. The Gobi occupies the southern part of Mongolia. The wet summer monsoons lose their moisture crossing the mountains rimming the desert. Lands covered by the sparse grass typical of the steppes stretch north of the Gobi.

Mongolia's continental climate features extreme temperatures. Temperatures in the winter may reach −57°F (−49°C). The summers are very hot and dry. Because of the harsh natural setting, agriculture is almost impossible except at the oases. In fact, food products, along with machinery and manufactured goods, stand as Mongolia's major imports.

**The Mongolian people.** The disadvantages for human settlement in Mongolia seem to outweigh the advantages; but Mongolians have modified the land and exploit its few natural gifts. Although some of Mongolia's 2 million people live in cities such as the capital of Ulaanbaatar (oo·lahn·BAH·tuhr) and the industrial city of Darhan

(DAHR·kahn), more than half the people live in rural areas. The major occupation of the people in the countryside is herding. In fact, Mongolia has more livestock per capita than any other nation. Along with minerals, meat and other animal products such as hides and leather make up the majority of the exports.

Large herds and little vegetation make nomadic herding a way of life. Sheep and goats survive on short grass and provide wool, hides, and hair for clothing and tents, and dairy products and meat for food. Under Mongolia's totalitarian dictatorship, most herders belong to government cooperatives. They move with the flocks part of the year and work at assigned jobs for the other part.

Nomads also rely on another type of animal for their existence—the pack animal. Mongolians use different kinds of pack animals depending on the topography. They use oxen and yak in rocky or mountainous areas. They use camels in the dry, sandy areas where the animals' large, padded feet keep them from sinking in the sand.

**635**

The Mongols of Inner and Outer Mongolia have fascinated scholars for many decades. Anthropologists study the traditional social organization of the Mongols. Historians study the history of these people, and political scientists research their political organization. Linguists study the Mongolian language, a language that is written in a unique form of the Cyrillic alphabet.

Another type of scholar—the cultural geographer—attempts to learn about the society and environment of people like the original Mongols. Cultural geographers study the land on which the Mongols lived, how they changed it, and how they utilized their resources in order to survive. By studying the history and culture of the Mongols, cultural geographers learn how the Mongols lived day to day and how they were able to obtain food, clothing, and other necessities in a harsh environment. They also study the diffusion patterns of the Mongol people and culture.

Cultural geographers have found in talking with Mongolians who continue to follow traditional life styles that the Mongolians' ancestors were nomadic herders who traveled with their animals from place to place. For protection from the harsh weather, these herders lived in tents called yurts. When the herders moved they simply collapsed the yurts and carried them to their new camp. Studying the traditional life style of the Mongols adds to a cultural geographer's understanding of the geographic themes of relationships within places and movement.

Long ago the Mongols faced and solved some of the same types of problems that modern society faces today. Cultural geographers study people such as the Mongols to find insights into how modern society can solve the same kinds of problems. If you enjoy studying about the life styles and cultural traditions of societies, cultural geography offers a fascinating career.

Mongolian customs reveal the importance of animals. Mongolians divide animals into two groups: warm-nosed and cold-nosed. They view warm-nosed horses and sheep as friends. They view cold-nosed cattle, goats, and camels as strangers. At meals Mongolians serve lamb to make a good impression on friends. Beef, however, would never be served to a friend.

## Taiwan

Taiwan became a part of China in the 1600s. Japan seized the island in 1895 and held it until 1945. In 1949, after the Communist party came to power on the Chinese mainland, 2 million refugees fled to Taiwan.

Taiwan remained under the control of China's Nationalist party headed by Chiang Kai-shek, who refused to accept defeat. The Nationalists set up a government-in-exile in Taipei (TY·PAY) and vowed to someday regain control of all of China.

**A small, crowded island.** Taiwan is a volcanic island covered with steep mountains. The mountains rise like a series of steps along the east coast of the island to more than 12,000 feet (4,000 meters) above sea level. From this rugged backbone the land slopes gently westward to a coastal plain. More than 80 percent of the island's 19.6 million people live on the coastal plain. Because much of Taiwan remains unsuited

for farming, the **physiological density,** or the number of people per square mile or square kilometer of arable land, ranks as one of the highest in the world.

Taiwan has a subtropical climate and receives heavy precipitation. Until the 1940s Taiwan produced most of the world's oolong tea and natural camphor. Today farmers grow rice, sugarcane, and yams. Rice remains the staple crop, and most areas produce two rice crops a year. Successful land reform included the redistribution of land to tenant farmers. Incentives, seed improvement, increased irrigation, special fertilizers, and new double-crop rotations have raised output. They have allowed Taiwanese farmers to more than double farm production, increase exports, and raise the standard of living. In recent years they have begun to use machinery to further increase yields.

**Taiwan's booming economy.** By the late 1970s industrial products accounted for two-thirds of Taiwan's gross national product, and the average annual per-person income was more than $1,300. Such economic strength was gained despite a lack of natural resources such as iron ore. Taiwan's industries, like those of Japan, must rely on imported raw materials. For example, Taiwan's leading industries—textiles and metals—use imported cotton, bauxite, and other minerals.

Today Taiwan is far more industrialized than the People's Republic of China. More than 33 percent of Taiwan's labor force work in manufacturing, compared with only 11 percent on the mainland. Only 19 percent of all Taiwanese workers earn a living as farmers, compared with more than 75 percent on the mainland. International trade on the tiny island roughly equals that of all mainland China. Taiwanese exports include steel, ships, chemicals, television and electronic equipment, clothing, and shoes.

**Learning from Pictures.** *Taiwan has developed industries such as iron and steel manufacturing. How has the success of Taiwan's farmers affected industrialization?*

**An uncertain future.** Taiwan's position in the world became more difficult with the recognition of the People's Republic of China in the 1970s. The People's Republic replaced Taiwan in the United Nations and the United States closed its embassy in Taiwan in 1979. Despite these changes, the United States still supports Taiwan with technical, financial, and military aid.

**SECTION 4 REVIEW**

1. **Define** physiological density
2. **Locate** Mongolia, Taipei
3. **Identifying Ideas** How does Mongolia's environment affect farming?
4. **Interpreting Ideas** (a) In what ways are animals important to Mongolians economically? (b) How is the importance of animals reflected socially in Mongolia?
5. **Contrasting Ideas** How are the labor forces of Taiwan different from those of mainland China?

637

# CHAPTER 32 REVIEW

## Chapter Summary

The following list contains the key concepts you have learned about China, Mongolia, and Taiwan.

1. The People's Republic of China is the world's third largest nation in land area. The land has a variety of landforms and climates, abundant mineral deposits, and ample water resources.
2. China is divided into six regions: North China, South China, the Northeast, Inner Mongolia, Xinjiang Uygur, and Tibet. Each of these regions has its own unique landscape and life style.
3. China has one of the world's longest continuous histories. Over time the country developed a distinct culture.
4. The Four Modernizations program aims to improve Chinese agriculture, industry, science and technology, and defense.
5. China's large population of more than 1 billion strains the country's resources. The government discourages population growth by penalizing couples who have more than one child.
6. Mongolia lies on China's northern border. It is a dry, harsh land of shepherds and farmers.
7. Mongolia has retained much of its traditional life style as the world around it has changed. Today most of its people still tend animals in a Communist economy.
8. Taiwan became the center of the anti-Communist activity in Asia after the Communist takeover of the Chinese mainland.
9. Taiwan has built a strong economy based on manufacturing and world trade. International trade on the island today roughly equals that of mainland China.
10. Taiwan's position in the world has become difficult, even though it has the support of the United States. Mainland China has replaced Taiwan in the United Nations.
11. Shanghai, one of the world's largest cities, is a truly international city.

On a separate sheet of paper, complete the following review exercises.

## Reviewing Geographic Terms

Match each of the following terms with the correct definition below.

a. physiological density
b. loess
c. arable land
d. contract responsibility system
e. commune
f. autonomous region
g. mandarin
h. dynasty
i. abdicate

_____ 1. Yellowish, fertile, fine-grained material that blows from the Gobi and settles over the uplands of China
_____ 2. Land suitable for cultivation
_____ 3. A succession of rulers from the same family
_____ 4. To give up the throne
_____ 5. Chinese official under the emperors
_____ 6. Political division set up by the Chinese government to provide minorities limited self-government
_____ 7. Large collective farm for which officials make all the decisions
_____ 8. System that leases government land to each family, which decides what to plant
_____ 9. Statistic indicating the number of people supported by a square mile or a square kilometer of arable land

## Developing Critical Thinking Skills

1. **Summarizing Ideas**   What are the principal resources of (a) North China, (b) South China, (c) Northeast China, and (d) Inner Mongolia?
2. **Investigating Ideas**   (a) Although the climate of Inner Mongolia ranges from semiarid to arid, farming is an important economic activity. How is this possible?   (b) Where does farming take place in Xinjiang Uygur, which has a similar climate?

3. **Interpreting Ideas** (a) What ideas are the Chinese expressing when they call their country the Middle Kingdom? (b) Why was China able to develop and preserve a unique culture?
4. **Comparing Ideas** (a) In what ways are Mongolia and Tibet similar? (b) How are they different?
5. **Analyzing Ideas** (a) Why is Taiwan's future position in the world uncertain? (b) What is the United States' position toward Taiwan?
6. **Writing About Geography** In a full-page essay, complete one of the following activities. (a) Explain the reason for the creation of the Republic of China and why the leaders of the Nationalist party continue to call Taiwan the seat of the true government of China. (b) Explain your opinion concerning the laws in China that deal with people's decisions to marry and have children.

## Using Primary Sources

In the following excerpt from *This Is Our China*, Madame Chiang Kai-shek writes about the strength of the Chinese people and their passive resistance to such things as revolution and change. As you study the reading, consider whether the People's Republic of China is a nation incapable of modern change.

Revolution is no easy thing to introduce, or easy to carry through, in a land like China. Hidebound with conservatism, suspicious of all things, superstitious, mostly illiterate, and void of all conception of the responsibilities of citizenship and public service, a huge population like that of China possesses, by virtue of its very ignorance, tremendous powers of passive resistance. This can impede, and delay, and frustrate reforms that . . . could easily be introduced because of their apparent practical value . . . logic . . . and their obvious necessity. . . . The launching of any major scheme of improvement, to say nothing of any potentially sweeping social reform, has consequently been equivalent to entering upon an endurance test, out of which come triumphant the ones having the greatest supply of patience, persistence, and philosophy, and, at times, physical strength.

1. What factors does Madame Chiang believe impede revolution in China?
2. What traits does the author say a reformer needs to possess to bring about change in China?

## Practicing Geography Skills

*Before completing this activity, review Developing Geography Skills on page 628.*

**Identifying Regions** Select one of the following regions. Research the region and identify the characteristics that define it as a region.

- New England
- Northeastern States
- Southeastern States
- Great Lakes States
- Plains States
- Southwestern States
- Pacific States
- French Canada
- The Guianas
- The Low Countries
- Alpine Europe
- The Middle East
- West Africa
- South Asia

## Exploring Geography

1. Construct a table showing the six regions of the People's Republic of China. Your table should include each region's location, landforms, major rivers, natural resources, economic activities, and important cities.
2. Reread the CITY FOCUS on Shanghai on page 624. Then use resources in your school or public library to write a similar essay on one of the other major cities of the People's Republic of China. Possible choices include: Beijing, Nanjing, Wuhu, Wuhan, Chongqing, Guangzhou, Shenyang, and Baotou.

# PUTTING THE CHAPTER IN FOCUS

Japan and the two Koreas—North and South—lie at the eastern edge of Asia. The three nations share similar physical and cultural traits. All three are mountainous and are closely linked to the sea. All three have imported many of their cultural traditions from China. Today, however, each nation has a distinct and unique way of life.

## Ideas to Understand

In studying about Japan and the two Koreas, use these ideas to give direction to your reading.

1 Japan is a beautiful land with few natural resources.
2 Japanese culture blends traditional and modern ways of life.
3 Two nations with a common past occupy the Korean Peninsula today.

## Terms to Define

The following terms are some of the key terms in the chapter. Defining them will help you understand Japan and the two Koreas.

| | |
|---|---|
| typhoon | shogun |
| tsunami | samurai |
| aquaculture | balance of trade |

## Places to Locate

Locating the following places will add to your knowledge of geography.

| | |
|---|---|
| Hokkaido | Korean Peninsula |
| Honshu | 38th parallel |
| Kyushu | July 27, 1953, truce |
| Shikoku | line |
| Ryukyu Islands | Seoul |
| Mount Fuji | Pusan |

## 1 Japan is a beautiful land with few natural resources.

Perched on the eastern edge of East Asia, the island archipelago of Japan arcs through the Pacific Ocean from 21° 30′ N to 45° 10′ N and 123° W to 146° W. This location provides both the links and the isolation that have been so important throughout Japan's history.

### Physical Setting

Japan occupies a land of spectacular physical beauty. A rugged coastline fringes the islands. Steep, forested mountains, snowcapped volcanic peaks, and a patchwork of green terraced fields combine to give Japan a varied and beautiful landscape.

◀ *Traditional and modern styles in Tokyo*

Four main islands—Hokkaido (hah·KYD·oh), Honshu (HAHN·shoo), Kyushu (kee·OO·shoo), and Shikoku (shi·KOH·koo)—and nearly 4,000 smaller ones including the Ryukyu (ree·YOO·kyoo) Islands make up Japan. The four main islands account for more than 98 percent of Japan's land area, which is slightly smaller than that of the state of California.

Lowlands occur as small plains near rivers and bays on the coast of southern Honshu and around the Inland Sea. This densely populated southern region forms Japan's historic cultural core and is today its chief urban-industrial region. Major cities in the area include, from east to west, Tokyo, Yokohama (yoh·kuh·HAHM·uh), Osaka (oh·SAHK·uh), Nagoya (nuh·GOY·uh), Kobe (KOH·bee), Hiroshima (hir·uh·SHEE·muh), and Nagasaki (nahg·uh·SAHK·ee).

## Natural Hazards

The tops of a submerged mountain chain located along the "Ring of Fire" (see page 72) form the Japanese islands. This ring lies along an active plate boundary where earthquakes and volcanic eruptions are still forming mountains. Hurricanes, called **typhoons** in the Pacific Ocean, also threaten the islands.

More than 1,500 earthquakes shake Japan each year. Although most of the earthquakes are minor tremors that cause little damage, others cause loss of life and destruction. The great 1923 earthquake killed more than 200,000 people and destroyed much of Tokyo and Yokohama.

Undersea earthquakes often cause **tsunamis** (suh·NAHM·eez), or giant ocean waves, that sweep onshore with great force. In the past tsunamis struck without warning and washed away entire fishing fleets and villages. Today Japanese scientists constantly monitor earthquakes likely to cause tsunamis and warn people in threatened coastal areas to move to higher ground.

Japan has 196 volcanoes, nearly 10 percent of the world's total. The most famous is Mount Fujiyama, more commonly known as Mount Fuji (FOO·jee), which rises to 12,388 feet (3,780 meters) on the island of Honshu. Mount Fuji is now inactive but more than 30 other volcanoes in Japan remain active. In recent years, however, volcanoes have not caused significant destruction in Japan.

## Climate

Japan's climates resemble the climates found in similar latitudes—31° N to 45° N—in the eastern United States. Continental influences dominate the climates of both areas (see page 94). In Japan, however, surrounding seas and ocean currents and the seasonal reversal of Asia's monsoon winds modify the climates.

In summer monsoon winds blow mainly from the south and east across open water, bringing abundant rain to the southern and eastern coasts. In winter the monsoon winds blow from central Asia in the north and west. Although dry, they pick up some moisture as they cross the Sea of Japan (see the map on this page) and are not as dry as winds in the rest of East Asia.

Hokkaido and northern Honshu have a humid continental climate similar to that of New England. Winds blowing onshore across the cold Oyashio (oy·AHSH·ee·oh) Current (see the map on page 130) keep summers cool. Cold and snowy conditions prevail during the winters. Annual precipitation in this region varies from 20 to 40 inches (50 to 100 centimeters).

**Learning from Maps.** *Japan is actually a collection of islands off the continental coast of Asia. How has this location influenced Japanese history?*

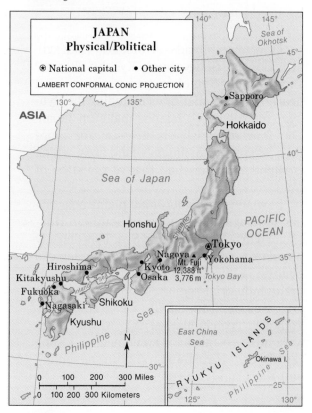

Southern Honshu, Kyushu, and Shikoku have a humid subtropical climate somewhat like that of the state of Georgia. The Japan Current (see the map on page 130) warms southeastern Japan as far north as Tokyo. Up to 80 inches (200 centimeters) of rain falls in places. The heavy rains support dense forests and swift streams suitable for hydroelectricity in the mountains and, together with a long growing season, high farm yields in the lowlands.

## Resources

Farmers cultivate less than 20 percent of all land in Japan. It is a tribute to the skills of Japanese farmers and the Japanese fishing fleet that they are able to supply over 75 percent of Japan's food needs.

**Agriculture.** Japanese farmers have worked hard to make the best use of their lands. Terraced fields painstakingly cut into the sides of hills cover the countryside. These terraced fields, carved over centuries, add a strong human imprint to the Japanese landscape.

Most Japanese farmers own their farms, which average a little over 2 acres (1 hectare). Most farmers use modern machinery and fertilizers developed for their special needs. Intensive farming and modern methods help Japanese farmers produce per-acre yields that rank among the world's highest.

Farmers throughout Japan plant two rice crops each year. In the south farmers also grow tea and soybeans, while northern farmers raise wheat, potatoes, and vegetables. In addition, farmers cultivate mulberry trees that provide food for silkworms. The silkworms produce the delicate thread from which silk is made.

**Forestry.** Forests cover more than two-thirds of Japan. The government, however,

***Learning from Pictures.*** *Terraces on hillsides make level farmland for growing rice out of slopes throughout Japan. Why is Japan's physiological density high?*

limits lumbering in order to conserve this valuable resource. As a result, Japan buys lumber from other nations.

**Fishing.** Just as they have with farming, the Japanese have applied modern techniques to large-scale fishing. Japanese fishers sail the world ocean on modern ships equipped with the latest scientific gear. Their catch accounts for more than 20 percent of the world's total annual catch.

Japan leads the world in **aquaculture,** the cultivation of fish and water plants for human consumption. The Japanese raise freshwater fish in ponds and flooded paddies, grow seaweed in ponds and aquariums, and harvest shellfish in shallow bays. They also are experimenting with algae and krill, tiny marine animals that constitute the main food for many whales, as sources of food.

**Mining.** Although Japan produces some coal, most is low-grade, soft coal that burns with a blue flame that is not hot enough for most industrial uses. For industrial purposes, the Japanese mix their own coal with coal imported from the United States or Australia. Japanese mines also yield lead, zinc, sulfur, and limestone, but not in the amounts needed for industry. As a result, Japan must import many of these minerals and other raw materials.

---

**SECTION 1 REVIEW**

1. **Define** typhoon, tsunami, aquaculture
2. **Locate** Hokkaido, Honshu, Kyushu, Shikoku, Ryukyu Islands, Mount Fuji
3. **Summarizing Ideas** **(a)** What is the "Ring of Fire"? **(b)** What natural hazards affect Japan?
4. **Organizing Ideas** What climatic influences modify Japan's climates?
5. **Analyzing Ideas** How are Japanese farmers and fishers able to supply over 75 percent of Japan's food needs?

---

## 2 Japanese culture blends traditional and modern ways of life.

Japan is one of the most rapidly changing nations in the world, but its culture rests upon traditions that reach far back in time. These traditions have created distinctive cultural patterns.

### A Brief History

Although China influenced early Japanese history, Japan's geographic isolation and closed society helped it move away from Chinese influences beginning about A.D. 800. For more than 750 years a succession of powerful Japanese military leaders called **shoguns** ruled the country in the name of the emperor. During this time the **samurai,** Japanese warriors known for their loyalty and bravery, enforced the will of the ruling shogun.

In the mid-1500s the first European traders and missionaries arrived in Japan. As contact with foreigners grew, however, Japanese leaders began to fear the loss of Japan's unique culture. They drove out most of the European traders and missionaries in 1639.

Japan remained isolated until 1853. In that year Commodore Matthew C. Perry, commanding a squadron of United States warships, entered Edo (present-day Tokyo) Bay and began trade with Japan. As trade with the United States and other nations increased, Japan began to industrialize.

As industrialization progressed so did Japan's need to acquire raw materials and desire to expand. By 1941 Japan controlled most of eastern China and Indochina (present-day Laos, Cambodia, and Vietnam) and sought to expand throughout the Pacific Ocean. Its attack on United States forces in Hawaii led to an escalation of World War II. By 1945, however, the United States and its allies had defeated the Japanese, and Japan was in ruins.

### Population Patterns

Japan has one of the world's most homogeneous populations. Because of Japan's isolation, the island country absorbed very few minority groups during its history. Instead most Japanese trace their roots to Mongol settlers who came to the islands from Asia thousands of years ago. This common ethnic and cultural heritage unites the Japanese people and gives them a strong national identity.

About 90 percent of Japan's 122 million people crowd onto small patches of level

*Text continues on page 646.*

# CASE STUDY
## GEOGRAPHY AND PEOPLE: The Ainu

The Mongol ancestors of most Japanese people arrived in Japan more than 2,000 years ago. These settlers found the islands inhabited by a people quite unlike the other people of eastern and northeastern Asia. They found a people who called themselves "Ainu" (EYE·noo), which means simply "man."

### A Different People

The physical traits of the descendants of the Ainu set them apart from the rest of the Japanese population. The Ainu have large bones, long arms, and large heads and are shorter than the Japanese. Ainu men average about 5 feet 2 inches (1.6 meters) in height; Ainu women average 4 inches (.1 meter) shorter than the men. The physical traits most often used to separate the Ainu from the rest of the Japanese population are eye shape and color, skin color, and amount of body hair. An Ainu's eyes are shaped differently from the eyes of other Japanese and are brown or hazel rather than black. The Ainu have light brown skin. Ainu men, unlike other Japanese men, have heavy beards. All three of these physical features are quite unusual among people of Asian descent.

Little is known about the Ainu's origins. Their language holds no clue, for it shows no relationship to any other known language. No form of Ainu writing exists. The Ainu use a numbering system based on 20 rather than 10. The system only goes up to the number 800. The Ainu measure distance in steps, quantities in handfuls, and have no terms for weight or area.

### The Ainu Today

About 15,000 Ainu live in rural villages on Hokkaido. Only a few of these Ainu follow the ways of their ancestors. Those who do live in small fishing villages. They make

*Ainu man in traditional clothes on Hokkaido*

their clothing by hand from animal skins or plant material. The men grow long beards and hair in the traditional Ainu way. Games, sports, and amusements continue to be rare among the Ainu.

For centuries other Japanese have discriminated against the Ainu. The Ainu were not permitted to go to school, join the army, or vote. In recent years, however, the Ainu have banded together to demand better treatment. Many Japanese with Ainu ancestors have called for government help for the Ainu. In response the government has set up special programs to help the Ainu improve their living standards while maintaining their unique way of life.

land near the coasts of the four major islands. Nearly 80 percent of the Japanese population lives on Honshu. Honshu also holds all of the largest Japanese cities—Tokyo, Yokohama, Nagoya, Kobe, Kyoto, and Osaka.

Japan's large population and its small land area make it one of the world's most densely populated nations. In fact, Japan's physiological density of 5,800 people for every square mile (2,239 per square kilometer) of cultivated land ranks as one of the highest in the world.

*Learning from Pictures.* *Japan exports a variety of goods, such as Suzuki motorcycles. How did limited resources influence Japan's development as a trading nation?*

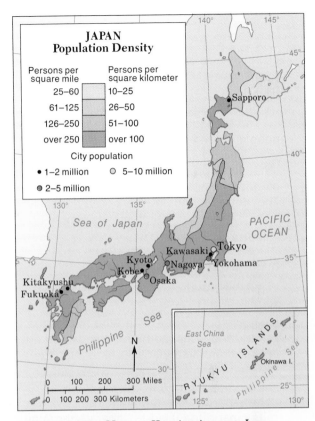

*Learning from Maps.* *Housing in some Japanese cities is so hard to find that people rent boxes large enough to sleep in. What accounts for Japan's sparsely settled areas?*

As elsewhere, more and more Japanese people are moving to cities in search of better job opportunities. Today more than 76 percent of the people live in urban areas, compared to only 68 percent in 1965. Several rural villages have been all but abandoned in recent years. Crowded Japanese metropolitan areas now spread over the landscape. But because of Japan's economic strength, the cities have experienced fewer of the problems common in rapidly growing urban areas.

Although urban dwellers enjoy a high standard of living, Japanese cities, like Western cities, face many problems. Urban leaders must deal with problems such as air and water pollution, housing shortages, and traffic jams. Officials are formulating strict pollution laws aimed at improving air

and water quality. Carefully planned urban growth and closely monitored waiting lists ease housing shortages. Widespread and efficient public transportation systems reduce traffic jams.

Japanese and Western cities reflect differences as well as similarities. The Japanese show a respect for law that often amazes Westerners and has helped make Japan's crime rate among the world's lowest. Its cities also have fewer slum areas. Every Japanese city has its poorer sections, but government services provide for the health and housing of less fortunate urban residents.

## Social Patterns

Almost everyone in Japan's homogeneous population speaks Japanese. An emphasis on education has given Japan one of the highest literacy rates and best-educated populations in the world.

Beauty and serenity have traditionally played an important role in Japan's culture. The Japanese have learned to take even the smallest piece of land, which is often all that is available, and with careful tending turn it into a garden. Bonsai, the dwarfing and shaping of trees, is a Japanese art. Japanese architects design buildings to harmonize with their natural surroundings. Carefully tended parks and gardens dot Japanese cities, and Japanese artists focus on the subtle beauty of nature.

Much of this serenity and devotion to beauty and nature comes from the Japanese view of life. This view of life is deeply rooted in Shintoism, an ancient nature religion. Many Japanese practice both Shintoism and Buddhism.

Since World War II Western styles and ideas have become part of the Japanese culture. Baseball and golf, not ancient sumo wrestling or even the martial arts, top the list of Japan's popular sports (see THE GEO-

*Learning from Pictures.* *About 60 percent of the Japanese people follow Buddhism, which was brought to Japan from China. Why is Buddhism an example of expansion diffusion?*

GRAPHIC WEB on pages 650–51). Even clothing styles and entertainment blend Eastern and Western influences. Many Japanese wear Western-style clothing outside the home. On holidays, at festivals, and at home, however, many people wear traditional kimonos (kuh·MOH·nuhz) and flat sandals. Western movies and rock music are popular, but people of all ages also flock to festivals to see Kabuki (kuh·BOO·kee)—ancient Japanese theater.

## Political Patterns

Japan is a fragmented nation with a constitutional monarchy and several political parties. Until the end of World War II the emperor, considered to be a direct link between the people and the gods, held absolute power. Today, however, the Diet, or legislature, makes laws and chooses a prime minister to direct government policy. The emperor's role as head of state is largely ceremonial, much as it is in Britain and other Western European countries.

*Text continues on page 649.*

**647**

# CITY FOCUS
## Tokyo, Japan

*Tokyo's famous Ginza district*

Nearly 8.5 million people now live in Tokyo's 223 square miles (578 square kilometers). This gives Tokyo a population density that, at 38,000 people per square mile (14,700 people per square kilometer), is nearly twice as high as the population density of New York City. Four other cities—Shanghai, Mexico City, Beijing, and Seoul—have more inhabitants than Tokyo, but none is more densely populated.

### Tokyo's Many Aspects

Tokyo reflects great diversity. In some ways it is very modern and cosmopolitan. Tall buildings, freeways jammed with traffic, and streets aglow with neon signs resemble their counterparts in many of the world's other great cities. So, too, do the crowded baseball stadiums, golf courses, and movie theaters.

In other ways, however, Tokyo retains many Japanese traditions. Though most people wear street clothes that would not be out of place in any modern city, on almost every corner there is likely to be a man or woman dressed in traditional Japanese clothes. Intermingled with modern restaurants that serve everything from hamburgers to the finest European dishes are shops selling local delicacies. Down many twisting alleys are ancient Japanese shrines. And if it is festival time, people dressed in styles of long ago may be carrying a shrine through the streets on their shoulders to allow the deity who lives in the shrine a yearly inspection of the neighborhood it protects.

### A Tokyo Address

Getting around in Tokyo can be difficult. Because only a few of the most important streets have names, few street signs exist. The numbering system for buildings is very confusing because buildings are not numbered up and down the street as in many Western cities. Instead the buildings are renumbered every time a new one is built.

Fortunately the excellent Tokyo subway system helps visitors untangle the confusing layout. Seven subway lines crisscross the city, carrying more than 3 million passengers a day. All subway stations have names and instructions in both Japanese and English. Each station also features an up-to-date map that shows the streets and the building numbers of the surrounding neighborhood.

### Hub of the Nation

Although much of Tokyo was leveled during a violent earthquake in 1923 and again in the bombing raids of World War II, the city has been rebuilt. Today, with earthquake-resistant skyscrapers, Tokyo remains the center of Japanese government, business, and industry. One of every four Japanese corporations has its headquarters in Tokyo and one of every six factories is located in the city or in a nearby community. Tokyo has become the focus of a vibrant nation and one of the world's great cities.

## Economic Patterns

Japan's economic growth stands as one of the wonders of recent history. Since 1945 Japan's capitalistic economic system has helped the nation rise from the ashes of defeat to become a major economic power with the world's third-largest gross national product.

The Japanese people themselves can take the credit for their nation's economic recovery from the devastation caused by World War II. Accepting responsibility and working hard are essential to being Japanese. Japanese workers show extreme loyalty to their employers. People often work for the same company all of their lives. They take great pride in the company or factory in which they are employed, the job

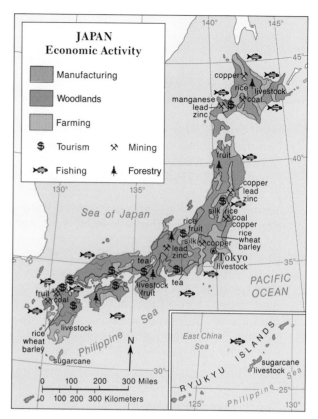

**Learning from Maps.** *As you can see from the map, Japan has a very diversified economy with strong agricultural and industrial sectors. What city on Hokkaido do many tourists visit?*

**Learning from Graphs.** *In recent years Japan's trade with North America has decreased slightly. What accounts for the large percentage of imports from the Middle East?*

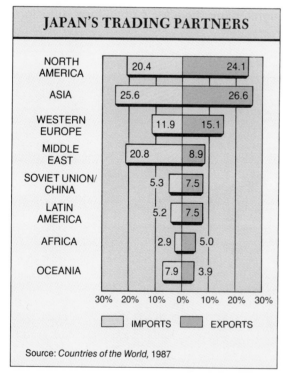

JAPAN'S TRADING PARTNERS

| | IMPORTS | EXPORTS |
|---|---|---|
| NORTH AMERICA | 20.4 | 24.1 |
| ASIA | 25.6 | 26.6 |
| WESTERN EUROPE | 11.9 | 15.1 |
| MIDDLE EAST | 20.8 | 8.9 |
| SOVIET UNION/ CHINA | 5.3 | 7.5 |
| LATIN AMERICA | 5.2 | 7.5 |
| AFRICA | 2.9 | 5.0 |
| OCEANIA | 7.9 | 3.9 |

Source: *Countries of the World,* 1987

that they perform, and the product or service they provide. In fact, several generations of a family often work for the same company. Japanese employers encourage such loyalty by providing special benefits for loyal employees, such as paid vacations at company-owned resorts.

Even though Japan must import most raw materials, it ranks as a leading exporter of manufactured goods. In fact, Japan's most important economic activity is manufacturing. Manufacturing employs one-fourth of all Japanese workers and earns 40 percent of Japan's gross national product.

The transportation equipment industry ranks first among Japan's industries. Japan produces about half of the world's new ships and its automobile and motorcycle industries rank among the world's largest.

*Text continues on page 652.*

# THE GEOGRAPHIC WEB
## Games of the World

Alfonso X, king of Castile on the Iberian Peninsula, compiled the first encyclopedia of games in 1283. In his introduction Alfonso stated, "God has intended [people] to enjoy themselves with many games" to "bring them comfort and dispel their boredom." Cultural geographers study such activities to discover the interactions of the physical environment and culture.

In studying games, sports, and recreation, geographers have made surprising discoveries. Among the most interesting findings are that these activities reflect important cultural values and traditions and that many activities have diffused around the world.

### The Impact of Setting

The way a civilization amuses itself explains much about its setting. The physical setting has a major influence on the development of games and sports. Darts, for example, was first played by hunters in the forests of northern Europe. Because of the dense woods, hunters could not hunt with bows and arrows effectively. Instead hunters carried short, heavy, throwing arrows. At the end of the day the hunters amused themselves and sharpened their skills by throwing the arrows at a target.

From a different setting, the frozen tundra of the north, comes *ajaqaq* (ah·JAK·ak). This game, easily played both indoors and outdoors, is played with a sharp piece of animal sinew attached to a whale bone or musk ox horn. The player must stick the sinew into a small hole in the bone by flipping the bone in the air and impaling it. The game provided entertainment and helped Eskimo hunters sharpen their hand-eye coordination. Variations of this game have been found among the Chinese and the Kwakiutl (kwah·kee·OOH·tl) Indians of the northwest coast of the United States, highlighting the effects of cultural diffusion.

*Baseball, from the United States to Japan*

*Ancient Aztec ball court in Mexico*

The natural surroundings also provide the raw materials for many games and sports. The Dogon children of Mali in West Africa use the sand and pebbles of their native land for their favorite game—*sey.* Using sleight of hand, players take turns hiding a pebble, or *tibi,* in the sand. The other children must guess where it is hidden. Several other West African games such as *dosu* and *godo* involve hiding objects in the sand, a material that is abundant in that area of the world.

## The Impact of Culture

Games and sports also mirror civilization. In the East African nation of Uganda, the game of *lawala* highlights the importance of a hunter's accuracy with a spear. The object of *lawala* is to throw a spear through a rolling hoop. A point is scored each time a spear passes through the hoop without touching it. The first team to reach the predetermined number of points wins.

There are few nations in the world where space is so important a consideration as in Japan. Many of the recreational pursuits in Japan reflect both this limitation and the traditions of Japanese culture. Many Japanese participate in *aikido, judo,* and *karate*—traditional martial arts that involve fighting without weapons. Such activities require little space and involve aspects of culture that play an important role in Japanese life.

Baseball and soccer are modern examples of cultural diffusion. Baseball developed in the United States and is now played in Japan, Taiwan, and throughout the Americas. Boys and girls of all ages play baseball and softball, both in organized programs and informal "pickup" games. Soccer is the most widely played game in the world. Today many youth leagues, high schools, and colleges have soccer teams.

Games and sports are an important part of every culture. They use the elements of the environment and reflect the relationships between humans and their natural surroundings. Cultural geographers who study games and sports focus on the settings of the regions where the games are played, the parallels among the activities, and the life styles of the people who developed them.

*Soccer, an example of worldwide diffusion*

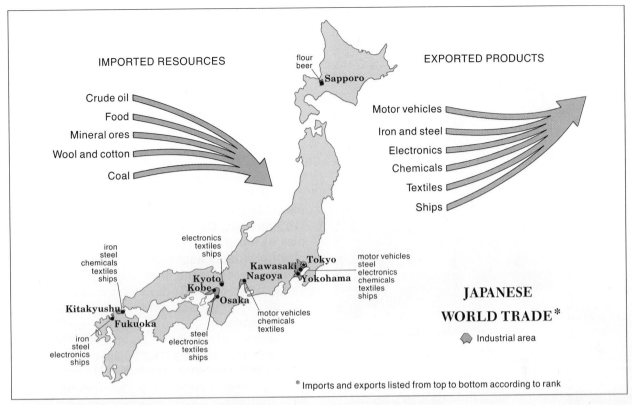

IMPORTED RESOURCES

flour
beer
Sapporo

Crude oil
Food
Mineral ores
Wool and cotton
Coal

EXPORTED PRODUCTS

Motor vehicles
Iron and steel
Electronics
Chemicals
Textiles
Ships

iron
steel
chemicals
textiles
ships

electronics
textiles
ships

Tokyo
Kawasaki
Nagoya
Yokohama

motor vehicles
steel
electronics
chemicals
textiles
ships

Kyoto
Kobe
Osaka

Kitakyushu
Fukuoka

iron
steel
electronics
ships

steel
electronics
textiles
ships

motor vehicles
chemicals
textiles

JAPANESE
WORLD TRADE*

⬡ Industrial area

* Imports and exports listed from top to bottom according to rank

**Learning from Maps.** *Japan produces more than 7 million automobiles and 4 million trucks each year. Which cities produce most of the motor vehicles?*

In addition, Japan produces electronic equipment such as stereos, televisions, and appliances; machinery; iron and steel; sporting goods; and petrochemicals.

The value of Japan's exports and imports totals more than $300 billion annually. Since the mid-1960s the value of Japan's exports has been greater than the value of its imports, giving Japan a favorable **balance of trade.** The Japanese maintain this favorable trade balance by keeping export prices low and restricting imports. In recent years Japan has exported many more products to its chief trading partner, the United States, than it imports from it. This situation has caused friction between the two countries and has led to threats of trade wars. American leaders currently are examining ways, including negotiating treaties, to improve the United States' unfavorable balance of trade.

**SECTION 2 REVIEW**

1. **Define** shogun, samurai, balance of trade
2. **Organizing Ideas** **(a)** Why did Japanese leaders drive out European traders and missionaries in 1639? **(b)** Who was responsible for opening Japanese trade in 1853?
3. **Summarizing Ideas** What is responsible for giving the Japanese people a strong sense of national identity?
4. **Analyzing Ideas** How is Japan dealing with the urban problems of **(a)** pollution and **(b)** overcrowding?
5. **Identifying Ideas** How has the role of the emperor changed?
6. **Relating Ideas** **(a)** How does Japan maintain its favorable balance of trade? **(b)** How has this affected the balance of trade in the United States?

## 3 Two nations with a common past occupy the Korean Peninsula today.

The Korean Peninsula extends from the East Asian mainland and is bordered by the Sea of Japan on the east and the Yellow Sea on the west. Communist North Korea—officially known as the Democratic People's Republic of Korea—and capitalist South Korea—officially known as the Republic of Korea—occupy the peninsula.

### Physical Setting

Notable differences mark the physical settings of North Korea, which occupies more than half of the peninsula, and South Korea.

**Landforms.** Mountains run like a backbone down the Korean Peninsula. They rise highest and steepest in the east and drop down to a broad lowland in the west. Although the entire peninsula is mountainous, North Korea is more rugged and has fewer lowlands than South Korea.

**Climate.** North Korea has a cold, dry continental climate. The rain-bearing summer monsoon winds are relatively dry by the time they reach North Korea and bring only sparse and erratic rainfall. Winter monsoon winds from Asia bring bitterly cold and dry conditions.

South Korea has a humid subtropical climate. In summer monsoon winds bring heavy rains. The surrounding seas moderate South Korea's winters.

### Cultural Setting

For most of its history Korea was a single nation. Even today, North Koreans and South Koreans have a common history, a common ancestry, and a common language—Korean. Since World War II, however, the two countries have been divided, each developing unique cultural patterns.

**From one nation to two.** For centuries, first China and then Japan controlled the Korean Peninsula. After Japan's defeat in World War II, the United States and the Soviet Union occupied the peninsula and divided Korea along the 38th parallel for administrative purposes. The Soviet Union took control of northern Korea. The United States administered southern Korea. The division was to last only until the Korean people could hold free elections and choose their own form of government.

*Learning from Maps.* *All of Korea's major rivers drain into the Yellow Sea, forming a series of fertile valleys along that coast. Why does North Korea have a continental climate?*

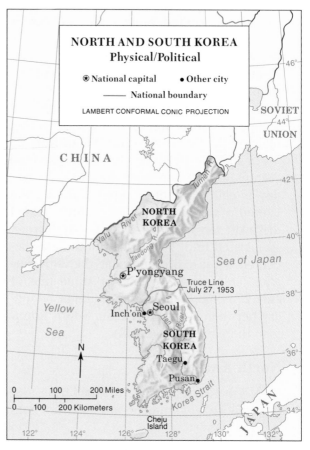

**NORTH AND SOUTH KOREA**
**Physical/Political**

⊛ National capital    • Other city

——— National boundary

LAMBERT CONFORMAL CONIC PROJECTION

SOVIET UNION

CHINA

Tumen R.

Yalu River

Taedong R.

NORTH KOREA

Sea of Japan

P'yongyang

Truce Line
July 27, 1953

Yellow Sea

Inch'on

Seoul

Han R.

SOUTH KOREA

Taegu

Pusan

Korea Strait

JAPAN

N

0    100    200 Miles
0    100    200 Kilometers

Cheju Island

122°   124°   126°   128°   130°   132°

34°   36°   38°   40°   42°   44°   46°

**653**

*Learning from Pictures. The production of iron and steel ranks as North Korea's leading industry. Why do many industrialized countries build steel industries?*

**War on the peninsula.** The Cold War between the United States and the Soviet Union kept Korea divided. In 1948 the United States allowed South Korea to hold elections and become an independent nation. North Korea declared itself a separate nation. By mid-1949 American and Soviet troops withdrew, and each new government claimed the authority to rule all of Korea.

In 1950 North Korean forces crossed the 38th parallel and invaded South Korea. Under a call from the United Nations, the United States and 16 other nations helped drive off the invaders. The bloody Korean War lasted until 1953, when both sides accepted a cease-fire line near the 38th parallel. This cease-fire line, or truce line of July 27, 1953, remains the political boundary between North Korea and South Korea (see the map on page 653).

## North Korea Today

North Korea remains a totalitarian system whose government attempts to hold complete power over the people. The government even discourages any traditional religious practices.

The partition of Korea in 1945 left North Korea with most of Korea's industrial resources but with scarce agricultural resources. Only about 18 percent of North Korea is suitable for farming. Rice and wheat are the chief crops. Although food shortages used to be common, the development of high-yield rice seeds adapted to North Korea's cool, dry conditions help North Korea meet the food needs of its 21.5 million people today.

North Korea's farmland is organized into collective farms similar to those in the Soviet Union. The government owns the land, makes the farming decisions, and sells farm products through state-owned stores. About 300 farm families live and work on each collective farm.

*Learning from Graphs. Though both Koreas are self-sufficient in producing food, North Korea has most of the other natural resources. How has South Korea built its industry?*

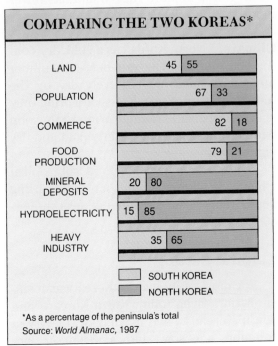

**COMPARING THE TWO KOREAS***

| | SOUTH KOREA | NORTH KOREA |
|---|---|---|
| LAND | 45 | 55 |
| POPULATION | 67 | 33 |
| COMMERCE | 82 | 18 |
| FOOD PRODUCTION | 79 | 21 |
| MINERAL DEPOSITS | 20 | 80 |
| HYDROELECTRICITY | 15 | 85 |
| HEAVY INDUSTRY | 35 | 65 |

*As a percentage of the peninsula's total
Source: *World Almanac*, 1987

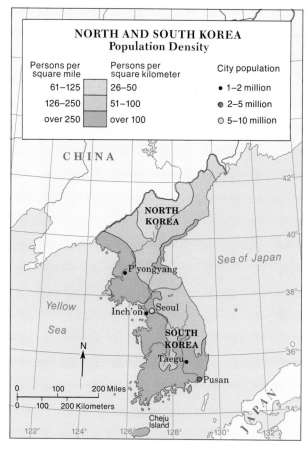

**Learning from Maps.** *People in both Koreas crowd the western coast. What physical features make the western coast more attractive for settlement than the eastern coast?*

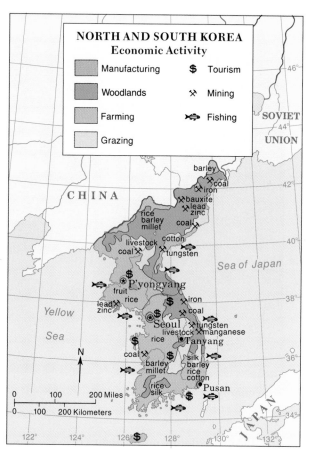

**Learning from Maps.** *South Korea's economy is more diversified than North Korea's. What mineral deposits help support North Korea's steel industry?*

North Korea's totalitarian dictatorship also owns and operates all factories. Government plans stress the development of steel, chemical, and textile industries to make North Korea's Communist economy self-reliant. Trade contributes little to the economy. The trade the nation does conduct is mostly with countries that also have Communist systems.

## South Korea Today

South Korea is a republic, although its leaders maintain tight control of the government. Recent protests have called for government reforms and new freedoms for the people. Confucianism is the dominant religion, although Christians and Buddhists form significant minorities.

South Korea has most of the peninsula's farmland but almost no industrial raw materials. Nonetheless, following the Japanese model, South Korea has built a vigorous industrial economy from imported raw materials and exports of manufactured goods.

A population of more than 42 million leaves South Korea far more densely populated than North Korea. Rapid urbanization marks all areas of the country. More than 65 percent of the people now live in urban areas. Seoul contains more than 11 million people in its ever-growing metropolitan area, making it the world's fourth-largest city. Pusan (POO·sahn) has more than

**Learning from Pictures.** *Electronic equipment now ranks as a major South Korean export. Why is trade so important to the South Korean economy?*

3 million residents and Taegu (ty·GOO) has more than 2 million.

About 33 percent of South Korea's workers farm the 23 percent of the land that is arable. Most farmers own their farms, which average less than 2 acres (1 hectare) in size. As in Japan, modern technology and intensive farming make the farms very productive. Today Korea is self-sufficient in producing food. Rice serves as the chief crop. Some farmers are able to grow two rice crops a year in the south.

Industries begun in the 1950s used South Korea's low wage rates to produce inexpensive clothing, toys, and shoes for export. Later the government encouraged the development of steel, chemicals, machinery, and other basic industries. These basic industries now produce a wide range of manufactured goods, including ships, automobiles, television sets, electronic equipment, and computers. Korea exports almost all of these products.

Like Japan, South Korea needs trade to overcome deficiencies in energy and raw materials. Exports give South Korea a favorable balance of trade in most years.

**SECTION 3 REVIEW**

1. **Locate** Korean Peninsula, 38th parallel, Seoul, Pusan
2. **Comparing Ideas** How does the population of North Korea compare to that of South Korea?
3. **Contrasting Ideas** What are the differences between North Korea and South Korea in terms of **(a)** landforms and **(b)** climate? **(c)** How do these differences affect agriculture in North and South Korea today?
4. **Identifying Ideas** Describe the major features of **(a)** North Korea's economic system and **(b)** South Korea's economic system.

# DEVELOPING GEOGRAPHY SKILLS
## STUDYING ECONOMIC GEOGRAPHY: Analyzing Trade

Countries and cultures interact in many different ways. One of the key forms of global interaction today is world trade. Most countries trade—exchange, buy, and sell—a number of goods with other countries.

Geography, economics, and politics influence world trade patterns. Countries that lack industrial resources or farmland import needed raw materials or food. Countries producing excess raw materials or finished products export them to world markets. In each case the location of the trading partner and the economy of the home country are important considerations.

*Unloading container ships in Kobe harbor*

### How to Analyze Trade

Follow these guidelines to analyze trade.

1. **Note imports and exports.** Study what a country produces and what it needs. This data will provide information about its physical setting and economy.
2. **Identify trading patterns.** Note with whom the country trades and where the trading partners are located. In this case, note both absolute and relative locations.
3. **Analyze trade interactions.** Ask yourself why such a trade pattern exists. Do these countries trade because the raw materials or products are available only from each other? Do these countries trade for geographic reasons? economic reasons? political reasons?

### Applying the Skill

Study the map titled "Japanese World Trade" on page 652. It indicates that most of Japan's imports are industrial raw materials and energy resources. From this information you can conclude that Japan has limited industrial resources. Food is Japan's second leading import, indicating Japan's farmers and fishers need help feed-

ing the population. Note on the same map that Japan exports motor vehicles, iron and steel, and electronic equipment. This data shows that Japan is heavily industrialized.

Next study the chart titled "Japan's Trading Partners" on page 649. It identifies North America, Asia, and Western Europe as the major markets for Japanese exports. Japan gets many of its imports from the Middle East, Asia, and North America.

Information on the map and chart indicates that free market economies influence Japan's trade. This influence is shown by the large volume of Japanese trade with North America and Western Europe. The trade with those nations contrasts with Japan's relatively small trade (7.5 percent) with the People's Republic of China and the Soviet Union, which are geographically closer to Japan than its major trading partners. From this you can conclude that political factors have helped determine Japan's principal trading partners.

*To practice this skill, see Practicing Geography Skills on page 659.*

# CHAPTER 33 REVIEW

## Chapter Summary

The following list contains the key concepts you have learned about Japan and the two Koreas.

1. Japan, North Korea, and South Korea lie on the eastern edge of Asia.
2. Earthquakes, volcanoes, typhoons, and tsunamis often threaten Japan.
3. Japan's climates resemble the continental climates in the eastern United States but with important monsoonal influences.
4. Japanese and Korean farmers have used modern methods of intensive farming to produce high yields on a limited amount of arable land.
5. Japanese and Korean cultures have ancient ties to China, but long ago their peoples developed distinct life styles of their own.
6. Most Japanese people live in cities that experience many of the same problems of Western cities. Today many Japanese have adopted elements of Western culture. Japanese economic and political patterns also reflect Western influences.
7. Japan's economic system has enabled it to become a leading economic power.
8. North Korea has a cold and dry continental climate. South Korea has a humid subtropical climate.
9. In 1945 the Korean Peninsula was divided into what would become two countries—North Korea and South Korea.
10. Today little contact takes place between the people of North Korea and the people of South Korea, accenting the many differences between the two countries.
11. Today North Korea attempts to become economically self-reliant while South Korea builds an economy based on imported raw materials.
12. The Ainu have a culture and life style very different from those of other Japanese.

On a separate sheet of paper, complete the following review exercises.

## Reviewing Geographic Terms

Supply the correct geographic term that completes each sentence.

1. Hurricanes in Japan are called ____.
2. Undersea earthquakes often cause ____, or giant ocean waves that sweep onshore with great force.
3. ____ is the cultivation of fish and water plants for human consumption.
4. Powerful Japanese military leaders called ____ ruled the country in the name of the emperor.
5. Japanese warriors known for their loyalty and bravery were called ____.
6. The difference in the value of a country's exports and imports is called the ____.

## Developing Critical Thinking Skills

1. **Summarizing Ideas** (a) What are the four major islands of Japan? (b) Where are the principal lowlands of Japan located?
2. **Investigating Ideas** Why do Japanese farmers cultivate mulberry trees?
3. **Interpreting Ideas** (a) How much of Japan is covered by forests? (b) Why does the Japanese government limit lumbering?
4. **Identifying Ideas** (a) What is a homogeneous population? (b) What features of the physical and cultural settings helped Japan develop a homogeneous population?
5. **Organizing Information** (a) When was Korea divided into two separate nations? (b) How did this division affect each nation's share of the peninsula's resources?
6. **Analyzing Ideas** Why does South Korea, like Japan, depend on trade?
7. **Writing About Geography** In a full-page essay, discuss one of the following ideas. (a) What is known about the Ainu's origins? Do you think their lack of writing skills and terms for weight and area are positive or negative cultural traits? (b) Do you think that the United States should limit imports from Japan? Why or why not?

## Using Primary Sources

In the following excerpt from *Modern China and Japan*, Conrad Schirokauer discusses how modern Japanese companies deal with their employees. As you study the reading, compare these techniques with the personnel policies of American companies.

For the most part, Japanese companies, especially the large modern concerns [businesses], retained the loyalty of their employees, who were made to feel that what was best for the company was also best for Japan. This business ideology gained credence from management's practice of plowing earnings back into the firm so that it could continue to grow and hopefully surpass its rivals. Since that rather than any increase in payouts to stockholders was the company's objective, management was long able to persuade workers to moderate their demands for wage increases and fringe benefits. Naturally, the threat of foreign competition was also used to good effect, and for many years Japanese companies enjoyed a lower labor bill and greater labor peace than many of their competitors in Europe and America. The threat of foreign competition helped to motivate employees to work harder at a time when the quest for increased GNP [gross national product] gave Japan a sense of national purpose. Government in many ways helped to advance that purpose.

1. According to the author, how do modern Japanese companies retain the loyalty of their workers?
2. What two advantages does the author say Japanese companies enjoyed over their European and American competitors?
3. According to the author, the threat of foreign competition helped to motivate employees to work harder. Why?

## Practicing Geography Skills

*Before completing this activity, review Developing Geography Skills on page 657.*

**Analyzing Trade**   Reread the subsections "North Korea Today" on pages 654–55 and "South Korea Today" on pages 655–56. Also study the graph titled "Comparing the Two Koreas" on page 654. Then answer the following questions.  **(a)** What nations are North Korea's main trading partners?  **(b)** Which factor—geographic, political, or economic—most strongly influences North Korea's trading patterns?  **(c)** What kind of economic system do the main trading partners of North Korea have?  **(d)** What are South Korea's major exports?  **(e)** In a brief paragraph, describe either North or South Korea's trading patterns.

## Exploring Geography

1. Use resources in your school or public library to conduct research and prepare an oral report on one or more of the innovative farming and fishing techniques employed by the Japanese.
2. Reread the CITY FOCUS on Tokyo on page 648. Then write a similar feature of approximately 250 words on one of the following Japanese cities: Sapporo, Yokohama, Kawasaki, Nagoya, Osaka, Kobe, Kyoto, Fukuoka, or Kitakyushu.
3. Look through magazines and newspapers to find advertisements for Japanese or South Korean products. Then construct a collage of all the advertisements. Note on your collage the prices of these products. Then prepare a second collage of comparable American-made products.
4. Reread Section 3 on pages 653–56. Then use the information in the section to construct a chart comparing North Korea and South Korea. Your completed chart should include the following headings: "Physical geography," "Culture," "Economy," and "Politics."

# UNIT 11 REVIEW

## Unit Summary

The following list contains the key concepts you have learned about East Asia.

1. China has a variety of landforms and climates, usable mineral deposits, and ample water resources.
2. China has one of the world's longest continuous histories, and it has produced a distinct Chinese culture.
3. The Four Modernizations program is designed to improve the People's Republic of China's defense, agriculture, industry, and science and technology.
4. The People's Republic of China has about 1 billion people and includes 55 ethnic groups.
5. Mongolians retain a traditional life style along the northern border of the People's Republic of China.
6. Taiwan became the focus of attention when the Nationalists refused to accept defeat and set up a government there to represent the Republic of China. Today international trade in Taiwan roughly equals that of mainland China.
7. Taiwan's position in the world has become difficult as it competes with mainland China for recognition. Today the People's Republic of China represents the Chinese in the United Nations.
8. Japan is a fragmented island nation with monsoonal versions of continental climates found in the eastern United States.
9. The Korean Peninsula has a humid subtropical climate in the south and a cold and dry continental climate in the north.
10. Japanese and Korean cultures have ancient ties to Chinese culture, but long ago their peoples developed distinct ways of life.
11. Modern intensive farming methods have produced high yields on the limited amounts of arable land available in Japan and the two Koreas.
12. In 1945 the Korean Peninsula was divided by the Soviet Union and the United States into two parts. Eventually the two parts became two nations—Communist North Korea and capitalist South Korea.
13. North Korea is trying to become economically self-reliant. South Korea bases its economy on imported raw materials.

On a separate sheet of paper, complete the following review exercises.

## Checking Your Understanding

1. What are the major philosophies of China?
2. Why did the Chinese government establish an official language?
3. **(a)** What type of economic system prevails in the People's Republic of China? **(b)** Who controls all the industry there? **(c)** What are the four major types of industry?
4. What are **(a)** Mongolia's and **(b)** Taiwan's leading economic activities?
5. **(a)** What minerals do Japanese mines yield? **(b)** Why does Japan import some of these same minerals?
6. What type of economic system is found in **(a)** North Korea and **(b)** South Korea?

## Applying Critical Thinking Skills

1. **Identifying Ideas** Why do Mongolians sometimes use camels instead of oxen or yaks as pack animals?
2. **Interpreting Ideas** **(a)** What will the People's Republic of China need to do in order to catch up with the technological advancement of other countries? **(b)** What steps have they taken toward this?
3. **Comparing Ideas** **(a)** How are the economic patterns of Japan and South Korea similar? **(b)** In what ways do these economic patterns differ from the economic patterns of the People's Republic of China and North Korea?
4. **Analyzing Ideas** Why are Japan's future economic prospects good?

## Reviewing Unit Features

1. **Geography in the Workplace** Why is it important for cultural geographers to study people like the Mongols?
2. **The Geographic Web** Why do cultural geographers study the games that people in different cultures play?
3. **City Focus** How does Shanghai reflect both European and Chinese influences?
4. **City Focus** Why is it easy for visitors to get lost in Tokyo?

## Using Map Skills

1. Study the map on page 627. During which dynasty did China add the most land to its territory?
2. Study the map on page 652. Which cities in Japan contribute most of the country's exports?
3. Study the map on page 655. **(a)** What are the main industrial resources of North Korea? **(b)** What are the main industrial resources of South Korea? **(c)** Which nation seems to have the stronger industrial base? Why?

## Investigating Geography

1. Investigate and report on the experiences of Marco Polo. Polo's book, *Description of the World*, includes an account of his observations and impressions of the lands along his route. Prepare a map showing the route taken by Polo (see the map on page 28), his father, and his uncle to accompany your report. Also collect samples of some of the products and ideas Polo and his group encountered for the first time.
2. Study the chart comparing North Korea and South Korea on page 654. Then write an essay based on the information contained in the chart that analyzes the geographic situations of the two Koreas. Your essay should evaluate and compare the two nations.

## Further Readings

**Chapter 32**

Allen, Thomas R. "Time Catches Up with Mongolia." *National Geographic*. Vol. 167, no. 2 (February 1985): 242–69. Presents photographs and text on modern Mongolia, Mongolia's past, and its orientation toward the Soviet Union.

Axelbank, Albert. *The China Challenge*. New York: Franklin Watts. Provides a personal journey through the People's Republic of China with visits to a commune, a village, and various factories.

Liao, Hung-ying, and Derek Bryan. *Let's Visit China*. London: Burke. Provides a regional view of China from Mongolia and the north to Tibet.

Loescher, Gil, with Ann Dull Loescher. *China: Pushing Toward the Year 2000*. Orlando: Harcourt Brace Jovanovich. Discusses the ongoing changes in the People's Republic of China as that nation attempts to modernize its society and understand its historical roots and its relationship with the West.

**Chapter 33**

*All-Japan: The Catalogue of Everything Japanese*. New York: William Morrow. Surveys hundreds of facets of Japanese life.

Cumings, Bruce. *The Two Koreas*. New York: Foreign Policy Association. Examines tensions between North and South Korea.

Dolan, Edward F., Jr., and Shan Finney. *The New Japan*. New York: Franklin Watts. Shows the mixture of East and West in Japan.

Masatsugu, Mitsuyuki. *The Modern Samurai Society: Duty and Dependence in Contemporary Japan*. New York: Amacom. Provides an overview of Japanese culture, giving extensive coverage to the historical development of the current management style of Japanese businesses.

Woronoff, Jon. *Japan's Commercial Empire*. Armonk, N.Y.: M. E. Sharpe. Illustrates similarities between Japanese and American foreign investments.

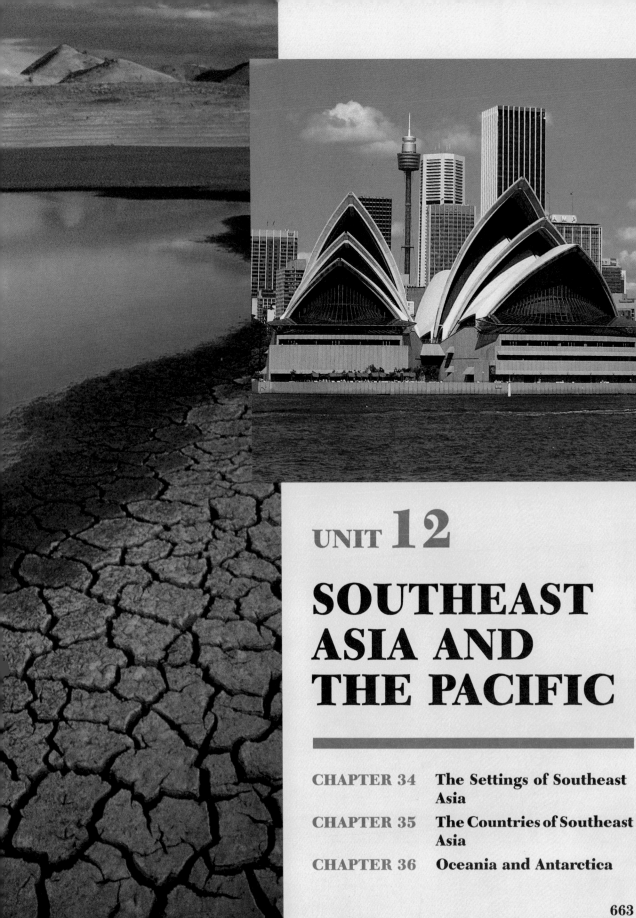

# UNIT 12

# SOUTHEAST ASIA AND THE PACIFIC

663

# The Settings of Southeast Asia

# PUTTING THE CHAPTER IN FOCUS

To the east of India and Sri Lanka stretch more than 3,000 miles (4,800 kilometers) of peninsulas, islands, and surrounding seas. Together they make up the complex and culturally diverse region known as Southeast Asia. Southeast Asia serves as one of the world's great historical and cultural crossroads. Hindu, Buddhist, and Muslim influences had already left their marks on the region by the time Europeans arrived in the 1500s. Each wave of human migrants contributed to the diverse cultural imprints that characterize Southeast Asia today.

## Ideas to Understand

In studying about the settings of Southeast Asia, use these ideas to give direction to your reading.

**1** Southeast Asia lies at the crossroads of world trade routes.

**2** Diverse traditions create a complex cultural setting in Southeast Asia.

## Terms to Define

The following terms are some of the key terms in the chapter. Defining them will help you understand the settings of Southeast Asia.

paddy            national language

## Places to Locate

Locating the following places will add to your knowledge of geography.

| | |
|---|---|
| Strait of Malacca | Borneo |
| Indochina | Java |
| Malay Peninsula | Mandalay |
| Irrawaddy River | Angkor |
| Menam River | Bali |
| Mekong River | Manila |
| Red River | Bangkok |

# 1 Southeast Asia lies at the crossroads of world trade routes.

Southeast Asia stretches like a fan from west to east toward the Pacific Ocean. There the fan breaks into chains of islands. In the distant past land bridges linked the peninsulas and islands, and prehistoric people traveled to places that are now separated by bodies of water. Accompanying these people were the many different ideas that make Southeast Asia such a complex cultural region.

## Physical Regions

Perhaps the key word in understanding Southeast Asia is *location*. Because of the region's pattern of peninsulas and island chains, almost all movements of people and goods throughout Southeast Asia pass from the Indian Ocean into the South China Sea through the narrow Strait of Malacca (muh·LAHK·uh). The strait's location between the Malay Peninsula and the island of Sumatra in Indonesia has focused attention on it for many centuries.

Geographers often divide Southeast Asia into two geographic parts. Peninsular Southeast Asia lies on the Asian mainland between India and the People's Republic of China and is often referred to as Indochina. Six of Southeast Asia's 10 countries—Burma; Thailand (TY·land); Laos (LAHWS); Cambodia, also called Kampuchea (kam·poo·CHEE·uh); Vietnam; and Malaysia (muh·LAY·zhuh)—lie in Peninsular Southeast

◀ *Rice terraces in the Philippines*

Asia. Geographers refer to the islands located off the Asian mainland as Insular Southeast Asia. Four island nations form this subregion—Singapore, Brunei (BROO·ny), Indonesia (in·doh·NEE·zhuh), and the Philippines.

Southeast Asia's peninsulas and islands offer three very different natural environments for human settlement—the mainland mountains, the alluvial river valleys, and the islands.

**Mainland mountains.** Five mountainous "fingers" project across Southeast Asia from a "hand" centered where Burma and China meet. One finger forms Burma's mountainous coast on the Bay of Bengal.

*Learning from Pictures. Several distributaries cross the Mekong Delta. Compare the picture below with the one on page 49 and state a generalization about the delta.*

The second finger forms the mountains of northern Burma. The third finger extends along eastern Burma's Shan Plateau and continues south as the mountainous backbone of the long Malay Peninsula. The fourth finger forms the mountains of northern Thailand and that country's Khorat Plateau in the east. The mountains of Laos and Vietnam stretch southward from China as the fifth finger.

**Alluvial river valleys.** Four great rivers—the Irrawaddy, the Menam (may·NAHM), the Mekong (may·KONG), and the Red River—flow southward between the knife-edged mountain ranges of Peninsular Southeast Asia. Each forms a fertile and densely populated alluvial valley that ends in a broad delta. The Irrawaddy River serves as the economic and cultural core of Burma. The Menam River, or Chao Phraya (CHAOO PRY·uh), lies at the economic and cultural heart of Thailand. The Mekong River forms the economic and cultural centers of Laos, Cambodia, and southern Vietnam. The Red River flows across northern Vietnam.

**Islands.** Islands of many different sizes, often forming long archipelagoes, dot Southeast Asia. Three different nations—Malaysia, Brunei, and Indonesia—share the region's largest island, Borneo. Many of the other islands are quite small. Except for Singapore, which remains an independent nation, all the other islands make up part of the countries of Indonesia or the Philippines (see the map on page 667).

Each of the islands in Insular Southeast Asia features a central mountainous core and an alluvial coastal plain of varying widths. Volcanic activity in some of the mountainous cores serves as a constant reminder that part of the area falls on the Pacific Rim in the Ring of Fire, a geographic region that encircles the Pacific Ocean.

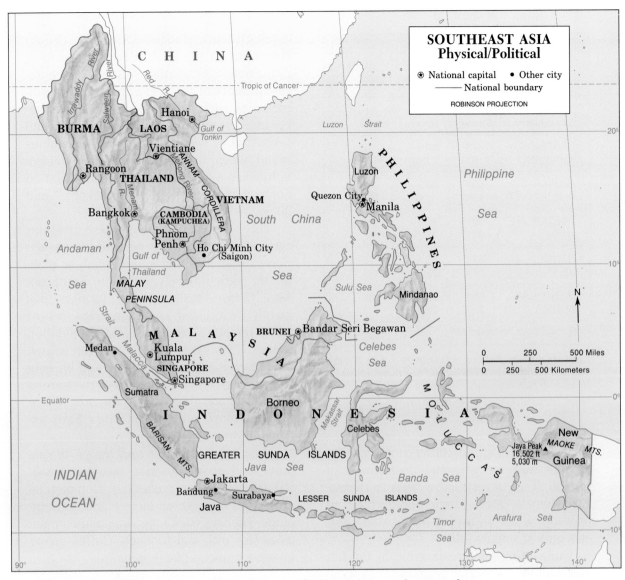

**Learning from Maps.** *Several of the countries of Southeast Asia are fragmented nations. About how far from east to west does Indonesia extend?*

## Climate

The parts of Southeast Asia that lie on or near the equator have a tropical wet climate. Days remain monotonously hot and humid throughout the year, although cooler conditions prevail in the mountains. Away from the equator the climate has a more seasonal rhythm of alternating rainy and dry seasons. As in South Asia, the monsoon winds cause the alternating seasons. In general, the summer monsoons bring heavy rains to thirsty crops in coastal and mountainous regions. The dry winter monsoons pick up moisture only when their paths take them over the sea.

## Vegetation

Dense forests originally covered much of Southeast Asia. Today large areas remain forested. Because the region never receives a frost, the forests generally stay green all year. The mixture of tree types, however,

## TEMPERATURES AND PRECIPITATION IN SELECTED SOUTHEAST ASIAN CITIES

| City/Country | January Low | July High | Precipitation (in/cm) |
|---|---|---|---|
| BANGKOK, THAILAND | 67°F 19°C | 90°F 32°C | 58/ 147 |
| MANILA, PHILIPPINES | 69°F 21°C | 88°F 31°C | 82/ 208 |
| SINGAPORE | 73°F 23°C | 88°F 31°C | 95/ 242 |
| HANOI, VIETNAM | 63°F 17°C | 85°F 29°C | 72/ 183 |
| MANDALAY, BURMA | 68°F 20°C | 85°F 29°C | 30/ 76 |

Sources: *World Almanac*, 1987

*Learning from Tables.* *Temperatures in Southeast Asia reflect little variation, but there are noticeable differences in precipitation. Why does precipitation vary more than temperature?*

varies according to differences in the amount and the seasonal distribution of rainfall. Teak forests grow well in Burma. Elsewhere a dense jungle undergrowth of bamboo, vines, and ferns makes many forests almost impassable.

Quite different forests grow in the hot and humid equatorial regions. They typically feature a mixture of tall trees that completely shade the forest floor, making it impossible for jungles to develop. The mixture of trees in these tropical rain forests hinders lumbering operations.

## Resources

Alluvial or volcanic soils form Southeast Asia's best farmland. Floods and volcanic eruptions constantly replenish the fertility of these soils. Heavy rains quickly leach nutrients from other types of soils, making them less fertile.

**Agriculture.** Geographers seem certain that some of the world's food crops were first planted in Southeast Asia. For centuries farmers of the region have grown edible roots such as taro and yams; rice; coconuts; ginger and various spices; and breadfruit, a seedless fruit that resembles bread when baked. Experts also believe Southeast Asian farmers were the first to domesticate dogs, pigs, chickens, and ducks.

Three types of farming—slash-and-burn agriculture, or shifting agriculture; paddy-rice subsistence; and commercial, or plantation, agriculture—coexist in Southeast Asia today. Slash-and-burn farmers live mainly in forested mountain areas, where land remains plentiful and population sparse. They clear small areas for subsistence farming by cutting down and burning trees in the forest. The ashes of the burned vegetation add nutrients to the soil. These farmers move after their crops have exhausted the soil's fertility.

Most other farmers tend crops in one place and grow wet rice (see the CASE STUDY feature on page 669). Commercial crops, often grown on large plantations, include rubber, coconuts, sugarcane, palm trees (for oil), and tobacco. Coffee grows in some cooler, upland areas.

**Forestry and fishing.** Forestry serves as a major economic activity in Southeast Asia. Lumbering operations make important contributions to the economies of Burma, Thailand, Laos, Malaysia, Indonesia, and the Philippines. Logs, wood, and wood products rank as major exports for all of these countries.

Not surprisingly, fishing is a major activity in a region so interspersed with water. Fishers supply seafood to local markets in all the countries. In addition, Thailand, Malaysia, Indonesia, and the Philippines export fish and seafood.

*Text continues on page 670.*

# CASE STUDY
## EXPLORING NATURE: Food for Crowded Lands

On a worldwide scale, rice ranks as the most important food crop. This is especially true in populous Southeast Asia. In many languages of the region the word for food and the word for rice are the same. In Thailand a common morning greeting translates, "Have you eaten rice?"

### An Adaptable Crop

Because many parts of the tropics have poor soils, farmers struggle to support their populations. This is an especially difficult problem in Southeast Asia, as long as there are millions of mouths to feed. How can farmers keep up?

The answer is rice—an amazingly adaptable crop. Because the rice plant gets most of its needed nutrients from water rather than from soil, it can grow in extremely poor soils where abundant water is available. Although rice can grow without irrigation, most cultivated rice is "wetland rice."

### The Rice Paddy

Wet rice requires both level land and access to water. In crowded, mountainous Southeast Asia people have changed the physical landscape to provide these two elements. In many areas people have created level land by terracing the hillsides to make planting fields called **paddies.**

Planted in the shallow water of the paddy, the rice plant elongates its stem as the water in the field rises—through irrigation or rainfall. The water covering the paddy must contain enough oxygen to nourish the young sprouts. Stagnant water contains so little oxygen that it is useless for rice cultivation.

### Hard Work, Huge Rewards

Growing rice requires a large labor force. Terracing the hillsides is a huge job.

*Drying rice on Borneo*

Planting, cultivating, and harvesting rice by hand also require the backbreaking efforts of many people. Fortunately the crowded lands of Southeast Asia have an ample supply of workers.

To the millions of people in Southeast Asia, rice and life are synonymous. Most people eat more than a pound of rice per day. It provides many of the vitamins and minerals needed for good nutrition as well as the calories needed for energy. In addition, few crops keep well in the heat and humidity of the tropics. Rice is very practical in this respect. Properly dried rice grains can be kept safely for months. This allows the people to store surplus rice as a safeguard against future shortages.

The resources of the physical setting and the ability of the farmers in Southeast Asia to produce rice literally made the region's development possible. They enabled the region to support much larger populations than most other tropical areas, which are sparsely populated. As the world becomes increasingly crowded, farmers in tropical Africa and the Americas may soon be following the rice-growing methods developed in Southeast Asia.

***Learning from Pictures.*** *Mines, mostly from colonial times and now outdated, tap some mineral resources in Southeast Asia. Why has development been slow in the region?*

**Mining.** Oil deposits underlie Burma, Indonesia, and Brunei. Indonesia also has large supplies of natural gas, which it exports in liquefied form. Much of the world's tin comes from deposits in Malaysia, Indonesia, and Thailand. Rushing streams wash the tin down from surrounding hills, and miners scoop up alluvial gravels and sands and separate out the tin. Other mineral resources include gold, copper, and coal.

---

### SECTION 1 REVIEW

1. **Define** paddy
2. **Locate** Strait of Malacca, Indochina, Malay Peninsula, Irrawaddy River, Menam River, Mekong River, Red River, Borneo
3. **Summarizing Ideas** What nations make up **(a)** Peninsular Southeast Asia and **(b)** Insular Southeast Asia?
4. **Outlining Ideas** What are the great Southeast Asian rivers and to which countries is each important?
5. **Identifying Ideas** What climates are typical of Southeast Asia?
6. **Analyzing Ideas** How have Southeast Asians made the most of their natural resources?

---

## 2 Diverse traditions create a complex cultural setting in Southeast Asia.

Magnificent ruins in the forests of Southeast Asia, similar to those in Mexico and Central America, whisper of ancient greatness and advanced cultures. Today, however, the region is noted more for its discord than its progress.

### A Brief History

Historians still wonder which early people first moved into Southeast Asia. Perhaps people from China were first. Or perhaps it was people from India. People with cultural links to each country dominated the region at one time or another.

The Chinese began moving into Southeast Asia several thousand years ago. By about 100 B.C. the Chinese ruled the northern part of Vietnam. Chinese control lasted until about A.D. 900, when Vietnam gained its independence.

People from India also began migrating to Southeast Asia several thousand years ago. They traveled down the Malay Peninsula, across Sumatra and Java, and into what is today Indonesia. Influences from India were strong in several kingdoms, including the Champa Empire on the Mekong Delta in Vietnam; a kingdom near Mandalay in Burma; an early Hindu–Buddhist kingdom on the island of Java; and the Khmer (kuh·MER) Empire, located at Angkor in present-day Cambodia.

Many great changes had occurred in the region by the 1200s. Thais moved southward, conquering Angkor and laying the foundations of modern Thailand (formerly Siam) and Laos. The Khmers moved southward and built a new capital at Phnom Penh (NAWM·pen). Annamese culture developed near Hanoi and spread southward along the

# DEVELOPING GEOGRAPHY SKILLS
## INTERPRETING VISUALS: Determining Locations

Location answers the geographic question *"where?"* As you have learned, location can be described either in *absolute* or *relative* terms. These two descriptions of location allow geographers to identify the positions of physical and cultural features on the earth.

Note that the map on page 69 provides the locations of tectonic plates, earthquakes, and volcanoes. You can use this map to determine both absolute and relative locations. For example, the absolute location of Krakatau—6° 15′ S, 105° 15′ E—tells you the location of the catastrophic eruption that took place between August 23 and August 26, 1883. The volcano's relative location helps explain why the effects of the eruption killed an estimated 36,000 people on western Java. It also helps you understand the magnitude of the explosion when you learn that it was heard in Turkey, Australia, and Japan.

### How to Determine Locations

Follow these steps to determine absolute and relative locations.

1. **Identify a purpose.** Decide whether absolute or relative location or both are needed to help you describe a place.

2. **Find the absolute location.** Use the map's grid to locate the latitude and longitude of the place. On some maps you may be able to find the exact latitude and longitude. On others you will have to approximate.

3. **Determine relative location.** Use one or more maps to identify the location of the place in relation to the locations of other places.

### Applying the Skill

Study the map on page 69 again. You can determine the approximate locations of many of the tectonic plates, major earthquake zones, and volcanoes. Mount St. Helens in southern Washington State has an absolute location of 46° N, 122° W. Mount Fuji in Japan has an absolute location of about 35° N, 138° W.

You can also determine relative locations from the map. Note that the major zone of earthquakes and volcanoes circles the Pacific Ocean. You can easily see that Indonesia is located in the center of a heavy zone of activity in the western Pacific.

*To practice this skill, see Practicing Geography Skills on page 677.*

coast of what is now Vietnam. Islam, brought by Arab traders, spread across the Malay Peninsula and into Sumatra and Java, replacing Hindu customs everywhere in the region except on the Indonesian island of Bali.

Europeans began trading in Southeast Asia in the 1400s and eventually established colonies throughout the region except in Thailand. The British held Burma, the Malay Peninsula, and parts of Borneo. The Dutch controlled what they called the Dutch East Indies—Sumatra, Java, and islands to the east. The French acquired Vietnam, Laos, and Cambodia and called their colony French Indochina. The Portuguese held the Indonesian island of Timor. Spain ruled the Philippines for over 300 years until control passed to the United States following the Spanish American War in 1898. After 1945 all the Southeast Asian colonies gained their independence.

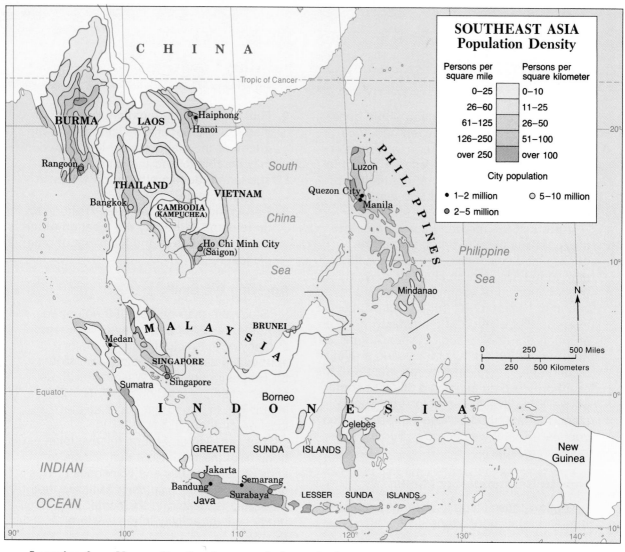

## SOUTHEAST ASIA
### Population Density

| Persons per square mile | Persons per square kilometer |
|---|---|
| 0–25 | 0–10 |
| 26–60 | 11–25 |
| 61–125 | 26–50 |
| 126–250 | 51–100 |
| over 250 | over 100 |

City population

- 1–2 million
- 2–5 million
- 5–10 million

**Learning from Maps.**  *Despite a large population and relatively small land area, most Southeast Asians live in villages. What are the region's largest cities?*

## Population Patterns

Southeast Asia has a total population of 421 million. The five most populous countries are Indonesia (175 million), Vietnam and the Philippines (62 million each), Thailand (54 million), and Burma (39 million). All five rank among the world's 25 most populous nations. The annual growth rate for the region averages about 2.2 percent, ranging from 1.1 percent in Singapore to 2.8 percent in the Philippines.

**Population composition.**  In many ways the boundary patterns drawn by European colonists in Southeast Asia resemble those drawn in Africa by colonial leaders and they have caused similar problems. The boundaries tend to run through sparsely populated uplands and often separate ethnic groups among different countries.

In addition, wave after wave of different peoples have moved into the region throughout its long and complex history. They brought influences from India, China,

and elsewhere that increased Southeast Asia's ethnic diversity. European colonists also added to the diverse imprint, as did the Chinese and Indian laborers who worked on their plantations.

**Population distribution.** Most Southeast Asians live on fertile alluvial or volcanic soils. The deltas of the Irrawaddy, Menam, Mekong, and Red rivers rank among the world's most densely populated areas. Equally as crowded is volcanic Java, where 62 percent of all Indonesians live (see the map on page 672). By contrast, few people live on Borneo and in the mountains throughout the region.

Most of the people of Southeast Asia continue to live in small villages. Urbanization averages a mere 20 percent. Only in Singapore, with an urbanization rate of 100 percent, and Brunei, with a rate of 64 percent, do more than half the people live in cities. As in other developing areas, however, urbanization constantly increases. Four cities—Jakarta, Indonesia; Manila, Philippines; Bangkok, Thailand; and Ho Chi Minh City (formerly called Saigon), Vietnam—rank among the world's 40 largest metropolitan areas.

## Social Patterns

Throughout Southeast Asia the cultural setting varies from one ethnic group to another. Each ethnic group has its own life styles and traditions but may be split into even smaller groups by differences in language and religion.

**Language.** Four Southeast Asian countries have adopted a **national language,** or official language to be used throughout the country, in order to promote unity and ease of communication among their multilingual populations. Bahasa Malaysia, or Malay, is a language that unites the multilingual people

of Malaysia. Malay also serves as the official language of Singapore. Indonesia adopted Bahasa Indonesia, which is similar to Malay, as the national language to help unify the people on its far-flung islands. The Indonesians speak some 250 different languages. The new constitution of the Philippines identifies a national language called Filipino (formerly called Pilipino), which is based on English and the Tagalog (tuh·GAHL·uhg) language spoken around Manila. People in the Philippines also speak more than 70 other languages and dialects.

In each of the other countries of the region a majority of the people speak the nation's official language. People speak Burmese in Burma, Thai in Thailand, Khmer

*Learning from Pictures.* The Shwe Dagon Pagoda in Rangoon is one of the many beautiful Buddhist temples in the region. Where did Buddhism originate?

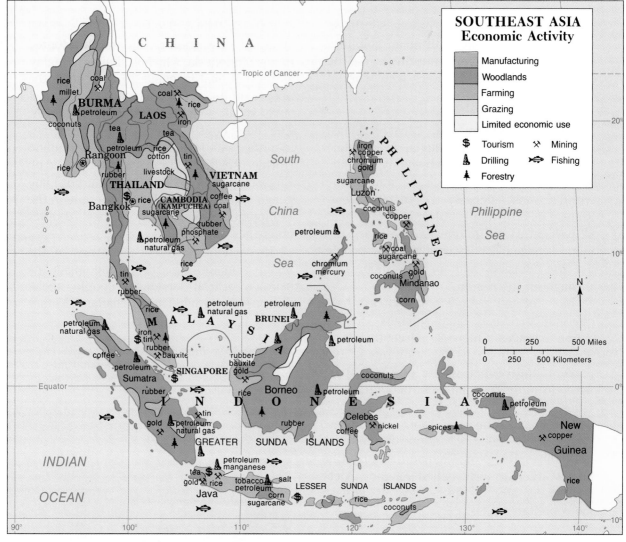

**Learning from Maps.** *Southeast Asia has relatively little suitable farmland. What valuable energy resources are abundant?*

in Cambodia, Lao in Laos, Vietnamese in Vietnam, and Malay in Brunei.

**Religion.** Buddhism flourished in Southeast Asia from the 600s through the 1300s. It remains the major religion in Vietnam, Cambodia, Burma, Thailand, and Laos. Hinduism serves as the major religion only on the island of Bali. Most of the people in the rest of Indonesia and in Malaysia, Brunei, and the southern Philippines follow Islam. The Roman Catholic religion brought to the Philippine islands by the Spanish now dominates only in the northern Philippines.

## Political Patterns

Long civil wars marked the independence movements of the countries of Southeast Asia. Today demands by minority groups for greater representation in government continue in Thailand, the Philippines, and other countries. In addition, Communist guerrillas threaten the area.

Many different types of government systems guide the region's countries. Nominal democracies govern some, including the Philippines. Monarchs rule others, such as Thailand. Dictatorships control still others, such as Vietnam. Many of the countries change governments frequently. Regardless of the type of government, political conflicts trouble all of the countries.

## Economic Patterns

A location astride world trade routes continues to serve as Southeast Asia's greatest asset. World trade between the Atlantic, Indian, and Pacific oceans funnels through the narrow Strait of Malacca. Singapore, the region's only developed nation, enjoys an especially advantageous location at one end of the Strait of Malacca.

***Learning from Pictures.*** *Warehouses line the wharves of Manila harbor, now a major seaport. Why are many of the major cities in Southeast Asia seaports?*

Singapore lacks natural resources of its own, but uses its well-equipped port and its location to export items its people make from imported raw materials.

Except for industrialized Singapore, the countries of Southeast Asia remain primarily agricultural. Singapore and oil-rich Brunei have the region's highest standards of living.

***Learning from Pictures.*** *Isolated farming villages, such as this Meo settlement in Thailand, dot the region's mountains. Why have such villages remained isolated?*

### SECTION 2 REVIEW

1. **Define**   national language
2. **Locate**   Java, Mandalay, Angkor, Bali, Singapore, Jakarta, Manila, Bangkok, Ho Chi Minh City
3. **Summarizing Ideas**   What groups of people outside Southeast Asia moved into the region and added to its cultural imprints?
4. **Analyzing Ideas**   **(a)** How do national languages help to promote national unity and ease of communication among populations?   **(b)** Why do you think that many of the countries have governmental instability and political problems?

## Chapter Summary

The following list contains the key concepts you have learned about the settings of Southeast Asia.

1. Ten nations occupy the region known as Southeast Asia.
2. Geographers often divide Southeast Asia into two parts. Peninsular Southeast Asia lies on the Asian mainland and is often referred to as Indochina. Geographers refer to the islands off the Asian mainland as Insular Southeast Asia.
3. The region's tropical climates range from year-round rain near the equator to alternating wet and dry monsoon seasons elsewhere.
4. Southeast Asian farmers work their lands in three entirely different ways.
5. A great diversity of ethnic and cultural groups coexist in Southeast Asia today.
6. The region's population is concentrated in four alluvial river valleys and on the volcanic island of Java.
7. Conflicts among different groups within the region continue to cause problems in several countries.
8. All of the Southeast Asian nations except industrialized Singapore and oil-rich Brunei depend on agriculture and rank as developing nations.
9. A location astride world trade routes serves as Southeast Asia's greatest asset.

On a separate sheet of paper, complete the following review exercises.

## Reviewing Geographic Terms

Decide whether each of the following sentences is true or false. If the sentence is false, replace the underlined term with the word or phrase that will make the sentence true.

1. Four countries that were troubled by language problems adopted <u>dialects</u> to unify the people and ease communication.

2. Throughout Southeast Asia, farmers build low walls and flood their fields to form <u>patches</u> for growing wet rice.

## Developing Critical Thinking Skills

1. **Summarizing Ideas** (a) Identify and describe the two parts into which geographers often divide Southeast Asia. (b) What are the three major physical features of the region?
2. **Seeing Relationships** (a) What are the most important rivers in Southeast Asia? (b) Discuss their importance to transportation, settlement patterns, and farming.
3. **Understanding Ideas** (a) What is the staple food crop of Southeast Asia? (b) Southeast Asia provides much of the world's supply of what mineral?
4. **Comparing Ideas** What are three things all the countries of Southeast Asia have in common?
5. **Tracing Ideas** (a) People from which two nearby civilizations were among the first to move to Southeast Asia? (b) Considering the landscapes of Southeast Asia and the areas from which those people came, who do you think came first? Why?
6. **Organizing Ideas** (a) How do Singapore and Brunei's population patterns differ from those of the rest of Southeast Asia? (b) Which four cities in Southeast Asia rank among the world's largest?
7. **Synthesizing Ideas** In what ways was European colonialism similar in Southeast Asia and Africa?
8. **Interpreting Ideas** In what ways do slash-and-burn agriculture and paddy rice subsistence agriculture reflect human interactions with Southeast Asia's unique natural environment?
9. **Analyzing Ideas** What evidence indicates that Southeast Asian farmers were innovative even in times long past?
10. **Writing About Geography** In a well-written essay, complete one of the following

activities. **(a)** Discuss how location has been both a benefit and a problem for Southeast Asia. **(b)** Describe the main features of farming in Southeast Asia today.

## Using Primary Sources

In the following excerpt from *A History of South-East Asia*, D. G. E. Hall describes the way that the Spanish conquerors organized land in the Philippines in the 1500s. As you study the reading, consider how this system might relate to current problems in the Philippines.

In taking over the islands the Spaniards left the existing system of food production unchanged and made few alterations in the [local labor] systems. An increased food supply was of course necessary, but the measures taken to ensure it brought no fundamental changes, though they involved forcing the Filipinos to grow a surplus. A fair price for their produce would have easily overcome this difficulty. The Spaniards did, however, introduce important changes in the land system, which were responsible for the growth of landlordism on a large scale, that was to become so prominent a feature of Filipino society in the nineteenth century.

In the first place they introduced the notion of ownership: the chieftains assumed the ownership of the *barangay* [group of 45 to 50 families into which a Philippine village is divided] lands which their dependents cultivated. Previously all landowning had been communal in character with the title vested in the *barangay*. In the second place under Spanish law all lands owned neither communally nor privately belonged to the royal domain, and could be assigned to Filipino chieftains as real estate. Little is known of the early history of these forms of landowning . . . but certain facts can be stated: (a) the religious orders acquired their estates by purchasing lands, once communally owned, from local chieftains; (b) the ecclesiastical estates became the largest item of the Spanish-owned *latifundia* [huge estates where workers similar to indentured servants practiced primitive agriculture], but represented only a small fraction of the total lands under cultivation, and (c) the bulk of all cultivated lands remained in the possession of the Filipinos.

1. Before the arrival of the Spanish, who owned the land?
2. Who benefited the most from the Spanish system of land ownership?

## Practicing Geography Skills

*Before completing this activity, review Developing Geography Skills on page 671.*

**Determining Locations**  Study the map on page 667. Then complete these activities.

1. Give the approximate absolute locations of the following places in Southeast Asia: **(a)** Manila, **(b)** Brunei, **(c)** Bangkok, **(d)** Java, and **(e)** Celebes.
2. Give the relative locations within Southeast Asia of the following places: **(a)** Rangoon, **(b)** Singapore, **(c)** Ho Chi Minh City, and **(d)** Brunei.
3. Using the maps in this textbook, determine Singapore's location relative to **(a)** Tokyo and **(b)** San Francisco.

## Exploring Geography

Use atlases and encyclopedias in your school or public library to construct a chart comparing the major urban centers of Southeast Asia. Include in your chart information on the urban centers' locations and populations, their places of interest, and their major economic activities.

# The Countries of Southeast Asia

# PUTTING THE CHAPTER IN FOCUS

Historically, the term "Indochina" refers to the former French colonies of Cambodia, also known as Kampuchea (kahm·poo·CHEE·uh); Laos; and Vietnam. Physical geographers, however, use the term to mean those three countries as well as Burma, Malaysia, and Thailand. In most of these countries diverse ethnic demands make government difficult and rapid population growth outpaces food supplies and jobs. The conflicting goals of a variety of special interest groups make the social and economic problems even worse.

Four other countries—Indonesia, the Philippines, Brunei, and Singapore—occupy the islands of Insular Southeast Asia. These countries also face problems as they try to modernize.

## Ideas to Understand

In studying about the countries of Southeast Asia, use these ideas to give direction to your reading.

1 Six countries make up Indochina.
2 Insular Southeast Asia includes four island countries.

## Terms to Define

The following terms are some of the key terms in the chapter. Defining them will help you understand the countries of Southeast Asia.

| | |
|---|---|
| sultan | free port |
| coalition | entrepôt |
| transmigration | |

## Places to Locate

Locating the following places will add to your knowledge of geography.

| | |
|---|---|
| Malay Peninsula | Hanoi |
| Irrawaddy River | Sumatra |
| Rangoon | New Guinea |
| East Malaysia | Spice Islands |
| Kuala Lumpur | Luzon |

## 1 Six countries make up Indochina.

Your small boat chugs slowly along a rain-swollen river that meanders through a soggy valley. In the steamy mist you catch a glimpse of steep mountains covered with seemingly impenetrable rain forests. On all sides of you snakes slither, monkeys screech, and lizards mimic the human voice. You are in Indochina, a land rich in history, resources, and people.

### Physical Setting

Indochina stretches more than 2,000 miles (3,200 kilometers) from north to south and almost 1,000 miles (1,600 kilo-

meters) from east to west. The Malay Peninsula juts south into the South China Sea and guards one of the world's most important sea-lanes—the Strait of Malacca.

Mountains line the region, and rivers such as the Irrawaddy, Chindwin, Sittang, Menam, and Mekong slice valleys through fertile plains and plateaus. Although not high, the mountains have very steep sides and are covered with dense rain forests. These rugged mountains have traditionally served as barriers to communication throughout Indochina.

As in South Asia, monsoons influence the climate. Coastal areas have a tropical wet climate, while interior areas have a tropical wet-and-dry climate. Abundant rain falls throughout the region.

◀ *Thai dancer at Wat Arun in Bangkok*

## Cultural Setting

All of the countries of Indochina have heterogeneous populations. However, all except Thailand, which was never a colony of a European power, still reflect the cultural imprints of their colonial rulers. Today people throughout Indochina practice Islam, Buddhism, Daoism, Hinduism, and Christianity.

A variety of political systems exists in Indochina. All the countries of the region remain developing nations. Each has an agricultural economy and its people follow traditional life styles.

## Countries of Western Indochina

Three countries—Burma, Malaysia, and Thailand—occupy the lands of the western part of Indochina.

**Burma.** Burma covers an area about the same size as Texas. Mountains run along most of Burma's borders in the west, north, and east and enclose a fertile plain in the center of the country. This plain serves as the country's historic and economic heartland. The Irrawaddy River and its principal tributaries, the Chindwin and Sittang rivers, drain the plain. The Irrawaddy ends in a large fertile delta, which is the site of Rangoon, Burma's capital, largest city, and chief port.

Unevenly distributed rainfall divides Burma into a wet zone in the south and west and a dry zone north of the city of Mandalay. Dense tropical forests of teak and other trees cover rainy slopes in the wet zone, drenched by summer monsoon rains. Scrub forests characterize the dry zone.

As they did in parts of Africa, colonial rulers drawing Burma's boundaries included a variety of ethnic groups within the country. Of Burma's 39 million people, about two-thirds are Burmans who are concentrated along the fertile plain of the central Irrawaddy River Valley. Burma's ethnic minorities inhabit the hills and mountains surrounding the central plain. The Karen and Shan form the largest minority groups. The country also includes people of Chinese and Indian descent, whose ancestors were brought to Burma as laborers by the British. Burmese, the language of the Burmans, serves as the nation's official language. Most members of minority groups, however, speak their own languages. The majority of the people practice Buddhism.

*Learning from Maps.* *Rivers have long served as key transportation routes in Indochina. In what landform do most of the rivers in Indochina originate?*

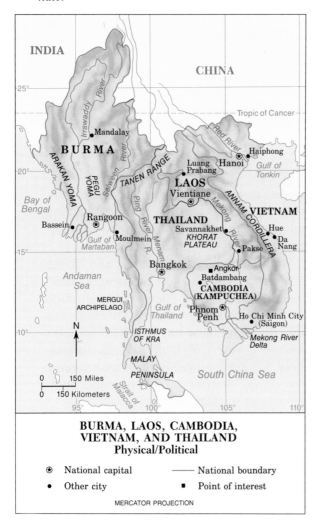

**BURMA, LAOS, CAMBODIA, VIETNAM, AND THAILAND**
**Physical/Political**

⊛ National capital ——— National boundary
● Other city ■ Point of interest

MERCATOR PROJECTION

Independent from Britain since 1948, Burma is officially a republic. The government, however, allows only one political party.

As in many other developing nations, most of Burma's workers engage in farming. Farmers on the fertile central plain and the delta of the Irrawaddy grow rice, sugarcane, beans, and peanuts. Fertile soil and abundant rain help make the country self-sufficient in food. Burma ranks as a leading rice exporter as well as the world's leading supplier of valuable teak.

Industry remains largely undeveloped in Burma, although cottage industries produce silk, carvings, and jewelry. Mineral resources include oil, copper, lead, tin, and jade.

**Malaysia.**    Malaysia can be divided into Peninsular Malaysia, which is larger than New Mexico, and East Malaysia. Peninsular Malaysia lies on the mainland's long and narrow Malay Peninsula. It is the economic and political heart of the country. East Malaysia consists of two states on the northern coast of the island of Borneo—Sabah, the size of Nebraska, and Sarawak (suh·RAH·wahk), the size of Arizona.

Peninsular Malaysia and the island states have mountainous interiors. Most of the people live on narrow coastal plains. Kuala Lumpur (KWAHL·uh LOOHM·poohr), located on Peninsular Malaysia, is the capital and largest city.

More than 80 percent of Malaysia's 16 million people live in Peninsular Malaysia. Almost half the people are ethnic Malays who refer to themselves as Bumiputras (boo·muh·POO·truhs). In order to form a majority and retain political control of Malaysia, the Bumiputras align themselves with several small, indigenous minority groups.

Malaysia's nonindigenous people include the Chinese, who make up about 34 percent of the population, and people of Indian or Pakistani ancestry, who make up

**Learning from Pictures.**   *Plantations set up by American companies in the 1920s still supply much of the world's natural rubber. What country is the leading producer of rubber?*

11 percent. The Bumiputras resent and fear the economic power of the Chinese and Indians, who now control much of Malaysia's wealth. Violence sometimes breaks out between the groups.

The government promotes Bahasa Malaysian as a national language to unite the multiethnic population. Some Malaysians also speak Chinese, Tamil, and English. Most Bumiputras practice Islam, Malaysia's official religion. Most Chinese follow Buddhism, while most Indians are Hindus.

Malaysia is a federal republic of nine states on the peninsula and the two self-governing island states—Sabah and Sarawak. Hereditary **sultans,** or Muslim rulers, still reign in each of the states on Peninsular Malaysia. The sultans choose the national head of state from among their group.

Most Malaysians farm, growing rice, coconuts, peppers, pineapples, and vegetables on small farms. The country ranks as the world's leading producer of natural rubber. Other exports include palm oil, tin, lumber,

and oil. Although industry still ranks behind farming in economic importance, the Malaysians are continuing to industrialize.

**Thailand.** Thailand's irregular borders enclose a land about the size of Texas and shaped like the head and trunk of an elephant. Peninsular Thailand, on the northern part of the Malay Peninsula, forms the elephant's trunk. Lowlands along the Menam River form the eye and lead down to a mouth near Bangkok. The flat rice-growing lands along the Menam are as vital to Thailand's food supply and economic health as the eye and mouth they resemble are to an elephant. High mountains in northern Thailand form the top of the elephant's head. The low Khorat Plateau in the east forms the elephant's ear.

About three-fourths of Thailand's 54 million people are Thais. Some 30 ethnic groups make up the rest of the population. Chinese, Malays, and refugees from war-torn Cambodia form the largest minorities.

*Learning from Pictures.* *Thai farmers domesticated the water buffalo for plowing and hauling. What crop ranks as Thailand's chief crop today?*

Thai is the dominant language, although some people speak regional and ethnic dialects. Most Thais practice Buddhism, worshiping in the many beautiful temples called *wats* (WAHTS) that dot the countryside.

In former times the Thai ruler governed as an absolute monarch. Today the country is a constitutional monarchy, although the monarch retains considerable power. Bangkok serves as the nation's capital.

As in neighboring Burma and Malaysia, most of Thailand's workers farm. Rice is the chief crop. Farmers also grow cassava, corn, cotton, pineapples, rubber, and sugarcane. Exports include rice, sugar, corn, rubber, tin, and tapioca.

## Countries of Eastern Indochina

Three former French colonies—Cambodia, Laos, and Vietnam—share eastern Indochina. Fierce civil wars have disrupted life in all these countries in recent years.

**Cambodia.** Cambodia, located in southern Indochina between Thailand, Laos, and Vietnam, is about the size of Missouri and ranks as one of the few countries of the world that has *lost* population in the last decade. The loss is the direct result of the civil wars that have wracked this mountainous land. Perhaps the worst period of the wars occurred between 1975 and 1979 when Communists known as the Khmer Rouge (kuh·MER ROOJ) controlled the government. The Khmer Rouge brutally reorganized Cambodians into Communist-style communes and forced urban dwellers to move to the countryside. They also murdered as many as 1 million Cambodians before Vietnamese troops overthrew them. Today a **coalition,** or group of political parties, is fighting a guerrilla war to drive the Vietnamese out of Cambodia.

Most Cambodians trace their descent to the Khmers. Almost all the people practice

*Text continues on page 684.*

# CITY FOCUS
## Bangkok, Thailand

On the east bank of the Menam River, 17 miles (27 kilometers) north of the Gulf of Thailand, lies a city of more than 5 million people. It is known to the Thai people as Krung Thep (kruhng·TEHP), or "City of Angels." We call it Bangkok, the capital and primate city of Thailand.

### A Royal City

Bangkok was a rural village in 1782 when King Rama I decided to make it the site of his palace. The Thais believe that the king's palace is the center of the universe, and Rama's goal was to construct a city worthy of this position. Rama first built his grand palace, overlooking the river. Magnificent temples and government buildings followed. He had buildings of lesser significance constructed farther from the palace.

### Bangkok Today

Bangkok, like many large cities, is overcrowded. Most of its citizens live in apartments above their shops or in fire-prone wooden houses. Frequent traffic jams and stifling air pollution mar the landscape.

*Venders on a Bangkok canal*

But Bangkok is distinctive. The city's canals carry floating markets of farm products. And each day somewhere in Bangkok a religious celebration takes place.

Bangkok's temples reflect the Thai people's love of beauty. The Temple of the Emerald Buddha, one of more than 300 Buddhist temples in the city, is considered one of Asia's greatest sights. Glowing in its own soft light, this Buddha sits high on a golden altar. The air in the temple carries the scents of flower offerings and smoldering incense. Three times each year, the king ceremonially changes the Buddha's robes. During the hot summer months, the statue is given a diamond-studded cloak.

For the rainy season, the Buddha wears a blue robe lined with gold threads. For the cool season, it has an enamel-coated wrap of solid gold.

From February 15 until the end of April, kites fill the skies of Bangkok, adding to the enchantment of the city. Late in the afternoon, when fresh breezes begin to defuse the tropical heat, children send up kites of every shape—snakes, tigers, dragons, frogs, and butterflies. These kites twist, turn, and dance high above the city's buildings, turning Bangkok into a land of color. Such ceremonies remind people that within this modern city much of the past remains.

Buddhism. Most of the country's 6.5 million people live on the fertile plains of the Mekong River and the Tonle Sap, or Great Lake.

Constant fighting and political turmoil have weakened Cambodia's predominantly agricultural economy. It remains a developing nation with practically no manufacturing. Large shipments of food from other countries help to supplement the meager harvests of the chief crop, rice, and prevent widespread starvation.

**Laos.** Mountains and rain forests dominate Laos, a landlocked country slightly larger than Utah. The most habitable lands lie along the Mekong River.

About half of the Laotian people are Lao, a people related to the Thais. The Lao language serves as the nation's official language. Members of many other ethnic groups live in sparsely populated mountain areas, where they work mainly as slash-and-burn farmers. The different life style, religion, language, and traditions of these upland people serve as sources of constant friction with the lowland Lao.

Since the overthrow of its monarch in 1975, Laos has been a totalitarian nation with a Communist economic system. Most of the workers are farmers, and rice ranks as the dominant crop. The Mekong floods in summer, making conditions on the floodplain ideal for growing wet rice. Fish from the Mekong provides protein for the Lao diet of rice and other grains. However, Laos is no longer self-sufficient in food, which ranks as the country's leading import. No major industries exist.

**Vietnam.** To the east of Laos lies Vietnam, a country the size of New Mexico. Vietnam consists of two flat and densely populated deltas separated by a narrow strip of sparsely populated mountains. Many people living near the delta at the mouth of the Red River in the north have long-standing ties to the People's Republic of China. This area is the site of Vietnam's capital city of Hanoi. People in the delta at the mouth of the Mekong River in the south have traditionally resisted Chinese influences. Smaller lowlands form Vietnam's narrow coastal plain along the South China Sea.

Rice flourishes on the two watery deltas during Vietnam's hot and rainy summer monsoon season. Virtually impenetrable jungles of bamboo and thickets cover the country's mountains.

Almost all of Vietnam's 62 million people are Vietnamese. Chinese make up the only significant minority group. Population densities on the Tonkin and Cochin deltas are among the highest in the world. Buddhism, Confucianism, Daoism, and Roman Catholicism rank as the leading religions. But Islam, Protestant religions, and several

*Learning from Pictures.* *Many small villages line the banks of the Mekong River. Why have life styles remained traditional in many of the region's rural areas?*

# GEOGRAPHY IN THE WORKPLACE
## Explorers and Foreign Area Specialists

Most people think of an explorer as someone who treks across unmapped sands or ice fields, climbs a peak that has never been climbed before, or charts a previously unknown island. And indeed explorers—many of them geographers—have done precisely these things. Some 80 professional geographers are members of The Explorers Club, an organization located in New York City that is devoted solely to promoting exploration on land, under the sea, and in space.

Geographers as explorers play a great variety of roles, few of which actually involve exploring new lands. Instead most act as foreign area specialists—experts on a country, groups of countries, or regions of the world. These geographers develop special knowledge of the attitudes and traditions of the people who live in the regions of their specialization. They study the regions' economic and political systems and know the locations and availability of the natural resources.

The demand for explorers and regional specialists is almost always greater than the supply. Colleges and universities, many branches of the federal government, intelligence departments in the armed forces, and businesses engaged in foreign trade employ such specialists.

If you are fascinated by life in distant places among people who speak little or no English, a career as an explorer or foreign area specialist might be made to order for you. If you can adjust to new living situations without prejudice and can observe objectively, an exciting career may be ahead of you.

But first you must learn a language. A thorough knowledge of the language of your region is essential. No one can gain a real understanding of the people of Burma, for example, without a command of Burmese. You also must take courses in the geography of the region. And most important of all, you must travel in the region as much and as often as possible. A foreign area specialist gains the broadest understanding of the region only by living among the people and visiting the land to be explored.

indigenous religions have sizable followings. Most people speak Vietnamese—the official language—and large numbers speak French, Chinese, English, and Khmer.

After it gained independence from France in 1954, Vietnam was divided into two countries along the 17th parallel. The People's Republic of China backed North Vietnam and installed a totalitarian dictatorship and a Communist economic system. The United States backed South Vietnam, which had its own democratic form of government. Civil war soon wracked the two Vietnams. Although the United States tried to stop the Communist takeover of South Vietnam, the American government withdrew its troops in 1973. North Vietnamese captured the South Vietnamese capital of Saigon, which they renamed Ho Chi Minh City, and reunified the country.

Most Vietnamese workers are subsistence farmers. Their main crops include rice, corn, sugarcane, and vegetables. Farms are very small, but farmers make the land unusually productive by farming intensively and using irrigation in the dry winter season. Human muscles, rather than machinery, do most of the farm work.

# 2 Insular Southeast Asia includes four island countries.

A variety of landforms, including fine-sand beaches constantly pounded by roaring surf and majestic volcanoes that belch smoke and lava, characterizes the islands of Southeast Asia. Their physical and cultural settings reflect wide diversity.

## Physical Setting

Insular Southeast Asia includes thousands of islands strung south and east of Indochina, forming part of the Ring of Fire. The tops of submerged volcanoes, some of which still cover the surrounding landscape with smoldering dust and lava, form many of these islands. Lava flows have created fertile soils throughout the area. These soils support some of the highest population densities in the world. Earthquakes also serve as reminders that the region lies atop a tectonic plate boundary. Monsoons influence the hot, tropical climate.

## Cultural Setting

The cultural setting of Insular Southeast Asia reflects its relative location near one of the world's busiest crossroads. For centuries people from many cultures have crisscrossed the islands, leaving evidence of their religions, languages, and cultures.

## Countries of Insular Southeast Asia

The island nations of Indonesia and the Philippines rank among the largest and most populous countries in Southeast Asia. Brunei, located on the island of Borneo, is one of the region's smallest and least populated countries. Singapore is a tiny island city-state that has become wealthy as a trading and industrial center.

**Indonesia.** Indonesia, the largest country in Southeast Asia, stretches across more than 10,000 mountainous islands located on or near the equator. Altogether it covers a land area about the same size as Alaska and California combined. The largest islands include Sumatra; Java; Kalimantan, or Indonesian Borneo; and spider-shaped Celebes (SEL·uh·beez). The sparsely populated Molucca (muh·LUHK·uh) Islands and western New Guinea (GIN·ee) make up most of eastern Indonesia. Formerly known as the Spice Islands, the Moluccas still produce nutmeg, clove, pepper, and other spices.

Indonesia ranks as the fifth most populous nation in the world. Its current population of 175 million, and its growth rate of 2.1 percent pose a major threat to the country's future. The population problem is greatest on Java, where 62 percent of all Indonesians live. To combat the problem of overcrowding, the Indonesian government encourages what it calls **transmigration,** or the voluntary migration of Javanese to less crowded islands. For those Javanese willing to migrate, the government gives land, housing, and supplies

*Text continues on page 688.*

Imagine that you are in an airplane, flying low over the South China Sea enroute from Thailand to Australia. Suddenly a huge tropical island comes into view. It is Borneo, the third-largest island in the world. One of the world's largest expanses of tropical rain forest covers the island.

From the air hundreds of shades of green blend in the seemingly unending canopy of leaves. The canopy rises and falls with changes in slope, covering hills, rocks, and soil. The trees appear to climb up and over the high mountainous backbone of the island. The great rivers that drain these remote highlands create the only break in the dense green blanket.

*Borneo's Great Argus Pheasant*

### Inhabitants of the Forests

But if you look closely, especially at an area where a tributary joins a main river, you might spot a long-house and a patchwork of tiny fields and clearings where the rain forest has been cut away. In a clearing you would find children splashing in the stream, dogs barking, chickens cackling, and smoke rising from the long-house. Nearby, old men would sit on their haunches and tell tales of their past bravery and exchange the legends of their tribe.

### Legends of the Birds

If you could listen closely you would hear legends about birds—for birds play important, almost magical, roles in the lives of the Dyak, the people of Borneo. Many Dyaks believe that birds, including those that appear in dreams, offer powerful omens of what will happen in the future. These omens can be good or bad.

Omens are an important part of life for the people of the rain forest. For example, if a group of hunters walks along a jungle trail and spots a small woodpecker, the group immediately stops. The hunters might wait for hours for an encouraging sign from the bird before they continue. Or they might even call off the hunt and return to their village. To the Dyak each of the more than 600 species of birds in Borneo carries a message.

Besides providing people with ways of seeing into the future, birds play a significant role in planting and harvesting activities. Because of Borneo's tropical climate, there are no real seasons to guide farmers. However, the tropical rain forest does provide a winter refuge for many migratory birds that spend their summers on the Asian mainland. The comings and goings of these migratory birds provide a rhythm for farming. In August when the yellow wagtail appears on the hillsides, it is time to clear the fields for planting. By October the brown shrike appears and farmers know that they must finish planting.

Perhaps it was these seasonal signals, carried by the birds, that first attracted the people's attention. But today the Dyaks watch the sky for a sign of what the future may hold.

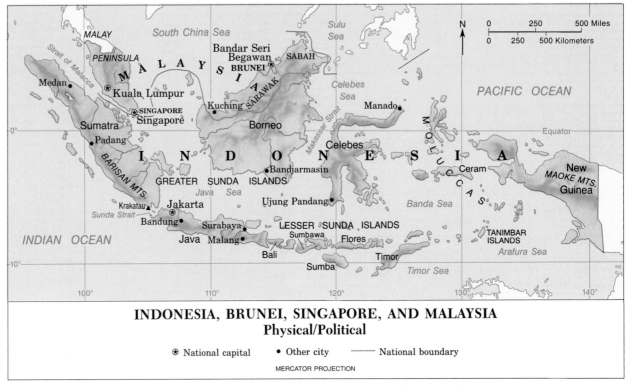

### INDONESIA, BRUNEI, SINGAPORE, AND MALAYSIA
#### Physical/Political

⊛ National capital     • Other city     —— National boundary

MERCATOR PROJECTION

*Learning from Maps.* *Indonesia provides an excellent example of a fragmented nation. What problems does fragmentation cause for a country?*

to help them prosper on their new islands. Money to pay for such government programs comes mainly from exports of oil and natural gas.

Buddhist and Hindu influences were strong in Indonesia from the 600s to the 1300s. Hinduism still survives as the principal religion on Bali and as a minority religion elsewhere, while almost 90 percent of Indonesians follow Islam.

Indonesia currently has a republican form of government. Since gaining its independence from the Netherlands in 1949, however, the country has had both military dictatorships and democracies.

Extensive oil and natural gas reserves have helped Indonesia in its ambitious drive to industrialize. Nonetheless, the country remains a developing nation. The per capita GNP is less than $600, and many of the people are subsistence farmers.

**The Philippines.** During the colonial years Spain and then the United States ruled the Philippines. Independent since 1946, the Philippines includes more than 7,100 mountainous, volcanic islands and contains about the same land area as Nevada. The two largest islands are Luzon (loo·ZAHN) in the north and Mindanao (min·duh·NAH·oh) in the south.

In winter the northeast monsoons cross the South China Sea, bringing heavy rains to the country's northeast coasts. The southwest monsoons in summer soak the southwest coasts with heavy rains. Sugarcane, bananas, coconuts, and rice flourish in the high heat and humidity.

Almost 50 percent of the 62 million people depend on farming as a livelihood. Almost all of the people belong to the Malay ethnic group, but they speak many different languages. Both Filipino, the national lan-

guage, and English serve as official languages. Roman Catholicism, introduced by the Spanish, remains the principal religion in the Philippines. A small minority of Filipinos in the south are Muslims.

As in Indonesia, the government of the Philippines has teetered back and forth

**Learning from Pictures.** *Singapore is a modern, major world city. How is Singapore's locational advantage similar to that of Great Lakes cities?*

between democracy and dictatorship since independence. In 1986 Filipinos overthrew a dictatorship. The country's new leader, Corazon Aquino, struggled to restore democracy in the fragmented nation. Muslims want more control over their local affairs. Communist guerrillas have many supporters among the poor, who feel that the government is not doing enough to improve their low standard of living.

The Philippines remains a developing nation with an agricultural economy. The country ranks as a leading exporter of rice. Farmers also grow coconuts, sugarcane, and tobacco for export. The country possesses rich deposits of copper, gold, chromite, iron ore, manganese, and nickel.

**Brunei.** Wedged along the northern coast of Malaysian Borneo lies Brunei, the newest country of Southeast Asia and the smallest in population, with 221,000 people. The tiny country is slightly larger than Delaware. Brunei gained its independence from Britain in 1984. Various groups speak Malay, English, and Chinese. Islam and support for the nation's sultan unite the people. Brunei's vast oil reserves have helped the country achieve a per capita GNP of over $7,000.

**Learning from Maps.** *The more than 7,100 islands of the Philippines are divided into 73 provinces. How are the settings of the Philippines similar to those of Indonesia?*

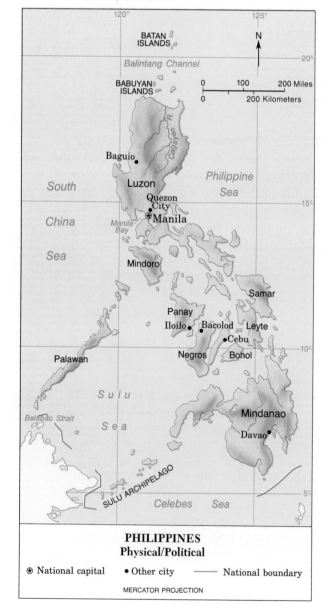

**PHILIPPINES**
Physical/Political

⊛ National capital    • Other city    —— National boundary

MERCATOR PROJECTION

**689**

| COMPARING SELECTED COUNTRIES IN SOUTHEAST ASIA | | | | | |
|---|---|---|---|---|---|
| Country | Population (in millions) | Population Density (in million sq. m/sq. km) | Area (sq. m/sq. km) | GNP (in billions) | Value of Exports (in millions) | Value of Imports (in millions) |
| VIETNAM | 63.6 | 463/179 | 127,207/ 329,707 | $18.1 | $ 500 | $ 1,900 |
| PHILIPPINES | 61.7 | 474/184 | 115,831/ 300,440 | $33.6 | $ 5,200 | $ 6,300 |
| CAMBODIA | 6.7 | 104/ 40 | 69,900/ 181,035 | NA | $ 43 | $ 103 |
| THAILAND | 53.8 | 259/100 | 198,500/ 514,820 | $52.4 | $ 7,400 | $10,400 |
| INDONESIA | 180.6 | 226/ 88 | 741,101/ 2,027,087 | $90.3 | $20,900 | $16,700 |

Source: *World Fact Book*, 1987

***Learning from Charts.*** *Most of the countries listed have developing economies. How are the region's development problems similar to those of African nations?*

**Singapore.** Smaller than New York City, the tiny island nation of Singapore, with a per capita GNP of more than $7,000, ranks as the most developed and industrialized nation in Southeast Asia. Singapore's relative location on the Strait of Malacca gives the country a unique advantage. One of the world's chief shipping routes runs through the strait, which connects Australia and the Pacific Islands to the Indian and Atlantic oceans. Singapore's location allows it to import raw materials and export them in the form of more valuable manufactured goods.

The British took advantage of Singapore's excellent natural harbor to develop the city as a **free port** open to all without the payment of a tax or duty on imported goods. Singapore still serves as an **entrepôt** (AHN·truh·poh), or distribution point, for goods moving to and from all of Southeast Asia. Related industries include banking, insurance, finance, and shipping.

After gaining independence from Britain in 1963, Singapore belonged to the Federation of Malaysia. It seceded in 1965 in part because of ethnic differences. Three-fourths of Singapore's 2.6 million people are Chinese. Minorities include Malays, Indians, Pakistanis, and Europeans. Malay, Chinese, Tamil, and English all serve as official languages, though the national language is Malay. Religions include Buddhism, Islam, Daoism, Hinduism, and Christianity.

**SECTION 2 REVIEW**

1. **Define** transmigration, free port, entrepôt
2. **Locate** Sumatra, New Guinea, Spice Islands, Luzon
3. **Identifying Ideas** (a) What is Indonesia's chief problem? (b) Where is the problem most serious?
4. **Illustrating Ideas** Which nations of Insular Southeast Asia have Muslim majorities?
5. **Analyzing Ideas** What common political problems do the Philippines and Indonesia share?
6. **Interpreting Ideas** How do Singapore and Brunei differ from Indonesia and the Philippines?

Geographers obtain information through their own analysis of the events and settings they study. As a student of geography, you must be able to analyze the writings of geographers. Often such writings contain viewpoints, conclusions, and hypotheses that geographers have drawn from their analyses of data.

Remember that to analyze information means to break it apart—into facts and opinions, causes and effects, time and other relationships—for study (see page 257). Then you should be able to put the pieces of information back together, like you do a jigsaw puzzle. In putting the puzzle together you will gain an understanding of the relationships among the pieces.

## How to Analyze Information

To effectively analyze information, follow these steps.

1. **Read the material carefully.** Read for understanding. Identify main ideas and supporting details.
2. **Ask yourself questions.** Study the information to answer *where, who, what, when,* and *why* questions.
3. **Separate fact from opinion.** Facts are provable and usually can be checked in more than one source. Opinions may or may not be proved true. Recognizing opinions helps you analyze the geographer's statements. Also note bias. Be alert for words, phrases, or facts that state only one viewpoint when more than one seems possible.
4. **Check for other relationships.** Look for clues that indicate causes or effects. Recognize the time relationships among events.
5. **Use your analysis.** Put your new understanding to use by drawing a conclusion, stating a generalization, or forming a hypothesis.

## Applying the Skill

Read the textbook excerpt given below. It is an example of one type of information geographers provide in their writings.

More than 80 percent of Malaysia's 16 million people live in Peninsular Malaysia. Almost half the people are ethnic Malays who refer to themselves as Bumiputras. In order to form a majority and retain political control of Malaysia, the Bumiputras align themselves with several small indigenous minority groups.

Malaysia's nonindigenous people include the Chinese, who make up about 34 percent of the population, and people of Indian or Pakistani ancestry, who make up 11 percent. The Bumiputras resent and fear the economic power of the Chinese and Indians, who now control much of Malaysia's wealth. Violence sometimes breaks out between the groups.

An analysis of the excerpt reveals the following pieces of information. Most of the information in the excerpt is factual and the geographer shows no bias. The *where* is Malaysia in Southeast Asia. The *who* of the excerpt are the Bumiputras. The *what* is the Bumiputras' attempts to retain political control. The *when* is today. And the *why* is the Bumiputras' desire to form a majority and retain political control of the country. Note that a cause—*the economic power of the Chinese and Indians*—and an effect—*resentment and fear by the Bumiputras*—are stated. Through further analysis you can discover even more about the political situation in Malaysia from this excerpt.

*To practice this skill, see Practicing Geography Skills on page 693.*

## Chapter Summary

The following list contains the key concepts you have learned about the countries of Southeast Asia.

1. Geographers divide Southeast Asia into two regions—Indochina and Insular Southeast Asia. The countries of Indochina include Burma, Malaysia, Thailand, Cambodia, Laos, and Vietnam. Insular Southeast Asia includes Indonesia, the Philippines, Brunei, and Singapore. Except for Thailand all of the countries of the region were once ruled by European powers.
2. Mountains crisscross Indochina. Although not high, these mountains are very steep and densely forested. Traditionally they have been barriers to transportation and communication in the region.
3. Climates in the region vary from tropical wet to tropical wet-and-dry.
4. The large total population of Southeast Asia and its distribution among narrow valleys and small islands give the region several of the world's most densely populated areas. The growing population also strains the region's resources.
5. Of all the nations of the region only tiny Singapore is classified as a developed nation. The other countries of the region are developing nations with agricultural economies and traditional life styles.
6. Farmers throughout the region grow rice, which is the basis for most of the people's diets.
7. Burma ranks as a leading rice exporter as well as the world's leading source of valuable teak. Oil has added great income to Brunei's economy.
8. Most people in Malaysia, Indonesia, and Brunei are Muslims. A variety of religions occur elsewhere.
9. Communists rule Vietnam, Cambodia, and Laos and are a force in the Philippines, which is attempting to restore democratic government after years of dictatorship.

On a separate sheet of paper, complete the following review exercises.

## Reviewing Geographic Terms

Supply the geographic term that correctly completes each sentence.

1. Hereditary Muslim rulers known as _____ still reign in Peninsular Malaysia.
2. A political organization formed from two or more political parties is called a _____.
3. _____ occurs when people move voluntarily from a densely populated region to a sparsely populated one.
4. A harbor city that is open to all trade without payment of taxes on imports or exports is called a _____ _____.

## Developing Critical Thinking Skills

1. **Summarizing Ideas** **(a)** Which physical features characterize the nations of the Indochina Peninsula? **(b)** How have these features influenced communication and settlement patterns?
2. **Organizing Ideas** How has Thailand's history differed from that of other Southeast Asian countries?
3. **Determining Cause and Effect** **(a)** How does Cambodia's population differ from the populations of its neighbors? **(b)** What caused this difference?
4. **Analyzing Ideas** Why do you think the Bumiputras in Malaysia fear Indian and Chinese minorities?
5. **Comparing Ideas** **(a)** In what ways are Singapore and Brunei similar? **(b)** In what ways do Singapore and Brunei differ from Indonesia and the Philippines?
6. **Interpreting Ideas** **(a)** What are the major problems facing Indonesia? **(b)** How are Indonesia's problems similar to those of Malaysia? **(c)** What steps might the governments of these two countries take to solve their problems?

**7. Writing About Geography** In a well-written essay, complete one of the following activities. **(a)** Trace Vietnam's history since 1954 and describe the role the United States played in it. **(b)** Explain the many challenges that the Philippine government must face today.

## Using Primary Sources

In the following excerpt from *Laos—A Country Study,* Donald P. Whitaker and others describe the system of choosing leaders in a tribal village in Laos. As you study the reading, compare this system with other ways of choosing political leaders.

In the political hierarchy the village is the smallest administrative unit. Its headman (*pho ban*), chosen from among the most respected heads of households, is generally elected for life or until he chooses to retire. He is usually one of the well-to-do men, respected by the other householders for his community and religious activities, the generosity of his hospitality when giving feasts, the quality of his house, and the contributions he makes to the *wat* and the *sangha* (sahng·HAH) [Buddhist monks and novices living in the wat].

The uses of wealth rather than its accumulation determine the choice of a village headman, for the way in which a man distributes his wealth reveals his character. A headman is, next to the head of the *wat,* the most important person in the village, and he must be able to maintain the dignity of his position—for which he is not paid. Thus, a poor man, though he might be highly respected for his industry, piety, generosity, and knowledge, would not be chosen as a headman because he could not meet the obligations the villagers feel to be necessary. In some villages the title tends to be hereditary, or

nearly so; a retiring headman usually designates his son or some other close relative to succeed him, after which the villagers formally elect his choice.

1. What qualities must a person have to be selected as a village headman?
2. Why would a poor man not normally be elected as a village headman?

## Practicing Geography Skills

*Before completing this activity, review Developing Geography Skills on page 691.*

**Analyzing Information** Read the following excerpt and complete the activities below.

Cambodia . . . ranks as one of the few countries of the world that has *lost* population in the last decade. The loss is the direct result of the civil wars that have wracked this mountainous land. Perhaps the worst period of the wars occurred between 1975 and 1979 when Communists known as the Khmer Rouge controlled the government. The Khmer Rouge brutally reorganized Cambodians into Communist-style communes and forced urban dwellers to move to the countryside. They also murdered as many as 1 million Cambodians before Vietnamese troops overthrew them.

1. Answer the excerpt's **(a)** where, **(b)** who, **(c)** what, **(d)** when, and **(e)** why questions.
2. Identify any statements you feel are opinions and explain your reasoning.

## Exploring Geography

Use resources in your school or public library to find information on the plight of refugees from Cambodia, Laos, and Vietnam. Then use the information to write a newspaper article on the problems that these refugees face.

**CHAPTER**
**36**

# Oceania and Antarctica

# PUTTING THE CHAPTER IN FOCUS

Ferdinand Magellan sighted and named the Pacific Ocean in the 1520s. His journey across the Pacific, however, was quite surprising. Except for Guam and two tiny uninhabited islands, Magellan's crew saw nothing but "a sea so vast that the human mind can scarcely grasp it." Later explorers found more. They found a region now called Oceania, made up of the island continent of Australia and thousands of tiny islands strung out like stepping-stones across the ocean. They also found Antarctica, an uninhabitable continent cloaked in ice far to the south.

## Ideas to Understand

In studying about Oceania and Antarctica, use these ideas to give direction to your reading.

1 A shortage of water hampers Australia's development.
2 New Zealand reflects Polynesian and European influences.
3 Oceania includes thousands of large and small islands.
4 The cold, ice-covered continent of Antarctica remains uninhabited.

## Terms to Define

The following terms are some of the key terms in the chapter. Defining them will help you understand Oceania and Antarctica.

| | |
|---|---|
| marsupial | geyser |
| playa | geothermal energy |
| artesian basin | atoll |
| aquifer | trust territory |
| Aborigine | |

## Places to Locate

Locating the following places will add to your knowledge of geography.

| | |
|---|---|
| Tasmania | Auckland |
| Great Barrier Reef | Papua New Guinea |
| Sydney | Samoa |
| Melbourne | Antarctica |

## 1 A shortage of water hampers Australia's development.

The largest of Oceania's many lands is Australia. On a visit to Australia you might see a variety of unusual animals—animals that you would otherwise see only in a zoo. Among Australia's unique animals are the duckbilled platypus and the **marsupials** (mahr·soo·pee·uhls), animals that raise their young in a pouch. The most widely known marsupials include kangaroos; wallabies, smaller cousins of the kangaroo; and koalas. Many of these animals are unique to Australia because it was cut off from other areas for thousands of years.

*Moorea, Society Islands, and Tahiti beyond*

## Physical Setting

Australia is the smallest continent and the only continent entirely occupied by one nation. Another distinction—the only inhabited continent located entirely in the Southern Hemisphere—has earned Australia the nickname "Land Down Under."

**Physical regions.** Geographers divide Australia's territory into four physical regions. They are the Great Dividing Range, the Central Lowlands, the Western Plateau, and the Great Barrier Reef.

Australia's highest lands lie in the Great Dividing Range, sometimes called the Eastern Highlands, which rises near the east coast. These mountains form Australia's

*Learning from Pictures.* In interior Australia rainwater collects in playas that eventually dry up from evaporation. What is Australia's main source of water?

continental divide. They extend from Cape York Peninsula to the island of Tasmania. The southeastern part of the range rises to 7,310 feet (2,230 meters) at Mount Kosciusko (kahz·ee·UHS·koh), the highest point.

The dry Central Lowlands are west of the Great Dividing Range. They cover about one-third of Australia, stretching north and south from the Gulf of Carpentaria to Spencer Gulf. Elevation in the lowlands averages less than 500 feet (150 meters). A huge lake in the lowlands, Lake Eyre (AUHR), dips below sea level. The lake is actually a **playa** (PLY·uh), or shallow desert lake that grows and shrinks with rainfall.

The Western Plateau lies on Australia's ancient core and boasts abundant supplies of minerals. Elevations on the plateau range from 750 to 1,500 feet (230 to 460 meters). The flat and treeless Nullarbor (meaning "no trees") Plain forms the region's southern edge along the Indian Ocean. Two deserts—the Great Sandy Desert and the Great Victoria Desert—cover large parts of the plateau's arid interior. Mile after mile of huge sand dunes mark the deserts. Held in place by scrub vegetation, these dunes are quite unlike the moving sand dunes found in other deserts of the world.

*Learning from Diagrams.* The Great Dividing Range acts as Australia's continental divide. What is a continental divide?

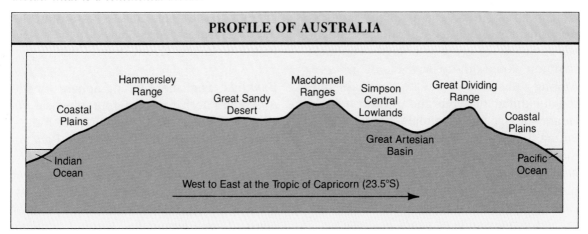

## PROFILE OF AUSTRALIA

Coastal Plains — Hammersley Range — Great Sandy Desert — Macdonnell Ranges — Simpson Central Lowlands — Great Dividing Range — Coastal Plains

Indian Ocean — Great Artesian Basin — Pacific Ocean

West to East at the Tropic of Capricorn (23.5°S)

The Great Barrier Reef lies under the sea along Australia's northeastern coast. It is the world's largest coral reef (see THE GEOGRAPHIC WEB on pages 700–01).

**Climate.**　Arid conditions characterize much of Australia's climate. Only Tasmania and the southeast coast between Brisbane and Melbourne receive enough rain to support non-irrigated farming. Deserts cover most of the Central Lowlands and Western Plateau, which receive less than 10 inches (25 centimeters) of rain a year.

Northern Australia has a tropical wet-and-dry climate. Droughts come in the winter months—June and July—and heavy rains fall from November through April. In southern and southwestern Australia, which have Mediterranean climates, droughts come in the summer months—December and January. Southeastern Australia experiences the four seasons typical of temperate climates.

**Vegetation.**　Forests cover only the few rainy areas scattered in Australia's mountains, along the southwestern corner of the Pacific coast, and in Tasmania. Open woodlands grow in semiarid areas inland. Australia's forests and woodlands contain many unique varieties of eucalyptus (yoo·kuh·LIP·tuhs) and acacia (uh·KAY·shuh) trees. Farther inland, along the edges of the desert, shrubs and grasslands grow.

**Resources.**　Australia lacks an essential resource—water. Few rivers and a drought-prone climate make Australia the driest of all the inhabited continents. Only Antarctica, whose water is trapped in ice, is drier.

Abundant underground water compensates to some extent for Australia's lack of surface water. The underground water lies in vast artesian basins. **Artesian basins** consist of slightly folded layers of porous rocks that fill with rainwater. The water

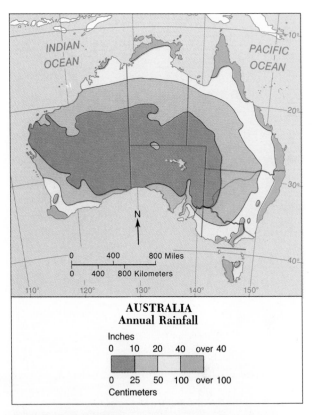

*Learning from Maps.*　Most of Australia's rain falls along the northern and eastern coasts. From what direction do you think the rain-bearing winds come? Why?

collects in underground **aquifers,** or water-bearing rock layers. When workers dig a well to an aquifer, pressure causes the water to rise naturally to the surface, making pumping unnecessary. The Great Artesian Basin, Australia's largest water reserve, underlies about one-fifth of the continent. Although slightly salty and unfit as drinking water, artesian water often serves as the main water supply for sheep and cattle in Australia's arid interior.

Australia possesses great mineral resources. Gold rushes in 1851 and 1892 attracted many early settlers, and mines still produce gold today. Australia also ranks among the world's leaders in iron ore, bauxite, nickel, and lead production. Electricity generated by coal mined near Newcastle supplies most of Australia's energy needs.

*Text continues on page 702.*

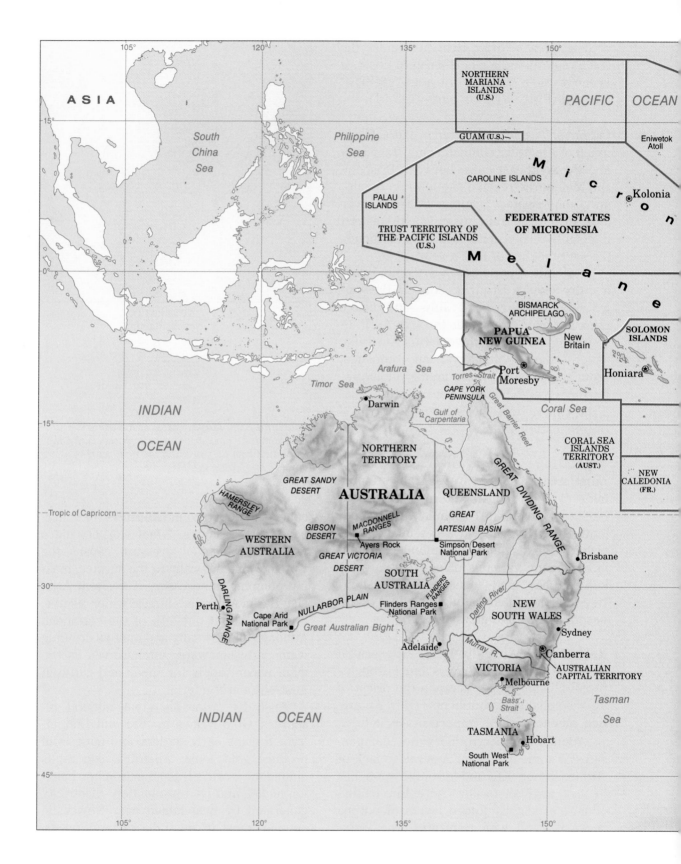

ASIA

PACIFIC OCEAN

South
China
Sea

Philippine
Sea

NORTHERN
MARIANA
ISLANDS
(U.S.)

GUAM (U.S.)

Eniwetok
Atoll

CAROLINE ISLANDS

Micronesia

Kolonia

PALAU
ISLANDS

FEDERATED STATES
OF MICRONESIA

TRUST TERRITORY OF
THE PACIFIC ISLANDS
(U.S.)

Melanesia

BISMARCK
ARCHIPELAGO

PAPUA
NEW GUINEA

New
Britain

SOLOMON
ISLANDS

Arafura    Sea

Timor Sea

Torres Strait

Port
Moresby

Honiara

INDIAN

OCEAN

Darwin

CAPE YORK
PENINSULA

Gulf of
Carpentaria

Coral Sea

CORAL SEA
ISLANDS
TERRITORY
(AUST.)

NEW
CALEDONIA
(FR.)

NORTHERN
TERRITORY

GREAT SANDY
DESERT

AUSTRALIA

QUEENSLAND

GREAT DIVIDING RANGE

HAMERSLEY
RANGE

Tropic of Capricorn

GIBSON
DESERT

MACDONNELL
RANGES

GREAT
ARTESIAN BASIN

WESTERN
AUSTRALIA

Ayers Rock

GREAT VICTORIA
DESERT

Simpson Desert
National Park

Brisbane

SOUTH
AUSTRALIA

FLINDERS RANGES

NEW
SOUTH WALES

DARLING RANGE

Perth

NULLARBOR PLAIN

Flinders Ranges
National Park

Darling River

Sydney

Cape Arid
National Park

Great Australian Bight

Adelaide

Murray R.

Canberra

AUSTRALIAN
CAPITAL TERRITORY

VICTORIA

Melbourne

INDIAN    OCEAN

Bass
Strait

Tasman

Sea

TASMANIA

Hobart

South West
National Park

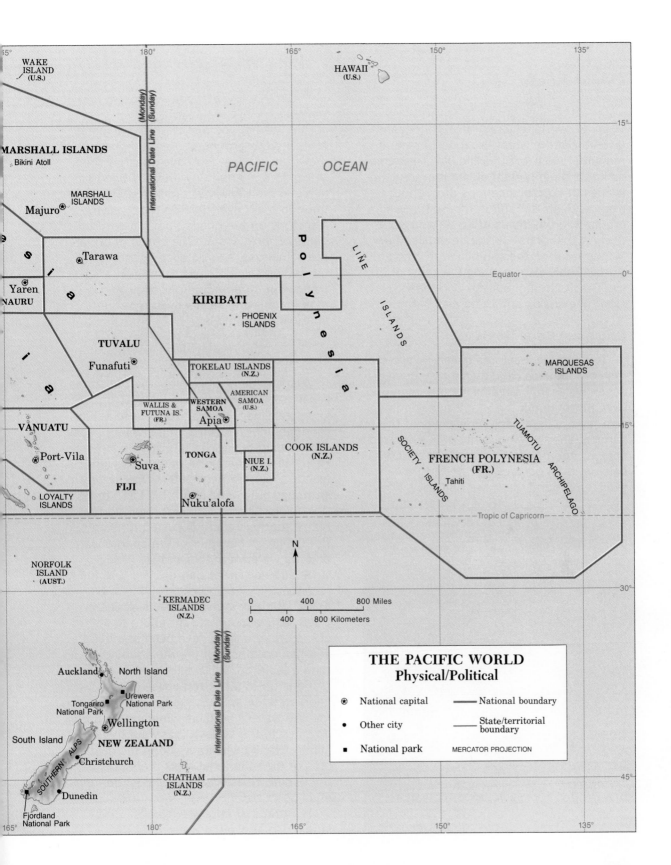

WAKE
ISLAND
(U.S.)

HAWAII
(U.S.)

MARSHALL ISLANDS

Bikini Atoll

PACIFIC OCEAN

MARSHALL
ISLANDS

Majuro⊛

Tarawa⊛

Yaren⊛
NAURU

Polynesia

LINE ISLANDS

KIRIBATI

Equator 0°

PHOENIX
ISLANDS

15°

TUVALU

Funafuti⊛

TOKELAU ISLANDS
(N.Z.)

MARQUESAS
ISLANDS

WALLIS &
FUTUNA IS.
(FR.)

WESTERN
SAMOA

AMERICAN
SAMOA
(U.S.)

TUAMOTU ARCHIPELAGO

VANUATU

Apia⊛

Port-Vila⊛

Suva⊛

TONGA

NIUE I.
(N.Z.)

COOK ISLANDS
(N.Z.)

SOCIETY ISLANDS

FRENCH POLYNESIA
(FR.)

15°

FIJI

Tahiti

LOYALTY
ISLANDS

Nuku'alofa⊛

Tropic of Capricorn

NORFOLK
ISLAND
(AUST.)

N

30°

KERMADEC
ISLANDS
(N.Z.)

0        400        800 Miles

0    400    800 Kilometers

Auckland ▪   North Island

Urewera
National Park

Tongariro
National Park

Wellington⊛

South Island

SOUTHERN ALPS

NEW ZEALAND

Christchurch

Dunedin

CHATHAM
ISLANDS
(N.Z.)

45°

Fjordland
National Park

## THE PACIFIC WORLD
### Physical/Political

⊛ National capital     —— National boundary

• Other city     —— State/territorial boundary

▪ National park     MERCATOR PROJECTION

International Date Line   (Monday) (Sunday)

In the warm waters of tropical oceans throughout the world lie wondrous coral reefs that teem with marine life. These reefs make up an important element in the landscapes of coastal locations throughout the tropics. Reefs abound in the South Pacific, around the coastlines of South and Southeast Asia, and around the huge island of Madagascar off the southeastern coast of Africa. Reefs also lie along the coast of tropical Brazil, throughout the Caribbean, and along the coasts of Florida and Bermuda.

### Origins of Coral Reefs

Tiny marine creatures called polyps create coral. Polyps can survive only in clear ocean water that remains warmer than 65°F (18°C) throughout the year. Because polyps also require light, they grow close to the surface. They grow in many different sizes, shapes, and colors. Each polyp extracts calcium from ocean water and secretes a skeleton around the lower half of its body.

*Erskine Reef in the Great Barrier Reef*

The formations that we know as coral reefs are the groups of untold thousands of individual polyps that have attached themselves to one another with both living tissue and their external skeletons. They continue to build over time on dead polyp skeletons on the ocean floor, on outcroppings of rock, around the cones of undersea volcanoes, and on such ocean debris as sunken ships. Coral reefs, then, are a living, self-repairing colony of polyps and rank among the earth's most amazing physical phenomena.

### The Great Barrier Reef

Just off the northeast coast of Australia lies a 100,000-square-mile (260,000-square-kilometer) maritime habitat of coral reefs, sandbars, coral islands, and sheltered seas. This habitat makes up the Great Barrier Reef—the largest coral reef in the world (see the map on pages 698–99). The reef stretches north and south for 1,260 miles (2,016 kilometers). The reef received the name "barrier reef" because it forms a barrier between the water of the open ocean and the water near the shore.

Australia's Great Barrier Reef is actually an enormously complex structure composed of many individual reefs. At least 2,500 reefs accounting for about one-third of the entire colony have been identified and named. Some of the reefs are no larger than a tabletop, while others are huge formations up to 20 square miles (52 square kilometers) in area. Some lie many feet below the water's surface, while others grow so close to the surface that waves constantly break over them. Along the eastern face of the outermost reefs the swells of the Pacific Ocean form an almost continuous line of surf.

Hundreds of coral keys (cays), or islands, rise above the water near the Great

*Tour boat near Port Douglas*

Barrier Reef. These keys originally came into being as reefs, perhaps partially exposed at low tide, but covered by water twice each day. Day after day, year after year, sand and coral debris washed over them and coral grew on them until finally the reef emerged permanently from the ocean. Once above the ocean's surface, plants produced from seeds carried by wind, waves, and birds grew on the islands.

### Exploring the Reef

In spite of the presence of luxurious tourist resorts on a few of the larger islands, most of the smaller keys remain virtually untouched. Their total number has never been counted and most have never been explored. And if the islands are so little touched, the underwater coral jungle is even less explored. Official maps of the Great Barrier Reef still contain areas that are marked "Unexamined but Considered Dangerous to Navigation."

In spite of what appear to be many openings in the line of outer reefs, ships still pass through it at just two clearly identified openings. One—Trinity Opening—lies just opposite Cairns. The other—Flinders Passage—opens near Townsville. Skippers of even small fishing boats avoid sailing over most reefs and often have to race rapidly dropping tides to clear the coral in safety.

### Life in a Reef

The underwater world of coral provides shelter for an unbelievable diversity of marine life, including oysters, mussels, lobsters, clams, octopi, starfish, sea urchins, sponges, sea worms, and millions of fish.

All of these organisms live in the interrelated complex. Most of the fish feed off of other fish. Sharks eat snapper, which eat mackerels, which eat herrings, which eat thousands of small fish every day. The smallest ocean creatures form the base of this food chain (see Chapter 6).

The entire biological spectrum of a coral reef such as the Great Barrier Reef is so complicated that, according to one Australian marine scientist, the world's largest computer would break down even attempting to unravel its mysteries. Surely, then, the Great Barrier Reef stands as one of the earth's last and largest unknowns—a world yet to be explored.

*Green Island—one of the largest on the reef*

Oil has now been found in the northwest, in Queensland, and beneath Bass Strait between Tasmania and the mainland.

## Cultural Setting

Although British ways dominate Australia's culture, immigrants from other countries add a cosmopolitan flavor to many of the larger cities. Australians speak an English that uses many unusual words and expressions. The usual greeting is not "hello" but "g'day." The popular song "Waltzing Matilda" makes sense only if you know it is about hiking (waltzing) with a backpack (matilda).

**A brief history.** Scholars estimate that the first Australians, known as **Aborigines** (ab·uh·RIJ·uh·nees), or native people, arrived on the continent about 50,000 years ago. Theories hold that the Aborigines migrated across a land bridge that then linked Australia to Southeast Asia.

For centuries the Aborigines were Australia's only inhabitants. Then in the 1600s

*Learning from Pictures. This aboriginal rock art depicts an emu, a large flightless bird of Australia. By what route do scientists believe Australia's first people traveled to the continent?*

Europeans "discovered" the isolated continent. Captain James Cook landed at Botany Bay in 1770 and claimed the entire east coast for Britain. The British decided to use its new territory as a penal colony and transported the first convicts there in 1788. The transportation of convicts to Australia ended by 1860.

Other colonists, attracted by lands suitable for growing wheat and grazing sheep, also moved to Australia. Australia's wheat and wool became especially valuable exports to Britain, where food and raw materials supported industrialization.

In time Australia's six original colonies—New South Wales, Victoria, Western Australia, South Australia, Queensland, and Tasmania—prospered. The six colonies, soon to become states, formed the Commonwealth of Australia in 1901 and gained complete independence from Britain in 1931. However, close links remain between Britain and Australia.

**Population patterns.** Ninety-nine percent of Australia's 16.2 million people trace their descent to European ancestors. Some 87 percent of the people live in urban areas located along the coasts. About 40 percent live in the two largest cities—Sydney and Melbourne.

Only 13 percent of all Australians live in rural areas. And very few people actually live in the vast interior of the country called the "Outback." For those who do, life can be extremely lonely. Some of the isolated ranches, called "stations," cover more than 1,000 square miles (2,600 square kilometers) and lie more than 100 miles (160 kilometers) from the nearest town. Children on remote stations do their schoolwork by listening and talking to the School of the Air teachers on two-way radios.

**Social patterns.** Although the Aborigines were Australia's first settlers, today they

*Text continues on page 704.*

# CITY FOCUS
## Perth, Australia

Perth serves as the capital of the state of Western Australia and is one of the world's most isolated large urban centers. As Western Australians say jokingly, Perth is located smack in the middle of nowhere. And in a way they are right. The nearest urban neighbor, Adelaide, lies 1,700 miles (2,735 kilometers) to the east, far beyond the desolate Nullarbor Plain. The road between Adelaide and Perth was not even paved until 1976.

### Coping with Isolation

Isolation has not kept Perth from becoming a large and dynamic city. Situated along the sweeping curves of the Swan River, Perth lies 12 miles (19 kilometers) from the Indian Ocean. Perth's major industrial plants sit far from the center of the city. This helps eliminate the smog and pollution that mars the beauty of so many urban centers. It also keeps much of the heavy traffic from the city's heart.

A warm, sunny climate enhances Perth's attractiveness. Rainfall is rare in summer, and winters are mild. The average temperature for July, the coldest month of the year, is 55°F (13°C). As one of the sunniest places on earth, Perth abounds in recreational opportunities, the most popular of which may be boating. In fact, some people say that on weekends Perth's people divide into two groups—one group heading for their sailboats and the other group already on board.

### Early Settlers

Unlike much of Australia, Perth's first settlers were not prisoners or guards from Britain. Most were British farmers determined to carve out farms and ranches in Australia's far west. But few were prepared for the hardships they encountered. Living

*Perth beyond the Royal Yacht Club*

in brush huts, they battled flies, sandstorms, unfamiliar soils, and a harsh climate. They were forced to work together to survive. That spirit of cooperation still unites the people today.

### Perth Today

Perth functions as a service center for the wheat farms and sheep stations scattered over the vast interior of Western Australia. And in more recent years Perth has prospered as Western Australia has become a major world producer of iron ore, uranium, gold, and diamonds. Nearby mines also produce bauxite, nickel, cobalt, chrome, molybdenum, tantalum, and vanadium. Adding to its luster is Perth's function as the business center for Australia's oil industry. Perth enjoys a boom from recent discoveries of oil and natural gas deposits offshore. The wealth from nearby natural resources, coupled with the generous spirit that comes from its people, hold great promise for growth for this isolated metropolis on the Swan River.

*Learning from Pictures.* *Parents act as monitors for students who receive instruction by shortwave radio. Why are schools impractical in the Outback?*

Roman Catholics. Another fourth belong to other Christian denominations. A few Aborigines practice traditional religions.

**Political patterns.** A single nation known as the Commonwealth of Australia occupies the entire continent of Australia. Six self-governing states and one territory make up Australia's federation. The Northern Territory became self-governing in 1978 as the first step toward statehood. Canberra (see the map on pages 698–99) serves as the nation's capital. Australia has a democratic, parliamentary government with a constitutional monarchy. In 1986 Australia removed its final legal ties with Britain, but Queen Elizabeth II continues as head of state.

*Learning from Maps.* *Comparing the map below with the one on page 697 shows how closely settlement and rainfall patterns relate. State a generalization about the location of Australian cities.*

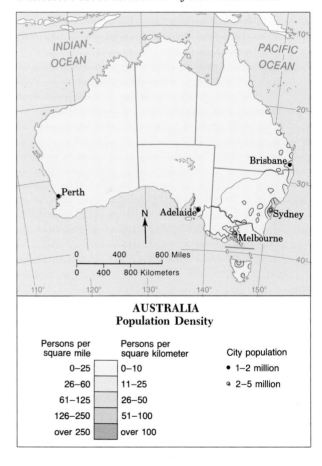

**AUSTRALIA**
**Population Density**

| Persons per square mile | Persons per square kilometer |
|---|---|
| 0–25 | 0–10 |
| 26–60 | 11–25 |
| 61–125 | 26–50 |
| 126–250 | 51–100 |
| over 250 | over 100 |

City population
● 1–2 million
◕ 2–5 million

number only 175,000, or 1 percent of the population. A few Aborigines retain their ancient way of life on reservations. The majority, however, live outside reservations on the fringes of Australian society. Often they lag far behind other Australians in education, housing, and health care.

People from England, Scotland, and Ireland were the first European immigrants to arrive in Australia and their imprint has been the strongest. When World War II ended in 1945 the Australian government encouraged other Europeans to immigrate. Over 4 million people from more than 100 different countries took advantage of special transportation fares and other bonuses. The largest numbers came from Britain, Italy, and Greece. Asians now account for many of the new immigrants.

About one-fourth of Australia's people are members of the Anglican Church, or Church of England, and one-fourth are

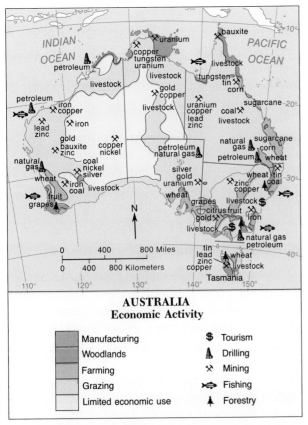

**AUSTRALIA**
**Economic Activity**

| | |
|---|---|
| Manufacturing | $ Tourism |
| Woodlands | ⚓ Drilling |
| Farming | ⚒ Mining |
| Grazing | 🐟 Fishing |
| Limited economic use | 🌲 Forestry |

***Learning from Maps.*** *Manufacturing in south-west Australia centers on metal-processing. From the data on this map, what type of product would you expect Australia to export?*

**Economic patterns.** Australia ranks as one of the world's most prosperous developed nations. The per capita GNP averages more than $11,700—higher than that of many European countries.

Farming is the basis of Australia's export economy. Agriculture employs only 7 percent of the work force but accounts for many important exports. Modern agricultural technologies and irrigation along the Murray River and its tributaries help farmers in that area produce grapes, apples, and hay. Farm products—beef, wheat, and wool—serve as its leading exports.

About one-fourth of Australia's labor force works in manufacturing. Leading products include chemicals, automobiles, electronics, textiles, and machinery.

## 2 New Zealand reflects Polynesian and European influences.

Although people often think of Australia and New Zealand together, in many ways the two nations are worlds apart. For example, plains and plateaus cover most of Australia, while ice-sculpted mountains cover much of New Zealand.

### Physical Setting

The island nation of New Zealand, roughly the size of Colorado, lies about 1,000 miles (1,600 kilometers) across the stormy Tasman Sea southeast of Australia.

**Physical regions.** New Zealand consists of two main islands—North Island and South Island—and several smaller islands. Cook Strait separates the two main islands.

A fertile volcanic plateau dominated by snowcapped Mount Egmont occupies narrow, hilly North Island. The conical mountain looms 8,261 feet (2,518 meters) above the fertile farmlands and forests that cover much of the island. Hot springs and **geysers**—jets of heated spring water and steam that shoot through cracks in the earth's crust—are sources of geothermal

**Learning from Pictures.** *Sheep ranches, or stations, cover much of New Zealand. What features of the country's physical setting make raising sheep an ideal activity?*

energy. **Geothermal energy** is energy produced by the heat of the earth's interior.

Longer, more mountainous South Island curls to the southwest of North Island. The Canterbury Plains, New Zealand's principal lowlands, are inland from the east coast near Christchurch. Behind them rise the snowcapped Southern Alps that form the island's backbone. Mount Cook—the highest peak—rises to 12,349 feet (3,766 meters). Spectacular fjords form the island's rugged southwestern coastline.

**Climate.** Because New Zealand is an island nation, the ocean dominates its climate. Marine influences blown onshore by prevailing northwest winds keep the climate mild and rainy throughout the year. Temperatures tend to be warmest in the north and coolest in the south.

**Vegetation.** In the 1800s forests covered some 75 percent of New Zealand. Today the development of pastures, farms, and towns has reduced the forests to only about 25 percent of the land. Many unique trees grow on the islands and are preserved in national parks.

**Resources.** Hydroelectricity meets 85 percent of New Zealand's electricity needs. Coal on South Island and geothermal energy and iron-bearing sands on volcanic North Island provide additional resources.

## Cultural Setting

People of Polynesian and European ancestry have contributed to New Zealand's cultural imprint. British ways, however, dominate the country's educational, judicial, and governmental systems.

**A brief history.** Polynesian colonists called Maori (MOWR·ee) settled New Zealand beginning about A.D. 800. Arriving from the Society Islands or from the Cook Islands, most of the Maori settled on North Island, with its warm climate, rather than on colder South Island.

In 1642 the Dutch explorer Abel Tasman, for whom Tasmania is named, sighted what would become New Zealand and named the islands for the Dutch province of Zeeland in the Netherlands. Captain James Cook visited the islands in the 1770s and claimed them for Britain.

British colonization of New Zealand began in the 1840s. The British made English the official language and established many of the country's cultural institutions.

**Population patterns.** Only about 3.3 million people live on sparsely populated New Zealand. Three out of every four New Zealanders live on North Island.

Urban life styles predominate in New Zealand. Auckland on North Island ranks as the largest city and chief port. Wellington,

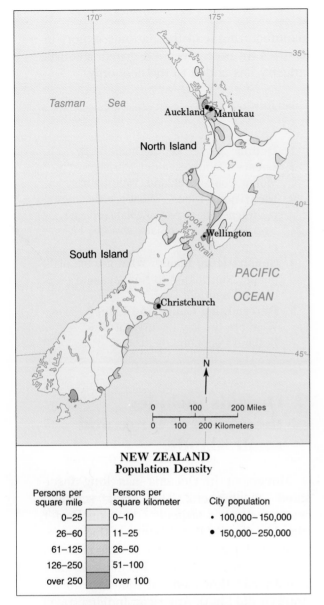

**NEW ZEALAND**
**Population Density**

| Persons per square mile | Persons per square kilometer | City population |
|---|---|---|
| 0–25 | 0–10 | • 100,000–150,000 |
| 26–60 | 11–25 | ● 150,000–250,000 |
| 61–125 | 26–50 | |
| 126–250 | 51–100 | |
| over 250 | over 100 | |

*Learning from Maps.* New Zealand's population-density patterns resemble those of Australia but for different reasons. What are these different reasons?

also on North Island, serves as New Zealand's capital. Christchurch is the largest city on South Island.

**Social patterns.** About 90 percent of all New Zealanders are of European ancestry. Contact with Europeans, however, proved disastrous to the lives of the Maori, much

as it did to the Indians of the Americas. Because they had no immunity to European diseases such as measles, thousands of Maoris became ill and died. Many others were killed in the Maori Wars of the 1860s. The number of Maori dropped to 42,000 in 1896. Today Maoris number 280,000 and make up 9 percent of the population.

More than 50 percent of the people are Protestants, belonging chiefly to either the

*Learning from Maps.* Several of South Island's higher mountains have alpine-style ski resorts. What are New Zealand's main natural resources?

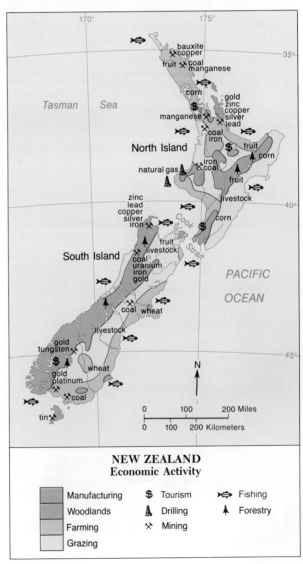

**NEW ZEALAND**
**Economic Activity**

Manufacturing
Woodlands
Farming
Grazing

$ Tourism
🛢 Drilling
⚒ Mining

🐟 Fishing
🌲 Forestry

Anglican or Presbyterian churches. Fifteen percent of the New Zealanders practice Roman Catholicism.

**Political patterns.** Like the government of Australia, New Zealand's government is a parliamentary democracy. The British monarch, represented by a governor-general, serves as the official head of state.

**Economic patterns.** Economists classify New Zealand as a developed nation. Its people enjoy one of the world's highest standards of living.

As in Australia, farm-related industries dominate New Zealand's economy. Grassland farming supplies 60 percent of all New Zealand's exports. Meat, especially lamb; wool; butter; and cheese rank as New Zealand's major agricultural products.

The small size of New Zealand's market, its distance from other trading nations, and its lack of mineral resources hamper industrialization. Food processing and textile manufacturing lead the nation's export industries. In recent years a growing tourist industry has added to the economy.

**SECTION 2 REVIEW**

1. **Define** geyser, geothermal energy
2. **Locate** Mount Egmont, Christchurch, Mount Cook, Auckland, Wellington
3. **Identifying Ideas** What are the main features of New Zealand's **(a)** landscape, **(b)** climate, and **(c)** energy resources?
4. **Summarizing Ideas** What groups of people contributed to New Zealand's cultural imprint?
5. **Determining Cause and Effect** What are the key features of New Zealand's economic patterns?

## 3 Oceania includes thousands of large and small islands.

Movement in Oceania has long fascinated geographers. The giant sculpted heads and other artifacts found on Easter Island in the mid-Pacific suggest that movements took place. But what people chiseled these works of art? Did Pacific Islanders actually sail thousands of miles to the island? Or did South American Indians travel those countless miles across the wide Pacific Ocean? Thor Heyerdahl's amazing journeys on the raft *Kon-Tiki* show that such voyages were possible. But many of the mysteries remain.

### Physical Setting

The Pacific Ocean contains some 25,000 islands. Geographers divide these islands into two basic types—high islands and low islands—according to their elevations above sea level. High islands have moun-

*Learning from Pictures.* *Workers set colored spools of wool in a pattern at a carpet factory in Christchurch. Why are sheep an especially useful agricultural product?*

708

tainous cores. They include a few large islands such as New Guinea and New Caledonia and many smaller, volcanic islands. Volcanoes formed the islands of Fiji, Samoa, the Solomons, the Marianas, and Vanuatu (vahn·uh·WAH·too).

Two types of coral reefs—atolls and exposed coral reefs—form the low islands. **Atolls,** rings of coral surrounding an inner body of water called a lagoon, form atop sunken volcanoes. Atolls seldom reach more than 3 to 5 feet (1 to 2 meters) above sea level. Examples of atolls include the Marshall Islands and Kiribati (KIR·uh·bas). Low islands built on exposed coral reefs, such as Nauru (nah·oo·roo), are flat like atolls but have no central lagoon. They form as movements of the earth or drops in sea level raise old coral reefs above the water's surface.

**Climate and vegetation.** Tropical climates dominate the Pacific Islands. Cool conditions prevail in higher elevations on the more mountainous high islands. Rainfall distribution varies greatly. The windward slopes of some high islands receive more than 150 inches (380 centimeters) of rain each year, while some low islands receive only a few inches. Vegetation reflects these differences, ranging from tropical rain forests in the mountains of high islands to a few palm trees on drier atolls.

**Resources.** Mines produce gold, copper, and nickel on New Guinea and other large islands. The volcanic and coral islands of Oceania, however, lack mineral resources. Miners throughout the region collect nodules of pure minerals from the seafloor where possible (see Chapter 6). The potential mineral wealth beneath each island's seas has created a new political map for Oceania on which sea boundaries are as important as land boundaries (see the map on pages 698–99).

***Learning from Pictures.*** *A worker splits coconuts to dry before selling the copra, dried coconut meat that yields coconut oil. What hinders the prospect of development on many islands?*

## Cultural Setting

Mysteries remain about where Oceania's first settlers came from. Many scholars believe that Polynesians used large canoes to travel throughout the region. Over the centuries they settled all but the very driest islands—a vast triangular-shaped area from Hawaii to Easter Island to New Zealand.

**Population patterns.** Papua New Guinea ranks as the most populous Pacific Island, with 3.7 million people. Of the other island countries, only Fiji has more than 500,000 people. Although Oceania has no large cities, many of its islands are overcrowded.

**Social patterns.** The people of the Pacific Islands can be divided into three groups—Melanesians, Polynesians, and Micronesians. Melanesians form a majority in the southwestern islands known collectively as Melanesia (see the map on pages 698–99).

*Text continues on page 711.*

# CASE STUDY
## GEOGRAPHY AND PEOPLE: Fa'a Samoa

*Matai at a title-granting ceremony*

In the sparkling blue waters of the South Pacific Ocean, about 4,800 miles (7,720 kilometers) southwest of San Francisco, lie the Samoan Islands. Foreign diplomats divided the islands in the 1890s into American Samoa, which remains an American possession, and German Samoa, which in 1962 became independent Western Samoa after more than 50 years as a trust territory of New Zealand.

Despite the division, the people who live in the two Samoas speak the same language and follow the same traditions. *Fa'a Samoa*—the Samoan way of thinking and acting—unites them. It sets the rules for conduct that make for harmonious living.

### Led by the Matai

Life on Samoa traditionally centers on the *aiga*, or extended family. Members of an aiga live in the same village and each aiga chooses a *matai,* or family chief.

The matai is a person of great importance. Fa'a Samoa requires the matai to be treated with honor and respect. Members of the aiga bring him gifts and serve food to him first. His meal always consists of the most desirable portions of food.

The matai also has great responsibilities. The matai must provide leadership and guidance in all matters. He plans for the aiga, settles disputes, and arranges marriages. Each morning the members of the aiga gather in front of their matai's house to await their daily work assignments.

### Changing Life Styles

Opposing fa'a Samoa is *fa'a papalagi,* meaning "way of the skybuster." Fa'a papalagi is the way of outsiders. With the coming of the papalagi, new ideas began to change the traditional Samoan way of life. For example, outsiders brought new ways to earn a living. Coconut plantations producing copra for export replaced traditional farms. People on the plantations eventually challenged the traditional authority of the matai to assign village workloads.

The modern technology of outsiders caused other changes. Television brought images of a way of life quite different from fa'a Samoa. Many young Samoan men and women, seeing new opportunities, chose to move away from Samoa. Today American Samoans often travel to the United States, while Western Samoans travel to New Zealand. Samoans returning to their villages cause further problems. Many see no reason to obey the matai and find the traditional ceremonies tedious and boring. Even those who have never left the village have begun to question fa'a Samoa. The changes have rapidly altered the unique and orderly ways of fa'a Samoa.

Melanesia includes the independent countries of Papua New Guinea, the Solomon Islands, Vanuatu, and Fiji, as well as France's colony of New Caledonia. Polynesia, meaning "many islands," extends from Easter Island, which belongs to Chile, to the International Date Line, which closely follows the 180° meridian (see the maps on pages 698–99 and 713). Micronesia, or "little islands," lies generally north of the equator in the western Pacific. Much of Micronesia consists of tiny atolls.

**Political patterns.** During the 1800s and early 1900s most of the Pacific Islands became the colonial possessions of Britain, France, Germany, and the United States. Japan took over many of the German possessions after World War I. These same islands became bloody battlegrounds in the Pacific campaigns of World War II. After the war the United Nations designated many of these islands as **trust territories,** or territories supervised by another nation until they can govern themselves. The United States, for example, administers most of Micronesia as the United Nations Trust Territory of the Pacific Islands. Since the 1960s many of the islands have gained independence.

**Economic patterns.** Most of the Pacific Islands are developing nations that lack mineral wealth, have low per capita GNPs, and high unemployment. Subsistence farming remains the chief economic activity. The Europeans introduced commercial agriculture and mining to some islands. The small size of many islands, however, limits farm output. Many islands export only copra. Some of the larger islands export bananas and coffee.

Tourism has developed on several islands, but it sometimes disrupts traditional life styles and brings more economic benefits to outsiders than to the islanders.

## SECTION 3 REVIEW

1. **Define**   atoll, trust territory
2. **Locate**   Papua New Guinea, New Caledonia, Fiji, Samoa, Solomon Islands, Mariana Islands, Vanuatu, Marshall Islands, Kiribati, Nauru, Melanesia, Polynesia, Micronesia
3. **Determining Cause and Effect** How are the different types of Pacific Islands formed?
4. **Interpreting Ideas**   What movements of people took place within Oceania in the past?
5. **Analyzing Ideas**   Why has building a strong economy been difficult for most of the new countries in Oceania?

# 4  The cold, ice-covered continent of Antarctica remains uninhabited.

Antarctica ranks as the world's third-smallest continent—larger than Europe and Australia. A mantle of ice thousands of feet thick makes Antarctica the highest continent, and its location at the South Pole makes it the coldest.

## A Frigid Land

Antarctica's bitter temperatures often reach −100°F (−73°C). The almost constant wind intensifies the cold. The enormous ice and snow mass that makes up Antarctica averages 8,000 feet (2,440 meters) thick. Despite the large amounts of ice and snow that cover the continent, geographers classify Antarctica as a desert because it receives little precipitation. The snow that does fall never melts and the pressure caused by the tremendous weight of the snow turns it to ice. Huge sections of this glacial mass break off the edges of the continent, filling the ocean with icebergs.

## Life in Antarctica

Abundant marine life, including seals and whales, inhabits the cold waters off Antarctica. Indigenous bird life provides a number of types of penguins. The Adélie penguin uses the same nest every year. The larger emperor penguin has no fixed nest and carries its eggs atop its feet.

With so much ice and cold it may seem surprising that lichens and mosses grow on the barren, windswept valleys of Antarctica. Tiny insects live on those plants during the short summers.

Explorers know that Antarctica has deposits of coal and reserves of other minerals. Unfortunately, no economically feasible way to extract these resources from beneath the ice is currently available.

Antarctica remained unknown for centuries. Its coast was not sighted until the 1800s, and the continent remained unexplored until this century. In 1911 a Norwegian team led by Roald Amundsen became the first to reach the South Pole. Since that time explorers and scientists have set up bases to observe the climate, soil, and

### GEOGRAPHIC HIGHLIGHTS OF OCEANIA AND ANTARCTICA

INDONESIA

HOTTEST SPOT
Cloncurry
128°F/53°C

AUSTRALIA

LOWEST SPOT
Lake Eyre
− 38 ft/− 12 m

COLDEST SPOT
Vostok*
− 127°F/− 88°C

ANTARCTICA
+
South Pole

HIGHEST SPOT
Vinson Massif
16,863 ft/5,140 m

*World Record

Source: *World Almanac and Book of Facts*, 1987

*Learning from Maps.* Australia and Antarctica have some examples of extreme weather and climate. How do their locations produce such extremes?

animal and marine life, but no people inhabit Antarctica permanently. In 1959 several countries, including the United States and the Soviet Union, agreed to allow freedom of scientific investigation on Antarctica and agreed to ban the testing of nuclear weapons there.

*Learning from Pictures.* Wildlife such as these penguins are Antarctica's only permanent inhabitants. In 1959 what agreement did world nations reach concerning Antarctica?

### SECTION 4 REVIEW

1. **Locate** Antarctica, South Pole
2. **Summarizing Ideas** What characteristics distinguish Antarctica from the other continents?
3. **Analyzing Ideas** What benefits might Antarctica provide for the people of the world in the future?

# DEVELOPING GEOGRAPHY SKILLS
## THINKING GEOGRAPHICALLY: Understanding Time Zones

As you have learned, the earth rotates on its axis. It makes one rotation, or complete circle of 360°, every 24 hours. This means the earth rotates 15° each hour. The system of world time zones divides the earth into 24 time zones—one for every 15° on a globe or map.

### How to Understand Time Zones

The map below shows world time zones. The numbers across the top indicate what time it is in each time zone when it is noon along the prime meridian (see Chapter 1). Note that the hours are earlier moving from east to west. This is because the earth rotates in that direction. The numbers at the bottom show the difference in hours at a zone from that at the prime meridian.

A map of time zones also contains two special features. First is the international date line, which falls 180° from the prime meridian. This line, set by international agreement, indicates where each day first begins. As you can see on the map it is Sunday to the east of the line and Monday to the west. The other special feature is the nonstandard time zones, areas that vary from agreed-upon time zones.

### Applying the Skill

Study the map below again. You can see the various time zones, times, and time differences in the United States and the world.

*To practice this skill, see Practicing Geography Skills on page 715.*

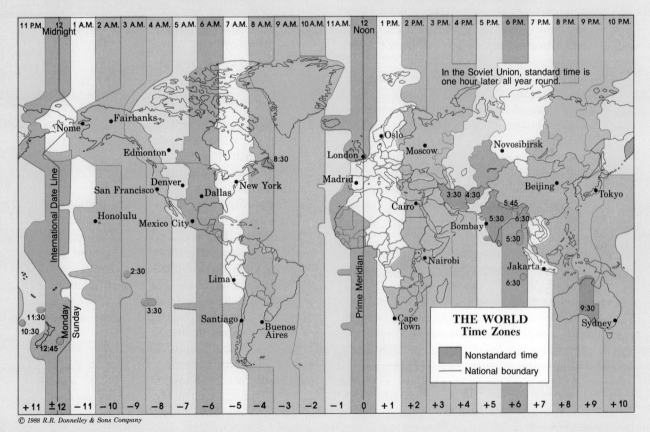

In the Soviet Union, standard time is one hour later all year round.

**THE WORLD Time Zones**

Nonstandard time

National boundary

© 1988 R.R. Donnelley & Sons Company

713

## Chapter Summary

The following list contains the key concepts you have learned about the countries of Oceania and the continent of Antarctica.

1. Australia's physical regions include the Great Dividing Range, the Central Lowlands, the Western Plateau, and the Great Barrier Reef.
2. Australia is sparsely populated because uninhabitable deserts cover much of the land. Most Australians live along the continent's southeast coast.
3. Abundant underground water collected in artesian basins compensates for Australia's lack of surface water.
4. Although the Aborigines were Australia's first inhabitants, they account for only 1 percent of the population today. Most Australians claim European descent.
5. Farming remains the basis of Australia's economy. Australia's leading farm products—beef, wheat, and wool—head the list of exports.
6. New Zealand has a mixed population of European and Polynesian ancestry.
7. New Zealand has an agricultural economy with an emphasis on sheep raising.
8. Manufacturing in New Zealand is limited by a small domestic market, isolation from other trading nations, and lack of minerals.
9. Geographers divide the Pacific Islands into two basic groups—high islands and low islands—according to their elevations above sea level.
10. Independence movements brought independence to many Pacific Islands since 1960.
11. Samoa remains a largely traditional society based on age-old ways even though contact with outsiders is influencing life today.
12. Antarctica is a frigid, dry, uninhabited continent in the Southern Hemisphere.

On a separate sheet of paper, complete the following review exercises.

## Reviewing Geographic Terms

Supply the geographic term that correctly completes each sentence.

1. The heat generated by the earth's interior is the source of ____ ____.
2. Koalas, kangaroos, and wallabies carry their young in pouches, making them ____.
3. In New Zealand, as elsewhere, heated spring water shoots up through cracks in the earth as ____.
4. Shallow sheets of water spread out over desert basins in the rainy season to form ____.
5. Underground water-bearing rocks, or ____, hold much of Australia's available water.
6. After World War II many of the small islands in the Pacific became ____ ____ administered by the United Nations.
7. Slightly folded porous rocks fill with rain water to form huge ____ ____ underneath Australia.
8. Rings of coral surrounding an inner body of water called a lagoon that form atop sunken volcanoes are known as ____.

## Developing Critical Thinking Skills

1. **Interpreting Ideas**  Why did Australian wool and wheat become so important in industrializing Britain?
2. **Understanding Ideas**  Why do most Australians live along the coast?
3. **Comparing Ideas**  Cite the similarities and differences between Australia's and New Zealand's **(a)** landscapes, **(b)** climates, **(c)** population patterns, **(d)** social patterns, and **(e)** economic patterns.
4. **Summarizing Ideas**  **(a)** Identify and describe the three types of islands in Oceania. **(b)** Into what three island groups are the Pacific Islands divided? **(c)** How is each of these island groups distinctive?
5. **Distinguishing Ideas**  **(a)** Which Pacific Islands are self-governing? **(b)** Which countries still control territories in Oceania? **(c)** Why do these countries retain control?

6. **Synthesizing Ideas**   How have the effects of modernization on the Masai of Africa and the Samoans of the Pacific been similar?
7. **Contrasting Ideas**   How is Antarctica different from the other continents?
8. **Writing About Geography**   In a clearly-written essay, complete one of the following activities.   **(a)** Discuss what effects the relative locations of Australia and New Zealand have had on economic development in those two nations. Why are their relative locations probably less influential than they were 50 years ago?   **(b)** Describe in detail what the Pacific Islands might do to develop stronger economic patterns.

## Using Primary Sources

In the following excerpt from *The Australians: How They Live and Work*, Nancy Learmonth discusses how the original settlers of Australia reached the continent. As you study the reading, consider whether the American Indians might have arrived and developed in a similar manner in the Americas.

The Aboriginal people probably reached Australia by a former land link with south-east Asia. Their arrival is estimated to have been spread over a period from 32,000 to 12,000 years ago, following the last ice age. They brought with them only the dingo [wild dog] and their nomadic way of life which depended entirely on what they could hunt or gather. Survival depended on a very thorough understanding of their environment, and they were really the first conservationists, for to destroy that environment meant starvation. Their migrations followed the seed time of grasses and the fruiting of trees and shrubs, the movements of fish and even of moths which took the tribes up to the high summer pastures. Kangaroo and wallaby were hunted by spear

and throwing-stick; these sticks did not return to the thrower like the boomerang, that fascinating aero-dynamic discovery the Aborigines kept only as a toy for their amusement. Game was flushed out by fire; but although widespread bushfires clearly affected the vegetation long before the white man came they were modest effects compared with those wrought by two centuries of European occupance. Only a few hundred Aborigines still follow the old tribal way of life out of contact with the white man.

1. According to the author, along what route did the Aborigines travel to reach Australia?
2. Why does the author describe the Aborigines as among the first conservationists?

## Practicing Geography Skills

*Before completing this activity, review Developing Geography Skills on page 713.*

**Understanding Time Zones**   Study the time zone map on page 713. Then answer the following questions.

1. If it is noon in London, what time is it in **(a)** Dallas, **(b)** Honolulu, and **(c)** Beijing?
2. If it is Friday in Nome, Alaska, what day is it in Sydney, Australia?

## Exploring Geography

1. Construct a time line showing the major events in Australian history from Captain James Cook's landing on the east coast in 1770 to the bicentennial celebrations of 1988.
2. New Zealand has long been a powerhouse in the sport of rugby. Use resources in your school or public library to find information on this sport and prepare an oral presentation on the similarities and differences between rugby and American football.

# UNIT 12 REVIEW

## Unit Summary

The following list contains the key concepts you have learned about Southeast Asia, Oceania, and Antarctica.

1. In many ways location and movement are the keys to understanding Southeast Asia, Oceania, and Australia.
2. Geographers divide Southeast Asia into Peninsular and Insular Southeast Asia.
3. Landscape varies throughout these regions. Mountains crisscross Indochina and New Zealand and form the islands of Southeast Asia, while most of Australia and the Pacific Islands are flat.
4. Southeast Asia's tropical climate ranges from wet to wet-and-dry. New Zealand and the Pacific Islands also receive abundant rainfall. Australia is very dry.
5. Wave after wave of human migrants have left a great diversity of ethnic and cultural groups in Southeast Asia today. The first settlers in Australia were eventually cut off from other areas. Different groups of people moved about the Pacific Islands in large canoes.
6. Farmers throughout Southeast Asia grow rice, which is the basis for most of the people's diets. Australian and New Zealand farmers and ranchers raise a wide variety of products. Farming is limited on most Pacific Islands.
7. Conflicts among different groups within the countries cause problems in several Southeast Asian countries. Australia, New Zealand, and the Pacific Islands are more homogeneous and stable.
8. Location astride world trade routes has long been a key to Southeast Asian development. Australia's industries produce mostly for local markets. Isolation has hindered the development of industry in New Zealand. Little industry exists on the Pacific Islands.
9. All of the Southeast Asian countries except industrializing Singapore are developing nations, as are the Pacific Islands. Brunei, while a developing nation, prospers from oil. Australia and New Zealand are developed nations.
10. Settlement patterns throughout the region are typical of elsewhere in the world. Most people live where water and fertile soil are available.
11. Political patterns vary throughout these lands depending on their historical and colonial pasts.

On a separate sheet of paper, complete the following review exercises.

## Checking Your Understanding

1. How do water sources and supplies in Southeast Asia and Australia differ?
2. How do volcanic activities affect Southeast Asia and Oceania?
3. (a) How are Australia and Antarctica alike? (b) How are they different?
4. (a) What are the major problems facing Southeast Asia today? (b) What are the major problems facing the Pacific Islands?
5. Why have the matai of Samoa lost much of their authority?

## Applying Critical Thinking Skills

1. **Organizing Ideas** How have India and China influenced Southeast Asia?
2. **Summarizing Ideas** (a) Along what route did prehistoric people travel to the islands of Southeast Asia and Australia? (b) How and why has that route changed?
3. **Determining Cause and Effect** (a) What causes the alternation of wet and dry seasons in Southeast Asia? (b) What causes the vast expanse of dry lands in Australia?
4. **Contrasting Ideas** (a) Why have some countries in Southeast Asia adopted national languages? (b) Why was it not necessary for Australia to do the same?

5. **Interpreting Ideas** (a) In what ways did the colonial experiences of Australia and New Zealand differ from those of the Southeast Asian colonies? (b) How have these differences in colonial experiences led to differences as independent countries?

6. **Analyzing Ideas** (a) In what ways do the problems facing Southeast Asian countries resemble those facing many Pacific Islands? (b) In what ways do their problems differ?

7. **Evaluating Ideas** Do you think the changes Samoan society is undergoing are beneficial or harmful? Support your answer.

## Reviewing Unit Features

1. **Geography in the Workplace** What special training must explorers and foreign area specialists have?

2. **City Focus** What aspects of Bangkok are particularly distinctive?

3. **The Geographic Web** How do barrier reefs form?

4. **City Focus** What gives Perth its economic vitality?

## Using Map Skills

1. Compare the maps on pages 672 and 704. How do the population distribution patterns of Southeast Asia and Australia differ?

2. Examine the map entitled "The Pacific World: Physical/Political" on pages 698–99. Why are most of the countries on this map considered fragmented nations?

## Investigating Geography

1. Select one of the countries of Southeast Asia and study the cultural setting. Report on the highlights of the culture—music, architecture, dance, art, and literature. If available, add pictures of the architecture, art, and clothing and samples of literature and music.

2. Investigate the research efforts underway in Antarctica. Prepare a report that answers the following questions. What nations have research stations there? What are the researchers studying and what have they discovered? What is life at such stations like?

## Further Readings

### Chapter 34
Cook, David C. *The Tribal People of Thailand.* New York: G. P. Putnam's Sons. Describes the author's travels among the tribal people of Thailand, focusing on their form of government, customs, and tribal religions.

### Chapter 35
Poole, Frederick King. *Malaysia and Singapore.* New York: Franklin Watts, Inc. Provides a pictorial essay of the people and activities of Singapore and Malaysia.

Smith, Datus C., Jr. *The Land and People of Indonesia.* New Revised Edition. New York: J. B. Lippincott. Deals with Indonesia's rich cultural tradition, the influence of the Dutch who once occupied Indonesia, and some of the men and women who have helped to unite Indonesia into a modern state.

### Chapter 36
Booth, Robert. "The Two Samoas, Still Coming of Age." *National Geographic*, 168; October 1985. Describes both traditional and current Samoan society and illustrates the changes the society is undergoing.

Frank, R. *Ice Island: The Story of Antarctica.* New York: Thomas Y. Crowell, Inc. Traces the history of Antarctica from its discovery to the famous expeditions to the South Pole of Amundsen, Scott, and Byrd.

Henderson, W. F. and R. A. Henderson. *Looking at Australia.* Philadelphia: J. B. Lippincott. Illustrates the land, people, and culture of Australia in pictures and text.

Lepthien, Emilie V. *Australia.* Chicago: Childrens Press. Highlights the physical and cultural uniqueness of Australia and discusses its aboriginal societies and later English development.

# THE REFERENCE LIBRARY

# Pronunciation Guide

Many of the key terms in this textbook have been respelled to help you pronounce them. The following Phonetic Respelling and Pronunciation Guide offers the simplest form of usage and is adapted from *Webster's Ninth New Collegiate Dictionary*, *Webster's New Geographical Dictionary*, and *Webster's New Biographical Dictionary*. The letter combinations used in the respellings are explained below.

| Phonetic Mark | As In | Respelling | Example |
|---|---|---|---|
| a | alphabet | a | *AL·fuh·bet |
| ā | Asia | ay | AY·zhuh |
| ä | cart, top | ah | KAHRT, TAHP |
| e | let, ten | e | LET, TEN |
| ē | even, leaf | ee | EE·vuhn, LEEF |
| i | it, tip, British | i | IT, TIP, BRIT·ish |
| ī | site, buy, Ohio | y | SYT, BY, oh·HY·oh |
| | iris | eye | EYE·ris |
| k | card | k | KARD |
| ō | over, rainbow | oh | oh·vuhr, RAYN·boh |
| u̇ | book, wood | ooh | BOOHK, WOOHD |
| ȯ | all, orchid | aw | AWL, AWR·kid |
| ȯi | foil, coin | oy | FOYL, KOYN |
| au̇ | out | ow | OWT |
| ə | cup, butter | uh | KUHP, BUHT·uhr |
| ü | rule, food | oo | ROOL, FOOD |
| yü | few | yoo | FYOO |
| zh | vision | zh | VIZH·uhn |

*A syllable printed in small capital letters receives heavier emphasis than the other syllables in a word.

## Pinyin

Most of the names of Chinese people and Chinese geographical names in this textbook use the Roman alphabet and pronunciation system introduced by the Chinese in the 1950s and in general use since the 1970s. This system, called Pinyin, most accurately reflects the sounds of the Chinese language. The United States government and many newspapers, magazines, and atlases accept and use Pinyin. Both the maps and narrative in this textbook consistently use Pinyin. Some exceptions occur where the names are so well known by their older spellings—using the Wade-Giles system—that the use of Pinyin would confuse rather than help you. Exceptions include Chiang Kai-shek, Tibet, Hong Kong, Mongolia, and the word "China" itself.

| NATION/ Capital/ Population/ Natural Increase | National Flag | Land Area/ { sq mi/ Density/ ∫ (sq km) Percent Urban/ Per Capita GNP | Land Use | Imports | Exports |
|---|---|---|---|---|---|
| **NORTH AMERICA**\*\* | | | | | |
| UNITED STATES Washington, D.C. 243,084,000 0.7% | | 3,615,123(9,399,320) 64.9(168.1) 74 $16,500 | 32% forests; 27% pastures; 19% cultivated; 22% wasteland, other | crude and partially refined petroleum, machinery, transport equipment | machinery, chemicals, transport equipment, agricultural products |
| CANADA Ottawa 25,857,943 0.8% | | 3,851,809(10,014,703) 7.1(18.4) 76 $13,670 | 44% forests; 4% cultivated; 2% pastures; 50% wasteland, other | transport equipment, crude petroleum, communication equipment, textiles, steel | transport equipment, wood and wood products, ores, crude petroleum |
| **MIDDLE AMERICA** | | | | | |
| ANTIGUA & BARBUDA St. John's 69,280 1.0% | | 171(445) 472.1(1,222.8) 34 $2,030 | 54% arable; 18% wasteland, built on; 14% forests; 9% unused; 5% pastures | fuel, food, machinery | clothing, rum, lobsters |
| BAHAMAS Nassau 238,817 1.8% | | 5,386(14,004) 42.7(110.6) 75 $7,150 | 70% built on; 29% forests; 1% cultivated | food, manufactured goods, mineral fuels | pharmaceuticals, cement, rum, crayfish |
| BARBADOS Bridgetown 323,839 0.9% | | 166(432) 1,522(3,942) 32 $4,680 | 60% cropland; 30% built on, unused, wasteland; 10% meadows | food, consumer durables, fuels, machinery | sugar, sugarcane byproducts, electrical parts, clothing |
| BELIZE Belmopan 168,204 2.7% | | 8,867(23,054) 18.8(48.7) 52 $1,130 | 46% forests; 38% agricultural; 16% wasteland, other | machinery and transport equipment, food, manufactured goods, fuels, chemicals | sugar, garments, seafood, molasses, citrus fruits, wood and wood products |
| COSTA RICA San José 2,811,652 2.7% | | 19,652(50,095) 128.9(333.9) 48 $1,290 | 60% forests; 30% agricultural; 10% wasteland, other | manufactured products, fuels, machinery, transport equipment, chemicals, food | coffee, beef, bananas, sugar, cocoa |
| CUBA Havana 10,259,473 1.2% | | 44,218(114,967) 235(609) 71 NA\* | 35% cultivated; 30% pastures; 15% forests; 20% wasteland, other | capital goods, industrial raw materials, food, petroleum | sugar, nickel, shellfish, tobacco, coffee, citrus |
| DOMINICA Roseau 94,191 1.7% | | 289(751) 256(663) 46 $1,160 | 67% forests; 24% arable; 2% pastures; 7% other | machinery and equipment, food, manufactured articles, cement | bananas, coconuts, lime juice and oil, cocoa |
| DOMINICAN REPUBLIC Santo Domingo 6,960,743 2.5% | | 18,657(48,508) 333.8(864.6) 52 $810 | 45% forests; 20% built on, wasteland; 17% pastures; 14% cultivated; 4% fallowland | food, petroleum, industrial raw materials, capital equipment | sugar, nickel, coffee, tobacco, cocoa, gold, silver |
| EL SALVADOR San Salvador 5,260,478 2.6% | | 8,260(21,476) 644.5(1,669.3) 43 $710 | 32% cropland; 31% nonagricultural; 26% pastures; 11% forests | machinery, intermediate goods, petroleum, construction materials, fertilizer, food | coffee, cotton, sugar, shrimp |

\*NA: Information not available.
\*\*Land area of Greenland 839,999 sq mi/2,183,997 sq km

Geodata Files

| NATION/ Capital/ Population/ Natural Increase | National Flag | Land Area/ sq mi/ Density/ (sq km) Percent Urban/ Per Capita GNP | Land Use | Imports | Exports |
|---|---|---|---|---|---|
| GRENADA St. George's 84,748 1.9% | | 120(312) 725.2(1,878.3) NA $970 | 44% cultivated; 17% unused; 12% forests; 4% pastures; 23% built on, wasteland, other | food, machinery and transport equipment, oil, building materials | cocoa beans, nutmeg, bananas, mace (spice) |
| GUATEMALA Guatemala 8,622,387 3.2% | | 42,042(109,309) 182.5(472.7) 39 $1,240 | 57% forests; 10% pastures; 14% cultivated; 19% other | manufactured products, machinery, transport equipment, chemicals, fuels | coffee, cotton, sugar, meat, bananas |
| HAITI Port-au-Prince 6,187,115 2.3% | | 10,714(27,856) 507(1,313) 26 $350 | 44% unproductive; 31% cultivated; 18% pastures; 7% forests | consumer durables, food, industrial equipment, petroleum products, construction materials | mangos, coffee, light industrial products, sisal, sugar |
| HONDURAS Tegucigalpa 4,823,818 3.1% | | 43,277(112,520) 101(262) 40 $730 | 36% wasteland and built on; 30% pastures; 27% forests; 7% cropland | manufactured products, machinery, transport equipment, chemicals | bananas, coffee, lumber, meat, petroleum products |
| JAMAICA Kingston 2,455,536 2.0% | | 4,471(11,625) 552.2(1,430.2) 54 $940 | 23% pastures; 21% arable; 19% forests; 37% wasteland, other | fuels, machinery, transportation and electrical equipment, food, fertilizer | alumina, bauxite, sugar, bananas, citrus, rum, cocoa |
| MEXICO Mexico City 82,860,566 2.5% | | 761,600(1,980,160) 103.5(268.1) 70 $2,080 | 40% pastures; 22% forests; 12% cropland; 26% wasteland, other | machinery, equipment, vehicles, intermediate goods | cotton, coffee, nonferrous minerals, shrimp, petroleum, sulfur, salt, cattle, meat |
| NICARAGUA Managua 3,319,059 3.4% | | 49,579(128,905) 66.5(172.2) 53 $850 | 50% forests; 7% arable; 7% pastures; 36% wasteland, other | food and nonfood agricultural products, chemicals and pharmaceuticals, transport equipment | cotton, coffee, chemical products, meat, sugar, seafood |
| PANAMA Panama 2,274,833 2.2% | | 33,659(87,513) 73.3(189) 51 $2,020 | 24% arable; 20% exploitable forests; 56% other forests, wasteland, other | petroleum, manufactured goods, machinery and transport equipment, chemicals | petroleum products, bananas, shrimp, sugar |
| ST. CHRISTOPHER-NEVIS Basseterre; Charlestown 54,775 1.6% | | 118(307) 455.9(1,180.1) 45 $1,520 | 40% arable; 33% wasteland, built on; 17% forests; 10% pastures | food, manufactures, fuel | sugar |
| SAINT LUCIA Castries 152,305 2.5% | | 238(619) 577.4(1,495.5) 40 $1,210 | 50% arable; 23% wasteland, built on; 27% forests; unused, other | food, machinery, equipment, fertilizer, petroleum products | bananas, cocoa |
| ST. VINCENT & THE GRENADINES Kingstown 131,215 2.0% | | 150(390) 698.6(1,809.4) 26 $840 | 50% arable; 44% forests; 3% pastures; 3% wasteland, other | food, machinery, equipment, chemicals, fertilizers, minerals, fuels | bananas, arrowroot, copra |
| TRINIDAD & TOBAGO Port-of-Spain 1,250,839 2.0% | | 1,980(5148) 600.5(1,555.3) 34 $6,010 | 42% cropland; 58% grasses, forests, built on, wasteland, other | crude petroleum, machinery, fabricated metals, transport equipment, manufactured goods | petroleum and petroleum products, ammonia, fertilizer, chemicals, sugar |

*NA: Information not available.

| NATION/ Capital/ Population/ Natural Increase | National Flag | Land Area/ sq mi/ Density/ (sq km) Percent Urban/ Per Capita GNP | Land Use | Imports | Exports |
|---|---|---|---|---|---|
| **SOUTH AMERICA** | | | | | |
| ARGENTINA Buenos Aires 31,144,775 1.6% | | 1,072,156(2,787,606) 28.5(73.8) 84 $2,130 | 57% agricultural; 25% forests; 18% mountains, wasteland, other | chemicals, machinery, fuel | wheat, corn, oilseed, hides, wool |
| BOLIVIA La Paz; Sucre 6,309,642 2.6% | | 424,162(1,102,821) 15.2(39.4) 48 $470 | 47% deserts, wasteland, other; 40% forests; 11% pastures; 2% cultivated | food, chemicals, capital goods, pharmaceuticals | tin, natural gas, silver, tungsten, zinc, antimony, gold, coffee, sugar, bismuth |
| BRAZIL Brasilia 147,094,739 2.1% | | 3,284,426(8,539,508) 41.2(106.7) 71 $1,640 | 60% forests; 23% built on, wasteland, other; 13% pastures; 4% cultivated | petroleum, machinery, chemicals, fertilizers, wheat, copper | soybeans, coffee, transport equipment, iron ore, steel products |
| CHILE Santiago 12,448,008 1.6% | | 292,257(759,868) 42.4(109.8) 83 $1,440 | 47% mountains, deserts, other; 29% forests; 15% pastures; 9% arable | petroleum, sugar, wheat, capital goods, vehicles | copper, molybdenum, iron ore, paper products, steel products, fishmeal, fruits |
| COLOMBIA Bogotá 30,660,504 2.1% | | 439,735(1,143,311) 65.4(169.4) 65 $1,320 | 72% forests and savanna; 14% pastures; 9% other; 5% cropland | transport equipment, machinery, industrial metals, raw materials, fuels | coffee, coal, fuel oil, cotton, tobacco, sugar, textiles, cattle hides |
| ECUADOR Quito 9,954,609 2.8% | | 109,483(284,656) 82.8(214.5) 51 $1,160 | 55% forests; 11% cultivated; 8% pastures; 26% wasteland, other | machinery, industrial raw materials, building supplies | petroleum, fish products, coffee, cocoa, bananas |
| GUYANA Georgetown 765,844 2.0% | | 83,000(215,800) 11.5(29.8) 32 $570 | 66% forests; 22% wasteland, other; 8% savanna; 3% pastures; 1% cropland | manufactures, machinery, food, petroleum | bauxite, sugar, rice, shrimp, molasses, timber, rum |
| GUYANE Cayenne 92,038 2.3% FRANCE | | 35,135(91,351) 2.3(6.0) 73 $3,230 | 82% forests; 18% other | food, other consumer goods, producer goods, petroleum | shrimp, timber, rum, rosewood essence |
| PARAGUAY Asunción 4,251,924 2.9% | | 157,043(408,312) 21.7(56.2) 43 $940 | 52% forests; 24% pastures; 22% wasteland; 2% cropland | fuels and lubricants, machinery and motors, motor vehicles, beverages, tobacco, food | cotton, oilseeds, meat products, tobacco, timber, coffee, essential oils, tung oil |
| PERU Lima 20,739,218 2.5% | | 496,222(1,290,177) 39.7(102.8) 69 $960 | 55% forests; 14% pastures; 2% cropland; 29% wasteland, other | food, machinery, transport equipment, iron and steel semimanufactures, chemicals | fishmeal, cotton, sugar, coffee, copper, iron ore, gold, refined silver, lead, zinc |
| SURINAME Paramaribo 388,636 2.1% | | 63,251(164,453) 6.2(16.1) 66 $2,570 | 76% forests; 16% built on, wasteland, other; 8% unused | capital equipment, petroleum, iron and steel, cotton, flour, meat, dairy products | alumina, bauxite, aluminum, rice, wood and wood products |
| URUGUAY Montevideo 2,964,052 0.8% | | 68,536(178,194) 44.3(114.7) 85 $1,660 | 84% agricultural; 16% forests, wasteland, other | fuels and lubricants, metals, machinery, transport equipment, industrial chemicals | wool, hides, meat, textiles, leather products, fish, rice, furs |
| VENEZUELA Caracas 18,300,000 2.7% | | 352,143(915,572) 49.2(127.4) 76 $3,110 | 21% forests; 18% pastures; 4% cropland; 57% wasteland, other | machinery and transport equipment, chemicals, food | petroleum |

| NATION/ Capital/ Population/ Natural Increase | National Flag | Land Area/ sq mi/ (sq km) Density/ Percent Urban/ Per Capita GNP | Land Use | Imports | Exports |
|---|---|---|---|---|---|
| **WESTERN EUROPE** | | | | | |
| ANDORRA Andorra la Vella 47,973 1.0% | | 180(468) 238.2(616.9) 66 $9,000 | Mostly pasture | consumer goods | agricultural products |
| AUSTRIA Vienna 7,569,283 0.0% | | 32,375(84,175) 233.2(604) 55 $9,150 | 33% forests; 26% pastures; 20% cultivated; 21% wasteland, other | machinery and equipment, chemicals, textiles and clothing, petroleum, food | iron and steel products, machinery and equipment, lumber, textiles, chemicals |
| BELGIUM Brussels 9,873,066 0.0% | | 11,781(30,631) 836.7(2,167.1) 95 $8,450 | 28% cultivated; 28% wasteland, other; 24% pastures; 20% forests | fuels, food, chemicals | cars, petroleum products, chemicals |
| DENMARK Copenhagen 5,121,766 −0.1% | | 16,629(43,235) 307.2(795.6) 84 $11,240 | 64% arable; 11% forests; 8% pastures; 17% other | industrial machinery, transport equipment, petroleum, textile fibers | meat, dairy products, machinery and equipment |
| FINLAND Helsinki 4,939,880 0.3% | | 130,128(338,333) 41.7(108) 60 $10,870 | 58% forests; 8% arable; 34% other | food, petroleum, chemicals, transport equipment, iron, steel, machinery | timber, paper, ships, machinery, clothing, footwear |
| FRANCE Paris 55,596,030 0.4% | | 212,918(553,587) 262.6(680.1) 73 $9,550 | 34% cultivated; 24% pastures; 27% forests; 15% wasteland, other | crude petroleum, machinery and equipment, agricultural products, chemicals | machinery and transport equipment, chemicals, food, agricultural products |
| GERMANY, FEDERAL REPUBLIC OF Bonn 60,989,419 −0.2% | | 182,426(474,308) 638.5(1,653.7) 85 $10,940 | 33% cultivated; 29% forests; 23% pastures; 15% wasteland, other | manufactures, fuels, agricultural products | machinery, vehicles, manufactures, agricultural products, fuels, raw materials |
| GREECE Athens 9,987,785 0.2% | | 50,944(132,454) 195.6(506.6) 70 $3,550 | 40% pastures; 29% arable; 20% forests; 11% wasteland, other | machinery and automotive equipment, petroleum, manufactured goods | tobacco, minerals, fruits, textiles |
| ICELAND Reykjavik 244,676 0.9% | | 39,702(103,225) 6.1(15.8) 89 $10,720 | 22% pastures; 78% other | machinery and transport equipment, petroleum, food, textiles | fish, animal products, aluminum, diatomite |
| IRELAND Dublin 3,534,553 0.8% | | 26,600(69,160) 135.9(352) 56 $4,840 | 51% pastures; 29% wasteland, other; 17% arable; 3% forests | machinery, petroleum, chemicals, semifinished goods, cereals | food, computers, live animals, machinery, chemicals, clothing |
| ITALY Rome 57,350,850 0.1% | | 116,313(302,422) 490.7(1,270.9) $6,520 | 50% cultivated; 21% forests; 17% pastures; 12% wasteland, other | petroleum, machinery and transport equipment, food, metals, wool, cotton | textiles, chemicals, footwear |
| LIECHTENSTEIN Vaduz 27,074 0.9% | | 62(161) 432.3(1,119.7) NA $20,960 | 18% forests; 38% pastures; 25% agricultural; 19% other | NA | electronics, metals, machinery, precision instruments, artificial teeth |
| LUXEMBOURG Luxembourg 366,136 0.0% | | 999(2,597) 366.6(949.5) 78 $13,380 | 15% wasteland; 33% forests; 27% pastures; 25% other | iron and steel products | minerals, metals, food, machinery |

*NA: Information not available.

| NATION/ Capital/ Population/ Natural Increase | National Flag | Land Area/ ⎰ sq mi/ Density/ ∫(sq km) Percent Urban/ Per Capita GNP | Land Use | Imports | Exports |
|---|---|---|---|---|---|
| MALTA Valletta 361,704 0.8% | | 122(317) 2,730(7,071) 85 $3,300 | 45% agricultural; 55% wasteland, other | machinery and transport equipment, fuels, food | clothing, textiles, ships, printed matter |
| MONACO Monaco 28,641 1.0% | | .58(1.5) NA/NA/ NA NA | 100% built on | pharmaceuticals, plastics, microelectronics | NA |
| NETHERLANDS Amsterdam 14,641,554 0.4% | | 14,140(36,764) 1,094(2,833) 89 $9,180 | 70% cultivated; 8% forests; 22% wasteland, other | machinery, transport equipment, crude petroleum, food, chemicals, raw cotton | food, machinery, chemicals, petroleum products, natural gas, textiles |
| NORWAY Oslo 4,178,545 0.2% | | 125,049(325,127) 33.2(86) 70 $13,890 | 21% forests; 2% pastures; 3% arable; 74% other | machinery, fuels, lubricants, transport equipment, chemicals, food, clothing, ships | oil, natural gas, metals, chemicals, machinery, fish and fish products, pulp and paper, ships |
| PORTUGAL Lisbon 10,314,727 0.3% | | 35,383(91,996) 284.6(737.1) 30 $1,970 | 49% arable; 31% forests; 6% pastures; 14% wasteland, other | petroleum, cotton, industrial machinery, iron and steel, chemicals | cotton textiles, cork, canned fish, wine, timber, resin, machinery, appliances |
| SAN MARINO San Marino 22,791 0.3% | | 24(62) 943.9(2,44.7) 91 $8,207 | 74% cultivated; 22% pastures; 4% built on | consumer manufactures | postage stamps, building stones, lime, wood, chestnuts, wheat, wine |
| SPAIN Madrid 39,000,804 0.5% | | 194,881(506,691) 198.9(515.2) 91 $4,360 | 41% arable and cropland; 27% pastures; 22% forests; 10% other | fuels, machinery, chemicals, iron and steel, vegetables, automobiles | iron and steel products, machinery, automobiles, fruits and vegetables, textiles |
| SWEDEN Stockholm 8,383,026 0.1% | | 173,665(451,529) 52.5(136) 83 $11,890 | 55% forests; 7% arable; 2% pastures; 36% other | machinery, petroleum and petroleum products, chemicals, motor vehicles, food, iron and steel, clothing | machinery, motor vehicles, paper products, pulp and wood, iron and steel products, chemicals |
| SWITZERLAND Bern 6,572,739 0.2% | | 15,941(41,447) 406(1,052) 57 $16,380 | 43% pastures; 24% forests; 33% wasteland, other | machinery and transport equipment, metals, and metal products, food, chemicals, textile fibers | machinery and equipment, chemicals, precision instruments, metal products, textiles, food |
| UNITED KINGDOM London 56,845,195 0.2% | | 93,598(243,355) 599.7(1,553.2) 90 $8,390 | 50% pastures; 30% arable; 13% wasteland, other; 7% forests | manufactured goods, machinery, semifinished goods, food, consumer goods | manufactured goods, machinery, fuels, chemicals, semifinished goods, transport equipment |
| VATICAN CITY Vatican City 738 0.0% | | .17(.44) NA 100 NA | 100% built on | None | None |
| **EASTERN EUROPE** | | | | | |
| ALBANIA Tiranë 3,085,985 2.0% | | 11,100(28,860) 374.8(970.7) 34 $850 | 43% forests; 21% arable; 19% pastures; 12% other; 5% cropland | machinery, machine tools, iron and steel products, textiles, chemicals | asphalt, bitumen, petroleum products, metals, ores, electricity, oil, vegetables |

*NA: Information not available.

| NATION/ Capital/ Population/ Natural Increase | National Flag | Land Area/ sq mi/ Density/ (sq km) Percent Urban/ Per Capita GNP | Land Use | Imports | Exports |
|---|---|---|---|---|---|
| BULGARIA Sofia 8,960,749 0.1% | | 42,823(101,398) 209.7(543.1) 66 $2,920 | 41% arable; 33% forests; 15% other; 11% agricultural | fuels and minerals, machinery, chemicals | machinery, agricultural products, fuels, mineral raw materials |
| CZECHOSLOVAKIA Prague 15,581,993 0.3% | | 49,371(111,340) 314.1(813.5) 74 $5,690 | 53% agricultural; 36% forests; 11% other | fuels, minerals, metals, machinery, equipment, agricultural and forestry products | machinery, equipment, manufactured consumer goods, fuels, minerals |
| GERMAN DEMOCRATIC REPUBLIC Berlin (East) 16,610,265 0.0% | | 41,766(108,592) 399.3(1,034.2) 77 $5,300 | 43% arable; 27% forests; 15% pastures; 15% other | machinery, transport equipment, fuels, raw materials, food | machinery, transport equipment, fuels, raw materials |
| HUNGARY Budapest 10,609,447 −0.2% | | 35,919(93,389) 296.3(767.4) 56 $1,940 | 70% agricultural; 18% forests; 12% other | fuels, raw materials, semifinished products, machinery and equipment | fuel, raw materials, food products, machinery and equipment |
| POLAND Warsaw 37,726,699 0.8% | | 120,756(313,966) 307.8(797.2) 60 $2,120 | 49% arable; 27% forests; 14% other agricultural; 10% other | machinery and equipment, fuels, minerals and metals, agricultural and forestry products | machinery and equipment, processed minerals and metals, manufactured goods |
| ROMANIA Bucharest 22,936,503 0.5% | | 91,699(238,417) 247.7(641.5) 53 $2,019 | 44% arable; 27% forests; 19% other agricultural; 10% other | machinery and equipment, fuels, minerals, agricultural and forestry products | machinery and equipment, processed minerals and metals, manufactured goods |
| YUGOSLAVIA Belgrade 23,430,830 0.7% | | 98,766(256,792) 235.3(656) 46 $2,070 | 34% forests; 32% arable; 25% pastures; 9% other | raw materials, semimanufactures, equipment, consumer goods | processed materials and semimanufactures, consumer goods, machinery and equipment |
| **SOVIET UNION** | | | | | |
| SOVIET UNION Moscow 284,008,160 0.9% | | 8,649,512 (22,488,731) 23.3(60.3) 65 $7,400 | 35% forests; 17% pastures; 10% cultivated; 38% other | grain, agricultural products, machinery, equipment, steel products, consumer manufactures | petroleum, natural gas, metals, wood, agricultural products, manufactured goods |
| **NORTH AFRICA** | | | | | |
| ALGERIA Algiers 23,460,614 3.2% | | 896,598(2,331,155) 23.6(61.1) 43 $2,530 | 80% deserts, wasteland; 16% pastures; 3% cultivated; 1% forests | capital goods, semifinished goods, food | petroleum and natural gas |
| EGYPT Cairo 51,939,962 2.6% | | 386,900(1,005,940) 125.9(326.1) 46 $680 | 97% deserts, wasteland, other; 3% cultivated | food, machinery and equipment, fertilizer, wood | crude petroleum, raw cotton, cotton yarn, fabric |
| LIBYA Tripoli 3,806,825 3.0% | | 679,358(1,766,331) 5.5(14.2) 76 $7,500 | 93% deserts, wasteland, other; 6% agricultural; 1% forests | manufactures, food | petroleum |
| MAURITANIA Nouakchott 1,863,208 3.0% | | 397,955(1,034,683) 4.2(10.9) 35 $410 | 90% deserts; 10% pastures | food, consumer goods, petroleum products, capital goods | iron ore, processed fish, gum arabic, gypsum, cattle |

| NATION/ Capital/ Population/ Natural Increase | National Flag | Land Area/ ⎱ sq mi/ Density/ ⎰ (sq km) Percent Urban/ Per Capita GNP | Land Use | Imports | Exports |
|---|---|---|---|---|---|
| MOROCCO Rabat 23,361,495 2.5% | | 172,413(448,274) 137.6(356.4) 43 $610 | 51% deserts, waste- land, other; 32% arable, pastures; 17% forests, grasses | petroleum products | phosphates |
| TUNISIA Tunis 7,561,641 2.5% | | 63,378(164,783) 120.4(311.8) 53 $1,220 | 43% deserts, waste- land, other; 28% cropland; 23% range; 6% forests | machinery, petro- leum, transport equipment, iron and steel | crude petroleum, tex- tiles, phosphates, chemicals |
| **MIDDLE EAST** | | | | | |
| AFGHANISTAN Kabul 15,183,671 2.6% | | 250,775(652,015) 71.9(186.2) 16 $214 | 75% deserts, waste- land, other; 12% cultivated; 10% pasture; 3% forests | food supplies, petro- leum products | fruits, nuts, natural gas, carpets |
| BAHRAIN Manama 464,102 2.8% | | 255(663) 1,647(4,266) 81 $9,560 | 95% deserts, wasteland, other; 5% cultivated | machinery and trans- port equipment, consumer goods, live animals | petroleum |
| CYPRUS Nicosia 683,651 1.1% | | 3,572(9,287) 191.8(496.8) 53 $3,790 | 60% arable; 15% forests; 25% wasteland, other | manufactured goods, machinery and trans- port equipment, fuels, food | food, beverages, cement, clothing |
| IRAN Tehran 50,407,763 3.2% | | 635,932(1,653,423) 70.9(183.6) 51 $2,123 | 51% deserts, wasteland; 30% cultivable; 11% forests; 8% pastures, other | machinery, military supplies | petroleum, carpets, fruits, nuts |
| IRAQ Baghdad 16,970,948 3.3% | | 168,927(439,210) 92.6(239.8) 68 $2,300 | 68% deserts, wasteland; 18% cultivated; 10% pastures; 4% forests | food, live animals, cereals, chemicals, machinery | mineral fuels, lubricants |
| ISRAEL Jerusalem 4,222,118 1.7% | | 7,992(20,779) 538.8(1,395.5) 75 $4,920 | 40% pastures; 20% cultivated; 4% forests; 36% deserts, other | military equipment, rough diamonds, oil, chemicals, machin- ery, iron and steel | polished diamonds, citrus, textiles and clothing, processed foods, fertilizer |
| JORDAN Amman 2,761,695 3.7% | | 37,737(98,116) 76.9(199.2) 60 $1,560 | 88% deserts, waste- land, other; 11% agricultural; 1% forests | crude oil, petroleum, textiles, capital goods, motor vehicles | fruits, vegetables, phosphates, fertilizers |
| KUWAIT Kuwait 1,863,615 3.2% | | 6,200(16,120) 259.5(672.1) 80 $14,270 | 99% deserts, wasteland, other; 1% cultivated | machinery and trans- port equipment, live animals, food | petroleum and petro- leum products |
| LEBANON Beirut 3,300,522 2.2% | | 3,949(10,267) 784.8(2,032.6) 80 $1,636 | 64% deserts, waste- land, other; 27% agricultural; 9% forests | precious metals and stones, machinery and electrical appara- tus, mineral products | vegetable products, precious metals and stones, machinery |
| OMAN Muscat 1,226,923 3.3% | | 82,000(213,200) 8.7(22.5) 9 $7,080 | Mostly deserts, wasteland, and built on | machinery, transport equipment, manufac- tured goods, food, livestock, lubricants | petroleum, reexports, processed copper |
| QATAR Doha 315,741 3.0% | | 4,400(11,440) 68.4(177.2) 86 $15,980 | Mostly desert, wasteland, and built on | machinery and trans- port equipment, manufactures, food, live animals | petroleum and petro- leum products |

| NATION/ Capital/ Population/ Natural Increase | National Flag | Land Area/ {sq mi/ Density/ {(sq km) Percent Urban/ Per Capita GNP | Land Use | Imports | Exports |
|---|---|---|---|---|---|
| SAUDI ARABIA Riyadh 14,904,794 3.1% | | 873,972(2,272,327) 13(34) 72 $8,860 | 98% deserts, waste-land, other; 1% agricultural; 1% forests | manufactured goods, transport equipment, construction materials | petroleum and petro-leum products |
| SYRIA Damascus 11,147,763 3.8% | | 71,498(185,895) 143.6(371.9) 49 $1,630 | 48% arable; 29% pastures; 21% deserts; 2% forests | petroleum, machin-ery, metal products, textiles, fuels, foods | petroleum, textiles and textile products, tobacco, fruit, and vegetables, cotton |
| TURKEY Ankara 52,987,778 2.1% | | 301,380(783,588) 157.7(408.4) 46 $1,130 | 35% cropland; 25% pastures; 23% forests; 17% other | crude oil, machinery, transport equipment, metals, pharma-ceuticals, dyes, plastics, rubber | cotton, tobacco, fruits, nuts, metals, livestock products, textiles, clothing, cement |
| UNITED ARAB EMIRATES Abu Dhabi 1,846,373 2.6% | | 30,000(78,000) 42.7(110.6) 81 $19,120 | Almost all desert or wasteland | food, consumer and capital goods | crude oil, natural gas, reexports, dried fish, dates |
| YEMEN, NORTH Sanaa 6,533,265 3.4% | | 75,290(195,754) 125.4(324.8) 15 $520 | 79% deserts, wasteland, other; 20% agricultural; 1% forests | textiles, manufac-tured consumer goods, petroleum products, sugar, grain, flour | cotton, coffee, hides, vegetables |
| YEMEN, SOUTH Aden 2,351,131 3.0% | | 112,075(291,395) 16.3(42.2) 40 $540 | 1% arable; 99% deserts, wasteland, other | machinery and trans-port equipment, food, live animals, petroleum | food, live animals, fish, petroleum |

## WEST AFRICA

| NATION/ Capital/ Population/ Natural Increase | National Flag | Land Area/ Density/ Percent Urban/ Per Capita GNP | Land Use | Imports | Exports |
|---|---|---|---|---|---|
| BENIN Porto-Novo 4,339,096 3.0% | | 43,483(113,056) 92.2(238.8) 39 $270 | 80% arable; 19% forests, game reserves; 1% nonarable | thread, cloth, cloth-ing, construction materials, iron, steel, fuels | palm products, cot-ton, agricultural products |
| BURKINA FASO Ouagadougou 8,276,272 2.8% | | 105,869(275,259) 64.5(167.1) 8 $140 | 50% pastures; 21% fallowland; 10% cultivated; 9% forests; 10% wasteland | textiles, food, trans-port equipment, machinery, fuels | livestock, peanuts, shea nut products, cotton, sesame |
| CAPE VERDE Praia 344,282 2.6% | | 1,557(4,048) 201.7(522.4) 27 $430 | 9% arable; 6% pastures; 85% other | petroleum products, corn, rice, textiles, machinery | fish, bananas, salt, flour |
| GAMBIA Banjul 760,362 2.1% | | 4,003(10,408) 181.5(470.1) 21 $230 | 55% cultivable, built on, other; 25% uncultivated savanna; 16% swampland; 4% forest park | textiles, food, tobacco, machinery, petroleum products, chemicals | peanuts and peanut products, fish, palm kernels |
| GHANA Accra 13,948,925 2.8% | | 92,100(239,460) 139.1(360.3) 31 $390 | 60% forests and bushland; 19% agricultural; 21% other | textiles, manufac-tured goods, foods, fuels, transport equipment | cocoa, wood, gold, diamonds, man-ganese, bauxite, aluminum |
| GUINEA Conakry 6,737,760 2.4% | | 94,925(246,805) 57.2(148.1) 22 $320 | 10% forests; 15% cultivated; 75% unused | petroleum products, metals, machinery, transport equipment, food, textiles | bauxite, alumina, diamonds, coffee, pineapples, bananas, palm kernels |
| GUINEA-BISSAU Bissau 928,425 2.0% | | 13,948(36,265) 62.6(162.1) 27 $170 | 9% arable; 46% pastures; 38% forests; 7% other | food, manufactured goods, fuels, trans-port equipment | peanuts, palm ker-nels, shrimp, fish, lumber |

Geodata Files

| NATION/ Capital/ Population/ Natural Increase | National Flag | Land Area/ sq mi/ Density/ (sq km) Percent Urban/ Per Capita GNP | Land Use | Imports | Exports |
|---|---|---|---|---|---|
| IVORY COAST Abidjan 10,766,632 3.0% | | 124,503(323,708) 82.1(212.6) 43 $620 | 52% pastures, fallowland, wasteland; 40% forests; 8% cultivated | manufactured goods and semifinished products, consumer goods, raw materials | cocoa, coffee, tropical woods, cotton, bananas, pineapples, palm oil |
| LIBERIA Monrovia 2,384,158 3.2% | | 43,000(111,800) 58.3(151) 40 $470 | 40% forests; 30% rain forests, swamps; 20% agricultural; 10% other | machinery, transport equipment, petroleum products, food | iron ore, rubber, diamonds, lumber, logs, coffee, cocoa |
| MALI Bamako 8,422,810 2.9% | | 478,652(1,244,495) 16.9(43.8) 18 $140 | 75% sparse pastures, deserts; 25% arable | textiles, vehicles, petroleum products, machinery, sugar, cereals | livestock, peanuts, dried fish, cotton, skins |
| NIGER Niamey 6,988,540 2.9% | | 459,073(1,193,590) 12.6(32.6) 16 $200 | 7% pastures; 3% arable; 2% forests; 88% other | petroleum products, primary materials, machinery, vehicles and parts, electronic equipment | uranium, livestock, cowpeas, onions, hides, skins |
| NIGERIA Lagos 108,579,764 2.8% | | 356,669(927,339) 269.2(697.2) 28 $760 | 35% forests; 24% arable; 41% deserts, wasteland, other | machinery and transport equipment, manufactured goods, chemicals, wheat | oil, cocoa, palm products, rubber, timber, tin |
| SENEGAL Dakar 7,064,025 2.8% | | 76,124(197,922) 85.8(222.2) 36 $370 | 40% agricultural; 13% forests; 47% built up, wasteland, other | food, consumer goods, machinery, transport equipment, petroleum | peanuts and peanut products, phosphate rock, fish, petroleum products |
| SIERRA LEONE Freetown 3,754,088 1.8% | | 27,699(7,199) 141.9(367.5) 28 $370 | 65% arable; 27% pastures; 4% swamps; 4% forests | machinery and transport equipment, manufactured goods, food, petroleum products | diamonds, iron ore, palm kernels, cocoa, coffee |
| TOGO Lomé 3,228,635 3.1% | | 21,853(56,818) 136.3(353) 22 $250 | 50% arable; 50% other | consumer goods, fuels, machinery, tobacco, food | phosphates, cocoa, coffee, palm kernels |
| **CENTRAL AFRICA** | | | | | |
| ANGOLA Luanda 7,950,244 2.5% | | 481,351(1,251,513) 17.8(46.1) 25 $1,032 | 44% forests; 22% pastures; 1% cultivated; 33% other | machinery and electrical equipment, wine, bulk iron, steel, metals, vehicles | oil, coffee, diamonds, sisal, fish, iron ore, timber, cotton |
| CAMEROON Yaoundé 10,256,332 2.7% | | 183,591(477,337) 53.6(138.8) 42 $810 | 50% forests; 18% meadows; 15% other; 13% fallowland; 4% cultivated | consumer goods, machinery and transport equipment, alumina for refining | crude oil, cocoa, coffee, timber, aluminum, cotton, natural rubber, bananas |
| CENTRAL AFRICAN REPUBLIC Bangui 2,669,293 2.5% | | 240,376(624,978) 11(28.5) 42 $270 | 15% cultivated; 5% forests; 80% other | textiles, petroleum products, machinery, electrical equipment | cotton, coffee, diamonds, timber |
| CHAD N'Djamena 4,646,054 2.0% | | 495,752(1,288,955) 10.(25.9) 27 $59 | 35% pastures; 17% arable; 2% forests and scrubland; 46% wasteland, other | cement, petroleum, flour, sugar, tea, machinery, textiles, motor vehicles | cotton, meat, fish, animal products |

*NA: Information not available.

**728**

| NATION/ Capital/ Population/ Natural Increase | National Flag | Land Area/ ⎰ sq mi/ Density/ ⎱ (sq km) Percent Urban/ Per Capita GNP | Land Use | Imports | Exports |
|---|---|---|---|---|---|
| CONGO Brazzaville 2,082,154 3.4% | | 132,047(343,322) 13.2(34.2) 48 $1,020 | 63% forests; 31% meadows; 4% wasteland, other; 2% cultivated | machinery, transport equipment, manufactured consumer goods, iron and steel | oil, lumber, tobacco, veneer, plywood, coffee, cocoa |
| EQUATORIAL GUINEA Malabo 340,434 1.3% | | 10,825(28,145) 29.3(75.9) 60 $197 | 5% arable; 4% permanent crops; 4% pastures; 61% forest and woodland; 26% other | food, chemicals, textiles | cocoa, coffee, wood |
| GABON Libreville 1,039,006 1.6% | | 102,317(266,024) 11.3(29.3) 41 $3,340 | 75% forests; 15% savanna; 1% cultivated; 9% wasteland, other | mining and road building equipment, electrical equipment, transport vehicles | crude petroleum, wood, minerals |
| SÃO TOMÉ AND PRINCIPE São Tomé 114,025 2.7% | | 327(850) 275.2(712.7) 35 $310 | 1% arable; 36% permanent crops; 1% pastures; 62% other | food products, machinery and electrical equipment, fuels | cocoa, copra, coffee, palm oil |
| ZAIRE Kinshasa 32,342,947 3.1% | | 905,063(2,353,164) 36.5(94.5) 34 $170 | 45% forests; 22% agricultural; 33% other | consumer goods, food, mining, machinery, transport equipment, fuels | copper, cobalt, diamonds, petroleum, coffee |
| ZAMBIA Lusaka 7,281,738 3.5% | | 290,585(755,521) 22.9(59.3) 43 $400 | 61% woodland, grasses; 13% forests; 10% grazing; 6% marsh; 10% other | machinery, transport equipment, food, fuels, manufactures | copper, zinc, cobalt, lead, tobacco |
| **EAST AFRICA** | | | | | |
| BURUNDI Bujumbura 5,005,504 2.9% | | 10,759(27,973) 477.6(1,237) 5 $240 | 37% arable; 23% pastures; 10% scrub forests and forests; 30% other | textiles, food, transport equipment, petroleum products | coffee, tea, cotton, hides, skins |
| DJIBOUTI Djibouti 312,405 2.5% | | 8,880(23,088) 48(124.3) 74 $760 | 89% deserts, wasteland; 10% pastures; 1% cultivated | almost all domestically needed goods | hides, skins, coffee, transit |
| ETHIOPIA Addis Ababa 46,706,229 2.3% | | 471,775(1,226,615) 92.2(238.8) 10 $100 | 55% pastures; 10% cropland, orchards; 6% forests; 29% wasteland, other | food, animals, beverages, chemicals, rubber, paper | coffee, hides, skins |
| KENYA Nairobi 22,377,802 3.9% | | 224,960(584,896) 92.1(238) 16 $290 | 66% grassland; 21% forests; 13% agricultural | machinery, transport equipment, crude oil, paper, iron and steel products | petroleum products, coffee, tea, sisal, livestock products, pyrethrum |
| MALAWI Lilongwe 7,437,911 3.2% | | 45,193(117,502) 187.9(486.7) 12 $170 | 34% arable; 25% forests; 6% meadows; 35% other | manufactured goods, machinery, transport equipment | coffee, tobacco, tea, sugar, peanuts, cotton, corn |
| MOZAMBIQUE Maputo 14,535,805 2.6% | | 297,846(774,400) 46.3(120) 13 $360 | 56% forests; 30% arable; 14% wasteland, other | refined petroleum products, machinery, transportation goods, spare parts | cashews, shrimp, sugar, tea, cotton |

*NA: Information not available.

| NATION/ Capital/ Population/ Natural Increase | National Flag | Land Area/ }sq mi/ Density/ }(sq km) Percent Urban/ Per Capita GNP | Land Use | Imports | Exports |
|---|---|---|---|---|---|
| RWANDA Kigali 6,811,336 3.7% | | 10,169(26,439) 601.3(1,557.4) 6 $290 | 33% cultivated; 33% pastures; 9% forests; 25% other | textiles, food, machinery, equipment, capital goods, steel, petroleum products | coffee, tea, cassiterite, wolframite, pyrethrum |
| SOMALIA Mogadishu 7,741,859 2.5% | | 246,154(640,000) 23.6(61.1) 34 $270 | 32% pastures; 14% scrubland, forests; 13% arable; 41% deserts, other | textiles, cereals, transport equipment, machinery, construction materials | livestock, hides, skins, bananas |
| SUDAN Khartoum 23,524,622 2.8% | | 967,500(2,515,500) 24.5(63.5) 20 $330 | 37% arable; 33% deserts; 15% pastures; 15% forests | textiles, petroleum products, food, transport equipment, manufactured goods | cotton, gum arabic, peanuts, sesame |
| TANZANIA Dar es Salaam 23,502,472 3.5% | | 364,943(948,852) 63.5(164.5) 18 $270 | 45% forests; 37% pastures; 4% arable; 1% cropland; 13% other | manufactured goods, machinery and transport equipment, cotton piece goods, crude oil, food | coffee, cotton, sisal, cashews, meat, cloves, tobacco, tea, coconut products |
| UGANDA Kampala 15,908,896 3.4% | | 91,134(236,948) 158.1(409.5) 10 $434 | 45% forests, grasses; 21% cultivated; 13% parks and reserves; 21% inland waters, swamps | petroleum products, machinery, cotton piece goods, metals, transport equipment, food | coffee, cotton, tea |
| **SOUTHERN AFRICA** | | | | | |
| BOTSWANA Gaborone 1,149,141 3.4% | | 219,916(57,781) 4.8(12.4) 22 $840 | 94% mostly deserts; 6% arable | food, vehicles, textiles, petroleum products | diamonds, cattle, animal products, copper, nickel |
| COMOROS Moroni 415,220 3.3% | | 863(2,244) 560.5(1,451.7) 23 $280 | 48% cultivated; 29% uncultivated; 16% forests; 7% pastures | rice, food, cement, fuels, chemicals, textiles | perfume oils, vanilla, copra, cloves |
| LESOTHO Maseru 1,621,932 2.6% | | 11,716(30,462) 127.9(331.3) 17 $480 | 10% cultivated; 6% forests; 64% pastures; 20% other | corn, building materials, clothing, machinery, medicines | labor, wool, mohair, wheat, cattle, peas, beans, corn, hides, skins |
| MADAGASCAR Antananarivo 10,730,754  2.3% | | 226,657(589,308) 42.3(109.6) 22 $250 | 58% pastures; 21% forests; 16% wasteland, other; 5% cultivated | raw materials, intermediate goods, food | coffee, vanilla, sugar, cloves |
| MAURITIUS Port Louis 1,079,627 1.2% | | 720(1,872) 1,300.6(3,368.6) 42 $1,070 | 50% agricultural; 39% forests; 11% built on wasteland, other | food, petroleum products, manufactured goods | sugar |
| NAMIBIA Windhoek 1,273,263 3.3% | SOUTH AFRICA | 317,887(826,506) 3.5(9.1) 51 $1,760 | 1% arable; 64% pastures; 22% forests; 13% other | NA | diamonds, uranium, copper, zinc, lead, tin, kerakui pelts, fish and fish products |
| SEYCHELLES Victoria 67,552 1.9% | | 107(278) 372(963.5) 37 $2,200 | 54% arable; 17% forests; 29% other | manufactured goods, food, tobacco, beverages, machinery and transport equipment | fish, copra, cinnamon bark |

*NA: Information not available.

| NATION/ Capital/ Population/ Natural Increase | National Flag | Land Area/ ⌐sq mi/ Density/ ⌐(sq km) Percent Urban/ Per Capita GNP | Land Use | Imports | Exports |
|---|---|---|---|---|---|
| SOUTH AFRICA Pretoria; Cape Town 34,313,356 2.3% | (FLAG OF SOUTH AFRICA) | 471,445(1,225,757) 63.2(145) 56 $2,010 | 86% deserts, wasteland, other; 12% arable; 2% forests | machinery, motor vehicle parts, petroleum products, textiles, chemicals | gold, coal, diamonds, corn, uranium, mineral and agricultural products |
| SWAZILAND Mbabane 700,000 3.1% | | 6,705(17,433) 96.6(250.2) 26 $650 | Mostly cropland or pastures | motor vehicles, chemicals, petroleum products, food | sugar, asbestos, wood and forest products, citrus, canned fruit |
| ZIMBABWE Harare 9,371,972 3.5% | | 150,820(392,132) 53.7(139.1) 24 $650 | 40% arable; 60% grazing | machinery, petroleum products, wheat, transport equipment | gold, tobacco, asbestos, cotton, copper, tin, chrome, nickel, meat, clothing, sugar |
| **SOUTH ASIA** | | | | | |
| BANGLADESH Dacca 107,087,586 2.7% | | 55,126(143,328) 1,775(4,597.3) 13 $150 | 66% arable; 18% uncultivated; 16% forests | food grains, fuels, raw cotton, fertilizer, manufactured products | raw and manufactured jute, leather, tea |
| BHUTAN Thimphu 1,472,911 2.0% | | 16,000(41,600) 78.6(203.6) 5 $160 | 70% forests; 15% deserts, wasteland; 15% agricultural | textiles, cereals, vehicles, fuels, machinery | agricultural and forestry products, coal |
| INDIA New Delhi 800,325, 817 2.1% | | 1,229,424(3,196,502) 605(1,567) 25 $250 | 50% arable; 22% forests; 23% deserts, wasteland, other; 5% pastures | machinery and transport equipment, petroleum, edible oils, fertilizer | engineering goods, textiles, clothing, tea |
| MALDIVES Male 195,837 3.8% | | 115(299) 1,577.8(4,086.5) 26 $290 | 10% arable; 3% pastures; 3% forests; 84% other | NA | fish, coconut oil |
| NEPAL Kathmandu 17,814,294 2.5% | | 54,362(141,341) 290.8(753.7) 7 $160 | 38% mountains, wasteland, other; 32% forests; 16% agricultural; 14% pastures | manufactured consumer goods, fuel, construction materials, fertilizer, food products | rice and other food, jute, timber, manufactured goods |
| PAKISTAN Islamabad 104,600,799 2.9% | | 310,403(807,048) 326.5(845.7) 28 $380 | 40% arable; 3% forests; 57% wasteland, nonarable | petroleum, cooking oil, defense equipment | rice, cotton, textiles |
| SRI LANKA Colombo 16,406,576 1.3% | | 25,332(65,863) 635.9(1,647) 22 $370 | 44% forests; 31% wasteland, other; 25% cultivated | petroleum, machinery, transport equipment, sugar, textiles, textile materials | tea, rubber, petroleum products, textiles, coconuts |
| **EAST ASIA** | | | | | |
| CHINA Beijing 1,064,147,038 1.3% | | 3,691,502(9,597,905) 282.3(731.2) 32 $310 | 76% deserts, wasteland, other; 11% cultivated; 13% forests | grain, chemical fertilizer, steel, industrial materials, machinery and equipment | manufactured goods, agricultural products, oil, minerals |
| JAPAN Tokyo 122,124,293 0.6% | | 143,619(373,409) 854(2,211) $11,330 | 69% forests; 16% arable; 12% wasteland, other; 3% grasses | fuels, manufactures, food, machinery | machinery, electrical equipment, motor vehicles, iron and steel |

*NA: Information not available.

| NATION/ Capital/ Population/ Natural Increase | National Flag | Land Area/ $\}$ sq mi/ Density/ $\int$ (sq km) Percent Urban/ Per Capita GNP | Land Use | Imports | Exports |
|---|---|---|---|---|---|
| KOREA, NORTH P'yongyang 21,447,977 2.5% | | 46,609(121,183) 426.6(1,104.9) 64 $790 | 74% forests and brush; 17% arable; 9% wasteland, other | petroleum, machinery and equipment, coking coal, grain | minerals, metallurgical products, agricultural products, manufactures |
| KOREA, SOUTH Seoul 41,986,669 1.4% | | 38,022(98,857) 1,077.3(2,709.2) 65 $2,180 | 66% forests; 23% arable; 11% other | machinery, oil, steel, transport equipment, textiles, organic chemicals, grains | textiles, clothing, electrical machinery, footwear, steel, ships, fish |
| MONGOLIA Ulaanbaatar 2,011,066 2.6% | | 604,247(1,571,042) 3.2(9.1) 51 $1,000 | 90% pastures, deserts; 10% forests | machinery and equipment, petroleum, clothing, building materials, sugar | livestock, animal products, wool, hides, fluorspar, nonferrous metals, minerals |
| TAIWAN Taipei 19,768,035 1.2% | | 13,887(36,106) 1,376.6(3,565.4) 67 $3,040 | 55% forests; 24% cultivated; 6% pastures; 15% wasteland, other | machinery and equipment, crude oil, chemicals, basic metals, food | textiles, electrical machinery and equipment, general machinery and equipment, telecommunications equipment |
| **SOUTHEAST ASIA** | | | | | |
| BRUNEI Begawan 249,961 2.6% | | 2,226(5,788) 100.6(260.6) 64 $17,580 | 75% forests; 22% wasteland, other; 3% arable | machinery and transport equipment, food, beverages | crude oil, liquefied natural gas, petroleum products |
| BURMA Rangoon 38,822,484 2.1% | | 261,789(680,651) 144.3(373.8) 24 $1,90 | 49% forests; 15% arable; 1% cultivated; 35% other | machinery and transport equipment, building material | teak, rice, peas, base metals, ores |
| CAMBODIA (KAMPUCHEA) Phnom Penh 6,534,079 2.1% | | 69,898(181,735) 104.1(269.6) 11 $159 | 75% forests; 25% other | agricultural products, mineral products, textiles, metals, chemicals | rice, rubber, haricot beans |
| INDONESIA Jakarta 180,425,534 2.1% | | 779,675(2,027,155) 226.1(585.6) 22 $530 | 64% forests; 24% wasteland, other; 12% small holdings and estates | rice, wheat, flour, cereals, textiles, chemicals, iron and steel products, machinery | petroleum and natural gas, timber, rubber, coffee, tin, palm oil, tea, copper |
| LAOS Vientiane 3,765,887 2.5% | | 91,428(237,713) 45(116.6) 16 $152 | 60% forests; 8% agricultural; 32% wasteland, other | rice, food, petroleum products, machinery, transport equipment | electric power, forest products, tin concentrates, coffee, opium, tobacco |
| MALAYSIA Kuala Lumpur 16,068,516 2.4% | | 128,727(334,690) 122.8(318.1) 32 $2,050 | 26% forest reserves; 20% cultivated; 54% other | machinery, transport equipment, basic manufactures, fuels and lubricants | natural rubber, palm oil, tin, timber, petroleum, light manufactures |
| PHILIPPINES Manila 61,524,761 2.8% | | 115,651(300,719) 472(1,222.5) 40 $600 | 53% forests; 30% arable; 5% pastures; 12% other | petroleum, industrial equipment, wheat | coconut products, sugar, logs, lumber, copper concentrates, bananas, garments, nickel |
| SINGAPORE Singapore 2,616,236 1.1% | | 225(585) 10,704(27,723.4) 100 $7,420 | 31% built on; 22% agricultural; 47% other | capital equipment, manufactured goods, petroleum | manufactured goods, petroleum, rubber, electronics |

| NATION/ Capital/ Population/ Natural Increase | National Flag | Land Area/ ⎱ sq mi/ Density/ ⎰ (sq km) Percent Urban/ Per Capita GNP | Land Use | Imports | Exports |
|---|---|---|---|---|---|
| THAILAND Bangkok 53,645,823 2.1% | | 198,455(515,983) 258.9(670.6) 17 $830 | 56% forests; 24% cropland; 20% other | machinery and transport equipment, fuels and lubricants, base metals, chemicals | rice, sugar, corn, rubber, tin, tapioca, textiles, garments, integrated circuits |
| VIETNAM Hanoi 63,585,121 2.6% | | 130,468(339,217) 462.6(1,198.1) 19 $170 | 50% forests; 14% cultivated; 36% other | petroleum, steel products, railroad equipment, chemicals, medicines, raw cotton, fertilizer | agricultural and handicraft products, coal, minerals, ores |
| **PACIFIC WORLD** | | | | | |
| AUSTRALIA Canberra 16,072,986 0.8% | | 2,967,909(7,716,563) 5.3(13.7) 86 $10,840 | 58% pastures; 6% arable; 2% forests; 34% other | manufactured raw materials, capital equipment, consumer goods | coal, wool, iron ore, lamb, meat, dairy products |
| FIJI Suva 727,902 2.3% | | 6,938(18,039) 98.1(254.1) 37 $1,700 | 13% arable; 3% pastures; 65% forests; 19% other | manufactured goods, food, machinery, fuel | sugar, copra |
| KIRIBATI Bairiki 66,441 2.1% | | 102(265) 234.7(607.9) 33 $492 | 51% cropland; 3% forests; 46% other | food, fuel, transport equipment | phosphates, copra |
| NAURU Yaren 8,448 2.5% | | 8.5(22) 975.6(2,526.8) 100 $21,400 | 80% phosphate deposits; 20% other | food, fuel, water | phosphates |
| NEW ZEALAND Wellington 3,307,239 0.8% | | 103,736(269,714) 31.8(82.4) 84 $7,310 | 50% pastures; 16% forests; 10% parks; 3% cultivated; 21% wasteland, other | petroleum, cars, trucks, machinery and electrical equipment, iron and steel | beef, wool, dairy products |
| PAPUA NEW GUINEA Port Moresby 3,563,743 2.4% | | 90,540(235,404) 18.7(48.4) 13 $710 | 70% forests; 3% cultivated; 2% pastures; 25% other | machinery and equipment, fuels and lubricants, food, chemicals | gold, copper, coffee, palm oil, logs, cocoa, copra, coconut oil, tea |
| SOLOMON ISLANDS Honiara 301,180 3.6% | | 15,220(39,572) 25.1(65) 9 $510 | 93% forests; 2% arable; 1% pastures; 4% other | NA | copra, timber, fish |
| TONGA Nuku'alofa 98,689 2.4% | | 270(702) 336.4(871.3) 20 $777 | 77% arable; 3% pastures; 13% forests; 7% other | food, machinery, petroleum | copra, bananas, coconut products |
| TUVALU Funafuti Atoll 8,329 2.9% | | 9(23) 927.5(2,402.2) 31 $680 | Mostly wooded | food, mineral fuels | copra |
| VANUATU Port-Vila 149,652 3.3% | | 5,700(14,820) 28.4(73.6) 18 $585 | 2% pastures; 6% arable; 1% forests; 91% other | food | frozen fish, meat |
| WESTERN SAMOA Apia 175,084 2.4% | | 1,113(2,894) 146.4(379.2) 21 $660 | 65% forests; 24% cultivated; 11% wasteland, other | food, manufactured goods, machinery | copra, cocoa, timber, mineral fuels, bananas |

*NA: Information not available.

# GAZETTEER

This GAZETTEER is an index of all the place names that appear on the maps in *WORLD GEOGRAPHY: The Earth and Its People*. It provides the name, a phonetic respelling of most names, the latitude and longitude of each place listed, and the page number of a map on which that place appears.

| NAME | LATITUDE | LONGITUDE | PAGE |
|---|---|---|---|
| **A** | | | |
| Abadan (ah·buh·DAHN) | 30° 15′N | 48° 30′E | 497 |
| Aberdeen, Scotland (ab·uhr·DEEN) | 57° 15′N | 2° 00′W | 397 |
| Aberdeen, S.D. (ab·uhr·DEEN) | 45° 30′N | 98° 30′W | 233 |
| Abidjan (ah·beed·ZHAHN) | 5° 15′N | 4° 00′W | 511 |
| Abilene (AB·i·leen) | 32° 30′N | 99° 45′W | 237 |
| Absaroka Range (ab·SAHR·uh·kuh) | 44° 45′N | 109° 45′W | 239 |
| Abu Dhabi (AH·boo DAH·bee) | 24° 15′N | 54° 30′E | 491 |
| Accra (AH·krah) | 5° 30′N | 0° 15′W | 528 |
| Aconcagua, Mount (ah·kawn·KAH·gwah) | 32° 15′S | 71° 00′W | 366 |
| Acquaviva (ahk·kwah·VEE·vah) | 44° 00′N | 12° 30′E | 408 |
| Adamawa Highlands (ad·uh·MAH·wuh) | 6° 30′N | 11° 45′E | 528 |
| Adana (AH·dah·nah) | 37° 00′N | 35° 30′E | 484 |
| Addis Ababa (ad·uhs AB·uh·buh) | 9° 00′N | 38° 45′E | 548 |
| Adelaide (AD·uh·layd) | 34° 45′S | 139° 15′E | 698 |
| Aden (AY·den) | 12° 45′N | 45° 00′E | 491 |
| Aden, Gulf of | 11° 45′N | 45° 45′E | 491 |
| Adirondack Mountains (ad·uh·RAWN·dak) | 43° 45′N | 73° 45′W | 225 |
| Adriatic Sea (ay·dree·AT·ik) | 43° 30′N | 14° 30′E | 407 |
| Aegean Sea (i·JEE·uhn) | 39° 00′N | 25° 00′E | 407 |
| Afghanistan (af·GAN·uh·stan) | 33° 00′N | 63° 00′E | 497 |
| Africa (AF·ri·cah) | 10° 00′N | 25° 00′E | 16 |
| Agulhas, Cape (ah·GOOL·yahs) | 34° 45′S | 20° 00′E | 557 |
| Ahaggar Mountains (uh·huh·GAHR) | 23° 15′N | 6° 00′E | 478 |
| Ahmadabad (ahm·uhd·uh·BAD) | 23° 00′N | 72° 45′E | 572 |
| Aïr (ah·IR) | 18° 00′N | 8° 00′E | 528 |
| Akron (AK·ruhn) | 41° 00′N | 81° 30′W | 231 |
| Akureyri (ak·kooh·RUH·ree) | 65° 45′N | 18° 00′W | 401 |
| Alabama (al·uh·BAM·uh) | 32° 45′N | 87° 30′W | 228 |
| Alabama River | 30° 45′N | 88° 00′W | 228 |
| Al-Akdar (ahl AK·dahr) | 23° 00′N | 57° 45′E | 491 |
| Alamo, The (AL·uh·moh) | 29° 30′N | 98° 30′W | 237 |
| Alaska (uh·LAS·kuh) | 64° 00′N | 150° 00′W | 241 |
| Alaska, Gulf of | 57° 45′N | 147° 00′W | 241 |
| Alaska Range | 62° 00′N | 152° 15′W | 195 |
| Albania (al·BAYN·ee·uh) | 41° 15′N | 20° 00′E | 422 |
| Albany, Ga. (AWL·ban·ee) | 31° 30′N | 84° 15′W | 228 |
| Albany, N.Y. | 42° 45′N | 73° 45′W | 225 |
| Albert, Lake (AL·buhrt) | 1° 45′N | 30° 45′E | 538 |
| Alberta (al·BUHR·tuh) | 54° 30′N | 117° 15′W | 253 |
| Ålborg (OHL·bohr) | 57° 00′N | 10° 00′E | 401 |
| Albuquerque (al·boo·KUHR·kee) | 35° 00′N | 106° 45′W | 237 |
| Aldan Mountains (ahl·DAHN) | 57° 45′N | 130° 30′E | 434 |
| Aleppo (uh·LEP·oh) | 36° 15′N | 37° 15′E | 487 |
| Aleutian Islands (uh·LOO·shuhn) | 54° 45′N | 177° 30′E | 241 |
| Alexandria, Egypt | 31° 15′N | 30° 00′E | 472 |
| Alexandria, Va. | 38° 45′N | 77° 00′W | 228 |
| Algeria (al·JEER·ee·uh) | 28° 45′N | 1° 00′E | 478 |
| Algiers (al·JEERS) | 36° 45′N | 3° 00′E | 478 |
| Alice Springs (AL·is) | 23° 45′S | 134° 00′E | 17 |
| Allegheny Mountains (al·uh·GAY·nee) | 37° 35′N | 82° 00′W | 225 |
| Allegheny River | 40° 30′N | 80° 00′W | 225 |
| Alma-Ata (AL·muh-AT·uh) | 45° 15′N | 73° 15′E | 434 |
| Alps | 46° 15′N | 8° 45′E | 397 |

| NAME | LATITUDE | LONGITUDE | PAGE |
|---|---|---|---|
| Altai Mountains (ah·TY) | 49° 15′N | 87° 15′E | 622 |
| Altiplano (al·ti·PLAHN·oh) | 18° 45′S | 68° 15′W | 352 |
| Amarillo (am·uh·RIL·oh) | 35° 15′N | 101° 45′W | 237 |
| Amazon Basin (AM·uh·zawn) | 5° 00′S | 62° 00′W | 366 |
| Amazon River | 0° 00′ | 50° 00′W | 366 |
| American Samoa (suh·MOH·uh) | 14° 00′S | 170° 00′W | 699 |
| Amman (AHM·mahn) | 32° 00′N | 36° 00′E | 487 |
| Amsterdam (AM·sturh·dam) | 52° 15′N | 4° 45′E | 397 |
| Amu Darya (ah·moo DAHR·ee·ah) | 54° 00′N | 60° 00′E | 434 |
| Amundsen-Scott (AH·muhn·suhn) | 90° 00′S | | 17 |
| Amundsen Sea | 72° 00′S | 110° 00′W | 17 |
| Amur River (ah·MOOR) | 54° 00′N | 140° 00′E | 434 |
| Anchorage (ANG·ker·uhj) | 61° 15′N | 149° 45′W | 241 |
| Andaman Islands (an·duh·MAN) | 11° 45′N | 92° 15′E | 572 |
| Andaman Sea | 12° 45′N | 95° 45′E | 572 |
| Andes (AN·deez) | 13° 00′S | 75° 00′W | 11 |
| Andorra (an·DOHR·uh) | 42° 45′N | 1° 30′E | 408 |
| Andorra La Vella (lah VEL·yah) | 42° 30′N | 1° 30′E | 408 |
| Angel Falls (AHN·hel) | 5° 45′N | 62° 30′W | 338 |
| Angkor (AHNG·kohr) | 13° 45′N | 103° 45′E | 680 |
| Angola (an·GOH·luh) | 14° 15′S | 16° 00′E | 538 |
| Angola Plateau | 13° 00′S | 16° 00′E | 538 |
| Anguilla (an·GWIL·uh) | 23° 30′N | 79° 30′W | 304 |
| Ankara (AN·kuh·ruh) | 40° 00′N | 33° 00′E | 484 |
| Ankaratra Mountains (ang·kuh·RAH·truh) | 20° 00′S | 48° 00′E | 557 |
| An Nafūd (an nuh·FOOHD) | 28° 30′N | 40° 30′E | 491 |
| Annam Cordillera (a·NAM) | 17° 30′N | 105° 45′E | 680 |
| Annapolis (an·NAP·oh·lis) | 39° 00′N | 76° 30′W | 225 |
| Ann Arbor (an AHR·buhr) | 42° 15′N | 83° 45′W | 231 |
| Anshan (AHN·shahn) | 41° 00′N | 123° 00′E | 622 |
| Antananarivo (an·tuh·nan·uh·REE·voh) | 18° 45′S | 47° 45′E | 557 |
| Antarctica (ant·AHRK·tik·uh) | 80° 15′S | 127° 00′E | 17 |
| Antarctic Peninsula | 70° 00′S | 65° 00′W | 17 |
| Antigua and Barbuda (an·TEE·gwuh and bar·BOO·duh) | 17° 15′N | 61° 15′W | 304 |
| Antofagasta (ahn·toh·fah·GAHS·tah) | 23° 30′S | 70° 15′W | 352 |
| Antsirabe (ahnt·see·RAH·bay) | 19° 45′S | 47° 15′E | 557 |
| Antsiranana (ahnt·suh·RAHN·uh·nuh) | 12° 15′S | 49° 15′E | 557 |
| Antwerp (ANT·wuhrp) | 51° 15′N | 4° 30′E | 397 |
| Apalachee Bay (ap·uh·LACH·ee) | 30° 00′N | 84° 00′W | 228 |
| Apennines (AP·uh·nynz) | 43° 45′N | 11° 00′E | 407 |
| Appalachian Mountains (ap·puh·LAY·chee·uhn) | 37° 15′N | 82° 00′W | 228 |
| Appleton (AP·uhl·tuhn) | 44° 15′N | 88° 30′W | 231 |
| Apure River (ah·POO·ray) | 7° 00′N | 67° 00′W | 338 |
| Aqaba (AH·kuh·buh) | 29° 30′N | 35° 00′E | 495 |
| Aqaba, Gulf of | 28° 30′N | 34° 45′E | 472 |
| Arabian Desert (uh·RAH·bee·uhn) | 27° 00′N | 32° 45′E | 472 |
| Arabian Peninsula | 28° 00′N | 40° 00′E | 491 |
| Arabian Sea | 16° 00′N | 55° 15′E | 491 |
| Arafura Sea (ahr·uh·FOOH·ruh) | 8° 45′S | 130° 00′E | 698 |
| Arakan Yoma (uh·ruh·KUHN YOH·muh) | 19° 45′N | 94° 15′E | 680 |
| Aral Sea (AR·uhl) | 45° 15′N | 60° 00′E | 434 |
| Ararat, Mount (A·ruh·rat) | 39° 45′N | 44° 15′E | 484 |
| Arctic Ocean (AHRK·tik) | 90° 00′N | | 2-3 |
| Arequipa (ah·ruh·KEEP·uh) | 16° 30′S | 71° 30′W | 352 |
| Argentina (ahr·jen·TEEN·uh) | 35° 30′S | 67° 00′W | 366 |
| Århus (OH·hoos) | 56° 15′N | 10° 15′E | 401 |
| Arizona (a·ri·ZOHN·uh) | 34° 00′N | 113° 00′W | 237 |
| Arkansas (AHR·kan·saw) | 34° 45′N | 93° 45′W | 228 |
| Arkansas River (ahr·KAN·suhs) | 32° 30′N | 91° 15′W | 233 |
| Arkhangelsk (ar·KAN·gelsk) | 64° 30′N | 40° 30′E | 13 |
| Armenian S.S.R. (ahr·MEEN·ee·uhn) | 41° 00′N | 44° 45′E | 434 |
| Aruba (uh·ROO·buh) | 12° 30′N | 70° 00′W | 304 |
| Asheville (ASH·vil) | 35° 30′N | 82° 30′W | 228 |
| Ashkhabad (uhsh·kah·BAHT) | 39° 45′N | 58° 15′E | 434 |

# GAZETTEER

| NAME | LATITUDE | LONGITUDE | PAGE |
|---|---|---|---|
| Asia (AY · zhuh) | 45° 00′N | 85° 00′E | 14–15 |
| Asia Minor | 38° 45′N | 32° 00′E | 484 |
| Asir, Ras (ah · SEER) | 12° 00′N | 51° 30′E | 548 |
| Asmara (az · MAHR · uh) | 15° 17′N | 39° 00′E | 548 |
| Astara (ahs · tuh · RAH) | 38° 00′N | 48° 00′E | 495 |
| Asunción (ah · soon · see · OHN) | 25° 30′S | 57° 30′W | 366 |
| Aswan Dam (ah · SWAHN) | 24° 00′N | 33° 00′E | 472 |
| Atacama Desert (ah · tah · KAH · mah) | 23° 15′S | 68° 45′W | 352 |
| Athabasca, Lake (ath · uh · BAS · kuh) | 59° 00′N | 109° 15′W | 253 |
| Athabasca River | 58° 00′N | 112° 00′W | 253 |
| Athens (ATH · enz) | 38° 00′N | 23° 45′E | 407 |
| Atlanta (at · LAN · tuh) | 33° 45′N | 83° 45′W | 228 |
| Atlantic Coastal Plain (at · LAN · tik) | 35° 00′N | 80° 00′W | 195 |
| Atlantic Ocean | 23° 30′N | 30° 00′W | 2 |
| Atlas Mountains (AT · las) | 31° 15′N | 5° 00′W | 454 |
| Auckland (AWK · land) | 37° 00′S | 174° 45′E | 698 |
| Augusta, Ga. (aw · GUHS · tuh) | 33° 30′N | 82° 00′W | 228 |
| Augusta, Me. | 44° 15′N | 69° 45′W | 224 |
| Aura River (AW · rah) | 44° 00′N | 12° 30′E | 401 |
| Austin (AWS · tin) | 30° 15′N | 97° 45′W | 237 |
| Australia (aws · TRAYL · yuh) | 25° 00′S | 135° 00′E | 698 |
| Australian Capital Territory | 35° 30′S | 149° 15′E | 698 |
| Austria (AWS · tree · uh) | 47° 15′N | 12° 00′E | 397 |
| Azerbaijan S.S.R. (az · uhr · by · JAHN) | 40° 30′N | 47° 30′E | 434 |
| Azores (AY · zohrs) | 37° 45′N | 29° 30′W | 16 |
| **B** | | | |
| Babuyan Islands (bah · boo · YAHN) | 19° 30′N | 122° 45′E | 689 |
| Babylon (BAB · i · lawn) | 32° 15′N | 45° 30′E | 497 |
| Bacolod (bah · COH · lawd) | 10° 45′N | 123° 00′E | 689 |
| Badlands National Park | 43° 45′N | 102° 00′W | 233 |
| Baffin Bay (BAF · in) | 72° 00′N | 65° 00′W | 253 |
| Baffin Island | 67° 15′N | 71° 00′W | 253 |
| Baghdad (BAG · dad) | 33° 15′N | 44° 15′E | 497 |
| Baguio (bahg · ee · OH) | 16° 30′N | 120° 30′E | 689 |
| Bahamas (bah · HAH · muhs) | 26° 15′N | 76° 00′W | 304 |
| Bahrain (bah · RAYN) | 26° 15′N | 51° 15′E | 491 |
| Baikal, Lake (by · KAHL) | 53° 00′N | 109° 30′E | 434 |
| Baja California (BAH · hah) | 27° 30′N | 113° 00′W | 272 |
| Bakersfield (BAY · kers · feeld) | 35° 30′N | 119° 00′W | 241 |
| Bakhtaran (BAK · tuh · ran) | 34° 00′N | 47° 00′E | 497 |
| Baku (ba · KOO) | 40° 30′N | 49° 45′E | 434 |
| Balabac Strait (BAH · lah · bahk) | 7° 30′N | 116° 30′E | 698 |
| Balaton, Lake (BAL · uh · tawn) | 46° 45′N | 18° 00′E | 422 |
| Balearic Islands (bal · ee · AR · ik) | 39° 30′N | 1° 30′E | 407 |
| Bali (BAL · ee) | 8° 00′S | 115° 15′E | 688 |
| Balintang Channel (bal · in · TAHNG) | 19° 45′N | 121° 15′E | 689 |
| Balkan Mountains (BAWL · kuhn) | 42° 45′N | 24° 45′E | 422 |
| Balkan Peninsula | 42° 00′N | 23° 00′E | 422 |
| Balkhash, Lake (bal · KASH) | 49° 00′N | 72° 15′E | 434 |
| Balsas River (BAWL · suhs) | 18° 00′N | 102° 30′W | 272 |
| Baltic Sea (BAWL · tik) | 55° 30′N | 16° 45′E | 401 |
| Baltimore (BAWL · ti · mohr) | 39° 15′N | 76° 45′W | 225 |
| Balzers (BAHL · zuhrs) | 47° 00′N | 9° 30′E | 408 |
| Bamako (bah · ma · KOH) | 12° 45′N | 8° 00′W | 528 |
| Bandar Abbas (buhn · DUHR uh · BAHS) | 27° 00′N | 56° 15′E | 497 |
| Bandar Seri Begawan (buhn · duhr ser · ee buh · GAW · wuhn) | 5° 00′N | 115° 00′E | 688 |
| Banda Sea (BAN · duh) | 6° 00′S | 127° 30′E | 688 |
| Bandjarmasin (bahn · jer · MAH · seen) | 3° 15′S | 114° 30′E | 688 |
| Bandung (BAHN · duhng) | 7° 00′S | 107° 15′E | 688 |
| Bangalore (BANG · guh · lohr) | 13° 00′N | 77° 45′E | 572 |
| Bangkok (BANG · kawk) | 13° 45′N | 100° 30′E | 680 |
| Bangladesh (bang · gluh · DESH) | 24° 15′N | 90° 00′E | 572 |
| Bangor (BANG · guhr) | 44° 45′N | 68° 45′W | 224 |
| Bangoran National Park (bahn · goh · RAHN) | 7° 30′N | 20° 15′E | 538 |
| Bangui (bahn · GEE) | 4° 15′N | 18° 30′E | 538 |
| Banjul (BAHN · jool) | 13°30′N | 16° 45′W | 528 |
| Barbados (bar · BAY · dohs) | 13° 30′N | 59° 00′W | 304 |
| Barcelona (bahr · thuh · LOH · nah) | 41° 30′N | 2° 15′E | 407 |
| Barents Sea (BAHR · rents) | 72° 15′N | 37° 30′E | 434 |
| Barisan Mountains (bahr · i · SAHN) | 2° 45′S | 101° 45′E | 688 |
| Barranquilla (bahr · ahn · KEEL · yuh) | 11° 00′N | 75° 00′W | 338 |
| Barrow, Point (BAR · oh) | 71° 15′N | 156° 00′W | 241 |
| Basel (BAH · zuhl) | 47° 30′N | 7° 30′E | 397 |
| Basra (BAHS · ruh) | 30° 30′N | 48° 00′E | 495 |
| Bassein (buh · SEEN) | 16° 45′N | 94° 45′E | 680 |
| Bass Strait | 39° 45′S | 145° 45′E | 698 |
| Batan Islands (bah · TAHN) | 21° 00′N | 122° 15′E | 689 |
| Batman (baht · MAHN) | 38° 30′N | 41° 00′E | 495 |
| Baton Rouge (bat · uhn ROOZH) | 30° 30′N | 91° 15′W | 228 |
| Bauchi Plateau (buh · OOCH · ee) | 10° 15′N | 9° 45′E | 528 |
| Beatrice (BEE · uh · tris) | 40° 15′N | 96° 45′W | 233 |
| Beaufort Sea (BOH · fuhrt) | 70° 30′N | 138° 45′W | 253 |
| Beaumont (BOH · mawnt) | 30° 00′N | 94° 00′W | 237 |
| Beijing (BAY · JING) | 40° 00′N | 116° 30′E | 622 |
| Beira (BAY · ruh) | 19° 45′S | 35° 00′E | 557 |
| Beirut (bay · ROOT) | 34° 00′N | 35° 00′E | 487 |
| Belém (buh · LEM) | 1° 15′S | 48° 30′W | 366 |
| Belfast (BEL · fast) | 54° 30′N | 5° 45′W | 397 |
| Belgium (BEL · juhm) | 51° 00′N | 2° 45′E | 397 |
| Belgrade (BEL · grahd) | 44° 45′N | 20° 30′E | 422 |
| Belize (be · LEEZ) | 17° 00′N | 88° 45′W | 288 |
| Belize City | 17° 30′N | 88° 45′W | 288 |
| Bellingham (BEL · ing · ham) | 48° 45′N | 122° 30′W | 241 |
| Bellinghausen Sea (BEL · ingz · how · zuhn) | 72° 00′S | 80° 30′W | 17 |
| Belmopan (bel · moh · PAN) | 17° 15′N | 88° 45′W | 288 |
| Belo Horizonte (BAY · loh her · uh · ZAHNT · ee) | 20° 00′N | 44° 00′W | 366 |
| Bemidji (buh · MIJ · ee) | 47° 30′N | 95° 00′W | 233 |
| Bengal, Bay of (ben · GAWL) | 17° 30′N | 87° 00′E | 572 |
| Benghazi (ben · GAH · zee) | 32° 00′N | 20° 00′E | 472 |
| Benin, (buh · NEEN) | 8° 00′N | 2° 00′E | 528 |
| Benin, Bight of | 6° 00′N | 3° 00′E | 528 |
| Benue River (BAY · noo · uh) | 8° 00′N | 9° 00′E | 528 |
| Berbera (BUHR · buhr · uh) | 10° 30′N | 45° 00′E | 548 |
| Bergen (BER · guhn) | 60° 30′N | 5° 15′E | 401 |
| Bering Sea (BER · ing) | 58° 00′N | 175° 00′W | 241 |
| Bering Strait | 64° 45′N | 169° 45′W | 241 |
| Berkeley (BUHRK · lee) | 37° 45′N | 122° 15′W | 241 |
| Berlin (ber · LIN) | 52° 30′N | 13° 30′E | 422 |
| Bermuda (ber · MYOO · duh) | 32° 15′N | 65° 45′W | 10 |
| Bern (bern) | 47° 00′N | 7° 30′E | 397 |
| Bethlehem (BETH · luh · hem) | 31° 45′N | 35° 15′E | 487 |
| Bhutan (boo · TAHN) | 27° 15′N | 90° 30′E | 572 |
| Big Belt Mountains | 47° 00′N | 111° 45′W | 239 |
| Big Bend National Park | 29° 15′N | 103° 15′W | 237 |
| Big Horn Mountains | 44° 45′N | 107° 45′W | 239 |
| Bighorn River | 46° 15′N | 107° 30′W | 239 |
| Big Sandy River | 38° 15′N | 83° 30′W | 228 |
| Bikini Atoll | 12° 00′N | 165° 00′E | 698 |
| Bilbao (bil · BAH · oh) | 43° 15′N | 2° 45′W | 407 |
| Billings (BIL · ingz) | 45° 45′N | 108° 30′W | 239 |
| Biloxi (bi · LAWKS · ee) | 30° 30′N | 88° 45′W | 228 |
| Birkirkara (bir · kuh · KAHR · uh) | 36° 00′N | 14° 30′E | 408 |
| Birmingham, Ala. | 33° 30′N | 86° 45′W | 228 |
| Birmingham, England | 52° 30′N | 1° 45′W | 397 |
| Biscay, Bay of (bis · KAY) | 45° 15′N | 3° 45′W | 397 |
| Bismarck (BIZ · mahrk) | 46° 45′N | 100° 45′W | 233 |
| Bismarck Archipelago | 3° 15′S | 150° 45′E | 698 |
| Bissau (buh · SAH · oo) | 11° 45′N | 15° 30′W | 528 |
| Bitterroot Range (BIT · uhr · root) | 46° 30′N | 114° 15′W | 239 |
| Black Forest | 48° 00′N | 8° 00′E | 397 |
| Black Hills | 44° 15′N | 103° 45′W | 233 |
| Black Range | 33° 15′N | 107° 00′W | 237 |
| Black Sea | 43° 00′N | 32° 15′E | 434 |
| Black Volta River (VOHL · tuh) | 9° 00′N | 1° 00′W | 528 |
| Blantyre (BLAN · tyr) | 15° 45′S | 35° 00′E | 557 |
| Bloemfontein (BLOOM · fawn · tayn) | 29° 15′S | 26° 15′E | 557 |

**735**

# GAZETTEER

Gazetteer

| NAME | LATITUDE | LONGITUDE | PAGE |
|------|----------|-----------|------|
| Blue Mountains | 45° 15′N | 118° 45′W | 241 |
| Blue Nile (NYL) | 15° 30′N | 32° 30′E | 548 |
| Blue Ridge Mountains | 35° 30′N | 82° 45′W | 228 |
| Bogotá (boh·goh·TAH) | 4° 45′N | 74° 00′W | 338 |
| Bohemian Forest (boh·HEEM·ee·uhn) | 49° 30′N | 12° 30′E | 397 |
| Bohol (boh·HAHL) | 9° 30′N | 124° 30′E | 689 |
| Boise (BOY·zee) | 43° 45′N | 116° 15′W | 239 |
| Bolivia (boh·LIV·ee·uh) | 17° 00′S | 64° 00′W | 352 |
| Bombay (bawm·BAY) | 19° 00′N | 72° 45′E | 572 |
| Bonaire (buh·NAYR) | 12° 15′N | 68° 15′W | 304 |
| Bonampak (boh·nahm·PAHK) | 16° 30′N | 91° 00′W | 276 |
| Bonn (BAWN) | 50° 45′N | 7° 00′E | 397 |
| Bordeaux (bohr·DOH) | 44° 45′N | 0° 30′W | 397 |
| Borneo (BOR·nee·oh) | 0° 30′N | 112° 45′E | 688 |
| Bornholm (BORN·hohlm) | 55° 15′N | 15° 15′E | 401 |
| Bosporus (BAHS·puhr·uhs) | 41° 15′N | 29° 15′E | 484 |
| Boston (BAWS·tuhn) | 42° 15′N | 71° 00′W | 224 |
| Bothnia, Gulf of (BAWTH·nee·uh) | 63° 45′N | 21° 30′E | 401 |
| Botswana (bawts·WAH·nah) | 22° 15′S | 23° 15′E | 557 |
| Bouaké (boo·ah·KAY) | 7° 45′N | 5° 00′W | 528 |
| Boulder (BOHL·duhr) | 40° 00′N | 105° 15′W | 239 |
| Brahmaputra River (brah·muh·POO·truh) | 26° 45′N | 92° 45′E | 572 |
| Brasilia (brah·ZIL·lyuh) | 15° 45′S | 47° 45′W | 366 |
| Braşov (brah·SHAWV) | 45° 45′N | 25° 30′E | 422 |
| Bratislava (BRAHT·is·lah·vuh) | 48° 15′N | 17° 00′E | 422 |
| Brazil (brah·ZIL) | 9° 00′S | 53° 00′W | 366 |
| Brazilian Highlands (brah·ZIL·yuhn) | 14° 00′S | 48° 00′W | 366 |
| Brazos River (BRAH·zohs) | 29° 00′N | 96° 15′W | 237 |
| Brazzaville (brah·zuh·VEEL) | 4° 15′S | 15° 15′E | 538 |
| Bremen (BRAY·men) | 53° 00′N | 8° 45′E | 397 |
| Bridgeport (BRIDJ·pohrt) | 41° 15′N | 73° 15′W | 224 |
| Bridgetown (BRIDJ·town) | 13° 15′N | 59° 30′W | 304 |
| Brisbane (BRIZ·buhn) | 27° 30′S | 153° 15′E | 698 |
| Bristol (BRIS·tuhl) | 51° 30′N | 2° 45′W | 397 |
| British Columbia (BRIT·ish koh·LUHM·bee·uh) | 56° 00′N | 125° 00′W | 253 |
| British Isles | 53° 00′N | 4° 00′W | 397 |
| British Virgin Islands | 18° 15′N | 63° 30′W | 304 |
| Brno (BUHR·noh) | 49° 15′N | 16° 30′E | 422 |
| Broken Hill | 32° 00′S | 141° 30′E | 698 |
| Brookings (BROOHK·ingz) | 44° 15′N | 96° 45′W | 233 |
| Brooks Range (broohks) | 68° 15′N | 159° 00′W | 241 |
| Brownsville (BROWNZ·vil) | 26° 00′N | 97° 30′W | 237 |
| Brunei (broo·NEYE) | 4° 45′N | 113° 45′E | 688 |
| Brussels (BRUHS·selz) | 50° 45′N | 4° 30′E | 397 |
| Bucharest (boo·kah·REST) | 44° 30′N | 26° 15′E | 422 |
| Budapest (BOO·duh·pest) | 47° 30′N | 19° 00′E | 422 |
| Buenos Aires (bway·nuh· SAHR·eez) | 34° 15′S | 58° 30′W | 366 |
| Buffalo (BUHF·uh·loh) | 43° 00′N | 78° 45′W | 225 |
| Bug River (BOOG) | 52° 15′N | 21° 05′E | 422 |
| Bujumbura (boo·juhm·BUHR·uh) | 3° 30′S | 29° 15′E | 548 |
| Bukavu (boo·KAH·voo) | 2° 30′S | 28° 45′E | 538 |
| Bulawayo (boo·luh·WAY·oh) | 20° 15′S | 28° 45′E | 557 |
| Bulgaria (boohl·GAR·ee·uh) | 42° 15′N | 24° 15′E | 422 |
| Burkina Faso (buhr·KEEN·nuh FAH·soh) | 11° 45′N | 3° 15′E | 528 |
| Burlington, Iowa (BUHR·ling·tuhn) | 40° 45′N | 91° 00′W | 233 |
| Burlington, Vt. | 44° 30′N | 73° 15′W | 224 |
| Burma (BUHR·muh) | 21° 00′N | 95° 15′E | 680 |
| Bursa (BOOR·suh) | 40° 15′N | 28° 15′E | 484 |
| Burundi (buh·ROON·dee) | 3° 00′S | 29° 30′E | 548 |
| Butte (BYOOT) | 46° 00′N | 112° 30′W | 239 |
| Byelorussian S.S.R. (bel·oh·RUHSH·uhn) | 53° 30′N | 25° 30′E | 434 |

### C

| NAME | LATITUDE | LONGITUDE | PAGE |
|------|----------|-----------|------|
| Cabinda (kuh·BIN·duh) | 5° 15′S | 10° 00′E | 538 |
| Cádiz (KAH·deez) | 36° 30′N | 6° 15′W | 407 |
| Cagayan River (kah·gah·YAHN) | 18° 15′N | 121° 45′E | 689 |
| Cairo (KY·roh) | 30° 00′N | 31° 15′E | 472 |

| NAME | LATITUDE | LONGITUDE | PAGE |
|------|----------|-----------|------|
| Calais (kal·AY) | 51° 00′N | 1° 45′E | 397 |
| Calcutta (kal·KUHT·uh) | 22° 30′N | 88° 15′E | 572 |
| Calgary (KAL·guh·ree) | 51° 00′N | 114° 00′W | 253 |
| Cali (KAH·lee) | 3° 30′N | 76° 30′W | 338 |
| California (kal·i·FOHR·nee·uh) | 38° 15′N | 121° 30′W | 241 |
| California, Gulf of | 30° 30′N | 114° 45′W | 272 |
| Callao (kal·YAH·oh) | 12° 00′S | 77° 00′W | 352 |
| Cambay, Gulf of (kam·BAY) | 21° 15′N | 72° 30′E | 572 |
| Cambodia (kam·BOH·dee·uh) | 12° 15′N | 104° 00′E | 680 |
| Camden (KAM·den) | 40° 00′N | 75° 00′W | 225 |
| Cameroon (KAM·uhr·oon) | 5° 45′N | 11° 00′E | 538 |
| Cameroon, Mount | 4° 15′N | 9° 15′E | 538 |
| Canada (KAN·uh·duh) | 50° 00′N | 100° 00′W | 253 |
| Canadian River (kuh·NAY·dee·uhn) | 36° 30′N | 95° 00′W | 253 |
| Canadian Shield | 55° 00′N | 88° 00′W | 253 |
| Canary Islands (kuh·NAY·ree) | 29° 15′N | 16° 30′W | 16 |
| Canaveral, Cape (kuh·NAV·uhr·uhl) | 28° 30′N | 80° 30′W | 228 |
| Canberra (KAN·buhr·uh) | 35° 15′S | 149° 15′E | 698 |
| Cantabrian Mountains (kan·TAB·ree·uhn) | 43° 00′N | 6° 00′W | 407 |
| Cape Arid National Park | 33° 30′S | 123° 00′E | 698 |
| Cape Girardeau (jee·rahr·DOH) | 37° 15′N | 89° 30′W | 233 |
| Cape Town | 33° 45′S | 18° 30′E | 557 |
| Cape Verde (vuhrd) | 15° 45′N | 26° 00′W | 528 |
| Cape York Peninsula | 12° 30′S | 142° 30′E | 698 |
| Caprivi Strip (kuh·PREE·vee) | 18° 00′S | 22° 00′E | 557 |
| Caquetá River (kah·kay·TAH) | 1° 45′S | 69° 30′W | 338 |
| Caracas (kah·RAH·kuhs) | 10° 30′N | 67° 00′W | 338 |
| Caribbean Sea (kar·i·BEE·uhn) | 14° 30′N | 75° 30′W | 304 |
| Carlsbad Caverns (KARLZ·bad) | 32° 15′N | 104° 30′W | 237 |
| Caroline Islands (KAR·oh·lyn) | 9° 30′N | 143° 00′E | 698 |
| Caroni River (kah·ROH·nee) | 8° 30′N | 62° 45′W | 338 |
| Carpathian Mountains (kahr·PAY·thee·uhn) | 49° 30′N | 20° 15′E | 422 |
| Carpentaria, Gulf of (kahr·puhn·TER·ee·uh) | 14° 45′S | 138° 45′E | 698 |
| Carson City (KAHR·suhn) | 39° 15′N | 119° 45′W | 239 |
| Casablanca (kah·sah·BLAHNG·KAH) | 33° 30′N | 7° 45′W | 478 |
| Cascade Range (kas·KAYD) | 42° 45′N | 122° 15′W | 241 |
| Casper (KAS·puhr) | 42° 45′N | 106° 15′W | 239 |
| Caspian Sea (KAS·pee·uhn) | 40° 00′N | 52° 00′E | 434 |
| Castries (kas·TREE) | 14° 00′N | 61° 00′W | 304 |
| Cauca River (KAW·kuh) | 9° 15′N | 75° 00′W | 338 |
| Caucasus Mountains (KAW·kuh·suhs) | 43° 30′N | 42°00 ′E | 434 |
| Caura River (KAW·rah) | 7° 15′N | 65° 00′W | 338 |
| Cayenne (keye·EN) | 4° 45′N | 52° 15′W | 338 |
| Cayman Islands (KAY·men) | 19° 30′N | 80° 30′W | 304 |
| Cebu (say·BOO) | 10° 15′N | 123° 45′E | 689 |
| Cedar Rapids (SEE·duhr RAP·idz) | 42° 00′N | 91° 45′W | 233 |
| Celebes (sel·uh·BEEZ) | 2° 15′S | 121° 30′E | 688 |
| Celebes Sea | 3° 45′N | 121° 45′E | 688 |
| Central African Republic | 7° 45′N | 21° 00′E | 538 |
| Central America | 10° 45′N | 87° 15′W | 288 |
| Central Kalahari Game Preserve (kal·uh·HAHR·ee) | 23° 30′S | 24° 00′E | 557 |
| Central Lowland | 41° 00′N | 89° 00′W | 195 |
| Central Valley | 38° 00′N | 121° 00′W | 241 |
| Ceram (SAY·rahm) | 2° 45′S | 129° 30′E | 688 |
| Ceuta (thay·OO·tah) | 36° 00′N | 5° 30′W | 478 |
| Chad | 17° 45′N | 19° 00′E | 511 |
| Chad, Lake | 13° 00′N | 14° 00′E | 511 |
| Champlain, Lake (sham·PLAYN) | 44° 54′N | 73° 15′W | 225 |
| Changchun (CHAHNG·CHOON) | 44° 00′N | 125° 30′E | 622 |
| Chang Jiang (CHAHNG JYAHNG) | 30° 00′N | 117° 30′E | 622 |
| Channel Islands, Calif. (CHAN·uhl) | 33° 15′N | 119° 00′W | 241 |
| Channel Islands, England | 49° 15′N | 3° 30′W | 397 |
| Chari River (shah·REE) | 13° 00′N | 14° 00′E | 538 |
| Charleston, S.C. (CHAHRLZ·tuhn) | 32° 45′N | 80° 00′W | 228 |
| Charleston, W.V. | 38° 15′N | 81° 30′W | 225 |
| Charlotte (SHAHR·luht) | 35° 15′N | 80° 45′W | 228 |

| NAME | LATITUDE | LONGITUDE | PAGE |
|---|---|---|---|
| Charlottesville (SHAHR·luhtz·vil) | 38° 00′N | 78° 30′W | 228 |
| Charlottetown (SHAHR·luht·town) | 46° 15′N | 63° 15′W | 253 |
| Chatham Islands (CHAT·uhm) | 44° 00′S | 178° 00′W | 699 |
| Chattahoochee River (chat·uh·HOO·chee) | 29° 45′N | 85° 15′W | 228 |
| Cheju Island (CHE·JOO) | 33° 30′N | 126° 45′E | 653 |
| Chelyabinsk (chel·yah·BEENSK) | 55° 15′N | 61° 30′E | 434 |
| Chengdu (CHUHNG·DOO) | 30° 30′N | 104° 15′E | 622 |
| Cherskogo Range (cher·SKOH·guh) | 66° 15′N | 138° 40′E | 434 |
| Chesapeake Bay (CHES·uh·peek) | 36° 45′N | 76° 15′W | 225 |
| Cheyenne (shy·AN) | 41° 15′N | 104° 45′W | 239 |
| Cheyenne River | 45° 00′N | 101° 00′W | 233 |
| Chicago (shi·CAW·goh) | 41° 45′N | 87° 30′W | 231 |
| Chichén Itzá (chee·CHEN eet·ZAH) | 20° 30′N | 88° 30′W | 276 |
| Chile (CHEE·lay) | 35° 00′S | 72° 00′W | 352 |
| China (CHY·nuh) | 36° 45′N | 93° 00′E | 622 |
| Chittagong (chit·uh·GAWNG) | 22° 30′N | 90° 45′E | 572 |
| Cholula (choh·LOO·lah) | 19° 00′N | 98° 15′W | 276 |
| Chongqing (CHOHNG·KING) | 29° 30′N | 107° 30′E | 622 |
| Christchurch (KRYST·chuhrch) | 43° 30′S | 172° 45′E | 698 |
| Chukchi Sea (CHUHK·chee) | 70° 00′N | 175° 00′E | 434 |
| Cimarron River (SIM·uh·ruhn) | 36° 15′N | 96° 15′W | 237 |
| Cincinnati (sin·sin·AT·ee) | 39° 15′N | 84° 30′W | 231 |
| Citlaltépetl (seet·lahl·TAY·petl) | 19° 00′N | 97° 15′W | 272 |
| Ciudad Bolivar (BOH·LEE·vahr) | 8° 00′N | 63° 45′W | 338 |
| Ciudad Juárez (HWAHR·ez) | 31° 45′N | 106° 30′W | 272 |
| Cleveland (CLEEV·land) | 43° 30′N | 81° 45′W | 231 |
| Cloud Peak | 44° 30′N | 107° 15′W | 239 |
| Cluj (KLOOZH) | 46° 45′N | 23° 30′E | 422 |
| Coast Mountains | 54° 15′N | 128° 00′W | 253 |
| Coast Range | 41° 30′N | 123° 30′W | 241 |
| Cod, Cape | 41° 30′N | 70° 30′W | 224 |
| Cologne (koh·LOHN) | 51° 00′N | 7° 00′E | 397 |
| Colombia (koh·LOHM·bee·uh) | 3° 30′N | 74° 45′W | 338 |
| Colombo (koh·LOHM·boh) | 7° 00′N | 80° 00′E | 572 |
| Colón (koh·LOHN) | 9° 15′N | 80° 00′W | 288 |
| Colorado (kaw·loh·RAH·doh) | 39° 30′N | 107° 00′W | 239 |
| Colorado Plateau | 36° 15′N | 109° 15′W | 239 |
| Colorado River, Mexico | 32° 00′N | 115° 00′W | 272 |
| Colorado River, Texas | 28° 45′N | 96° 00′W | 237 |
| Colorado Springs | 38° 45′N | 104° 45′W | 239 |
| Columbia, Cape | 83° 00′N | 61° 00′W | 17 |
| Columbia, Mo. (koh·LUHM·bee·uh) | 39° 00′N | 92° 15′W | 233 |
| Columbia Plateau | 47° 00′N | 117° 15′W | 241 |
| Columbia River | 46° 15′N | 124° 00′W | 241 |
| Columbia, S.C. | 34° 00′N | 81° 00′W | 228 |
| Columbus, Ga. (koh·LUHM·buhs) | 32° 30′N | 85° 00′W | 228 |
| Columbus, Ohio | 40° 00′N | 83° 00′W | 231 |
| Comorin, Cape (KAW·moh·rin) | 8° 00′N | 78° 00′E | 572 |
| Comoros (KAHM·uh·rohs) | 12° 30′S | 42° 45′E | 557 |
| Conakry (koh·nuh·KREE) | 9° 30′N | 13° 45′W | 528 |
| Concepción (kohn·sep·see·OHN) | 36° 45′S | 73° 00′W | 352 |
| Concord (KONG·kuhrd) | 43° 15′N | 71° 30′W | 224 |
| Congo (KAWN·goh) | 3° 00′S | 13° 45′E | 538 |
| Congo Basin | 3° 45′S | 21° 00′E | 538 |
| Congo River. See Zaire River. | | | |
| Connecticut (kuh·NET·uh·kuht) | 41° 45′N | 73° 15′W | 224 |
| Connecticut River | 41° 15′N | 73° 00′W | 224 |
| Constanța (kohn·STAN·tsuh) | 44° 15′N | 28° 30′E | 422 |
| Cook Islands | 20° 00′S | 158° 00′W | 699 |
| Cook Strait | 40° 30′S | 174° 15′E | 698 |
| Copàn (koh·PAHN) | 14° 45′N | 89° 15′W | 276 |
| Copenhagen (koh·pen·HAY·guhn) | 55° 45′N | 12° 30′E | 401 |
| Coral Sea | 13° 30′S | 150° 00′E | 698 |
| Coral Sea Islands Territory | 13° 30′S | 150° 00′E | 698 |
| Córdoba (KOHR·doh·buh) | 30° 15′S | 64° 00′W | 366 |
| Corfu (KOHR·foo) | 39° 30′N | 19° 30′E | 407 |
| Corpus Christi (KOHR·puhs KRIS·tee) | 27° 45′N | 97° 30′W | 237 |
| Corsica (KOHR·see·kah) | 42° 15′N | 9° 00′E | 397 |
| Costa Rica (KOS·tah REE·kah) | 10° 30′N | 84° 30′W | 288 |
| Cotopaxi (koht·uh·PAK·see) | 0° 45′S | 78° 30′W | 352 |
| Council Bluffs (KOWN·suhl bluhfs) | 41° 15′N | 96° 00′W | 233 |
| Covington (KUHV·ing·tuhn) | 39° 00′N | 84° 30′W | 228 |
| Crater Lake National Park | 43° 00′N | 122° 45′W | 241 |
| Crete (kreet) | 35° 15′N | 24° 30′E | 407 |
| Cuango River (KWAHNG·goh) | 3° 15′S | 17° 15′E | 538 |
| Cuba (KYOO·buh) | 22° 00′N | 79° 00′W | 304 |
| Cúcuta (KOO·koo·tah) | 8° 00′N | 72° 30′W | 338 |
| Cuernavaca (kwayr·nah·VAH·kah) | 19° 00′N | 99° 15′W | 10 |
| Cumberland Plateau (KUHM·buhr·luhnd) | 35° 30′N | 85° 30′W | 228 |
| Cunene River (koo·NAY·nuh) | 17° 15′S | 11° 45′E | 538 |
| Curaçao (koo·ruh·SAH·oh) | 12° 15′N | 69° 00′W | 304 |
| Curitiba (koo·ree·TEE·bah) | 25° 15′S | 49° 15′W | 366 |
| Cuzco (KOOS·koh) | 13° 30′S | 71° 45′W | 352 |
| Cyclades (SIK·luh·deez) | 37° 45′N | 27° 45′E | 407 |
| Cyprus (SY·pruhs) | 35° 00′N | 31° 00′E | 484 |
| Czechoslovakia (chek·oh·sloh·VAHK·ee·uh) | 49° 30′N | 16° 00′E | 422 |
| **D** | | | |
| Dacca (DAH·kah) | 23° 45′N | 90° 30′E | 572 |
| Dakar (duh·KAHR) | 14° 45′N | 17° 30′W | 528 |
| Dallas (DAHL·luhs) | 32° 45′N | 97° 45′W | 237 |
| Damascus (duh·MAS·kuhs) | 33° 30′N | 36° 15′E | 487 |
| Damman (dam·MAN) | 26° 30′N | 50° 00′E | 495 |
| Da Nang (dah NAHNG) | 16° 15′N | 108° 15′E | 680 |
| Danube (DAN·yoob) | 47° 00′N | 29° 30′E | 422 |
| Dardanelles (dahrd·uhn·ELZ) | 40° 00′N | 25° 45′E | 484 |
| Dar es Salaam (dahr es suh·LAHM) | 6° 45′S | 37° 15′E | 548 |
| Darling Range | 30° 30′S | 115° 45′E | 698 |
| Darling River | 24° 00′S | 142° 00′E | 698 |
| Darwin (DAHR·win) | 12° 30′S | 131° 00′E | 698 |
| Davao (DAH·vaoo ) | 7° 00′N | 125° 30′E | 689 |
| Davenport (DAV·uhn·pohrt) | 41° 30′N | 90° 45′W | 233 |
| Davis Sea (DAY·vis) | 65° 00′S | 90° 00′E | 17 |
| Davis Strait | 66° 00′N | 60° 00′W | 253 |
| Dayton (DAY·tuhn) | 40° 00′N | 84° 15′W | 231 |
| Dead Sea | 31° 30′N | 35° 45′E | 487 |
| Death Valley | 37° 00′N | 117° 15′W | 241 |
| Debrecen (DEB·ret·sen) | 47° 30′N | 21° 45′E | 422 |
| Decatur (dee·KAY·tuhr) | 39° 45′N | 89° 00′W | 231 |
| Deccan Plateau (DEK·uhn) | 17° 00′N | 77° 00′E | 572 |
| Delaware (DEL·uh·wauhr) | 38° 45′N | 75° 30′W | 225 |
| Delaware River | 39° 45′N | 75° 30′W | 225 |
| Delhi (DEL·ee) | 29° 00′N | 77° 15′E | 572 |
| Denali National Park (duh·NAHL·ee) | 64° 00′N | 150° 00′W | 241 |
| Denmark (DEN·mahrk) | 56° 15′N | 8° 30′E | 401 |
| Denver (DEN·vuhr) | 39° 45′N | 105° 00′W | 239 |
| Deschutes River (day·SHOOT) | 45° 30′N | 120° 45′W | 241 |
| Des Moines (duh MOYN) | 41° 30′N | 93° 30′W | 233 |
| Des Moines River | 40° 30′N | 91° 30′W | 233 |
| Detroit (dee·TROYT) | 42° 15′N | 83° 15′W | 231 |
| Dickinson (DIK·in·suhn) | 46° 45′N | 102° 45′W | 233 |
| Dijon (dee·ZHAHN) | 47° 15′N | 5° 00′E | 397 |
| Dinaric Alps (di·NAHR·ik) | 44° 00′N | 16° 00′E | 422 |
| Djibouti (juh·BOO·tee) | 11° 30′N | 43° 00′E | 548 |
| Djibouti (city) | 11° 30′N | 43° 15′E | 548 |
| Dnepropetrovsk (DNYEP·roh·puh·trohfsk) | 48° 30′N | 34° 15′E | 434 |
| Dniester River (NEES·tuhr) | 46° 00′N | 30° 30′E | 13 |
| Doha (DOH·hah) | 25° 00′N | 51° 30′E | 495 |
| Dominica (doh·min·EEK·uh) | 15° 30′N | 60° 45′W | 304 |
| Dominican Republic (doh·MIN·ik·uhn) | 19° 00′N | 70° 45′W | 304 |
| Donetsk (duh·NETSK) | 48° 00′N | 37° 30′E | 434 |
| Don River | 47° 00′N | 39° 15′E | 13 |
| Door Peninsula | 44° 45′N | 87° 30′W | 231 |
| Dortyol (duhrt·YAWL) | 37° 00′N | 36° 00′E | 495 |
| Douala (doo·AH·lah) | 4° 00′N | 9° 45′E | 538 |
| Dover, Del. (DOH·vuhr) | 39° 15′N | 75° 30′W | 225 |
| Dover, England | 51° 15′N | 1° 15′E | 12 |
| Dover, Strait of | 51° 00′N | 1° 15′E | 397 |

**737**

# GAZETTEER

| NAME | LATITUDE | LONGITUDE | PAGE |
|---|---|---|---|
| Drakensberg Mountains (DRAYK · uhnz · buhrg) | 29° 15′S | 29° 00′E | 557 |
| Drava River (DRAH · vah) | 43° 30′N | 21° 15′E | 422 |
| Dresden (DREZ · den) | 51° 00′N | 13° 45′E | 422 |
| Dublin (DUHB · lin) | 53° 15′N | 6° 15′W | 397 |
| Dubrovnik (doo · BRAWV · nik) | 42° 45′N | 18° 15′E | 422 |
| Dubuque (duh · BYOOK) | 42° 30′N | 90° 45′W | 233 |
| Duero River (DWER · oh) | 41° 15′N | 8° 45′W | 407 |
| Duluth (duh · LOOTH) | 46° 45′N | 92° 00′W | 233 |
| Dumont d'Urville (doo · MAWNT duhr · VEEL) | 66° 30′S | 140° 00′E | 17 |
| Dunedin (duh · NEE · duhn) | 45° 45′S | 170° 30′E | 699 |
| Durban (DUHR · buhn) | 29° 45′S | 31° 00′E | 557 |
| Durham (DUHR · uhm) | 36° 00′N | 79° 00′W | 228 |
| Dushanbe (doo · SHAN · buh) | 38° 30′N | 68° 45′E | 434 |
| Düsseldorf (DOO · suhl · dohrf) | 51° 15′N | 6° 45′E | 397 |
| **E** | | | |
| East China Sea | 30° 30′N | 125° 45′E | 622 |
| Eastern Ghats (GAWTS) | 13° 45′N | 78° 45′E | 572 |
| East St. Louis | 38° 45′N | 90° 15′W | 231 |
| East Siberian Sea | 77° 30′N | 153° 30′E | 434 |
| Eau Claire (oh CLAYR) | 44° 45′N | 91° 30′W | 231 |
| Ebro River (AY · broh) | 41° 45′N | 0° 45′E | 407 |
| Ecuador (EK · wuh · dohr) | 3° 00′S | 78° 30′W | 352 |
| Edinburgh (ED · in · buhr · uh) | 56° 00′N | 3° 15′W | 397 |
| Edmonton (ED · muhn · tuhn) | 53° 30′N | 113° 30′W | 253 |
| Edward, Lake | 0° 30′S | 29° 45′E | 548 |
| Edwards Plateau (ED · wahrdz) | 31° 00′N | 101° 00′W | 237 |
| Egypt (EE · jipt) | 27° 00′N | 27° 00′E | 472 |
| El Aaiún (el eye · OON) | 26° 45′N | 13° 15′W | 454 |
| El Amiriya (ah · mee · REE · yuh) | 29° 00′N | 27° 00′E | 495 |
| Elat (ay · LAHT) | 29° 00′N | 35° 00′E | 487 |
| Elbe River (EL · buh) | 53° 45′N | 9° 00′E | 422 |
| Elburz Mountains (el · BOOHRZ) | 36° 30′N | 51° 00′E | 497 |
| Elgon, Mount (EL · gawn) | 1° 00′N | 34° 30′E | 548 |
| Ellesmere Island (ELZ · meer) | 81° 00′N | 80° 00′W | 253 |
| Ellsworth Land (ELZ · wuhrth) | 77° 00′S | 90° 00′W | 17 |
| El Paso (PAS · oh) | 31° 45′N | 106° 30′W | 237 |
| El Salvador (sal · vah · DOHR) | 14° 00′N | 89° 30′W | 288 |
| El Serrat (ser · RAHT) | 42° 30′N | 1° 30′E | 408 |
| Emporia (em · POHR · ee · uh) | 38° 30′N | 96° 15′W | 233 |
| Ems River (EMZ) | 53° 15′N | 7° 15′E | 397 |
| Enderby Land (EN · duhr · bee) | 72° 00′S | 52° 00′E | 17 |
| England (ING · land) | 51° 30′N | 1° 45′W | 397 |
| English Channel (ING · lish) | 49° 45′N | 3° 00′W | 397 |
| Enid (EE · nid) | 36° 30′N | 97° 45′W | 237 |
| Eniwetok Atoll (en · i · WEE · tahk) | 11° 00′N | 162° 00′E | 698 |
| Equatorial Guinea (GI · nee) | 2° 00′N | 7° 15′E | 538 |
| Erie (EER · ee) | 42° 00′N | 80° 00′W | 225 |
| Erie, Lake | 42° 15′N | 81° 30′W | 195 |
| Eritrea (ay · ruh · TRAY · uh) | 16° 15′N | 38° 30′E | 548 |
| Essen (ES · en) | 51° 30′N | 7° 00′E | 397 |
| Essequibo River (es · uh · KEE · boh) | 7° 00′N | 57° 30′W | 338 |
| Es Sider (es · SEE · der) | 31° 00′N | 18° 00′E | 495 |
| Estonian S.S.R. (es · TOH · nee · uhn) | 59° 15′N | 25° 00′E | 434 |
| Ethiopia (eeth · ee · OH · pee · uh) | 8° 00′N | 38° 00′E | 548 |
| Ethiopian Plateau (eeth · ee · OH · pee · uhn) | 8° 00′N | 38° 00′E | 548 |
| Etna, Mount (ET · nuh) | 37° 45′N | 15° 00′E | 407 |
| Eugene (yoo · JEEN) | 44° 00′N | 123° 00′W | 241 |
| Euphrates River (yoo · FRAY · teez) | 30° 30′N | 47° 30′E | 454 |
| Eureka (yoo · REE · kuh) | 40° 45′N | 124° 15′W | 241 |
| Europe (YOOR · uhp) | 50° 00′N | 15° 00′E | 12–13 |
| Evansville (EV · uhns · vil) | 38° 00′N | 87° 30′W | 231 |
| Everest, Mount (EV · urh · est) | 28° 00′N | 87° 00′E | 572 |
| Everglades (EV · uhr · glaydz) | 25° 45′N | 81° 00′W | 228 |
| **F** | | | |
| Faetano (fah · et · AHN · oh) | 44° 00′N | 12° 30′E | 408 |
| Fairbanks (FAYR · banks) | 64° 00′N | 147° 45′W | 241 |
| Faisalabad (fy · SAHL · uh · bahd) | 31° 30′N | 73° 00′E | 589 |
| Falkland Islands (FAWK · land) | 50° 45′S | 61° 00′W | 366 |
| Fall Line | 33° 00′N | 82° 00′W | 195 |

| NAME | LATITUDE | LONGITUDE | PAGE |
|---|---|---|---|
| Fao (FOW) | 30° 00′N | 48° 00′E | 495 |
| Fargo (FAHR · goh) | 47° 00′N | 96° 45′W | 233 |
| Fayetteville (fay · YET · vil) | 36° 00′N | 94° 15′W | 228 |
| Federated States of Micronesia (my · kroh · NEE · zhuh) | 10° 00′N | 152° 00′E | 698 |
| Fès (FES) | 34° 15′N | 5° 00′W | 478 |
| Fiji (FEE · jee) | 18° 45′S | 175° 00′E | 699 |
| Finland (FIN · land) | 62° 45′N | 26° 15′E | 401 |
| Finland, Gulf of | 59° 30′N | 23° 30′E | 401 |
| Fjordland National Park (FYOHRD · land) | 45° 00′S | 167° 00′E | 699 |
| Flagstaff (FLAG · staf) | 35° 15′N | 111° 45′W | 237 |
| Flinders Ranges (FLIN · duhrz) | 32° 15′S | 138° 45′E | 698 |
| Flinders Ranges National Park | 32° 30′S | 139° 00′E | 698 |
| Flint | 43° 00′N | 83° 45′W | 231 |
| Florence (FLOHR · ens) | 43° 45′N | 11° 15′E | 407 |
| Flores (FLOHR · ays) | 8° 15′S | 121° 15′E | 688 |
| Florida (FLAWR · uh · duh) | 30° 30′N | 84° 45′W | 228 |
| Florida Keys | 24° 30′N | 81° 15′W | 228 |
| Florida, Straits of | 24° 15′N | 81° 00′W | 228 |
| Fortaleza (fohr · tah · LAY · zuh) | 3° 30′S | 38° 30′W | 366 |
| Fort Collins (KAW · linz) | 40° 30′N | 105° 00′W | 239 |
| Fort-de-France (fohrd · duh · FRAHNS) | 14° 30′N | 61° 00′W | 304 |
| Fort Knox (nawks) | 38° 00′N | 86° 00′W | 228 |
| Fort Lauderdale (LAW · duhr · dayl) | 26° 00′N | 80° 15′W | 228 |
| Fort Peck Reservoir | 47° 45′N | 107° 00′W | 239 |
| Fort Smith | 35° 30′N | 94° 30′W | 228 |
| Fort Sumter (SUHM · tuhr) | 32° 45′N | 80° 00′W | 228 |
| Fort Wayne | 41° 00′N | 85° 15′W | 231 |
| Fort Worth | 32° 45′N | 97° 15′W | 237 |
| Fouta Djallon (FOO · tuh jah · lohn) | 11° 30′N | 12° 30′W | 528 |
| France (FRANS) | 46° 45′N | 0° 45′E | 397 |
| Francis Case, Lake | 43° 15′N | 99° 00′W | 233 |
| Frankfort (FRANK · fuhrt) | 38° 15′N | 85° 00′W | 228 |
| Frankfurt | 52° 45′N | 13° 30′E | 397 |
| Franz Josef Land (frahnts YOH · sef) | 81° 30′N | 40° 00′E | 434 |
| Fraser River (FRAY · zuhr) | 49° 15′N | 123° 00′W | 253 |
| Fredericton (FRED · uhr · ik · tuhn) | 45° 45′N | 66° 45′W | 253 |
| Freetown (FREE · town) | 8° 30′N | 13° 15′W | 528 |
| French Guiana (gee · AN · uh) | 4° 15′N | 53° 00′W | 338 |
| French Polynesia (paw · luh · NEE · zhuh) | 15° 00′S | 140° 00′W | 699 |
| Fresno (FREZ · noh) | 37° 00′N | 120° 30′W | 241 |
| Frisian Islands (FREE · zhuhn) | 53° 30′N | 5° 15′E | 397 |
| Front Range | 42° 15′N | 106° 00′W | 239 |
| Frunze (FROON · zuh) | 49° 45′N | 74° 45′E | 434 |
| Fuji, Mount (FOO · jee) | 35° 30′N | 138° 45′E | 642 |
| Fukuoka (foo · kooh · OH · kuh) | 33° 30′N | 130° 30′E | 642 |
| Funafuti (fyoo · nuh · FYOO · tee) | 8° 00′S | 179° 00′E | 699 |
| Fushun (FOO · SHOON) | 41° 45′N | 124° 00′E | 622 |
| **G** | | | |
| Gabon (guh · BOHN) | 0° 30′S | 10° 45′E | 538 |
| Gaborone (gah · buh · ROHN) | 24° 30′S | 26° 00′E | 557 |
| Galilee, Sea of (GAL · i · lee) | 33° 00′N | 35° 30′E | 487 |
| Gallinas, Punta (PUHN · tuh gahl · YEE · nuhs) | 12° 15′N | 72° 15′W | 338 |
| Galveston (GAL · vuhs · tuhn) | 29° 15′N | 94° 45′W | 237 |
| Gambia (GAM · bee · uh) | 13° 45′N | 19° 45′W | 528 |
| Gambia River | 13° 30′N | 16° 45′W | 528 |
| Ganges Delta (GAN · jeez) | 22° 00′N | 88° 45′E | 572 |
| Ganges River | 21° 15′N | 88° 45′E | 572 |
| Gannett Peak (GAN · et) | 43° 15′N | 109° 45′W | 239 |
| Garonne River (gah · ROHN) | 44° 45′N | 0° 30′W | 397 |
| Gary (GAR · ree) | 41° 30′N | 87° 15′W | 231 |
| Gaza Strip (GAH · zah) | 31° 30′N | 34° 30′E | 487 |
| Gdansk (guh · DAHNSK) | 54° 15′N | 18° 45′E | 422 |
| Geelong (jee · LONG) | 38° 00′S | 144° 15′E | 17 |
| General Belgrano (bel · GRAHN · oh) | 78° 00′S | 38° 00′W | 17 |
| Geneva (jen · EEV · uh) | 46° 15′N | 6° 00′E | 397 |
| Genoa (JEN · oh · uh) | 44° 30′N | 9° 45′E | 407 |
| Georgetown (JOHRJ · town) | 7° 45′N | 58° 00′W | 338 |
| Georgia (JOHR · juh) | 32° 45′N | 83° 45′W | 228 |

Gazetteer

| NAME | LATITUDE | LONGITUDE | PAGE |
|---|---|---|---|
| Georgian Bay (JOHR·juhn) | 45° 15′N | 80° 45′W | 231 |
| Georgian S. S. R. | 42° 15′N | 43° 00′E | 434 |
| Germany, East (JER·man·ee) | 53° 30′N | 12° 30′E | 422 |
| Germany, West | 51° 45′N | 8° 30′E | 397 |
| Ghana (GAHN·uh) | 8° 00′N | 2° 00′W | 528 |
| Gibraltar (ji·BRAWL·tuhr) | 36° 15′N | 5° 15′W | 407 |
| Gibraltar, Strait of | 36° 00′N | 5° 45′W | 407 |
| Gibson Desert (GIB·suhn) | 24° 45′S | 123° 15′E | 698 |
| Gila River (HEE·luh) | 32° 45′N | 114° 45′W | 237 |
| Giza (GEE·zuh) | 30° 00′N | 31° 15′E | 472 |
| Glacier Bay National Park | 58° 00′N | 136° 45′W | 241 |
| Glacier National Park | 48° 45′N | 114° 00′W | 239 |
| Glåma River (GLAW·muh) | 54° 15′N | 11° 00′E | 401 |
| Glasgow (GLAS·goh) | 56° 00′N | 4° 30′W | 397 |
| Glen Canyon Dam | 37° 00′N | 111° 30′W | 237 |
| Gobi (GOH·bee) | 43° 30′N | 103° 15′E | 622 |
| Godavari River (goh·DAH·vuh·ree) | 16° 45′N | 82° 15′E | 572 |
| Golan Heights (GOH·lan) | 33° 00′N | 36° 15′E | 487 |
| Gold Coast | 5° 00′N | 2° 00′W | 528 |
| Good Hope, Cape of | 34° 15′S | 18° 30′E | 511 |
| Gor'kiy (GAW·kee) | 56° 15′N | 44° 00′E | 434 |
| Göteborg (YOO·te·bohrg) | 57° 45′N | 12° 00′E | 401 |
| Gotland (GAHT·land) | 57° 30′N | 17° 30′E | 401 |
| Gozo (GOH·zoh) | 36° 00′N | 14° 15′E | 408 |
| Grampian Mountains (GRAM·pee·uhn) | 56° 30′N | 5° 00′W | 397 |
| Gran Chaco (grahn CHAH·coh) | 25° 30′S | 62° 15′W | 366 |
| Grand Canal | 34° 30′N | 118° 00′E | 622 |
| Grand Canyon National Park | 36° 15′N | 112° 15′W | 237 |
| Grand Erg Occidental (erg ok·si·DEN·tuhl) | 29° 30′N | 6° 00′E | 478 |
| Grand Forks | 48° 00′N | 97° 00′W | 233 |
| Grand Harbor | 36° 00′N | 14° 30′E | 408 |
| Grand Island | 41° 00′N | 98° 30′W | 233 |
| Grand Junction (JUHNGK·shuhn) | 39° 00′N | 108° 30′W | 239 |
| Grand Rapids (RAP·idz) | 43° 00′N | 85° 45′W | 231 |
| Grand Teton Mountain (TEE·tuhn) | 43° 45′N | 110° 45′W | 239 |
| Graz (grahts) | 47° 00′N | 15° 30′E | 397 |
| Great Artesian Basin (ahr·TEE·zhuhn) | 23° 15′S | 143° 30′E | 698 |
| Great Australian Bight (byt) | 33° 30′S | 127° 00′E | 698 |
| Great Barrier Reef | 16° 45′S | 146° 30′E | 698 |
| Great Bear Lake | 66° 15′N | 120° 00′W | 253 |
| Great Comoro Island (KAHM·uh·roh) | 11° 45′S | 43° 15′E | 557 |
| Great Divide Basin | 42° 15′N | 108° 15′W | 239 |
| Great Dividing Range | 25° 15′S | 146° 45′E | 698 |
| Greater Antilles (an·TIL·eez) | 20° 00′N | 76° 00′W | 304 |
| Greater Khingan Range (SHING·AHN) | 46° 30′N | 120° 00′E | 622 |
| Greater Sunda Islands (SOON·duh) | 4° 00′S | 108° 00′E | 688 |
| Great Falls | 47° 30′N | 111° 15′W | 239 |
| Great Karoo (KUH·roo) | 32° 45′S | 22° 00′E | 557 |
| Great Nevada Basin (nuh·VAD·uh) | 39° 00′N | 117° 00′W | 239 |
| Great Plains | 45° 30′N | 100° 00′W | 195 |
| Great Rift Valley | 4° 00′N | 37° 00′E | 548 |
| Great Salt Desert | 34° 45′N | 53° 30′E | 497 |
| Great Salt Lake | 41° 15′N | 112° 45′W | 239 |
| Great Sandy Desert | 21° 45′S | 123° 15′E | 698 |
| Great Slave Lake | 61° 30′N | 115° 00′W | 253 |
| Great Smoky Mountains National Park | 35° 45′N | 84° 15′W | 228 |
| Great Victoria Desert | 29° 45′S | 124° 00′E | 698 |
| Great Wall | 38° 00′N | 110° 00′E | 622 |
| Greece (GREES) | 39° 00′N | 21° 30′E | 407 |
| Green Bay | 44° 30′N | 88° 00′W | 231 |
| Greenland (GREEN·land) | 74° 00′N | 40° 00′W | 10 |
| Green Mountains | 43° 15′N | 73° 00′W | 224 |
| Green River | 38° 15′N | 110° 00′W | 239 |
| Greensboro (greenz·BUHR·oh) | 36° 00′N | 79° 45′W | 228 |
| Greenville (GREEN·vil) | 34° 45′N | 82° 30′W | 228 |
| Grenada (gren·AY·duh) | 12° 00′N | 61° 15′W | 304 |
| Guadalajara (gwah·duh·lah·HAH·ruh) | 20° 45′N | 103° 15′W | 272 |

| NAME | LATITUDE | LONGITUDE | PAGE |
|---|---|---|---|
| Guadalquivir River (GWAHD·uhl·kweev·EEHR) | 36° 45′N | 6° 45′W | 407 |
| Guadeloupe (gwahd·uh·LOOP) | 16° 45′N | 61° 15′W | 304 |
| Guadiana River (gwahd·ee·AHN·uh) | 37° 15′N | 7° 30′W | 407 |
| Guam (GWAHM) | 14° 00′N | 143° 15′E | 698 |
| Guangzhou (GOO·AHNG·JOH) | 24° 30′N | 118° 00′E | 622 |
| Guaporé River (gwahp·uh·RAY) | 3° 00′S | 58° 15′W | 352 |
| Guatemala (gwaht·uh·MAHL·ah) | 15° 45′N | 91° 45′W | 288 |
| Guatemala (city) | 14° 30′N | 90° 30′W | 288 |
| Guaviare River (gwahv·YAHR·ee) | 4° 00′N | 67° 45′W | 338 |
| Guayaquil (gwy·ah·KEEL) | 2° 15′S | 80° 00′W | 352 |
| Guiana Highlands (gee·AN·uh) | 3° 15′N | 60° 00′W | 338 |
| Guinea (GIN·ee) | 10° 45′N | 12° 30′W | 528 |
| Guinea-Bissau (GIN·ee·buh·SAH·OO) | 12° 00′N | 20° 00′W | 528 |
| Guinea, Gulf of | 2° 00′N | 1° 00′E | 528 |
| Guinea Plateau | 11° 00′N | 10° 00′W | 528 |
| Gulf Coastal Plain | 32° 00′N | 91° 00′W | 195 |
| Guri Reservoir (GOO·ree) | 7° 30′N | 63° 00′W | 338 |
| Guyana (gy·AN·uh) | 7° 45′N | 59° 00′W | 338 |
|  |  |  |  |
| **H** |  |  |  |
| Hague, The (HAYG) | 52° 00′N | 4° 15′E | 397 |
| Haifa ('IY·fuh) | 32° 45′N | 35° 00′E | 487 |
| Hainan (HY·NAHN) | 19° 00′N | 111° 15′E | 622 |
| Haiphong (HY·FAWNG) | 20° 45′N | 106° 45′E | 680 |
| Haiti (HAY·tee) | 19° 00′N | 72° 15′W | 304 |
| Halifax (HAL·i·faks) | 44° 45′N | 63° 30′W | 253 |
| Halley (HAL·ee) | 76° 00′S | 25° 30′W | 17 |
| Hama (HAH·mah) | 35° 15′N | 37° 00′E | 487 |
| Hamburg (HAM·boorg) | 53° 30′N | 10° 00′E | 397 |
| Hamersley Range (HAM·uhrs·lee) | 22° 15′S | 117° 45′E | 698 |
| Hamilton (HAM·uhl·tuhn) | 43° 15′N | 79° 45′W | 253 |
| Hannibal (HAN·i·buhl) | 39° 45′N | 91° 45′W | 233 |
| Hannover (HAHN·oh·vuhr) | 52° 15′N | 9° 45′E | 397 |
| Hanoi (han·OY) | 21° 00′N | 105° 45′E | 680 |
| Han River, China (HAHN) | 31° 30′N | 112° 00′E | 622 |
| Han River, Korea | 37° 30′N | 126° 45′E | 653 |
| Harare (huh·RAH·ray) | 17° 45′S | 31° 00′E | 557 |
| Harbin (HAHR·buhn) | 45° 45′N | 126° 30′E | 622 |
| Harrisburg (HAR·uhs·buhrg) | 40° 15′N | 76° 45′W | 225 |
| Hartford (HAHRT·fuhrd) | 41° 45′N | 72° 45′W | 224 |
| Havana (hah·VAN·uh) | 20° 15′N | 82° 15′W | 304 |
| Hawaii (haw·WY·ee) (island) | 19° 45′N | 157° 15′W | 195 |
| Hawaii (state) | 20° 00′N | 157° 45′W | 241 |
| Hawaii Volcanoes National Park | 19° 30′N | 156° 30′W | 241 |
| Hejaz (he·JAZ) | 23° 45′N | 39° 15′E | 491 |
| Hekla (HEK·luh) | 64° 00′N | 19° 30′W | 401 |
| Helena (hel·LEN·uh) | 46° 30′N | 112° 00′W | 239 |
| Helmand River (HEL·muhnd) | 31° 00′N | 64° 00′E | 497 |
| Helsinki (HEL·sin·kee) | 60° 15′N | 25° 00′E | 401 |
| Helwan (he·WAN) | 28° 00′N | 31° 15′E | 495 |
| Herāt (he·RAHT) | 34° 30′N | 62° 15′E | 497 |
| Hilo (HEE·loh) | 19° 45′N | 155° 00′W | 241 |
| Himalaya, The (him·uh·LAY·uh) | 29° 30′N | 85° 00′E | 572 |
| Hindu Kush (HIN·doo koosh) | 36° 15′N | 68° 45′E | 572 |
| Hiroshima (hee·roh·SHEE·mah) | 34° 15′N | 133° 30′E | 642 |
| Hispaniola (his·pan·YOH·lah) | 17° 30′N | 73° 15′W | 304 |
| Hobart (HOH·bahrt) | 43° 00′S | 147° 30′E | 698 |
| Ho Chi Minh City (HOH CHEE MIN) | 10° 45′N | 106° 30′E | 680 |
| Hodeida (ho·DAY·duh) | 14° 15′N | 43° 00′E | 491 |
| Hofuf (huh·FOOF) | 25° 15′N | 49° 45′E | 491 |
| Hokkaido (hoh·KY·doh) | 43° 30′N | 142° 45′E | 642 |
| Homs (HOHMS) | 34° 45′N | 36° 45′E | 487 |
| Honduras (hawn·DOOR·uhs) | 14° 30′N | 88° 00′W | 288 |
| Honduras, Gulf of | 16° 30′N | 87° 30′W | 288 |
| Hong Kong (HAWNG KAWNG) | 21° 45′N | 115° 00′E | 622 |
| Honiara (hoh·nee·AHR·uh) | 9° 15′S | 159° 45′E | 698 |
| Honolulu (hon·oh·LOO·loo) | 21° 15′N | 157° 45′W | 241 |
| Honshu (HAWN·shoo) | 36° 45′N | 136° 15′E | 642 |
| Hood, Mount | 45° 15′N | 121° 45′W | 241 |
| Hoover Dam | 36° 00′N | 115° 00′W | 237 |

# GAZETTEER

| NAME | LATITUDE | LONGITUDE | PAGE |
|------|----------|-----------|------|
| Hormuz, Strait of (hohr · MOOZ) | 26° 30'N | 56° 30'E | 497 |
| Horn, Cape | 56° 00'S | 67° 00'W | 11 |
| Hot Springs | 34° 30'N | 93° 00'W | 228 |
| Houston (HYOOS · tuhn) | 30° 00'N | 89° 00'W | 237 |
| Huambo (WAHM · boh) | 12° 45'S | 15° 45'E | 538 |
| Huang He (HOO · AHNG HUH) | 35° 00'N | 113° 45'E | 622 |
| Huascarán, Nevado | | | |
| (wahs · kah · RAHN nev · AH · doh) | 9° 00'S | 77° 45'W | 352 |
| Hudson Bay (HUHD · suhn) | 60° 15'N | 85° 30'W | 253 |
| Hudson River | 42° 45'N | 74° 00'W | 225 |
| Hudson Strait | 63° 30'N | 74° 30'W | 253 |
| Hue (oo · AY) | 16° 30'N | 107° 45'E | 680 |
| Humboldt River (HUHM · bohlt) | 40° 30'N | 116° 45'W | 239 |
| Hungarian Plain | | | |
| (huhn · GAR · ee · uhn) | 47° 00'N | 20° 00'E | 422 |
| Hungary (HUHNG · guh · ree) | 46° 45'N | 18° 00'E | 422 |
| Huntington (HUHNT · ing · tuhn) | 38° 30'N | 82° 30'W | 225 |
| Huntsville (HUHNTS · vil) | 34° 45'N | 86° 30'W | 228 |
| Huron, Lake (HOO · ron) | 45° 15'N | 82° 45'W | 195 |
| Hyderabad, India | | | |
| (hy · der · uh · BAD) | 17° 30'N | 79° 30'E | 572 |
| Hyderabad, Pakistan | 25° 30'N | 68° 30'E | 572 |
| Hyndman Peak (HIND · muhn) | 43° 45'N | 114° 00'E | 239 |
| **I** | | | |
| Ibadan (ee · BAHD · ahn) | 7° 15'N | 3° 30'E | 528 |
| Iberian Peninsula | | | |
| (y · BEER · ee · uhn) | 41° 00'N | 0° 15'W | 407 |
| Iceland (YS · land) | 65° 15'N | 19° 45'W | 401 |
| Idaho (Y · duh · hoh) | 44° 00'N | 115° 15'W | 239 |
| Idaho Falls | 43° 00'N | 112° 00'W | 239 |
| Iguidi, Erg (erg ee · guh · DEE) | 26° 15'N | 7° 00'W | 478 |
| Illinois (il · in · OY) | 40° 30'N | 90° 45'W | 231 |
| Illinois River | 39° 00'N | 90° 30'W | 231 |
| Iloilo (ee · loh · EE · loh) | 10° 45'N | 122° 30'E | 689 |
| Imperial Valley (im · PEER · ee · uhl) | 33° 00'N | 115° 15'W | 241 |
| Inch'on (IN · chuhn) | 37° 30'N | 126° 45'E | 653 |
| Independence (in · dee · PEN · duhnts) | 39° 00'N | 94° 30'W | 233 |
| India (IN · dee · uh) | 23° 00'N | 77° 30'E | 572 |
| Indiana (in · dee · AH · uh) | 39° 45'N | 86° 45'W | 231 |
| Indiana Dunes National Lakeshore | 41° 45'N | 87° 00'W | 231 |
| Indianapolis | | | |
| (in · dee · uh · NAP · uh · luhs) | 39° 45'N | 86° 15'W | 231 |
| Indian Ocean (IN · dee · uhn) | 0° 00' | 70° 00'E | 14-15 |
| Indonesia (in · do · NEE · zhuh) | 4° 45'S | 118° 45'E | 688 |
| Indus River (IN · duhs) | 24° 00'N | 68° 00'E | 572 |
| Inner Hebrides (HEB · ruh · deez) | 57° 15'N | 6° 15'W | 397 |
| Innsbruck (INZ · broohk) | 47° 15'N | 11° 30'E | 397 |
| Interior Plains | 53° 00'N | 110° 00'W | 253 |
| International Falls | 48° 30'N | 93° 30'W | 233 |
| Iona National Park (ee · OHN · uh) | 16° 30'S | 12° 00'E | 538 |
| Ionian Islands (y · OHN · ee · uhn) | 39° 15'N | 20° 00'E | 407 |
| Ionian Sea | 39° 00'N | 18° 45'E | 407 |
| Iowa (Y · oh · wuh) | 42° 00'N | 94° 15'W | 233 |
| Iowa City | 41° 45'N | 91° 30'W | 233 |
| Iquitos (ee · KEE · tohs) | 3° 45'S | 73° 15'W | 352 |
| Iran (i · RAHN) | 31° 15'N | 53° 30'E | 497 |
| Iraq (i · RAK) | 32° 00'N | 42° 30'E | 497 |
| Irbid (ir · BEED) | 32° 30'N | 35° 45'E | 487 |
| Ireland (YR · land) | 53° 30'N | 8° 00'W | 397 |
| Irish Sea (YR · ish) | 54° 00'N | 5° 30'W | 397 |
| Irkutsk (ir · KOOTSK) | 52° 15'N | 104° 00'E | 434 |
| Irrawaddy River (ir · uh · WAHD · ee) | 16° 30'N | 95° 00'E | 680 |
| Irtysh River (ir · TISH) | 61° 00'N | 69° 00'E | 434 |
| Isfahan (es · fuh · HAHN) | 32° 45'N | 51° 30'E | 497 |
| Islamabad (is · LAHM · uh · bahd) | 34° 00'N | 73° 00'E | 572 |
| Isle of Man | 54° 30'N | 4° 15'W | 397 |
| Isle Royale National Park | | | |
| (il roy · AHL) | 48° 00'N | 88° 30'W | 231 |
| Israel (IZ · ree · uhl) | 32° 45'N | 35° 00'E | 487 |
| Istanbul (is · tuhm · BOOL) | 41° 00'N | 29° 00'E | 484 |
| Italy (IT · uh · lee) | 44° 00'N | 11° 15'E | 407 |
| Ivory Coast (country) | 7° 45'N | 6° 30'W | 528 |
| Ivory Coast | 5° 00'N | 5° 00'W | 528 |

| NAME | LATITUDE | LONGITUDE | PAGE |
|------|----------|-----------|------|
| Izalco (ee · ZAHL · coh) | 13° 45'N | 89° 45'W | 288 |
| Izmir (iz · MEER) | 38° 30'N | 27° 00'E | 484 |
| **J** | | | |
| Jackson, Miss. | 32° 15'N | 90° 15'W | 228 |
| Jacksonville | 30° 15'N | 81° 30'W | 228 |
| Jackson, Wyo. | 43° 30'N | 113° 45'W | 239 |
| Jakarta (juh · KAHR · tuh) | 6° 15'S | 106° 45'E | 688 |
| Jamaica (juh · MAY · kuh) | 17° 45'N | 78° 00'W | 304 |
| James River, S.D. | 42° 45'N | 97° 15'W | 233 |
| James River, Va. | 37° 00'N | 76° 15'W | 228 |
| Jammu and Kashmir | | | |
| (JUHM · oo and kash · MEER) | 39° 15'N | 75° 00'E | 572 |
| Japan (juh · PAN) | 36° 30'N | 133° 30'E | 642 |
| Japan, Sea of | 40° 15'N | 133° 00'E | 642 |
| Java (JAH · vah) | 8° 30'S | 111° 15'E | 688 |
| Java Sea | 5° 15'S | 110° 30'E | 688 |
| Jaya Peak (JAH · yah) | 4° 00'S | 136° 15'E | 667 |
| Jefferson City | 38° 30'N | 92° 15'W | 233 |
| Jerusalem (je · ROO · suh · luhm) | 31° 45'N | 35° 15'E | 487 |
| Jiddah (JID · uh) | 21° 30'N | 39° 15'E | 491 |
| Jilin (jyee · lin) | 44° 00'N | 126° 45'E | 633 |
| Jinan (jyee · nahn) | 35° 45'N | 117° 00'E | 622 |
| Johannesburg | | | |
| (yoh · HAHN · uhs · boohrg) | 26° 15'S | 28° 00'E | 557 |
| Joplin (JAWP · lin) | 37° 00'N | 94° 30'W | 233 |
| Jordan (JOHR · duhn) | 30° 15'N | 38° 00'E | 487 |
| Jordan River | 31° 30'N | 35° 30'E | 487 |
| Juan de Fuca, Strait of | | | |
| (whahn duh FYOO · kah) | 48° 30'N | 124° 30'W | 241 |
| Juba River (JOO · buh) | 0° 15'S | 42° 30'E | 548 |
| Juneau (JOO · noh) | 58° 15'N | 134° 30'W | 241 |
| Jutland (JUHT · land) | 56° 00'N | 9° 00'E | 401 |
| **K** | | | |
| Kabul (KAH · bool) | 34° 45'N | 69° 15'E | 497 |
| Kabul River | 34° 00'N | 72° 00'E | 497 |
| Kafue National Park | | | |
| (kuhn · FOO · ee) | 15° 00'S | 25° 30'E | 538 |
| Kalahari Desert | | | |
| (kahl · uh · HAHR · ee) | 23° 00'S | 22° 00'E | 557 |
| Kalahari Gemsbok National Park | | | |
| (GEMZ · bahk) | 26° 00'S | 21° 00'E | 557 |
| Kamchatka Peninsula | | | |
| (kam · CHAT · kuh) | 55° 15'N | 157° 45'E | 434 |
| Kampala (kahm · PAH · luh) | 0° 15'N | 32° 30'E | 548 |
| Kampuchea. See Cambodia. | | | |
| Kananga (kuh · NAHN · guh) | 6° 15'S | 22° 15'E | 538 |
| Kanawha River (kuh · NAH · wuh) | 38° 45'N | 82° 00'W | 225 |
| Kandahār (kan · duh · HAHR) | 31° 45'N | 66° 00'E | 497 |
| Kangan (kahng · GAHN) | 27° 45'N | 51° 45'E | 495 |
| Kano (KAHN · oh) | 12° 00'N | 8° 30'E | 528 |
| Kanpur (KAHN · poohr) | 26° 00'N | 82° 45'E | 572 |
| Kansas (KAN · zuhs) | 38° 30'N | 99° 45'W | 233 |
| Kansas City, Kans. | 39° 00'N | 94° 45'W | 233 |
| Kansas City, Mo. | 39° 00'N | 94° 30'W | 233 |
| Kansas River | 39° 00'N | 95° 30'W | 233 |
| Kaohsiung (kah · oh · SYOONG) | 22° 30'N | 120° 30'E | 622 |
| Karachi (kuh · RACH · ee) | 25° 00'N | 69° 00'E | 572 |
| Karakoram Range | | | |
| (kahr · uh · KOHR · oohm) | 35° 30'N | 76° 45'E | 572 |
| Karakum Desert (kahr · uh · KOOM) | 40° 00'N | 57° 00'E | 434 |
| Kara Sea (KAH · rah) | 74° 00'N | 68° 00'E | 434 |
| Kariba, Lake (kuh · REE · buh) | 17° 15'S | 28° 00'E | 538 |
| Karisimbi, Mount | | | |
| (kar · uh · SIM · bee) | 1° 45'S | 29° 30'E | 538 |
| Karl-Marx-Stadt | | | |
| (kahrl · mahrks · shtaht) | 50° 45'N | 13° 00'E | 422 |
| Karnaphuli Reservoir | | | |
| (kahr · nuh · FOO · lee) | 22° 30'N | 92° 00'E | 572 |
| Kasai River (kuh · SY) | 3° 00'S | 16° 45'E | 538 |
| Katmandu (kat · man · DOO) | 27° 45'N | 85° 15'E | 572 |
| Katowice (kaht · uh · WEET · suh) | 50° 15'N | 19° 00'E | 422 |
| Kattegat (KAT · i · gat) | 57° 00'N | 11° 30'E | 401 |

Gazetteer

| NAME | LATITUDE | LONGITUDE | PAGE |
|---|---|---|---|
| Kauai (KAW·eye) | 22° 15′N | 159° 15′W | 241 |
| Kawasaki (kah·wah·SAH·kee) | 35° 30′N | 139° 45′E | 642 |
| Kazakh S.S.R. (kuh·ZAHK) | 48° 45′N | 69° 00′E | 434 |
| Kazan (kuh·ZAHN) | 55° 45′N | 49° 15′E | 434 |
| Kemmuna (kem·MOO·nuh) | 36° 00′N | 14° 15′E | 408 |
| Kenosha (ken·OH·shuh) | 42° 30′N | 87° 45′W | 231 |
| Kentucky (ken·TUHK·ee) | 37° 30′N | 87° 30′W | 228 |
| Kentucky River | 38° 45′N | 85° 15′W | 228 |
| Kenya (KEN·yuh) | 1° 00′N | 37° 00′E | 548 |
| Kermadec Islands (ker·MAD·ek) | 30° 30′S | 177° 00′W | 699 |
| Kerman (ker·MAHN) | 30° 30′N | 57° 15′E | 497 |
| Kerulen River (KER·uh·len) | 48° 00′N | 113° 30′E | 622 |
| Khabur River (kah·BOOHR) | 35° 00′N | 40° 15′E | 487 |
| Khangai Mountains (KAHNG·gy) | 48° 00′N | 99° 45′E | 622 |
| Kharg Island (KAHRG) | 28° 30′N | 50° 30′E | 495 |
| Kharkov (KAHR·kof) | 50° 00′N | 36° 15′E | 434 |
| Khartoum (kahr·TOOM) | 15° 30′N | 32° 30′E | 548 |
| Khorat Plateau (koh·RAHT) | 17° 00′N | 103° 00′E | 680 |
| Khyber Pass (KY·ber) | 34° 30′N | 71° 15′E | 497 |
| Kiel Canal (KEEL) | 54° 00′N | 9° 30′E | 397 |
| Kiev (KEE·yef) | 50° 30′N | 30° 30′E | 434 |
| Kigali (kee·GAH·lee) | 2° 00′S | 30° 00′E | 548 |
| Kilauea (kee·lah·oo·AY·ah) | 22° 15′N | 159° 30′W | 241 |
| Kilimanjaro, Mount (kil·uh·man·JAHR·oh) | 3° 15′S | 37° 15′E | 548 |
| Kingston (KINGZ·tuhn) | 18° 00′N | 76° 45′W | 304 |
| Kingstown (KINGZ·town) | 13° 15′N | 61° 15′W | 304 |
| Kinshasa (kin·SHAH·suh) | 4° 15′N | 15° 15′E | 538 |
| Kirghiz S. S. R. (ker·GHEEZ) | 41° 45′N | 74° 45′E | 434 |
| Kirghiz Steppe | 49° 30′N | 57° 00′E | 434 |
| Kiribati (KIR·uh·bas) | 1° 30′S | 173° 00′W | 699 |
| Kirinyaga, Mount (kir·in·YAH·gah) | 0° 15′N | 37° 15′E | 548 |
| Kisangani (kee·suhn·GAHN·ee) | 0° 30′N | 25° 15′E | 538 |
| Kishinev (kih·shuh·NYOF) | 47° 00′N | 28° 45′E | 434 |
| Kitakyushu (KEE·tuh·kyoo·shoo) | 34° 15′N | 130° 30′E | 642 |
| Kitwe (KIT·wuh) | 12° 45′S | 28° 15′E | 538 |
| Kivu, Lake (KEE·voo) | 1° 45′S | 29° 00′E | 538 |
| Kizil River (KIZ·il) | 42° 00′N | 36° 00′E | 497 |
| Kjølen Mountains (CHUHL·uhn) | 68° 00′N | 17° 00′E | 401 |
| Knoxville (NAWKS·vil) | 36° 00′N | 84° 00′W | 228 |
| Kobe (KOH·be) | 34° 30′N | 135° 15′E | 15 |
| Kolonia (koh·LOHN·ee·uh) | 9° 00′N | 160° 00′E | 698 |
| Kolyma River (kuh·LEE·muh) | 69° 00′N | 161° 00′E | 434 |
| Kopet Mountains (KOH·pet) | 37° 30′N | 58° 30′E | 497 |
| Korea, North (kuh·REE·uh) | 40° 00′N | 127° 00′E | 653 |
| Korea, South | 36° 30′N | 128° 00′E | 653 |
| Korea Strait | 34° 30′N | 128° 30′E | 653 |
| Kra, Isthmus of (krah) | 9° 30′N | 99° 45′E | 680 |
| Krakatau (krak·uh·TOW) | 6° 15′S | 105° 15′E | 688 |
| Kraków (KRAH·kaw) | 50° 00′N | 20° 00′E | 422 |
| Krasnoyarsk (krahs·noh·YAHRSK) | 56° 15′N | 90° 15′E | 434 |
| Krishna River (KRISH·nuh) | 16° 15′N | 81° 15′E | 572 |
| Kruger National Park (KROO·guhr) | 23° 15′S | 30° 15′E | 557 |
| Kuala Lumpur (KWUH·lah loohm·POOR) | 3° 15′N | 101° 45′E | 688 |
| Kuching (KOO·ching) | 1° 30′N | 110° 30′E | 688 |
| Kuibyshev (KOO·ee·bi·shif) | 53° 15′N | 50° 00′E | 13 |
| Kumasi (koo·MAH·see) | 6° 45′N | 1° 30′W | 528 |
| Kunlun Mountains (KOON·LOON) | 35° 30′N | 83° 00′E | 622 |
| Kuril Islands (KOO·ril) | 46° 15′N | 149° 30′E | 434 |
| Kutch, Gulf of (KUHCH) | 22° 45′N | 68° 30′E | 572 |
| Kutch, Rann of | 24° 00′N | 69° 15′E | 572 |
| Kuwait (kuh·WAYT) | 29° 00′N | 48° 45′E | 491 |
| Kyoga, Lake (kee·OH·guh) | 1° 30′N | 32° 45′E | 548 |
| Kyoto (kee·OH·toh) | 35° 00′N | 135° 45′E | 642 |
| Kyushu (KYOO·SHOO) | 32° 30′N | 131° 00′E | 642 |
| **L** | | | |
| Labrador (LAB·ruh·dohr) | 53° 00′N | 63° 30′W | 253 |
| Labrador Sea | 50° 45′N | 55° 00′W | 253 |
| Laccadive Islands (LAK·uh·div) | 11° 00′N | 73° 00′E | 572 |
| Lafayette (lahf·ee·ET) | 30° 15′N | 92° 00′W | 228 |
| Lågen River (LAH·gen) | 56° 30′N | 12° 45′E | 401 |
| Lagos (LAY·gaws) | 6° 30′N | 3° 30′E | 528 |

| NAME | LATITUDE | LONGITUDE | PAGE |
|---|---|---|---|
| Lahore (lah·HOHR) | 32° 00′N | 74° 15′E | 572 |
| Lake Charles | 30° 15′N | 93° 15′W | 228 |
| La Massana (lah mahs·SAH·nah) | 42° 30′N | 1° 30′E | 408 |
| Lanai (luh·NY) | 20° 45′N | 157° 00′W | 241 |
| Lands End | 50° 00′N | 5° 45′W | 397 |
| Lansing (LANT·sing) | 42° 45′N | 84° 30′W | 231 |
| Lanzhou (lahn·joh) | 36° 00′N | 104° 00′E | 622 |
| Laos (LAOOS) | 20° 15′N | 102° 00′E | 680 |
| La Paz (lah PAZ) | 16° 30′S | 68° 00′W | 352 |
| Lapland (LAP·land) | 68° 00′N | 22° 00′E | 401 |
| Laptev Sea (LAP·tef) | 79° 45′N | 120° 00′E | 434 |
| Laramie (LAR·uh·mee) | 41° 15′N | 105° 45′W | 239 |
| La Rochelle (lah roh·SHEL) | 46° 15′N | 1° 15′W | 397 |
| Las Cruzes (lahs KROO·suhs) | 32° 15′N | 106° 45′W | 237 |
| Las Vegas (VAY·guhs) | 36° 15′N | 115° 15′W | 239 |
| Latvian S.S.R. (LAT·vee·uhn) | 57° 30′N | 24° 30′E | 434 |
| Laurentian Highlands (law·REN·shuhn) | 49° 00′N | 74° 45′W | 253 |
| Lawrence (LAW·rens) | 39° 00′N | 95° 15′W | 233 |
| Lawton (LAW·tuhn) | 34° 30′N | 98° 30′W | 237 |
| Lebanon (LEB·uh·nuhn) | 34° 00′N | 36° 00′E | 487 |
| Lebanon Mountains | 33° 30′N | 35° 30′E | 487 |
| Leeds (LEEDZ) | 53° 45′N | 1° 30′W | 397 |
| Leeward Islands (LEE·wuhrd) | 16° 30′N | 62° 15′W | 304 |
| Le Havre (luh HAVRUH) | 49° 30′N | 0° 15′E | 397 |
| Leipzig (LYP·sig) | 51° 15′N | 12° 30′E | 422 |
| Lena River (LEE·nuh) | 72° 00′N | 127° 00′E | 434 |
| Leningrad (LEN·in·grahd) | 60° 00′N | 30° 15′E | 434 |
| León (lay·OHN) | 21° 15′N | 101° 45′W | 272 |
| Lesotho (luh·SOH·thoh) | 29° 45′S | 28° 00′E | 557 |
| Lesser Khingan Range (SHING·AHN) | 49° 45′N | 129° 30′E | 622 |
| Lesser Sunda Islands (SOON·duh) | 9° 00′S | 120° 00′E | 688 |
| Lewiston, Id. (LOO·is·tuhn) | 46° 30′N | 117° 00′W | 239 |
| Lewiston, Me. | 44° 00′N | 70° 15′W | 224 |
| Lexington (LEKS·ing·tuhn) | 38° 00′N | 84° 30′W | 224 |
| Leyte (LAY·tay) | 10° 30′N | 125° 30′E | 689 |
| Lhasa (LAH·sah) | 29° 45′N | 91° 00′E | 622 |
| Liberia (ly·BEER·ee·uh) | 6° 30′N | 10° 00′W | 528 |
| Libreville (lee·bruh·VEEL) | 0° 30′N | 9° 30′E | 538 |
| Libya (LIB·ee·uh) | 27° 45′N | 15° 00′E | 472 |
| Libyan Desert (LIB·ee·uhn) | 28° 30′N | 23° 30′E | 472 |
| Liechtenstein (LIK·ten·shtyn) | 47° 15′N | 10° 00′E | 408 |
| Liège (lee·AYZH) | 50° 45′N | 5° 30′E | 397 |
| Lille (LEEL) | 50° 45′N | 3° 00′E | 397 |
| Lilongwe (li·LAWNG·way) | 14° 00′S | 33° 45′E | 557 |
| Lima (LEE·mah) | 12° 00′S | 77° 00′W | 352 |
| Limassol (lim·uh·SOHL) | 34° 45′N | 33° 00′E | 484 |
| Limpopo River (lim·POH·poh) | 25° 00′S | 33° 45′E | 557 |
| Lincoln, Neb. | 40° 50′N | 96° 45′W | 233 |
| Line Islands | 3° 00′S | 162° 00′W | 699 |
| Linz (LINTS) | 48° 15′N | 14° 15′E | 397 |
| Lisbon (LIZ·buhn) | 38° 45′N | 9° 00′W | 407 |
| Lithuanian S.S.R. (lith·oo·AY·nee·uhn) | 55° 45′N | 23° 30′E | 434 |
| Little Colorado River | 36° 15′N | 111° 45′W | 237 |
| Little Missouri River | 47° 45′N | 102° 00′W | 233 |
| Little Rock | 34° 45′N | 92° 15′W | 228 |
| Liverpool (LIV·uhr·pool) | 53° 30′N | 2° 45′W | 397 |
| Ljubljana (lyoo·BLYAHN·uh) | 46° 00′N | 15° 30′E | 422 |
| Llano Estacado (LAHN·oh es·tuh·CAH·doh) | 34° 30′N | 103° 00′W | 195 |
| Llanos (LAHN·ohs) | 4° 00′N | 71° 15′W | 338 |
| Łódź (WOOHDZH) | 51° 45′N | 19° 15′E | 422 |
| Logan (LOH·guhn) | 41° 45′N | 111° 45′W | 239 |
| Logan, Mount | 61° 00′N | 140° 30′W | 253 |
| Loire River (LWAHR) | 47° 15′N | 2° 15′E | 397 |
| Lomami River (loh·MAHM·ee) | 0° 45′N | 20° 15′E | 538 |
| Lomé (loh·MAY) | 6° 15′N | 1° 15′E | 528 |
| London, Canada (LUHN·duhn) | 43° 00′N | 81° 15′W | 253 |
| London, England | 51° 30′N | 0° 00′ | 397 |
| Long Beach | 33° 45′N | 118° 15′W | 241 |
| Long Island | 40° 45′N | 72° 45′W | 225 |

Gazetteer

# GAZETTEER

| NAME | LATITUDE | LONGITUDE | PAGE |
|------|----------|-----------|------|
| Longs Peak | 40° 15′N | 105° 30′W | 239 |
| Los Angeles (laws AN · je · luhs) | 34° 00′N | 118° 15′W | 241 |
| Louisiana (loo · ee · zee · AN · uh) | 30° 45′N | 92° 45′W | 228 |
| Louisville (LOO · ee · vil) | 38° 15′N | 85° 45′W | 228 |
| Loyalty Islands (LOY · yahl · tee) | 21° 15′S | 168° 15′E | 699 |
| Lualaba River (loo · uh · LAH · buh) | 0° 45′N | 20° 15′E | 538 |
| Luanda (loo · AHN · duh) | 8° 45′S | 13° 15′E | 538 |
| Luang Prabang (loo · ANG prah · BAHNG) | 19° 45′N | 102° 15′E | 680 |
| Luapula River (loo · uh · POO · luh) | 9° 30′S | 28° 00′E | 538 |
| Lubbock (LUHB · uhk) | 33° 30′N | 101° 45′W | 237 |
| Lublin (loo · bluhn) | 51° 15′N | 22° 30′E | 422 |
| Lubumbashi (loo · boohm · BAHSH · ee) | 11° 45′S | 27° 30′E | 538 |
| Lüda (loo · dah) | 39° 00′N | 121° 30′E | 622 |
| Lusaka (loo · SAH · kuh) | 15° 30′S | 28° 15′E | 538 |
| Luvua River (LOO · vooh · uh) | 6° 30′S | 27° 00′E | 538 |
| Luxembourg (LUHKS · uhm · buhrg) | 49° 30′N | 6° 30′E | 397 |
| Luxembourg (city) | 49° 45′N | 6° 30′E | 397 |
| Luzon (loo · ZAWN) | 17° 15′N | 119° 45′E | 689 |
| Lyon (lee · OHN) | 45° 45′N | 4° 45′E | 397 |

**M**

| NAME | LATITUDE | LONGITUDE | PAGE |
|------|----------|-----------|------|
| Macao (muh · KOW) | 22° 00′N | 113° 00′E | 622 |
| Macdonnell Ranges | 23° 45′S | 131° 30′E | 698 |
| Machu Picchu (MAH · choo PEEK · choo) | 13° 00′S | 72° 30′W | 352 |
| Mackenzie River (muh · KEN · zee) | 63° 45′N | 123° 30′W | 253 |
| Mackinac Island (MAK · uh · nak) | 45° 30′N | 84° 30′W | 231 |
| Macon (MAY · kuhn) | 32° 45′N | 82° 45′W | 228 |
| Madagascar (mad · uh · GAS · kahr) | 18° 00′S | 43° 15′E | 557 |
| Madeira Islands (mah · DIR · uh) | 33° 30′N | 16° 45′W | 16 |
| Madison (MAD · i · suhn) | 43° 00′N | 89° 30′W | 231 |
| Madras (muh · DRUHS) | 13° 15′N | 80° 15′E | 572 |
| Madrid (mah · DRID) | 40° 30′N | 3° 45′W | 407 |
| Magdalena River (mag · duh · LAY · nuh) | 11° 00′N | 75° 00′W | 11 |
| Magdeburg (MAHG · duh · boohrg) | 52° 00′N | 11° 45′E | 422 |
| Magellan, Strait of (muh · JEL · uhn) | 52° 30′S | 68° 45′W | 366 |
| Mahajanga (muh · huh · JENG · guh) | 15° 15′S | 46° 30′E | 557 |
| Mahé Island (ma · HAY) | 4° 30′S | 55° 30′E | 557 |
| Mai-Ndombe, Lac (my · en · DOHM · bee) | 2° 15′S | 19° 00′E | 538 |
| Maine (MAYN) | 45° 30′N | 69° 45′W | 224 |
| Majorca (muh · JOHR · kah) | 39° 15′N | 2° 15′E | 407 |
| Majuro (muh · JOOHR · oh) | 7° 00′N | 171° 00′E | 699 |
| Makassar Strait (muh · KAS · uhr) | 2° 00′S | 118° 00′E | 688 |
| Malabo (mah · LAH · boh) | 3° 45′N | 8° 45′E | 538 |
| Malacca, Strait of (muh · LAK · uh) | 4° 15′N | 99° 45′E | 688 |
| Malang (muh · LAHNG) | 8° 00′S | 112° 45′E | 688 |
| Malawi (muh · LAH · wee) | 11° 15′S | 33° 45′E | 557 |
| Malawi, Lake | 10° 45′S | 34° 30′E | 557 |
| Malay Peninsula (muh · LAY) | 7° 45′N | 101° 00′E | 688 |
| Malaysia (muh · LAY · zhuh) | 4° 15′N | 101° 15′E | 688 |
| Male (MAHL · ee) | 4° 00′N | 72° 00′E | 14 |
| Mali (MAH · lee) | 15° 45′N | 0° 15′W | 511 |
| Malmö (MAL · muh) | 55° 30′N | 13° 00′E | 401 |
| Malta (MAHL · tah) | 35° 45′N | 14° 30′E | 408 |
| Mammoth Cave National Park | 37° 15′N | 86° 15′W | 228 |
| Mamoré River (mah · moh · RAY) | 12° 00′S | 65° 00′W | 352 |
| Manado (men · AH · doh) | 1° 30′N | 124° 45′E | 688 |
| Managua (man · AH · gwah) | 12° 15′N | 86° 15′W | 288 |
| Manama (muh · NAM · uh) | 26° 00′N | 50° 30′E | 495 |
| Manaus (muh · NAWS) | 3° 00′S | 60° 00′W | 366 |
| Manchester, England (MAN · ches · tuhr) | 53° 30′N | 2° 15′W | 397 |
| Manchester, N.H. | 43° 00′N | 71° 30′W | 224 |
| Manchuria (man · CHOOR · ee · uh) | 48° 00′N | 125° 00′E | 622 |
| Mandalay (MAN · duh · lay) | 22° 00′N | 96° 15′E | 680 |
| Mandara Mountains (mahn · DAH · rah) | 10° 15′N | 13° 30′E | 538 |
| Manila (muh · NIL · uh) | 14° 30′N | 121° 00′E | 689 |
| Manila Bay | 14° 45′N | 120° 45′E | 689 |
| Manitoba (man · i · TOH · buh) | 55° 15′N | 97° 30′W | 253 |

| NAME | LATITUDE | LONGITUDE | PAGE |
|------|----------|-----------|------|
| Mannar, Gulf of (muh · NAHR) | 8° 45′N | 78° 30′E | 572 |
| Manukau (MAHN · uh · kaws) | 37° 00′S | 174° 45′E | 698 |
| Maoke Mountains (MOW · kay) | 4° 00′S | 138° 00′E | 688 |
| Maputo (mah · POO · toh) | 26° 45′S | 32° 30′E | 557 |
| Maracaibo (mar · uh · KY · boh) | 10° 45′N | 71° 45′W | 338 |
| Maracaibo, Lake | 10° 00′N | 72° 15′W | 338 |
| Marana River (mah · RAH · nah) | 44° 00′N | 12° 30′E | 688 |
| Marañón River (mah · rahn · YOHN) | 4° 00′S | 73° 30′W | 352 |
| Marie Byrd Land (muh · REE buhrd) | 78° 00′S | 130° 00′W | 17 |
| Marmara, Sea of (MAHR · muh · ruh) | 40° 45′N | 28° 00′E | 484 |
| Maroni River (muh · ROH · nee) | 5° 45′N | 54° 15′W | 338 |
| Marquesas Islands (mahr · KAY · suhs) | 8° 45′S | 141° 00′W | 699 |
| Marrakech (muh · RAH · kesh) | 31° 45′N | 8° 00′W | 478 |
| Marsabit Reserve (mahr · SAH · bit) | 2° 15′N | 38° 00′E | 548 |
| Marsalforn (mahr · SAHL · fohrn) | 36° 00′N | 14° 15′E | 408 |
| Marseille (mahr · SAY) | 43° 15′N | 5° 30′E | 397 |
| Marshall Islands (MAHR · shuhl) | 10° 00′N | 165° 00′E | 699 |
| Martaban, Gulf of (mahr · tuh · BAHN) | 16° 30′N | 97° 30′E | 680 |
| Martinique (mahr · uhn · EEK) | 14° 45′N | 60° 45′W | 304 |
| Maryland (MER · uh · land) | 39° 15′N | 76° 30′W | 225 |
| Masai Steppe (mah · SY) | 4° 30′S | 36° 45′E | 548 |
| Maseru (maz · ER · oo) | 29° 15′S | 27° 15′E | 557 |
| Mashhad (muh · SHAD) | 36° 15′N | 59° 30′E | 495 |
| Massachusetts (mas · uh · CHOO · sets) | 42° 15′N | 72° 30′W | 224 |
| Massif Central (mah · SEEF sen · TRAHL) | 45° 15′N | 3° 00′E | 397 |
| Mato Grosso (MAH · tooh GROHS · ooh) | 13° 45′S | 55° 45′W | 366 |
| Maui (MAOW · ee) | 20° 45′N | 156° 00′W | 241 |
| Mauna Kea (MAWN · uh KAY · ah) | 19° 45′N | 155° 30′W | 241 |
| Mauna Loa (LOH · ah) | 19° 30′N | 155° 45′W | 241 |
| Mauritania (maw · ri · TAY · nee · uh) | 13° 45′N | 10° 30′W | 478 |
| Mauritius (maw · RISH · ee · uhs) | 20° 15′S | 57° 30′E | 557 |
| Mawson (MAW · suhn) | 67° 00′S | 63° 00′E | 17 |
| Mayapán (my · ah · PAHN) | 20° 30′N | 89° 30′W | 276 |
| Mayotte (muh · YAWT) | 13° 00′S | 45° 30′E | 557 |
| Mbabane (em · bah · BAHN) | 26° 15′S | 31° 15′E | 557 |
| M'Bakaou Reservoir (uhm · bah · KAH · ooh) | 6° 15′N | 13° 00′E | 538 |
| Mbandaka (em · bahn · DAHK · uh) | 0° 00′ | 18° 15′E | 538 |
| Mbuji-Mayi (em · boo · jee · MY · uh) | 6° 15′S | 23° 30′E | 538 |
| McKinley, Mount (muh · KIN · lee) | 63° 00′N | 151° 00′W | 241 |
| McMurdo (mik · MUHR · doh) | 76° 00′S | 168° 00′W | 17 |
| Mead, Lake | 36° 15′N | 114° 15′W | 239 |
| Mecca (MEK · uh) | 21° 30′N | 39° 45′E | 491 |
| Medan (may · DAHN) | 3° 30′N | 98° 30′E | 688 |
| Medellín (med · uh · YEEN) | 6° 15′N | 75° 30′W | 338 |
| Medford (MED · fuhrd) | 42° 15′N | 122° 45′W | 241 |
| Medina (muh · DEE · nuh) | 24° 30′N | 39° 45′E | 491 |
| Mediterranean Sea (med · i · tuh · RAY · nee · uhn) | 36° 15′N | 13° 30′E | 407 |
| Mekong River (MAY · KONG) | 10° 30′N | 107° 00′E | 667 |
| Mekong River Delta | 10° 30′N | 107° 00′E | 680 |
| Melanesia (mel · uh · NEE · zhuh) | 5° 00′S | 160° 00′E | 698 |
| Melbourne (MEL · buhrn) | 37° 45′S | 145° 15′E | 698 |
| Memphis (MEM · fis) | 35° 00′N | 90° 00′W | 228 |
| Menam River (may · NAHM) | 13° 45′N | 100° 30′E | 680 |
| Mendocino, Cape (men · doh · SEE · noh) | 40° 30′N | 123° 15′W | 241 |
| Mergui Archipelago (muhr · GWEE) | 12° 00′N | 97° 00′E | 680 |
| Merrimack River (MER · uh · mak) | 42° 45′N | 71° 00′W | 224 |
| Mesabi Range (muh · SAHB · ee) | 47° 15′N | 93° 00′W | 233 |
| Mesa Verde National Park (MAY · suh VER · day) | 37° 15′N | 108° 30′W | 239 |
| Meta River (MET · ah) | 6° 30′N | 67° 30′W | 338 |
| Metz (METZ) | 49° 15′N | 6° 15′E | 397 |
| Mexican Plateau (MEKS · ee · kahn) | 24° 00′N | 103° 00′W | 272 |
| Mexico (MEKS · i · koh) | 23° 45′N | 104° 00′W | 272 |
| Mexico City | 19° 30′N | 99° 15′W | 272 |

Gazetteer

| NAME | LATITUDE | LONGITUDE | PAGE |
|---|---|---|---|
| Mexico, Gulf of | 25° 15′N | 93° 45′W | 195 |
| Mgarr (EMGAHR) | 36° 00′N | 14° 15′E | 408 |
| Miami (my·AM·ee) | 25° 45′N | 80° 15′W | 228 |
| Miami River | 39° 00′N | 84° 45′W | 231 |
| Michigan (MISH·i·guhn) | 46° 00′N | 87° 00′W | 231 |
| Michigan, Lake | 43° 15′N | 87° 15′W | 195 |
| Micronesia (my·kroh·NEE·zhuh) | 8° 00′N | 160° 00′E | 698 |
| Midland (MID·land) | 32° 00′N | 102° 00′W | 237 |
| Milan (mi·LAN) | 45° 30′N | 9° 15′E | 407 |
| Milk River | 48° 00′N | 106° 15′W | 239 |
| Milwaukee (mil·WAW·kee) | 43° 00′N | 88° 00′W | 231 |
| Mindanao (min·duh·NOW) | 7° 30′N | 125° 15′E | 689 |
| Mindoro (min·DOH·roh) | 13° 00′N | 121° 00′E | 689 |
| Minneapolis (min·ee·AP·oh·lis) | 45° 00′N | 93° 15′W | 233 |
| Minnesota (min·uh·SOH·tuh) | 46° 15′N | 93° 15′W | 233 |
| Minnesota River | 45° 00′N | 93° 15′W | 233 |
| Minorca (men·OHR·kah) | 40° 00′N | 4° 00′E | 407 |
| Minot (MY·nawt) | 48° 15′N | 101° 15′W | 233 |
| Minsk | 54° 00′N | 27° 30′E | 434 |
| Miskolc (MISH·kohlts) | 48° 00′N | 20° 45′E | 422 |
| Mississauga (mis·is·SAW·guh) | 43° 30′N | 79° 30′W | 253 |
| Mississippi (mis·uh·SIP·ee) | 32° 30′N | 89° 45′W | 228 |
| Mississippi Delta | 29° 00′N | 89° 15′W | 228 |
| Mississippi River | 29° 00′N | 89° 15′W | 195 |
| Missoula (mi·ZOO·luh) | 46° 30′N | 114° 00′W | 239 |
| Missouri (mi·ZOOR·ee) | 38° 00′N | 93° 45′W | 233 |
| Missouri Coteau (cuh·TOH) | 47° 30′N | 101° 00′W | 233 |
| Missouri River | 38° 45′N | 90° 00′W | 195 |
| Mitchell (MICH·uhl) | 43° 45′N | 98° 00′W | 233 |
| Mitchell, Mount | 35° 35′N | 82° 15′W | 228 |
| Mitumba Mountains (mit·OOHM·buh) | 10° 45′S | 27° 00′E | 538 |
| Mobile (moh·BEEL) | 30° 45′N | 88° 00′W | 228 |
| Mobile Bay | 30° 30′N | 88° 00′W | 228 |
| Mogadishu (MAHG·uh·dish·OO) | 2° 15′N | 45° 15′E | 548 |
| Mojave Desert (moh·HAV·ee) | 35° 00′N | 117° 30′W | 241 |
| Moldau River (MOHL·dow) | 50° 15′N | 14° 15′E | 422 |
| Moldavian Plateau | 47° 15′N | 27° 15′E | 422 |
| Moldavian S.S.R. | 48° 00′N | 28° 00′E | 434 |
| Molokai (moh·luh·KY) | 21° 15′N | 157° 00′W | 241 |
| MOMBASA (MAWM·BAH·sah) | 4° 00′S | 39° 45′E | 548 |
| Monaco (MAWN·uh·coh) | 43° 45′N | 7° 45′E | 397 |
| Monaco, Harbor of | 43° 45′N | 7° 45′E | 408 |
| Mona Passage (MOH·nuh) | 18° 00′N | 68° 15′W | 304 |
| Mongolia (mon·GOHL·ee·uh) | 46° 00′N | 100° 00′E | 622 |
| Monrovia (mawn·ROH·vee·uh) | 6° 15′N | 10° 45′W | 528 |
| Montana (mawn·TAN·uh) | 47° 15′N | 111° 45′W | 239 |
| Montevideo (mawn·tuh·vi·DAY·oh) | 34° 45′S | 56° 15′W | 366 |
| Montpelier (mawnt·PEEL·yuhr) | 44° 15′N | 72° 30′W | 224 |
| Morgantown (MOR·guhn·town) | 39° 45′N | 80° 00′W | 225 |
| Moroni (moh·ROH·nee) | 11° 45′S | 43° 15′E | 557 |
| Moulmein (mawl·MAYN) | 16° 30′S | 97° 45′E | 680 |
| Mount Rushmore National Monument | 43° 45′N | 103° 30′W | 233 |
| Mozambique (moh·zuhm·BEEK) | 20° 15′S | 34° 00′E | 557 |
| Mozambique Channel | 24° 00′S | 38° 00′E | 557 |
| Muchinga Mountains (moo·CHING·guh) | 12° 50′S | 32° 00′E | 538 |
| Muir Woods (MYOOR) | 38° 00′N | 123° 15′W | 241 |
| Multan (mooh·TAHN) | 30° 15′N | 71° 15′E | 572 |
| Munich (MYOO·nik) | 48° 15′N | 11° 30′E | 397 |
| Murray River (MUHR·ee) | 39° 15′S | 139° 30′E | 698 |
| Muscat (MUHS·kat) | 23° 30′N | 58° 30′E | 491 |
| Mwali Island (uhm·WAHL·ee) | 12° 15′S | 43° 45′E | 557 |
| Mweru, Lake (muh·WER·oo) | 8° 45′S | 28° 45′E | 538 |
| **N** | | | |
| Nagasaki (nah·gah·SAH·kee) | 32° 45′N | 130° 00′E | 642 |
| Nagoya (nah·GOY·uh) | 35° 15′N | 137° 00′E | 642 |
| Nagpur (NAHG·poor) | 21° 15′N | 79° 15′E | 572 |
| Nairobi (ny·ROH·bee) | 1° 15′S | 36° 45′E | 548 |
| Namada River (nuh·MAH·duh) | 21° 45′N | 73° 00′E | 572 |
| Namib Desert (nah·MIB) | 18° 45′S | 12° 45′E | 557 |

| NAME | LATITUDE | LONGITUDE | PAGE |
|---|---|---|---|
| Namibia (nuh·MIB·ee·uh) | 19° 30′S | 16° 15′E | 557 |
| Nampula (nam·POO·luh) | 15° 00′S | 39° 15′E | 557 |
| Nanjing (NAHN·JYING) | 32° 00′N | 118° 45′E | 622 |
| Nan Ling (NAN LING) | 25° 15′N | 111° 45′E | 622 |
| Nantes (NAHNT) | 47° 15′N | 1° 30′W | 397 |
| Nantucket Island (nan·TUHK·et) | 41° 15′N | 70° 00′W | 224 |
| Naples (NAY·puhls) | 40° 30′N | 14° 15′E | 407 |
| Narvik (NAHR·veek) | 68° 15′N | 17° 15′E | 401 |
| Nashua (NASH·OO·uh) | 42° 45′N | 71° 30′W | 224 |
| Nashville (NASH·vil) | 36° 15′N | 86° 45′W | 228 |
| Nassau (NAS·saw) | 25° 00′N | 77° 15′W | 304 |
| Nasser, Lake (NAS·uhr) | 23° 45′N | 32° 45′E | 472 |
| Nauru (nah·OO·roo) | 0° 30′S | 167° 00′E | 699 |
| N'Djamena (en·JAHM·uh·nuh) | 12° 00′N | 15° 00′E | 538 |
| Ndola (en·DOH·luh) | 13° 00′S | 28° 45′E | 538 |
| Nebraska (neb·RAS·kuh) | 41° 45′N | 101° 30′W | 233 |
| Negev Desert (NEG·ev) | 30° 30′N | 34° 45′E | 487 |
| Negro River (NAY·grooh) | 3° 00′S | 60° 00′W | 366 |
| Negros (NAY·grohs) | 9° 45′N | 121° 45′E | 689 |
| Neisse River (NYS·suh) | 52° 00′N | 14° 30′E | 422 |
| Neka (NE·kah) | 37° 00′N | 54° 15′E | 495 |
| Nelson River (NEL·suhn) | 57° 00′N | 92° 30′W | 10 |
| Nepal (nuh·PAWL) | 28° 45′N | 83° 00′E | 572 |
| Ness, Loch (LAWK NES) | 57° 30′N | 4° 15′W | 397 |
| Netherlands (NETH·uhr·lands) | 53° 00′N | 4° 00′E | 397 |
| Netzahualcóyotl (net·zah·wahl·COH·yohtl) | 19° 30′N | 99° 00′W | 272 |
| Nevada (nuh·VAHD·uh) | 39° 30′N | 117° 00′W | 239 |
| Newark (NOO·uhrk) | 40° 45′N | 74° 15′W | 225 |
| New Bedford (BED·fuhrd) | 43° 30′N | 71° 00′W | 224 |
| New Britain (BRIT·uhn) | 6° 45′S | 149° 45′E | 698 |
| New Brunswick (BRUHNZ·wik) | 47° 15′N | 66° 30′W | 253 |
| New Caledonia (kal·uh·DOH·nee·uh) | 21° 30′S | 164° 45′E | 698 |
| New Delhi (DEL·ee) | 28° 45′N | 77° 15′E | 572 |
| New England (ING·land) | 44° 00′N | 70° 00′W | 224 |
| Newfoundland (noo·fuhnd·LAND) | 48° 15′N | 57° 00′W | 253 |
| New Guinea (GIN·ee) | 5° 45′S | 140° 00′E | 698 |
| New Hampshire (HAMP·shuhr) | 44° 00′N | 71° 45′W | 224 |
| New Haven (HAY·vuhn) | 41° 15′N | 73° 00′W | 224 |
| New Jersey (JURH·zee) | 40° 30′N | 74° 45′W | 225 |
| New Mexico (MEKS·i·koh) | 34° 30′N | 107° 15′W | 237 |
| New Orleans (AWR·lee·uhns) | 30° 00′N | 90° 00′W | 228 |
| Newport (NOO·pohrt) | 41° 30′N | 71° 15′W | 224 |
| Newport News | 37° 00′N | 76° 30′W | 228 |
| New Siberian Islands (sy·BEER·ee·uhn) | 55° 00′N | 83° 00′E | 434 |
| New South Wales | 32° 45′S | 146° 15′E | 698 |
| New York City | 40° 45′N | 74° 00′W | 225 |
| New York (state) | 42° 45′N | 78° 00′W | 225 |
| New Zealand (ZEE·land) | 42° 00′S | 175° 00′E | 699 |
| Niamey (nee·ah·MUH) | 13° 30′N | 2° 00′E | 528 |
| Nicaragua (ni·cuh·RAH·gwah) | 12° 45′N | 86° 15′W | 288 |
| Nicaragua, Lake | 11° 45′N | 85° 30′W | 288 |
| Nice (NEES) | 44° 45′N | 7° 15′E | 397 |
| Nicobar Islands (NIK·uh·bahr) | 7° 30′N | 94° 00′E | 572 |
| Nicosia (ni·coh·SEE·uh) | 35° 15′N | 33° 15′E | 484 |
| Niger (NY·juhr) | 18° 00′N | 8° 30′E | 528 |
| Nigeria (ny·JEER·ee·uh) | 9° 00′N | 6° 30′E | 528 |
| Niger River | 4° 45′N | 5° 15′E | 528 |
| Niihau (NEE·ee·hah·oo) | 21° 45′N | 160° 00′W | 241 |
| Nile River (nyl) | 32° 00′N | 31° 00′E | 472 |
| Nineveh (NIN·uh·vuh) | 36° 30′N | 43° 15′E | 497 |
| Niobrara River (ni·oh·BRAH·ruh) | 42° 45′N | 98° 00′W | 233 |
| Niue Island (NI·OO) | 19° 45′S | 167° 00′W | 699 |
| Nome (NOHM) | 64° 30′N | 165° 15′W | 241 |
| Norfolk Island | 27° 15′S | 166° 45′E | 699 |
| Norfolk, Neb. (NAWR·fuhk) | 42° 15′N | 97° 30′W | 233 |
| Norfolk, Va. | 37° 00′N | 76° 15′W | 228 |
| Norman (NAWR·muhn) | 35° 15′N | 97° 30′W | 237 |
| North America | 41° 00′N | 98° 00′W | 10 |
| North Carolina (kar·oh·LY·nuh) | 35° 45′N | 81° 30′W | 228 |
| North China Plain | 34° 00′N | 115° 00′E | 622 |

# GAZETTEER

Gazetteer

| NAME | LATITUDE | LONGITUDE | PAGE |
|------|----------|-----------|------|
| North Dakota (duh · KOH · tuh) | 47° 15′N | 102° 00′W | 233 |
| North Dvina River (duh· VEEN · ah) | 64° 30′N | 40° 30′E | 13 |
| Northern Ireland (YR · land) | 54° 45′N | 7° 00′W | 397 |
| Northern Mariana Islands (mar · ee · AHN · uh) | 17° 15′N | 145° 00′E | 698 |
| Northern Territory | 18° 15′S | 133° 00′E | 698 |
| North Island | 27° 15′S | 173° 30′E | 699 |
| North Platte (PLAT) | 41° 15′N | 100° 45′W | 233 |
| North Platte River | 41° 15′N | 100° 45′W | 233 |
| North Sea | 56° 15′N | 3° 15′E | 397 |
| Northwest Territories | 64° 45′N | 119° 15′W | 253 |
| North York | 43° 45′N | 79° 30′W | 253 |
| Norway (NAWR· way) | 63° 45′N | 11° 15′E | 401 |
| Nouakchott (nuh · AHK · shaht) | 18° 00′N | 16° 00′W | 478 |
| Nova Iguaçu (NOH · vah ee· gwah · SOO) | 22° 45′S | 43° 30′W | 330 |
| Nova Scotia (NOH · vah SKOH · shuh) | 44° 30′N | 65° 00′W | 253 |
| Novaya Zemlya (NOH · vuh · yah zem · LYAH) | 72° 00′N | 54° 45′E | 434 |
| Novosibirsk (noh · voh · see · BEERSK) | 55° 00′N | 83° 00′E | 434 |
| Nubian Desert (NOO · bee · uhn) | 21° 15′N | 33° 15′E | 511 |
| Nuku'alofa (noo · kuh · wuh · LAW · fah) | 21° 00′S | 175° 15′E | 699 |
| Nullarbor (nuhe· UH · baw) | 31° 45′S | 126° 30′E | 698 |

## O

| NAME | LATITUDE | LONGITUDE | PAGE |
|------|----------|-----------|------|
| Oahe, Lake (uh · WAH · hee) | 45° 15′N | 100° 00′W | 233 |
| Oahu (oh· WAH · hoo) | 21° 45′N | 157° 45′W | 241 |
| Oakland (OHK · land) | 38° 00′N | 122° 15′W | 241 |
| Oaxaca (wah · HAH · kah) | 17° 00′N | 96° 45′W | 10 |
| Ob River (OHB) | 66° 30′N | 70° 00′E | 434 |
| Oconee River (oh · KOH · nee) | 31° 15′N | 81° 15′W | 228 |
| Odense (OH · den · suh) | 55° 30′N | 10° 15′E | 401 |
| Oder River (OH · duhr) | 54° 00′N | 14° 15′E | 422 |
| Odessa, Texas, (oh · DES · uh) | 31° 45′N | 102° 15′W | 237 |
| Odessa, U.S.S.R. | 46° 30′N | 30° 45′E | 434 |
| Ogbomosho (awg · boh · MOH · shoh) | 8° 15′N | 4° 15′E | 528 |
| Ogden (AWG · den) | 41° 15′N | 112° 00′W | 239 |
| Ohio (oh · HY · oh) | 40° 30′N | 83° 15′W | 231 |
| Ohio River | 37° 00′N | 89° 15′W | 195 |
| Okavango Basin (oh · kuh · VANG · goh) | 19° 30′S | 23° 00′E | 557 |
| Okavango River | 19° 30′S | 23° 00′E | 557 |
| Okeechobee, Lake (oh · kuh · CHOH · bee) | 27° 00′N | 80° 45′W | 228 |
| Okhotsk, Sea of (oh · KOHTSK) | 56° 45′N | 146° 00′E | 434 |
| Okinawa Island (oh · kuh · NAH · wah) | 26° 30′N | 128° 30′E | 642 |
| Oklahoma (ohk · luh · HOH · muh) | 36° 00′N | 98° 15′W | 237 |
| Oklahoma City | 35° 30′N | 97° 30′W | 237 |
| Öland (oo · LAHND) | 57° 00′N | 17° 15′E | 401 |
| Olympia (oh · LIM · pee · uh) | 47° 00′N | 122° 45′W | 241 |
| Olympic National Park (oh· LIM · pik) | 48° 00′N | 123° 00′W | 241 |
| Omaha (OH · muh · haw) | 41° 15′N | 97° 00′W | 233 |
| Oman (oh · MAHN) | 20° 00′N | 57° 45′E | 491 |
| Oman, Gulf of | 24° 30′N | 59° 00′E | 491 |
| Omdurman (ahm · duhr · MAN) | 15° 45′N | 32° 30′E | 548 |
| Omo River (OH· moh) | 4° 30′N | 36° 15′E | 548 |
| Omsk (OHMSK) | 55° 15′N | 73° 15′E | 434 |
| Ontario (awn · TAR · ee · oh) | 50° 45′N | 88° 45′W | 253 |
| Ontario, Lake | 43° 30′N | 79° 00′W | 195 |
| Oporto (oh· POHRT · ooh) | 41° 15′N | 8° 45′W | 407 |
| Oran (oh · RAHN) | 35° 45′N | 0° 45′W | 478 |
| Orange River (AWR· inj) | 28° 30′S | 16° 15′E | 557 |
| Örebro (OH · ree · broh) | 59° 15′N | 15° 15′E | 401 |
| Oregon (AWR· i · guhn) | 43° 45′N | 121° 45′W | 241 |
| Ore Mountains | 50° 30′N | 12° 45′E | 422 |
| Orinoco River (oh · rin · OH · koh) | 9° 00′N | 62° 00′W | 338 |
| Orkney Islands (AWRK · nee) | 59° 00′N | 2° 15′W | 397 |
| Orlando (ohr · LAN · doh) | 28° 30′N | 81° 15′W | 228 |
| Orléans (awr · lay · AHN) | 48° 00′N | 2° 00′E | 397 |
| Orontes River (oh · RAHN · teez) | 36° 15′N | 35° 45′E | 487 |
| Osaka (OH · sahk · ah) | 34° 45′N | 135° 30′E | 642 |
| Oshogbo (oh · SHOHG · boh) | 7° 45′N | 4° 30′E | 528 |

| NAME | LATITUDE | LONGITUDE | PAGE |
|------|----------|-----------|------|
| Oslo (AWS · loh) | 60° 00′N | 10° 45′E | 401 |
| Ostrava (oh · STRAH · vuh) | 49° 45′N | 18° 15′E | 422 |
| Otranto, Strait of (oh · TRAHN · toh) | 40° 30′N | 18° 45′E | 407 |
| Ottawa (AWT· uh · wuh) | 45° 30′N | 75° 45′W | 253 |
| Ouachita Mountains (WAHSH · uh · taw) | 34° 30′N | 95° 00′W | 237 |
| Ouagadougou (wah · guh · DOO · goo) | 12° 15′N | 1° 30′W | 528 |
| Outer Hebrides (HEB · ruh · deez) | 57° 15′N | 7° 45′W | 397 |
| Owensboro (OH · wenz · buhr · oh) | 37° 45′N | 87° 00′W | 228 |
| Oyapock River (oh · yuh · PAWK) | 4° 30′N | 51° 45′W | 338 |
| Ozark Mountains (OH · zahrk) | 36° 30′N | 94° 00′W | 228 |
| Ozark Plateau | 37° 00′N | 94° 00′W | 233 |
| Ozarks, Lake of the | 38° 00′N | 93° 30′W | 233 |

## P

| NAME | LATITUDE | LONGITUDE | PAGE |
|------|----------|-----------|------|
| Pacific Ocean (puh · SIF · ik) | 0° 00′ | 170° 00′W | 2-3 |
| Padang (pah · DAHNG) | 1° 00′S | 100° 00′E | 688 |
| Padre Island National Seashore (PAH · dray) | 27° 00′N | 97° 15′W | 237 |
| Paducah (puh · DOO · kuh) | 37° 00′N | 88° 30′W | 228 |
| Painted Desert | 36° 15′N | 111° 30′W | 237 |
| Pakistan (PAK · is · tan) | 28° 00′N | 67° 30′E | 572 |
| Pakse (PAHK· suh) | 14° 45′N | 106° 00′E | 680 |
| Palau Islands (pah · LAH · ooh) | 7° 15′N | 134° 30′E | 698 |
| Palawan (pah · LAH · wuhn) | 9° 45′N | 117° 45′E | 689 |
| Palenque (pah · LEN · kay) | 17° 30′N | 92° 00′W | 276 |
| Palermo (pah · LAYR · moh) | 38° 15′N | 13° 30′E | 407 |
| Palmas (PAHL· muhs) | 4° 15′N | 7° 45′W | 528 |
| Pampas (PAHM· puhs) | 37° 00′S | 64° 30′W | 366 |
| Panama (pan · uh · MAH) | 8° 30′N | 81° 15′W | 288 |
| Panamá (city) | 9° 00′N | 79° 30′W | 288 |
| Panama Canal | 9° 15′N | 79° 45′W | 288 |
| Panamá, Gulf of | 7° 45′N | 79° 15′W | 288 |
| Panay (pah · NY) | 11° 15′N | 121° 45′E | 689 |
| Papua New Guinea (PAH · poo · uh noo GI · nee) | 7° 00′S | 142° 15′E | 698 |
| Paraguay (pah · rah · GWY) | 24° 00′S | 57° 00′W | 366 |
| Paramaribo (pah · rah · MAH · ree · boh) | 5° 45′N | 55° 15′W | 338 |
| Paraná River (pah · ran · UH) | 34° 00′S | 58° 00′W | 366 |
| Paricutín (pahr · ee · coo · TEEN) | 19° 30′N | 102° 15′W | 272 |
| Paris (PAR · is) | 48° 45′N | 2° 15′E | 397 |
| Parkersburg (PAHR · kuhrz · buhrg) | 39° 15′N | 81° 30′W | 225 |
| Paropamisus Mountains (pahr · uh · puh · MY · suhs) | 34° 45′N | 64° 00′E | 497 |
| Pascagoula (pas · kuh · GOO · luh) | 30° 15′N | 88° 30′W | 228 |
| Patagonia (pah · tah · GOH · nee · uh) | 46° 45′S | 69° 30′W | 366 |
| Peace River | 58° 45′N | 111° 15′W | 253 |
| Pearl River | 30° 15′N | 89° 45′W | 228 |
| Pecos River (PAY· kohs) | 29° 45′N | 101° 30′W | 237 |
| Pegu Yoma (pe · GOO YOH · mah) | 19° 15′N | 96° 00′E | 680 |
| Peloponnesus (pel · uh · poh · NEE · suhs) | 37° 30′N | 22° 15′E | 407 |
| Pemba (PEM · buh) | 5° 15′S | 40° 00′E | 548 |
| Pennine Chain (PEN· nyn) | 54° 30′N | 2° 00′W | 397 |
| Pennsylvania (pen · sil · VAY · nee · uh) | 41° 00′N | 78° 15′W | 225 |
| Penobscot River (pen · AHB · skuht) | 44° 30′N | 68° 45′W | 224 |
| Pensacola (pen · suh · KOH · luh) | 30° 30′N | 87° 15′W | 228 |
| Peoria (pee · OHR· ee · uh) | 40° 45′N | 89° 30′W | 231 |
| Perm | 58° 00′N | 56° 15′E | 434 |
| Persian Gulf (PER · zhuhn) | 27° 45′N | 50° 30′E | 454 |
| Perth (PUHRTH) | 31° 45′S | 116° 15′E | 698 |
| Peru (puh · ROO) | 10° 00′S | 75° 00′W | 352 |
| Philadelphia (fil · uh · DEL · fee · uh) | 40° 00′N | 75° 15′W | 225 |
| Philippines (FIL · uh · peenz) | 14° 30′N | 125° 00′E | 689 |
| Philippine Sea (FIL · uh · peen) | 16° 00′N | 123° 00′E | 689 |
| Phnom Penh (NAWM PEN) | 11° 45′N | 105° 00′E | 680 |
| Phoenix (FEE · niks) | 33° 30′N | 112° 00′W | 237 |
| Phoenix Islands | 4° 00′S | 174° 00′W | 699 |
| Piedmont (PEED · mahnt) | 32° 30′N | 82° 00′W | 195 |
| Pierre (PEER) | 44° 15′N | 100° 15′W | 233 |
| Pikes Peak | 38° 45′N | 105° 00′W | 239 |

| NAME | LATITUDE | LONGITUDE | PAGE |
|------|----------|-----------|------|
| Pindus Mountains (PIN · duhs) | 39° 45′N | 21° 15′E | 407 |
| Pine Bluff | 34° 15′N | 92° 00′W | 228 |
| Ping River | 15° 45′N | 100° 00′E | 680 |
| Pittsburgh (PITS · buhrg) | 40° 30′N | 80° 00′W | 225 |
| Plata, Río de la | | | |
| (REE · oh day lah PLAHT · uh) | 34° 30′S | 54° 15′W | 366 |
| Platte River | 41° 00′N | 98° 00′W | 233 |
| Pleven (PLE · ven) | 43° 30′N | 24° 30′E | 422 |
| Ploesti (plaw · YESHT · ee) | 45° 00′N | 26° 00′E | 422 |
| Plovdiv (PLAWV · dif) | 42° 15′N | 24° 45′E | 422 |
| Pocatello (poh · kuh · TEL · oh) | 43° 00′N | 112° 30′W | 239 |
| Pointe Noire (NWAWR) | 4° 45′S | 11° 45′E | 538 |
| Poland (POH · land) | 52° 30′N | 17° 00′E | 422 |
| Polynesia (paw · luh · NEE · zhuh) | 0° 00′ | 165° 00′W | 699 |
| Ponchartrain, Lake | | | |
| (PAWN · chah · trayn) | 30° 15′N | 90° 15′W | 228 |
| Pontic Mountains (PON · tik) | 41° 15′N | 37° 30′E | 484 |
| Poona (POO · nuh) | 18° 45′N | 74° 00′E | 572 |
| Popocatépetl | | | |
| (poh · poh · kah · TAY · petl) | 19° 00′N | 98° 45′W | 272 |
| Po River | 45° 00′N | 12° 30′E | 407 |
| Port-au-Prince (POHRT OH PRINS) | 18° 30′N | 71° 15′W | 304 |
| Port Brega (BREG · uh) | 31° 00′N | 20° 00′E | 495 |
| Port Elizabeth (ee · LIZ · uh · beth) | 34° 00′S | 25° 30′E | 557 |
| Port Harcourt (HAHR· kuhrt) | 4° 45′N | 7° 00′E | 528 |
| Portland, Me. (POHRT · luhnd) | 43° 45′N | 70° 15′W | 224 |
| Portland, Ore. | 45° 30′N | 123° 30′W | 241 |
| Port Louis | 20° 00′S | 57° 30′E | 557 |
| Port Macquarie (muh · KWOHR · ee) | 31° 30′S | 152° 45′E | 17 |
| Port Moresby (MOHRZ · bee) | 13° 30′S | 147° 15′E | 698 |
| Pôrto Alegre | | | |
| (POHR · tooh ah · LAY · gruh) | 30° 00′S | 51° 15′W | 366 |
| Port of Spain (SPAYN) | 10° 45′N | 61° 30′W | 304 |
| Porto-Novo (POHR · toh NOH · voh) | 6° 30′N | 2° 30′E | 528 |
| Port Said (sah· EED) | 31° 15′N | 32° 15′E | 472 |
| Portsmouth (PORTS · muhth) | 43° 00′N | 70° 45′W | 224 |
| Portugal (POHRT · uh · gahl) | 38° 15′N | 8° 15′W | 407 |
| Port-Vila (VIL· uh) | 18° 00′S | 168° 00′E | 699 |
| Potomac River (poh · TOH · muhk) | 38° 00′N | 76° 15′W | 225 |
| Potosí (poh · toh · SEE) | 19° 45′N | 65° 45′W | 352 |
| Powder River (POW· duhr) | 46° 45′N | 105° 30′W | 239 |
| Powell, Lake (POW· uhel) | 37° 30′N | 110° 30′W | 239 |
| Poznań (pawz · NAHN) | 52° 30′N | 17° 00′E | 422 |
| Prague (PRAHG) | 50° 00′N | 14° 30′E | 422 |
| Praia (PRAH · yah) | 15° 00′N | 23° 30′W | 528 |
| Presidente Frei (FRAY) | 62° 00′S | 59° 00′W | 17 |
| Pretoria (pree · TOR · ee · uh) | 25° 45′S | 28° 15′E | 557 |
| Prince Edward Island (ED · whurd) | 46° 45′N | 63° 15′W | 253 |
| Príncipe (PRINC · suh · puh) | 2° 00′N | 7° 00′E | 538 |
| Providence (PRAWV· uh · dens) | 41° 45′N | 71° 30′W | 224 |
| Provo (PROH · voh) | 40° 15′N | 111° 45′W | 239 |
| Prudhoe Bay (PROOD · hoh) | 70° 45′N | 147° 30′W | 241 |
| Prut River (PROOT) | 45° 30′N | 28° 18′E | 422 |
| Puebla (PWAY · bluh) | 19° 00′N | 98° 15′W | 272 |
| Pueblo (PWAY · bloh) | 38° 15′N | 104° 30′W | 239 |
| Puerto Rico (PWERT· oh REE· koh) | 18° 15′N | 66° 45′W | 304 |
| Puget Sound (POO · jet) | 48° 45′N | 122° 30′W | 241 |
| Punta Arenas | | | |
| (POOHN · tah ah · RAY · nahs) | 53° 15′S | 70° 45′W | 352 |
| Pusan (POO · sahn) | 35° 15′N | 129° 00′E | 653 |
| Putumayo River | | | |
| (pooh · too · MAH · yoh) | 3° 00′S | 67° 45′W | 338 |
| P'yongyang (pee · AWNG · yang) | 39° 00′N | 125° 45′E | 653 |
| Pyrenees (PEER · uh · neez) | 43° 00′N | 2° 30′E | 397 |
| **Q** | | | |
| Qatar (KAH · tahr) | 25° 00′N | 52° 45′E | 491 |
| Qattara Depression (kuh · TAHR · uh) | 30° 00′N | 27° 30′E | 472 |
| Qilian Shan (CHYEE · LYEN SHAHN) | 38° 45′N | 98° 00′E | 622 |
| Qingdao (CHYIN · DOW) | 36° 00′N | 120° 00′E | 622 |
| Qin Ling (CHYIN LING) | 33° 30′N | 109° 00′E | 622 |
| Qom (KOOHM) | 34° 30′N | 51° 00′E | 497 |
| Québec (kwee · BEK) | 51° 00′N | 70° 30′W | 253 |
| Québec (city) | 46° 45′N | 71° 15′W | 253 |

| NAME | LATITUDE | LONGITUDE | PAGE |
|------|----------|-----------|------|
| Queen Charlotte Islands | | | |
| (SHAHR · luht) | 53° 30′N | 132° 30′W | 253 |
| Queen Elizabeth Islands | 79° 15′N | 110° 00′W | 253 |
| Queen Maud Land (MAWD) | 75° 00′S | 10° 00′E | 17 |
| Queensland (KWEENZ· land) | 22° 45′S | 141° 00′E | 698 |
| Quezon City (KAY · sohn) | 14° 45′N | 121° 00′E | 689 |
| Quiçama National Park | | | |
| (kee · KAHM · muh) | 10° 00′S | 13° 30′E | 538 |
| Quito (KEE· toh) | 0° 15′S | 78° 30′W | 352 |
| **R** | | | |
| Rabat (ruh· BAHT), Malta | 36° 00′N | 14° 15′E | 408 |
| Rabat, Morocco | 34° 00′N | 6° 45′W | 478 |
| Race, Cape | 46° 45′N | 53° 15′W | 253 |
| Rainier, Mount (ray · NEER) | 46° 45′N | 121° 45′W | 241 |
| Raleigh (RAHW · lee) | 35° 45′N | 78° 45′W | 228 |
| Rangoon (rang · GOON) | 16° 45′N | 96° 15′E | 680 |
| Rapid City | 44° 00′N | 103° 15′W | 233 |
| Rappahannock River | | | |
| (rap · uh · HAN · uhk) | 37° 15′N | 76° 15′W | 228 |
| Rasht (RASHT) | 37° 15′N | 49° 45′E | 495 |
| Ras Tanura (rahs tuh · NOOHR · uh) | 26° 30′N | 50° 00′E | 495 |
| Recife (ruh · SEE · fuh) | 8° 15′S | 35° 00′W | 366 |
| Red River, Canada | 50° 30′N | 97° 00′W | 253 |
| Red River, Louisiana | 31° 00′N | 91° 45′W | 228 |
| Red River, North Vietnam | 20° 45′N | 106° 45′E | 680 |
| Red Sea | 23° 15′N | 37° 00′E | 454 |
| Redwood National Park | 41° 30′N | 124° 00′W | 241 |
| Regina (ruh · JY · nuh) | 50° 30′N | 104° 45′W | 253 |
| Reno (REE· noh) | 39° 30′N | 119° 45′W | 239 |
| Republican River | | | |
| (ree · PUHB · li · kuhn) | 39° 00′N | 96° 45′W | 233 |
| Réunion (ray · oon · ee · OHN) | 21° 00′S | 55° 30′E | 557 |
| Reykjavík (RAY · kyah · veek) | 64° 15′N | 21° 45′W | 401 |
| Rhine River (RYN) | 51° 30′N | 3° 45′E | 397 |
| Rhode Island (ROHD) | 41° 30′N | 71° 45′W | 224 |
| Rhodes (ROHDZ) | 36° 30′N | 28° 15′E | 407 |
| Rhodope Mountains | | | |
| (RAW · doh · pe) | 42° 00′N | 24° 15′E | 422 |
| Rhône River (ROHN) | 43° 15′N | 4° 45′E | 397 |
| Richmond (RICH · muhnd) | 37° 30′N | 77° 30′W | 228 |
| Rift Valley | 3° 15′N | 31° 30′E | 511 |
| Riga (REE· guh) | 57° 00′N | 24° 00′E | 434 |
| Rijeka (ri · YEK · uh) | 45° 15′N | 14° 30′E | 422 |
| Rio de Janeiro | | | |
| (REE · oh day zhahn · AY · rooh) | 23° 00′S | 43° 00′W | 366 |
| Rio Grande (REE· oh GRAND · ay) | 26° 00′N | 97° 00′W | 195 |
| Rio Muni (REE· oh MOO· nee) | 1° 45′N | 10° 00′E | 538 |
| Riyadh (ree · YAHD) | 24° 30′N | 46° 45′E | 491 |
| Roanoke (ROH· uh · nohk) | 37° 15′N | 80° 00′W | 228 |
| Roanoke River | 36° 00′N | 76° 30′W | 228 |
| Rochester, Minn. (ROCH · es · tuhr) | 44° 00′N | 92° 30′W | 233 |
| Rochester, N.Y. | 43° 15′N | 77° 30′W | 225 |
| Rockford (ROK · ferd) | 42° 15′N | 89° 00′W | 231 |
| Rock River | 41° 30′N | 90° 45′W | 231 |
| Rocky Mountain National Park | 40° 30′N | 106° 00′W | 239 |
| Rocky Mountains | 40° 00′N | 115° 00′W | 195 |
| Romania (roh · MAY · nee · uh) | 46° 15′N | 23° 00′E | 422 |
| Rome (ROHM) | 41° 45′N | 12° 30′E | 407 |
| Ronne Ice Shelf (ROH· nuh) | 77° 30′S | 38° 00′E | 17 |
| Rosario (roh · ZAHR · ee · oh) | 33° 00′S | 60° 45′W | 11 |
| Roseau (roh · ZOH) | 15° 15′N | 61° 30′W | 304 |
| Ross Ice Shelf (RAWS) | 81° 30′S | 175° 00′W | 17 |
| Ross Sea | 76° 00′S | 178° 00′W | 17 |
| Rostock (RAWS · tuhk) | 54° 00′N | 12° 00′E | 422 |
| Roswell (RAWS · wel) | 33° 30′N | 104° 30′W | 237 |
| Rotterdam (ROT · uhr · dam) | 52° 00′N | 4° 30′E | 397 |
| Rouen (roo · AHN) | 49° 30′N | 1° 00′E | 397 |
| Ruaha National Park | 8° 00′S | 35° 00′E | 548 |
| Rub' al Khali (roohb al KAHL· ee) | 20° 30′N | 49° 15′E | 491 |
| Ruggell (ROOH · guhl) | 47° 15′N | 9° 30′E | 408 |
| Rukwa, Lake (rook · WAH) | 8° 00′S | 32° 30′E | 548 |
| Russian S. F. S. Republic | | | |
| (RUHSH · uhn) | 61° 00′N | 60° 00′E | 434 |

Gazetteer

# GAZETTEER

| NAME | LATITUDE | LONGITUDE | PAGE |
|------|----------|-----------|------|
| Rutland (RUHT · land) | 43° 30′N | 73° 00′W | 224 |
| Ruvuma River (rooh · VOO · muh) | 10° 30′S | 40° 30′E | 548 |
| Rwanda (roo · AN · duh) | 2° 15′S | 29° 30′E | 548 |
| Ryukyu Islands (ree · YOO · kyoo) | 27° 30′N | 127° 00′E | 642 |
| **S** | | | |
| Saba (SAH · bah) | 17° 45′N | 63° 15′W | 304 |
| Sabah (SAH · buh) | 5° 15′N | 116° 30′E | 688 |
| Sabine River (suh · BEEN) | 29° 45′N | 94° 00′W | 237 |
| Sacramento (sak · ruh · MEN · toh) | 38° 30′N | 121° 30′W | 241 |
| Sacramento River | 38° 00′N | 122° 00′W | 241 |
| Sacramento Valley | 39° 00′N | 122° 00′W | 241 |
| Saginaw (SAG · i · naw) | 43° 30′N | 84° 00′W | 231 |
| Sahara (suh · HAH · ruh) | 23° 45′N | 1° 45′W | 454 |
| Sahel (suh · HEL) | 14° 00′N | 6° 00′W | 511 |
| Saigon. *See* Ho Chi Minh City. | | | |
| St. Augustine (SAYNT AW · guhs · teen) | 30° 00′N | 81° 15′W | 228 |
| St. Barthélemy (san bar · tay · luh · mee) | 18° 00′N | 62° 30′W | 304 |
| St. Christopher-Nevis (NEE · vuhs) | 17° 30′N | 63° 30′W | 304 |
| St. Clair, Lake (CLAYR) | 42° 30′N | 82° 30′W | 231 |
| St. Cloud (CLOWD) | 45° 30′N | 94° 15′W | 233 |
| St. Croix River (CROY) | 45° 00′N | 92° 45′W | 231 |
| St. Denis (DEN · is) | 21° 00′S | 55° 30′E | 397 |
| St. Georges (JOHR · jez) | 12° 00′N | 62° 00′W | 304 |
| St. Helens, Mount (HE · lenz) | 46° 15′N | 122° 15′W | 241 |
| St. John River (JAWN) | 45° 15′N | 66° 00′W | 253 |
| St. John's, Antigua & Barbuda | 17° 00′N | 61° 45′W | 304 |
| St. John's, Canada | 47° 30′N | 52° 45′W | 253 |
| St. Johns River | 31° 15′N | 81° 30′W | 228 |
| St. Joseph (JOH · sef) | 39° 45′N | 94° 45′W | 233 |
| St. Lawrence River (LAW · rens) | 49° 15′N | 67° 15′W | 253 |
| St. Louis (LOO · is) | 38° 45′N | 90° 15′W | 233 |
| St. Lucia (LOO · shuh) | 14° 00′N | 60° 45′W | 304 |
| St. Martin (MAR · tin) | 18° 00′N | 63° 00′W | 304 |
| St. Paul | 45° 00′N | 93° 00′W | 233 |
| St. Petersburg | 27° 45′N | 82° 30′W | 228 |
| St. Vincent and the Grenadines (gren · uh · DEENZ) | 13° 15′N | 60° 45′W | 304 |
| Sakakawea, Lake (sak · uh · kuh · WEE · uh) | 48° 00′N | 102° 00′W | 233 |
| Sakhalin (SAK · uh · leen) | 52° 45′N | 144° 15′E | 434 |
| Salem (SAY · luhm) | 45° 00′N | 123° 00′W | 241 |
| Salif (sal · EEF) | 16° 45′N | 40° 15′E | 495 |
| Salinas (suh · LEE · nuhs) | 36° 45′N | 121° 45′W | 241 |
| Salmon River Mountains (SAM · uhn) | 44° 15′N | 115° 45′W | 239 |
| Salonika (sah · LOHN · ik · uh) | 40° 45′N | 23° 00′E | 407 |
| Salt Lake City | 40° 45′N | 111° 45′W | 239 |
| Salton Sea (SAHL · tuhn) | 33° 30′N | 115° 45′W | 241 |
| Salvador (sahl · vah · DOHR) | 13° 00′S | 38° 30′W | 366 |
| Salween River (sal · WEEN) | 17° 00′N | 98° 15′E | 680 |
| Salzburg (SAHL · boohrg) | 47° 45′N | 13° 00′E | 397 |
| Samar (SAH · mahr) | 11° 30′N | 125° 00′E | 689 |
| Samarkand (sa · mar · KAHNT) | 39° 45′N | 68° 00′E | 434 |
| Samina River (sam · EE · nah) | 47° 15′N | 9° 45′E | 408 |
| Sam Rayburn Reservoir | 31° 15′N | 94° 15′W | 237 |
| Sanaa (SAHN · ah) | 15° 15′N | 44° 00′E | 491 |
| Sanaga River (sah · NAH · gah) | 4° 00′N | 9° 45′E | 538 |
| San Andres Mountains (an · DRAYS) | 32° 45′N | 106° 45′W | 237 |
| San Antonio (an · TOHN · ee · oh) | 29° 30′N | 98° 30′W | 237 |
| San Bernardino (ber · nahr · DEE · noh) | 34° 00′N | 117° 15′W | 241 |
| Sand Hills | 42° 00′N | 101° 30′W | 233 |
| San Diego (dee · AY · goh) | 32° 45′N | 117° 15′W | 241 |
| San Francisco (fran · SIS · koh) | 37° 45′N | 122° 30′W | 241 |
| Sangre de Cristo Mountains (SANG · ray day KREES · toh) | 37° 45′N | 105° 45′W | 239 |
| San Joaquin River (wah · KEEN) | 38° 15′N | 121° 45′W | 241 |
| San Joaquin Valley | 36° 45′N | 120° 30′W | 241 |

| NAME | LATITUDE | LONGITUDE | PAGE |
|------|----------|-----------|------|
| San Jose (hoh · ZAY) | 37° 15′N | 122° 00′W | 241 |
| San José (hoh · SAY) | 10° 00′N | 84° 00′W | 288 |
| San Juan (HWAHN) | 18° 30′N | 66° 15′W | 304 |
| San Juan Mountains | 37° 45′N | 107° 30′W | 239 |
| San Juan River | 11° 30′N | 84° 00′W | 288 |
| San Juan River, Utah | 37° 15′N | 110° 00′W | 239 |
| San Marino (mah · REE · noh) | 44° 00′N | 12° 30′E | 408 |
| San Marino (city) | 44° 00′N | 12° 30′E | 408 |
| San Marino River | 44° 00′N | 12° 30′E | 408 |
| San Pedro (PAY · droh) | 4° 30′N | 7° 30′W | 528 |
| San Pedro Sula (SOO · lah) | 15° 30′N | 88° 30′W | 288 |
| San Salvador (sahl · vah · DOHR) | 13° 45′N | 89° 15′W | 288 |
| Santa Barbara (SAN · tuh BAHR · buh · ruh) | 34° 30′N | 119° 45′W | 241 |
| Santa Cruz (KROOZ) | 17° 45′S | 63° 00′W | 352 |
| Santa Fe (fay) | 35° 15′N | 106° 00′W | 237 |
| Santiago (sahn · tee · AH · goh) | 33° 30′S | 70° 45′W | 352 |
| Santiago de Cuba (KOO · buh) | 20° 00′N | 75° 45′W | 304 |
| Santiago Mountains | 30° 00′N | 103° 00′W | 237 |
| Santo Domingo (SAHN · toh doh · MIN · goh) | 18° 30′N | 70° 00′W | 304 |
| São Francisco River (sown frahn · SEESH · kooh) | 10° 15′S | 36° 30′W | 366 |
| São Paulo (POW · looh) | 22° 45′S | 45° 45′W | 366 |
| São Tomé (toh · MAY) | 0° 15′N | 7° 00′E | 538 |
| São Tomé (city) | 0° 15′N | 6° 45′E | 538 |
| São Tomé and Príncipe (PRIN · suh · puh) | 1° 00′N | 6° 00′E | 538 |
| Sapporo (sahp · POHR · roh) | 43° 00′N | 141° 30′E | 642 |
| Sarajevo (sah · ruh · YEV · oh) | 43° 15′N | 18° 30′E | 422 |
| Sarawak (suh · RAH · wahk) | 2° 30′N | 112° 45′E | 688 |
| Sardinia (sahr · DIN · ee · uh) | 40° 15′N | 9° 00′E | 407 |
| Saskatchewan (sas · KACH · uh · wahn) | 53° 45′N | 103° 30′W | 253 |
| Saskatchewan River | 53° 45′N | 100° 30′W | 253 |
| Saskatoon (sas · kuh · TOON) | 52° 00′N | 106° 45′W | 253 |
| Saudi Arabia (SOW · dee uh · RAY · bee · uh) | 22° 45′N | 46° 00′E | 491 |
| Savannah (suh · VAN · uh) | 32° 00′N | 81° 00′W | 228 |
| Savannakhet (suh · VAHN · uh · ket) | 16° 30′N | 104° 45′E | 680 |
| Sava River (SAH · vah) | 44° 45′N | 20° 30′E | 422 |
| Sayan Mountains (suh · YAHN) | 51° 30′N | 90° 00′E | 434 |
| Scandinavia (skan · di · NAY · vee · uh) | 62° 00′N | 14° 00′E | 401 |
| Schaan (SHAHN) | 47° 15′N | 9° 30′E | 408 |
| Scotland (SKAWT · land) | 57° 00′N | 5° 15′W | 397 |
| Scottsbluff (SKAWTZ · bluhf) | 42° 00′N | 103° 30′W | 233 |
| Scranton (SKRAN · tuhn) | 41° 45′N | 75° 45′W | 225 |
| Seattle (see · AT · uhl) | 47° 30′N | 122° 15′W | 241 |
| Ségou (say · GOO) | 13° 30′N | 6° 15′W | 528 |
| Seine River (SEN) | 49° 30′N | 0° 00′ | 397 |
| Senegal (sen · e · GAWL) | 15° 00′N | 15° 00′W | 528 |
| Senegal River | 16° 00′N | 16° 30′W | 528 |
| Seoul (SOHL) | 37° 30′N | 127° 00′E | 653 |
| Serengeti National Park (ser · uhn · GET · ee) | 2° 30′S | 34° 45′E | 548 |
| Serengeti Plain | 2° 45′S | 35° 00′E | 548 |
| Serravalle (SER · rah · vahl · le) | 44° 00′N | 12° 30′E | 408 |
| Sevastopol (suh · VAS · tuh · pohl) | 44° 30′N | 33° 30′E | 13 |
| Severnaya Zemlya (se · vir · NY · uh zem · LYAH) | 79° 30′N | 101° 15′E | 434 |
| Severn River (SEV · urhn) | 51° 30′N | 2° 45′W | 397 |
| Seville (suh · VIL) | 37° 30′N | 6° 00′W | 407 |
| Seychelles (say · SHEL) | 5° 15′S | 55° 15′E | 557 |
| Shaba Plateau (SHAH · buh) | 10° 00′S | 23° 00′E | 538 |
| Shanghai (SHAHNG · HY) | 31° 15′N | 121° 30′E | 622 |
| Shantou (SHAHN · TOH) | 23° 30′N | 116° 45′E | 622 |
| Shasta, Mount (SHAS · tuh) | 41° 30′N | 122° 15′W | 241 |
| Shenandoah River (shen · uhn · DOH · uh) | 39° 15′N | 77° 45′W | 228 |
| Shenyang (SHUHN · YAHNG) | 41° 45′N | 122° 30′E | 622 |
| Sheridan (SHER · i · duhn) | 44° 45′N | 107° 00′W | 239 |
| Shikoku (SHEE · koh · koo) | 33° 45′N | 133° 30′E | 642 |

| NAME | LATITUDE | LONGITUDE | PAGE |
|------|----------|-----------|------|
| Shiraz (shi · RAHZ) | 29° 30′N | 52° 30′E | 495 |
| Shreveport (SHREEV · pohrt) | 32° 30′N | 93° 45′W | 228 |
| Sicily (SI · si · lee) | 37° 45′N | 13° 30′E | 407 |
| Sidra, Gulf of (SID · ruh) | 31° 30′N | 18° 30′E | 472 |
| Sierra Leone (see · ER · uh lay · OHN · ay) | 8° 45′N | 12° 30′W | 528 |
| Sierra Madre Occidental (MAH · dray awks · ee · den · TAHL) | 24° 45′N | 105° 15′W | 272 |
| Sierra Madre Oriental (or · ree · uhn · TAHL) | 22° 00′N | 100° 00′W | 272 |
| Sierra Morena (moh · RAY · nah) | 38° 30′N | 5° 45′W | 407 |
| Sierra Nevada, Calif. (ne · VAH · duh) | 38° 00′N | 119° 15′W | 241 |
| Sierra Nevada, Spain | 36° 45′N | 3° 15′W | 407 |
| Sikhote-Alin Mountains (se · KOH · tuh-uh · LEEN) | 45° 00′N | 135° 45′E | 434 |
| Simpson Desert National Park | 25° 15′S | 138° 00′E | 698 |
| Sinai Peninsula (SY · ny) | 29° 30′N | 33° 30′E | 472 |
| Singapore (sin · guh · POHR) | 1° 15′N | 103° 45′E | 688 |
| Singapore (city) | 1° 15′N | 103° 45′E | 688 |
| Sioux City (SOO) | 42° 30′N | 96° 30′W | 233 |
| Sioux Falls | 43° 30′N | 96° 45′W | 233 |
| Sitka (SIT · kuh) | 57° 15′N | 135° 15′W | 241 |
| Sjaelland (SHEL · lan) | 55° 45′N | 11° 30′E | 401 |
| Skagerrak (skah · gee · RAHK) | 57° 45′N | 8° 30′E | 401 |
| Skopje (SKAWP · ye) | 42° 00′N | 21° 30′E | 422 |
| Slave Coast | 6° 30′N | 2° 30′E | 528 |
| Sliema (SLEE · muh) | 36° 00′N | 14° 30′E | 408 |
| Smoky Hill River | 39° 00′N | 98° 45′W | 233 |
| Snake River | 44° 30′N | 117° 00′W | 239 |
| Society Islands | 15° 00′S | 157° 30′W | 699 |
| Socotra (saw · KOH · truh) | 13° 00′N | 52° 30′E | 491 |
| Sofia (SOH · fee · uh) | 42° 45′N | 23° 15′E | 422 |
| Soldeu (sohl · DOOH) | 42° 30′N | 1° 45′E | 408 |
| Solomon Islands (SAWL · oh · muhn) | 7° 00′S | 160° 00′E | 698 |
| Somalia (soh · MAH · lee · uh) | 3° 30′N | 44° 45′E | 548 |
| Sonoran Desert (suh · NOH · ruhn) | 33° 30′N | 113° 15′W | 237 |
| South Africa (AF · ri · kah) | 28° 00′S | 24° 45′E | 557 |
| South America (ah · MER · ik · uh) | 10° 00′S | 58° 00′W | 11 |
| South Australia (aws · TRAYL · yuh) | 29° 45′S | 132° 00′E | 698 |
| South Bend | 41° 30′N | 86° 30′W | 231 |
| South Carolina (kar · oh · LY · nuh) | 34° 15′N | 81° 15′W | 228 |
| South China Sea (CHY · nuh) | 18° 30′N | 114° 15′E | 622 |
| South Dakota (duh · KOH · tuh) | 44° 15′N | 102° 00′W | 233 |
| Southern Alps (ALPS) | 43° 30′S | 170° 00′E | 699 |
| South Georgia Island (JOHR · juh) | 54° 00′S | 37° 00′W | 11 |
| South Island | 42° 45′S | 169° 00′E | 698 |
| South Platte River (PLAT) | 41° 15′N | 102° 45′W | 233 |
| South West National Park | 43° 45′S | 146° 00′E | 698 |
| Soweto (soh · WET · oh) | 26° 15′S | 28° 00′E | 557 |
| Spain (SPAYN) | 40° 15′N | 4° 30′W | 407 |
| Spartanburg (SPAHR · tuhn · buhrg) | 35° 00′N | 82° 15′W | 228 |
| Spokane (spoh · KAYN) | 47° 45′N | 117° 30′W | 241 |
| Springfield, Mass. (SPRING · feeld) | 42° 00′N | 72° 30′W | 224 |
| Springfield, Mo. | 37° 45′N | 93° 30′W | 233 |
| Sri Lanka (sree · LAHNG · kuh) | 8° 45′N | 82° 30′E | 572 |
| Stamford (STAM · fuhrd) | 41° 00′N | 73° 30′W | 224 |
| Stanley (STAN · lee) | 51° 45′S | 58° 00′W | 11 |
| Stanovoi Range (stuhn · uh · VOY) | 56° 15′N | 117° 15′E | 434 |
| Stavanger (stah · VANG · uhr) | 59° 30′N | 5° 45′E | 401 |
| Stockholm (STAWK · hohlm) | 59° 30′N | 18° 00′E | 401 |
| Stockton Plateau (STAHK · tuhn) | 30° 30′N | 103° 00′W | 237 |
| Strasbourg (STRAHS · buhrg) | 48° 30′N | 7° 45′E | 397 |
| Stuttgart (STOOT · gahrt) | 48° 45′N | 9° 15′E | 397 |
| Sucre (SOO · kray) | 19° 00′S | 65° 15′W | 352 |
| Sudan (SOO · DAN) | 14° 00′N | 28° 00′E | 548 |
| Sudan (region) | 10° 00′N | 7° 00′E | 511 |
| Sudetic Mountains (SOO · DET · ik) | 50° 45′N | 15° 30′E | 422 |
| Suez (SOO · EZ) | 30° 00′N | 32° 30′E | 472 |
| Suez Canal | 31° 00′N | 32° 15′E | 472 |
| Suez, Gulf of | 30° 00′N | 32° 30′E | 472 |

| NAME | LATITUDE | LONGITUDE | PAGE |
|------|----------|-----------|------|
| Sulaiman Range (soo · lah · ee · MAHN) | 29° 45′N | 69° 15′E | 572 |
| Sulu Archipelago (SOO · loo) | 5° 45′N | 122° 00′E | 689 |
| Sulu Sea | 8° 00′N | 120° 00′E | 689 |
| Sumatra (sooh · MAH · truh) | 2° 00′N | 99° 45′E | 688 |
| Sumba (SUHM · buh) | 9° 45′S | 119° 00′E | 688 |
| Sumbawa (soohm · BAH · wah) | 9° 00′S | 118° 15′E | 688 |
| Sunda Strait (SOON · duh) | 5° 45′S | 106° 15′E | 688 |
| Sungari River (SOOHNG · guh · ree) | 46° 00′N | 128° 00′E | 622 |
| Superior (soo · PEER · ee · uhr) | 46° 45′N | 92° 00′W | 231 |
| Superior, Lake | 47° 45′N | 89° 30′W | 195 |
| Surabaya (suhr · uh · BY · uh) | 7° 30′S | 112° 45′E | 688 |
| Suriname (soo · ruh · NAHM) | 4° 00′N | 56° 00′W | 338 |
| Sutlej River (SUHT · lej) | 28° 00′N | 71° 00′E | 572 |
| Suva (SOO · vuh) | 18° 00′S | 178° 00′E | 699 |
| Sverdlovsk (sverd · LOFSK) | 56° 45′N | 60° 30′E | 434 |
| Swaziland (SWAH · zee · land) | 26° 45′S | 31° 30′E | 557 |
| Sweden (SWEE · den) | 60° 15′N | 14° 15′E | 401 |
| Switzerland (SWIT · zuhr · land) | 46° 30′N | 7° 45′E | 397 |
| Sydney, Australia (SID · nee) | 34° 00′S | 151° 15′E | 698 |
| Sydney, Canada | 46° 15′N | 60° 15′W | 253 |
| Syoma (see · OH · mah) | 68° 30′S | 40° 00′E | 17 |
| Syracuse (SEER · uh · koos) | 43° 00′N | 76° 15′W | 225 |
| Syria (SEER · ee · uh) | 35° 00′N | 37° 15′E | 487 |
| Syrian Desert (SEER · ee · uhn) | 32° 00′N | 39° 30′E | 487 |
| Szczecin (SHCHE · tsin) | 53° 30′N | 14° 30′E | 422 |
| Szeged (se · GED) | 46° 15′N | 20° 15′E | 422 |

**T**

| NAME | LATITUDE | LONGITUDE | PAGE |
|------|----------|-----------|------|
| Tabrīz (tuh · BREEZ) | 38° 00′N | 46° 15′E | 497 |
| Tacoma (tuh · COH · muh) | 47° 15′N | 122° 30′W | 241 |
| Tadzhik S. S. R. (tah · JIK) | 39° 15′N | 69° 30′E | 434 |
| Taedong River (TAY · DOWNG) | 38° 45′N | 125° 30′E | 653 |
| Taegu (ty · GOO) | 35° 45′N | 128° 45′E | 653 |
| Tagus River (TAY · guhs) | 38° 45′N | 9° 15′W | 407 |
| Tahiti (tah · HEE · tee) | 17° 30′S | 149° 30′W | 699 |
| Tahoe, Lake (TAH · hoh) | 39° 15′N | 120° 15′W | 241 |
| Taipei (TY · PAY) | 25° 00′N | 121° 45′E | 622 |
| Taiwan (TY · WAHN) | 23° 30′N | 122° 30′E | 622 |
| Taiyuan (TY · YOO · AHN) | 37° 30′N | 112° 45′E | 622 |
| Takla Makan (TAHK · luh muh · KAHN) | 39° 15′N | 82° 30′E | 622 |
| Tallahassee (tal · uh · HAS · ee) | 30° 30′N | 84° 15′W | 228 |
| Tallinn (TAL · een) | 59° 30′N | 24° 45′E | 434 |
| Tambora (tahm · BOHR · uh) | 7° 45′S | 116° 00′E | 688 |
| Tampa (TAM · puh) | 28° 00′N | 82° 30′W | 228 |
| Tampa Bay | 27° 30′N | 82° 45′W | 228 |
| Tampere (TAM · pe · re) | 61° 15′N | 23° 45′E | 401 |
| Tanana River (TA · nuh · naw) | 65° 15′N | 152° 30′W | 241 |
| Tana River (TAH · nah) | 2° 15′S | 40° 15′E | 548 |
| Tanen Range (TAH · nen) | 20° 00′N | 100° 00′E | 680 |
| Tanganyika, Lake (tan · gan · YEE · kuh) | 5° 15′S | 29° 45′E | 548 |
| Tangier (tan · JEER) | 35° 45′N | 6° 00′W | 478 |
| Tanimbar Islands (tuh · NIM · bahr) | 8° 00′S | 132° 00′E | 688 |
| Tanzania (tan · zan · EE · uh) | 6° 45′S | 34° 00′E | 548 |
| Tarawa (tuh · RAH · wuh) | 2° 00′N | 172° 00′E | 699 |
| Tartus (TAHR · tuhs) | 34° 30′N | 35° 45′E | 495 |
| Tashkent (TASH · kent) | 41° 00′N | 69° 00′E | 434 |
| Tasmania (taz · MAY · nee · uh) | 41° 30′S | 142° 30′E | 698 |
| Tasman Sea (TAZ · man) | 39° 30′S | 155° 00′E | 698 |
| Taurus Mountains (TAW · ruhs) | 37° 00′N | 32° 45′E | 484 |
| Tbilisi (tbil · YEE · see) | 41° 30′N | 44° 45′E | 434 |
| Tegucigalpa (tuh · goo · si · GAHL · pah) | 14° 15′N | 87° 15′W | 288 |
| Tehran (te · RAHN) | 35° 45′N | 51° 30′E | 497 |
| Tehuantepec, Isthmus of (tay · HWAHN · tay · pek) | 18° 00′N | 94° 30′W | 272 |
| Tel Aviv (tel ah · VEEV) | 32° 00′N | 34° 45′E | 487 |
| Tempe (TEM · pee) | 33° 30′N | 112° 00′W | 237 |
| Ténéré (tay · nayr · AY) | 19° 30′N | 10° 15′E | 528 |
| Tennessee (ten · uh · SEE) | 35° 45′N | 88° 00′W | 228 |
| Tennessee River | 37° 15′N | 88° 30′N | 228 |
| Tenochtitlán (ten · ohch · teet · LAN) | 19° 30′N | 99° 00′W | 276 |

# GAZETTEER

| NAME | LATITUDE | LONGITUDE | PAGE |
|---|---|---|---|
| Texarkana (teks · ahr · KAN · uh) | 33° 30′N | 94° 00′W | 228 |
| Texas (TEKS · uhs) | 31° 00′N | 100° 00′W | 237 |
| Thailand (TY · land) | 16° 30′N | 101° 00′E | 680 |
| Thailand, Gulf of | 11° 30′N | 100° 45′E | 680 |
| Thames River (TEMZ) | 51° 00′N | 1° 00′E | 397 |
| Thar Desert (TAHR) | 27° 30′N | 71° 30′E | 572 |
| Thimbu (THIM · boo) | 27° 30′N | 89° 45′E | 572 |
| Tianjin (TYEN · JYIN) | 39° 00′N | 117° 15′E | 622 |
| Tiber River (TY · buhr) | 41° 45′N | 12° 15′E | 407 |
| Tibesti Mountains (tuh · BES · tee) | 20° 45′N | 17° 45′E | 538 |
| Tibet, Plateau of (ti · BET) | 32° 15′N | 82° 30′E | 622 |
| Tien Shan (DI · EN SHAHN) | 41° 00′N | 80° 30′E | 622 |
| Tierra del Fuego (TYAYR · uh del FWAY · goh) | 53° 45′S | 68° 45′W | 11 |
| Tigris River (TY · gris) | 31° 30′N | 47° 30′E | 497 |
| Tijuana (tee · HWAHN · uh) | 32° 30′N | 117° 00′W | 272 |
| Tikal (tee · KAHL) | 17° 15′N | 90° 00′W | 276 |
| Timişoara (tee · mish · uh · WAHR · uh) | 45° 45′N | 21° 15′E | 422 |
| Timor (tee · MOHR) | 10° 15′S | 125° 00′E | 688 |
| Timor Sea | 12° 45′S | 125° 00′E | 688 |
| Tirane (tee · RAH · nah) | 41° 45′N | 19° 45′E | 422 |
| Titicaca, Lake (ti · ti · KAH · kah) | 16° 15′S | 70° 30′W | 352 |
| Toamasina (toh · uh · muh · SEE · nuh) | 18° 15′S | 49° 30′E | 557 |
| Tobago (toh · BAY · goh) | 11° 15′N | 60° 30′W | 304 |
| Tobruk (toh · BROOHK) | 32° 00′N | 24° 00′E | 495 |
| Togo (TOH · goh) | 8° 00′N | 0° 45′E | 528 |
| Tokelau Islands (toh · kee · LAH · ooh) | 8° 00′S | 176° 00′W | 699 |
| Tokyo (TOH · kee · oh) | 35° 45′N | 139° 45′E | 642 |
| Tokyo Bay | 34° 00′N | 140° 00′E | 642 |
| Toledo (toh · LEE · doh) | 41° 45′N | 83° 30′W | 231 |
| Tolima (toh · LEE · muh) | 4° 45′N | 75° 15′W | 338 |
| Tombouctou (tawm · book · TOO) | 16° 45′N | 3° 00′W | 528 |
| Tonga (TAWNG · guh) | 18° 45′S | 175° 15′W | 699 |
| Tongariro National Park (tahn · guh · RIR · oh) | 37° 15′S | 175° 30′E | 699 |
| Tonkin, Gulf of (TANG · kin) | 20° 30′N | 108° 15′E | 680 |
| Topeka (toh · PEEK · uh) | 39° 00′N | 95° 45′W | 233 |
| Toronto (toh · RAHN · toh) | 43° 45′N | 79° 30′W | 253 |
| Torres Strait (TAW · res) | 10° 30′S | 141° 30′E | 698 |
| Toulouse (too · LOOZ) | 43° 30′N | 1° 30′E | 397 |
| Trabzon (TRUHB · zohn) | 41° 00′N | 39° 45′E | 484 |
| Trans-Alaska Pipeline | 66° 00′N | 150° 00′W | 241 |
| Transylvanian Alps (tranz · sil · VAY · nee · uhn) | 45° 30′N | 23° 30′E | 422 |
| Trenton (TREN · tuhn) | 40° 15′N | 74° 45′W | 225 |
| Trieste (tree · ES · tay) | 45° 45′N | 13° 45′E | 407 |
| Trinidad (TRIN · i · dad) | 10° 00′N | 61° 00′W | 304 |
| Trinidad and Tobago (toh · BAY · goh) | 11° 00′N | 61° 00′W | 304 |
| Trinity River (TRIN · i · tee) | 29° 45′N | 94° 45′W | 237 |
| Tripoli, Lebanon (TRIP · oh · lee) | 34° 30′N | 35° 45′E | 495 |
| Tripoli, Libya | 32° 45′N | 13° 15′E | 472 |
| Tromsø (TRAWM · suh) | 69° 45′N | 19° 15′E | 401 |
| Trondheim (TRAWN · haym) | 63° 30′N | 11° 30′E | 401 |
| Trujillo (troo · HEE · yoh) | 8° 15′S | 79° 00′W | 352 |
| Trust Territory of the Pacific Islands | 10° 00′N | 135° 00′E | 698 |
| Tsaratanana Massif (sahr · uh · TAHN · uh · nuh) | 15° 00′S | 48° 00′E | 557 |
| Tsavo National Park (SAHV · oh) | 3° 30′S | 38° 00′E | 548 |
| Tuamotu Archipelago (too · ah · MOH · too) | 19° 00′S | 141° 15′W | 699 |
| Tucson (TOO · sawn) | 32° 15′N | 111° 00′W | 237 |
| Tula (TOO · lah) | 20° 00′N | 99° 15′W | 276 |
| Tulsa (TUHL · suh) | 36° 15′N | 96° 00′W | 237 |
| Tumen River (TOO · MUHN) | 42° 00′N | 130° 30′E | 653 |
| Turin (TOO · rin) | 45° 00′N | 7° 45′E | 407 |
| Turkmen S. S. R. (toork · MEN) | 40° 45′N | 66° 00′E | 434 |
| Turks and Caicos Islands (tuhrks and KAY · kuhs) | 21° 45′N | 71° 45′W | 304 |
| Turku (TOOHR · kooh) | 60° 30′N | 22° 15′E | 401 |
| Tuscaloosa (tuhs · kuh · LOO · suh) | 33° 15′N | 87° 30′W | 228 |
| Tuvalu (TOO · vah · loo) | 5° 15′S | 174° 00′E | 699 |

| NAME | LATITUDE | LONGITUDE | PAGE |
|---|---|---|---|
| Tuz, Lake (TOOZ) | 39° 00′N | 33° 30′E | 484 |
| Twin Falls | 42° 30′N | 114° 30′W | 239 |
| Tyrrhenian Sea (ti · REEN · ee · uhn) | 39° 15′N | 12° 15′E | 407 |
| **U** | | | |
| Ubangi River (oo · BANG · gee) | 0° 45′S | 17° 45′E | 511 |
| Ucayali River (oo · kah · YAH · lee) | 4° 00′S | 73° 30′W | 352 |
| Uele River (WAY · luh) | 4° 00′N | 22° 30′E | 538 |
| Ufa (OOHF · uh) | 55° 45′N | 56° 00′E | 434 |
| Uganda (oo · GAHN · duh) | 2° 00′N | 32° 30′E | 548 |
| Uinta Mountains (yoo · IN · tuh) | 40° 45′N | 110° 15′W | 239 |
| Ujung Pandang (oo · juhng pahn · DAHNG) | 5° 15′S | 119° 30′E | 688 |
| Ukrainian S.S.R. (yoo · KRAY · nee · uhn) | 49° 15′N | 30° 15′E | 434 |
| Ulaanbaatar (oo · lahn · BAH · tawr) | 48° 00′N | 107° 00′E | 622 |
| Ume River (oo · may) | 63° 45′N | 20° 30′E | 401 |
| Ungava Peninsula (uhn · GAH · vuh) | 60° 00′N | 74° 00′W | 253 |
| Union of Soviet Socialist Republics | 63° 30′N | 64° 00′E | 434 |
| United Arab Emirates (EM · uhr · ets) | 24° 00′N | 54° 00′E | 491 |
| United Kingdom | 56° 30′N | 1° 45′E | 12-13 |
| United States | 38° 00′N | 110° 00′W | 8-9 |
| Upemba National Park (oo · PEM · buh) | 9° 15′S | 26° 15′E | 538 |
| Upper Peninsula | 46° 30′N | 87° 45′W | 231 |
| Uppsala (OOP · suh · lah) | 60° 00′N | 17° 45′E | 401 |
| Ural Mountains (YOOHR · uhl) | 56° 00′N | 58° 15′E | 434 |
| Ural River | 46° 30′N | 52° 00′E | 434 |
| Urewera National Park (oo · ruh · WER · uh) | 38° 30′S | 177° 00′E | 699 |
| Urmia, Lake (OOHR · mee · uh) | 38° 00′N | 45° 15′E | 497 |
| Uruguay (oo · rah · GWY) | 32° 45′S | 56° 00′W | 366 |
| Uruguay River | 33° 00′S | 58° 00′W | 366 |
| Utah (YOO · tah) | 39° 30′N | 112° 45′W | 239 |
| Uzbek S. S. R. (ooz · BEK) | 42° 45′N | 60° 00′E | 434 |
| **V** | | | |
| Vaal River (VAHL) | 29° 45′S | 22° 45′E | 557 |
| Vaduz (vah · DOOHTS) | 47° 15′N | 9° 30′E | 408 |
| Valdez (VAL · deez) | 61° 15′N | 146° 15′W | 241 |
| Valdivia (vahl · DEEV · ee · uh) | 39° 45′S | 73° 15′W | 352 |
| Valencia (vah · LEN · thee · uh) | 39° 30′N | 0° 30′W | 407 |
| Valira del Orient River (del oh · ree · ENT) | 42° 30′N | 1° 45′E | 408 |
| Valira River (vah · LEE · rah) | 42° 30′N | 1° 30′E | 408 |
| Valletta (vahl · LET · ah) | 36° 00′N | 14° 30′E | 408 |
| Valparaíso (vahl · pahr · ah · EE · soh) | 33° 00′S | 71° 30′W | 352 |
| Van Blommenstein Reservoir (van BLOHM · ens · tayn) | 4° 00′N | 56° 00′W | 338 |
| Vancouver (van · KOO · vuhr) | 49° 15′N | 123° 00′W | 253 |
| Vancouver Island | 49° 45′N | 125° 00′W | 253 |
| Vänern, Lake (VAY · nuhrn) | 58° 45′N | 13° 15′E | 401 |
| Van, Lake (VAN) | 38° 45′N | 43° 00′E | 484 |
| Vanuatu (van · uh · WAH · too) | 16° 00′S | 169° 15′E | 699 |
| Varna (VAHR · nuh) | 43° 15′N | 28° 00′E | 422 |
| Västeras (VES · ter · aws) | 59° 45′N | 16° 30′E | 401 |
| Vatican City (VAT · i · kan) | 42° 00′N | 12° 15′E | 408 |
| Vatnajökull (VAHT · nuh · yoo · kool) | 64° 30′N | 16° 45′W | 401 |
| Venezuela (ven · uh · ZWAY · luh) | 8° 00′N | 65° 00′W | 338 |
| Venice (VEN · is) | 45° 30′N | 12° 15′E | 407 |
| Veracruz (vayr · uh · KROOZ) | 19° 15′N | 96° 00′W | 10 |
| Verkhoyansk Mountains (vyer · koh · YANSK) | 67° 45′N | 128° 00′E | 434 |
| Vermont (ver · MAWNT) | 43° 45′N | 72° 45′W | 224 |
| Vert, Cape (VAYR) | 14° 45′N | 17° 30′W | 528 |
| Vesuvius, Mount (ve · SOO · vee · uhs) | 40° 30′N | 14° 30′E | 407 |
| Vicksburg (VIKS · buhrg) | 32° 15′N | 90° 45′W | 228 |
| Victoria, Australia | 36° 45′S | 143° 15′E | 698 |
| Victoria, Canada | 48° 30′N | 123° 30′W | 253 |
| Victoria Falls | 18° 00′S | 25° 45′E | 557 |
| Victoria Island | 70° 15′N | 107° 45′W | 253 |
| Victoria, Lake | 0° 45′S | 32° 45′E | 548 |

| NAME | LATITUDE | LONGITUDE | PAGE |
|---|---|---|---|
| Victoria Land | 75° 00′S | 160° 00′E | 17 |
| Victoria, Malta | 36° 00′N | 14° 15′E | 408 |
| Victoria, Seychelles | 4° 30′S | 55° 30′E | 557 |
| Vienna (vee·EN·uh) | 48° 15′N | 16° 15′E | 397 |
| Vientiane (VYEN·TYAHN) | 18° 00′N | 102° 30′E | 680 |
| Vietnam (vee·et·NAHM) | 18° 00′N | 107° 00′E | 680 |
| Vilnius (VIL·nee·oohs) | 54° 45′N | 25° 30′E | 434 |
| Vindhya Range (VIND·yah) | 22° 30′N | 75° 00′E | 572 |
| Virginia (ver·JIN·yuh) | 37° 00′N | 80° 45′W | 228 |
| Virginia Beach | 36° 45′N | 76° 00′W | 228 |
| Virgin Islands (VUHR·jin) | 18° 15′N | 64° 00′W | 304 |
| Vistula River (VIS·too·lah) | 54° 15′N | 19° 00′E | 422 |
| Vladivostok (vlad·uh·vuh·STAHK) | 43° 00′N | 131° 45′E | 434 |
| Volga River (VOHL·guh) | 46° 00′N | 48° 00′E | 434 |
| Volgograd (vohl·goh·GRAT) | 48° 45′N | 42° 15′E | 13 |
| Volta, Lake (VAWL·tuh) | 7° 15′N | 0° 30′W | 528 |
| Vosges (VOHZH) | 48° 15′N | 7° 00′E | 397 |
| Vostok (VAWS·tawk) | 78° 00′S | 108° 00′E | 17 |

## W

| NAME | LATITUDE | LONGITUDE | PAGE |
|---|---|---|---|
| Wabash River (WAW·bash) | 38° 00′N | 88° 00′W | 231 |
| Waco (WAY·koh) | 31° 30′N | 97° 00′W | 237 |
| Wake Island (WAYK) | 19° 30′N | 167° 00′E | 699 |
| Walachian Plain (wah·LAY·kee·uhn) | 45° 15′N | 24° 45′E | 422 |
| Wales (WAYLZ) | 52° 15′N | 3° 45′W | 397 |
| Walla Walla (WAH·luh WAH·luh) | 46° 00′N | 118° 15′W | 241 |
| Wallis and Futuna (WAH·lis and fuh·TOO·nuh) | 13° 00′S | 176° 15′E | 699 |
| Walvis Bay (WAWL·vis) | 22° 45′S | 14° 30′E | 557 |
| Warsaw (WAWR·saw) | 52° 15′N | 21° 00′E | 422 |
| Wasatch Range (WAW·satch) | 41° 15′N | 111° 30′W | 239 |
| Washington (WAHSH·ing·tuhn) | 47° 30′N | 121° 15′W | 241 |
| Washington, D.C. | 38° 45′N | 77° 00′W | 225 |
| Washington, Mount | 44° 15′N | 71° 15′W | 224 |
| Waterbury (WAW·tuhr·buhr·ee) | 41° 30′N | 73° 00′W | 224 |
| Waterloo, Ia. (waw·tuhr·LOO) | 42° 30′N | 92° 15′W | 233 |
| Weddell Sea (WED·uhl) | 73° 00′S | 45° 00′W | 17 |
| Wei He (WAY HUH) | 34° 00′N | 108° 00′E | 622 |
| Wellington (WEL·ling·tuhn) | 41° 15′S | 174° 45′E | 699 |
| Western Australia (aws·TRAYL·yuh) | 24° 15′S | 121° 30′E | 698 |
| Western Ghats (GAWTS) | 17° 30′N | 74° 00′E | 572 |
| Western Sahara (sah·HAH·ruh) | 23° 00′N | 15° 30′W | 478 |
| Western Samoa (suh·MOH·uh) | 14° 30′S | 172° 00′W | 699 |
| West Indies (IN·deez) | 19° 00′N | 78° 30′W | 304 |
| West Siberian Plain (sy·BEER·ee·uhn) | 63° 30′N | 79° 45′E | 434 |
| West Virginia (ver·JIN·yuh) | 39° 00′N | 80° 45′W | 225 |
| Wheeler Peak (HWEE·luhr) | 39° 00′N | 114° 15′W | 239 |
| Wheeling (HWEE·ling) | 40° 00′N | 80° 45′W | 225 |
| Whitehorse (HWYT·hohrs) | 60° 45′N | 135° 00′W | 253 |
| White Mountains | 44° 15′N | 71° 00′W | 224 |
| White Nile | 15° 30′N | 32° 30′E | 548 |
| White Volta River (VOHL·tuh) | 9° 00′N | 1° 00′W | 528 |
| Whitney, Mount (HWIT·nee) | 36° 30′N | 118° 15′W | 241 |
| Wichita (WICH·i·taw) | 37° 45′N | 97° 30′W | 233 |
| Wichita Falls | 34° 00′N | 98° 30′W | 237 |
| Wight, Isle of (WYT) | 50° 45′N | 1° 15′W | 397 |
| Wilkes Land (WILKS) | 71° 00′S | 126° 00′E | 17 |
| Willamette River (wuh·LAM·uht) | 45° 30′N | 123° 45′W | 241 |
| Willamette Valley | 44° 45′N | 121° 15′W | 241 |
| Williamsburg (WIL·yuhmz·buhrg) | 37° 15′N | 76° 45′W | 228 |
| Williston (WIL·is·tuhn) | 48° 15′N | 103° 45′W | 233 |
| Wilmington, Del. (WIL·ming·tuhn) | 39° 45′N | 75° 30′W | 225 |
| Wilmington, N.C. | 34° 15′N | 78° 00′W | 228 |
| Windhoek (VINT·hoohk) | 22° 00′S | 17° 15′E | 557 |
| Wind River Range | 43° 15′N | 109° 45′W | 239 |
| Windsor (WIN·zuhr) | 42° 15′N | 83° 00′W | 253 |

| NAME | LATITUDE | LONGITUDE | PAGE |
|---|---|---|---|
| Windward Islands (WIND·wuhrd) | 12° 45′N | 61° 45′W | 304 |
| Windward Passage | 19° 30′N | 74° 15′W | 304 |
| Winnebago, Lake (win·uh·BAY·goh) | 44° 15′N | 88° 15′W | 231 |
| Winnipeg (WIN·i·peg) | 50° 00′N | 97° 15′W | 253 |
| Winnipeg, Lake | 52° 00′N | 97° 00′W | 253 |
| Winston-Salem (win·stuhn-SAY·luhm) | 36° 00′N | 80° 15′W | 228 |
| Wisconsin (wis·KON·sin) | 44° 30′N | 91° 00′W | 231 |
| Wisconsin River | 43° 15′N | 91° 15′W | 231 |
| Woods, Lake of the | 49° 30′N | 95° 30′W | 233 |
| Worcester (WOOHS·ter) | 42° 15′N | 71° 45′W | 224 |
| Wrangel Island (RANG·ghuhl) | 71° 30′N | 178° 30′E | 434 |
| Wrocław (VRAWTS·lahv) | 51° 00′N | 17° 15′E | 422 |
| Wuhan (WOO·HAHN) | 30° 30′N | 114° 15′E | 622 |
| Wyoming (wy·OH·ming) | 42° 45′N | 108° 30′W | 239 |
| Wyoming Basin | 42° 00′N | 109° 00′W | 239 |
| Wyoming Range | 42° 45′N | 110° 30′W | 239 |

## X

| NAME | LATITUDE | LONGITUDE | PAGE |
|---|---|---|---|
| Xiamen (SHYAH·MUHN) | 24° 30′N | 118° 15′E | 622 |
| Xi'an (SHYEE·AHN) | 34° 30′N | 109° 00′E | 622 |
| Xinjiang (SHYIN·JYAHNG) | 40° 15′N | 82° 15′E | 622 |
| Xi River (SHYEE) | 22° 30′N | 113° 15′E | 622 |

## Y

| NAME | LATITUDE | LONGITUDE | PAGE |
|---|---|---|---|
| Yalu River (YAH·LOO) | 41° 30′N | 126° 30′E | 622 |
| Yamuna River (YUH·muh·nuh) | 25° 30′N | 82° 00′E | 572 |
| Yaoundé (yuh·oon·DAY) | 3° 45′N | 11° 30′E | 528 |
| Yaren (YAH·ren) | 0° 00′ | 166° 00′E | 699 |
| Yellowknife (YEL·oh·nyf) | 62° 30′N | 114° 45′W | 253 |
| Yellow Sea | 35° 30′N | 122° 15′E | 622 |
| Yellowstone National Park | 44° 45′N | 110° 30′W | 239 |
| Yellowstone River | 46° 00′N | 106° 00′W | 239 |
| Yemen (YEM·uhn) | 15° 45′N | 44° 30′E | 491 |
| Yemen, People's Democratic Republic of | 14° 45′N | 46° 45′E | 491 |
| Yenbo (YEN·buh) | 24° 00′N | 38° 00′E | 495 |
| Yenisei River (ye·nee·SE·ee) | 70° 00′N | 85° 00′E | 434 |
| Yerevan (ye·re·VAHN) | 40° 15′N | 44° 30′E | 434 |
| Yokohama (yoh·koh·HAM·ah) | 35° 30′N | 139° 45′E | 642 |
| Yosemite National Park (yoh·SEM·i·tee) | 38° 00′N | 119° 30′W | 241 |
| Youngstown (YUHNGZ·town) | 41° 00′N | 80° 45′W | 231 |
| Yucatán Peninsula (yoo·cuh·TAN) | 20° 00′N | 89° 00′W | 272 |
| Yugoslavia (yoo·goh·SLAH·vee·uh) | 44° 45′N | 17° 30′E | 422 |
| Yukon (YOO·kawn) | 63° 15′N | 135° 30′W | 253 |
| Yukon River | 63° 00′N | 165° 00′W | 241 |
| Yuma (YOO·mah) | 32° 45′N | 114° 45′W | 237 |
| Yunnan Plateau (yoo·NAHN) | 26° 00′N | 101° 30′E | 622 |

## Z

| NAME | LATITUDE | LONGITUDE | PAGE |
|---|---|---|---|
| Zagreb (ZAH·greb) | 45° 45′N | 16° 00′E | 422 |
| Zagros Mountains (ZAG·ruhs) | 33° 30′N | 46° 30′E | 497 |
| Zaire (zah·EER) | 1° 00′S | 22° 15′E | 538 |
| Zaire River | 0° 45′S | 18° 00′E | 538 |
| Zakouma National Park (zah·KOO·mah) | 10° 45′N | 19° 15′E | 538 |
| Zambezi River (zam·BAY·zee) | 17° 45′S | 36° 30′E | 557 |
| Zambia (ZAM·bee·uh) | 14° 30′S | 24° 15′E | 538 |
| Zanzibar (ZAN·zi·bahr) | 6° 15′S | 39° 30′E | 548 |
| Zarqa (ZAHR·kuh) | 32° 00′N | 36° 00′E | 487 |
| Zibo (DZEE·BOH) | 36° 45′N | 118° 00′E | 622 |
| Zimbabwe (zim·BAHB·wee) | 17° 45′S | 29° 30′E | 557 |
| Zimbabwe National Park | 21° 00′S | 31° 00′E | 557 |
| Zion National Park (ZY·uhn) | 37° 15′N | 113° 00′W | 239 |
| Zürich (TSOO·rik) | 47° 15′N | 8° 30′E | 397 |

Gazetteer

# GLOSSARY

This GLOSSARY contains many of the terms you need to understand as you study geography. After each term there is a brief definition or explanation of the meaning of the term as it is usually used in geography. The page number in parentheses after each definition refers to the page on which the term is boldfaced in the textbook. A phonetic respelling is provided to help you pronounce many of the terms. (Please refer to the Pronunciation Guide on page 719.)

The brief definitions in this glossary do not always provide all the information that you may need to know about these terms. Therefore, you may find it useful to turn to the page listed in parentheses to read more about a term.

## A

**abdicate** (AB·di·kayt)  to give up the throne **(p. 626)**

**Aborigine** (ab·uh·RIJ·uh·nee) native person, especially one of the first Australians **(p. 702)**

**absolute humidity**  measure of the actual weight of water vapor in the air **(p. 82)**

**absolute location**  precise spot of a place on the earth's surface **(p. 30)**

**absolute monarchy**  form of government in which the ruler has no restrictions on his or her power **(p. 463)**

**abyssal plain** (uh·BIHS·uhl)  very wide, smooth, flat section of seafloor **(p. 133)**

**acculturation** (uh·kul·chuh·RAY·shuhn) process by which a person from one culture adopts traits of another culture **(pp. 149, 210)**

**acid rain**  polluted precipitation that results when chemicals in pollutants combine with the chemicals in water vapor **(p. 33)**

**aerial photograph**  picture taken from above the earth **(p. 48)**

**age distribution**  relative sizes of different age groups in a population **(p. 212)**

**agriculture**  art and science of farming **(p. 171)**

**alluvial soil** (uh·LOO·vee·uhl)  soil deposited by flowing water; also called "alluvium" (uh·LOO·vee·uhm) **(p. 289)**

**alpine meadow**  tundra-covered field above the tree line **(p. 386)**

**Altiplano** (al·ti·PLAHN·oh)  high-altitude plateau in the Andes **(p. 323)**

**altitude** (AL·ti·tood)  distance above the earth's surface **(p. 84)**

**alumina** (uh·LOO·muh·nuh)  semifinished form of bauxite from which aluminum is made **(p. 347)**

**apartheid** (uh·PAHR·tayt)  official policy of South Africa which separates the races and ensures white control **(p. 557)**

**aquaculture** (AK·wuh·kuhl·chuhr)  cultivation of water plants and animals for human consumption **(p. 643)**

**aquifer** (AK·wuh·fuhr)  water-bearing rock layers **(pp. 123, 697)**

**arable land** (AR·uh·buhl)  land suitable for cultivation **(p. 622)**

**archipelago** (ahr·kuh·PEL·uh·goh)  chain of islands **(p. 304)**

**arithmetic density** (ar·ith·MET·ik DEN·suht·ee)  average number of people per square mile or square kilometer in a given country **(p. 154)**

**artesian basin** (ahr·TEE·zhuhn)  folded layers of porous rocks that fill with rainfall **(p. 697)**

**atlas**  collection of maps and related material **(p. 41)**

**atmosphere** (AT·muh·sfehr)  various gases that surround a planet **(p. 79)**

**atmospheric pressure**  weight of the air **(p. 84)**

**atoll** (A·tawl)  ring of coral surrounding an inner body of water called a lagoon **(pp. 597, 709)**

**authoritarian socialism** (ah·thar·uh·TER·ee·uhn SOH·shuh·liz·uhm)  economic system in which the government owns almost all of the businesses and controls the entire economy. *See* **communism** **(p. 167)**

**autonomous republic** (or **region**) (aw·TAHN·uh·muhs)  political division that provides limited self-government **(pp. 441, 627)**

**axis** (AK·sehs)  imaginary line extending through the center of a sphere **(p. 30)**

**azimuthal map** (az·uh·MUHTH·uhl)  map using a projection that shows true compass direction **(p. 47)**

## B

**balance of trade**  difference in value between a nation's imports and its exports **(pp. 477, 652)**

**balkanization** (BAWL·kuh·nuh·zay·shuhn)  process of breaking up a larger area into many small states **(p. 418)**

**basin**  broad depression in the earth's surface **(p. 510)**

**basin and range**  desert landscape consisting of steep, rugged mountain chains with dry basins between **(p. 456)**

**bazaar** (buh·ZAR)  marketplace **(p. 472)**

**bedouin** (BED·uh·wuhn)  Arab nomad **(p. 463)**

**bilingual** (by·LIN·gwuhl)  fluent in two languages **(p. 217)**

**biodegradable** (by·oh·dee·GRAYD·uh·buhl)  easily broken down by natural means **(p. 140)**

**biome** (BY·ohm)  plant and animal community living in a particular climate region; also called an **ecosystem** **(p. 98)**

**biophysical geography**  study of the natural environment and the interrelationships of all the living things in that environment; also called "biogeography" **(p. 28)**

**birth rate** number of children born per 1,000 people **(p. 150)**

**boreal** (BOHR·ee·uhl) northern, especially a northern climate zone or forest **(p. 252)**

**boycott** agreement to refuse to buy certain goods **(p. 588)**

**break-of-bulk center** location where goods are transferred from one form of transportation to another **(p. 175)**

**buffer state** country lying between two rivals **(p. 611)**

## C

**canton** (KANT·uhn) political unit in Switzerland **(p. 405)**

**capitalism** economic system in which individuals and private corporations own most of the businesses **(p. 167)**

**capital resource** money, tools, machinery, and inventory needed to industrialize **(pp. 162, 542)**

**cardinal directions** north, south, east, and west **(p. 42)**

**cartography** (kahr·TAHG·ruh·fee) art and science of mapmaking **(p. 29)**

**cash crop** crop or animal raised to be sold **(p. 118)**

**caste system** (KAST) system in which people are placed into life-long hereditary social classes according to Hindu beliefs **(p. 590)**

**cataract** (KAT·uh·rakt) waterfall that interrupts a river **(p. 550)**

**cay** (KEE; KAY) low-lying island of coral; also spelled **key** as in Key West **(p. 303)**

**cease-fire line** political boundary established when fighting stops **(p. 605)**

**central business district** commercial center of a city or town **(p. 182)**

**central place** function of a city as the location of specialized activities and services for the surrounding area **(p. 175)**

**centrifugal force** (sen·TRIF·uh·guhl) element of disunity, such as different languages, cultures, or racial groups, that tend to divide people within a country **(p. 441)**

**centripetal force** (sen·TRIP·uh·tuhl) element, such as common language, shared history, or even a good network of transportation, that binds a nation together **(p. 441)**

**chernozem** (cher·nuh·ZYAWM) fertile black soils that cover southern areas of the Fertile Triangle of the Soviet Union **(p. 436)**

**city** center of population larger than a town or village **(p. 171)**

**climate** (CLY·muht) average of daily weather conditions over a long period of time **(p. 92)**

**climatic control** factor influencing the distribution of climates over the earth's surface **(p. 92)**

**climax community** (CLY·maks) plant community that takes over in the last phase of plant succession. *See* **plant succession (p. 99)**

**coalition** (koh·uh·LISH·uhn) group of political parties with common goals **(p. 682)**

**collective** several ejidos grouped together. *See* **ejido (p. 283)**

**collective farm** form of agricultural organization in which the farmers rent the land from the government, work it cooperatively, and earn wages and receive a share of the farm's profits **(p. 421)**

**commercial farming** type of agriculture based on growing crops or animals to sell **(p. 118)**

**commonwealth** self-governing territory belonging to another country **(p. 312)**

**commune** (KAHM·yoon) large collective farm on which officials make all decisions **(p. 630)**

**communism** (KAM·yuh·niz·uhm) another name for **authoritarian socialism (p. 167)**

**compact nation** country with a generally round or rectangular shape, having a land area not divided by large bodies of water or by the territory of other countries, and in which all points on the country's borders are about the same distance from the geographic center of the country **(p. 160)**

**compass rose** symbol that indicates direction on a map—the arms of the symbol point to north, south, east, and west on the map **(p. 42)**

**condensation** (kahn·den·SAY·shuhn) process in which gaseous water vapor changes to a liquid **(p. 82)**

**conformal map** (kuh·FAWRM·uhl) map using a projection that maintains true shape **(p. 45)**

**conservationist** (kahn·suhr·VAY·shuhn·uhst) person who works to protect natural resources and natural environments **(p. 114)**

**constitutional monarchy** (kahn·stuh·TOO·shuhn·uhl MAHN·uhr·kee) form of government in which the powers of the ruler is limited and shared with elected or appointed officials **(pp. 393, 463)**

**continent** (KAHNT·uhn·ent) one of the seven large landmasses on the earth's surface **(p. 60)**

**continental divide** line, usually along a mountain range, dividing the flow of rivers **(p. 198)**

**continental drift** theory applied to Francis Bacon's idea that the continents were joined in the past, have separated, and are still moving **(p. 67)**

**continental influence** climatic effect on areas separated from the ocean by mountains or by hundreds of miles of land **(p. 94)**

**continental shelf** edge of continent extending beneath the ocean **(p. 132)**

**continental slope** steep drop at the outer edge of the continental shelf **(p. 132)**

**contour** (KAHN·toor) changes in elevation **(p. 234)**

**contour line** line on a map that connects points of equal elevation on the earth's surface **(p. 42)**

**contract responsibility system** system in which the government leases land to each family, which decides what to plant **(p. 630)**

**cordillera** (kaurd·uhl·YER·uh) mountain system or chain **(pp. 250, 337)**

Glossary

# GLOSSARY

**core** center of the earth **(p. 62)**

**core sample** piece of rock from deep in the earth **(p. 68)**

**Coriolis force** (kor·ee·OH·les) effect produced by the earth's rotation that deflects winds to the right of their intended course in the Northern Hemisphere and to the left in the Southern Hemisphere **(p. 85)**

**cottage industry** workshops run by craftspeople in their homes **(p. 595)**

**coup d'etat** (KOOD ay·TAH) overthrow of a government **(p. 479)**

**crust** solid outermost layer of the earth **(p. 64)**

**cultivate** (KUHL·tuh·vayt) to farm **(p. 121)**

**cultural diffusion** (KUHLCH·uh·ruhl dif·YOO·zhehn) spread of certain parts of cultures from one area of the world to another **(pp. 26, 149)**

**cultural geography** study of the impact of human ideas and actions on the earth **(p. 26)**

**cultural hearth** (HAHRTH) region where colonial settlement begins and many cultural institutions and attitudes develop **(p. 368)**

**cultural landscape** imprint or effect a group of people leaves on its human habitat. *See* **human habitat (p. 26)**

**cultural pluralism** (PLUHR·uh·liz·uhm) way of life in which people share a common culture while retaining many parts of their traditional culture **(p. 217)**

**cultural region** area in which people share similar cultural characteristics; area identified by cultural characteristics **(pp. 158, 194)**

**cultural setting** an area's various cultural features **(p. 149)**

**culture** sum of what a human group acquires through living together, including language, knowledge, skills, art, literature, laws, customs, and life styles **(pp. 26, 149)**

## D

**death rate** number of people who die per 1,000 people **(p. 150)**

**deciduous** (di·SIDZH·uh·wuhs) broadleaf trees that stop growing and shed their leaves when it gets cold or dry **(p. 102)**

**deep** another term for trench. *See* **trench (p. 133)**

**deforest** to remove forests **(p. 574)**

**democracy** rule by the people **(p. 161)**

**democratic socialism** (dem·uh·KRAT·ik) economic system in which the government owns the major means of production and distribution but individuals maintain basic human rights and control over economic planning through the election of government officials **(p. 167)**

**demographer** (dih·MOG·reh·fer) scientist who studies population trends **(p. 150)**

**demographic transition** (dem·uh·GRAF·ik trans·ISH·uhn) stages of population growth **(p. 150)**

**dependency** (di·PEN·duhn·see) territory ruled by, but not part of, another nation **(p. 306)**

**depose** (di·POHZ) to remove a government leader from office **(p. 474)**

**desalinization** (dee·SAL·uh·nuh·zay·shuhn) removal of salts from seawater **(pp. 112, 496)**

**desertification** (di·zuhrt·uh·fuh·KAY·shuhn) process by which fertile land becomes desert **(p. 464)**

**détente** (day·TAHNT) gradual relaxing of tensions between nations **(p. 442)**

**developed nation** highly industrialized nation with high standard of living **(p. 162)**

**developing nation** nation that features an agricultural economy, traditional life styles, and little or no industry **(p. 166)**

**dialect** (DY·uh·lekt) variation of a language **(p. 463)**

**dictatorship** (dik·TAYT·uhr·ship) government with all power held by a single ruler or group of rulers **(pp. 161, 291)**

**distortion** (dis·TAWR·shuhn) inaccuracy **(p. 41)**

**distributary** (dis·TRIB·yuh·ter·ee) small stream that carries water away from the main stream of a river **(p. 606)**

**dome mountain** landform created as molten rock from within the earth pushes up layers of soft rock **(p. 72)**

**doubling time** number of years it will take for the population of a country to double in size if current rates of growth continue **(p. 578)**

**duty** tax on imports or exports **(p. 298)**

**dynasty** (DY·nuh·stee) succession of rulers from the same family **(p. 626)**

## E

**earthquake** sudden vibration of the earth **(p. 70)**

**economic geography** study of resources and resource use, agriculture and land use, and global trade interactions **(p. 28)**

**ecosystem** (EE·koh·sis·tuhm) another term for biome. *See* **biome (pp. 98, 606)**

**ejido** (ee·HEE·doh) Spanish term for "public land" **(p. 281)**

**elevation** (el·uh·VAY·shuhn) distance above or below sea level **(p. 60)**

**emigration** (em·uh·GRAY·shuhn) movement of people out of a country **(p. 155)**

**emir** (ih·MIR) hereditary Muslim ruler **(p. 495)**

**enclave** territory enclosed within a foreign country **(p. 478)**

**entrepôt** (AHN·truh·poh) distribution point for trade **(p. 690)**

**environment** (in·VY·rehn·mehnt) physical surroundings **(p. 25)**

**epicenter** (EHP·ih·sent·uhr) point on earth's surface directly above an earthquake **(p. 70)**

**equal-area map** map using a projection that shows relative sizes correctly **(p. 45)**

**equator** (ee·KWAY·tur) imaginary line drawn around the earth halfway between the North and South poles **(p. 30)**

**equidistant map** (ee·kweh·DIHS·tehnt) map using a projection that shows distances correctly **(p. 47)**

**equinox** (EE·kwuh·nahks) time of the year when the sun's rays strike the equator directly **(p. 92)**

**erg** large sand dune **(p. 456)**

**erosion** (i·ROH·zhuhn) gradual wearing away of the earth's surface **(p. 74)**

**escarpment** (is·KAHRP·muhnt) rock cliff **(p. 547)**

**estuary** (ES·chuh·wer·ee) water passage where the tide meets a river current **(p. 194)**

**evaporation** process by which water changes from a liquid form to a gaseous water vapor **(p. 82)**

**exotic river** (ig·ZAHT·ik) river that flows through desert area where it is least expected **(p. 457)**

## F

**factor of production** natural resource or raw material, human resource or labor, or capital resource **(p. 162)**

**fall line** place where rivers drop from the foothills to the coastal plain in small waterfalls **(p. 194)**

**fault** break in the earth's crust **(p. 68)**

**fault-block mountain** landform that develops in places where the earth's crust is broken into enormous blocklike pieces **(p. 72)**

**federal system** system in which the national government and regional, state, or local governments share the responsibilities of government and the authority to govern **(p. 160)**

**finca** (FINK·uh) plantation in El Salvador **(p. 296)**

**fjord** (fee·OOHRD) steep-sided inlet along a coastal area **(p. 384)**

**floodplain** level area made of sediments deposited along a river or stream **(p. 289)**

**folded mountain** landform created when stress on the earth's surface results in the squeezing together of rocks into a series of rounded waves that appear as great folds **(p. 72)**

**food chain** complex feeding system **(p. 137)**

**fossil fuel** energy source such as oil or coal that formed from the remains of plants and animals that died millions of years ago **(p. 115)**

**fragmented nation** country in which part of the territory is geographically separated from other parts **(p. 160)**

**free enterprise system** economic system in which business is conducted freely and with limited government intervention **(pp. 167, 219)**

**free port** place of trade where a government levies little taxes on imports and exports **(pp. 478, 690)**

**front** leading edge of an air mass **(p. 84)**

## G

**gaucho** (GOW·choh) Argentine term for a "cowhand" **(p. 373)**

**gazetteer** (gaz·uh·TIUHR) geographic index of place names **(p. 556)**

**geographer** scientist who studies the relationship between people and their environments **(p. 26)**

**geography** study of the relationship between people and their physical surroundings **(p. 25)**

**geologist** (jee·AHL·uh·juhst) scientist who specializes in the study of the earth's crust, including its different rock formations **(p. 64)**

**geopolitics** (jee·oh·PAHL·uh·tiks) study of the relationship between geography and political policy **(p. 108)**

**geothermal energy** (jee·oh·THURM·uhl) energy produced by heat from the earth's interior **(pp. 116, 706)**

**geyser** (GY·zuhr) jet of heated spring water and steam that shoots through cracks in the earth's crust **(pp. 402, 705)**

**glaciated** (GLAY·she·ayt·ed) covered by ice **(p. 196)**

**glacier** (GLAY·sher) large mass of moving ice **(p. 74)**

**glasnost** (GLAHS·nuhst) new Soviet policy, meaning "openness," that promises greater political and economic freedom **(p. 438)**

**glen** sheltered valley **(p. 384)**

**global language** language spoken by millions of people **(p. 157)**

**globe** three-dimensional model of the earth **(p. 39)**

**great circle** edge of any imaginary plane that divides the earth into two equal parts **(p. 40)**

**greenhouse effect** process in which the heat from sunlight is trapped by the lower atmosphere and continues to warm the earth **(p. 81)**

**gross national product** (GNP) dollar value of all goods and services produced in a country in a year **(p. 458)**

**guerrilla** (guh·RIL·uh) member of an organized opposition group that uses violent methods to oppose the existing government **(p. 479)**

## H

**hacienda** (hahs·ee·EN·duh) Spanish term for an estate similar to a plantation **(p. 281)**

**hammada** (huh·MAH·duh) rocky, dry plateau **(p. 456)**

**hemisphere** (HEM·eh·sfehr) half of the earth **(p. 30)**

**heterogeneous population** (het·uh·ruh·GEE·nee·uhs) population made up of people from a wide variety of backgrounds **(p. 559)**

**hill** generally rounded land that rises at least 500 feet (152 meters) and has local relief of less than 2,000 feet (610 meters) **(p. 61)**

**historical geography** study of the ways in which the relationship between people and their environments has changed over time **(p. 28)**

**homelands** land set aside by the government of South Africa as independent nations for black South Africans, but which are not recognized as nations by the rest of the world **(p. 558)**

**homogeneous population** (hoh·moh·GEE·nee·uhs) population drawn from one group **(p. 551)**

**human habitat** (HAB·eh·tat) place where a group of people lives **(p. 26)**

# GLOSSARY

**human resource**   worker **(p. 162)**

**human rights**   basic rights of all people **(p. 441)**

**humidity** (hyoo·MIHD·eht·ee)   amount of moisture in the air **(p. 82)**

**humus** (HYOO·muhs)   soil layer that consists of decayed plants and animals **(p. 109)**

**hurricane**   violent tropical storm formed over large low-pressure areas of the Gulf of Mexico and the Atlantic Ocean during summer and fall **(p. 90)**

**hypothesis** (hi·PAHTH·uh·suhs)   scientific assumption adopted as a tentative explanation of observed facts **(p. 65)**

## I

**immigration** (im·uh·GRAY·shuhn)   movement of people into a country **(p. 155)**

**indentured laborer** (in·DEN·churd)   person who agrees to work for a specified time in exchange for transportation to a new location **(p. 306)**

**Indian reserve**   areas of Canada set aside for Indians **(p. 258)**

**indigenous** (in·DIJ·uh·nuhs)   native to a region **(p. 582)**

**industrialization**   (in·duhs·tree·uh·luh·ZAY·shuhn) replacement of human power by machine power as the major source of labor **(p. 172)**

**insolation** (in·soh·LAY·suhn)   process by which sunlight warms the earth **(p. 80)**

**international city**   city governed by an international council **(p. 489)**

**isthmus** (IS·muhs)   narrow piece of land that connects two landmasses **(p. 274)**

## J

**jet stream**   bands of swiftly moving, high-altitude winds **(p. 88)**

**jungle**   thick growth of plants in a tropical rain forest **(p. 512)**

## K

**key**   another name for the map legend. *See* **legend, cay (p. 41)**

**kibbutz** (kib·OOTS)   large collective farm in Israel **(p. 489)**

## L

**ladino** (luh·DEE·noh)   Guatemalan term for mestizos; *See* **mestizo (p. 290)**

**land bridge**   small isthmus connecting two larger landmasses **(p. 287)**

**landfill**   site for the disposal of garbage **(p. 156)**

**landform**   shape on the earth's surface **(p. 59)**

**land reform**   program designed to allow more people to own land **(p. 281)**

**Landsat**   satellite that circles the earth and transmits images to computers at receiving stations **(p. 49)**

**language family**   group of languages with common origins **(p. 157)**

**lava** (LAHV·uh)   molten rock **(p. 71)**

**leach**   wash out nutrients from the soil **(pp. 289, 368)**

**leeward**   side of a mountain facing away from the wind **(p. 84)**

**legend**   key that explains the meaning of symbols and colors used on a map **(p. 41)**

**life expectancy**   average number of years a person is expected to live **(p. 150)**

**line of latitude** (LAT·uh·tood)   another name for parallel. *See* **parallel (p. 31)**

**line of longitude** (LAHN·jeh·tood)   another name for meridian. *See* **meridian (p. 31)**

**literacy rate** (LIHT·uh·ruh·see)   percentage of people who can read and write **(p. 166)**

**literate** (LIHT·uh·ruht)   able to read and write **(p. 291)**

**local language**   language spoken by relatively small numbers of people **(p. 157)**

**local relief**   difference in elevation between the highest and lowest points in an area **(p. 60)**

**locational advantage**   benefit of location **(p. 230)**

**loch** (LAHK)   long lake in the Scottish Highlands **(p. 384)**

**loess** (LES) fine soil deposited by wind **(pp. 414, 622)**

## M

**malnutrition** (mal·noo·TRISH·uhn)   lack of a proper diet **(p. 122)**

**mandarin** (MAN·duh·ruhn)   Chinese official during imperial times **(p. 629)**

**mangrove forest**   marshy coastal lands filled with mangrove trees that protect the coast from erosion and are breeding grounds for marine life **(p. 606)**

**mantle**   material that lies directly above the earth's liquid outer core **(p. 62)**

**map**   flat representation of the earth **(p. 41)**

**map projection**   method by which the features of the earth's curved surface are transferred onto a flat map **(p. 42)**

**map scale**   line or bar used to measure distances on a map **(p. 42)**

**marine biologist**   scientist who studies ocean plants and animals **(p. 136)**

**marine influence**   climatic effect on lands swept by winds from the ocean **(p. 94)**

**marsupial** (mahr·SOO·pee·uhl)   animal that raises its young in a pouch **(p. 695)**

**martial law** (MAHR·shuhl)   rule imposed by the military **(p. 339)**

**material culture**   all the physical objects that people make, including buildings, clothing, tools, paintings, and other artifacts **(p. 149)**

**megalopolis** (meg·uh·LAHP·oh·luhs)   supercity consisting of several cities that have grown together; continuous urban corridor **(pp. 214, 225)**

**mercenary** (MUHRS·uhn·er·ee)   soldier paid to serve in the army of another country **(p. 611)**

**meridian** (meh·RIHD·ee·ehn) imaginary line drawn on the earth from pole to pole **(p. 31)**

**mesa** (MAY·suh)  elevated plateau with steep sides (**p. 271**)

**mestizo** (meh·STEE·zoh)  person of mixed Spanish and Indian ancestry (**p. 277**)

**metropolitan area** (me·truh·PAHL·uht·uhn) place that includes both the city proper and the dependent smaller cities and suburbs nearby (**p. 182**)

**microclimate**  characteristics of temperature and rainfall that are locally determined, especially on mountains (**p. 203**)

**microstate**  nation so small that it can be walked across in a single day (**p. 159**)

**migration** (my·GRAY·shuhn)  movement of people from place to place (**p. 155**)

**mineral**  inorganic substance found in the earth's crust (**p. 107**)

**mistral** (MIS·truhl)  cold, dry wind that brings blasts of cold air down the Rhône River Valley to southern France (**p. 385**)

**mixed economy**  economy that combines a variety of methods to produce, distribute, and exchange goods and services (**p. 167**)

**molten material** (MOHLT·uhn)  rocks and stones melted by heat (**p. 62**)

**monotheism** (MAHN·uh·thee·iz·uhm)  belief in only one God (**p. 459**)

**monsoon** (mahn·SOON)  seasonal winds named for the direction from which they blow or the season in which they occur, and which determine the climate of a region such as the Indian subcontinent (**p. 574**)

**montane** (mahn·TAYN)  rain forest on rainy slopes of the Andes (**p. 325**)

**moor**  rainy, windswept upland in northern and western Great Britain (**p. 386**)

**moraine** (muh·RAYN)  combination of earth and stone left by glaciers as they melted and retreated (**p. 413**)

**mountain**  landform distinguished by steep slopes, local relief of at least 2,000 feet (610 meters), and high elevation (**p. 61**)

**movement**  interaction of humans with each other (**p. 33**)

**mulatto** (moo·LAT·oh)  person of mixed black and European ancestry (**p. 295**)

**multinational state**  country that includes many different nationalities (**p. 439**)

**multispectral scanner** (muhl·tee·SPEC·trahl) instrument that electronically records observations from space and sends them to ground stations where computers translate the data into electronic images (**p. 49**)

## N

**nationalism**  sense of national identity, usually reinforced by a common language, history, culture, and patriotic displays (**p. 390**)

**nationalized industry**  industry owned by the government (**p. 423**)

**national language**  language adopted by countries to promote unity and ease of communication among the multilingual population (**p. 673**)

**native peoples**  Canada's first inhabitants (**p. 258**)

**natural landscape**  another name for physical setting. *See* **physical setting** (**p. 59**)

**natural resource**  naturally occurring material that can be used to produce goods and services (**p. 107**)

**neutral** (NOO·truhl)  not taking sides (**p. 405**)

**nodule** (NAHJ·ooul)  mineral occurring in a potato-sized lump on the ocean floor (**p. 136**)

**nomad** (NOH·mad)  person who is always on the move hunting game and gathering food that grows wild (**p. 171**)

**nonaligned nation** (nahn·uhl·EYEND)  nation that refuses to take sides in the political struggles between the Communist and non-Communist systems (**p. 592**)

**nonmaterial culture**  ideas of a society expressed in its language, values, and political and economic systems (**p. 149**)

**nonrenewable resource** (nahn·ri·NOO·uh·buhl) material that is almost impossible to replace so that its supply diminishes with each use (**p. 109**)

## O

**oasis** (oh·AY·suhs)  fertile area surrounded by desert (**p. 354**)

**ocean acoustic tomography** (uh·KOO·stik toh·MAHG·reh·fee)  technique that provides a three-dimensional image of water movement (**p. 130**)

**ocean current**  riverlike stream that circulates ocean waters (**p. 129**)

**oceanic ridge** (oh·shee·AN·ik)  range of submarine mountains (**p. 132**)

**oceanographer** (oh·shuh·NAHG·ruh·fuhr) scientist who studies the ocean (**p. 130**)

**one-crop economy**  economy that relies on the production of one or a few goods (**p. 161**)

**overfish**  to take more fish from the sea than can be naturally replaced (**p. 140**)

**overpopulate**  supporting too many people with too few resources (**p. 306**)

## P

**paddy**  flooded field well suited for growing rice (**p. 669**)

**paleomagnetism** (pay·lee·oh·MAG·neh·tihz·ehm) study of the ancient patterns of magnetism recorded in rocks (**p. 68**)

**pampa** (PAM·puh)  Spanish word for "grassy plain" (**p. 370**)

**parallel**  imaginary line parallel to the equator that measures latitude (**p. 31**)

**paramos** (PAH·rah·mohs)  treeless upland plain in South America (**p. 351**)

**parent material**  soil layer that consists of solid rock (**p. 109**)

Glossary

# GLOSSARY

**pass** routeway through rugged mountains **(p. 573)**

**passive resistance** (PAS·iv ri·ZIS·tuhnts) nonviolent protest **(p. 588)**

**peninsula** (puh·NIN·suh·luh) narrow piece of land surrounded on three sides by water **(p. 250)**

**per capita gross national product** measure of wealth obtained by dividing total dollar value of all goods and services produced in a country by the number of people living in that country **(p. 166)**

**permafrost** (PUHR·muh·frawst) permanently frozen subsoil **(p. 435)**

**petrochemical** (pe·troh·KEM·i·kuhl) oil-based material used to manufacture plastics, synthetic fibers, fertilizers, insecticides, and pesticides **(p. 115)**

**petroleum** (puh·TROH·lee·uhm) liquid fossil fuel **(p. 115)**

**physical geography** study of the physical features and changes of the earth's surface **(p. 26)**

**physical region** area identified by shapes on the earth's surface **(p. 193)**

**physical setting** combination of physical features of a place **(p. 59)**

**physiological density** (fihz·ee·uh·LAHJ·ih·kuhl) number of people per square mile (square kilometer) of cultivated land **(pp. 154, 637)**

**place** physical and cultural aspects of a location **(p. 32)**

**plain** landform characterized by nearly level or gently rolling land and with little slope and low local relief **(p. 60)**

**plane** flat surface that divides the earth into two equal parts **(p. 40)**

**planet** object or body composed of various solids and gases that circles a star **(p. 25)**

**plantation** (plan·TAY·shuhn) very large farm **(pp. 120, 326)**

**plant community** varieties of plants existing in the same location **(p. 98)**

**plant succession** (suhk·SESH·uhn) process by which one type of vegetation replaces another **(p. 99)**

**plateau** (pla·TOH) generally flat area that rises far above surrounding land on at least one side and has little slope, high elevation, and low local relief **(p. 60)**

**plate tectonics** (tek·TON·iks) theory that states that the earth's rigid outer crust—including both the crust and parts of the upper mantle—is not continuously solid but is broken into huge slabs or plates **(p. 68)**

**playa** (PLY·uh) shallow desert lake that grows and shrinks depending on rainfall **(p. 696)**

**polder** (POHL·duhr) drained lands that once lay beneath the sea **(p. 404)**

**political geography** study of the political organization of areas **(p. 28)**

**polytheism** (PAHL·i·thee·iz·uhm) belief in many gods **(p. 590)**

**population** number of people living on the earth **(p. 150)**

**population density** number of people per square mile (or per square kilometer) of a given land area **(p. 150)**

**precipitation** (pri·sip·uh·TAY·shuhn) condensation in the form of rain, snow, sleet, or hail **(p. 82)**

**prehistory** time before written records were kept **(p. 459)**

**prevailing wind** (pri·VAY·ling) continuous air flow between global pressure belts **(p. 85)**

**primary source** any firsthand or eyewitness account **(p. 257)**

**primate city** (PRY·mayt) a city so much larger than any other city that it dominates an area **(p. 179)**

**prime meridian** line passing through Greenwich, England, that was accepted by international agreement as 0° longitude **(p. 31)**

**prime minister** chief public official who runs the affairs of government **(p. 258)**

## R

**race** group of people having similar physical traits **(p. 555)**

**rate of natural increase** difference between the birth rate and the death rate **(p. 150)**

**recycling** process by which products that have been used and discarded can be reused **(p. 114)**

**reforestation** (ree·fawr·uh·STAY·shuhn) process of planting new trees on lands that were once covered by forests **(p. 224)**

**region** unit of the earth's surface that has one or more characteristics that set it apart from other regions of the world **(p. 33)**

**reincarnation** (ree·in·kahr·NAY·shuhn) belief that souls go through a series of births, deaths, and rebirths **(p. 592)**

**relationships within places** interactions between people and their environments **(p. 33)**

**relative humidity** at a given temperature, the ratio of water vapor in the air to the maximum amount of water vapor the air could hold—stated as a percentage **(p. 82)**

**relative location** position of places in relation to other places on the earth **(p. 32)**

**relief** (ri·LEEF) elevations of the landforms illustrated on a map **(p. 42)**

**religion** set of beliefs, especially in a supreme being or beings **(p. 158)**

**remote sensing** (ri·MOHT) gathering and recording of information through aerial photographs and satellite images **(p. 48)**

**renewable resource** material replaced naturally and which can be used over and over again **(p. 109)**

**reservation** (rez·uhr·VAY·shuhn) land that the United States government set aside for Indians **(p. 209)**

**resource** material that people use to meet basic needs and wants **(p. 107)**

**Richter scale** (RIK·tuhr) technical device that measures the intensity of earthquakes **(p. 71)**

**rift** wide crack at the crest of an oceanic ridge **(p. 132)**

**rift valley** long, narrow depression along a fault **(p. 272)**

**rotate** (ROH·tayt) to spin on an axis **(p. 30)**

**rural area** (ROOR·uhl) term, borrowed from the Latin word for "countryside," for places outside cities **(p. 179)**

## S

**safari** (suh·FAWR·ee) Swahili word for "journey" **(p. 509)**

**salinity** (say·LIN·uht·ee) salt content **(p. 136)**

**samurai** (SAM·uh·ry) Japanese warrior **(p. 644)**

**satellite nation** (SAT·uhl·eyet) nation controlled by a more powerful nation **(p. 419)**

**savanna** (suh·VAN·uh) grassland found in tropical wet-and-dry climates **(p. 102)**

**secede** (si·SEED) to withdraw **(pp. 256, 531)**

**sediment** (SED·uh·muhnt) solid deposited by water **(p. 68)**

**seismic wave** (SYS·mik) vibration of the earth **(p. 62)**

**selva** (SEL·vuh) rain forest in Amazon Basin **(p. 325)**

**separatism** (SEP·uh·ruht·iz·uhm) breaking away from the current government to form a new national government **(p. 592)**

**service area** area around the city for which the city provides services **(p. 175)**

**shield** area of exposed ancient rock **(p. 196)**

**shogun** (SHOH·guhn) Japanese military leader who ruled the country in the name of the emperor **(p. 644)**

**sierra** (see·ER·uh) Spanish term for "mountain range" **(p. 271)**

**silt** moist soil carried as sediment in a river's waters **(p. 472)**

**sirocco** (suh·RAHK·oh) hot wind that brings dry and dusty air from North Africa's deserts **(p. 385)**

**site** physical features of the place that a city occupies **(p. 172)**

**situation** a city's relative location **(p. 173)**

**slash-and-burn agriculture** type of farming that involves cutting and burning trees and brush to clear and fertilize the soil **(p. 120)**

**slope** slant of the land **(p. 60)**

**snow line** elevation above which snow and ice lie permanently on the ground **(p. 103)**

**social geography** study of interrelationships among groups and communities **(p. 28)**

**socialism** (SOH·shuh·liz·uhm) economic system in which the government owns or controls the major means of production **(p. 167)**

**social legislation** government programs designed to help people **(p. 361)**

**society** (suh·SY·uht·ee) group of people who share traditions, institutions, activities, and interests **(p. 26)**

**solar system** star, such as the sun, and the planets and related bodies, such as asteroids, that revolve around it **(p. 25)**

**solstice** (SAWL·stuhs) time of year when the earth's poles reach their maximum tilt toward or away from the sun **(p. 92)**

**sonar** (SOH·nar) equipment that uses sound waves to detect underwater objects **(p. 67)**

**soviet** (SOHV·ee·et) council of Communist party members **(p. 441)**

**spatial distribution of population** (SPAY·shul) pattern of where people live on the earth **(p. 150)**

**spatial relationship** distribution pattern on the earth **(p. 159)**

**specialization of labor** (spesh·uh·luh·ZAY·shuhn) division of tasks among workers **(p. 172)**

**staple crop** main food crop **(p. 593)**

**state farm** form of agricultural organization operated by the government in which workers receive wages and the government keeps the profits **(pp. 311, 421)**

**steppe** (STEP) natural flat grasslands, especially in the southern Soviet Union **(pp. 102, 436)**

**stereoplotter** viewing instrument that gives a more accurate three-dimensional view of the earth shown in aerial photos **(p. 49)**

**stereoscope** instrument that converts a pair of overlapping aerial photos into a single three-dimensional view of the area shown **(p. 48)**

**strait** (STRAYT) narrow waterway linking larger bodies of water **(pp. 128, 483)**

**stratosphere** (STRAT·uh·sfir) upper atmosphere **(p. 80)**

**subcontinent** landmass smaller than a continent but still of great size **(p. 571)**

**subregion** smaller unit of a region **(pp. 194, 453)**

**subsidy** (SUHB·suhd·ee) payment made to farmer to keep food costs low **(p. 283)**

**subsistence farmer** (suhb·SIS·tuhns) farmer who produces only enough food for family members **(p. 281)**

**subsistence farming** type of agriculture in which farmers raise only enough food to feed themselves and their families **(p. 118)**

**suburb** (SUHB·uhrb) community just outside a city **(p. 179)**

**sultan** (SULT·uhn) hereditary Muslim leader of state **(pp. 484, 681)**

**summit** highest point of a mountain **(p. 61)**

**Sun Belt** area made up of warm-weather southern and southwestern states **(p. 215)**

Glossary

# GLOSSARY

## T

**taiga** (TY·guh) hardy needleleaf forests that cover areas having a subarctic climate **(p. 436)**

**temperature** measure of heat and cold **(p. 80)**

**territorial limit** (TER·uh·tohr·ee·uhl) government claim to an area of the ocean **(p. 138)**

**theocracy** (thee·AWK·ruh·see) government led by a religious leader or leaders **(p. 463)**

**theory** (THE·uh·ree) idea for explaining something not proven **(p. 65)**

**tidal bore** condition that exists when a bay narrows inland, causing tides to pile up a gigantic wall of water **(p. 131)**

**tide** regular rise and fall of the ocean **(p. 131)**

**tierra helada** (tee·ER·uh huh·LAHD·uh) frozen land where snow permanently covers the ground **(p. 338)**

**topography** (tuh·PAHG·ruh·fee) shapes of the land and the bodies of water in a given location **(p. 28)**

**tornado** (tawr·NAYD·oh) violent storm consisting of a twisting, funnel-shaped cloud with winds between 300 and 500 miles (480 and 800 kilometers) per hour **(p. 90)**

**trade surplus** situation occurring when the value of exports is greater than the value of imports **(p. 533)**

**traditional economy** economy based on the customs, habits, laws, and religious beliefs that were developed long ago **(p. 167)**

**transmigration** (trans·my·GRAY·shuhn) voluntary migration of people to less-populated areas **(p. 686)**

**transportation hub** center where road, rail, river, or air routes cross **(p. 175)**

**tree line** elevation beyond which it is too cold for trees to grow **(pp. 103, 252)**

**trench** V-shaped valley that forms the deepest part of the ocean floor **(p. 133)**

**tribe** group of people who share a common language and culture **(p. 516)**

**tributary** (TRIB·yuh·ter·ee) stream or river flowing into a larger river **(p. 196)**

**tropical rain forest** vast broadleaf evergreen forest **(p. 512)**

**tropics** area between the Tropic of Cancer (23.5° N) and the Tropic of Capricorn (23.5° S); generally characterized by warm climates **(p. 325)**

**truck farming** type of agriculture in which farmers grow fresh fruits and vegetables for sale in the city **(p. 224)**

**trust territory** territory supervised by another nation until it can become self-governing **(p. 711)**

**tsar** (ZAHR) Russian emperor **(p. 437)**

**tsunami** (suh·NAHM·ee) giant ocean wave **(p. 642)**

**tundra** (TUN·druh) cold deserts found where summers last three months or less and it is too cold for trees and most other plants to live **(p. 103)**

**twin cities** pair of cities located on facing banks of a river **(p. 235)**

**typhoon** (ty·FOON) violent tropical storm that forms over large low-pressure areas of the Pacific Ocean **(pp. 90, 642)**

## U

**ujamaa** (oo·jah·MUH) Swahili word for "working together for the good of all" that refers to a government program in Tanzania **(p. 552)**

**unitary system** (YOO·nuh·tehr·ee) system in which a central government has the complete authority to govern **(p. 160)**

**untouchable** in Hindu belief, a person born without a caste **(p. 590)**

**urban area** (UHR·buhn) towns and cities **(p. 179)**

**urban geography** study of the locations of cities, the services cities provide, and the movements of goods and people to and from cities **(p. 29)**

**urbanization** (uhr·buh·nuh·ZAY·shuhn) large-scale movement of people from rural to urban areas **(p. 179)**

## V

**volcano** (vahl·KAY·noh) mountain created by layers of lava that solidify after an eruption; also called **volcanic mountain (pp. 71, 73)**

**voodoo** type of religion based on West African practices **(p. 311)**

## W

**wadi** (WAHD·ee) dry valley with steep sides and narrow floor cut through a plateau **(p. 456)**

**water cycle** process in which water is changed from a liquid to a gaseous water vapor and back to a liquid **(p. 81)**

**water table** level of underground water supply **(pp. 113, 489)**

**weather** condition of the atmosphere for a short period of time in a specific area **(p. 80)**

**weathering** slow process that breaks rocks down into smaller and smaller pieces **(p. 73)**

**wind** movement that occurs when air moves from high-pressure to low-pressure areas **(p. 85)**

**windward** side of a mountain facing the wind **(p. 84)**

## Y

**yield** (YEELD) amount grown per acre or hectare **(p. 121)**

**yunga** (YUHNG·uh) valley in the eastern cordillera of Bolivia **(p. 355)**

## Z

**zero population growth** point at which the birth rate and the death rate are about equal **(p. 150)**

**zone of transition** area lying between cultures **(p. 479)**

## Abbreviation Guide

Where appropriate, the following abbreviations have been used in the Index.

Index

# INDEX

Index

# INDEX

# INDEX

Index

Index

# INDEX

Index

*(Acknowledgments continued from page iv)*

*East,* Revised Edition, by Carleton S. Coon. Copyright 1951, © 1958 by Henry Holt and Company, Inc. *Holt, Rinehart and Winston, Inc.:* From p. 17 in *The Australians: How They Live and Work* by Nancy Learmonth. © 1973 by Nancy Learmonth. *Houghton Mifflin Company:* From pp. 326–327 in *The Old Patagonian Express* by Paul Theroux. Copyright © 1979 by Cape Cod Scriveners Company. *Jean Kistler Kendall:* From pp. 22–23 in *The Story of India* by Jean Bothwell. Published by Harcourt Brace Jovanovich, Inc., 1952. *Lexington Books, a division of D. C. Heath & Company, Lexington, MA:* From "Lebanon, Syria, Jordan and Iraq" by Albert H. Hourani in *The Middle East: Oil, Conflict & Hope,* Volume X, Critical Choices for Americans (Titled: "The Middle East: Oil, Conflict and Hope"), edited by A. L. Udovitch. Copyright © 1976 by The Third Century Corporation. *Library of Congress:* From p. 46 in *Laos: a country study* by Donald P. Whitaker et al. Copyright © 1979 by The American University. *Little, Brown and Company:* From *God's Country and Mine: A Declaration of Love Spiced With a Few Harsh Words* by Jacques Barzun. From *Memoirs, 1950–1963,* Volume II by George F. Kennan. *McIntosh & Otis, Inc.:* From *Their Blood Is Strong* by John Steinbeck. Copyright © 1938 by John Steinbeck. Published by Simon J. Lubin Society of California, Inc. *Natalia D. Murray:* From pp. 439–440 in *Paris Journal, 1944–1965* by Janet Flanner (Genêt), edited by William Shawn. Published by Atheneum Publishers, 1965. *National Geographic Society:* From pp. 152–167 in "Africa's Sahel: The Stricken Land" by William S. Ellis in *National Geographic,* Volume 172, No. 2, August 1987. *Oxford University Press, Inc.:* From *The Sea Around Us,* Revised Edition by Rachel L. Carson. Copyright © 1950, 1951, 1961 by Rachel L. Carson, renewed 1979 by Roger Christie. *Rand McNally & Company:* Mileage chart from p. 105 in *Rand McNally Road Atlas.* Copyright © 1988 by Rand McNally & Company, R. L. 88-S-9. *Random House, Inc.:* From p. 6 in *Out of Africa* by Isak Dinesen. Copyright 1937, 1938 by Random House, Inc., copyright renewed 1965 by Rungstedlundfonden. *Charles Scribner's Sons, an imprint of Macmillan Publishing Company:* From pp. 112–113 in *In Morocco* by Edith Wharton. Copyright 1919, 1920 by Charles Scribner's Sons; copyright renewed. *Thomas & Hudson, Ltd.:* From p. 79 in *The Ottoman Impact on Europe* by Paul Coles. Copyright © © 1968 by P. H. Coles and Thames and Hudson, London. *The University of Michigan Press:* From p. 209 in *Africa to 1875: A Modern History* by Robin Hallett, Published by The University of Michigan Press, 1970. *Verso Editions and Editorial Argos Vergara, S. A.:* From p. 23 in *I, Rigoberta Menchú: An Indian Woman in Guatemala,* edited and introduced by Elisabeth Burgos-Debray, translated by Ann Wright. © 1984 by Verso Editions. Originally published in Spain under the title *Me Llamo Rigoberta Menchú Y Así Me Nació La Corciencia. Viking Penguin Inc.:* From p. vii in *Diary of the Cuban Revolution* by Carlos Franqui. Copyright © 1976 by Editions de Seuil. English-language translation copyright © 1980 by Viking Penguin. All rights reserved. *The Frank Lloyd Wright Foundation:* From *The Living City* by Frank Lloyd Wright. Copyright © 1958 by The Frank Lloyd Wright Foundation.

**PICTURE CREDITS:** The positions of photographs and illustrations are indicated by the following abbreviations: (t) top, (b) bottom, (l) left, (r) right, (c) center.

**Cover:** METEOSAT image suplied by the European Space Agency; (tl), Selwyn Tait/Time Magazine: (tr), Bob Long/The Stock Shop; (cl), Anthony Edgeworth/The Stock Market; (c), Robert Frerck/Odyssey Productions; (cr), Jaroslav Kubec/The Stock Market; (b) Steve Vidler/Leo de Wys, Inc.

**FRONTPIECES:** Page ii, David Muench/H. Armstrong Roberts, Inc.; v, Don Rutledge/Tom Stack & Assoc.; vi, Sorlie/H. Armstrong Roberts, Inc.; vii, Richard Steedman/The Stock Market; viii, Casimir/Leo de Wys, Inc.; ix, David Hiser/Photographers Aspen; x, Luis Villota/The Stock Market; xi, Gala/Telephoto; xii, Four By Five; xiii, Fujihira/Monkmeyer Press Photo Service; xiv, Antje Gunnar/FPG; xv(t), Carl Purcell/Words and Pictures; xv (b), Peter Hendrie/The Image Bank.

**UNIT 1:** Page 22(tl), The Granger Collection; 22(tr), R. Hamilton Smith/Frozen Images; 22(bl), The Granger Collection; 22(br), Shostal Assoc.; 23(l), Don Rutledge/Tom Stack & Assoc.; 23(r), Russ Kinne/Comstock; 24, NASA; 27, The Granger Collection; 30, The Granger Collection; 33, Don Rutledge/Tom Stack & Assoc.; 38, Historical Pictures Service; 40, Richard Laird/FPG; 41, © 1987 Universal Press Syndicate; 42, Shostal Assoc.; 43, Douglas Waugh/Peter Arnold, Inc.; 48, Photri; 49, EOSAT; 51, R. Hamilton Smith/Frozen Images.

**Index**

6(tr), Everett Johnson/Leo de Wys, Inc.; 56(bl), Holton Collection/Four By Five; 56(br), Grant Heilman Photography; ...ASA; 58, Michael Collier/Stock, Boston; 65, The Granger Collection; 68, Dr. David Schwimmer/Bruce Coleman, ...Photri; 74, Gene Ahrens/Shostal Assoc.; 78, NASA; 84, Robert H. Glaze/Artstreet; 89, Sorlie/H. Armstrong ...l, NOAA from Science Photo Library/Photo Researchers; 92, Brent Jones; 94, J. Beckner/Shostal Assoc.; 99, ...ocki Stock Photo; 103, Karl Kummels/Shostal Assoc.; 106, T.J. Florian/Nawrocki Stock Photo; 108, Werner ...Luce/Tom Stack & Assoc.; 114, David Aronson/Stock, Boston; 115, Kenneth Garrett/Woodfin Camp & ...Photography; 121, Holton Collection/Four by Five; 122, Wernher Krutein/Photovault; 126, Photri; 129, ...139, Andre Fatras/The Image Works; 141, J.A. Fernandez/Woodfin Camp & Assoc.

...Stock Market; 146(bl), Michael J. Johnson/Valan Photos; 146(br), Bob Daemrich/Stock, Boston; 147(l), ...nk; 148, Jehangir Gazdar/Woodfin Camp & Assoc.; 151, The Granger Collection; 154, U.N. Fund for ...he Stock Market; 160, Paul Harper/West Stock; 162, Michael J. Johnson/Valan Photos; 166, Bill ...R. Krubner/H. Armstrong Roberts, Inc.; 175, DPI; 177, Bob Daemrich/Stock, Boston.

...o Strauss/Woodfin Camp & Assoc.; 190(bl), Malak/Shostal Assoc.; 190(br), Nashua River Watershed Assoc.; ...om Click/Chicago; 192, Ed Cooper; 196, David Muench/H. Armstrong Roberts, Inc.; 199, Ann & Myron ...Inc.; 208, J. Messerschmidt/H. Armstrong Roberts, Inc.; 211, Brian Seed from Click/Chicago; 216, Bob ...Stockhouse; 222, P. Buddle/H. Armstrong Roberts, Inc.; 226, John Marmaras/Woodfin Camp & Assoc.; 229, Philip ...avid R. Frazier; 236, Robert Frerck/Odyssey Productions; 238, Bob Strauss/Woodfin Camp & Assoc.; 244, William A. ...stal Assoc.; 251, Shostal Assoc.; 252, Casimir/Leo de Wys, Inc.; 254, Winston Fraser; 261, Malak/Shostal Assoc.; 262, Hal ...om Stack & Assoc.

...(tr), James P. Rowan/Hillstrom Stock Photo; 268(bl), W. Bayer/Bruce Coleman, Inc.; 268(br), Robert Frerck/Odyssey Productions; ...spen; 269(r), Kathy Sloane/Light Images; 270, K. Reinhard/FPG; 272, Robert Frerck/Odyssey Productions; 276, Mark Godfrey/Archive; ...c.; 281, David Hiser/Photographers Aspen; 282, Robert Frerck/Odyssey Productions; 286, J.Y. Rabeuf/The Image Works; 288, Larry ...orge Archer/DPI; 292, Kevin P. Gale/Taurus Photos; 293, Eugene Gordon; 294, William Floyd Holdman/Royce Bair & Assoc.; 295, Alon ...Assoc.; 296, Bob Nickelsberg/Woodfin Camp & Assoc.; 298, Joe Viesti; 299, Instituto Costarricense de Turismo; 302, Wendell Metzen/H. ...308(t), Steve Smith/Wheeler Pictures; 308(b), Robert Frerck/Odyssey Productions; 310, H. Armstrong Roberts, Inc.; 313, Richard Steedman/The ...mes P. Rowan/Hillstrom Stock Photo; 315, Adam Woolfitt/Woodfin Camp & Assoc.

...Joe Viesti; 320(tr), Bob Long/The Stock Shop; 320(bl), Karl Kummels/Shostal Assoc.; 320(br), Shostal Assoc.; 321(l), Luis Villota/The Stock Market; 321(r), ...ck/Odyssey Productions; 322, Robert Frerck/Odyssey Productions; 324, Thomas S. England; 328, Victor Englebert; 330, Shostal Assoc.; 331, Karl ...Shostal Assoc.; 336, Randa Bishop/After-Image; 339, Bob Long/The Stock Shop; 340, Anthony Scullion/Valan Photos; 342, Hugh Rogers/Monkmeyer Press Photo ...; 343, Cameramann International; 344(t), Hubertus Kanus/Shostal Assoc.; 344(b), W. King/FPG; 346, Index/Stock International; 350, Cameramann International; 353, ...Villota/The Stock Market; 354, Susanna Burton/Horizon; 356(l), Robert Holland; 356(r), Robert Holland; 357, U.S. Dept. of Education; 358, Luis Villota/The Stock ...Market; 359, Loren McIntyre; 364, Karl Kummels/Shostal Assoc.; 367, FPG; 369, Nicholas DeVore III/Bruce Coleman, Inc.; 370, Luis Villota/The Stock Market; 372, Joe Viesti; 373, Joe Viesti; 375, Luis Villota/The Stock Market.

**UNIT 7:** 380(tl), Jaroslav Kubec/The Stock Market; 380(tr), Fred W. Henstridge; 380(bl), Shostal Assoc.; 380(br), Photri; 381(l), Gala/Telephoto; 381(r), Shostal Assoc. 382, Gala/Telephoto; 384, J. Messerschmidt/The Stock Market; 388, Photri; 389(l), Photri; 389(r), Photri; 392, Dallas & John Heaton from Click/Chicago; 393, John Bryson/Photo Researchers; 395, Photri; 396, Topham/The Image Works; 399, Gala/Telephoto; 400, Cameramann International; 403, Randall Hyman/Stock, Boston; 405, Joy Spurr/Bruce Coleman, Inc.; 409, HBJ Photo; 412, Dallas & John Heaton from Click/Chicago; 415, Shostal Assoc.; 416, Cameramann International; 418, Jaroslav Kubec/The Stock Market; 420, Photri; 423, Fred W. Henstridge; 424, Chuck Fishman/Woodfin Camp & Assoc.; 425, Cameramann International; 426, Vera Bradshaw/Hillstrom Stock Photo; 430, Steve Vidler/Nawrocki Stock Photo; 433, Shostal Assoc.; 436, Photri; 439, Anthony Edgeworth/The Stock Market; 440, Shostal Assoc.; 441, M. Koene/H. Armstrong Roberts, Inc.; 444, Martin Gastelan/Bruce Coleman, Inc.

**UNIT 8:** 450(tl), Michael Coyne/Black Star; 450(tr), Diane M. Love/Stock, Boston; 450(bl), Shostal Assoc.; 450(br), Lee Boltin; 451(l), Four By Five; 451(r), Steve Vidler/Four By Five; 452, Baer, ZEFA/H. Armstrong Roberts, Inc.; 455, Gerald Clyde/FPG; 458, Victor Englebert; 460, Manley Photo/Shostal Assoc.; 461(t), Lee Boltin; 461(b), Lee Boltin; 463, Steve Vidler/Leo de Wys, Inc.; 464, Tony Howarth/Woodfin Camp & Assoc.; 468, Richard Steedman/The Stock Market; 470, Richard Steedman/The Stock Market; 471, Steve Vidler/Nawrocki Stock Photo; 472, Marcus Brooke/FPG; 474, Derek Bayes/Photri; 475, James R. Holland/Stock, Boston; 476, EOSAT; 477, Shostal Assoc.; 482, Shostal Assoc.; 485, Berlitz from Click/Chicago; 488, Four By Five; 489, Cameramann International; 492, Robert Azzi/Woodfin Camp & Assoc.; 493, Diane M. Love/Stock, Boston; 494, W. Eastep/The Stock Market; 498, Herbert Lanks/Shostal Assoc.; 499, Michael Coyne/Black Star; 500, Steve McCurry/Magnum Photos.

**UNIT 9:** 506(tl), George Holton/Photo Researchers; 506(tr), Bruno Barbey/Magnum Photos; 506(bl), Marc & Evelyne Bernheim/Woodfin Camp & Assoc.; 506(br), Travelpix/FPG; 507(l), Fujihira/Monkmeyer Press Photo Service; 507(r), Selwyn Tait/Time Magazine; 508, H. Schwarz, Bildagentur Mauritius/The Stock Shop; 513, Bruno Barbey/Magnum Photos; 514, Marc & Evelyne Bernheim/Woodfin Camp & Assoc.; 516, Lee Boltin; 517, George Holton/Photo Researchers; 520, Dieter Blum/Peter Arnold, Inc.; 523, Peter Davis/Black Star; 526, Richard Saunders/Leo de Wys, Inc.; 529, Owen Franken/Stock, Boston; 531, Marc & Evelyne Bernheim/Woodfin Camp & Assoc.; 532, Shostal Assoc.; 533, Abbas/Magnum Photos; 534, Marvin E. Newman/The Image Bank; 536, M. Huet/Hoa-Qui; 537, Bruno Barbey/Magnum Photos; 539, Steele Perkins/Magnum Photos; 541, Jason Laure/Nawrocki Stock Photo; 542, Fujihira/Monkmeyer Press Photo Service; 543, Marc & Evelyne Bernheim/Woodfin Camp & Assoc.; 546, Stephen J. Krasemann/Valan Photos; 549, Robert Frerck/Odyssey Productions; 550, Brian Gustafson; 551, Robert Caputo/Stock, Boston; 553, James P. Rowan/The Marilyn Gartman Agency; 554, Robert Caputo/Stock, Boston; 558, Travelpix/FPG; 560, Gideon Mendel/Magnum Photos; 561(t), Louise Gubb/JB Pictures; 561(b), Cameramann International; 562, R. Nolan/Leo de Wys, Inc.

**UNIT 10:** 568(tl), Shostal Assoc.; 568(tr), Chad Ehlers/International Stock Photography; 568(bl), Robert Frerck/Odyssey Productions; 568(br), Bruno Barbey/Magnum Photos; 569(l), Antje Gunnar/FPG; 569(r), Robert Frerck/Odyssey Productions; 570, E.R. Degginger; 573, Rameshwar Das/Monkmeyer Press Photo Service; 575, Steve McCurry/Magnum Photos; 577, Robert Frerck/Odyssey Productions; 578, Bruno Barbey/Magnum Photos; 581, Shostal Assoc.; 582, Robert Frerck/Odyssey Productions; 583, Marc & Evelyne Bernheim/Woodfin Camp & Assoc.; 586, Joe Viesti; 588, Robert Frerck/Odyssey Productions; 590, John C. Hillery; 591, Shostal Assoc.; 593, Robert Frerck/Odyssey Productions; 594, Jackie Foryst/Bruce Coleman, Inc.; 597, Robert Frerck/After-Image; 598, Agricultural Research Service/USDA; 599(t), Fusa Sudzuki, Escuela de Agronomia, Departamento Produccion Agricola, Campus Antumapu, Santiago, Chile/National Research Council; 599(b), Agricultural Research Service/USDA; 602, Keith Gunnar/FPG; 604, Steve McCurry/Magnum Photos; 605, Philippe Gontier/The Image Works; 607, Shostal Assoc.; 609, John Paul Kay/Peter Arnold, Inc.; 610, Keith Gunnar/Bruce Coleman, Inc.; 612, Antje Gunnar/FPG; 613, Chad Ehlers/International Stock Photography.

**UNIT 11:** 618(tl), Steve Vidler/Leo de Wys, Inc.; 618(tr), Steve Vidler/Leo de Wys, Inc.; 618(bl), Kurt Scholz/Shostal Assoc.; 618(br), Dallas & John Heaton from Click/Chicago; 619(l), Carl Purcell/Words and Pictures; 619(r), M. Koene/H. Armstrong Roberts, Inc.; 620, Hiroji Kubota/Magnum Photos; 623, Edwin Hoffman/Illustrator's Stock Photos; 624, Bruno Barbey/Magnum Photos; 626, Kurt Scholz/Shostal Assoc.; 630, Steve Vidler/Leo de Wys, Inc.; 631, Tompix/Peter Arnold, Inc.; 634, Gamma-Liaison; 635(l), Carl Purcell/Words and Pictures; 635(r), G & J Images/The Image Bank; 637, Armand Borlant/Gamma-Liaison; 640, Steve Vidler/Leo de Wys, Inc.; 643, Suzanne J. Engelmann/Shostal Assoc.; 645, Robert H. Glaze/Artstreet; 646, Richard Kalvar/Magnum Photos; 647, Steve Vidler/Leo de Wys, Inc.; 648, Dallas & John Heaton from Click/Chicago; 650(l), Four By Five; 650(r), Ronald C. Modra/Sports Illustrated; 651(t), A.J. Hartman/Comstock; 651(b), Billy Stickland/Photo Researchers; 654, Hiroji Kubota/Magnum Photos; 656, Cameramann International; 657, Lou Jones.

**UNIT 12:** 662(tl), Juli Weber/The Stockhouse; 662(tr), Ron Sanford from F/Stop Pictures; 662(bl), Jean Kugler/FPG; 662(br), Manley Photo/Shostal Assoc.; 663(l), Peter Hendrie/The Image Bank; 663(r), Dallas & John Heaton/The Stock Shop; 664, Steve Vidler/After-Image; 666, J. Gifford/Leo de Wys, Inc.; 669, Leo de Wys, Inc.; 670, John Elk III/Bruce Coleman, Inc.; 673, Steve Vidler/Four By Five; 675(t), Dallas & John Heaton/After-Image; 675(b), Jane Lewis from Click/Chicago; 678, Robert Frerck/Odyssey Productions; 681, Manley Photo/Shostal Assoc.; 682, Juli Weber/The Stockhouse; 683, Ron Sanford from F/Stop Pictures; 684, Shostal Assoc.; 687, Tom McHugh/Photo Researchers; 689, Jean Kugler/FPG; 694, Nicholas DeVore III/Bruce Coleman, Inc.; 696, Peter Hendrie/The Image Bank; 700, David R. Austen/Stock, Boston; 701(t), Dallas & John Heaton/The Stock Shop; 701(b), Dallas & John Heaton/The Stock Shop; 702, John Cancalosi/Tom Stack & Assoc.; 703, Dallas & John Heaton/After-Image; 704, David R. Austen from Click/Chicago; 706, Robert Frerck/Woodfin Camp & Assoc.; 708, G.R. Roberts; 709, G.R. Roberts; 710, Melinda Berge/Photographers Aspen; 712, SuperStock International.

Charts by Tom Scelza and Ruth Soffer.

Maps prepared by R.R. Donnelley & Sons Company Cartographic Services, the computer-generated shaded relief on pages 134–35 by The National Geophysical Data Center, NOAA.

1
2
3
G 4
H 5
I 6
J 7